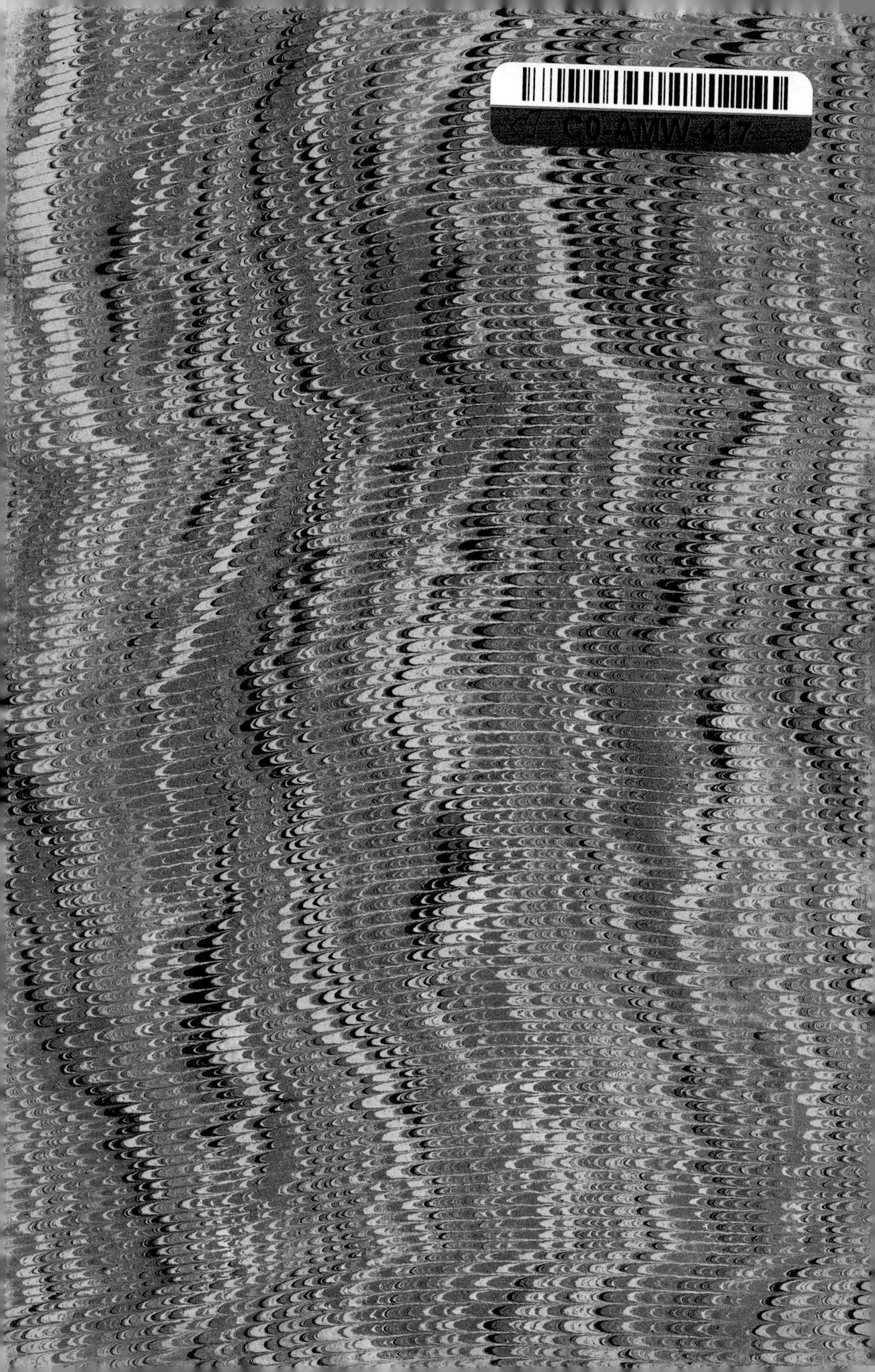
C0-AMW-417

15^{00}

J. Norton Oember

Robert Southey.

London, Longman, Brown, Green & Longmans, 1849.

THE
DOCTOR
&c.
Complete
IN ONE VOLUME.

Car. Southey, del. J. T. Willmore.

View from the Author's Study Window.

LONDON:
LONGMAN, BROWN, GREEN & LONGMANS.
PATERNOSTER ROW 1849.

THE DOCTOR,

&c.

BY THE LATE

Robert Southey.

EDITED BY

HIS SON-IN-LAW,

JOHN WOOD WARTER, B.D.

NEW EDITION,

COMPLETE IN ONE VOLUME.

LONDON:
LONGMAN, BROWN, GREEN, AND LONGMANS,
PATERNOSTER-ROW
1849.

"THOUGH THOU HADST MADE A GENERAL SURVEY
OF ALL THE BEST OF MEN'S BEST KNOWLEDGES,
AND KNEW SO MUCH AS EVER LEARNING KNEW;
YET DID IT MAKE THEE TRUST THYSELF THE LESS,
AND LESS PRESUME. — AND YET WHEN BEING MOV'D
IN PRIVATE TALK TO SPEAK; THOU DIDST BEWRAY
HOW FULLY FRAUGHT THOU WERT WITHIN; AND PROV'D
THAT THOU DIDST KNOW WHATEVER WIT COULD SAY.
WHICH SHOW'D THOU HADST NOT BOOKS AS MANY HAVE,
FOR OSTENTATION, BUT FOR USE; AND THAT
THY BOUNTEOUS MEMORY WAS SUCH AS GAVE
A LARGE REVENUE OF THE GOOD IT GAT.
WITNESS SO MANY VOLUMES, WHERETO THOU
HAST SET THY NOTES UNDER THY LEARNED HAND,
AND MARK'D THEM WITH THAT PRINT, AS WILL SHOW HOW
THE POINT OF THY CONCEIVING THOUGHTS DID STAND;
THAT NONE WOULD THINK, IF ALL THY LIFE HAD BEEN
TURN'D INTO LEISURE, THOU COULDST HAVE ATTAIN'D
SO MUCH OF TIME, TO HAVE PERUS'D AND SEEN
SO MANY VOLUMES THAT SO MUCH CONTAIN'D."

DANIEL. *Funeral Poem upon the Death of the late Noble Earl of Devonshire.*

"WELL-LANGUAGED DANIEL," as Browne called him in his "Britannia's Pastorals," was one of Southey's favourite poets. Let the above extract speak of the Author of "THE DOCTOR, &c."

THE EDITOR.

EDITOR'S PREFACE.

THE intrinsic beauty, and, what is of more consequence, the moral and religious value of the sentiments contained in "THE DOCTOR, &c.," has called for a new and popular Edition of that work. It has fallen to my lot, — otherwise laboriously occupied, — to edit it. What is done, ought to be done well, — whether it be so or not, competent readers will be the best judges. Not unversed in books, and familiar with ancient and modern languages as toward circumstances have made me, I trust the endeavour has not been unattained, — though some errors —

. . . Quas aut incuria fudit
Aut humana parum cavit natura —

will unavoidably be detected and charitably overlooked.

Five out of six, it has been said by those quite able to form an unbiassed and judicious opinion, were assured as to the authorship of "THE DOCTOR, &c." It is now well known that the lamented Southey played with its pages as he did with his kittens,— as a relaxation from his bread-earning and every-day pursuits. It is not too much to say that no one but Southey could have written it. Line upon line, —page upon page, — shows the man that feared God, and honoured the King, and loved his Country, and despised all political tinkers, whether in matters ecclesiastical or civil.

The extract following from a letter to Miss Caroline Bowles, — the present no less talented than amiable and excellent Mrs. Southey, and my much valued friend, — contains the most interesting particulars relative to the work. It is dated, Keswick, June, 1835.

"Miss B., who then lived in the next house, was the Bhow Begum. That whole chapter" (that is, Chapter VII. A. I.) "is from the life, and the Book grew out of that night's conversation, exactly as there related. But to go farther back with its history. There is a story of Dr. D. D. of D., and of his horse Nobs, which has, I believe, been made into a Hawker's Book. Coleridge used to tell it, and the humour lay in making it as long-winded as possible; — it suited, however, my long-windedness better than his, and I was frequently called upon for it by those who enjoyed it, and sometimes I volunteered it, when Coleridge protested against its being told.

As you may suppose, it was never twice told alike, except as to names, and the leading features. With something of Tristram Shandy, something of Rabelais, and more of Montaigne, and a little of old Burton, the predominant characteristic is still my own."

Though railroads outrun literature, and Mammon has more votaries than religious and useful learning, it says something for us that a book such as "THE DOCTOR, &c." should again be called for, the more so when it is considered that its readers, after all, must be rather fit and few than many. But, well said Walter Savage Landor, — "Southey was the first, and remains to the present day almost the only critic, who was constantly guided by truth and conscience. Added to which, his judgment, especially in works of imagination, was incomparably more correct than any other man's."

It only remains to add that the "AUTHOR OF THE DOCTOR, &c., IN HIS STUDY," and the "SKETCH OF THE BUST," are by Nash, — "Edward Nash," — (as he is described in the Colloquies, i. 238.) — "My dear, kind-hearted friend and fellow traveller, whose death has darkened some of the blithest recollections of my latter life." Both of these are excellent in their way, — but the engraving of the Bust, in the eyes of myself, and Southey's eldest daughter, Edith May Warter, is perfect. "THE VIEW OF KESWICK FROM THE STUDY WINDOW" is by Mrs. Southey, and it is a view not to be forgotten. For the few foot-notes not marked *R. S.*, the Editor is responsible.

I had laid down the pen, when these words of old Fuller — (an especial favourite of Southey's) — flashed across my mind. Reader! "NO DISCREET PERSON WILL CONCLUDE OUR FAITH THE WORSE, BECAUSE OUR CHARITY IS THE MORE." Apply them as thou readest!

JOHN WOOD WARTER.

VICARAGE HOUSE, WEST TARRING, SUSSEX,
May 15th, 1848

PRELUDE OF MOTTOES.

Now they that like it may: the rest may chuse.

G. WITHER.

Je veux à face descouverte qu'on sçache que je fay le fol. Et pourquoy ne me le sera-t-il permis, si le grand Solon dans Athenes, ne douta de le faire pour apporter un grand bien à sa Republique? La Republique dont j'ay charge, est ce petit monde que Dieu a estably en moy; pour la conservation duquel je ne scay meilleur moyen que de tromper mes afflictions par quelques honnestes jeux d'esprit; appellez-les bouffonneries si ainsi le voulez.

PASQUIER.

If you are so bold as to venture a blowing-up, look closely to it! for the plot lies deadly deep, and 'twill be between your legs before you be aware of it. — But of all things have a care of putting it in your pocket, for fear it takes fire, or runs away with your breeches. And if you can shun it, read it not when you are alone; or at least not late in the evening; for the venom is strongest about midnight, and seizes most violently upon the head when the party is by himself. I shall not tell you one line of what is in it; and therefore consider well what you do, and look to yourself. But if you be resolved to meddle, be sure have a care of catching cold, and keep to a moderate diet; for there is danger and jeopardy in it besides.

DR. EACHARD.

— For those faults of barbarism, Doric dialect, extemporanean stile, tautologies, apish imitation, a rhapsody of rags gathered together from several dung-hills, excrements of authors, toyes and fopperies, confusedly tumbled out, without art, invention, judgement, wit, learning, harsh, raw, rude, phantasticall, absurd, insolent, indiscreet, ill-composed, indigested, vain, scurrile, idle, dull, and dry: — I confess all; ('tis partly affected;) thou canst not think worse of me than I do of myself. 'Tis not worth the reading! I yield it. I desire thee not to lose time in perusing so vain a subject. I should be peradventure loth myself to read him or thee so writing; 'tis not *operæ pretium*. All I say is this, that I have precedents for it.

BURTON.

A foolish extravagant spirit, full of forms, figures, shapes, objects, ideas, apprehensions, motions, revolutions; these are begot in the ventricle of memory, nourished in the womb of *pia mater*, and delivered upon the mellowing of the occasion. But the gift is good in those in whom it is acute, and I am thankful for it.

LOVE'S LABOUR LOST.

If the world like it not, so much the worse for them.

COWPER.

— un boschetto,
Donne per quello givan fior cogliendo,
Con diletto, co' quel, co' quel dicendo;
Eccolo, eccol! . . che à? — è fiordaliso!
Va là per le viole;
Più colà per le rose, cole, cole,
Vaghe amorose.
O me, che' l prun mi punge!
Quell' altra me v' aggiunge.
U', ù, o, ch' è quel che salta?
Un grillo! un grillo!
Venite qua, correte,
Ramponzoli cogliete;
E' non con essi!
Si, son! — colei o colei
Vien qua, vien qua per funghi, un micolino
Piu colà, più cola per sermollino.

UGOLINO UBALDINI *or*
FRANCO SACCHETTI.

If the particulars seem too large or to be over tediously insisted upon, consider in how many impertinent and trifling discourses and actions the best of us do consume far more hours than the perusal of this requires minutes, and yet think it no tediousness: and let them call to mind how many volumes this age imprints and reads which are foolish if not wicked. Let them be persuaded likewise, that I have not written this for those who have no need thereof, or to shew my own wit or compendiousness but to instruct the ignorant; to whom I should more often speak in vain, if I did not otherwhile by repetitions and circumlocutions, stir up their affections, and beat into their understandings the knowledge and feeling of those things which I deliver. Yea, let them know that I know those expressions will be both pleasing and profitable to some which they imagine to be needless and superabundant; and that I had rather twenty nice critics should censure me for a word here and there superfluous than that one of those other should want that which might explain my meanings to their capacities, and so make frustrate all my labour to those who have most need of it, and for whom it was chiefly intended.

G. WITHER.

Tempus ad hoc mecum latuit, portuque resedit,
Nec fuit audaces impetus ire vias.
Nunc animi venere; juvat nunc denique funem
Solvere: —
Ancora sublata est; terræ, portusque valete!
Imus; habet ventos nostra carina suos.

WALLIUS.

POSTSCRIPT.

There was a certain Pisander whose name has been preserved in one of the proverbial sayings of the Greeks, because he lived in continual fear of seeing his own ghost. How often have I seen mine while arranging these volumes for publication, and carrying them through the press!

Twenty years have elapsed since the intention of composing them was conceived, and the composition commenced, in what manner and in what mood the reader will presently be made acquainted. The vicissitudes which in the course of those years have befallen every country in Europe are known to every one; and the changes, which, during such an interval, must have occurred in a private family, there are few who may not, from their own sad experience, readily apprehend.

Circumstances which when they were touched upon in these volumes were of present importance, and excited a lively interest, belong now to the history of the past. They who were then the great performers upon the theatre of public life have fretted their hour and disappeared from the stage. Many who were living and flourishing when their names were here sportively or severely introduced are gone to their account. The domestic circle which the introduction describes has in the ordinary course of things been broken up; some of its members are widely separated from others, and some have been laid to rest. The reader may well believe that certain passages which were written with most joyousness of heart, have been rendered purely painful to the writer by time and change: and that some of his sweetest thoughts come to him in chewing the cud, like wormwood and gall. — But it is a wholesome bitterness.

He has neither expunged nor altered any thing on any of these accounts. It would be weakness to do this on the score of his own remembrances, and in the case of allusions to public affairs and to public men it would be folly. The Almanack of the current year will be an old one as soon as next year begins.

It is the writer's determination to remain unknown; and they who may suppose that

> By certain signs here set in sundry place,

they have discovered him, will deceive themselves. A Welsh Triad says that the three unconcealable traits of a person by which he shall be known, are the glance of his eye, the pronunciation of his speech, and the mode of his self-motion; — in briefer English, his look, his voice, and his gait. There are no such characteristics by which an author can be identified. He must be a desperate mannerist who can be detected by his style, and a poor proficient in his art if he cannot at any time so vary it, as to put the critic upon a false scent. Indeed every day's experience shows that they who assume credit to themselves, and demand it from others for their discrimination in such things, are continually and ridiculously mistaken.

On that side the author is safe; he has a sure reliance upon the honour as well as the discretion of the very few to whom he is naturally or necessarily known; and if the various authors to whom the Book will be ascribed by report, should derive any gratification from the perusal, he requests of them in return that they will favour his purpose by allowing such reports to pass uncontradicted.

[*Prefixed to Vol. III. in the original Edition.*]

PRELUDE OF MOTTOES.

Ἄγε νῦν, ὦ . . . καρδία
ἄπελθ' ἐκεῖσε, ...
. . . . εἰποῦσ' ἅττ' ἂν αὐτῇ σοι δοκῇ,
τόλμησον, ἴθι, χώρησον, ἄγαμαι καρδίας.

ARISTOPHANES.

Je vas de nouveau percer mon tonneau, et de la traicte, laquelle par deux precedents volumes vous est assez cogneuë, vous tirer du creux de nos passetemps epicenaires un galant tiercin, et consecutivement un joyeux quart de sentences Pantagruelliques. Par moy vous sera licite les appeller Diogeniques. — Et peur n'ayez que le vin faille. — Autant que vous en tireray par la dille, autant en entonneray per le bondon. Ainsi demourcra le tonneau inexpuisible. Il a source vive et veine perpetuelle.

RABELAIS.

The wholesom'st meats that are will breed satiety
Except we should admit of some variety.
In music, notes must be some high, some base.
And this I say, these pages have intendment,
Still kept within the lists of good sobriety,
To work in men's ill manners good amendment.
Wherefore if any think the book unseasonable,
Their stoic minds are foes to good society,
And men of reason may think them unreasonable.
It is an act of virtue and of piety,
To warn men of their sins in any sort,
In prose, in verse, in earnest, or in sport.

SIR JOHN HARRINGTON.

The great cement that holds these several discourses together is one main design which they jointly drive at, and which, I think, is confessedly generous and important, namely, the knowledge of — true happiness, so far as reason can cut her way through those darknesses and difficulties she is encumbered with in this life: which though they be many and great, yet I should belie the sense of my own success, if I should pronounce them insuperable; as also, if I were deprived of that sense, should lose many pleasures and enjoyments of mind, which I am now conscious to myself of: amongst which, there is none so considerable as that tacit reflection within myself, what real service may be rendered to religion by these my labours. HENRY MORE.

Scribere fert animus multa et diversa, nec uno
Gurgite versari semper ; quo flamina ducent
Ibimus, et nunc has, nunc illas nabimus undas ;
Ardua nunc ponti, nunc littora tuta petemus.
Et quanquam interdum fretus ratione, latentes
Naturæ tentabo vias, atque abdita pandam,
Præcipuè tamen illa sequar quæcunque videntur
Prodesse, ac sanctos mortalibus addere mores,
Heu penitus (liceat verum mihi dicere) nostro
Extinctos ævo. PALINGENIUS.

Ja n'est besoin (amy Lecteur!) t'escrire
Par le menu le prouffit et plaisir
Que recevras si ce livre veux lire,
Et d'icelluy le sens prendre au desir ;
Veuille donc prendre à le lire loisir,
Et que ce soit avecq intelligence.
Si tu le fais, propos de grand plaisance
Tu y verras, et moult prouffiteras ;
Et si tiendras en grand resjouissance
Le tien esprit, et ton temps passeras. JEAN FAVRE.

" Gods me ! how now ! what present have we here ? "
" A Book that stood in peril of the press ;
But now it's past those pikes, and doth appear
To keep the lookers on from heaviness."
" What stuff contains it ? " — " Fustian, perfect spruce,
Wit's gallimalfry, or wit fried in steaks."
" From whom came it, a God's name ? " — " From his Muse,
(Oh do not tell !) that still your favour seeks."
" And who is that ? " — " Truth that is I." — " What I ?
I per se I, great I, you would say." — " No !
Great I indeed *you* well may say ; but I
Am little i, the least of all the row."

DAVIES OF HEREFORD.

Lector, esto libro te ofrezco, sin que me aya mandado Señor alguno que le escriva, ni menos me ayan importunado mis amigos que le estampe, sino solamente por mi gusto, por mi antojo y por mi voluntad. MONTALVAN.

The reader must not expect in this work merely the private uninteresting history of a single person. He may expect whatever curious particulars can with any propriety be connected with it. Nor must the general disquisitions and the incidental narratives of the present work be ever considered as actually digressionary in their natures, and as merely useful in their notices. They are all united with the rest, and form proper parts of the whole. They have some of them a necessary connexion with the history of the Doctor ; they have many of them an intimate relation, they have all of them a natural affinity to it. And the Author has endeavoured, by a judicious distribution of them through the work, to prevent that disgusting uniformity, and to take off that uninteresting personality, which must necessarily result from the merely barren and private annals of an obscure individual. He has thus in some measure adopted the elegant principles of modern gardening. He has thrown down the close hedges and the high walls that have confined so many biographers in their views. He has called in the scenes of the neighbouring country to his aid, and has happily combined them into his own plan. He has drawn off the attention from the central point before it became languid and exhausted, by fetching in some objects from society at large, or by presenting some view of the philosophy of man. But he has been cautious of multiplying objects in the wantonness of refinement, and of distracting the attention with a confused variety. He has always considered the history of the Doctor, as the great fixed point, the enlivening centre, of all his excursions. Every opening is therefore made to carry an actual reference, either mediate or immediate, to the regular history of the Doctor. And every visto is employed only for the useful purpose of breaking the stiff straight lines, of lighting up the dark, of heightening the little, and of colouring over the lifeless, in the regular history of the Doctor.

Preface to WHITAKER's History of Manchester,
mutatis mutandis.

Chi tristezza da se cacciar desia,
Legga quest' opra saporita e bella. BERTOLDO.

I exhort all People, gentle and simple, men, women and children, to buy, to read, to extol, these labours of mine. Let them not fear to defend every article ; for I will bear them harmless. I have arguments good store, and can easily confute, either logically, theologically, or metaphysically, all those who oppose me. ARBUTHNOT.

Scripta legis passim quamplurima, lector, in orbe,
Quæ damni plus quam commoditatis habent.
Hæc fugienda procul cum sint, sic illa petenda,
Jucunda utilibus quæ bene juncta docent.
P. RUBIGALLUS PANNONIUS.

Out of the old fieldes, as men saith,
Cometh all this new corn fro' year to year;
And out of old bookes, in good faith,
Cometh all this new science that men lere.
CHAUCER.

[*Prefixed to Vol. IV. in the original Edition.*]

PRELUDE OF MOTTOES.

TO THE READER IN ORDINARY.

The Muses forbid that I should restrain your meddling, whom I see already busy with the title, and tricking over the leaves: it is your own. I departed with my right, when I let it first abroad; and now so secure an interpreter I am of my chance, that neither praise nor dispraise from you can affect me. — The commendation of good things may fall within a many, the approbation but in a few; for the most commend out of affection, self-tickling, an easiness or imitation; but men judge only out of knowledge. That is the trying faculty; and to those works that will bear a judge, nothing is more dangerous than a foolish praise. You will say, I shall not have yours therefore; but rather the contrary, all vexation of censure. If I were not above such molestations now, I had great cause to think unworthily of my studies, or they had so of me. But I leave you to your exercise. Begin.
BEN JONSON.

Je n'adresse point ce Livre à un Grand, sur une vaine opinion que j'aurois de la garantir ou de l'envie, ou de le faire vivre contre les rudes assauts du temps, d'autant que sa principale recommendation doit deriver de son propre fonds, et non de l'appuy de celuy à qui je le dedierois: car rien ne l'auctorisera, s'il n'est remply de belles conceptions, et tissu d'un langage bref, nerveux, et escrit d'une plume franche, resoluë et hardie. La rondeur d'escrire plaist; ces choses sont pour donner prix et pointe à nos escrits, et dépiter le temps et la mort. Je prie Dieu que ces Tomes ressemblent à la beauté d'un jardin, duquel l'un cueille une belle rose, l'autre une violette, ou une giroflee; ainsi souhaitay-je qu'en ceste diversité de sujects, dont elles sont plaines, chacun tire dequoy resveiller, resjouyr et contenter son esprit. NICOLAS PASQUIER.

Non ego me methodo astringam serviliter ullâ,
Sed temeré Hyblææ more vagabor apis,
Quò me spes prædæ, et generandi gloria mellis,
Liberaque ingenii quo feret ala mei. COWLEY.

Take not too much at once, lest thy brain turn edge; Taste it first as a potion for physic, and by degrees thou shalt drink it as beer for thirst. FULLER.

Qui l'a fait? Quiconque il soit, en ce a esté prudent, qu'il n'y a point mis son nom. RABELAIS.

Io me n' andrò con la barchetta mia,
Quanto l' acqua comporta un picciol legno;
E ciò ch' io penso con la fantasia,
Di piacere ad ognuno è 'l mio disegno:
Convien che varie cose al mondo sia,
Come son varj volti e vario ingegno,
E piace a l' uno il bianco, a l' altro il perso,
O diverse materie in prosa o in verso.

Forse coloro ancor che leggeranno
Di questa tanto piccola favilla
La mente con poca esca accenderanno
De' monti o di Parnaso o di Sibilla:
E de' miei fior come ape piglieranno
I dotti, s' alcun dolce ne distilla;
Il resto a molti pur darà diletto,
E lo autore ancor fia benedetto. PULCI.

Most Prefaces are effectually apologies, and neither the Book nor the Author one jot the better for them. If the Book be good, it will not need an apology; if bad it will not bear one: for where a man thinks by calling himself noddy in the epistle, to atone for shewing himself to be one in the text, he does, with respect to the dignity of an author, but bind up two fools in one cover.
SIR ROGER D'ESTRANGE.

Inter cuncta leges, —
Quâ ratione queas traducere leniter ævum;
Ne te semper inops agitet vexetque cupido,
Ne pavor, et rerum mediocriter utilium spes; —
Quid minuat curas; quid te tibi reddat amicum;
Quid purè tranquillet, honos, an dulce lucellum,
An secretum iter, et fallentis semita vitæ. HORACE.

Si ne suis je toutesfois hors d'esperance, que si quelqu'un daigne lire, et bien gouster ces miens escrits, (encores que le langage n'en soit eslevé, ny enflé) il ne les trouvera du tout vuides de saveur; ny tant desgarniz d'utilité, qu'ils n'en puissent tirer plaisir et profit, pourveu que leurs esprits ne soyent auparavant saisiz de mal vueillance, ou imbuz de quelques autres mauvaises opinions. Je prie doncques tous Lecteurs entrer en la lecture des presents discours, delivres de toute passion et emulation. Car quand l'amertume d'envie ou mal vueillance, est detrempee en desir de contredire, elle ne laisse jamais le goust que depravé et mal jugeant.
PIERRE DE ST. JULIEN.

Here are no forced expressions, no rack'd phrase,
No Babel compositions to amaze
The tortured reader, no believed defence
To strengthen the bold Atheist's insolence,
No obscene syllable that may compel
A blush from a chaste maid. MASSINGER.

Read, and fear not thine own understanding; this book will create a clear one in thee; and when thou hast considered thy purchase, thou wilt call the price of it a charity to thyself. SHIRLEY.

One caveat, good Reader, and then God speed thee! —— Do not open it at adventures, and by reading the broken pieces of two or three lines, judge it; but read it through, and then I beg no pardon if thou dislikest it. Farewell.
THOMAS ADAMS.

Listen while my tongue
Reveals what old Harmodius wont to teach
My early age; Harmodius, who had weigh'd
Within his learned mind whate'er the schools
Of Wisdom, or thy lonely whispering voice,
O faithful Nature, dictate of the laws
Which govern and support this mighty frame
Of universal being. AKENSIDE.

Δεῦρ' ἔλθ', ὅπως ἂν καὶ σοφώτερος γένῃ.
EURIPIDES.

[*Prefixed to Vol. V. in the original Edition.*]

PRELUDE OF MOTTOES.

See here, see here, a Doctor rare,
  Who travels much at home;
Come take his pills, — they cure all ills,
  Past, present, and to come.
  Take a little of his nif-naf,
  Put it on your tif-taf.

THE BISHOPRICK GARLAND.

Quod virgo proba, quod stolata mater,
Quod purus positâ severitate
Jam post pulpita perlegat sacerdos.

T. L. ON SIR WM. KILLIGREW'S SELINDRA.

I entered on this work certainly with considerable materials, and since engaging in it, in reading, in thinking, in correcting and improving, I have proportioned my labours to my undertaking. Every step I advanced, I did but more clearly see how much farther I might go. Here too readers and some writers may be reminded of the effect produced by finding a pleasure in your employment; some burdens are sweet; you lose the sense of weight by the deceptions of fancy and occasional rests; and in proportion as your journey becomes more agreeable, you are in danger of growing more dilatory.

GEORGE DYER.

*Si tu tombes entre les mains de ceux qui ne voyent rien d'autruy que pour y trouver sujet de s'y desplaire, et qu'ils te reprochent que ton Docteur est ennuyeux; responds leur qu'il est à leur choix de lui voir ou ne lui voir point. — Si tu te trouves parmy ceux qui font profession d'interpreter les songes, et descouvrir les pensées plus secrettes d'autruy, et qu'ils asseurent que * * est un tel homme et * * une telle femme; ne leur respond rien; car ils sçavent assez qu'ils ne sçavent pas ce qu'ils disent: mais supplie ceux qui pourroient estre abusez de leurs fictions, de considerer que si ces choses ne m'importent, j'aurois eu bien peu d'esprit de les avoir voulu dissimuler et ne l'avoir sceu faire. Que si en ce qu'ils diront, il n'y a guere d'apparence, il ne les faut pas croire: et s'il y en a beaucoup, il faut penser que pour couvrir la chose que je voulois tenir cachée et ensevelie, je l'eusse autrement desguisée.*

ASTRÉE — mutatis mutandis.

I would not be in danger of that law of Moses, that if a man dig a pit and cover it not, he must recompense those which are damnified by it; which is often interpreted of such as shake old opinions, and do not establish new as certain, but leave consciences in a worse danger than they found them in. I believe that law of Moses hath in it some mystery and appliableness; for by that law men are only then bound to that indemnity and compensation, if an ox or an ass, (that is such as are of a strong constitution and accustomed to labour) fall therein; but it is not said so, if a sheep or a goat fall: no more are we if men in a silliness or wantonness will stumble or take a scandal, bound to rectify them at all times. And therefore because I justly presume you strong and watchful enough, I make account that I am not obnoxious to that law; since my meditations are neither too wide nor too deep for you.

DONNE'S LETTERS.

Such an author consulted in a morning sets the spirits for the vicissitudes of the day, better than the glass does a man's person. SIR RICHARD STEELE.

The Load-stone of Attraction I find out,
The Card of Observation guides about,
The Needle of Discretion points the way.

DUTCHESS OF NEWCASTLE.

—— βροτοὶ παύσασθε μάταιοι.
'Ρεμβόμενοι σκοτίῃ και ἀφεγγέϊ νυκτὶ μελαίνῃ·
Καὶ λίπετε σκοτίην νυκτὸς, φωτὸς δὲ λάβεσθε·
Οὗτος ἰδοὺ πάντεσσι σαφὴς, ἀπλάνητος ὑπάρχει.
Ἔλθετε, μὴ σκοτίην δὲ διώκετε, καὶ γνόφον αἰεί·
Ἠελίου γλυκυδερκὲς ἰδοὺ φάος ἔξοχα λάμπει.

SIBYLLINE VERSES.

Of things that be strange
  Who loveth to read
In this book let him range
  His fancy to feed. RICHARD ROBINSON.

At ego tibi sermone isto —
Varias fabulas conseram, auresque tuas
Benevolus lepido susurro permulceam.

APULEIUS.

Whoso doth attempt the Author's works to read
Must bring with him a stayed head, and judgement to proceed;
For as there be most wholesome hests and precepts to be found,
So are there rocks and shallow shelves to run the ship aground. ARTHUR GOLDING.

I am studying the art of patience: — to drive six snails before me from this town to Moscow, neither use goad nor whip to them, but let them take their own time. The patientest man i' the world match me for an experiment!

WEBSTER.

He says and he says not, cares and he cares not, he's king and he's no king; his high-born soul is above this sublunary world; he reigns, he rides in the clouds and keeps his court in the Horizon: he's Emperor of the Superlative Heights, and lives in pleasure among the Gods; he plays at bowls with the Stars, and makes a football of the Globe; he makes that to fly far, far out of the reach of Thought. HURLOTHRUMBO.

Lo libres fo be faitz, e de bos motz complit;
E sil voletz entendre, li gran e li petit
Podon i mot apendre de sen e de bel dit;
Car aisel qui le fe nal ventre tot farsit,
E sel que nol conoish, ni nol a resentit.
  Ja no so cujaria.

CANSOS DE LA CROZADA
CONTR ELS EREGES DALBREGES.

Something oddly
The book-man prated; yet he talked it weeping.

FORD.

We content ourselves to present to thinking minds, the original seeds from whence spring vast fields of new theories, that may be further cultivated, beautified and enlarged. Truth however being of a coherent nature, it is impossible to separate one branch from another and see it in all its beauty. I beg therefore my readers not to judge of the work by parcels, but to continue to the end, that so they may see the connection of every part with the whole. Scattered rays do not always enlighten; but when reunited they give a mutual lustre to each other.

THE CHEVALIER RAMSAY.

I must be allowed my freedom in my studies, for I substitute my writings for a game at the tennis-court or a club at the tavern. I never counted among my honours these *opuscula* of mine, but merely as harmless amusements. It is my partridge, as with St. John; my cat, as with Pope St. Gregory; my little dog, as with St. Dominic; my lamb, as with St. Francis; (my pig, he might have said as with St. Antony,) my great black mastiff, as with Cornelius Agrippa; and my tame hare, as with Justus Lipsius. CATHERINOT.

As quoted and translated by D'ISRAELI.

To ignorants obdurde, quhair wilfull errour lyis,
Nor zit to curious folks, quhilks carping dois deject thee,
Nor zit to learned men, quha thinks thame onelie wyis,
But to the docile bairns of knowledge I direct thee.

JAMES I.

Albeit I have studied much and learned little, yet I have learned to glean some handfulls of corn out of the rankest cockle; to make choice of the most fragrant flowers of humanity, the most virtuous herbs of philosophy, the most sovereign fruits of government, and the most heavenly manna of divinity; to be acquainted with the fairest, provided for the foulest, delighted with the temperatest, pleased with the meanest, and contented with all weather—greater men may profess and can achieve greater matters: I thank God I know the length, that is the shortness of my own foot. If it be any man's pleasure to extenuate my sufficiency in other knowledge, or practise to empeach my ability in words or deeds, to debase my fortune, to abridge my commendations, or to annihilate my fame, he shall find a cold adversary of him that hath laid hot passions watering, and might easily be induced to be the invective of his own non proficiency.

GABRIEL HARVEY.

[*Prefixed to Vol. VI. in the original Edition.*]

PRELUDE OF MOTTOES.

Two thyngys owyth every clerk
To advertysyn, begynnyng a werk,
If he procedyn wyl ordeneely,
The fyrste is *what*, the secunde is *why*.
In wych two wurdys, as it semyth me,
The Foure causys comprehendyd be
Wych as our philosofyrs us do teche,
In the begynnyng men owe to seche
Of every book; and aftyr there entent,
The fyrst is clepyd cause efficyent:
The secunde they clepe cause materyal,
Formal the thrydde; the fourte fynal.
The efficyent cause is the auctour,
Wych aftyr hys cunnyng doth hys labour
To a complyse the begunne matere,
Wych cause is secunde; and the more clere
That it may be, the formal cause
Settyth in dew ordre clause be clause.
And these thre thyngys, longyn to what,
Auctour, matere and forme ordinat,
The fynal cause declaryth pleynly
Of the werk begunne the cause why;
That is to seyne what was the entent
Of the auctour fynally, and what he ment.

OSBERN BOKENAM.

Look for no splendid painted outside here,
But for a work devotedly sincere;
A thing low prized in these too high-flown days:
Such solid sober works get little praise.
Yet some there be
Love true solidity.

And unto such brave noble souls I write,
In hopes to do them and the subject right.
I write it not to please the itching vein
Of idle-headed fashionists, or gain
Their fond applause;
I care for no such noise.

I write it only for the sober sort,
Who love right learning, and will labour for't;
And who will value worth in art, though old,
And not be weary of the good, though told
'Tis out of fashion
By nine-tenths of the nation.

I writ it also out of great good will
Unto my countrymen; and leave my skill
Behind me for the sakes of those that may
Not yet be born; but in some after day
May make good use
Of it, without abuse.

But chiefly I do write it, for to show
A duty to the Doctor which I owe.

THOMAS MACE.

Physicians are many times forced to leave such methods of curing as themselves know to be the fittest, and being overruled by their patient's impatiency are fain to try the best they can in taking that way of cure, which the cured will yield unto: in like sort, considering how the case doth stand with this present age, full of tongue and weak of brain, behold we yield to the stream thereof: into the causes of goodness we will not make any curious or deep inquiry; to touch them now and then it shall be sufficient, when they are so near at hand that easily they may be conceived without any far removed discourse. That way we are contented to prove, which being the worse in itself, is notwithstanding now, by reason of common imbecility, the fitter and likelier to be brooked. HOOKER.

Qui lit beaucoup et jamais ne medite,
Semble à celuy qui mange avidement,
Et de tous mets surcharge tellement
Son estomach que rien ne luy profit.

QUATRAINE DE PIBRAC.

Thus Englished by Sylvester,

Who readeth much and never meditates,
Is like a greedy eater of much food,
Who so surcloys his stomach with his cates
That commonly they do him little good.

Je sçay qu'en ce discours l'on me pourra reprendre, que j'ay mis beaucoup de particularitez qui sont fort superflues. Je le crois: mais, je sçay, que si elles desplaisent à aucuns, elles plairont aux autres: me semblant, que ce n'est pas assez, quand on louë des personnes, dire qu'elles sont belles, sages, vertueuses, valeureuses, vaillantes, magnanimes, libérales, splendides et très-parfaites. Ce sont loüanges et descriptions genérales, et lieux-communs empruntez de tout le monde. Il en faut specifier bien le tout, et descrire particulièrement les perfections, afin que mieux on les touche au doigt: et telle est mon opinion.

BRANTOME.

Non sai se l' arte, o il caso abbia fornita
Così bell' opra, o siano entrambi a parte;
Perocchè l' arte è tal che il caso imita,
E' l caso è tal che rassomiglia all' arte:
E questo a quella, e quella a questo unita,
Quanto può, quanto sa, mesce e comparte.
Un la materia al bel lavor dispose,
L'altra meglio adornolla, e poi s' ascose.

METASTASIO.

Tous ceux qui ont quelquesfois pesé le grand travail et le labeur de l'imagination, l'ont jugé pour le plus grand qui se puisse trouver, et ont eu raison; d'autant que celuy lequel veut et desire en contenter plusieurs, doit aussi chercher des moyens differens, afin que ce qui est ennuyeux à l'un, l'autre le trouve doux et agreable; car de le donner à tous, il est impossible; veu, qu'entre trois personnes seulement que l'on aura conviées, il se trouvera une grande diference de gouts, ainsi que l'a dit Horace, luy dis-je qui l'avoit si bien experimenté: par ainsi il n'est pas possible qu'en une si longue histoire que celle dont je vay traictant, que je ne donne de la peine par la diversité des chapitres. Toutesfois si le jugement s'en faict par des personnes privees et libres de toute passion, ils diront que c'est le vray moyen d'entretenir les esprits curieux.

L'HISTOIRE DU CHEVALIER DU SOLEIL.

Be rather wise than witty, for much wit hath commonly much froth; and 'tis hard to jest and not sometimes jeer too; which many times sinks deeper than was intended or expected; and what was designed for mirth, ends in sadness. CALEB TRENCHFIELD, (probably a fictitious name,) RESTITUTA.

In some passages you will observe me very satirical. Writing on such subjects I could not be otherwise. I can write nothing without aiming, at least, at usefulness. It were beneath my years to do it, and still more dishonourable to my religion. I know that a reformation of such abuses as I have censured is not to be expected from the efforts of an author; but to contemplate the world, its follies, its vices, its indifferences to duty, and its strenuous attachment to what is evil, and not to reprehend, were to approve it. From this charge, at least, I shall be clear; for I have neither tacitly, nor expressly flattered either its characters or its customs. COWPER.

Nemo eo sapientius desipuisse, nemo stultius sapuisse videtur.

Said of Cardan by I know not who.

Il y en a qui pensent que les lecteurs reçoivent peu d'instruction, quand on leur représente des choses qui n'ont pas esté achevées, qu'eux appellent œuvres imparfaites; mais je ne suis pas de leur advis; car quand quelque fait est descrit à la verité, et avec ses circonstances, encor qu'il ne soit parvenu qu'à mychemin, si peut-on tousjours en tirer du fruict. LA NOUE.

Authors, you know of greatest fame,
Thro' modesty suppress their name;
And would you wish me to reveal
What these superior wits conceal?
Forego the search, my curious friend,
And husband time to better end.
All my ambition is, I own,
To profit and to please unknown,
Like streams supplied from springs below
Which scatter blessings as they flow.

DR. COTTON.

Thus have I, as well as I could, gathered a posey of observations as they grew,—and if some rue and wormwood be found amongst the sweeter herbs, their wholesomeness will make amends for their bitterness.

ADAM LITTLETON.

This worthy work in which of good examples are so many,
This orchard of Alcinous, in which there wants not any
Herb, tree, or fruit that may mans use for health or pleasure serve;
This plenteous horn of Acheloy, which justly doth deserve
To bear the name of Treasury of Knowledge, I present
To your good worships once again,—desiring you therefore
To let your noble courtesy and favour countervail
My faults, where art or eloquence on my behalf doth fail,
For sure the mark whereat I shoot is neither wreaths of bay,
Nor name of author, no, nor meed; but chiefly that it may
Be liked well of you and all the wise and learned sort;
And next, that every wight that shall have pleasure for to sport
Him in this garden, may as well bear wholesome fruit away
As only on the pleasant flowers his retchless senses stay.

GOLDING.

Doubtless many thoughts have presented, and are still presenting themselves to my mind, which once I had no idea of. But these, in I believe every instance, are as much the growth of former rooted principles, as multiplied branches grow from one and the same main stem. Of such an inward vegetation I am always conscious; and I equally seem to myself to perceive the novelty of the fresh shoot, and its connexion with what had been produced before.

ALEXANDER KNOX.

The extensive argument and miscellaneous nature of the work led him to declare his sentiments on a multitude of questions, on which he thought differently from other writers, and of course, to censure or confute their opinions. Whole bodies of men, as well as individuals of the highest reputation, were attacked by him, and his manner was to speak his sense of all with freedom and force. So that most writers, and even readers, had some ground of complaint against him. Not only the free-thinkers and unbelievers, against whom the tenour of his book was directed, but the heterodox of every denomination were treated without much ceremony, and of the orthodox themselves, some tenet or other, which till then they had held sacred, was discussed and reprobated by him. Straggling heresies, or embodied systems, made no difference with him; as they came in his way, no quarter was given to either, "his end and manner of writing," as Dr. Middleton truly observed, "being to pursue truth wherever he found it." HURD'S LIFE OF WARBURTON.

Thou art like my rappee, here, a most ridiculous superfluity; but a pinch of thee now and then is a more delicious treat. CLANDESTINE MARRIAGE.

Yea—but what am I?
A scholar, or a schoolmaster, or else some youth?
A lawyer, a student, or else a country clown?
A brumman, a basket-maker, or a baker of pies?
A flesh, or a fishmonger, or a sower of lies?
A louse, or a louser, a leek or a lark,
A dreamer, a drommell, a fire or a spark?

A caitiff, a cut-throat, a creeper in corners,
A hairbrain, a hangman, or a grafter of horners?
A merchant, a maypole, a man or a mackarel,
A crab or a crevise, a crane or a cockerell?

APPIUS AND VIRGINIA.

It may appear to some ridiculous
Thus to talk knave and madman, and sometimes
Come in with a dried sentence, stuft with sage.

WEBSTER.

Etsi verò, quæ in isto opere desiderentur, rectiùs forsan quàm quivis alius, perspiciam; et si meo plane voto standum fuisset, id, in tantâ, quæ hodie est librorum copiâ, vel plane suppressissem, vel in multos annos adhuc pressissem; tamen aliquid amicis, aliquid tempori dandum; et cum iis qui aliquid fructus ex eo sperant, illud communicandum putavi. Hunc itaque meum qualemcunque laborem, Lector candide, boni consule; quod te facilè facturum confido, si eum animum ad legendum attuleris, quem ego ad scribendum, veritatis nimirum aliisque inserviendi cupidum.

SENNERTUS.

[*Prefixed to Vol. VII. in the original Edition.*]

PRELUDE OF MOTTOES.

Well: we go on. MERIC CASAUBON.

Ventri utinam pax sit, sic variante cibo.

VENANTIUS FORTUNATUS.

I had forgot one half, I do protest,
And now am sent again to speak the rest. DRYDEN.

Well said, Master Doctor, well said;
By the mass we must have you into the pulpit.

LUSTY JUVENTUS.

Why this is quincy quarie pepper de watchet single goby, of all that ever I tasted! ROBERT GREENE.

Alonso. Prythee no more! thou dost talk nothing to me.
Gonzalo. I did it to minister occasion to these gentlemen who are of such sensible and nimble lungs, that they always use to laugh at nothing. TEMPEST.

Comme l'on voit, à l'ouvrir de la porte
D'un cabinet royal, maint beau tableau,
Mainte antiquaille, et tout ce que de beau
Le Portugais des Indes nous apporte;

Aussi deslors que l'homme qui medite,
Et est sçavant, commence de s'ouvrir,
Un grand thresor vient à se descouvrir,
Thresor caché au puits de Democrite.

QUATRAINS DE PIBRAC.

Cum enim infelicius nihil sit iis ingeniis, ut rectè J. Cæs. Scaliger censet, quæ mordicùs sentiunt Majores nostros nihil ignorasse, mancipium alienarum opinionum nunquam esse volui. Contra nec me puduit ab aliis discere, et quædam ex iis in mea scripta transferre; quod omnibus seculis ab omnibus viris doctis factitatum video, neminemque adhuc inventum existimo, qui omnia, quæ in publicum edidit, in suo cerebro nata esse gloriari potuerit. Invenient tamen, qui volent, in meis aliqua, eaque à veritate non aliena, quæ in aliorum scriptis forsan non ita sunt obvia. Verùm omnibus placere impossibile; et, ut J. Cæs. Scaliger ait

Qui sevit, ab alto pluviam satis precatur;
At iter faciens imbribus imprecatur atris,
Non sæpe Deus placet; et tu placere credis?

Ideoque invidorum obtrectationibus nihil motus, tomum sextum Doctoris *in publicum edidi, ac septimum jam in manus sumam, et in eo quousque D. O. M. placuerit, progredior. In quo ipso etiam etsi non pauca quæ obtrectationi malevolorum et invidorum obnoxia esse poterunt, dicenda erunt, proferam tamen ea liberè.* SENNERTUS.

Tired of thee, my Opus? that is impossible!

οὐδὲ μεστὸς σοῦ γέγον' οὐδεὶς πώποτε.
τῶν μὲν γὰρ ἄλλων ἐστὶ πάντων πλησμονή·
ἔρωτος,
ἄρτων,
μουσικῆς,
τραγημάτων,
τιμῆς,
πλακούντων,
ἀνδραγαθίας,
ἰσχάδων,
φιλοτιμίας,
μάζης,
στρατηγίας,
φακῆς.
σοῦ δ' ἐγένετ' οὐδεὶς μεστὸς οὐδεπώποτε.

ARISTOPHANES.

I desire the unlearned readers not to be offended for that I have in some places intermixed Greek and Latin—(and other tongues) with the English. For I have an especial regard unto young scholars and students, unto whom it is not possible to be expressed what great utility, benefit, and knowledge doth redound, of conferring one strange language with another. Neither is it to be doubted, but that such as are towards the discipline of good literature in divers tongues, may of such doings as this pick out as much utility and furtherance of their studies, as the unlearned shall take pleasure and fruit of the English for their use. Whoso careth not for the Latin may pass it over, and satisfy himself with the English. Who passeth not on the Greek, may semblably pass it over, and make as though he see none such. There is in this behalf no man's labour lost but mine, and yet not that all lost neither, if my good zeal and honest intent to do good to all sorts, be in good part interpreted and accepted. NICHOLAS UDALL.

Truly for the Englishman to be offended with the admixtion of Latin, or the Latin-man to dislike the powdering of Greek, appeareth unto me a much like thing, as if at a feast with variety of good meats and drinks furnished, one that loveth to feed of a capon should take displeasure that another man hath appetite to a coney; or one that serveth his stomach with a partridge should be angry with another that hath a mind to a quail; or one that drinketh small beer, should be grieved with his next fellow for drinking ale or wine. NICHOLAS UDALL.

If food and amusement are wanted for the body, what does he deserve who finds food and amusement for the mind? GNOMICA.

Mai voi,—seguitate il ragionamento del Dottore; *et mostrateci, come havete bona memoria; che credo se saperete ritaccarlo ove lo lasciaste, non farete poco.*

CASTIGLIONE.

If any complain of obscurity, they must consider, that in these matters it cometh no otherwise to pass than in sundry the works both of art and also of nature, where that which hath greatest force in the very things we see, is, notwithstanding, itself oftentimes not seen. The stateliness of horses, the goodliness of trees, when we behold them, delighteth the eye; but that foundation which beareth up the one, that root which ministereth unto the other nourishment and life, is in the bosom of the earth concealed; and if there be at any time occasion to search into it, such labour is then more necessary than pleasant, both to them which undertake it, and for the lookers on. HOOKER.

Alcuni — dicono ch' io ho creduto formar me stesso, persuadendomi che le conditioni ch' io al Dottore *attribuisco, tutte siano in me. A' questi tali non voglio già negar di non haver tentato tutto quello, ch' io vorrei che sapesse il* Dottore; *et penso che chi non havesse havuto qualche notitia delle cose che nel libro si trattano, per erudito che fosse stato, male haverebbe potuto scriverle: ma io non son tanto privo di giudicio in conoscere me stesso, che mi presuma saper tutto quello, che so desiderare.*

CASTIGLIONE.

In a building, — if it be large, there is much to be done in preparing and laying the foundation, before the walls appear above ground; much is doing within, when the work does not seem, perhaps, to advance without, and when it is considerably forward, yet being encumbered with scaffolds and rubbish, a bystander sees it at great disadvantage, and can form but an imperfect judgment of it. But all this while the architect himself, even from the laying of the first stone, conceives of it according to the plan and design he has formed; he prepares and adjusts the materials, disposing each in its proper time and place, and views it in idea as already finished. In due season it is compleated, but not in a day. The top-stone is fixed, and then, the scaffolds and rubbish being removed, it appears to others as he intended it should be.

JOHN NEWTON.

Non si dea adunque l' uomo contentare di fare le cose buone, ma dee studiare di farle anco leggiadre. E non è altro leggiadria, che una cotale quasi luce, che risplende dalla convenevolezza delle cose, che sono ben composte, e ben divisate l' una con l' altra, e tutte insieme; senza la quel misura eziandio il bene non è bello, e la bellezza non è piacevole.

M. GIO. DELLA CASA, GALATEO.

Pick out of mirth, like stones out of thy ground,
  Profaneness, filthiness, abusiveness;
These are the scum with which coarse wits abound;
  The few may spare them well.

HERBERT.

The wise, — weighs each thing as it ought,
  Mistakes no term, nor sentence wrests awry;
The fond will read awhile, but cares for nought,
  Yet casts on each man's work a frowning eye.
  This neither treats of matters low nor high,
But finds a meane, that each good meaning might
In all true means take Charity aright.

CHURCHYARD.

While others fish with craft for great opinion,
I with great truth catch mere simplicity.
Whilst some with cunning gild their copper crowns,
With truth and plainness I do wear mine bare.
Fear not my truth; the moral of my wit
Is — plain and true; — there's all the reach of it.

SHAKSPEARE.

τούτων οὖν οὕνεκα πάντων,
ὅτι σωφρονικῶς, κοὐκ ἀνοήτως ἐσπήδησας ἐφλυάρει,
αἴρεσθ' αὐτῷ πολὺ τὸ ῥόθιον, παραπέμψατ' ἐφ' ἕνδεκα κώπαις
θόρυβον χρηστὸν ληναΐτην,
ἵν' ὁ ποιητὴς ἀπίῃ χαίρων,
κατὰ νοῦν πράξας,
φαιδρὸς λάμποντι μετώπῳ.

ARISTOPHANES.

Io vorrei, Monsignor, solo tant' arte
Ch' io potessi, per longo e per traverso,
Dipengervi il mio cor in queste carte.

LUDOVICO DOLCE.

Nous nous aimons un peu, c'est notre faible à tous;
Le prix que nous valons qui le sçait mieux que nous?
Et puis la mode en est, et la cour l'autorise,
Nous parlons de nous-mêmes avec tout franchise.

CORNEILLE.

Mes paroles sont un peu de dure digestion pour la foiblesse des estomacs d'à present. Mais si on les remâche bien, on en tirera beaucoup de substance.

MADEMOISELLE BOURIGNON.

Supersunt etiam plurima quæ dici possint in hanc materiam, quibus pro vitando fastidio, supersedendum puto; ut si quis eadem conari velit, habeat etiamnum aliquid in quo exerceat industriam.

REN. RAPIN.

I wish thee as much pleasure in the reading as I had in the writing.

QUARLES.

CONTENTS.

THE DOCTOR,

&c.

Eccoti il libro; mettivi ben cura
Iddio t' ajuti e dia buona ventura.
ORL. INNAM.

Pand. Ay, the bolting; but you must tarry the leavening.

Troilus. Still have I tarried.

Pand. Ay, to the leavening: but here's yet in the word hereafter, the kneading, the making of the cake, the heating of the oven, and the baking. Nay, you must stay the cooling too; or you may chance to burn your lips.

TROILUS AND CRESSIDA.

Enobarbus. Every time
Serves for the matter that is then born in it.
Lepidus. But small to greater matters must give way.
Enobarbus. Not if the small come first.

SHAKESPEARE.

Lass mich den Stunde gedenken, und jedes kleineren unstands.
Ach, wer ruft nicht so gern unwiederbringliches an!
Jenes süsse Gedränge der leichtesten irdischen Tage,
Ach, wer schätzt ihn genug, diesen vereilenden Werth!
Klein erscheinet es nun, doch ach! nicht kleinlich dem Herzen;
Macht die Liebe, die Kunst, jegliches kleine doch gross.

GOETHE.

Que sea Medico mas grave
Quien mas aforismos sabe,
Bien puede ser.
Mas que no sea mas experto
El que mas huviere muerto,
No puede ser.

GONGORA.

I wander 'twixt the poles
And heavenly hinges, 'mongst eccentricals,
Centers, concentricks, circles and epicycles.

ALBUMAZAR.

Diré aqui una maldad grande del Demonio.

PEDRO DE CIEÇA DE LEON.

Quid de pulicibus? vitæ salientia puncta. COWLEY.

Voulant doncques satisfaire à la curiosité de touts bons compagnons, j'ay revolvé toutes les Pantarches des Cieux, calculé les quadrats de la Lune, crocheté tout ce que jamais penserent touts les Astrophiles, Hypernephelistes, Anemophylaces, Uranopetes et Ombrophores. RABELAIS.

Si j'avois dispersé ceci en divers endroits de mon ouvrage, j'aurois évité la censure de ceux qui appelleront ce chapitre un fatras de petit recueils. Mais comme je cherche la commodité de mes lecteurs plutôt que la mienne, je veux bien au depens de cette censure, leur épargner la peine de rassembler ce que j'aurois dispersé. BAYLE.

A man that travelleth to the most desirable home, hath a habit of desire to it all the way; but his present business is his travel; and horse, and company, and inns, and ways, and weariness, &c., may take up more of his sensible thoughts, and of his talk and action, than his home.

BAXTER.

Ὦ πολλὰ λέξας ἄρτι κἀνόνητ' ἔπη,
Οὐ μνημονεύεις οὐκέτ' οὐδέν; SOPHOCLES.

Opinion is the rate of things,
From hence our peace doth flow;
I have a better fate than kings,
Because I think it so. KATHARINE PHILIPS.

—Now I love,
And so as in so short a time I may;
Yet so as time shall never break that so,
And therefore so accept of Elinor.

ROBERT GREENE.

Un mal que se entra por medio los ojos,
Y va se derecho hasta el corazon;
Alli en ser llegado se torna aficion,
Y da mil pesares, plazeres y enojos;
Causa alegrias, tristezas, antojos;
Haze llorar, y haze reir,
Haze cantar, y haze plañir;
Da pensamientos dos mil a manojos.

QUESTION DE AMOR.

Ἔνθα γάρ τι δεῖ ψεῦδος λέγεσθαι λεγέσθω.

HERODOTUS.

Ha, ha, ha, now ye will make me to smile,
To see if I can all men beguile.
Ha, my name, my name would ye so fain know?
Yea, I wis, shall ye, and that with all speed.
I have forgot it, therefore I cannot show.
A, a, now I have it! I have it indeed!
My name is Ambidexter, I signify one
That with both hands finely can play.

KING CAMBYSES.

Hark how the birds do sing,
And woods do ring!
All creatures have their joy, and Man hath his:
Yet if we rightly measure,
Man's joy and pleasure
Rather hereafter, than in present is. HERBERT.

In midst of plenty only to embrace
Calm patience, is not worthy of your praise;
But he that can look sorrow in the face
And not be daunted, he deserves the bays.
This is prosperity, where'er we find
A heavenly solace in an earthly mind.

HUGH CROMPTON.

It seems that you take pleasure in these walks, Sir.
Cleanthes. Contemplative content I do, my Lord;
They bring into my mind oft meditations
So sweetly precious, that in the parting
I find a shower of grace upon my cheeks,
They take their leave so feelingly.

MASSINGER.

If we present a mingle-mangle, our fault is to be excused, because the whole world is become a hodge-podge.

LYLY.

And sure there seem of human kind
Some born to shun the solemn strife;
Some for amusive tasks design'd
To soothe the certain ills of life,
Grace its lone vales with many a budding rose,
New founts of bliss disclose,
Call forth refreshing shades and decorate repose.

SHENSTONE.

Perhaps some Gull, as witty as a Goose,
Says with a coy skew look, "it's pretty, pretty!"
But yet that so much wit he should dispose
For so small purpose, faith" saith he, "'tis pity!"
DAVIES OF HEREFORD.

Theo. Look to my Horse, I pray you, well.
Diego. He shall, Sir.
Inc. Oh! how beneath his rank and call was that now!
Your Horse shall be entreated as becomes
A Horse of fashion, and his inches.
BEAUMONT AND FLETCHER.

Every man can say B to a battledore, and write in praise of virtue and the seven liberal sciences; thresh corn out of full sheaves, and fetch water out of the Thames. But out of dry stubble to make an after-harvest, and a plentiful crop without sowing, and wring juice out of a flint, that is Pierce a God's name, and the right trick of a workman. NASH.

—— his birth day, the eleventh of June
When the Apostle Barnaby the bright
Unto our year doth give the longest light.
BEN JONSON.

Lady Percy. But hear you, my Lord!
Hotspur. What say'st thou, my lady?
Lady Percy. What is it carries you away?
Hotspur. Why my Horse, my love, my Horse.
SHAKESPEARE.

Moreover there are many more things in the World than there are names for them; according to the saying of the Philosopher; *Nomina sunt finita, res autem infinitæ; ideo unum nomen plura significat:* which saying is by a certain, or rather uncertain, author approved: *Multis speciebus non sunt nomina; idcirco necessarium est nomina fingere, si nullum ante erit nomen impositum.* GWILLIM.

Quoiqu'il en soit, je ne tairai point cette histoire; je l'abandonne à la credulité, ou à l'incredulité des Lecteurs, ils prendront à cet égard quel parti il leur plaira. Je dirai seulement, s'ils ne la veulent pas croire, que je les defie de me prouver qu'elle soit absolument impossible; ils ne le prouveront jamais. GOMGAM.

Oh penny Pipers, and most painful penners
Of bountiful new Ballads, what a subject,
What a sweet subject for your silver sounds!
BEAUMONT AND FLETCHER.

Neither is it a thing impossible or greatly hard, even by such kind of proofs so to manifest and clear that point, that no man living shall be able to deny it, without denying some apparent principle such as all men acknowledge to be true. HOOKER.

Quant à moi, je desirerois fort sçavoir bien dire, ou que j'eusse eu une bonne plume, et bien taillée à commandement, pour l'exalter et louër comme il le mérite. Toutesfois, telle quelle est, je m'en vais l'employer au hazard. BRANTOME.

Renowned beast! (forgive poetic flight!)
Not less than man, deserves poetic right.
THE BRUCIAD.

There is a word, and it is a great word in this Book,* ἐπὶ τὸ αὐτὸ, — *In id ipsum,* that is, to look to the thing itself, the very point, the principal matter of all; to have our eye on that, and not off it, upon *alia omnia*, any thing but it. — To go to the point, drive all to that, as also to go to the matter real, without declining from it this way or that, to the right hand or to the left. BP. ANDREWES.

* The New Testament which the Preacher had before him.

Perseveremus, peractis quæ rem continebant, scrutari etiam ea quæ, si vis verum, connexa sunt, non cohærentia; quæ quisquis diligenter inspicit, nec facit operæ prætium, nec tamen perdit operam. SENECA.

As I have gained no small satisfaction to myself, — so I am desirous that nothing that occurs here may occasion the least dissatisfaction to others. And I think it will be impossible anything should, if they will be but pleased to take notice of my design. HENRY MORE.

Parolles. Go to, thou art a witty fool, I have found thee.
Clown. Did you find me in yourself, Sir? or were you taught to find me? The search, Sir, was profitable; and much fool may you find in you, even to the world's pleasure and the increase of laughter.
ALL'S WELL THAT ENDS WELL.

Perhaps when the Reader considers the copiousness of the argument, he will rather blame me for being too brief than too tedious. DR. JOHN SCOTT.

Mirths and toys
To cozen time withal: for o' my troth, Sir,
I can love, — I think well too, — well enough;
And think as well of women as they are, —
Pretty fantastic things, some more regardful,
And some few worth a service. I'm so honest
I wish 'em all in Heaven, and you know how hard, Sir,
'Twill be to get in there with their great farthingals.
BEAUMONT AND FLETCHER.

And not much easier now with their great sleeves.
AUTHOR. A. D. 1830.

Sing of the nature of women, and then the song shall be surely full of variety, old crotchets, and most sweet closes: It shall be humourous, grave, fantastic, amorous, melancholy, sprightly, one in all and all in one. MARSTON.

If there sit twelve women at the table, let a dozen of them be — as they are. TIMON OF ATHENS.

If thy name were known that writest in this sort,
By womankind, unnaturally, giving evil report,
Whom all men ought, both young and old, defend with all their might,
Considering what they do deserve of every living wight,
I wish thou should exiled be from women more and less,
And not without just cause thou must thyself confess.
EDWARD MORE.

O voi ch' avete gl' intelletti sani,
Mirate la dottrina, che s' asconde
Sotto 'l velame degli versi strani. DANTE.

THE DOCTOR,

&c.

CHAPTER VII. A. I.

A FAMILY PARTY AT A NEXT DOOR NEIGHBOUR'S.

> Good Sir, reject it not, although it bring
> Appearances of some fantastic thing
> At first unfolding!
>
> George Wither to the King.

I was in the fourth night of the story of the Doctor and his horse, and had broken it off, not like Scheherezade because it was time to get up, but because it was time to go to bed. It was at thirty-five minutes after ten o'clock, on the 20th of July, in the year of our Lord 1813. I finished my glass of punch, tinkled the spoon against its side, as if making music to my meditations, and having my eyes fixed upon the Bhow Begum, who was sitting opposite to me at the head of her own table, I said, "It ought to be written in a book!"

There had been a heavy thunder-storm in the afternoon; and though the thermometer had fallen from 78 to 70, still the atmosphere was charged. If that mysterious power by which the nerves convey sensation and make their impulses obeyed, be (as experiments seem to indicate) identical with the galvanic fluid; and if the galvanic and electric fluids be the same (as philosophers have more than surmised); and if the lungs (according to a happy hypothesis) elaborate for us from the light of heaven this pabulum of the brain, and material essence, or essential matter of genius,—it may be that the ethereal fire which I had inhaled so largely during the day produced the bright conception, or at least impregnated and quickened the latent seed. The punch, reader, had no share in it.

I had spoken as it were abstractedly, and the look which accompanied the words was rather cogitative than regardant. The Bhow Begum laid down her snuff-box and replied, entering into the feeling, as well as echoing the words, "It *ought* to be written in a book,—certainly it ought."

They may talk as they will of the dead languages. Our auxiliary verbs give us a power which the ancients, with all their varieties of mood, and inflections of tense, never could attain. "It *must* be written in a book," said I, encouraged by her manner. The mood was the same, the tense was the same; but the gradation of meaning was marked in a way which a Greek or Latin grammarian might have envied as well as admired.

"Pshaw! nonsense! stuff!" said my wife's eldest sister, who was sitting at the right hand of the Bhow Begum; "I say, write it in a book indeed!" My wife's youngest sister was sitting diagonally opposite to the last speaker; she lifted up her eyes and smiled. It was a smile which expressed the same opinion as the late vituperative tones; there was as much of incredulity in it; but more of wonder and less of vehemence.

My wife was at my left hand, making a cap for her youngest daughter, and with her tortoiseshell-paper work-box before her. I turned towards her, and repeated the words, "It *must* be written in a book!" But I smiled while I was speaking, and was conscious of that sort of meaning in my eyes which calls out contradiction for the pleasure of sporting with it.

"Write it in a book!" she replied, "I am sure you won't;" and she looked at me with a frown. Poets have written much upon their ladies' frowns, but I do not remember that they have ever described the thing with much accuracy. When my wife frowns, two perpendicular wrinkles, each three quarters of an inch in length, are formed in the forehead, the base of each resting upon the top of the nose, and equidistant from each other. The poets have also attributed dreadful effects to the frown of those whom they love. I cannot say that I ever experienced any thing very formidable in my wife's. At present she knew her eyes would give the lie to it if they looked at me steadily for a moment; so they wheeled to the left about quick, off at a tangent, in a direction to the Bhow Begum, and then she smiled. She could not prevent the smile; but she tried to make it scornful.

My wife's nephew was sitting diagonally with her, and opposite his mother, on the left hand of the Bhow Begum. "Oh!" he exclaimed, "it ought to be written in a book! it will be a glorious book! write it, uncle, I beseech you!" My wife s nephew is a sensible lad. He reads my writings, likes my stories, admires my singing, and thinks as I do in politics:—a youth of parts and considerable promise.

"He *will* write it!" said the Bhow Begum, taking up her snuff-box, and accompanying the words with a nod of satisfaction and encouragement. "He will never be so foolish!" said my wife. My wife's eldest sister rejoined, "he is foolish enough for any thing."

CHAPTER VI. A. I.

SHOWING THAT AN AUTHOR MAY MORE EASILY BE KEPT AWAKE BY HIS OWN IMAGINATIONS THAN PUT TO SLEEP BY THEM HIMSELF, WHATEVER MAY BE THEIR EFFECT UPON HIS READERS.

> Thou sleepest worse than if a mouse should be forced to take up her lodging in a cat's ear: a little infant that breeds its teeth, should it lie with thee, would cry out as if thou wert the more unquiet bedfellow. WEBSTER.

WHEN I ought to have been asleep the "unborn pages crowded on my soul." The Chapters ante-initial and post-initial appeared in delightful prospect "long drawn out:" the beginning, the middle and the end were evolved before me: the whole spread itself forth, and then the parts unravelled themselves and danced the hays. The very types rose in judgment against me, as if to persecute me for the tasks which during so many years I had imposed upon them. Capitals and small letters, pica and long-primer, brevier and bourgeois, English and nonpareil, minion and pearl, Romans and Italics, black-letter and red, passed over my inward sight. The notes of admiration ! ! ! stood straight up in view as I lay on the one side; and when I turned on the other to avoid them, the notes of interrogation cocked up their hump-backs ? ? ? Then came to recollection the various incidents of the eventful tale. "Visions of glory spare my aching sight!" The various personages, like spectral faces in a fit of the vapours, stared at me through my eyelids. The Doctor oppressed me like an incubus; and for the Horse,—he became a perfect night-mare. "Leave me, leave me to repose!"

Twelve by the kitchen clock!—still restless!—One! O Doctor, for one of thy comfortable composing draughts!—Two! here's a case of insomnolence! I, who in summer close my lids as instinctively as the daisy when the sun goes down; and who in winter could hybernate as well as Bruin, were I but provided with as much fat to support me during the season, and keep the wick of existence burning:—I, who, if my pedigree were properly made out, should be found to have descended from one of the Seven Sleepers, and from the Sleeping Beauty in the Wood!

I put my arms out of bed. I turned the pillow for the sake of applying a cold surface to my cheek. I stretched my feet into the cold corner. I listened to the river, and to the ticking of my watch. I thought of all sleepy sounds and all soporific things: the flow of water, the humming of bees, the motion of a boat, the waving of a field of corn, the nodding of a mandarine's head on the chimney-piece, a horse in a mill, the opera, Mr. Humdrum's conversation, Mr. Proser's poems, Mr. Laxative's speeches, Mr. Lengthy's sermons. I tried the device of my own childhood, and fancied that the bed revolved with me round and round. Still the Doctor visited me as perseveringly as if I had been his best patient; and, call up what thoughts I would to keep him off, the Horse charged through them all.

At last Morpheus reminded me of Dr. Torpedo's divinity lectures, where the voice, the manner, the matter, even the very atmosphere, and the streamy candle-light were all alike somnific; — where he who by strong effort lifted up his head, and forced open the reluctant eyes, never failed to see all around him fast asleep. Lettuces, cowslip-wine, poppy-syrup, mandragora, hop-pillows, spiders-web pills, and the whole tribe of narcotics, up to bang and the black drop, would have failed: but this was irresistible; and thus twenty years after date I found benefit from having attended the course.

CHAPTER V. A. I.

SOMETHING CONCERNING THE PHILOSOPHY OF DREAMS, AND THE AUTHOR'S EXPERIENCE IN AERIEL HORSEMANSHIP.

If a dream should come in now to make you afear'd,
With a windmill on his head and bells at his beard,
Would you straight wear your spectacles here at your toes,
And your boots on your brows and your spurs on your nose?
BEN JONSON.

THE wise ancients held that dreams are from Jove. Virgil hath told us from what gate of the infernal regions they go out, but at which of the five entrances of the town of Mansoul they get in John Bunyan hath not explained. Some have conceited that unembodied spirits have access to us during sleep, and impress upon the passive faculty, by divine permission, presentiments of those things whereof it is fitting that we should be thus dimly forewarned. This opinion is held by Baxter, and to this also doth Bishop Newton incline. The old atomists supposed that the likenesses or spectres of corporeal things (*excuviæ scilicet rerum, vel effluvia*, as they are called by Vaninus, when he takes advantage of them to explain the *Fata Morgana*), the atomists I say, supposed that these spectral forms which are constantly emitted from all bodies,

Omne genus quoniam passim simulacra feruntur *,

assail the soul when she ought to be at rest; according to which theory all the lathered faces that are created every morning in the looking-glass, and all the smiling ones that my Lord Simper and Mr. Smallwit contemplate there with so much satisfaction during the day, must at this moment be floating up and down the world. Others again opine, as if in contradiction to those who pretend life to be a dream, that dreams are realities, and that sleep sets the soul free like a bird from a cage. John Henderson saw the spirit of a slumbering cat pass from her in pursuit of a visionary mouse; — (I know not whether he would have admitted the fact as an argument for materialism;) and the soul of Hans Engelbrecht not only went to hell, but brought back from it a stench which proved to all the bystanders that it had been there. — Faugh!

Whether then my spirit that night found its way out at the nose (for I sleep with my mouth shut), and actually sallied out seeking adventures; or whether the spectrum of the Horse floated into my chamber; or some benevolent genius or dæmon assumed the well-known and welcome form; or whether the dream were merely a dream, —

si fuè en espiritu, ò fuè
en cuerpo, no sè ; que yo
solo sè, que no lo sè ; †

so however it was that in the visions of the night I mounted Nobs. Tell me not of Astolfo's hippogriff, or Pacolet's wooden steed; nor

Of that wonderous horse of brass
Whereon the Tartar King did pass;

nor of Alborak, who was the best beast for a night-journey that ever man bestrode. Tell

---

* LUCRETIUS. † CALDERON.

me not even of Pegasus! I have ridden him many a time; by day and by night have I ridden him; high and low, far and wide, round the earth, and about it, and over it, and under it. I know all his earth-paces, and his sky-paces. I have tried him at a walk, at an amble, at a trot, at a canter, at a hand-gallop, at full gallop, and at full speed. I have proved him in the *manège* with single turns and the *manège* with double turns, his bounds, his curvets, his *pirouettes*, and his *pistes*, his *croupade* and his *balotade*, his gallop-galliard, and his capriole. I have been on him when he has glided through the sky with wings outstretched and motionless, like a kite or a summer cloud; I have bestrode him when he went up like a bittern with a strong spiral flight, round, round, and round, and upward, upward, upward, circling and rising still; and again when he has gone full sail, or full fly, with his tail as straight as a comet's behind him. But for a hobby or a night horse, Pegasus is nothing to Nobs.

Where did we go on that memorable night? What did we see? — What did we do? — Or rather what did we not see? and what did we not perform?

CHAPTER IV. A. I.

A CONVERSATION AT THE BREAKFAST TABLE.

Tel condamne mon Coq-à-l'âne qui un jour en justifiera e bon sens. LA PRETIEUSE.

I WENT down to breakfast as usual, overflowing with joyous thoughts. For mirth and for music, the skylark is but a type of me. I warbled a few wood notes wild, and then, full of the unborn work, addressed myself to my wife's eldest sister, and asked if she would permit me to dedicate the Book to her. "What book?" she replied. "The History," said I, "of Doctor Daniel Dove, of Doncaster, and his Horse Nobs." She answered, "No, indeed! I will have no such nonsense dedicated to me!" — and with that she drew up her upper lip, and the lower region of the nose. I turned to my wife's youngest sister: "Shall I have the pleasure of dedicating it to you?" She raised her eyes, inclined her head forwards with a smile of negation, and begged leave to decline the honour. "Commandante," said I, to my wife and Commandress, "shall I dedicate it then to you?" My Commandante made answer, "Not unless you have something better to dedicate."

"So Ladies!" said I; "the stone which the builders rejected," — and then looking at my wife's youngest sister — "Oh, it will be such a book!" The manner and the tone were so much in earnest, that they arrested the bread and butter on the way to her mouth; and she exclaimed, with her eyes full of wonder and incredulity at the same time, "Why, you never can be serious?" "Not serious," said I; "why I have done nothing but think of it and dream of it the whole night." "He told me so," rejoined my Commandante, "the first thing in the morning." "Ah, Stupey!" cried my wife's eldest sister, accompanying the compliment with a protrusion of the head, and an extension of the lips, which disclosed not only the whole remaining row of teeth, but the chasms that had been made in it by the tooth drawer; *hiatus valde lacrymabiles.*

"Two volumes," said I, "and this in the title-page!" So taking out my pencil, I drew upon the back of a letter the mysterious monogram, erudite in its appearance as the diagamma of Mr. A. F. Valpy.

It past from hand to hand. "Why, he is not in earnest;" said my wife's youngest sister. "He never can be," replied my wife. And yet beginning to think that peradventure I was, she looked at me with a quick turn of the eye, — "a pretty subject, indeed, for you to employ your time upon! — You, — *vema whehaha yohu almad otenba twandri athancod!*" I have thought proper to translate this part of my Commandante's speech into the Garamna tongue.

CHAPTER III. A. I.

THE UTILITY OF POCKETS. A COMPLIMENT PROPERLY RECEIVED.

La tasca è proprio cosa da Christiani.
BENEDETTO VARCHI.

My eldest daughter had finished her Latin lessons, and my son had finished his Greek; and I was sitting at my desk, pen in hand and in mouth at the same time, (a substitute for biting the nails which I recommend to all onygophagists), when the Bow Begum came in with her black velvet reticule, suspended as usual from her arm by its silver chain.

Now, of all the inventions of the Tailor (who is of all artists the most inventive), I hold the pocket to be the most commodious, and, saving the fig leaf, the most indispensable. Birds have their craw; ruminating beasts their first or ante-stomach; the monkey has his cheek, the opossum her pouch; and, so necessary is some convenience of this kind for the human animal, that the savage who cares not for clothing, makes for himself a pocket if he can. The Hindoo carries his snuff-box in his turban. Some of the inhabitants of Congo make a secret fob in their woolly toupet, of which, as P. Labat says, the worst use they make is — to carry poison in it. The Matolas, a long-haired race, who border upon the Caffres, form their locks into a sort of hollow cylinder in which they bear about their little implements; certes a more sensible bag than such as is worn at court. The New Zealander is less ingenious; he makes a large opening in his ear, and carries his knife in it. The Ogres, who are worse than savages, and whose ignorance and brutality is in proportion to their bulk, are said, upon the authority of tradition, when they have picked up a stray traveller or two more than they require for their supper, to lodge them in a hollow tooth, as a place of security till breakfast; whence it may be inferred that they are not liable to tooth-ache, and that they make no use of tooth-picks. Ogres, savages, beasts, and birds, all require something to serve the purpose of a pocket. Thus much for the necessity of the thing. Touching its antiquity, much might be said; for it would not be difficult to show, with that little assistance from the auxiliaries *must* and *have* and *been*, which enabled Whitaker, of Manchester, to write whole quartos of hypothetical history in the potential mood, that pockets are coeval with clothing: and, as erudite men have maintained that language and even letters are of divine origin, there might with like reason be a conclusion drawn from the twenty-first verse of the third chapter of the book of Genesis, which it would not be easy to impugn. Moreover, nature herself shows us the utility, the importance, nay, the indispensability, or, to take a hint from the pure language of our diplomatists, the *sinequanonniness* of pockets. There is but one organ which is common to all animals whatsoever: some are without eyes, many without noses; some have no heads, others no tails; some neither one nor the other; some there are who have no brains, others very pappy ones; some no hearts, others very bad ones; but all have a stomach, — and what is the stomach but a live inside pocket? Hath not Van Helmont said of it, "*Saccus vel pera est, ut ciborum olla?*"

Dr. Towers used to have his coat pockets made of capacity to hold a quarto volume — a wise custom; but requiring stout cloth, good buckram, and strong thread well waxed. I do not so greatly commend the humour of Dr. Ingenhouz, whose coat was lined with pockets of all sizes, wherein, in his latter years, when science had become to him as a plaything, he carried about various materials for chemical experiments: among the rest, so many compositions for fulminating powders in glass tubes, separated only by a cork in the middle of the tube, that, if any person had unhappily given him a blow with a stick, he might have blown up himself and the Doctor too. For myself, four coat pockets of the ordinary dimensions content me; in these a sufficiency of conveniences may be carried, and that sufficiency methodically arranged. For mark me, gentle or ungentle reader! there is nothing like method in pockets, as well as in composition: and what orderly and methodical man would have his pocket-handkerchief, and his pocket-book, and the key of his door (if he be a batchelor living in chambers), and his knife, and his loose pence and half-pence, and the letters which peradventure he might just have received, or peradventure he may intend to drop in the post-office, two-penny or general, as he passes by, and his snuff, if he be accustomed so to regale his olfactory conduits, or his tobacco-box if he prefer the masticable to the pulverized weed, or his box of lozenges if he should be troubled with a tickling cough; and the sugar-plumbs, and the gingerbread nuts which he may be carrying home to his own children, or to any other small men and women upon whose hearts he may have a design;—who, I say, would like to have all this in chaos and confusion, one lying upon the other, and the thing which is wanted first fated alway to be undermost! (Mr. Wilberforce knows the inconvenience)—the snuff working its way out to the gingerbread, the sugar-plumbs insinuating themselves into the folds of the pocket-handkerchief, the pence grinding the lozenges to dust for the benefit of the pocket-book, and the door key busily employed in unlocking the letters?

Now, forasmuch as the commutation of female pockets for the reticule leadeth to inconveniences like this (not to mention that the very name of commutation ought to be held in abhorrence by all who hold day-light and fresh air essential to the comfort and salubrity of dwelling-houses), I abominate that bag of the Bhow Begum, notwithstanding the beauty of the silver chain upon the black velvet. And perceiving at this time that the clasp of its silver setting was broken, so that the mouth of the bag was gaping pitiably, like a sick or defunct oyster, I congratulated her as she came in upon this farther proof of the commodiousness of the invention; for here, in the country, there is no workman who can mend that clasp, and the bag must therefore either be laid aside, or used in that deplorable state.

When the Bhow Begum had seated herself I told her how my proffered dedication had been thrice rejected with scorn, and repeating the offer I looked for a more gracious reply. But, as if scorn had been the influenza of the female mind that morning, she answered, "No; indeed she would not have it after it had been refused by every body else." "Nay, nay," said I; "it is as much in your character to accept, as it was in theirs to refuse." While I was speaking she took a pinch of snuff; the nasal titillation co-operated with my speech, for when any one of the senses is pleased, the rest are not likely to continue out of humour. "Well," she replied, "I will have it dedicated to me, because I shall delight in the book." And she powdered the carpet with tobacco dust as she spake.

CHAPTER II. A. I.

CONCERNING DEDICATIONS, PRINTERS' TYPES, AND IMPERIAL INK.

Il y aura des clefs, et des ouvertures de mes secrets.
LA PRETIEUSE.

MONSIEUR Dellon, having been in the Inquisition at Goa, dedicated an account of that tribunal, and of his own sufferings to Mademoiselle du Cambout de Coislin, in these words:

Mademoiselle,

J'aurois tort de me plaindre des rigueurs de l'Inquisition, et des mauvais traitements que j'ay éprouvez de la part de ses ministres, puisqu'en me fournissant la matière de cet ouvrage, ils m'ont procuré l'avantage de vous le dédier.

This is the book which that good man Claudius Buchanan with so much propriety put into the hands of the Grand Inquisitor of India, when he paid him a visit at the Inquisition, and asked him his opinion of the accuracy of the relation upon the spot!

The Frenchman's compliment may truly be said to have been far-fetched and dearly bought. Heaven forefend that I should either go so far for one, or purchase it at such a price!

A dedication has oftentimes cost the unhappy author a greater consumption of thumb and finger nail than the whole book besides, and all varieties of matter and manner have been resorted to. Mine must be so far in character with the delectable history which it introduces, that it shall be unlike all which have ever gone before it. I knew a man (one he was who would have been an ornament to his country if methodism and madness had not combined to overthrow a bright and creative intellect), who, in one of his insaner moods, printed a sheet and a half of muddy rhapsodies with the title of the "Standard of God Displayed:" and he prefaced it by saying that the price of a perfect book, upon a perfect subject, ought to be a perfect sum in a perfect coin; that is to say, one guinea. Now as Dr. Daniel Dove was a perfect Doctor, and his horse Nobs was a perfect horse, and as I humbly hope their history will be a perfect history, so ought the Dedication thereunto to be perfect in its kind. Perfect therefore it shall be, as far as kalotypography can make it. For though it would be hopeless to exceed all former Dedications in the turn of a compliment or of a sentence, in the turn of the letters it is possible to exceed them all. It was once my fortune to employ a printer who had a love for his art; and having a taste that way myself, we discussed the merits of a new font one day when I happened to call in upon him. I objected to the angular inclination of a capital italic *A* which stood upon its pins as if it were starting aghast from the next letter on the left, and was about to tumble upon that to the right; in which case down would go the rest of the word, like a row of soldiers which children make with cards. My printer was too deeply enamoured with the beauties of his font, to have either ear or eye for its defects; and hastily waving that point he called my attention to a capital *R* in the same line, which cocked up its tail just as if it had been nicked; that cock of the tail had fascinated him. "Look Sir," said he, while his eyes glistened with all the ardour of an amateur; "look at that turn! —that's sweet, Sir!" and drawing off the hand with the forefinger of which he had indicated it, he described in the air the turn that had delighted him, in a sort of heroic flourish, his head with a diminished axis, like the inner stile of a Pentegraph, following the movement. I have never seen that R since without remembering him. ** *** ** **** ** *** ******** ** *** ***** ******* ** *******, *** ********* *****, ***, *** ** *** ******* ***** ** **********, *** *** *******. He who can read the stars, may read in them the secret which he seeketh.

But the turns of my Dedication to the Bhow Begum shall not be trusted to the letter founders, a set of men remarkable for involving their craft in such mystery that no one ever taught it to another, every one who has practised it having been obliged either surreptitiously to obtain the secret, or to invent a method for himself. It shall be in the old English letter, not only because that alphabet hath in its curves and angles, its frettings and redundant lines, a sort of picturesque similitude with Gothic architecture, but also because in its breadth and beauty it will display the colour of the ink to most advantage. For the Dedication shall not be printed in black after the ordinary fashion, nor in white like the Sermon upon the Excise Laws, nor in red after the mode of Mr. Dibdin's half titles, but in the colour of that imperial encaustic ink, which by the laws of the Roman Empire it was death for any but the Roman Emperor himself to use. We Britons live in a free country, wherein every man may use what coloured ink seemeth good to him, and put as much gall in it as he pleases, or any other ingredient whatsoever. Moreover this is an imperial age, in which to say nothing of M. Ingelby, the Emperor of the Conjurors, we have seen no fewer than four new Emperors. He of Russia, who did not think the old title of Peter the Great good enough for him; he of France, for whom any name but that of Tyrant or Murderer is too good; he of Austria, who took up one imperial appellation to cover over the humiliating manner in which he laid another down; and he of Hayti, who if he be wise will order all public business to be carried on in the talkee-talkee tongue, and make it high treason for any person to speak or write French in his dominions. We also must dub our old Parliament imperial forsooth! that we may not be behindhand with the age. Then we have Imperial Dining Tables! Imperial Oil for nourishing the hair! Imperial Liquid for Boot Tops! Yea, and, by all the Cæsars deified and damnified, Imperial Blacking! For my part I love to go with the stream, so I will have an Imperial Dedication.

Behold it, Reader. Therein is mystery.

To
The Bhow Begum
KEDORA
NIABARMA.

CHAPTER I. A. I.

NO BOOK CAN BE COMPLETE WITHOUT A PREFACE.

I see no cause but men may pick their teeth,
Though Brutus with a sword did kill himself.

TAYLOR, THE WATER POET.

WHO was the Inventor of Prefaces? I shall be obliged to the immortal Mr. Urban (immortal, because like the king in law he never dies,) if he will propound this question for me in his Magazine, that great lumber-room wherein small ware of all kinds has been laid up higgledy-piggledy by half-penny-worths or farthing-worths at a time for four-score years, till, like broken glass, rags, or rubbish, it has acquired value by mere accumulation. To send a book like this into the world without a Preface would be as impossible as it is to appear at Court without a bag at the head and a sword at the tail; for as the perfection of dress must be shown at Court, so in this history should the perfection of histories be exhibited. The book must be *omni genere absolutum;* it must prove and exemplify the perfectibility of books: yea, with all imaginable respect for the "Delicate Investigation," which I leave in undisputed possession of an appellation so exquisitely appropriate, I conceive that the title of THE BOOK, as a popular designation κατ' ἐξοχὴν, should be transferred from the edifying report of that Inquiry, to the present unique, unrivalled, and unrivalable production;—a production the like whereof hath not been, is not, and will not be. Here however let me warn my Greek and Arabian translators how they render the word, that if they offend the Mufti or the Patriarch, the offence as well as the danger may be theirs: I wash my hands of both. I write in plain English, innocently and in the simplicity of my heart: what may be made of it in heathen languages concerns not me.

ANTE-PREFACE.

I here present thee with a hive of bees, laden some with wax, and some with honey. Fear not to approach! There are no Wasps, there are no Hornets here. If some wanton Bee should chance to buzz about thine ears, stand thy ground and hold thy hands: there's none will sting thee if thou strike not first. If any do, she hath honey in her bag will cure thee too.

QUARLES.

"PREFACES," said Charles Blount, Gent., who committed suicide because the law would not allow him to marry his brother's widow,—(a law, be it remarked in passing, which is not sanctioned by reason, and which, instead of being in conformity with scripture, is in direct opposition to it, being in fact the mere device of a corrupt and greedy church)—"Prefaces," said this flippant, ill-opinioned and unhappy man, "ever were, and still are but of two sorts, let other modes and fashions vary as they please. Let the profane long peruke succeed the godly cropt hair; the cravat, the ruff; presbytery, popery; and popery presbytery again, yet still the author keeps to his old and wonted method of prefacing; when at the beginning of his book he enters, either with a halter about his neck, submitting himself to his reader's mercy whether he shall be hanged, or no; or else in a huffing manner he appears with the halter in his hand, and threatens to hang his reader, if he gives him not his good word. This, with the excitement of some friends to his undertaking, and some few apologies for want of time, books, and the like, are the constant and usual shams of all scribblers as well ancient as modern." This was not true then, nor is it now; but when he proceeds to say, "for my part I enter the lists upon another score,"—so say I with him; and my Preface shall say the rest.

PREFACE.

Oh for a quill pluck'd from a Seraph's wing!
YOUNG.

So the Poet exclaimed; and his exclamation may be quoted as one example more of the vanity of human wishes; for, in order to get a Seraph's quill it would be necessary, according to Mrs. Glasse's excellent item in her directions for roasting a hare, to begin by catching a Seraph. A quill from a Seraph's wing is, I confess, above my ambition; but one from a Peacock's tail was within my reach; and be it known unto all people, nations and languages, that with a Peacock's quill this Preface hath been penned—literally—truly, and *bona-fidely* speaking. And this is to write, as the learned old Pasquier says, *pavonesquement*, which in Latin minted for the nonce may be rendered *pavonicè*, and in English peacockically or peacockishly, whichever the reader may like best. That such a pen has verily and indeed been used upon this occasion I affirm. I affirm it upon the word of a true man; and here is a Captain of his Majesty's Navy at my elbow, who himself made the pen, and who, if evidence were required to the fact, would attest it by as round an oath as ever rolled over a right English tongue. Nor will the time easily escape his remembrance, the bells being at this moment ringing, June 4. 1814, to celebrate the King's birth-day, and the public notification that peace has been concluded with France.

I have oftentimes had the happiness of seeing due commendation bestowed by gentle critics, unknown admirers and partial friends upon my pen, which has been married to all amiable epithets:—classical, fine, powerful, tender, touching, pathetic, strong, fanciful, daring, elegant, sublime, beautiful. I have read these epithets with that proper satisfaction which, when thus applied, they could not fail to impart, and sometimes qualified the pride which they inspired by looking at the faithful old tool of the Muses beside me, worn to the stump in their service: the one end mended up to the quick in that spirit of economy which becomes a son of the Lackland family, and shortened at the other by the gradual and alternate processes of burning and biting, till a scant inch only is left above the finger place. Philemon Holland was but a type of me in this respect. Indeed I may be allowed to say that I have improved upon his practice, or at least that I get more out of a pen than he did, for in the engraved title-page to his Cyrupædia, where there appears the Portrait of the *Interpres* marked by a great D inclosing the Greek letter Φ (which I presume designates Doctor Philemon) *ætatis suæ* 80. A°. 1632, it may be plainly seen that he used his pen only at one end. Peradventure he delighted not, as I do, in the mitigated ammoniac odour.

But thou, O gentle reader, who in the exercise of thy sound judgment and natural benignity wilt praise this Preface, thou mayest with perfect propriety bestow the richest epithets upon the pen wherewith its immortal words were first clothed in material forms. Beautiful, elegant, fine, splendid, fanciful, will be to the very letter of truth: versatile it is as the wildest wit; flexible as the most monkey-like talent; and shouldst thou call it tender, I will whisper in thine ear—that it is only too soft. Yet softness may be suitable; for of my numerous readers one half will probably be soft by sex, and of the other half a very considerable proportion soft by nature. Soft therefore be the Pen and soft the strain.

I have drawn up the window-blinds (though sunshine at this time acts like snuff upon the mucous membrane of my nose) in order that the light may fall upon this excellent Poet's wand as I wave it to and fro, making cuts five and six of the broad-sword exercise. Every feather of its fringe is now lit up by the sun; the hues of green and gold and amethyst are all brought forth; and that predominant lustre which can only be likened to some rich metallic oxyd; and that spot of deepest purple, the pupil of an eye for whose glorious hue neither metals nor flowers nor precious stones afford a resemblance: its likeness is only to be found in animated life, in birds and insects whom nature seems to have formed when she was most prodigal of beauty *: I have seen it indeed upon the sea, but it has been in some quiet bay when the reflection of the land combined with the sky and the ocean to produce it.

And what can be more emblematic of the work which I am beginning than the splendid instrument wherewith the Preface is traced? What could more happily typify the combination of parts, each perfect in itself when separately considered, yet all connected into one harmonious whole; the story running through like the stem or back-bone, which the episodes and digressions fringe like so many featherlets, leading up to that catastrophe, the gem or eye-star, for which the whole was formed, and in which all terminate.

They who are versed in the doctrine of sympathies and the arcana of correspondences as revealed to the Swedish Emanuel, will doubtless admire the instinct or inspiration which directed my choice to the pavonian Pen. The example should be followed by all consumers of ink and quill. Then would the lover borrow a feather from the turtle dove. The lawyer would have a large assortment of kite, hawk, buzzard and vulture: his clients may use pigeon or gull. Poets according to their varieties. Mr. ——, the Tom Tit. Mr. ——, the Water-wagtail. Mr. ——, the Crow. Mr. ——, the Mocking-bird. Mr. ——, the Magpie. Mr. ——, the Sky-lark. Mr. ——, the Eagle. Mr. ——, the Swan. Lord ——, the Black Swan. Critics some the Owl, others the Butcher Bird. Your challenger must indite with one from the wing of a game cock: he who takes advantage of a privileged situation to offer the wrong and shrink from the atonement will find a white feather. Your dealers in public and private scandal, whether Jacobins or Anti-Jacobins, the pimps and panders of a profligate press, should use none but duck feathers, and those of the dirtiest that can be found in the purlieus of Pimlico or St. George's Fields. But for the Editor of the Edinburgh Review, whether he dictates in morals or in taste, or displays his peculiar talent in political prophecy, he must continue to use goose quills. Stick to the goose, Mr. Jeffrey; while you live, stick to the Goose!

* "Framed in the prodigality of nature."
Richard III.

INITIAL CHAPTER.

'Εξ οὗ δὴ τὰ πρῶτα. — Homer.

They who remember the year 1800 will remember also the great controversy whether it was the beginning of a century, or the end of one; a controversy in which all Magazines, all Newspapers, and all persons took part. Now as it has been deemed expedient to divide this work, or to speak more emphatically this Opus, or more emphatically still this Ergon, into Chapters Ante-Initial and Post-Initial, a dispute of the same nature might arise among the commentators in after ages, if especial care were not now taken to mark distinctly the beginning. This therefore, is the Initial Chapter, neither Ante nor Post, but standing between both; the point of initiation, the goal of the *Antes*, the starting place of the *Posts;* the mark at which the former end their career, and from whence the latter take their departure.

THE DOCTOR,

ETC.

Eccoti il libro; mettivi ben cura,
Iddio t' ajuti e dia buona ventura.

ORL. INNAM.

CHAPTER I. P. I.

THE SUBJECT OF THIS HISTORY AT HOME AND AT TEA.

If thou be a severe sour complexioned man, then I here disallow thee to be a competent judge.

IZAAK WALTON.

THE clock of St. George's had struck five. Mrs. Dove had just poured out the Doctor's seventh cup of tea. The Doctor was sitting in his arm-chair. Sir Thomas was purring upon his knees; and Pompey stood looking up to his mistress, wagging his tail, sometimes whining with a short note of impatience, and sometimes gently putting his paw against her apron to remind her that he wished for another bit of bread and butter. Barnaby was gone to the farm: and Nobs was in the stable.

CHAPTER II. P. I.

WHEREIN CERTAIN QUESTIONS ARE PROPOSED CONCERNING TIME, PLACE, AND PERSONS.

Quis? quid? ubi? quibus auxiliis? cur? quomodo? quando?

TECHNICAL VERSE.

THUS have I begun according to the most approved forms; not like those who begin the Trojan War from Leda's egg, or the History of Great Britain from Adam, or the Life of General Washington from the Discovery of the New World; but in conformity to the Horatian precept, rushing into the middle of things. Yet the Giant Moulineau's appeal to his friend the story-telling Ram may well be remembered here; *Belier, mon ami, si tu voulois commencer par le commencement, tu me ferois grand plaisir.* For in the few lines of the preceding chapter how much is there that requires explanation? — Who was Nobs? — Who was Barnaby? — Who was the Doctor? — Who was Mrs. Dove? — The place, where? — The time, when? — The persons, who? —

I maie not tell you all at once;
But as I maie and can, I shall
By order tellen you it all.

So saith Chaucer; and in the same mind, *facilius discimus quæ congruo dicuntur ordine quam quæ sparsim et confusim*, saith Erasmus. Think a moment I beseech thee, Reader, what order is! Not the mere word which is so often vociferated in the House of Commons or uttered by the Speaker *ore rotundo*, when it is necessary for him to assume the tone of Ζεὺς ὑψιβρεμέτης; but order in its essence and truth, in itself and in its derivatives.

Waving the Orders in Council, and the Order of the Day, a phrase so familiar in the disorderly days of the French National Convention, think, gentle Reader, of the order of Knighthood, of Holy Orders, of the orders of architecture, the Linnæan orders, the orderly Serjeant, the ordinal numbers, the Ordinary of Newgate, the Ordinary on Sundays at 2 o'clock in the environs of the Metropolis, the ordinary faces of those who partake of what is ordinarily provided for them there;

and under the auspices of Government itself, and *par excellence* the Extraordinary Gazette. And as the value of health is never truly and feelingly understood except in sickness, contemplate for a moment what the want of order is. Think of disorder in things remote, and then as it approaches thee. In the country wherein thou livest, bad; in the town whereof thou art an inhabitant, worse; in thine own street, worser; in thine own house, worst of all. Think of it in thy family, in thy fortune, in thine intestines. In thy affairs, distressing; in thy members, painful; in thy conduct, ruinous. Order is the sanity of the mind, the health of the body, the peace of the city, the security of the state. As the beams to a house, as the bones to the microcosm of man, so is order to all things. Abstract it from a Dictionary, and thou mayest imagine the inextricable confusion which would ensue. Reject it from the Alphabet, and Zerah Colburne himself could not go through the chriscross row. How then should I do without it in this history?

A Quaker, by name Benjamin Lay, (who was a little cracked in the head though sound at heart,) took one of his compositions once to Benjamin Franklin that it might be printed and published. Franklin, having looked over the manuscript, observed that it was deficient in arrangement; it is no matter, replied the author, print any part thou pleasest first. Many are the speeches and the sermons and the treatises and the poems and the volumes which are like Benjamin Lay's book; the head might serve for the tail, and the tail for the body, and the body for the head, — either end for the middle, and the middle for either end; — nay, if you could turn them inside out like a polypus, or a glove, they would be no worse for the operation.

When the excellent Hooker was on his death-bed, he expressed his joy at the prospect of entering a World of Order.

CHAPTER III. P. I.

WHOLESOME OBSERVATIONS UPON THE VANITY OF FAME.

Whosoever shall address himself to write of matters of instruction, or of any other argument of importance, it behoveth that before he enter thereinto, he should resolutely determine with himself in what order he will handle the same; so shall he best accomplish that he hath undertaken, and inform the understanding, and help the memory of the Reader.

GWILLIM'S DISPLAY OF HERALDRY.

WHO was the Doctor?

We will begin with the persons for sundry reasons, general and specific. Doth not the Latin grammar teach us so to do, wherein the personal verbs come before the impersonal, and the *Propria quæ maribus* precede all other nouns? Moreover by replying to this question all needful explanation as to time and place will naturally and of necessity follow in due sequence.

Truly I will deliver and discourse
The sum of all.*

Who was the Doctor?

Can it then be necessary to ask? — Alas the vanity of human fame! Vanity of vanities, all is Vanity! "How few," says Bishop Jeremy Taylor, "have heard of the name of Veneatapadino Ragium! He imagined that that there was no man in the world that knew him not: how many men can tell me that he was the King of Narsinga?" When I mention Arba, who but the practised textualist can call to mind that he was "a great man among the Anakim," that he was the father of Anak, and that from him Kirjath-Arba took its name? A great man among the Giants of the earth, the founder of a city, the father of Anak! — and now there remaineth nothing more of him or his race than the bare mention of them in one of the verses of one of the chapters of the Book of Joshua: except for that only record it would not now be known that Arba had ever lived, or that Hebron was originally called after his name. *Vanitas vanitatum! Omnia vanitas.* An old woman in a village in the West of England was told one day

* G. PEELE.

that the King of Prussia was dead, such a report having arrived when the great Frederic was in the noon-day of his glory. Old Mary lifted up her great slow eyes at the news, and fixing them in the fulness of vacancy upon her informant, replied, "Is a! is a! — The Lord ha' marcy! — Well, well! The King of Prussia! And who's he?" — The "Who's he" of this old woman might serve as text for a notable sermon upon ambition. "Who's he" may now be asked of men greater as soldiers in their day than Frederic, or Wellington; greater as discoverers than Sir Isaac, or Sir Humphrey. Who built the Pyramids? Who ate the first Oyster? *Vanitas vanitatum! Omnia vanitas.*

Why then doth flesh, a bubble-glass of breath,
Hunt after honour and advancement vain,
And rear a trophy for devouring Death,
With so great labour and long-lasting pain,
As if his days for ever should remain?
Sith all that in this world is great or gay,
Doth as a vapour vanish and decay.

Look back who list unto the former ages,
And call to count what is of them become;
Where be those learned wits and antique sages
Which of all wisdom knew the perfect sum?
Where those great warriors which did overcome
The world with conquest of their might and main,
And made one mear * of the earth and of their reign? †

Who was the Doctor?

Oh that thou hadst known him, Reader! Then should I have answered the question, — if orally, by an emphasis upon the article, — *the* Doctor; or if in written words, THE DOCTOR — thus giving the word that capital designation to which, as the head of his profession within his own orbit, he was so justly entitled. But I am not writing to those only who knew him, nor merely to the inhabitants of the West Riding, nor to the present generation alone: — No! to all Yorkshire, — all England; all the British Empire; all the countries wherein the English tongue is, or shall be, spoken or understood; yea to all places, and all times to come. *Para todos*, as saith the famous Doctor Juan Perez de Montalvan, *Natural de Madrid*, which is, being interpreted, a Spanish Cockney — *para todos; porque es un aparato de varias materias, donde el Filosofo, el Cortesano, el Humanista, el Poeta, el Predicador, el Teologo, el Soldado, el Devoto, el Jurisconsulto, el Matematico, el Medico, el Soltero, el Casado, el Religioso, el Ministro, el Plebeyo, el Señor, el Oficial, y el Entretenido, hallaran juntamente utilidad y gusto, erudicion y divertimiento, doctrina y desahogo, recreo y enseñanza, moralidad y alivio, ciencia y descanso, provecho y passatiempo, alabanzas y reprehensiones, y ultimamente exemplos y donaires, que sin ofender las costumbres delecten el animo, y sazonen el entendimiento.*

Who was the Doctor?

The Doctor was Doctor Daniel Dove.

* A *mear* or *meer*-stone, still means a *boundary* stone. The word is used in our Homilies. See fourth part of the Sermon for Rogation Week.

† Spenser.

CHAPTER IV. P. I.

BIRTH AND PARENTAGE OF DOCTOR DOVE, WITH THE DESCRIPTION OF A YEOMAN'S HOUSE IN THE WEST RIDING OF YORKSHIRE A HUNDRED YEARS AGO.

Non possidentem multa vocaveris
Recte beatum; rectius occupat
Nomen beati, qui Deorum
Muneribus sapienter uti,
Duramque callet pauperiem pati,
Pejusque letho flagitium timet.

Horat. Od.

Daniel, the son of Daniel Dove and of Dinah his wife, was born near Ingleton in the West Riding of Yorkshire, on Monday the twenty-second of April, old style, 1723, nine minutes and three seconds after three in the afternoon; on which day Marriage came in and Mercury was with the Moon; and the aspects were □ ♄ ♀ : a week earlier, it would have been a most glorious Trine of the Sun and Jupiter; — circumstances which were all duly noted in the blank leaf of the family Bible.

Daniel, the father, was one of a race of men who unhappily are now almost extinct. He lived upon an estate of six and twenty acres which his fathers had possessed before him, all Doves and Daniels, in uninterrupted succession from time immemorial, farther than registers or title deeds could ascend. The little church, called Chapel le Dale, stands about a bow-shot from the family house. There they had all been carried to the font; there they had each led his bride to the altar; and thither they had, each in his turn, been borne upon the shoulders of their friends and neighbours. Earth to earth they had been consigned there for so many generations, that half of the soil of the churchyard consisted of their remains. A hermit who might wish his grave to be as quiet as his cell, could imagine no fitter resting place. On three sides there was an irregular low stone wall, rather to mark the limits of the sacred ground, than to inclose it; on the fourth it was bounded by the brook whose waters proceed by a subterraneous channel from Wethercote cave. Two or three alders and rowan trees hung over the brook, and shed their leaves and seeds into the stream. Some bushy hazels grew at intervals along the lines of the wall; and a few ash trees, as the winds had sown them. To the east and west some fields adjoined it, in that state of half cultivation which gives a human character to solitude: to the south, on the other side the brook, the common with its limestone rocks peering every where above ground, extended to the foot of Ingleborough. A craggy hill, feathered with birch, sheltered it from the north.

The turf was as soft and fine as that of the adjoining hills; it was seldom broken, so scanty was the population to which it was appropriated; scarcely a thistle or a nettle deformed it, and the few tomb-stones which had been placed there were now themselves half buried. The sheep came over the wall when they listed, and sometimes took shelter in the porch from the storm. Their voices, and the cry of the kite wheeling above, were the only sounds which were heard there, except when the single bell which hung in its niche over the entrance tinkled for service on the Sabbath day, or with a slower tongue gave notice that one of the children of the soil was returning to the earth from which he sprung.

The house of the Doves was to the east of the church, under the same hill, and with the same brook in front; and the intervening fields belonged to the family. It was a low house, having before it a little garden of that size and character which showed that the inhabitants could afford to bestow a thought upon something more than mere bodily wants. You entered between two yew trees clipt to the fashion of two pawns. There were hollyhocks and sunflowers displaying themselves above the wall; roses and sweet peas under the windows, and the everlasting pea climbing the porch. Over the door was a stone with these letters.

D
D + M
A.D.
1608.

The A. was in the Saxon character. The rest of the garden lay behind the house, partly on the slope of the hill. It had a hedge of gooseberry-bushes, a few apple-trees, pot-herbs in abundance, onions, cabbages, turnips and carrots; potatoes had hardly yet found their way into these remote parts: and in a sheltered spot under the crag, open to the south, were six bee-hives which made the family perfectly independent of West India produce. Tea was in those days as little known as potatoes, and for all other things honey supplied the place of sugar.

The house consisted of seven rooms, the dairy and cellar included, which were both upon the ground floor. As you entered the kitchen there was on the right one of those open chimneys which afford more comfort in a winter's evening than the finest register stove; in front of the chimney stood a wooden bee-hive chair, and on each side was a long oak seat with a back to it, the seats serving as chests in which the oaten bread was kept. They were of the darkest brown, and well polished by constant use. On the back of each were the same initials as those over the door, with the date 1610. The great oak table, and the chest in the best kitchen which held the house-linen, bore the same date. The chimney was well hung with bacon, the rack which covered half the ceiling bore equal marks of plenty; mutton hams were suspended from other parts of the ceiling; and there was an odour of cheese from the adjoining dairy, which the turf fire, though perpetual as that of the Magi, or of the Vestal Virgins, did not overpower. A few pewter dishes were ranged above the trenchers, opposite the door, on a conspicuous shelf. The other treasures of the family were in an open triangular cupboard, fixed in one of the corners of the best kitchen, half way from the floor, and touching the ceiling. They consisted of a silver saucepan, a silver goblet, and four apostle spoons. Here also King Charles's Golden Rules were pasted against the wall, and a large print of Daniel in the Lion's Den. The Lions were bedaubed with yellow, and the Prophet was bedaubed with blue, with a red patch upon each of his cheeks: if he had been like his picture he might have frightened the Lions; but happily there were no "judges" in the family, and it had been bought for its name's sake. The other print which ornamented the room had been purchased from a like feeling, though the cause was not so immediately apparent. It represented a Ship in full sail, with Joseph, and the Virgin Mary, and the Infant on board, and a Dove flying behind as if to fill the sails with the motion of its wings. Six black chairs were ranged along the wall, where they were seldom disturbed from their array. They had been purchased by Daniel the grandfather upon his marriage, and were the most costly purchase that had ever been made in the family; for the goblet was a legacy. The backs were higher than the head of the tallest man when seated; the seats flat and shallow, set in a round frame, unaccommodating in their material, more unaccommodating in shape; the backs also were of wood rising straight up, and ornamented with balls and lozenges and embossments; and the legs and cross bars were adorned in the same taste. Over the chimney were two Peacocks' feathers, some of the dry silky pods of the honesty flower, and one of those large "sinuous shells" so finely thus described by Landor: —

> Of pearly hue
> Within, and they that lustre have imbib'd
> In the sun's palace porch; where, when unyok'd,
> His chariot wheel stands midway in the wave.
> Shake one, and it awakens; then apply
> Its polish'd lips to your attentive ear,
> And it remembers its august abodes,
> And murmurs as the ocean murmurs there.

There was also a head of Indian corn there, and a back scratcher, of which the hand was ivory and the handle black. This had been a present of Daniel the grandfather to his wife. The three apartments above served equally for store-rooms and bed-chambers. William Dove the brother slept in one, and Agatha the maid, or Haggy as she was called, in another.

CHAPTER V. P. I.

EXTENSION OF THE SCIENCE OF PHYSIOGNOMY, WITH SOME REMARKS UPON THE PRACTICAL USES OF CRANIOLOGY.

Hanc ergo scientiam blande excipiamus, hilariterque amplectamur, ut vere nostram et de nobismet ipsis tractantem; quam qui non amat, quam qui non amplectitur, nec philosophiam amat, neque suæ vitæ discrimina curat.
BAPTISTA PORTA.

THEY who know that the word physiognomy is not derived from phiz, and infer from that knowledge that the science is not confined to the visage alone, have extended it to handwritings also, and hence it has become fashionable in this age of collectors to collect the autographs of remarkable persons. But now that Mr. Rapier has arisen, "the Reformer of illegible hands," he and his rival Mr. Carstairs teach all their pupils to write alike. The countenance however has fairer play in our days than it had in old times, for the long heads of the sixteenth century were made by the nurses, not by nature. Elongating the nose, flattening the temples, and raising the forehead are no longer performed by manual force, and the face undergoes now no other artificial modelling than such as may be impressed upon it by the aid of the looking-glass. So far physiognomy becomes less difficult, the data upon which it has to proceed not having been falsified *ab initio;* but there arises a question in what state ought they to be examined? Dr. Gall is for shaving the head, and overhauling it as a Turk does a Circassian upon sale, that he may discover upon the outside of the skull the organs of fighting, murder, cunning, and thieving (near neighbours in his *mappa cerebri*), of comparing colours, of music, of sexual instinct, of philosophical judgment, &c. &c., all which, with all other qualities, have their latitudes and longitudes in the brain, and are conspicuous upon the outward skull, according to the degree in which they influence the character of the individual.

It must be admitted that if this learned German's theory of craniology be well founded, the Gods have devised a much surer, safer, and more convenient means for discovering the real characters of the Lords and Ladies of the creation, than what Momus proposed, when he advised that a window should be placed in the breast. For if his advice had been followed, and there had actually been a window in the sternum, — it is, I think, beyond all doubt that a window-shutter would soon have been found indispensably necessary in cold climates, more especially in England, where pulmonary complaints are so frequent; and, secondly, the wind would not be more injurious to the lungs in high latitudes, than the sun would be to the liver in torrid regions; indeed, every where during summer it would be impossible to exist without a green curtain, or Venetian blinds to the window; and after all, take what precautions we might, the world would be ten times more bilious than it is. Another great physical inconvenience would also have arisen; for if men could peep into their insides at any time, and see the motions and the fermentations which are continually going on, and the rise and progress of every malady distinctly marked in the changes it produced, so many nervous diseases would be brought on by frequent inspection, and so many derangements from attempting to regulate the machine, that the only way to prevent it from making a full stop would be to put a lock upon the shutter, and deliver the key to the Physician.

But upon Dr. Gall's theory how many and what obvious advantages result! Nor are they merely confined to the purposes of speculative physiognomy; the uses of his theory as applied to practice offer to us hopes scarcely less delightful than those which seemed to dawn upon mankind with the discovery of the gasses, and with the commencement of the French Revolution, and in these later days with the progress of the Bible Society. In courts of Justice, for instance, how beautifully would this new science supply any little deficiency of evidence upon trial! If a man were arraigned for murder, and the case were doubtful, but he were found to have a decided organ for the crime, it would be of little matter whether he had committed the specific fact in the indictment or not; for hanging, if not applicable as punishment, would be proper for prevention. Think also in State Trials what infinite advantages an Attorney General might derive from the opinion of a Regius Professor of Craniology! Even these are but partial benefits. Our Generals, Ministers, and Diplomatists would then unerringly be chosen by the outside of the head, though a criterion might still be wanted to ascertain when it was too thick and when too thin. But the greatest advantages are those which this new system would afford to education; for by the joint efforts of Dr. Gall and Mr. Edgeworth we should be able to breed up men according to any pattern which Parents or Guardians might think proper to bespeak. The Doctor would design the mould, and Mr. Edgeworth, by his skill in mechanics, devise with characteristic ingenuity the best means of making and applying it. As soon as the child was born the professional cap, medical, military, theological, commercial, or legal, would be put on, and thus he would be perfectly prepared for Mr. Edgeworth's admirable system of professional education. I will pursue this subject no farther than just to hint that the materials of the mould may operate sympathetically, and therefore that for a lawyer in *rus* the cap should be made of brass, for a divine of lead, for a politician of base-metal, for a soldier of steel, and for a sailor of heart of English oak.

Dr. Gall would doubtless require the naked head to be submitted to him for judgement. Contrariwise I opine,—and all the Ladies will agree with me in this opinion,—that the head ought neither to be stript, nor even examined in undress, but that it should be taken with all its accompaniments, when the owner has made the best of it, the accompaniments being not unfrequently more indicative than the features themselves. Long ago the question whether a man is most like himself drest or undrest, was propounded to the British Apollo; and it was answered by the Oracle that a man of God Almighty's making is most like himself when undrest; but a man of a tailor's, periwig-maker's, and sempstress's making, when drest. The Oracle answered rightly; for no man can select his own eyes, nose, or mouth,—but his wig and his whiskers are of his own choosing. And to use an illustrious instance, how much of character is there in that awful wig which alway in its box accompanies Dr. Parr upon his visits of ceremony, that it may be put on in the hall, with all its feathery honours thick upon it, not a curl deranged, a hair flattened, or a particle of powder wasted on the way!

But if we would form a judgement of the interior of that portentous head which is thus formidably obumbrated, how could it be done so well as by beholding the Doctor among his books, and there seeing the food upon which his terrific intellect is fed. There we should see the accents, quantities, dialects, digammas, and other such small gear as in these days constitute the complete armour of a perfect scholar; and by thus discovering what goes into the head we might form a fair estimate of what was likely to come out of it. This is a truth which, with many others of equal importance, will be beautifully elucidated in this nonpareil history. For Daniel Dove, the Father, had a collection of books; they were not so numerous as those of his contemporary Harley, famous for his library, and infamous for the Peace of Utrecht; but he was perfectly conversant with all their contents, which is more than could be said of the Earl of Oxford.

Reader, whether thou art man, woman, or child, thou art doubtless acquainted with the doctrine of association as inculcated by the great Mr. Locke and his disciples. But never hast thou seen that doctrine so richly and so entirely exemplified as in this great history, the association of ideas being, in oriental phrase, the silken thread upon which its pearls are strung. And never wilt thou see it so clearly and delightfully illustrated, not even if the ingenious Mr. John Jones should one day give to the world the whole twelve volumes in which he has proved the authenticity of the Gospel History, by bringing the narratives of the Four Evangelists to the test of Mr. Locke's metaphysics.

"Desultoriness," says Mr. Danby, "may often be the mark of a full head; connection must proceed from a thoughtful one."

CHAPTER VI. P. I.

A COLLECTION OF BOOKS NONE OF WHICH ARE INCLUDED AMONGST THE PUBLICATIONS OF ANY SOCIETY FOR THE PROMOTION OF KNOWLEDGE RELIGIOUS OR PROFANE.—HAPPINESS IN HUMBLE LIFE.

Felix ille animi, divisque simillimus ipsis,
Quem non mordaci resplendens gloria fuco
Solicitat, non fastosi mala gaudia luxus,
Sed tacitos sinit ire dies, et paupere cultu
Exigit innocuæ tranquilla silentia vitæ.

POLITIAN.

HAPPILY for Daniel, he lived before the age of Magazines, Reviews, Cyclopædias, Elegant Extracts and Literary Newspapers, so that he gathered the fruit of knowledge for himself, instead of receiving it from the dirty fingers of a retail vender. His books were few in number, but they were all weighty either in matter or in size. They consisted of the Morte d'Arthur in the fine black-letter edition of Copeland; Plutarch's Morals and Pliny's Natural History, two goodly folios, full as an egg of meat, and both translated by that old worthy Philemon, who for the service which he rendered to his contemporaries and to his countrymen deserves to be called the best of the Hollands, without disparaging either the Lord or the Doctor of that appellation. The whole works of Joshua Sylvester (whose name, let me tell the reader in passing, was accented upon the first syllable by his contemporaries, not as now upon the second);—Jean Petit's History of the Netherlands, translated and continued by Edward Grimeston, another worthy of the Philemon order; Sir Kenelm Digby's Discourses; Stowe's Chronicle; Joshua Barnes's Life of Edward III.; "Ripley Revived by Eirenæus Philalethes, an Englishman styling himself Citizen of the World," with its mysterious frontispiece representing the *Domus Naturæ*, to which, *Nil deest, nisi clavis:* the Pilgrim's Progress: two volumes of Ozell's translation of Rabelais; Latimer's Sermons; and the last volume of Fox's Martyrs, which latter book had been brought him by his wife. The Pilgrim's Progress was a godmother's present to his son: the odd volumes of Rabelais he had picked up at Kendal, at a sale, in a lot with Ripley Revived and Plutarch's Morals: the others he had inherited.

Daniel had looked into all these books, read most of them, and believed all that he read, except Rabelais, which he could not tell what to make of. He was not, however, one of those persons who complacently suppose every thing to be nonsense, which they do not perfectly comprehend, or flatter themselves that they do. His simple heart judged of books by what they ought to be, little knowing what they are. It never occurred to him that any thing would be printed which was not worth printing, any thing which did not convey either reasonable delight or useful instruction: and he was no more disposed to doubt the truth of what he read, than to question the veracity of his neighbour, or any one who had no interest in deceiving him. A book carried with it to him authority in its very aspect. The Morte d'Arthur therefore he received for authentic history, just as he did the painful chronicle of honest John Stowe, and the Barnesian labours of Joshua the self-satisfied: there was nothing in it indeed which stirred his English blood like the battles of Cressy and Poictiers and Najara; yet on the whole he preferred it to Barnes's story, believed in Sir Tor, Sir Tristram, Sir Lancelot and Sir Lamorack as entirely as in Sir John Chandos, the Captal de Buche and the Black Prince, and liked them better.

Latimer and Du Bartas he used sometimes to read aloud on Sundays; and if the departed take cognizance of what passes on earth, and poets derive any satisfaction from that posthumous applause which is generally the only reward of those who deserve it, Sylvester might have found some compensation for the undeserved neglect into which his works had sunk, by the full and devout delight which his rattling rhymes and quaint collocations afforded to this reader. The silver-tongued Sylvester, however, was reserved for a Sabbath book; as a week-day author Daniel preferred Pliny, for the same reason that bread and cheese, or a rasher of hung mutton, contented his palate better than a syllabub. He frequently regretted that so knowing a writer had never seen or heard of Wethercote and Yordas caves; the ebbing and flowing spring at Giggleswick, Malham Cove, and Gordale Scar, that he might have described them among the wonders of the world. *Omne ignotum pro magnifico* is a maxim which will not in all cases hold good. There are things which we do not undervalue because we are familiar with them, but which are admired the more the more thoroughly they are known and understood; it is thus with the grand objects of nature and the finest works of art,—with whatsoever is truly great and excellent. Daniel was not deficient in imagination; but no description of places which he had never seen, however exaggerated (as such things always are) impressed him so strongly as these objects in his own neighbourhood, which he had known from childhood. Three or four times in his life it had happened that strangers with a curiosity as uncommon in that age as it is general in this, came from afar to visit these wonders of the West Riding, and Daniel accompanied them with a delight such as he never experienced on any other occasion.

But the Author in whom he delighted most was Plutarch, of whose works he was lucky enough to possess the worthier half: if the other had perished Plutarch would not have been a popular writer, but he would have held a higher place in the estimation of the judicious. Daniel could have posed a candidate for university honours, and perhaps the examiner too, with some of the odd learning which he had stored up in his memory from these great repositories of ancient knowledge. Refusing all reward for such services, the strangers to whom he officiated as a guide, though they perceived that he was an extraordinary person, were little aware how much information he had acquired, and of how strange a kind. His talk with them did not go beyond the subjects which the scenes they came to visit naturally suggested, and they wondered more at the questions he asked, than at any thing which he advanced himself. For his disposition was naturally shy, and that which had been bashfulness in youth assumed the appearance of reserve as he advanced in life; for having none to communicate with upon his favourite studies, he lived in an intellectual world of his own, a mental solitude as complete as that of Alexander Selkirk or Robinson Crusoe. Even to the Curate his conversation, if he had touched upon his books, would have been heathen Greek; and to speak the truth plainly, without knowing a letter of that language, he knew more about the Greeks, than nine-tenths of the clergy at that time, including all the dissenters, and than nine-tenths of the schoolmasters also.

Our good Daniel had none of that confidence which so usually and so unpleasantly characterizes self-taught men. In fact he was by no means aware of the extent of his acquirements, all that he knew in this kind having been acquired for amusement not for use. He had never attempted to teach himself any thing. These books had lain in his way in boyhood, or fallen in it afterwards, and the perusal of them, intently as it was followed, was always accounted by him to be nothing more than recreation. None of his daily business had ever been neglected for it; he cultivated his fields and his garden, repaired his walls, looked to the stable, tended his cows and salved his sheep, as diligently and as contentedly as if he had possessed neither capacity nor inclination for any higher employments. Yet Daniel was one of those men, who, if disposition and aptitude were not overruled by circumstances, would have grown pale with study, instead of being bronzed and hardened by sun and wind and rain. There were in him undeveloped talents which might have raised him to distinction as an antiquary, a virtuoso of the Royal Society, a poet, or a theologian, to whichever course the bias in his ball of fortune had inclined. But he had not a particle of envy in his composition. He thought indeed that if he had had grammar learning in his youth like the curate, he would have made more use of it; but there was nothing either of the sourness or bitterness (call it which you please) of repining in this natural reflection.

Never indeed was any man more contented with doing his duty in that state of life to which it had pleased God to call him. And well he might be so, for no man ever passed through the world with less to disquiet or to sour him. Bred up in habits which secured the continuance of that humble but sure independence to which he was born, he had never known what it was to be anxious for the future. At the age of twenty-five he had brought home a wife, the daughter of a little landholder like himself, with fifteen pounds for her portion: and the true-love of his youth proved to him a faithful helpmate in those years when the dream of life is over, and we live in its realities. If at any time there had been some alloy in his happiness, it was when there appeared reason to suppose that in him his family would be extinct; for though no man knows what parental feelings are till he has experienced them, and Daniel therefore knew not the whole value of that which he had never enjoyed, the desire of progeny is natural to the heart of man; and though Daniel had neither large estates, nor an illustrious name to transmit, it was an unwelcome thought that the little portion of the earth which had belonged to his fathers time out of mind, should pass into the possession of some stranger, who would tread on their graves and his own without any regard to the dust that lay beneath. That uneasy apprehension was removed after he had been married fifteen years, when to the great joy of both parents, because they had long ceased to entertain any hope of such an event, their wishes were fulfilled in the birth of a son. This their only child was healthy, apt and docile, to all appearance as happily disposed in mind and body as a father's heart could wish. If they had fine weather for winning their hay or shearing their corn, they thanked God for it; if the season proved unfavourable, the labour was only a little the more and the crop a little the worse. Their stations secured them from want, and they had no wish beyond it. What more had Daniel to desire?

The following passage in the divine Du Bartas he used to read with peculiar satisfaction, applying it to himself: —

O thrice, thrice happy he, who shuns the cares
Of city troubles, and of state-affairs;
And, serving Ceres, tills with his own team,
His own *free land*, left by his friends to him!

Never pale Envy's poisony heads do hiss
To gnaw his heart: nor Vulture Avarice:
His fields' bounds, bound his thoughts: he never sups
For nectar, poison mixed in silver cups;
Neither in golden platters doth he lick
For sweet ambrosia deadly arsenic:
His hand's his bowl (better than plate or glass)
The silver brook his sweetest hippocrass:
Milk cheese and fruit, (fruits of his own endeavour)
Drest without dressing, hath he ready ever.

False counsellors (concealers of the law)
Turncoat attorneys that with both hands draw;
Sly pettifoggers, wranglers at the bar,
Proud purse-leeches, harpies of Westminster
With feigned-chiding, and foul jarring noise,
Break not his brain, nor interrupt his joys;
But cheerful birds chirping him sweet good-morrows
With nature's music do beguile his sorrows;
Teaching the fragrant forests day by day
The diapason of their heavenly lay.

His wandering vessel, reeling to and fro
On th' ireful ocean (as the winds do blow)
With sudden tempest is not overwhurled,
To seek his sad death in another world:
But leading all his life at home in peace,
Always in sight of his own smoke, no seas
No other seas he knows, no other torrent,
Than that which waters with its silver current
His native meadows: and that very earth
Shall give him burial which first gave him birth.

To summon timely sleep, he doth not need
Æthiop's cold rush, nor drowsy poppy-seed;
Nor keep in consort (as Mecænas did)
Luxurious Villains — (Viols I should have said);
But on green carpets thrum'd with mossy bever,
Fringing the round skirts of his winding river,
The stream's mild murmur, as it gently gushes,
His healthy limbs in quiet slumber hushes.

Drum fife and trumpet, with their loud alarms,
Make him not start out of his sleep, to arms;
Nor dear respect of some great General,
Him from his bed unto the block doth call.
The crested cock sings "*Hunt-is-up*"* to him,
Limits his rest, and makes him stir betime,
To walk the mountains and the flow'ry meads
Impearl'd with tears which great Aurora sheds.

Never gross air poisoned in stinking streets,
To choke his spirit, his tender nostril meets;
But th' open sky where at full breath he lives,
Still keeps him sound, and still new stomach gives.
And Death, dread Serjeant of the Eternal Judge,
Comes very late to his sole-seated lodge.

CHAPTER VII. P. I.

RUSTIC PHILOSOPHY. AN EXPERIMENT UPON MOONSHINE.

Quien comienza en juventud
A bien obrar,
Señal es de no errar
En senetud.
Proverbios del Marques de Santillana.

It is not, however, for man to rest in absolute contentment. He is born to hopes and aspirations as the sparks fly upward, unless he has brutified his nature and quenched the spirit of immortality which is his portion. Having nothing to desire for himself, Daniel's ambition had taken a natural direction and fixed upon his son. He was resolved that the boy should be made a scholar; not with the prospect of advancing him in the

* See Drayton's Poems, and Nare's Gloss. in v. *J. W. W.*

world, but in the hope that he might become a philosopher, and take as much delight in the books which he would inherit as his father had done before him. Riches and rank and power appeared in his judgment to be nothing when compared to philosophy; and herein he was as true a philosopher as if he had studied in the Porch, or walked the groves of Academus.

It was not however for this,—for he was as little given to talk of his opinions as to display his reading,—but for his retired habits, and general character, and some odd practices into which his books had led him, that he was commonly called Flossofer Daniel by his neighbours. The appellation was not affixed in derision, but respectfully and as his due; for he bore his faculties too meekly ever to excite an envious or an ill-natured feeling in any one. Rural Flossofers were not uncommon in those days, though in the progress of society they have disappeared like Crokers, Bowyers, Lorimers, Armourers, Running Footmen, and other descriptions of men whose occupations are gone by. But they were of a different order from our Daniel. They were usually Philomaths, Students in Astrology, or the Cœlestial Science, and not unfrequently Empirics or downright Quacks. Between twenty and thirty almanacs used to be published every year by men of this description, some of them versed enough in mathematics to have done honour to Cambridge, had the fates allowed; and others such proficients in roguery, that they would have done equal honour to the whipping-post.

A man of a different stamp from either came in declining life to settle at Ingleton in the humble capacity of schoolmaster, a little before young Daniel was capable of more instruction than could be given him at home. Richard Guy was his name; he is the person to whom the lovers of old rhyme are indebted for the preservation of the old poem of Flodden Field, which he transcribed from an ancient manuscript, and which was printed from his transcript by Thomas Gent of York. In his way through the world, which had not been along the King's high Dunstable road, Guy had picked up a competent share of Latin, a little Greek, some practical knowledge of physic, and more of its theory; astrology enough to cast a nativity, and more acquaintance with alchemy than has often been possessed by one who never burnt his fingers in its processes. These acquirements were grafted on a disposition as obliging as it was easy; and he was beholden to nature for an understanding so clear and quick that it might have raised him to some distinction in the world if he had not been under the influence of an imagination at once lively and credulous. Five and fifty years had taught him none of the world's wisdom; they had sobered his mind without maturing it; but he had a wise heart, and the wisdom of the heart is worth all other wisdom.

Daniel was too far advanced in life to fall in friendship; he felt a certain degree of attractiveness in this person's company; there was, however, so much of what may better be called reticence than reserve in his own quiet habitual manners, that it would have been long before their acquaintance ripened into any thing like intimacy, if an accidental circumstance had not brought out the latent sympathy which on both sides had till then rather been apprehended than understood They were walking together one day when young Daniel, who was then in his sixth year, looking up in his father's face, proposed this question: "Will it be any harm, Father, if I steal five beans when next I go into Jonathan Dowthwaites, if I can do it without any one's seeing me?"

"And what wouldst thou steal beans for?" was the reply, "when any body would give them to thee, and when thou knowest there are plenty at home?"

"But it won't do to have them given, Father," the boy replied. "They are to charm away my warts. Uncle William says I must steal five beans, a bean for every wart, and tie them carefully up in paper, and carry them to a place where two roads cross, and then drop them, and walk away without ever once looking behind me. And then the warts will go away from me, and come upon the hands of the person that picks up the beans."

"Nay boy," the Father made answer; "that charm was never taught by a white witch! If thy warts are a trouble to thee, they would be a trouble to any one else; and to get rid of an evil from ourselves Daniel, by bringing it upon another, is against our duty to our neighbour. Have nothing to do with a charm like that!"

"May I steal a piece of raw beef then," rejoined the boy, "and rub the warts with it and bury it? For Uncle says that will do, and as the beef rots, so the warts will waste away."

"Daniel," said the Father, "those can be no lawful charms that begin with stealing; I could tell thee how to cure thy warts in a better manner. There is an infallible way, which is by washing the hands in moonshine, but then the moonshine must be caught in a bright silver basin. You wash and wash in the basin, and a cold moisture will be felt upon the hands, proceeding from the cold and moist rays of the moon."

"But what shall we do for a silver basin?" said little Daniel.

The Father answered, "a pewter dish might be tried if it were made very bright; but it is not deep enough. The brass kettle perhaps might do better."

"Nay," said Guy, who had now begun to attend with some interest, "the shape of a kettle is not suitable. It should be a concave vessel, so as to concentrate the rays. Joshua Wilson I dare say would lend his brass basin, which he can very well spare at the hour you want it, because nobody comes to be shaved by moonlight. The moon rises early enough to serve at this time. If you come in this evening at six o'clock I will speak to Joshua in the mean time, and have the basin as bright and shining as a good scouring can make it. The experiment is curious and I should like to see it tried. Where Daniel didst thou learn it?" "I read it," replied Daniel, "in Sir Kenelm Digby's Discourses, and he says it never fails."

Accordingly the parties met at the appointed hour. Mambrino's helmet, when new from the armourer's, or when furbished for a tournament, was not brighter than Guy had rendered the inside of the barber's basin. Schoolmaster, Father and Son retired to a place out of observation, by the side of the river, a wild stream tumbling among the huge stones which it had brought down from the hills. On one of these stones sate Daniel the elder, holding the basin in such an inclination toward the moon that there should be no shadow in it; Guy directed the boy where to place himself so as not to intercept the light, and stood looking complacently on, while young Daniel revolved his hands one in another within the empty basin, as if washing them. "I feel them cold and clammy, Father!" said the boy. (It was the beginning of November) "Ay," replied the father, "that's the cold moisture of the moon!" "Ay!" echoed the schoolmaster, and nodded his head in confirmation.

The operation was repeated on the two following nights; and Daniel would have kept up his son two hours later than his regular time of rest to continue it on the third if the evening had not set in with clouds and rain. In spite of the patient's belief that the warts would waste away and were wasting, (for Prince Hohenlohe could not require more entire faith than was given on this occasion,) no alteration could be perceived in them at a fortnight's end. Daniel thought the experiment had failed because it had not been repeated sufficiently often, nor perhaps continued long enough. But the Schoolmaster was of opinion that the cause of failure was in the basin: for that silver being the lunar metal would by affinity assist the influential virtues of the moonlight, which finding no such affinity in a mixed metal of baser compounds, might contrariwise have its potential qualities weakened, or even destroyed when received in a brasen vessel, and reflected from it. Flossofer Daniel assented to this theory. Nevertheless as the child got rid of his troublesome excrescences in the course of three or four months, all parties disregarding the lapse of time at first, and afterwards fairly forgetting it, agreed that the remedy had been effectual, and Sir Kenelm, if he had been living, might have procured the solemn attestation of men more veracious than himself that moonshine was an infallible cure for warts.

CHAPTER VIII. P. I.

A KIND SCHOOLMASTER AND A HAPPY SCHOOLBOY.

> Though happily thou wilt say that wands be to be wrought when they are green, lest they rather break than bend when they be dry, yet know also that he that bendeth a twig because he would see if it would bow by strength may chance to have a crooked tree when he would have a straight. EUPHUES.

FROM this time the two Flossofers were friends. Daniel seldom went to Ingleton without looking in upon Guy, if it were between school hours. Guy on his part would walk as far with him on the way back, as the tether of his own time allowed, and frequently on Saturdays and Sundays he strolled out and took a seat by Daniel's fireside. Even the wearying occupation of hearing one generation of urchins after another repeat *a-b-ab*, hammering the first rules of arithmetic into leaden heads, and pacing like a horse in a mill the same dull dragging round day after day, had neither diminished Guy's good-nature, nor lessened his love for children. He had from the first conceived a liking for young Daniel, both because of the right principle which was evinced by the manner in which he proposed the question concerning stealing the beans, and of the profound gravity (worthy of a Flossofer's son) with which he behaved in the affair of the moonshine. All that he saw and heard of him tended to confirm this favourable prepossession; and the boy, who had been taught to read in the Bible and in Stowe's Chronicle, was committed to his tuition at seven years of age.

Five days in the week (for in the North of England Saturday as well as Sunday is a Sabbath to the Schoolmaster) did young Daniel, after supping his porringer of oatmeal pottage, set off to school, with a little basket containing his dinner in his hand. This provision usually consisted of oat-cake and cheese, the latter in goodly proportion, but of the most frugal quality, whatever cream the milk afforded having been consigned to the butter tub. Sometimes it was a piece of cold bacon or of cold pork; and in winter there was the luxury of a shred pie, which is a coarse north country edition of the pie abhorred by puritans. The distance was in those days called two miles; but miles of such long measure that they were for him a good hour's walk at a cheerful pace. He never loitered on the way, being at all times brisk in his movements, and going to school with a spirit as light as when he returned from it, like one whose blessed lot it was never to have experienced, and therefore never to stand in fear of severity or unkindness. For he was not more a favourite with Guy for his docility, and regularity and diligence, than he was with his schoolfellows for his thorough good-nature and a certain original oddity of humour.

There are some boys who take as much pleasure in exercising their intellectual faculties, as others do when putting forth the power of arms and legs in boisterous exertion. Young Daniel was from his childhood fond of books. William Dove used to say he was a chip of the old block; and this hereditary disposition was regarded with much satisfaction by both parents, Dinah having no higher ambition nor better wish for her son, than that he might prove like his father in all things. This being the bent of his nature, the boy having a kind master as well as a happy home, never tasted of what old Lily calls (and well might call) the wearisome bitterness of the scholar's learning. He was never subject to the brutal discipline of the Udals and Busbys and Bowyers, and Parrs, and other less notorious tyrants who have trodden in their steps; nor was any of that inhuman injustice ever exercised upon him to break his spirit, for which it is to be hoped Dean Colet has paid in Purgatory; — to be hoped, I say, because if there be no Purgatory, the Dean may have gone farther and fared worse. Being the only *Latiner* in the school, his lessons were heard with more interest and less formality. Guy observed his progress with almost as much delight and as much hope as Daniel himself. A schoolmaster who likes his vocation feels toward the boys who deserve his favour something like a thrifty and thriving father toward the children for whom he is scraping together wealth; he is contented that his humble and patient industry should produce fruit not for himself, but for them, and looks with pride to a result in which it is impossible for him to partake, and which in all likelihood he may never live to see. Even some of the old Phlebotomists have had this feeling to redeem them.

"Sir," says the Compositor to the Corrector of the Press, "there is no heading in the Copy for this Chapter. What must I do?"

"Leave a space for it," the Corrector replies. "It is a strange sort of book; but I dare say the Author has a reason for every thing that he says or does, and most likely you will find out his meaning as you set up."

Right, Mr. Corrector! you are a judicious person, free from the common vice of finding fault with what you do not understand. My meaning will be explained presently. And having thus prologized, we will draw a line if you please, and begin.

Ten measures of garrulity, says the Talmud, were sent down upon the earth, and the women took nine.

I have known in my time eight terrific talkers; and five of them were of the masculine gender.

But supposing that the Rabbis were right in allotting to the women a ninefold proportion of talkativeness, I confess that I have inherited my mother's share.

I am liberal of my inheritance, and the Public shall have the full benefit of it.

And here if my gentle Public will consider to what profitable uses this gift might have been applied, the disinterestedness of my disposition in having thus benevolently dedicated it to their service, will doubtless be appreciated as it deserves by their discrimination and generosity. Had I carried it to the pulpit, think how I might have filled the seats, and raised the prices of a private chapel! Had I taken it to the bar, think how I could have mystified a judge, and bamboozled a jury! Had I displayed it in the senate, think how I could have talked against time, for the purpose of delaying a division, till the expected numbers could be brought together; or how efficient a part I could have borne in the patriotic design of impeding the business of a session, prolonging and multiplying the debates, and worrying a minister out of his senses and his life.

Diis aliter visum — I am what I was to be, — what it is best for myself that I should be, — and for you, my Public, also. The rough-hewn plans of my destination have been better shaped for me by Providence than I could have shaped them for myself.

But to the purpose of this chapter, which is as headless as the Whigs — Observe, my Public, I have not said as brainless. . If it were, the book would be worth no more than a new Tragedy of Lord Byron's; or an old number of Mr. Jeffrey's Review, when its prophecies have proved false, its blunders have been exposed, and its slander stinks.

Every thing here shall be in order. The digressions into which this gift of discourse may lead me must not interrupt the arrangement of our History. Never shall it be said of the Unknown that "he draweth out the thread of his verbosity finer than the staple of his argument." We have a journey to perform from Dan to Beersheba, and we must halt occasionally by the way. Matter will arise contingent to the story, correlative to it, or excrescent from it; not necessary to its progress, and yet indispensable for your delight, my gentle Public, and for mine own ease. My Public would not have me stifle the *afflatus* when I am labouring with it, and in the condition of Elihu as described by himself in the 18th and 19th verses of the xxxii. chapter of the book of Job.

*Quemadmodum cælator oculos diu intentos ac fatigatos remittit atque avocat, et, ut dici solet, pascit; sic nos animum aliquando debemus relaxare et quibusdam oblectamentis reficere. Sed ipsa oblectamenta opera sint; ex his quoque si observaveris, sumes quod possit fieri salutare.**

But that the beautiful structure of this history may in no wise be deranged, such matter shall be distributed into distinct chapters in the way of intercalation; a device of which as it respects the year, Adam is believed to have been the inventor; but according to the Author of the book of Jalkut, it was only transmitted by him to his descendants, being one of the things which he received by revelation.

How then shall these Chapters be annominated? Intercalary they shall not. That word will send some of my readers to Johnson's Dictionary for its meaning; and others to Sheridan, or Walker for its pronunciation. Besides, I have a dislike to all mongrel words, and an especial dislike for strange compounds into which a preposition enters. I owe them a grudge. They make one of the main difficulties in Greek and German.

From our own Calendars we cannot borrow an appellation. In the Republican one of our neighbours, when the revolutionary fever was at its height, the supplemental days were called *Sans-culottedes*. The Spaniards would call them *Dias Descamisados*. The holders of liberal opinions in England would term them Radical Days. A hint might be taken hence, and we might name them radical chapters, as having the root of the matter in them; — or *ramal*, if there were such a word, upon the analogy of the Branch Bible societies. Or *ramage* as the king of Cockayne hath his Foliage. But they would not be truly and philosophically designated by these names. They are not branches from the tree of this history, neither are they its leaves; but rather choice garlands suspended there to adorn it on festival days. They may be likened to the waste weirs of a canal, or the safety valves of a steam engine; (my gentle Public would not have me stifle the *afflatus !*) — interludes; — symphonies between the acts; — voluntaries during the service; — resting places on the ascent of a church tower; angular recesses of an old bridge, into which foot passengers may retire from carriages or horsemen; — houses-of-call upon the road; seats by the way side, such as those which were provided by the Man of Ross, or the not less meritorious Woman of Chippenham, Maud Heath of Langley Burrel, — Hospices on the passages of the Alps, — Capes of Good Hope, or Isles of St. Helena, — yea, Islands of Tinian or Juan Fernandez, upon the long voyage whereon we are bound.

Leap-chapters they cannot properly be called; and if we were to call them Ha Has! as being chapters which the Reader may leap if he likes, the name would appear rather strained than significant, and might be justly censured as more remarkable for affectation than for aptness. For the same reason I reject the designation of Intermeans, though it hath the sanction of great Ben's authority.

Among the requisites for an accomplished writer Steele enumerates the skill whereby common words are started into new significations. I will not presume so far upon that talent (— modesty forbids me —) as to call these intervening chapters either Interpellations or Interpositions, or Interlocutions, or Intervals. Take this, Reader, for a general rule, that the readiest and plainest style is the most forcible (if the head be but properly stored;) and that in all ordinary cases the word which first presents itself is the best; even as in all matters of right and wrong, the first feeling is that which the heart owns and the conscience ratifies.

But for a new occasion, a new word or a new composite must be formed. Therefore I will strike one in the mint of analogy, in

* Seneca, Epist. 58.

which alone the king's English must be coined, and call them Interchapters — and thus endeth

INTERCHAPTER I.

REMARKS IN THE PRINTING OFFICE. THE AUTHOR CONFESSES A DISPOSITION TO GARRULITY. PROPRIETY OF PROVIDING CERTAIN CHAPTERS FOR THE RECEPTION OF HIS EXTRANEOUS DISCOURSE. CHOICE OF AN APPELLATION FOR SUCH CHAPTERS.

Perque vices aliquid, quod tempora longa videri
Non sinat, in medium vacuas referamus ad aures.
OVID.

CHAPTER IX. P. I.

EXCEPTIONS TO ONE OF KING SOLOMON'S RULES — A WINTER'S EVENING AT DANIEL'S FIRESIDE.

These are my thoughts; I might have spun them out into a greater length, but I think a little plot of ground, thick sown, is better than a great field which, for the most part of it, lies fallow. NORRIS.

"TRAIN up a child in the way he should go, and when he is old his feet will not depart from it." Generally speaking it will be found so; but is there any other rule to which there are so many exceptions?

Ask the serious Christian as he calls himself, or the Professor (another and more fitting appellative which the Christian Pharisees have chosen for themselves) — ask him whether he has found it hold good? Whether his sons when they attained to years of discretion (which are the most indiscreet years in the course of human life) have profited as he expected by the long extemporaneous prayers to which they listened night and morning, the sad sabbaths which they were compelled to observe, and the soporific sermons which closed the domestic religiosities of those melancholy days? Ask him if this discipline has prevented them from running headlong into the follies and vices of the age? from being birdlimed by dissipation? or caught in the spider's web of sophistry and unbelief? "It is no doubt a true observation," says Bishop Patrick*, "that the ready way to make the minds of youth grow awry, is to lace them too hard, by denying them their just freedom."

Ask the old faithful servant of Mammon, whom Mammon has rewarded to his heart's desire, and in whom the acquisition of riches has only increased his eagerness for acquiring more — ask him whether he has succeeded in training up his heir to the same service? He will tell you that the young man is to be found upon race-grounds, and in gaming-houses, that he is taking his swing of extravagance and excess, and is on the high road to ruin.

Ask the wealthy Quaker, the pillar of the meeting — most orthodox in heterodoxy, — who never wore a garment of forbidden cut or colour, never bent his body in salutation, or his knees in prayer, — never uttered the heathen name of a day or month, nor ever addressed himself to any person without religiously speaking illegitimate English, — ask him how it has happened that the tailor has converted his sons? He will fold his hands, and twirl his thumbs mournfully in silence. It has not been for want of training them in the way wherein it was his wish that they should go.

You are about, Sir, to send your son to a public school; Eton or Westminster; Winchester or Harrow; Rugby or the Charter House, no matter which. He may come from either an accomplished scholar to the utmost extent that school education can make him so; he may be the better both for its discipline and its want of discipline; it may serve him excellently well as a preparatory school for the world into which he is about to enter. But also he may come away an empty coxcomb or a hardened brute — a spendthrift — a profligate — a blackguard or a sot.

To put a boy in the way he should go, is like sending out a ship well found, well manned and stored, and with a careful captain; but there are rocks and shallows in her course,

---

* Fuller has the same remark in his notes on Jonah. "As for cards to play with, let us not wholly condemn them, lest lacing our consciences too straight, we make them to grow awry on the wrong side." p. 40.

winds and currents to be encountered, and all the contingencies and perils of the sea.

How often has it been seen that sons, not otherwise deficient in duty toward their parents, have, in the most momentous concerns of life, taken the course most opposite to that in which they were trained to go, going wrong where the father would have directed them aright, or taking the right path in spite of all inducements and endeavours for leading them wrong! The son of Charles Wesley, born and bred in Methodism and bound to it by all the strongest ties of pride and prejudice, became a papist. This indeed was but passing from one erroneous persuasion to another, and a more inviting one. But Isaac Casaubon also had the grief of seeing a son seduced into the Romish superstition, and on the part of that great and excellent man, there had been no want of discretion in training him, nor of sound learning and sound wisdom. Archbishop Leighton, an honour to his church, his country, and his kind, was the child of one of those firebrands who kindled the Great Rebellion. And Franklin had a son, who notwithstanding the example of his father (and such a father!) continued stedfast in his duty as a soldier and a subject; he took the unsuccessful side — but

——*nunquam successu crescat honestum.**

No such disappointment was destined to befal our Daniel. The way in which he trained up his son was that into which the bent of the boy's own nature would have led him; and all circumstances combined to favour the tendency of his education. The country abounding in natural objects of sublimity and beauty (some of these singular in their kind) might have impressed a duller imagination than had fallen to his lot; and that imagination had time enough for its workings during his solitary walks to and from school morning and evening. His home was in a lonely spot; and having neither brother nor sister, nor neighbours near enough in any degree to supply their place as playmates, he became his father's companion imperceptibly as he ceased to be his fondling. And the effect was hardly less apparent in Daniel than in the boy. He was no longer the same taciturn person as of yore; it seemed as if his tongue had been loosened, and when the reservoirs of his knowledge were opened they flowed freely.

* Lucan.

Their chimney corner on a winter's evening presented a group not unworthy of Sir Joshua's pencil. There sate Daniel, richer in marvellous stories than ever traveller who in the days of mendacity returned from the East; the peat fire shining upon a countenance which weather-hardened as it was, might have given the painter a model for a Patriarch, so rare was the union which it exhibited of intelligence, benevolence and simplicity. There sate the boy with open eyes and ears, raised head, and fallen lip, in all the happiness of wonder and implicit belief. There sate Dinah, not less proud of her husband's learning than of the towardly disposition and promising talents of her son, — twirling the thread at her spinning-wheel, but attending to all that past; and when there was a pause in the discourse, fetching a deep sigh, and exclaiming, "Lord bless us! what wonderful things there are in the world!" There also sate Haggy, knitting stockings, and sharing in the comforts and enjoyments of the family when the day's work was done. And there sate William Dove;—but William must have a chapter to himself.

CHAPTER X. P. I.

ONE WHO WAS NOT SO WISE AS HIS FRIENDS COULD HAVE WISHED, AND YET QUITE AS HAPPY AS IF HE HAD BEEN WISER. NEPOTISM NOT CONFINED TO POPES.

There are of madmen as there are of tame,
All humoured not alike. —— Some
Apish and fantastic;
And though 'twould grieve a soul to see God's image
So blemished and defaced, yet do they act
Such antic and such pretty lunacies,
That spite of sorrow, they will make you smile.

Dekker.

William Dove was Daniel's only surviving brother, seven years his junior. He was born with one of those heads in which the thin partition that divides great wits from folly is wanting. Had he come into the world a century sooner, he would have been taken *nolens volens* into some Baron's household, to wear motley, make sport for the guests and domestics, and live in fear of the rod. But it was his better fortune to live in an age when this calamity rendered him liable to no such oppression, and to be precisely in that station which secured for him all the enjoyments of which he was capable, and all the care he needed. In higher life, he would probably have been consigned to the keeping of strangers who would have taken charge of him for pay; in a humbler degree he must have depended upon the parish for support; or have been made an inmate of one of those moral lazar-houses in which age and infancy, the harlot and the idiot, the profligate and the unfortunate are herded together.

William Dove escaped these aggravations of calamity. He escaped also that persecution to which he would have been exposed in populous places where boys run loose in packs, and harden one another in impudence, mischief and cruelty. Natural feeling, when natural feeling is not corrupted, leads men to regard persons in his condition with a compassion not unmixed with awe. It is common with the country people when they speak of such persons to point significantly at the head and say *'tis not all there;*— words denoting a sense of the mysteriousness of our nature which perhaps they feel more deeply on this than on any other occasion. No outward and visible deformity can make them so truly apprehend how fearfully and wonderfully we are made.

William Dove's was not a case of fatuity. Though *all* was not there, there was a great deal. He was what is called *half-saved.* Some of his faculties were more than ordinarily acute, but the power of self conduct was entirely wanting in him. Fortunately it was supplied by a sense of entire dependence which produced entire docility. A dog does not obey his master more dutifully than William obeyed his brother; and in this obedience there was nothing of fear; with all the strength and simplicity of a child's love, it had also the character and merit of a moral attachment.

The professed and privileged fool was generally characterised by a spice of knavery, and not unfrequently of maliciousness: the unnatural situation in which he was placed, tended to excite such propensities and even to produce them. William had shrewdness enough for the character, but nothing of this appeared in his disposition; ill-usage might perhaps have awakened it, and to a fearful degree, if he had proved as sensible to injury as he was to kindness. But he had never felt an injury. He could not have been treated with more tenderness in Turkey (where a degree of holiness is imputed to persons in his condition) than was uniformly shown him within the little sphere of his perambulations. It was surprising how much he had picked up within that little sphere. Whatever event occurred, whatever tale was current, whatever traditions were preserved, whatever superstitions were believed, William knew them all; and all that his insatiable ear took in, his memory hoarded. Half the proverbial sayings in Ray's volume were in his head, and as many more with which Ray was unacquainted. He knew many of the stories which our children are now receiving as novelties in the selections from Grimm's *Kinder und Haus-Marchen*, and as many of those which are collected in the Danish Folk-Sagn. And if some zealous lover of legendary lore, (like poor John Leyden, or Sir Walter Scott,) had fallen in with him, the Shakesperian commentators might perhaps have had the whole story of St. Withold; the Wolf of the World's End might have been identified with Fenris and found to be a relic of the Scalds. and Rauf Collyer and John the Reeve might still have been as well known as Adam Bell, and Clym of the Clough, and William of Cloudeslie.

William had a great fondness for his nephew. Let not Protestants suppose that Nepotism is an affection confined to the dignitaries of the Roman Catholic Church. In its excess indeed it is peculiarly a Papal vice, — which is a degree higher than a Cardinal one; but like many other sins it grows out of the corruption of a good feeling. It may be questioned whether fond uncles are not as numerous as unkind ones, notwithstanding our recollections of King Richard and the Children in the Wood. We may use the epithet nepotious for those who carry this fondness to the extent of doting, and as expressing that degree of fondness it may be applied to William Dove: he was a nepotious uncle. The father regarded young Daniel with a deeper and more thoughtful, but not with a fonder affection, not with such a doting attachment. Dinah herself, though a fond as well as careful mother, did not more thoroughly

> —— delight to hear
> Her early child mis-speak half-uttered words ;*

and perhaps the boy, so long as he was incapable of distinguishing between their moral qualities, and their relative claims to his respect and love and duty, loved his uncle most of the three. The father had no idle hours; in the intervals when he was not otherwise employed, one of his dear books usually lay open before him, and if he was not feeding upon the page, he was ruminating the food it had afforded him. But William Dove, from the time that his nephew became capable of noticing and returning caresses seemed to have concentred upon him all his affections. With children affection seldom fails of finding its due return; and if he had not thus won the boy's heart in infancy, he would have secured it in childhood by winning his ear with these marvellous stories. But he possessed another talent which would alone have made him a favourite with children, — the power of imitating animal sounds with singular perfection. A London manager would have paid him well for performing the cock in Hamlet. He could bray in octaves to a nicety, set the geese gabbling by addressing them in their own tongue, and make the turkey-cock spread his fan, brush his wing against the ground, and angrily gob-gobble in answer to a gobble of defiance. But he prided himself more upon his success with the owls, as an accomplishment of more difficult attainment. In this Mr. Wordsworth's boy of Winander was not more perfect. Both hands were used as an instrument in producing the notes; and if Pope could have heard the responses which came from barn and doddered oak and ivied crag, he would rather, (satirist as he was,) have left Ralph unsatirised, than have vilified one of the wildest and sweetest of nocturnal sounds.

He was not less expert to a human ear in hitting off the wood-pigeon's note, though he could not in this instance provoke a reply. This sound he used to say ought to be natural to him, and it was wrong in the bird not to acknowledge his relation. Once when he had made too free with a lass's lips, he disarmed his brother of a reprehensive look, by pleading that as his name was William Dove it behoved him both to *bill* and to *coo*.

* Donne.

CHAPTER XI. P. I.

A WORD TO THE READER, SHOWING WHERE WE ARE, AND HOW WE CAME HERE, AND WHEREFORE; AND WHITHER WE ARE GOING.

> 'Tis my venture
> On your retentive wisdom.
> BEN JONSON.

Reader, you have not forgotten where we are at this time: you remember I trust, that we are neither at Dan nor Beersheba; nor anywhere between those two celebrated places; nor on the way to either of them: but that we are in the Doctor's parlour, that Mrs. Dove has just poured out his seventh cup of tea, and that the clock of St. George's has struck five. In what street, parade, place, square, row, terrace or lane, and in what town, and in what county; and on what day, and in what month, and in what year, will be explained in due time. You cannot but remember what was said in the second chapter *post initium* concerning the importance and the necessity of order in an undertaking like this. "All things," says Sir Thomas Brown, "began in order; so shall they end, and so shall they begin again; according to the ordainer of order, and mystical mathematics of the City of Heaven:" This awful sentence was uttered by the Philosopher of Norwich upon occasion of a subject less momentous than that whereon we have entered, for what are the mysteries of the *Quincunx* compared to the delineation of a human mind? Be pleased only at present to bear in mind where we are. Place but as much confidence in me as you do in your review, your newspaper, and your apothecary; give me but as much credit as you expect from your tailor; and if your apothecary deserves that confidence as well, it will be well for you, and if your credit is as punctually redeemed, it will be well for your tailor. It is not without cause that I have gone back to the Doctor's childhood and his birth-place. Be thou assured, O Reader! that he never could have been seated thus comfortably in that comfortable parlour where we are now regarding him, — never by possibility could have been at that time in that spot, and in those circumstances;—never could have been the Doctor that he was, — nay, according to all reasonable induction, all tangible or imaginable probabilities, — never would have been a Doctor at all, — consequently thou never couldst have had the happiness of reading this delectable history, nor I the happiness of writing it for thy benefit and information and delight, —had it not been for his father's character, his father's books, his schoolmaster Guy, and his Uncle William, with all whom and which, it was therefore indispensable that thou shouldst be made acquainted.

A metaphysician, or, as some of my contemporaries would affect to say a psychologist, if he were at all a master of his art bablative (for it is as much an *ars bablativa* as the law, which was defined to be so by that old traitor and time-server Serjeant Maynard) — a metaphysician I say, would not require more than three such octavo volumes as those of Mr. Malthus's Essay on Population, to prove that no existing circumstance could at this time be what it is, unless all preceding circumstances had from the beginning of time been precisely what they were. But, my good reader, I have too much respect for you, and too much regard for your precious time, and too much employment, or amusement (which is a very rational kind of employment) for my own, to waste it in demonstrating a truism. No man knows the value of time more feelingly than I do!

> Man's life, Sir, being
> So short, and then the way that leads unto
> The knowledge of ourselves, so long and tedious,
> Each minute should be precious.*

It is my wish and intention to make you acquainted with a person most worthy to be known, for such the subject of this history will be admitted to be: one whom when you once know him it will be impossible that you should ever forget: one for whom I have the highest possible veneration and regard; (and though it is not possible that your feelings towards him should be what mine are) one who, the more he is known, will and must be more and more admired. I wish to introduce this person to you. Now, Sir, I appeal to your good sense, and to your own standard of propriety, should I act with sufficient respect either to yourself or him, if, without giving you any previous intimation, any information, concerning his character and situation in life; or in any way apprising you who and what he was, I were to knock at your door and simply present him to you as Doctor Dove? No, my dear Sir! it is indispensable that you should be properly informed who it is whom I thus introduce to your acquaintance; and if you are the judicious person that I suppose you to be, you will be obliged to me as long as you live. "For why," as old Higgins hath it, —

> For why, who writes such histories as these
> Doth often bring the Reader's heart such ease
> As when they sit and see what he doth note,
> Well fare his heart, say they, this book that wrote!

Ill fare that reader's heart who of this

* Beaumont and Fletcher.

book says otherwise! "*Tam suavia dicam facinora, ut malè sit ei qui talibus non delectetur!*" said a very different person from old Higgins, writing in a different vein. I have not read his book, but so far as my own is concerned, I heartily adopt his malediction.

Had I been disposed, as the Persians say, to let the steed of the pen expatiate in the plains of prolixity, I should have carried thee farther back in the generations of the Doves. But the good garrulous son of Garcilasso my Lord (Heaven rest the soul of the Princess who bore him, — for Peru has never produced any thing else half so precious as his delightful books,) — the Inca-blooded historian himself, I say, was not more anxious to avoid that failing than I am. Forgive me, Reader, if I should have fallen into an opposite error; forgive me if in the fear of saying too much I should have said too little. I have my misgivings: — I may have run upon Scylla while striving to avoid Charybdis. Much interesting matter have I omitted; much have I passed by on which I "cast a longing lingering look behind;" — much which might worthily find a place in the History of Yorkshire; — or of the West Riding (if that history were tripartitively distributed;) — or in the Gentleman's Magazine; — or in John Nichols's Illustrations of the Literary History of the Eighteenth Century: (I honour John Nichols, I honour Mr. Urban!) — much more might it have had place — much more might it be looked for here!

I might have told thee, Reader, of Daniel the Grandfather, and of Abigail his second wife, who once tasted tea in the housekeeper's apartments at Skipton Castle; and of the Great Grandfather who at the age of twenty-eight died of the small-pox, and was the last of the family that wore a leathern jerkin; and of his father Daniel the *atavus*, who was the first of the family that shaved, and who went with his own horse and arms to serve in that brave troop, which during the wreck of the King's party the heir of Lowther raised for the loyal cause: and of that Daniel's Grandfather, (the *tritavus*) who going to Kentmere to bring home a wife was converted from the Popish superstition by falling in with Bernard Gilpin on the way. That apostolic man was so well pleased with his convert, that he gave him his own copy of Latimer's sermons, — that copy which was one of our Daniel's Sunday books, and which was religiously preserved in reverence for this ancestor, and for the Apostle of the North (as Bernard Gilpin was called), whose autograph it contained.

The history of any private family, however humble, could it be fully related for five or six generations, would illustrate the state and progress of society better than could be done by the most elaborate dissertation. And the History of the Doves might be rendered as interesting and as instructive as that of the Seymours or the Howards. Frown not, my Lord of Norfolk, frown not, your Grace of Somerset, when I add, that it would contain less for their descendants to regret.

CHAPTER XII. P. I.

A HISTORY NOTICED WHICH IS WRITTEN BACKWARD. THE CONFUSION OF TONGUES AN ESPECIAL EVIL FOR SCHOOLBOYS.

> For never in the long and tedious tract
> Of slavish grammar was I made to plod;
> No tyranny of Rules my patience rackt;
> I served no prenticehood to any Rod;
> But in the freedom of the Practic way
> Learnt to go right, even when I went astray.
>
> DR. BEAUMONT.

IT has been the general practice of historians, from the time of Moses, to begin at the beginning of their subject: but as a river may be traced either from its sources or its mouth, so it appears that a history may be composed in the reversed order of its chronology; and a French author of very considerable ability and great learning has actually written a history of the Christian religion from his own times upwards. It forms part of an elaborate and extensive work entitled *Parallele des Religions*, which must have been better known than it appears to be at present if it had not happened to be published in Paris during the most turbulent year of the Revolution. Perhaps if I had carried back the memoirs of the Dove family, I might have followed his example in choosing the up-hill way, and have proceeded from son to father in the ascending line. But having resolved (whether judiciously or not) not to go farther back in these family records than the year of our Lord 1723, being the year of the Doctor's birth, I shall continue in the usual course, and pursue his history *ab incunabulis* down to that important evening on which we find him now reaching out his hand to take that cup of tea which Mrs. Dove has just creamed and sugared for him. After all the beaten way is usually the best, and always the safest. "He ought to be well mounted," says Aaron Hill, "who is for leaping the hedges of custom." For myself I am not so adventurous a horseman as to take the hazards of a steeple chace.

Proceeding, therefore, after the model of a Tyburn biography, which being an ancient as well as popular form is likely to be the best, — we come after birth and parentage to education. "That the world from Babel was scattered into divers tongues, we need not other proof," says a grave and good author, "than as Diogenes proved that there is motion, — by walking; — so we may see the confusion of languages by our confused speaking. Once all the earth was of one tongue, one speech and one consent; for they all spake in the holy tongue wherein the world was created in the beginning. But *pro peccato dissentionis humanæ* (as saith St. Austin,) — for the sin of men disagreeing, — not only different dispositions but also different languages came into the world. — They came to Babel with a disagreeing agreement; and they came away punished with a speechless speech. They disagree among themselves, while every one strives for dominion. They agree against God in their *Nagnavad lan Liguda*, — we will make ourselves a rendezvous for idolatry. But they come away speaking to each other, but not understood of each other; and so speak to no more purpose than if they spake not at all. This punishment of theirs at Babel is like Adam's corruption, hereditary to us; for we never come under the rod at the Grammar School, but we smart for our ancestor's rebellion at Babel."

Light lie the earth upon the bones of Richard Guy, the Schoolmaster of Ingleton! He never consumed birch enough in his vocation to have made a besom; and his ferule was never applied unless when some moral offence called for a chastisement that would be felt. There is a closer connection between good-nature and good sense than is commonly supposed. A sour ill-tempered pedagogue would have driven Daniel through the briars and brambles of the Grammar and foundered him in its sloughs; Guy led him gently along the green-sward. He felt that childhood should not be made altogether a season of painful acquisition, and that the fruits of the sacrifices then made are uncertain as to the account to which they may be turned, and are also liable to the contingencies of life at least, if not otherwise jeopardized. "*Puisque le jour peut lui manquer, laissons le un peu jouir de l'Aurore!*" The precept which warmth of imagination inspired in Jean Jacques was impressed upon Guy's practice by gentleness of heart. He never crammed the memory of his pupil with such horrific terms as Prothesis, Aphæresis, Epenthesis, Syncope, Paragoge, and Apocope; never questioned him concerning Appositio, Evocatio, Syllepsis, Prolepsis, Zeugma, Synthesis, Antiptosis, and Synecdoche; never attempted to deter him (as Lily says boys are above all things to be deterred) from those faults which Lily also says, seem almost natural to the English, — the heinous faults of Iotacism, Lambdacism, (which Alcibiades affected,) — Ischnotesism, Trauli'sm and Plateasm. But having grounded him well in the nouns and verbs, and made him understand the concords, he then followed in part the excellent advice of Lily thus given in his address to the Reader:

"When these concords be well known unto them (an easy and pleasant pain, if the foregrounds be well and thoroughly beaten in) let them not continue in learning of the rules orderly, as they lie in their Syntax, but rather learn some pretty book wherein is contained not only the eloquence of the tongue, but also a good plain lesson of honesty and godliness; and thereof take some little sentence as it lieth, and learn to make the same first out of English into Latin, not seeing the book, or construing it thereupon. And if there fall any necessary rule of the Syntax to be known, then to learn it, as the occasion of the sentence giveth cause that day; which sentence once made well, and as nigh as may be with the words of the book, then to take the book and construe it; and so shall he be less troubled with the parsing of it, and easiliest carry his lesson in mind."

Guy followed this advice in part; and in part he deviated from it, upon Lily's own authority, as "judging that the most sufficient way which he saw to be the readiest mean;" while, therefore, he exercised his pupil in writing Latin pursuant to this plan, he carried him on faster in construing, and promoted the boy's progress by gratifying his desire of getting forward. When he had done with Cordery, Erasmus was taken up, —for some of Erasmus's colloquies were in those days used as a school book, and the most attractive one that could be put into a boy's hands. After he had got through this, the aid of an English version was laid aside. And here Guy departed from the ordinary course, not upon any notion that he could improve upon it, but merely because he happened to possess an old book composed for the use of Schools, which was easy enough to suit young Daniel's progress in the language, and might therefore save the cost of purchasing Justin or Phædrus or Cornelius Nepos, or Eutropius,—to one or other of which he would otherwise have been introduced.

CHAPTER XIII. P. I.

A DOUBT CONCERNING SCHOOL BOOKS, WHICH WILL BE DEEMED HERETICAL: AND SOME ACCOUNT OF AN EXTRAORDINARY SUBSTITUTE FOR OVID OR VIRGIL.

They say it is an ill mason that refuseth any stone; and there is no knowledge but in a skilful hand serves, either positively as it is, or else to illustrate some other knowledge.
HERBERT'S REMAINS.

I AM sometimes inclined to think that pigs are brought up upon a wiser system, than boys at a grammar school. The Pig is allowed to feed upon any kind of offal, however coarse, on which he can thrive, till the time approaches when pig is to commence pork, or take a degree as bacon; and then he is fed daintily. Now it has sometimes appeared to me that in like manner, boys might acquire their first knowledge of Latin from authors very inferior to those which are now used in all schools; provided the matter was unexceptionable and the Latinity good; and that they should not be introduced to the standard works of antiquity till they are of an age in some degree to appreciate what they read.

Understand me, Reader, as speaking doubtfully,—and that too upon a matter of little moment; for the scholar will return in riper years to those authors which are worthy of being studied, and as for the blockhead—it signifies nothing whether the book which he consumes by thumbing it in the middle and dog-earing it at the corners be worthy or not of a better use. Yet if the dead have any cognizance of posthumous fame, one would think it must abate somewhat of the pleasure with which Virgil and Ovid regard their earthly immortality, when they see to what base purposes their productions are applied. That their verses should be administered to boys in regular doses, as lessons or impositions, and some dim conception of their meaning whipt into the tail when it has failed to penetrate the head, cannot be just the sort of homage to their genius which they anticipated or desired.

Not from any reasonings or refinements of this kind, but from the mere accident of possessing the book, Guy put into his pupil's hands the Dialogues of Johannes Ravisius Textor. Jean Tixier, Seigneur de Ravisy, in the Nivernois, who thus latinised his name, is a person whose works, according to Baillet's severe censure, were buried in the dust of a few petty colleges and unfrequented shops, more than a century ago. He was, however, in his day a person of no mean station in the world of letters, having been Rector of the University of Paris, at the commencement of the sixteenth century; and few indeed are the writers whose books have been so much used; for perhaps no other author ever contributed so largely to the manufacture of exercises whether in prose or verse, and of sermons also. Textor may be considered as the first compiler of the *Gradus ad Parnassum;* and that collection of Apophthegms was originally formed by him, which Conrade Lycosthenes enlarged and re-arranged; which the Jesuits adopted after expurgating it; and which, during many generations, served as one of the standard common-place books for common-place divines in this country as well as on the continent.

But though Textor was continually working in classical literature with a patience and perseverance which nothing but the delight he experienced in such occupations could have sustained, he was without a particle of classical taste. His taste was that of the age wherein he flourished, and these his Dialogues are Moralities in Latin verse. The designs and thoughts which would have accorded with their language, had they been written either in old French or old English, appear, when presented in Latinity, which is always that of a scholar, and largely interwoven with scraps from familiar classics, as strange as Harlequin and Pantaloon would do in heroic costume.

Earth opens the first of these curious compositions with a bitter complaint for the misfortunes which it is her lot to witness. Age (*Ætas*) overhears the lamentation and inquires the cause; and after a dialogue in which the author makes the most liberal use of his own common-places, it appears that the perishable nature of all sublunary things is the cause of this mourning. *Ætas* endeavours to persuade *Terra* that her grief is altogether unreasonable by such brief and cogent observations as *Fata jubent*, *Fata volunt*, *Ita Diis placitum.* Earth asks the name of her philosophic consoler, but upon discovering it, calls her *falsa virago*, and *meretrix*, and abuses her as being the very author of all the evils that distress her. However *Ætas* succeeds in talking *Terra* into better humour, advises her to exhort man that he should not set his heart upon perishable things, and takes her leave as *Homo* enters. After a recognition between mother and son, *Terra* proceeds to warn *Homo* against all the ordinary pursuits of this world. To convince him of the vanity of glory she calls up in succession the ghosts of Hector, Achilles, Alexander, and Samson, who tell their tales and admonish him that valour and renown afford no protection against Death. To exemplify the vanity of beauty Helen, Lais, Thisbe and Lucretia are summoned, relate in like manner their respective fortunes, and remind him that *pulvis et umbra sumus.* Virgil preaches to him upon the emptiness of literary fame. Xerxes tells him that there is no avail in power, Nero that there is none in tyranny, Sardanapalus that there is none in voluptuousness. But the application which *Homo* makes of all this, is the very reverse to what his mother intended: he infers that seeing he must die at last, live how he will, the best thing he can do is to make a merry life of it, so away he goes to dance and revel and enjoy himself: and *Terra* concludes with the mournful observation that men will still pursue their bane, unmindful of their latter end.

Another of these Moralities begins with three Worldlings (*Tres Mundani*) ringing changes upon the pleasures of profligacy, in Textor's peculiar manner, each in regular succession saying something to the same purport in different words. As thus —

Primus Mundanus.
Si breve tempus abit,
Secundus Mundanus.
Si vita caduca recedit;
Tertius Mundanus.
Si cadit hora.
Primus Mundanus.
Dies abeunt,
Secundus Mundanus.
Perit Omne,
Tertius Mundanus.
Venit Mors,
Primus Mundanus.
Quidnam prodesset fati meminisse futuri?
Secundus Mundanus.
Quidnam prodesset lachrymis consumere vitam?
Tertius Mundanus.
Quidnam prodesset tantis incumbere curis?

Upon which an unpleasant personage who has just appeared to interrupt their trialogue observes,

Si breve tempus abit, si vita caduca recedit,
Si cadit hora, dies abeunt, perit omne, venit Mors,
Quidnam lethiferæ Mortis meminisse nocebit?

It is *Mors* herself who asks the question. The three Worldlings, however, behave as resolutely as Don Juan in the old drama; they tell Death that they are young, and rich, and active, and vigorous, and set all admonition at defiance. Death, or rather Mrs. Death, (for *Mors*, being feminine, is called *læna*, and *meretrix*, and *virago*,) takes all this patiently, and letting them go off in a dance, calls up Human Nature, who has been asleep meantime, and asks her how she can sleep in peace while her sons are leading a life of dissipation and debauchery? Nature very coolly replies by demanding why they should not? and Death answers, because they must go to the infernal regions for so doing. Upon this Nature, who appears to be liberally inclined, asks if it is credible that any should be obliged to go there? and Death, to convince her, calls up a soul from bale to give an account of his own sufferings. A dreadful account this *Damnatus* gives; and when Nature, shocked at what she hears, inquires if he is the only one who is tormented in *Orcus*, *Damnatus* assures her that hardly one in a thousand goes to Heaven, but that his fellow-sufferers are in number numberless; and he specifies among them Kings and Popes, and Senators, and severe Schoolmasters, — a class of men whom Textor seems to have held in great and proper abhorrence — as if like poor Thomas Tusser he had suffered under their inhuman discipline.

Horrified at this, Nature asks advice of *Mors*, and *Mors* advises her to send a Son of Thunder round the world, who should reprove the nations for their sins, and sow the seeds of virtue by his preaching. *Peregrinus* goes upon this mission and returns to give an account of it. Nothing can be worse than the report. As for the Kings of the Earth, it would be dangerous, he says, to say what they were doing. The Popes suffered the ship of Peter to go wherever the winds carried it. Senators were won by intercession or corrupted by gold. Doctors spread their nets in the temples for prey, and Lawyers were dumb unless their tongues were loosened by money. — Had he seen the Italians? — Italy was full of dissensions, ripe for war, and defiled by its own infamous vice. The Spaniards? — They were suckled by Pride. The English? —

Gens tacitis prægnans arcanis, ardua tentans,
Edita tartareis mihi creditur esse tenebris.

In short the Missionary concludes that he has found every where an abundant crop of vices, and that all his endeavours to produce amendment have been like ploughing the sea shore. Again afflicted Nature asks advice of *Mors*, and *Mors* recommends that she should call up Justice and send her abroad with her scourge to repress the wicked. But Justice is found to be so fast asleep that no calling can awaken her. *Mors* then advises her to summon *Veritas;* alas! unhappy *Veritas* enters complaining of pains from head to foot and in all the intermediate parts, within and without; she is dying and entreats that Nature will call some one to confess her. But who shall be applied to? — Kings? They will not come. — Nobles? *Veritas* is a hateful personage to them. — Bishops, or mitred Abbots? They have no regard for Truth. — Some Saint from the desert? Nature knows not where to find one! Poor *Veritas* therefore dies "unhouseled, disappointed, unanealed;" and forthwith three Demons enter rejoicing that Human Nature is left with none to help her, and that they are Kings of this world. They call in their Ministers, *Caro* and *Voluptas* and *Vitium*, and send them to do their work among mankind. These successful missionaries return, and relate how well they have sped every where; and the Demons being by this time hungry, after washing in due form, and many ceremonious compliments among themselves, sit down to a repast which their ministers have provided. The bill of fare was one which Beelzebub's Court of Aldermen might have approved. There were the brains of a fat monk,—a roasted Doctor of Divinity who afforded great satisfaction,—a King's sirloin,—some broiled Pope's flesh, and part of a Schoolmaster; the joint is not specified, but I suppose it to have been the rump. Then came a Senator's lights and a Lawyer's tongue.

When they have eaten of these dainties till the distended stomach can hold no more, *Virtus* comes in, and seeing them send off the fragments to their Tartarean den, calls upon mankind to bestow some sustenance upon her, for she is tormented with hunger. The Demons and their ministers insult her and drive her into banishment; they tell Nature that to-morrow the great King of Orcus will come and carry her away in chains; off they go in a dance, and Nature concludes the piece by saying that what they have threatened must happen, unless Justice shall be awakened, Virtue fed, and *Veritas* restored to life by the sacred book.

There are several other Dialogues in a similar strain of fiction. The rudest and perhaps oldest specimen of this style is to be found in Pierce Ploughman, the most polished in Calderon, the most popular in John Bunyan's Holy War, and above all in his Pilgrim's Progress. It appears from the Dialogues that they were not composed for the use of youth alone as a school book, but were represented at College; and poor as they are in point of composition, the oddity of their combinations, and the wholesome honesty of their satire, were well adapted to strike young imaginations and make an impression there which better and wiser works might have failed to leave.

A schoolmaster who had been regularly bred would have regarded such a book with scorn, and discerning at once its obvious faults, would have been incapable of perceiving any thing which might compensate for them. But Guy was not educated well enough to despise a writer like old Textor. What he knew himself, he had picked up where and how he could, in bye ways and corners. The book was neither in any respect above his comprehension, nor below his taste; and Joseph Warton, never rolled off the hexameters of Virgil or Homer, *ore rotundo*, with more delight, when expatiating with all the feelings of a scholar and a poet upon their beauties, to such pupils as Headley and Russell and Bowles, than Guy paraphrased these rude but striking allegories to his delighted Daniel.

CHAPTER XIV. P. I.

AN OBJECTION ANSWERED.

> Is this then your wonder?
> Nay then you shall understand more of my skill. BEN JONSON.

"This account of Textor's Dialogues," says a critical Reader, "might have done very well for the Retrospective Review, or one of the Magazines, or D'Israeli's Curiosities of Literature. But no one would have looked for it here, where it is completely out of place."

"My good Sir, there is quite enough left untouched in Textor to form a very amusing paper for the journal which you have mentioned, and the Editor may thank you for the hint. But you are mistaken in thinking that what has been said of those Dialogues is out of place here. May I ask what you expected in these volumes?"

"What the Title authorised me to look for."

"Do you know, Sir, what mutton broth means at a city breakfast on the Lord Mayor's Day, mutton broth being the appointed breakfast for that festival? It means according to established usage—by liberal interpretation—mutton broth and every thing else that can be wished for at a breakfast. So, Sir, you have here not only what the title seems to specify, but every thing else that can be wished for in a book. In treating of the Doctor, it treats *de omnibus rebus et quibusdam aliis*. It is the Doctor &c., and that &c., like one of Lyttleton's, implies every thing that can be deduced from the words preceding.

But I maintain that the little which has been said of comical old Textor (for it is little compared to what his Dialogues contain) strictly relates to the main thread of this most orderly and well-compacted work. You will remember that I am now replying to the question proposed in the third chapter P. I. "Who was the Doctor?" And as he who should undertake to edite the works of Chaucer, or Spenser, or Shakespear would not be qualified for the task, unless he had made himself conversant with the writings of those earlier authors, from whose storehouses (as far as they drew from books) their minds were fed; so it behoved me (as far as my information and poor ability extend) to explain in what manner so rare a character as Dr. Dove's was formed.

Quo semel est imbuta recens,—you know the rest of the quotation, Sir. And perhaps you may have tasted water out of a beery glass,—which it is not one or two rinsings that can purify.

You have seen yew trees cut into the forms of pyramids, chess-kings, and peacocks:—nothing can be more unlike their proper growth—and yet no tree except the yew could take the artificial figures so well. The garden passes into the possession of some new owner who has no taste for such ornaments: the yews are left to grow at their own will; they lose the preposterous shape which had been forced upon them, without recovering that of their natural growth, and what was formal becomes grotesque—a word which may be understood as expressing the incongruous combination of formality with extravagance or wildness.

The intellectual education which young Daniel received at home was as much out of the ordinary course as the book in which he studied at school. Robinson Crusoe had not yet reached Ingleton. Sandford and Merton had not been written, nor that history of Pecksey and Flapsey and the Robin's Nest, which is the prettiest fiction that ever was composed for children, and for which its excellent authoress will one day rank high among women of genius when time shall have set its seal upon desert. The only book within his reach, of all those which now come into the hands of youth, was the Pilgrim's Progress, and this he read at first without a suspicion of its allegorical import. What he did not understand was as little remembered as the sounds of the wind, or the motions of the passing clouds; but the imagery and the incidents took possession of his memory and his heart. After a while Textor became an interpreter of the immortal Tinker, and the boy acquired as much of the meaning by glimpses as was desirable, enough to render some of the personages more awful by spiritualising them, while the tale itself remained as a reality. Oh! what blockheads are those wise persons who think it necessary that a child should comprehend every thing it reads!

CHAPTER XV. P. I.

THE AUTHOR VENTURES AN OPINION AGAINST THE PREVAILING WISDOM OF MAKING CHILDREN PREMATURELY WISE.

> Pray you, use your freedom;
> And so far, if you please allow me mine,
> To hear you only; not to be compelled
> To take your moral potions. MASSINGER.

"WHAT, SIR," exclaims a Lady, who is bluer than ever one of her naked and woad-stained ancestors appeared at a public festival in full dye,—"what, Sir, do you tell us that children are not to be made to understand what they are taught?" And she casts her eyes complacently toward an assortment of those books which so many writers, male and female, some of the infidel, some of the semi-fidel, and some of the super-fidel schools have composed for the laudable purpose of enabling children to understand every thing. — "What, Sir," she repeats, "are we to make our children learn things by rote like parrots, and fill their heads with words to which they cannot attach any signification?"

"Yes, Madam, in very many cases."

"I should like, Sir, to be instructed why?"

She says this in a tone, and with an expression both of eyes and lips, which plainly show, in direct opposition to the words, that the Lady thinks herself much fitter to instruct, than to be instructed. It is not her fault. She is a good woman, and naturally a sensible one, but she has been trained up in the way women should not go. She has been carried from lecture to lecture, like a student who is being crammed at a Scotch University. She has attended lectures on chemistry, lectures on poetry, lectures on phrenology, lectures on mnemonics; she has read the latest and most applauded essays on Taste: she has studied the newest and most approved treatises practical and theoretical upon Education: she has paid sufficient attention to metaphysics to know as much as a professed philosopher about matter and spirit: she is a proficient in political economy, and can discourse upon the new science of population. Poor Lady, it would require large draughts of Lethe to clear out all this undigested and undigestible trash, and fit her for becoming what she might have been! Upon this point, however, it may be practicable to set her right.

"You are a mother, Madam, and a good one. In caressing your infants you may perhaps think it unphilosophical to use what I should call the proper and natural language of the nursery. But doubtless you talk to them; you give some utterance to your feelings, and whether that utterance be in legitimate and wise words, or in good extemporaneous nonsense, it is alike to the child. The conventional words convey no more meaning to him than the mere sound; but he understands from either all that is meant, all that you wish him to understand, all that is to be understood. He knows that it is an expression of your love and tenderness, and that he is the object of it.

"So too it continues after he is advanced from infancy into childhood. When children are beginning to speak they do not and cannot affix any meaning to half the words which they hear; yet they learn their mother tongue. What I say is, do not attempt to force their intellectual growth. Do not feed them with meat till they have teeth to masticate it.

"There is a great deal which they ought to learn, can learn, and must learn, before they can or ought to understand it. How many questions must you have heard from them which you have felt to be best answered, when they were with most dexterity put aside! Let me tell you a story which the Jesuit Manuel de Vergara used to tell of himself. When he was a little boy he asked a Dominican Friar what was the meaning of the seventh commandment, for he said he could not tell what committing adultery was. The Friar not knowing how to answer, cast a perplexed look round the room, and thinking he had found a safe reply pointed to a kettle on the fire, and said the Commandment meant that he must never put his hand in the pot while it was boiling. The very next day, a loud scream alarmed the family, and behold there was little Manuel running about the room holding up his scalded finger, and exclaiming "Oh dear, oh dear, I've committed adultery! I've committed adultery! I've committed adultery!"

CHAPTER XVI. P.I.

USE AND ABUSE OF STORIES IN REASONING, WITH A WORD IN BEHALF OF CHIMNEY-SWEEPERS AND IN REPROOF OF THE EARL OF LAUDERDALE.

My particular inclination moves me in controversy especially to approve his choice that said, *fortia mallem quam formosa.*
DR. JACKSON.

I ENDED that last chapter with a story, and though "I say it who should not say it," it is a good story well applied. Of what use a story may be even in the most serious debates may be seen from the circulation of old Joes in Parliament, which are as current there as their sterling namesakes used to be in the city some threescore years ago. A jest, though it should be as stale as last week's newspaper, and as flat as Lord Flounder's face, is sure to be received with laughter by the Collective Wisdom of the Nation: nay, it is sometimes thrown out like a tub to the whale, or like a trail of carrion to draw off hounds from the scent.

The Bill which should have put an end to the inhuman practice of employing children to sweep chimneys, was thrown out on the third reading in the House of Lords (having passed the Commons without a dissentient voice) by a speech from Lord Lauderdale, the force of which consisted in, literally, a Joe Millar jest. He related that an Irishman used to sweep his chimney by letting a rope down, which was fastened round the legs of a goose, and then pulling the goose after it. A neighbour to whom he recommended this as a convenient mode objected to it upon the score of cruelty to the goose: upon which he replied, that a couple of ducks might do as well. Now if the Bill before the house had been to enact that men should no longer sweep chimneys but that boys should be used instead, the story would have been applicable. It was no otherwise applicable than as it related to chimney-sweeping: but it was a joke, and that sufficed. The Lords laughed; his Lordship had the satisfaction of throwing out the Bill, and the home Negro trade has continued from that time, now seven years, till this day, and still continues. His Lordship had his jest, and it is speaking within compass to say that in the course of those seven years two thousand children have been *sacrificed* in consequence.

The worst actions of Lord Lauderdale's worst ancestor admit of a better defence before God and Man.

Had his Lordship perused the evidence which had been laid before the House of Commons when the Bill was brought in, upon which evidence the Bill was founded? Was he aware of the shocking barbarities connected with the trade, and inseparable from it? Did he know that children inevitably lacerate themselves in learning this dreadful occupation? that they are frequently crippled by it? frequently lose their lives in it by suffocation, or by slow fire? that it induces a peculiar and dreadful disease? that they who survive the accumulated hardships of a childhood during which they are exposed to every kind of misery, and destitute of every kind of comfort, have at the age of seventeen or eighteen to seek their living how they can in some other employment, — for it is only by children that this can be carried on? Did his Lordship know that girls as well as boys are thus abused? that their sufferings begin at the age of six, sometimes a year earlier? finally that they are sold to this worst and most inhuman of all slaveries, and sometimes stolen for the purpose of being sold to it?

I bear no ill-will towards Lord Lauderdale, either personally or politically: far from it. His manly and honourable conduct on the Queen's trial, when there was such an utter destitution of honour in many quarters where it was believed to exist, and so fearful a want of manliness where it ought to have been found, entitles him to the respect and gratitude of every true Briton. But I will tell his Lordship that rather than have spoken as he did against an act which would have lessened the sum of wickedness and suffering in this country, — rather than have treated a question of pure humanity with contempt and ridicule, — rather than have employed my tongue for such a purpose and with such success, I would —— But no: I will not tell him how I had concluded. I will not tell him what I had added in the sincerity of a free tongue and an honest heart. I leave the sentence imperfect rather than that any irritation which the strength of my language might excite should lessen the salutary effects of self-condemnation.

James Montgomery! these remarks are too late for a place in thy Chimney Sweepers' Friend: but insert them, I pray thee, in thy newspaper, at the request of one who admires and loves thee as a Poet, honours and respects thee as a man, and reaches out in spirit at this moment a long arm to shake hands with thee in cordial good will.

My compliments to you, Mr. Bowring! your little poem in Montgomery's benevolent album is in a strain of true poetry and right feeling. None but a man of genius could have struck off such stanzas upon such a theme. But when you wrote upon Humanity at Home, the useful reflection might have occurred that Patriotism has no business abroad. Whatever cause there may be to wish for amendment in the government and institutions of other countries, keep aloof from all revolutionary schemes for amending them, lest you should experience a far more painful disappointment in their success than in their failure. No spirit of prophecy is required for telling you that this must be the result. Lay not up that cause of remorse for yourself, and time will ripen in you what is crude, confirm what is right, and gently rectify all that is erroneous; it will abate your political hopes, and enlarge your religious faith, and stablish both upon a sure foundation. My good wishes and sincere respects to you, Mr. Bowring!

INTERCHAPTER II.

ABALLIBOOZOBANGANORRIBO.

Io 'l dico dunque, e dicol che ognun m'ode.

BENEDETTO VARCHI.

WHETHER the secret of the Freemasons be comprised in the mystic word above is more than I think proper to reveal at present. But I have broken no vow in uttering it.

And I am the better for having uttered it.

Mahomet begins some of the chapters of the Koran with certain letters of unknown signification, and the commentators say that the meaning of these initials ought not to be inquired. So Gelaleddin says, so sayeth Taleb. And they say truly. Some begin with A. L. M. Some with K. H. I. A. S.; some with T. H.; — T. S. M.; — T. S. or I. S. others with K. M.; — H. M. A. S. K.; — N. M.; — a single *Kaf*, a single *Nun* or a single *Sad*, and *sad* work would it be either for *Kaffer* or Mussulman to search for meaning where *none* is. Gelaleddin piously remarks that there is only One who knoweth the import of these letters; — I reverence the name which he uses too much to employ it upon this occasion. Mahomet himself tells us that they are the signs of the Book which teacheth the true doctrine, — the Book of the Wise, — the Book of Evidence, the Book of Instruction. When he speaketh thus of the Koran he lieth like an impostor as he is: but what he has said falsely of that false book may be applied truly to this. It is the Book of Instruction inasmuch as every individual reader among the thousands and tens of thousands who peruse it will find something in it which he did not know before. It is the Book of Evidence because of its internal truth. It is the Book of the Wise, because the wiser a man is the more he will delight therein; yea, the delight which he shall take in it will be the measure of his intellectual capacity. And that it teacheth the true doctrine is plain from this circumstance, that I defy the British Critic, the Antijacobin, the Quarterly and the Eclectic Reviews, — ay, and the Evangelical, the Methodist, the Baptist, and the Orthodox Churchman's Magazine, with the Christian Observer to boot, to detect any one heresy in it. Therefore I say again,

Aballiboozobanganorribo,

and, like Mahomet, I say that it is the Sign of the Book; and therefore it is that I have said it;

Nondimen nè la lingua degli Hebrei
Nè la Latina, nè la Greca antica,
*Nè quella forse ancor degli Aramei.**

Happen it may, — for things not less strange have happened, and what has been may be again, — for may be and has been are only tenses of the same verb, and that verb is eternally being declined: —— Happen I say it may; and peradventure if it may it must; and certainly if it must it will: — but what with indicatives and subjunc-

* MOLZA.

tives, presents, præterperfects and paulo-post-futura, the parenthesis is becoming too long for the sentence, and I must begin it again. A prudent author should never exact too much from the breath or the attention of his reader, — to say nothing of the brains.

Happen then it may that this Book may outlive Lord Castlereagh's Peace, Mr. Pitt's reputation (we will throw Mr. Fox's into the bargain); Mr. Locke's Metaphysics, and the Regent's Bridge in St. James's Park. It may outlive the eloquence of Burke, the discoveries of Davy, the poems of Wordsworth, and the victories of Wellington. It may outlive the language in which it is written; and, in heaven knows what year of heaven knows what era, be discovered by some learned inhabitant of that continent which the insects who make coral and madrepore are now, and from the beginning of the world have been, fabricating in the Pacific Ocean. It may be dug up among the ruins of London, and considered as one of the sacred books of the sacred Island of the West, — for I cannot but hope that some reverence will always be attached to this most glorious and most happy island when its power and happiness and glory, like those of Greece, shall have passed away. It may be deciphered and interpreted, and give occasion to a new religion called Dovery or Danielism, which may have its Chapels, Churches, Cathedrals, Abbeys, Priories, Monasteries, Nunneries, Seminaries, Colleges, and Universities; — its Synods, Consistories, Convocations, and Councils; — its Acolytes, Sacristans, Deacons, Priests, Archdeacons, Rural Deans, Chancellors, Prebends, Canons, Deans, Bishops, Archbishops, Prince Bishops, Primates, Patriarchs, Cardinals, and Popes; its most Catholic Kings, and its Kings most Dovish or most Danielish. It may have Commentators and Expounders — (who can doubt that it will have them?) — who will leave unenlightened that which is dark, and darken that which is clear. Various interpretations will be given, and be followed by as many sects. Schisms must ensue; and the tragedies, comedies, and farces, with all the varieties of tragi-comedy and tragi-farce or farcico-tragedy which have been represented in this old world, be enacted in that younger one. Attack on the one side, defence on the other; high Dovers and low Dovers; Danielites of a thousand unimagined and unimaginable denominations; schisms, heresies, seditions, persecutions, wars, — the dismal game of Puss-catch-corner played by a nation instead of a family of children, and in dreadful earnest, when power, property, and life are to be won and lost!

But, without looking so far into the future history of Dovery, let me exhort the learned Australian to whom the honour is reserved of imparting this treasure to his countrymen, that he abstain from all attempts at discovering the mysteries of Aballiboozobanganorribo! The unapocalyptical arcana of that stupendous vocable are beyond his reach; — so let him rest assured. Let him not plunge into the fathomless depths of that great word; let him not attempt to soar to its unapproachable heights. Perhaps, — and surely no man of judgement will suppose that I utter any thing lightly, — perhaps, if the object were attainable, he might have cause to repent its attainment. If too "little learning be a dangerous thing," too much is more so;

*Il saper troppo qualche volta nuoce.**

"Curiosity," says Fuller, "is a kernel of the Forbidden Fruit, which still sticketh in the throat of a natural man, sometimes to the danger of his choaking."

There is a knowledge which is forbidden because it is dangerous. Remember the Apple! Remember the beautiful tale of Cupid and Psyche! Remember Cornelius Agrippa's library; the youth who opened in unhappy hour his magical volume; and the choice moral which Southey, who always writes so morally, hath educed from that profitable story! Remember Bluebeard! But I am looking far into futurity. Bluebeard may be forgotten; Southey may be

* Molza.

forgotten; Cornelius Agrippa may be no more remembered; Cupid and Psyche may be mere names which shall have outlived all tales belonging to them; Adam and Eve — Enough.

Eat beans, if thou wilt, in spite of Pythagoras. Eat bacon with them, for the Levitical law hath been abrogated: and indulge in black-puddings, if thou likest such food, though there be Methodists who prohibit them as sinful. But abstain from Aballiboozobanganorribo.

CHAPTER XVII. P. I.

THE HAPPINESS OF HAVING A CATHOLIC TASTE.

> There's no want of meat, Sir;
> Portly and curious viands are prepared
> To please all kinds of appetites. MASSINGER.

A FASTIDIOUS taste is like a squeamish appetite; the one has its origin in some disease of mind, as the other has in some ailment of the stomach. Your true lover of literature is never fastidious. I do not mean the *helluo librorum*, the swinish feeder, who thinks that every name which is to be found in a title-page, or on a tombstone, ought to be rescued from oblivion; nor those first cousins of the moth, who labour under a bulimy for black-letter, and believe every thing to be excellent which was written in the reign of Elizabeth. I mean the man of robust and healthy intellect, who gathers the harvest of literature into his barns, threshes the straw, winnows the grain, grinds it at his own mill, bakes it in his own oven, and then eats the true bread of knowledge. If he bake his loaf upon a cabbage leaf, and eat onions with his bread and cheese, let who will find fault with him for his taste, — not I!

The Doves, father as well as son, were blest with a hearty intellectual appetite, and a strong digestion: but the son had the more catholic taste. He would have relished caviare; would have ventured upon laver undeterred by its appearance — and would have liked it.

> What an excellent thing did God bestow on man,
> When he did give him a good stomach! *

He would have eaten sausages for breakfast at Norwich, sally-luns at Bath, sweet butter in Cumberland, orange marmalade at Edinburgh, Findon haddocks at Aberdeen, and drunk punch with beef-steaks to oblige the French if they insisted upon obliging him with a *dejeûner à l'Angloise.*

> A good digestion turneth all to health.†

He would have eaten squab-pie in Devonshire, and the pie which is squabber than squab in Cornwall; sheep's head with the hair on in Scotland, and potatoes roasted on the hearth in Ireland; frogs with the French, pickled herrings with the Dutch, sour-krout with the Germans, maccaroni with the Italians, aniseed with the Spaniards, garlic with any body; horse-flesh with the Tartars; ass-flesh with the Persians; dogs with the North Western American Indians, curry with the Asiatic East Indians, birds' nests with the Chinese, mutton roasted with honey with the Turks, pismire cakes on the Orinoco, and turtle and venison with the Lord Mayor; and the turtle and venison he would have preferred to all the other dishes, because his taste, though catholic, was not indiscriminating. He would have tried all, tasted all, thriven upon all, and lived contentedly and cheerfully upon either, but he would have liked best that which was best. And his intellectual appetite had the same happy catholicism.

He would not have said with Euphues, "If I be in Crete, I can lie; if in Greece, I can shift; if in Italy, I can court it:" but he might have said with him, "I can carouse with Alexander; abstain with Romulus; eat with the Epicure; fast with the Stoic; sleep with Endymion; watch with Chrysippus."

The reader will not have forgotten, I trust, (but if he should I now remind him of it,) that in the brief inventory of Daniel's library there appeared some odd volumes of that "book full of Pantagruelism," the in-

---

* BEAUMONT and FLETCHER. † HERBERT.

estimable life of the Great Gargantua. The elder Daniel could make nothing of this book; and the younger, who was about ten years old when he began to read it, less than he could of the Pilgrim's Progress. But he made out something.

Young Daniel was free from all the *isms* in Lily, and from rhotacism to boot; he was clear too of schism, and all the worse *isms* which have arisen from it: having by the blessing of Providence been bred up not in any denomination ending in *ist* or *inian*, or *erian* or *arian*, but as a dutiful and contented son of the Church of England. In humour, however, he was by nature a Pantagruelist. And, indeed, in his mature years he always declared that one of the reasons which had led him to reject the old humoral pathology was, that it did not include Pantagruelism, which, he insisted, depended neither upon heat or cold, moisture or dryness, nor upon any combination of those qualities; but was itself a peculiar and elementary humour; a truth, he said, of which he was feelingly and experimentally convinced, and lauded the gods therefore.

Mr. Wordsworth, in that poem which Mr. Jeffrey has said *won't do* — (Mr. Jeffrey is always lucky in his predictions whether as a politician or a critic, — bear witness, Wellington! bear witness, Wordsworth and Southey! bear witness, Elia and Lord Byron!) — Mr. Wordsworth, in that poem which

> The high and tender Muses shall accept
> With gracious smile deliberately pleased,
> And listening Time reward with sacred praise:

Mr. Wordsworth, in that noble poem, observes,

> Oh many are the Poets that are sown
> By nature!

Among the emblems of Daniel Heinsius — (look at his head, reader, if thou hast a collection of portraits to refer to, and thou wilt marvel how so queer a conceit should have entered it, for seldom has there been a face more gnarled and knotted with crabbed cogitation than that of this man, who was one of the last of the Giants;) — among his emblems, I say, is one which represents Cupid sowing a field, and little heads springing out of the ground on all sides, some up to the neck, others to the shoulders, and some with the arms out. If the crop were examined, I agree with Mr. Wordsworth, that poets should be found there as thick as darnel in the corn; — and grave counsellors would not be wanting whose advice would be that they should be weeded out.

The Pantagruelists are scarcer. Greece produced three great tragic poets, and only one Aristophanes. The French had but one Rabelais when the seven Pleiades shone in their poetical hemisphere. We have seen a succession of great Tragedians from Betterton to the present time; and in all that time there has been but one Grimaldi in whom the Pantagruelism of Pantomine has found its perfect representative.

And yet the reader must not hastily conclude that I think Pantagruelism a better thing than Poetry, because it is rarer; that were imputing to me the common error of estimating things by their rarity rather than their worth, an error more vulgar than any which Sir Thomas Brown has refuted. But I do hold this, that all the greatest poets have had a spice of Pantagruelism in their composition, which I verily believe was essential to their greatness. What the world lost in losing the Margites of Homer we know not, we only know that Homer had there proved himself a Pantagruelist. Shakespear was a Pantagruelist; so was Cervantes; and till the world shall have produced two other men in whom that humour has been wanting equal to these, I hold my point established.

Some one objects Milton. I thank him for the exception; it is just such an exception as proves the rule; for look only at Milton's Limbo and you will see what a glorious Pantagruelist he might have been, — if the Puritans had not spoilt him for Pantagruelism.

CHAPTER XVIII. P. I.

ALL'S WELL THAT ENDS WELL.

Τὰ δ' ἂν ἐπιμνησθῶ — ὑπὸ τοῦ λόγου ἐξαναγκαζόμενος ἐπιμνησθήσομαι. HERODOTUS.

IF William Dove had been installed in office, with cap and bells and bauble, he would have been a Professor of Pantagruelism, and might have figured in Flögel's History of such Professors with Tyll Eulenspiegel, Piovano Arlotto, and Peter the Lion; and in Douce's Illustrations of Shakespear with Muckle John, Rees Pengelding, and Robin Rush. The humour lay latent till the boy his nephew hit the spring by reading to him some of those chapters in Rabelais which in their literal grotesqueness were level to the capacity of both. These readings led to a piece of practical Pantagruelism, for which William would have been whipt if he had worn a Fool's coat.

One unlucky day, Dan was reading to him that chapter wherein young Gargantua relates the course of experiments which he had made with a velvet mask, a leaf of vervain, his mother's glove, a lappet worked with gold thread, a bunch of nettles, and other things more or less unfit for the purpose to which they were applied. To those who are acquainted with the history of Grandgousier's royal family, I need not explain what that purpose was; nor must I to those who are not, (for reasons that require no explanation,) farther than to say, it was the same purpose for which that wild enigma (the semi-composition of the Sphinx's Ghost) was designed, — that enigma of all enigmas the wildest,

On which was written Ρηγμάρωλ.

William had frequently interrupted him with bursts of laughter; but when they came to that crowning experiment in which Gargantua thought he had found the *beau idéal* of what he was seeking, William clapt his hands, and with an expression of glee in his countenance worthy of Eulenspiegel himself, exclaimed, "Thou shalt try the Goose, Dan! thou shalt try the Goose!"

So with William's assistance the Goose was tried. They began with due prudence, according to rule, by catching a Goose. In this matter a couple of Ducks, Lord Lauderdale knows, would not have answered as well. The boy then having gone through the ceremony which the devotees of Baal are said to have performed at the foot of his Image, as the highest act of devotion, (an act of super-reverence it was,) and for which the Jews are said to have called him in mockery Baalzebul instead of Baalzebub; — cried out that he was ready. He was at that moment in the third of those eight attitudes which form a *Rik'ath.* My readers who are versed in the fashionable poets of the day — (*this* day I mean — their fashion not being insured for to-morrow) — such readers, I say, know that a rose is called a ghul, and a nightingale a bulbul, and that this is one way of dressing up English Poetry in Turkish Costume. But if they desire to learn a little more of what Mahometan customs are, they may consult D'Ohsson's *Tableau* of the Ottoman Empire, and there they may not only find the eight attitudes described, but see them represented. Of the third attitude or *Rukeou*, as it is denominated, I shall only say that the Ancients represented one of their Deities in it, and that it is the very attitude in which *As in præsenti* committed that notorious act for which he is celebrated in scholastic and immortal rhyme, and for which poor Syntax bore the blame. *Verbum sit sat sapienti.* During the reign of Liberty and Equality a Frenchman was guillotined for exemplifying it under Marat's Monument in the *Place du Carousal.*

The bird was brought, but young Daniel had not the strength of young Gargantua; the goose, being prevented by William from drawing back, pressed forward; they were by the side of the brook, and the boy by this violent and unexpected movement was, as the French would say in the politest and most delicate of all languages, *culbuté*, or in sailors' English, capsized into the water. The misfortune did not end there; for, falling with his forehead against a stone, he received a cut upon the brow, which left a scar as long as he lived.

It was not necessary to prohibit a repetition of what William called the *speriment.* Both had been sufficiently frightened; and William never felt more pain of mind than on this occasion, when the Father, with a shake of the head, a look of displeasure, and a low voice, told him he ought to have known better than to have put the lad upon such pranks!

The mishap, however, was not without its use. For, in after life, when Daniel felt an inclination to do any thing which might better be left undone, the recollection that he had *tried the goose* served as a salutary memento, and saved him, perhaps, sometimes from worse consequences.

CHAPTER XIX. P. I.

A CONVERSATION WITH MISS GRAVEAIRS.

Operi suscepto inserviendum fuit; so Jacobus Mycillus pleadeth for himself in his translation of Lucian's Dialogues, and so do I; I must and will perform my task.

BURTON.

"It does not signify, Miss Graveairs! you may flirt your fan, and overcloud that white forehead with a frown; but I assure you the last chapter could not be dispensed with. The Doctor used to relate the story himself to his friends; and often alluded to it as the most wholesome lesson he had ever received. My dear Miss Graveairs, let not those intelligent eyes shoot forth in anger arrows which ought to be reserved for other execution. You ought not to be displeased; ought not, must not, can not, shall not!"

"But you ought not to write such things, Mr. Author; really you ought not. What can be more unpleasant than to be reading aloud, and come unexpectedly upon something so strange that you know not whether to proceed or make a full stop, nor where to look, nor what to do? It is too bad of you, Sir, let me tell you! and if I come to any thing more of the kind, I must discard the book. It is provoking enough to meet with so much that one does not understand; but to meet with any thing that one ought not to understand, is worse. Sir, it is not to be forgiven; and I tell you again, that if I meet with any thing more of the same kind, I must discard the book."

"Nay, dear Miss Graveairs!"

"I must, Mr. Author; positively I must."

"Nay, dear Miss Graveairs! Banish Tristram Shandy! banish Smollett, banish Fielding, banish Richardson! But for the Doctor, — sweet Doctor Dove, kind Doctor Dove, true Doctor Dove, banish not him! Banish Doctor Dove, and banish all the world! — Come, come, good sense is getting the better of preciseness. That stitch in the forehead will not long keep the brows in their constrained position; and the incipient smile which already brings out that dimple, is the natural and proper feeling."

"Well, you are a strange man!"

"Call me a rare one, and I shall be satisfied. 'O rare Ben Jonson,' you know, was epitaph enough for one of our greatest men."

"But seriously, why should you put any thing in your book, which, if not actually exceptionable, exposes it at least to that sort of censure which is most injurious?"

"That question, dear Madam, is so sensibly proposed, that I will answer it with all serious sincerity. There is nothing exceptionable in these volumes; 'Certes,' as Euphues Lily has said, 'I think there be more speeches here which for gravity will mislike the foolish, than unseemly terms which for vanity may offend the wise.' There is nothing in them that I might not have read to Queen Elizabeth, if it had been my fortune to have lived in her golden days; nothing that can by possibility taint the imagination, or strengthen one evil propensity, or weaken one virtuous principle. But they are not composed like a forgotten novel of Dr. Towers's, to be read aloud in dissenting families instead of a moral essay, or a sermon; nor like Mr. Kett's Emily, to complete the education of young ladies by supplying them with an abstract of universal knowledge. Neither have they any pretensions to be placed on the same shelf with Cœlebs. But the book is a moral book; its tendency is good, and the morality is both the wholesomer and pleasanter because it is not administered as physic, but given as food. I don't like morality in doses."

"But why, my good Mr. Author, why lay yourself open to censure?"

"Miss Graveairs, nothing excellent was ever produced by any author who had the fear of censure before his eyes. He who would please posterity must please himself by choosing his own course. There are only two classes of writers who dare do this, the best and the worst, — for this is one of the many cases in which extremes meet. The mediocres in every grade aim at pleasing the public, and conform themselves to the fashion of their age whatever it may be."

My Doctor, like the Matthew Henderson of Burns, was a queer man, and in that respect, I, his friend and biographer, humbly resemble him. The resemblance may be natural, or I may have caught it, — this I pretend not to decide, but so it is. Perhaps it might have been well if I had resolved upon a farther designation of Chapters, and distributed them into Masculine and Feminine; or into the threefold arrangement of virile, feminile, and puerile; considering the book as a family breakfast, where there should be meat for men, muffins for women, and milk for children. Or I might have adopted the device of the Porteusian Society, and marked my chapters as they (very usefully) have done the Bible, pointing out what should be read by all persons for edification, and what may be passed over by the many, as instructive or intelligible only to the learned.

Here, however, the book is, —

An orchard bearing several trees,
And fruits of several taste.*

Ladies and Gentlemen, my gentle Readers, one of our liveliest and most popular old Dramatists knew so well the capricious humour of an audience that he made his Prologue say —

He'd rather dress upon a Triumph-Day
My Lord Mayor's Feast, and make them sauces too,
Sauce for each several mouth; nay further go,
He'd rather build up those invincible Pies
And Castle-Custards that affright all eyes, —
Nay, eat them all and their artillery, —
Than dress for such a curious company,
One single dish.

But I, gentle Readers, have set before you a table liberally spread. It is not expected or desired that every dish should suit the palate of all the guests, but every guest will find something that he likes. You, Madam, may prefer those boiled chicken, with stewed celery, — or a little of that fricandeau; — the Lady opposite will send her plate for some pigeon pie. The Doctor has an eye upon the venison — and so I see has the Captain. — Sir, I have not forgotten that this is one of your fast days — I am glad, therefore, that the turbot proves so good, — and that dish has been prepared for you. Sir John, there is garlic in the fricassee. The Hungarian wine has a bitterness which everybody may not like; the Ladies will probably prefer Malmsey. The Captain sticks to his Port, and the Doctor to his Madeira. — Sir John, I shall be happy to take Sauterne with you. — There is a splendid trifle for the young folks, which some of the elders also will not despise: — and I only wish my garden could have furnished a better dessert; but, considering our climate, it is not amiss. — Is not this entertainment better than if I had set you all down to a round of beef and turnips?

If any thing be set to a wrong taste,
'Tis not the meat there, but the mouth's displaced;
Remove but that sick palate, all is well.*

Like such a dinner I would have my book, — something for everybody's taste, and all good of its kind.

It ought also to resemble the personage of whom it treats; and

If ony whiggish whingin sot
To blame the Doctor dare, man;
May dool and sorrow be his lot,
For the Doctor was a rare man! †

Some whiggish sots, I dare say, will blame him, and whiggish sots they will be who do!

* Middleton and Rowley's Spanish Gipsey.

* Ben Jonson. † Burns.

"*En un mot; mes amis, je n'ai entrepris de vous contenter tous en général; ainsi uns et autres en particulier, et par spécial, moy-même.*" *

CHAPTER XX. P. I.

HOW TO MAKE GOLD.

L'Alchimista non travaglia a voto;
Ei cerca l' oro, ei cerca l' oro, io dico
Ch' ei cerca l' oro; e s' ei giungesse in porto
Fora ben per se stesso e per altrui.
L' oro e somma posanza infra mortali;
Chiedine a Cavalier, chiedine a Dame,
Chiedine a tutto il Mondo. CHIABRERA.

WILLIAM had heard so much about experiments that it is not surprising he should have been for making some himself. It was well indeed for his family that the speculative mind, which lay covered rather than concealed under the elder Daniel's ruminating manners, and quiet contented course of life, was not quickened by his acquaintance with the schoolmaster into an experimental and dangerous activity, instead of being satisfied with theoretical dreams. For Guy had found a book in that little collection which might have produced more serious consequences to the father than the imitation of Gargantua had done to the son.

This book was the Exposition of Eirenæus Philalethes upon Sir George Ripley's Hermetico-Poetical works. Daniel had formerly set as little value upon it as upon Rabelais. He knew indeed what its purport was; thus much he had gathered from it: but although it professed to contain "the plainest and most excellent discoveries of the most hidden secrets of the Ancient Philosophers that were ever yet published," it was to him as unintelligible as the mysteries of Pantagruelism. He could make nothing of the work that was to ascend in *Bus* and *Nubi* from the Moon up to the Sun, though the Expositor had expounded that this was in *Nubibus;* nor of the Lake which was to be boiled with the ashes of Hermes's Tree, night and day without ceasing, till the Heavenly Nature should ascend and the Earthly descend: nor of the Crow's bill, the White Dove, the Sparkling Cherubim, and the Soul of the Green Lion. But he took those cautions simply and honestly as cautions, which were in fact the lures whereby so many infatuated persons had been drawn on to their own undoing. The author had said that his work was not written for the information of the illiterate, and illiterate Daniel knew himself to be. "Our writings," says the dark Expositor, "shall prove as a curious edged knife; to some they shall carve out dainties, and to others it shall serve only to cut their fingers. Yet we are not to be blamed; for we do seriously profess to any that shall attempt the work, that he attempts the highest piece of philosophy that is in Nature; and though we write in English, yet our matter will be as hard as Greek to some, who will think they understand us well, when they misconstrue our meaning most perversely; for is it imaginable that they who are fools in Nature should be wise in our Books, which are testimonies unto Nature?" And again, "Make sure of thy true matter, which is no small thing to know; and though we have named it, yet we have done it so cunningly, that thou mayest sooner stumble at our Books than at any thou ever didst read in thy life.—Be not deceived either with receipt or discourse; for we verily do not intend to deceive you; but if you will be deceived, be deceived!—Our way, which is an easy way, and in which no man may err, —our broad way, our *linear* way, we have vowed never to reveal it but in metaphor. I, being moved with pity, will hint it to you. Take that which is not yet perfect, nor yet wholly imperfect, but in a way to perfection, and out of it make what is most noble and most perfect. This you may conceive to be an easier receipt than to take that which is already perfect, and extract out of it what is imperfect and make it perfect, and after out of that perfection to draw a *plusquam* perfection; and yet this is true, and we have wrought it. But this last discovery, which I hinted in few words, is it which no man

* PASQUIER.

ever did so plainly lay open; nor may any make it more plain upon pain of an anathema."

All this was heathen Greek to Daniel, except the admonition which it contained. But Guy had meddled with this perilous pseudo-science, and used to talk with him concerning its theory, which Daniel soon comprehended, and which like many other theories wanted nothing but a foundation to rest upon. That every thing had its own seed as well as its own form seemed a reasonable position; and that the fermental virtue, "which is the wonder of the world, and by which water becomes herbs, trees and plants, fruits, flesh, blood, stones, minerals and every thing, works only in kind. Was it not then absurd to allow that the fermentive and multiplicative power existed in almost all other things, and yet deny it to Gold, the most perfect of all sublunary things?"—The secret lay in extracting from Gold its hidden seed.

Ben Jonson has with his wonted ability presented the theory of this delusive art. His knavish Alchemist asks of an unbeliever,

> Why, what have you observed, Sir, in our art,
> Seems so impossible?
> *Surly.* But your whole work, no more!
> That you should hatch gold in a furnace, Sir,
> As they do eggs in Egypt.
> *Subtle.* Sir, do you
> Believe that eggs are hatch'd so?
> *Surly.* If I should?
> *Subtle.* Why, I think that the greater miracle.
> No egg but differs from a chicken more
> Than metals in themselves.
> *Surly.* That cannot be.
> The egg's ordained by nature to that end,
> And is a chicken *in potentiâ.*
> *Subtle.* The same we say of lead and other metals,
> Which would be gold if they had time.
> *Mammon.* And that
> Our art doth further.
> *Subtle.* Ay, for 'twere absurd
> To think that nature in the earth bred gold
> Perfect in the instant: something went before.
> There must be remote matter.
> *Surly.* Ay, what is that?
> *Subtle.* Marry we say—
> *Mammon.* Ay, now it heats; stand, father;
> Pound him to dust.
> *Subtle.* It is, of the one part,
> A humid exhalation, which we call
> *Materia liquida*, or the unctuous water;
> On the other part a certain crass and viscous
> Portion of earth; both which concorporate
> Do make the elementary matter of gold;
> Which is not yet *propria materia*,
> But common to all metals and all stones;
> For where it is forsaken of that moisture,
> And hath more dryness, it becomes a stone;
> Where it retains more of the humid fatness,
> It turns to sulphur, or to quicksilver,
> Who are the parents of all other metals.
> Nor can this remote matter suddenly
> Progress so from extreme unto extreme,
> As to grow gold, and leap o'er all the means.
> Nature doth first beget the imperfect, then
> Proceeds she to the perfect. Of that airy
> And oily water, mercury is engendered;
> Sulphur of the fat and earthy part; the one,
> Which is the last, supplying the place of male,
> The other of the female in all metals.
> Some so believe hermaphrodeity,
> That both do act and suffer. But these too
> Make the rest ductile, malleable, extensive.
> And even in gold they are; for we do find
> Seeds of them, by our fire, and gold in them;
> And can produce the species of each metal
> More perfect thence than nature doth in earth.

I have no cause to say here, with Sheik Mohammed Ali Hazin, that "taste for poetical and elegant composition has turned the reins of my ink-dropping pen away from the road which lay before it:" for this passage of learned Ben lay directly in the way; and no where, Reader, couldst thou find the theory of the Alchemists more ably epitomised.

"Father," said the boy Daniel one day, after listening to a conversation upon this subject, "I should like to learn to make gold."

"And what wouldst thou do, Daniel, if thou couldst make it?" was the reply.

"Why I would build a great house, and fill it with books; and have as much money as the King, and be as great a man as the Squire."

"Mayhap, Daniel, in that case thou wouldst care for books as little as the Squire, and have as little time for them as the King. Learning is better than house or land. As for money, enough is enough; no man can enjoy more; and the less he can be contented with the wiser and better he is likely to be. What, Daniel, does our good poet tell us in the great verse-book?

> Nature's with little pleased; enough's a feast:
> A sober life but a small charge requires:
> But man, the author of his own unrest,
> The more he hath, the more he still desires.

No, boy, thou canst never be as rich as the

King, nor as great as the Squire; but thou mayest be a Philosopher, and that is being as happy as either."

"A great deal happier," said Guy. "The Squire is as far from being the happiest man in the neighbourhood, as he is from being the wisest or the best. And the King, God bless him! has care enough upon his head to bring on early grey hairs.

Uneasy lies the head that wears a crown."

"But what does a Philosopher do?" rejoined the boy. "The Squire hunts and shoots and smokes, and drinks punch and goes to Justice-Meetings. And the King goes to fight for us against the French, and governs the Parliament, and makes laws. But I cannot tell what a Philosopher's business is. Do they do any thing else besides making Almanacks and gold?"

"Yes," said William, "they read the stars."

"And what do they read there?"

"What neither thou nor I can understand, Daniel," replied the father, "however nearly it may concern us!"

CHAPTER XXI. P. I.

A DOUBT CONCERNING THE USES OF PHILOSOPHY.

El comienzo de salud
es el saber,
distinguir y conocer
qual es virtud.
PROVERBIOS DEL MARQUES DE SANTILLANA.

THAT grave reply produced a short pause. It was broken by the boy, who said, returning to the subject, "I have been thinking, Father, that it is not a good thing to be a Philosopher."

"And what, my Son, has led thee to that thought?"

"What I have read at the end of the Dictionary, Father. There was one Philosopher that was pounded in a mortar."

"That, Daniel," said the Father, "could neither have been the Philosopher's fault nor his choice."

"But it was because he was a Philosopher, my lad," said Guy, "that he bore it so bravely, and said, beat on, you can only bruise the shell of Anaxarchus! If he had not been a Philosopher they might have pounded him just the same, but they would never have put him in the Dictionary. Epictetus in like manner bore the torments which his wicked master inflicted upon him, without a groan, only saying, 'Take care, or you will break my leg;' and when the leg was broken, he looked the wretch in the face and said, 'I told you you would break it.'"

"But," said the youngster, "there was one Philosopher who chose to live in a tub; and another who, that he might never again see any thing to withdraw his mind from meditation, put out his eyes by looking upon a bright brass basin, such as I cured my warts in."

"He might have been a wise man," said William Dove, "but not wondrous wise: for if he had, he would not have used the basin to put his eyes out. He would have jumped into a quickset hedge, and scratched them out, like the Man of our Town; because when he saw his eyes were out, he might then have jumped into another hedge and scratched them in again. The Man of our Town was the greatest philosopher of the two."

"And there was one," continued the boy, "who had better have blinded himself at once, for he did nothing else but cry at every thing he saw. Was not this being very foolish?"

"I am sure," says William, "it was not being merry and wise."

"There was another who said that hunger was his daily food."

"He must have kept such a table as Duke Humphrey," quoth William; "I should not have liked to dine with him."

"Then there was Crates," said the persevering boy; "he had a good estate and sold it and threw the money into the sea, saying, 'Away ye paltry cares! I will drown you that you may not drown me.'"

"I should like to know," quoth William, "what the overseers said to that chap, when he applied to the parish for support."

"They sent him off to Bedlam, I suppose," said the Mother, "it was the fit place for him, poor creature."

"And when Aristippus set out upon a journey he bade his servants throw away all their money, that they might travel the better. Why they must have begged their way, and it cannot be right to beg if people are not brought to it by misfortune. And there were some who thought there was no God. I am sure they were fools, for the Bible says so."

"Well, Daniel," said Guy, "thou hast studied the end of the Dictionary to some purpose!"

"And the Bible too, Master Guy!" said Dinah, — her countenance brightening with joy at her son's concluding remark.

"It's the best part of the book," said the boy, replying to his schoolmaster; "there are more entertaining and surprising things there than I ever read in any other place, except in my Father's book about Pantagruel."

CHAPTER XXII. P. I.

Τὸν δ' ἀπαμειβόμενος.

O felice colui, che intender puote
Le cagion de le cose di natura,
Che al piu di que' che vivon sono ignote;
E sotto il piè si mette ogni paura
De fati, e de la morte, ch'è si trista,
Nè di vulgo gli cal, nè d'altro ha cura.

Tansillo.

The elder Daniel had listened to this dialogue in his usual quiet way, smiling sometimes at his brother William's observations. He now stroked his forehead, and looking mildly but seriously at the boy addressed him thus.

"My son, many things appear strange or silly in themselves if they are presented to us simply, without any notice when and where they were done, and upon what occasion. If any strangers, for example, had seen thee washing thy hands in an empty basin, without knowing the philosophy of the matter, they would have taken thee for an innocent, and thy master and me for little better; or they might have supposed some conjuring was going on. The things which the old Philosophers said and did, would appear, I dare say, as wise to us as they did to the people of their own times, if we knew why and in what circumstances they were done and said.

"Daniel, there are two sorts of men in all ranks and ways of life, the wise and the foolish; and there are a great many degrees between them. That some foolish people have called themselves Philosophers, and some wicked ones, and some who were out of their wits, is just as certain as that persons of all these descriptions are to be found among all conditions of men.

"Philosophy, Daniel, is of two kinds: that which relates to conduct, and that which relates to knowledge. The first teaches us to value all things at their real worth, to be contented with little, modest in prosperity, patient in trouble, equal-minded at all times. It teaches us our duty to our neighbour and ourselves. It is that wisdom of which King Solomon speaks in our rhyme-book. Reach me the volume!" Then turning to the passage in his favourite Du Bartas he read these lines:

"She's God's own mirror; she's a light whose glance
Springs from the lightening of his countenance.
She's mildest heaven's most sacred influence;
Never decays her beauties' excellence,
Aye like herself; and she doth always trace
Not only the same path but the same pace.
Without her honour, health and wealth would prove
Three poisons to me. Wisdom from above
Is the only moderatrix, spring and guide,
Organ and honour of all gifts beside."

"But let us look in the Bible: — aye, this is the place.

"For in her is an understanding spirit, holy, one only, manifold, subtil, lively, clear, undefiled, plain, not subject to hurt, loving the thing that is good, quick, which cannot be letted, ready to do good;

"Kind to man, steadfast, sure, free from

care, having all power, overseeing all things, and going through all understanding, pure, and most subtil, spirits.

"For wisdom is more moving than any motion: she passeth and goeth through all things by reason of her pureness.

"For she is the breath of the power of God, and a pure influence, flowing from the glory of the Almighty; therefore can no defiled thing fall into her.

"For she is the brightness of the everlasting light, the unspotted mirror of the power of God, and the image of his goodness.

"And being but one she can do all things; and remaining in herself she maketh all things new: and in all ages entering into holy souls she maketh them friends of God, and prophets.

"For God loveth none but him that dwelleth with wisdom.

"For she is more beautiful than the Sun, and above all the order of Stars: being compared with the light she is found before it.

"For after this cometh night: but vice shall not prevail against wisdom."

He read this with a solemnity that gave weight to every word. Then closing the book, after a short pause, he proceeded in a lower tone.

"The Philosophers of whom you have read in the Dictionary possessed this wisdom only in part, because they were heathens, and therefore could see no farther than the light of mere reason sufficed to show the way. The fear of the Lord is the beginning of wisdom, and they had not that to begin with. So the thoughts which ought to have made them humble produce pride, and so far their wisdom proved but folly. The humblest Christian who learns his duty, and performs it as well as he can, is wiser than they. He does nothing to be seen of men; and that was their motive for most of their actions.

"Now for the philosophy which relates to knowledge. Knowledge is a brave thing. I am a plain, ignorant, untaught man, and know my ignorance. But it is a brave thing when we look around us in this wonderful world to understand something of what we see: to know something of the earth on which we move, the air which we breathe, and the elements whereof we are made: to comprehend the motions of the moon and stars, and measure the distances between them, and compute times and seasons: to observe the laws which sustain the universe by keeping all things in their courses: to search into the mysteries of nature, and discover the hidden virtue of plants and stones, and read the signs and tokens which are shown us, and make out the meaning of hidden things, and apply all this to the benefit of our fellow-creatures.

"Wisdom and knowledge, Daniel, make the difference between man and man, and that between man and beast is hardly greater.

"These things do not always go together. There may be wisdom without knowledge, and there may be knowledge without wisdom. A man without knowledge, if he walk humbly with his God, and live in charity with his neighbours, may be wise unto salvation. A man without wisdom may not find his knowledge avail him quite so well. But it is he who possesses both that is the true Philosopher. The more he knows, the more he is desirous of knowing; and yet the farther he advances in knowledge the better he understands how little he can attain, and the more deeply he feels that God alone can satisfy the infinite desires of an immortal soul. To understand this is the height and perfection of philosophy."

Then opening the Bible which lay before him, he read these verses from the Proverbs.

"My son, if thou wilt receive my words,—

"So that thou incline thine ear unto wisdom and apply thine heart to understanding;

"Yea, if thou criest after knowledge, and liftest up thy voice for understanding;

"If thou seekest after her as silver, and searchest for her as for hid treasures;

"Then shalt thou understand the fear of the Lord and find the knowledge of God.

"For the Lord giveth wisdom; out of His mouth cometh knowledge and understanding.

"He layeth up sound wisdom for the righteous; He is a buckler to them that walk uprightly.

"He keepeth the paths of judgement and preserveth the way of his Saints.

"Then shalt thou understand righteousness and judgement and equity; yea, every good path.

"When wisdom entereth into thine heart, and knowledge is pleasant unto thy soul;

"Discretion shall preserve thee, understanding shall keep thee,

"To deliver thee from the way of the evil." *

"Daniel, my son," after a pause he pursued, "thou art a diligent good lad. God hath given thee a tender and a dutiful heart; keep it so, and it will be a wise one, for thou hast the beginning of wisdom. I wish thee to pursue knowledge, because in pursuing it happiness will be found by the way. If I have said any thing now which is above thy years, it will come to mind in after time, when I am gone perhaps, but when thou mayest profit by it. God bless thee, my child!"

He stretched out his right hand at these words, and laid it gently upon the boy's head. What he said was not forgotten, and throughout life the son never thought of that blessing without feeling that it had taken effect.

CHAPTER XXIII. P. I.

ROWLAND DIXON AND HIS COMPANY OF PUPPETS.

Alli se ve tan eficaz el llanto,
las fabulas y historias retratadas,
que parece verdad, y es dulce encanto.

* * * *

Y para el vulgo rudo, que ignorante
aborrece el manjar costoso, guisa
el plato del gracioso extravagante;

Con que les hartas de contento y risa,
gustando de mirar sayal grossero,
mas que sutil y candida camisa.

JOSEPH ORTIZ DE VILLENA.

WERE it not for that happy facility with which the mind in such cases commonly satisfies itself, my readers would find it not more easy to place themselves in imagination at Ingleton a hundred years ago, than at Thebes or Athens, so strange must it appear to them, that a family should have existed, in humble but easy circumstances, among whose articles of consumption neither tea nor sugar had a place, who never raised potatoes in their garden, nor saw them at their table, and who never wore a cotton garment of any kind.

Equally unlike any thing to which my contemporaries have been accustomed, must it be for them to hear of an Englishman whose talk was of philosophy, moral or speculative, not of politics; who read books in folio and had never seen a newspaper; nor ever heard of a magazine, review, or literary journal of any kind. Not less strange must it seem to them who, if they please, may travel by steam at the rate of thirty miles an hour upon the Liverpool and Manchester railway, or at ten miles an hour by stage upon any of the more frequented roads, to consider the little intercourse which, in those days, was carried on between one part of the kingdom and another. During young Daniel's boyhood, and for many years after he had reached the age of manhood, the whole carriage of the northern counties, and indeed of all the remoter parts, was performed by pack-horses, the very name of which would long since have been as obsolete as their use, if it had not been preserved by the sign or appellation of some of those inns at which they were accustomed to put up. Rarely, indeed, were the roads about Ingleton marked by any other wheels than those of its indigenous carts.

That little town, however, obtained considerable celebrity in those days, as being the home and head quarters of Rowland Dixon, the Gesticulator Maximus, or Puppet show-master-general, of the North; a person not less eminent in his line than Powel, whom the Spectator has immortalised.

My readers must not form their notion of Rowland Dixon's company from the ambulatory puppet-shows which of late years have added new sights and sounds to the

---

* I am not sure whether *man* is left out advisedly, but I suspect it is.

spectacles and cries of London. Far be it from me to depreciate those peripatetic street exhibitions, which you may have before your window at a call, and by which the hearts of so many children are continually delighted: Nay, I confess that few things in that great city carry so much comfort to the cockles of my own, as the well-known voice of Punch;

—the same which in my school-boy days
I listened to, —

as Wordsworth says of the Cuckoo,

And I can listen to it yet —
And listen till I do beget
That golden time again.

It is a voice that seems to be as much in accord with the noise of towns, and the riotry of fairs, as the note of the Cuckoo, with the joyousness of spring fields and the fresh verdure of the vernal woods.

But Rowland Dixon's company of puppets would be pitifully disparaged, if their size, uses, or importance, were to be estimated by the street performances of the present day.

The Dramatis Personæ of these modern exhibitions never, I believe, comprehends more than four characters, and these four are generally the same, to wit, Punch, Judy, as she who used to be called Joan is now denominated, the Devil and the Doctor, or sometimes the Constable in the Doctor's stead. There is, therefore, as little variety in the action as in the personages; and their dimensions are such, that the whole company and the theatre in which they are exhibited are carried along the streets at quick time and with a light step by the two persons who manage the concern.

But the Rowlandian, Dixonian, or Ingletonian puppets were large as life; and required for their removal a caravan — (in the use to which that word is now appropriated), — a vehicle of such magnitude and questionable shape, that if Don Quixote had encountered its like upon the highway, he would have regarded it as the most formidable adventure which had ever been presented to his valour. And they went as far beyond our street-puppets in the sphere of their subjects as they exceeded them in size; for in that sphere *quicquid agunt homines* was included, — and a greal deal more.

In no country, and in no stage of society, has the drama ever existed in a ruder state than that in which this company presented it. The Drolls of Bartholomew Fair were hardly so far below the legitimate drama, as they were above that of Rowland Dixon; for the Drolls were written compositions: much ribaldry might be, and no doubt was, interpolated as opportunity allowed or invited; but the main dialogue was prepared. Here, on the contrary, there was no other preparation than that of frequent practice. The stock pieces were founded upon popular stories or ballads, such as Fair Rosamond, Jane Shore, and Bateman, who hanged himself for love; with scriptural subjects for Easter and Whitsun-week, such as the Creation, the Deluge, Susannah and the Elders, and Nebuchadnezzar or the Fall of Pride. These had been handed down from the time of the old mysteries and miracle-plays, having, in the progress of time and change, descended from the monks and clergy to become the property of such managers as Powel and Rowland Dixon. In what manner they were represented when thus

Fallen, fallen, fallen, fallen,
Fallen from their high estate,

may be imagined from a play-bill of Queen Anne's reign, in which one of them is thus advertised:

"At Crawley's Booth, over against the Crown Tavern in Smithfield, during the time of Bartholomew Fair, will be presented a little Opera, called the Old Creation of the World, yet newly revived; with the addition of Noah's flood. Also several fountains playing water during the time of the play. The last scene does present Noah and his family coming out of the Ark, with all the beasts two and two, and all the fowls of the air seen in a prospect sitting upon trees. Likewise over the Ark is seen the Sun rising in a most glorious manner. Moreover, a multitude of Angels will be seen in a double rank, which presents a double prospect, one for the Sun, the other for a palace, where will be seen six Angels, ringing of bells. Likewise machines descend from above double and treble, with Dives rising out of Hell, and Lazarus seen in Abraham's bosom; besides several figures dancing jigs, sarabands and country dances, to the admiration of the spectators; with the merry conceits of Squire Punch, and Sir John Spendall."

I have not found it any where stated at what time these irreverent representations were discontinued in England, nor whether (which is not unlikely) they were put an end to by the interference of the magistrates. The *Autos Sacramentales*, which form the most characteristic department of the Spanish drama, were prohibited at Madrid in 1763, at the instance of the Conde de Teba, then Archbishop of Toledo, chiefly because of the profaneness of the actors, and the indecency of the places in which they were represented: it seems, therefore, that if they had been performed by clerks, and within consecrated precincts, he would not have objected to them. The religious dramas, though they are not less extraordinary and far more reprehensible, because in many instances nothing can be more pernicious than their direct tendency, were not included in the same prohibition; the same marks of external reverence not being required for Saints and Images as for the great object of Romish Idolatry. These, probably, will long continue to delight the Spanish people. But facts of the same kind may be met with nearer home. So recently as the year 1816, the Sacrifice of Isaac was represented on the stage at Paris: Samson was the subject of the ballet; the unshorn son of Manoah delighted the spectators by dancing a solo with the gates of Gaza on his back; Dalilah clipt him during the intervals of a jig; and the Philistines surrounded and captured him in a country dance!

That Punch made his appearance in the puppet-show of the Deluge, most persons know; his exclamation of "hazy weather, master Noah," having been preserved by tradition. In all of these wooden dramas, whether sacred or profane, Punch indeed bore a part, and that part is well described in the verses entitled *Pupæ gesticulantes*, which may be found among the *Selecta Poemata Anglorum Latina*, edited by Mr. Popham.

Ecce tamen subitò, et medio discrimine rerum,
Ridiculus vultu procedit Homuncio, tergum
Cui riget in gibbum, immensusque protruditur alvus:
PUNCHIUS *huic nomen, nec erat petulantior unquam*
Ullus; quinctiam media inter seria semper
Importunus adest, lepidusque et garrulus usque
Perstat, permiscetque jocos, atque omnia turbat.
Sæpe puellarum densa ad subsellia sese
Convertens, — sedet en! pulchras mea, dixit, amica
Illic inter eas! Oculo simul improbus uno
Connivens, aliquam illarum quasi noverat, ipsam
Quæque pudens se signari pudefacta rubescit;
Totaque subridet juvenumque virumque corona.
Cum vero ambiguis obscœnas turpia dictis
Innuit, effuso testantur gaudia risu.

In one particular only this description is unlike the Punch of the Ingleton Company. He was not an *homuncio*, but a full-grown personage, who had succeeded with little alteration either of attributes or appearance to the Vice of the old Mysteries, and served like the Clown of our own early stage, and the *Gracioso* of the Spaniards, to scatter mirth over the serious part of the performance, or turn it into ridicule. The wife was an appendage of later times, when it was not thought good for Punch to be alone; and when, as these performances had fallen into lower hands, the quarrels between such a pair afforded a standing subject equally adapted to the capacity of the interlocutor and of his audience.

A tragic part was assigned to Punch in one of Rowland Dixon's pieces, and that one of the most popular, being the celebrated tragedy of Jane Shore. The Beadle in this piece, after proclaiming in obvious and opprobrious rhyme the offence which had drawn upon Mistress Shore this public punishment, prohibited all persons from relieving her on pain of death, and turned her out, according to the common story, to die of hunger in the streets. The only person who ventured to disobey this prohibition was Punch the Baker; and the reader may judge of the dialogue of these pieces by this Baker's words, when he stole behind her, and nudging her furtively, while he spake, offered her a loaf, saying, "*Tak it Jenny, tak it!*" for which act so little consonant with his general character, Punch died a martyr to humanity by the hangman's hands.

Dr. Dove used to say he doubted whether Garrick and Mrs. Cibber could have affected him more in middle life, than he had been moved by Punch the Baker and this wooden Jane Shore in his boyhood. For rude as were these performances (and nothing could possibly be ruder), the effect on infant minds was prodigious, from the accompanying sense of wonder, an emotion which of all others is, at that time of life, the most delightful. Here was miracle in any quantity to be seen for two-pence, and be believed in for nothing. No matter how confined the theatre, how coarse and inartificial the scenery, or how miserable the properties; the mind supplied all that was wanting.

"Mr. Guy," said young Daniel to the schoolmaster, after one of these performances, "I wish Rowland Dixon could perform one of our Latin dialogues!"

"Ay, Daniel," replied the schoolmaster, entering into the boy's feelings; "it would be a grand thing to have the Three Fatal Sisters introduced, and to have them send for Death; and then for Death to summon the Pope and jugulate him; and invite the Emperor and the King to dance; and disarm the soldier, and pass sentence upon the Judge; and stop the Lawyer's tongue; and feel the Physician's pulse; and make the Cook come to be killed; and send the Poet to the shades; and give the Drunkard his last draught. And then to have Rhadamanthus come in and try them all! Methinks, Daniel, that would beat Jane Shore and Fair Rosamond all to nothing, and would be as good as a sermon to boot."

"I believe it would, indeed!" said the Boy; "and then to see MORS and NATURA; and have DAMNATUS called up; and the Three Cacodæmons at supper upon the sirloin of a King, and the roasted Doctor of Divinity, and the cruel Schoolmaster's rump! Would not it be nice, Mr. Guy?"

"The pity is, Daniel," replied Guy, "that Rowland Dixon is no Latiner, any more than those who go to see his performances."

"But could not you put it into English for him, Mr. Guy?"

"I am afraid, Daniel, Rowland Dixon would not thank me for my pains. Besides, I could never make it sound half so noble in English as in those grand Latin verses, which fill the mouth, and the ears, and the mind, — ay and the heart and soul too. No, boy! schools are the proper places for representing such pieces, and if I had but Latiners enough we would have them ourselves. But there are not many houses, my good Daniel, in which learning is held in such esteem as it is at thy father's; if there were, I should have more Latin scholars;—and what is of far more consequence, the world would be wiser and better than it is!"

CHAPTER XXIV. P. I.

QUACK AND NO QUACK, BEING AN ACCOUNT OF DOCTOR GREEN AND HIS MAN KEMP. POPULAR MEDICINE, HERBARY, THEORY OF SIGNATURES, WILLIAM DOVE, JOHN WESLEY, AND BAXTER.

> Hold thy hand! health's dear maintainer;
> Life perchance may burn the stronger:
> Having substance to maintain her
> She untouch'd may last the longer.
> When the Artist goes about
> To redress her flame, I doubt
> Oftentimes he snuffs it out.
> QUARLES.

IT was not often that Rowland Dixon exhibited at Ingleton. He took his regular circuits to the fairs in all the surrounding country far and wide; but in the intervals of his vocation, he, who when abroad was the servant of the public, became his own master at home. His puppets were laid up in ordinary, the voice of Punch ceased, and the master of the motions enjoyed *otium cum dignitate*. When he favoured his friends and neighbours with an exhibition, it was *speciali gratiâ*, and in a way that rather enhanced that dignity than derogated from it.

A performer of a very different kind used in those days to visit Ingleton in his rounds, where his arrival was always expected by some of the community with great anxiety. This was a certain Dr. Green, who having been regularly educated for the profession of medicine, and regularly graduated in it, chose to practise as an itinerant, and take the field with a Merry Andrew for his aide-de-camp. He was of a respectable and wealthy family in the neighbourhood of Doncaster, which neighbourhood on their account he never approached in his professional circuits, though for himself he was far from being ashamed of the character that he had assumed. The course which he had taken had been deliberately chosen, with the twofold object of gratifying his own humour, and making a fortune; and in the remoter as well as in the immediate purpose, he succeeded to his heart's content.

It is not often that so much worldly prudence is found connected with so much eccentricity of character. A French poetess, Madame de Villedieu, taking as a text for some verses the liberal maxim *que la vertu dépend autant du temperament que des loix*, says,

> *Presque toujours chacun suit son caprice ;*
> *Heureux est le mortel que les destins amis*
> *Ont partagé d'un caprice permis.*

He is indeed a fortunate man who, if he *must* have a hobby-horse, which is the same as saying if he *will* have one, keeps it not merely for pleasure, but for use, breaks it in well, has it entirely under command, and gets as much work out of it as he could have done out of a common roadster. Dr. Green did this; he had not taken to this strange course because he was impatient of the restraints of society, but because he fancied that his constitution both of body and of mind required an erratic life; and that, within certain bounds which he prescribed for himself, he might indulge in it, both to his own advantage, and that of the community,—that part of the community at least among whom it would be his lot to labour. Our laws had provided itinerant Courts of Justice for the people. Our church had formerly provided itinerant preachers; and after the Reformation, when the Mendicant Orders were abolished by whom this service used to be performed, such preachers have never failed to appear during the prevalence of any religious influenza. Dr. Green thought that itinerant physicians were wanted; and that if practitioners regularly educated and well qualified would condescend to such a course, the poor ignorant people would no longer be cheated by travelling quacks, and sometimes poisoned by them!

One of the most reprehensible arts to which the Reformers resorted in their hatred of popery, was that of adapting vulgar verses to church tunes, and thus associating with ludicrous images, or with something worse, melodies which had formerly been held sacred. It is related of Whitefield that he, making a better use of the same device, fitted hymns to certain popular airs, because, he said, "there was no reason why the Devil should keep all the good tunes to himself." Green acted upon a similar principle when he took the field as a Physician Errant, with his man Kemp, like another Sancho for his Squire. But the Doctor was no Quixote; and his Merry Andrew had all Sancho's shrewdness, without any alloy of his simpleness.

In those times medical knowledge among the lower practitioners was at the lowest point. Except in large towns the people usually trusted to domestic medicine, which some Lady Bountiful administered from her family receipt book; or to a Village Doctress whose prescriptions were as likely sometimes to be dangerously active, as at others to be ridiculous and inert. But while they held to their garden physic it was seldom that any injury was done either by exhibiting wrong medicines or violent ones.

> Herbs, Woods and Springs, the power that in you lies
> If mortal man could know your properties! *

* Fletcher.

There was at one time abundant faith in those properties. The holy Shepherdess in Fletcher's fine pastoral drama, which so infinitely surpasses all foreign compositions of that class, thus apostrophises the herbs which she goes out to cull:

O you best sons of earth,
You only brood unto whose happy birth
Virtue was given, holding more of Nature
Than man, her first-born and most perfect creature,—
Let me adore you, you that only can
Help or kill Nature, drawing out that span
Of life and breath even to the end of time!

So abundantly was the English garden stocked in the age of the Tudors, that Tusser, after enumerating in an Appendix to one of his Chapters two and forty herbs for the kitchen, fourteen others for sallads or sauces, eleven to boil or butter, seventeen as strewing herbs, and forty "herbs, branches, and flowers for windows and pots," adds a list of seventeen herbs "to still in summer," and of five and twenty "necessary herbs to grow in the garden for physic, not rehearsed before;" and after all advises his readers to seek more in the fields. He says,

The nature of Flowers dame Physic doth shew;
She teacheth them all to be known to a few.

Elsewhere he observes that

The knowledge of stilling is one pretty feat,
The waters be wholesome, the charges not great.

In a comedy of Lord Digby's, written more than a hundred years after Tusser's didactics, one of the scenes is laid in a lady's laboratory, "with a fountain in it, some stills, and many shelves, with pots of porcelain and glasses;" and when the lady wishes to keep her attendant out of the way, she sends her there, saying

I have a task to give you, —— carefully
To shift the oils in the perfuming room,
As in the several ranges you shall see
The old begin to wither. To do it well
Will take you up some hours, but 'tis a work
I oft perform myself.

And Tusser among "the Points of Housewifery united to the Comfort of Husbandry," includes good housewifely physic, as inculcated in these rhymes;

Good houswife provides ere an sickness do come,
Of sundry good things in her house to have some;
Good *aqua composita*, and vinegar tart,
Rose water, and treacle to comfort the heart;
Cold herbs in her garden for agues that burn,
That over-strong heat to good temper may turn;
White endive, and succory, with spinage enow,
All such with good pot-herbs should follow the plough.
Get water of fumitory liver to cool,
And others the like, or else go like a fool;
Conserves of barberry, quinces and such,
With syrups that easeth the sickly so much.

Old Gervase Markham in his "Approved Book called the English Housewife, containing the inward and outward virtues which ought to be in a complete woman," places her skill in physic as one of the most principal; "you shall understand," he says, "that sith the preservation and care of the family touching their health and soundness of body consisteth most in her diligence, it is meet that she have a physical kind of knowledge, how to administer any wholesome receipts or medicines for the good of their healths, as well to prevent the first occasion of sickness, as to take away the effects and evil of the same, when it hath made seizure upon the body." And "as it must be confessed that the depths and secrets of this most excellent art of physic, are far beyond the capacity of the most skilful woman," he relates for the Housewife's use some "approved medecines and old doctrines, gathered together by two excellent and famous physicians, and in a manuscript given to a great worthy Countess of this land."

The receipts collected in this and other books for domestic practice are some of them so hyper-composite that even Tusser's garden could hardly supply all the indigenous ingredients; others are of the most fantastic kind, and for the most part they were as troublesome in preparation, and many of them as disgusting, as they were futile. That "Sovereign Water" which was invented by Dr. Stephens, was composed of almost all known spices, and all savoury and odorous herbs, distilled in claret. With this Dr. Stephens "preserved his own life until such extreme old age that he could neither go nor ride; and he did continue his life, being bed-rid five years, when other physicians did judge he could not live one year; and he confessed a little before his death, that if he were sick at any time, he never used any thing but this water only. And also the Archbishop of Canterbury used it, and found such goodness in it that he lived till he was not able to drink out of a cup, but sucked his drink through a hollow pipe of silver."

Twenty-nine plants were used in the composition of Dr. Adrian Gilbert's most sovereign Cordial Water, besides hartshorn, figs, raisins, gillyflowers, cowslips, marygolds, blue violets, red rose-buds, ambergris, bezoar stone, sugar, aniseed, liquorice, and to crown all, "what else you please." But then it was sovereign against all fevers; and one who in time of plague should take two spoonsful of it in good beer, or white wine, "he might walk safely from danger, by the leave of God."—The Water of Life was distilled from nearly as many ingredients, to which were added a fleshy running capon, the loins and legs of an old coney, the red flesh of the sinews of a leg of mutton, four young chickens, twelve larks, the yolks of twelve eggs, and a loaf of white bread, all to be distilled in white wine.

For consumption, there were pills in which powder of pearls, of white amber and of coral, were the potential ingredients; there was cockwater, the cock being to be chased and beaten before he was killed, or else plucked alive! and there was a special water procured by distillation, from a peck of garden shell-snails and a quart of earth worms, besides other things; this was prescribed not for consumption alone, but for dropsy and all obstructions. For all faintness, hot agues, heavy fantasies and imaginations, a cordial was prepared in tabulates, which were called *Manus Christi:* the true receipt required one ounce of prepared pearls to twelve of fine sugar, boiled with rose water, violet water, cinnamon water, "or howsoever one would have them." But apothecaries seldom used more than a drachm of pearls to a pound of sugar, because men would not go to the cost thereof; and the *Manus Christi simplex* was made without any pearl at all. For broken bones, bones out of joint, or any grief in the bones or sinews, oil of swallows* was pronounced exceeding sovereign, and this was to be procured by pounding twenty live swallows in a mortar with about as many different herbs! A mole, male or female according to the sex of the patient, was to be dried in an oven whole as taken out of the earth, and administered in powder for the falling evil. A grey eel with a white belly was to be closed in an earthen pot, and buried alive in a dunghill, and at the end of a fortnight its oil might be collected to "help hearing." A mixture of rose leaves and pigeon's dung quilted in a bag, and laid hot upon the parts affected, was thought to help a stitch in the side; and for a quinsey, "give the party to drink," says Markham, "the herb mouse-ear, steept in ale or beer; and look when you see a swine rub himself, and there upon the same place rub a slick-stone, and then with it slick all the swelling, and it will cure it."

To make hair grow on a bald part of the head, garden snails were to be plucked out of their houses, and pounded with horse-leaches, bees, wasps and salt, an equal quantity of each; and the baldness was to be anointed with the moisture from this mixture after it had been buried eight days in a hotbed. For the removal and extirpation of superfluous hairs, a depilatory was to be made by drowning in a pint of wine as many green frogs as it would cover (about twenty was the number), setting the pot forty days in the sun, and then straining it for use.

A water specially good against gravel or dropsy might be distilled from the dried and pulverised blood of a black buck or he-goat, three or four years old. The animal was to be kept by himself, in the summer time when the sun was in Leo, and dieted for three weeks upon certain herbs given in prescribed order, and to drink nothing but red wine, if you would have the best preparation, though some persons allowed him his

* I have known it used in the present century. The Old Doctor who used it,—Blacksmith, Farrier, Phlebotomist, and Tooth-drawer combined,—is now consigned to his resting place,—ætat. 81.

fill of water every third day. But there was a water of man's blood which in Queen Elizabeth's days was a new invention, "whereof some princes had very great estimation, and used it for to remain thereby in their force, and, as they thought, to live long." A strong man was to be chosen, in his flourishing youth, and of twenty-five years, and somewhat choleric by nature. He was to be well dieted for one month with light and healthy meats, and with all kinds of spices, and with good strong wine, and moreover to be kept with mirth; at the month's end veins in both arms were to be opened, and as much blood to be let out as he could "tolerate and abide." One handful of salt was to be added to six pounds of this blood, and this was to be seven times distilled, pouring the water upon the residuum after every distillation, till the last. This was to be taken three or four times a year, an ounce at a time. One has sight of a theory here; the life was thought to be in the blood, and to be made transferable when thus extracted.

Richard Brathwait, more famous since Mr. Haslewood has identified him with Drunken Barnaby, than as author of "the English Gentleman and the English Gentlewoman, presented to present times for ornaments, and commended to posterity for precedents," says of this Gentlewoman, "herbals she peruseth, which she seconds with conference; and by degrees so improves her knowledge, as her cautelous care perfits many a dangerous cure." But herbals were not better guides than the medical books of which specimens have just been set before the reader, except that they did not lead the practitioner so widely and perilously astray. "Had Solomon," says the author of Adam in Eden, or the Paradise of Plants, "that great proficient in all sublunary experiments, preserved those many volumes that he wrote in this kind, for the instruction of future ages, so great was that spaciousness of mind that God had bestowed on him, that he had immediately under the Deity been the greatest of Doctors for the preservation of mankind: but with the loss of his books so much lamented by the Rabbins and others, the best part of this herbarary art hath since groaned under the defects of many unworthy authors, and still remains under divers clouds and imperfections." This writer, "the ingeniously learned and excellent Herbarist Mr. William Coles," professing as near as possible to acquaint all sorts of people with the very pith and marrow of herbarism, arranges his work according to the anatomical application of plants, "appropriating," says he, "to every part of the body, (from the crown of the head, with which I begin, and proceed till I come to the sole of the foot,) such herbs and plants whose grand uses and virtues do most specifically, and by signature thereunto belong, not only for strengthening the same, but also for curing the evil effects whereunto they are subjected:"—the signatures being, as it were, the books out of which the ancients first learned the virtues of herbs; Nature, or rather the God of Nature, having stamped on divers of them legible characters to discover their uses, though he hath left others without any, "that after he had showed them the way, they, by their labour and industry, which renders every thing more acceptable, might find out the rest." It was an opinion often expressed by a physician of great and deserved celebrity, that in course of time specifics would be discovered for every malady to which the human frame is liable. He never supposed, (though few men have ever been more sanguine in their hopes and expectations,) that life was thus to be indefinitely prolonged, and that it would be man's own fault, or his own choice, if he did not live for ever; but he thought that when we should thus have been taught to subdue those diseases which cut our life short, we should, like the Patriarchs, live out the number of our days, and then fall asleep,—Man being by this physical redemption restored to his original corporeal state.

Then shall like four straight pillars, the four Elements
Support the goodly structure of Mortality:
Then shall the four Complexions, like four heads
Of a clear river, streaming in his body,

> Nourish and comfort every vein and sinew :
> No sickness of contagion, no grim death,
> Or deprivation of health's real blessings,
> Shall then affright the creature, built by Heaven,
> Reserved for immortality.*

He had not taken up this notion from any religious feeling; it was connected in him with the pride of philosophy, and he expected that this was one of the blessings which we were to obtain in the progress of knowledge.

Some specific remedies being known to exist, it is indeed reasonable to suppose that others will be found. Old theorists went farther; and in a world which everywhere bears such undeniable evidences of design in every thing, few theories should seem more likely to be favourably received than the one which supposed that every healing plant bears, in some part of its structure, the type or signature of its peculiar virtues: now this could in no other way be so obviously marked, as by a resemblance to that part of the human frame for which its remedial uses were intended. There is a fable, indeed, which says that he who may be so fortunate as to taste the blood of a certain unknown animal, would be enabled thereby to hear the voice of plants and understand their speech; and if he were on a mountain at sunrise, he might hear the herbs which grow there, when freshened with the dews of night they open themselves to the beams of the morning, return thanks to the Creator for the virtues with which he has indued them, each specifying what those virtues were, *le quali veramente son tante e tali che beati i pastori che quelle capessero.* A botanical writer who flourished a little before the theory of signatures was started complains that herbal medicine had fallen into disuse; he says, *antequam chemia patrum nostrorum memoriâ orbi restitueretur, contenti vivebant* οἱ τῶν ἰατρῶν κομψοὶ καὶ χαριέστατοι *pharmacis ex vegetabilium regno accersitis parum solliciti de Solis sulphure et oleo, de Lunæ sale et essentiâ, de Saturni saccaro, de Martis tincturâ et croco, de vitriolo Veneris, de Mercurio præcipitato, et Antimonii floribus, de Sulphuris spiritu et Tartari crystallis: nihilominus masculè debellabant morbos, et tutè et jucundè. Nunc sæculi nostri infelicitas est, quod vegetabilibus contemptim habitis, plerique nihil aliud spirant præter metallica ista, et extis parata horribilia secreta.** The new theory came in timely aid of the Galenists; it connected their practice with a doctrine hardly less mysterious than those of the Paracelsists, but more plausible because it seemed immediately intelligible, and had a natural religious feeling to strengthen and support it.

The Author of Adam in Eden refers to Oswald Crollius, as "the great discoverer of signatures," and no doubt has drawn from him most of his remarks upon this theory of physical correspondence. The resemblance is in some cases very obvious; but in many more the Swedenborgian correspondences are not more fantastic; and where the resemblances exist the inference is purely theoretical.

Walnuts are said to have the perfect signature of the head; the outer husks or green covering represents the *pericranium*, or outward skin of the skull, whereon the hair groweth, — and therefore salt made of those husks is exceeding good for wounds in the head. The inner woody shell hath the signature of the skull, and the little yellow skin or peel, that of the *dura* and *pia mater* which are the thin scarfs that envelope the brain. The kernel hath "the very figure of the brain, and therefore it is very profitable for the brain and resists poisons." So too the Piony, being not yet blown, was thought to have "some signature and proportion with the head of man, having sutures and little veins dispersed up and down, like unto those which environ the brain: when the flowers blow they open an outward little skin representing the skull:" the piony, therefore, besides its other virtues was very available against the falling sickness. Poppy heads with their crowns somewhat represent the head and brain, and

* Ford.

* Petri Laurembergii *Rostochiensis Horticultura.* — Præloquium, p. 10.

therefore decoctions of them were used with good success in several diseases of the head. And Lilies of the Valley, which in Coles's days grew plentifully upon Hampstead-heath, were known by signature to cure the apoplexy; "for as that disease is caused by the dropping of humours into the principal ventricles of the brain, so the flowers of this lilly hanging on the plants as if they were drops, are of wonderful use herein."

All capillary herbs were of course sovereign in diseases of the hair; and because the purple and yellow spots and stripes upon the flowers of Eyebright very much resemble the appearance of diseased eyes, it was found out by that signature that this herb was very effectual "for curing of the same." The small Stone-crop hath the signature of the gums, and is therefore good for scurvy. The exquisite Crollius observed that the woody scales of which the cones of the pine tree are composed resemble the fore teeth; and therefore pine leaves boiled in vinegar make a gargle which relieves the tooth-ache. The Pomegranate has a like virtue for a like reason. Thistles and Holly leaves signify by their prickles that they are excellent for pleurisy and stiches in the side. Saxifrage manifesteth in its growth its power of breaking the stone. It had been found experimentally that all roots, barks and flowers which were yellow, cured the yellow jaundice; and though Kidney beans as yet were only used for food, yet having so perfect a signature, practitioners in physic were exhorted to take it into consideration, and try whether there were not in this plant some excellent faculty to cure nephritic diseases. In pursuing this fantastic system, examples might be shown of that mischief, which, though it may long remain latent, never fails at some time or other to manifest itself as inherent in all error and falsehood.

When the mistresses of families grounded their practice of physic upon such systems of herbary, or took it from books which contained prescriptions like those before adduced, (few being either more simple or more rational,) Dr. Green might well argue that when he mounted his hobby and rode out seeking adventures as a Physician Errant, he went forth for the benefit of his fellow-creatures. The guidance of such works, or of their own traditional receipts, the people in fact then generally followed. Burton tells us that Paulus Jovius in his description of Britain, and Levinus Lemnius have observed, of this our island, how there was of old no use of physic amongst us, and but little at this day, except, he says, "it be for a few nice idle citizens, surfeiting courtiers, and stall-fed gentlemen lubbers. The country people use kitchen physic." There are two instances among the papers of the Berkeley family, of the little confidence which persons of rank placed upon such medical advice and medicinal preparations as could be obtained in the country, and even in the largest of our provincial cities. In the second year of Elizabeth's reign, Henry Lord Berkeley "having extremely heated himself by chasing on foot a tame deer in Yate Park, with the violence thereof fell into an immoderate bleeding of the nose, to stay which, by the ill counsel of some about him, he dipt his whole face into a basin of cold water, whereby," says the family chronicler, "that flush and fulness of his nose which forthwith arose could never be remedied, though for present help he had physicians in a few days from London, and for better help came thither himself not long after to have the advice of the whole College, and lodged with his mother at her house in Shoe-lane." He never afterwards could sing with truth or satisfaction the old song,

> Nose, Nose, jolly red Nose,
> And what gave thee that jolly red Nose?
> Cinnamon and Ginger, Nutmegs and Cloves,
> And they gave me this jolly red Nose.

A few years later, "Langham, an Irish footman of this Lord, upon the sickness of the Lady Catherine, this Lord's wife, carried a letter from Callowdon to old Dr. Fryer, a physician dwelling in Little Britain in London; and returned with a glass bottle in his hand, compounded by the doctor for the recovery of her health, a journey of an hundred and forty-eight miles performed by him in less than forty-two hours, notwithstanding his stay of one night at the physician's and apothecary's houses, which no one horse could have so well and safely performed." No doubt it was for the safer conveyance of the bottle, that a footman was sent on this special errand, for which the historian of that noble family adds, "the lady shall after give him a new suit of cloaths."

In those days, and long after, they who required remedies were likely to fare ill, under their own treatment, or that of their neighbours; and worse under the travelling quack, who was always an ignorant and impudent impostor, but found that human sufferings and human credulity afforded him a never-failing harvest. Dr. Green knew this: he did not say, with the Romish priest, *populus vult decipi, et decipietur!* for he had no intention of deceiving them; but he saw that many were to be won by buffoonery, more by what is called *palaver*, and almost all by pretensions. Condescending, therefore, to the common arts of quackery, he employed his man Kemp to tickle the multitude with coarse wit; but he stored himself with the best drugs that were to be procured, distributed as general remedies such only as could hardly be misapplied and must generally prove serviceable; and brought to particular cases the sound knowledge which he had acquired in the school of Boerhaave, and the skill which he had derived from experience aided by natural sagacity. When it became convenient for him to have a home, he established himself at Penrith, in the County of Cumberland, having married a lady of that place; but he long continued his favourite course of life and accumulated in it a large fortune. He gained it by one maggot, and reduced it by many: nevertheless, there remained a handsome inheritance for his children. His son proved as maggoty as the father, ran through a good fortune, and when confined in the King's Bench prison for debt, wrote a book upon the Art of cheap living in London!

The father's local fame, though it has not reached to the third and fourth generation, survived him far into the second; and for many years after his retirement from practice, and even after his death, every travelling mountebank in the northern counties adopted the name of Dr. Green.

At the time to which this chapter refers, Dr. Green was in his meridian career, and enjoyed the highest reputation throughout the sphere of his itinerancy. Ingleton lay in his rounds, and whenever he came there he used to send for the schoolmaster to pass the evening with him. He was always glad if he could find an opportunity also of conversing with the elder Daniel, as the Flossofer of those parts. William Dove could have communicated to him more curious things relating to his own art; but William kept out of the presence of strangers, and had happily no ailments to make him seek the Doctor's advice; his occasional indispositions were but slight, and he treated them in his own way. That way was sometimes merely superstitious, sometimes it was whimsical, and sometimes rough. If his charms failed when he tried them upon himself, it was not for want of faith. When at any time it happened that one of his eyes was blood-shot, he went forthwith in search of some urchin whose mother, either for laziness, or in the belief that it was wholesome to have it in that state, allowed his ragged head to serve as a free warren for certain "small deer." One of these hexapeds William secured, and "using him as if he loved him," put it into his eye; when according to William's account the insect fed upon what it found, cleared the eye, and disappearing he knew not where or how, never was seen more.

His remedy for the cholic was a pebble posset; white pebbles were preferred, and of these what was deemed a reasonable quantity was taken in some sort of milk porridge. Upon the same theory he sometimes swallowed a pebble large enough as he said to clear all before it; and for that purpose they have been administered of larger calibre than any bolus that ever came from the hands of the most merciless apothecary, as large indeed sometimes as a common sized walnut. Does the reader hesitate at believing this of an ignorant man, living in a remote part of the country? Well might William Dove be excused, for a generation later than his John Wesley prescribed, in his Primitive Physic, quicksilver to be taken ounce by ounce, to the amount of one, two, or three pounds, till the desired effect was produced. And a generation earlier, Richard Baxter of happy memory and unhappy digestion, having read in Dr. Gerhard "the admirable effects of the swallowing of a gold bullet upon his father," in a case which Baxter supposed to be like his own, got a gold bullet of between twenty and thirty shillings weight, and swallowed it. "Having taken it," says he, "I knew not how to be delivered of it again. I took clysters and purges for about three weeks, but nothing stirred it; and a gentleman having done the like, the bullet never came from him till he died, and it was cut out. But at last my neighbours set a day apart to fast and pray for me, and I was freed from my danger in the beginning of that day!"

CHAPTER XXV. P. I.

Hiatus valde lacrymabilis.

> Time flies away fast,
> The while we never remember
> How soon our life here
> Grows old with the year
> That dies with the next December! HERRICK.

I MUST pass over fourteen years, for were I to pursue the history of our young Daniel's boyhood and adolescence into all the ramifications which a faithful biography requires, fourteen volumes would not contain it. They would be worth reading, for that costs little; they would be worth writing, though that costs much. They would deserve the best embellishments that the pencil and the graver could produce. The most poetical of artists would be worthily employed in designing the sentimental and melancholy scenes; Cruikshank for the grotesque; Wilkie and Richter for the comic and serio-comic; Turner for the actual scenery; Bewick for the head and tail pieces. They ought to be written; they ought to be read. They should be written — and then they would be read. But time is wanting:

> *Eheu! fugaces Posthume, Posthume,*
> *Labuntur anni!*

and time is a commodity of which the value rises as long as we live. We must be contented with doing not what we wish, but what we can, — our *possible* as the French call it.

One of our Poets* — (which is it?) — speaks of an *everlasting now.* If such a condition of existence were offered to us in this world, and it were put to the vote whether we should accept the offer and fix all things immutably as they are, who are they whose voices would be given in the affirmative?

Not those who are in pursuit of fortune, or of fame, or of knowledge, or of enjoyment, or of happiness; though with regard to all of these, as far as any of them are attainable, there is more pleasure in the pursuit than in the attainment.

Not those who are at sea, or travelling in a stage coach.

Not the man who is shaving himself.

Not those who have the tooth-ache, or who are having a tooth drawn.

The fashionable beauty might; and the fashionable singer, and the fashionable opera dancer, and the actor who is in the height of his power and reputation. So might the alderman at a city feast. So would the heir who is squandering a large fortune faster than it was accumulated for him. And the thief who is not taken, and the convict who is not hanged, and the scoffer at religion whose heart belies his tongue.

---

* Cowley's Davideis, book i. vol. i. p. 302., and note p. 364. The Latin version is in vol. ii. p. 513.

> "Nothing is there to come, and nothing past,
> But an *eternal now* does always last."

It is needless to add that the term originated with the Schoolmen.

Not the wise and the good.

Not those who are in sickness or in sorrow.

Not I.

But were I endowed with the power of suspending the effect of time upon the things around me, methinks there are some of my flowers which should neither fall nor fade: decidedly my kitten should never attain to cathood: and I am afraid my little boy would continue to "mis-speak half-uttered words;" and never, while I live, outgrow that epicene dress of French grey, half European, half Asiatic in its fashion.

CHAPTER XXVI. P. I.

DANIEL AT DONCASTER; THE REASON WHY HE WAS DESTINED FOR THE MEDICAL PROFESSION, RATHER THAN HOLY ORDERS; AND SOME REMARKS UPON SERMONS.

Je ne veux dissimuler, amy Lecteur, que je n'aye bien préveu, et me tiens pour dellement adverty, que ne puis eviter la reprehension d'aucuns, et les calomnies de plusieurs, ausquels cest éscrit désplaira du tout.

CHRISTOFLE DE HERICOURT.

FOURTEEN years have elapsed since the scene took place which is related in the twenty-second chapter: and Daniel the younger, at the time to which this present chapter refers, was residing at Doncaster with Peter Hopkins who practised the medical art in all its branches. He had lived with him eight years, first as a pupil, latterly in the capacity of an assistant, and afterwards as an adopted successor.

How this connection between Daniel and Peter Hopkins was brought about, and the circumstances which prepared the way for it, would have appeared in some of the non-existent fourteen volumes, if it had pleased Fate that they should have been written.

Some of my readers, and especially those who pride themselves upon their knowledge of the world, or their success in it, will think it strange, perhaps, that the elder Daniel, when he resolved to make a scholar of his son, did not determine upon breeding him either to the Church or the Law, in either of which professions the way was easier and more inviting. Now though this will not appear strange to those other readers who have perceived that the father had no knowledge of the world, and could have none, it is nevertheless proper to enter into some explanation upon that point.

If George Herbert's Temple, or his Remains, or his life by old Izaak Walton, had all or any of them happened to be among those few but precious books which Daniel prized so highly and used so well, it is likely that the wish of his heart would have been to train up his Son for a Priest to the Temple. But so it was that none of his reading was of a kind to give his thoughts that direction; and he had not conceived any exalted opinion of the Clergy from the specimens which had fallen in his way. A contempt which was but too general had been brought upon the Order by the ignorance or the poverty of a great proportion of its members. The person who served the humble church which Daniel dutifully attended was almost as poor as a Capuchine, and quite as ignorant. This poor man had obtained in evil hour from some easy or careless Bishop a licence to preach. It was reprehensible enough to have ordained one who was destitute of every qualification that the office requires; the fault was still greater in promoting him from the desk to the pulpit.

"A very great Scholar" is quoted by Dr. Eachard as saying, "that such preaching as is usual is a hindrance of salvation rather than the means to it." This was said when the fashion of conceited preaching, which is satirised in Frey Gerundio, had extended to England, and though that fashion has so long been obsolete, that many persons will be surprised to hear it had ever existed among us, it may still reasonably be questioned whether sermons, such as they commonly are, do not quench more devotion than they kindle.

My Lord! put not the book aside in displeasure! (I address myself to whatever Bishop may be reading it.) Unbiassed I will not call myself, for I am a true and orthodox churchman, and have the interests of the Church zealously at heart, because I believe and know them to be essentially and inseparably connected with those of the commonwealth. But I have been an attentive observer, and as such, request a hearing. Receive my remarks as coming from one whose principles are in entire accord with your Lordship's, whose wishes have the same scope and purport, and who, while he offers his honest opinion, submits it with proper humility to your judgment.

The founders of the English Church did not intend that the sermon should invariably form a part of the Sunday services.* It became so in condescension to the Puritans, of whom it has long been the fashion to speak with respect, instead of holding them up to the contempt and infamy and abhorrence which they have so richly merited. They have been extolled by their descendants and successors as models of patriotism and piety; and the success with which this delusion has been practised is one of the most remarkable examples of what may be effected by dint of effrontery and persevering falsehood.

That sentence I am certain will not be disapproved at Fulham or Lambeth. Dr. Southey, or Dr. Phillpots, might have written it.

The general standard of the Clergy has undoubtedly been very much raised since the days when they were not allowed to preach without a licence for that purpose from the Ordinary. Nevertheless it is certain that many persons who are in other, and more material respects well, or even excellently, qualified for the ministerial functions, may be wanting in the qualifications for a preacher. A man may possess great learning, sound principles and good sense, and yet be without the talent of arranging and expressing his thoughts well in a written discourse: he may want the power of fixing the attention, or reaching the hearts of his hearers; and in that case the discourse, as some old writer has said in serious jest, which was designed for edification turns to *te*dification. The evil was less in Addison's days, when he who distrusted his own abilities availed himself of the compositions of some approved Divine, and was not disparaged in the opinion of his congregation by taking a printed volume into the pulpit. This is no longer practised; but instead of this, which secured wholesome instruction to the people, sermons are manufactured for sale, and sold in manuscript, or printed in a cursive type imitating manuscript. The articles which are prepared for such a market are, for the most part, copied from obscure books, with more or less alteration of language, and generally for the worse; and so far as they are drawn from such sources they are not likely to contain any thing exceptionable on the score of doctrine: but the best authors will not be resorted to, for fear of discovery, and therefore when these are used, the congregation lose as much in point of instruction, as he who uses them ought to lose in self-esteem.

But it is more injurious when a more scrupulous man composes his own discourses, if he be deficient either in judgment or learning. He is then more likely to entangle plain texts than to unravel knotty ones; rash positions are sometimes advanced by such preachers, unsound arguments are adduced by them in support of momentous doctrines, and though these things neither offend the ignorant and careless, nor injure the well-minded and well-informed, they carry poison with them when they enter a diseased ear. It cannot be doubted that such sermons act as corroboratives for infidelity.

Nor when they contain nothing that is actually erroneous, but are merely unimproving, are they in that case altogether harmless. They are not harmless if they are felt to be tedious. They are not harmless if they torpify the understanding: a chill that begins there may extend to the vital regions. Bishop Taylor (the great

* Selden's words are not to be readily forgotten. "Preaching, for the most part, is the glory of the Preacher, to show himself a fine man. Catechising would do much better." TABLE TALK.

Jeremy) says of devotional books, that "they are in a large degree the occasion of so great indevotion as prevails among the generality of nominal Christians, being," he says, "represented naked in the conclusions of spiritual life, without or art or learning; and made apt for persons who can do nothing but believe and love, not for them that can consider and love." This applies more forcibly to bad sermons than to common-place books of devotion; the book may be laid aside if it offend the reader's judgment, but the sermon is a positive infliction upon the helpless hearer.

The same Bishop, — and his name ought to carry with it authority among the wise and the good, — has delivered an opinion upon this subject, in his admirable Apology for Authorized and Set Forms of Liturgy. "Indeed," he says, "if I may freely declare my opinion, I think it were not amiss, if the liberty of making sermons were something more restrained than it is; and that such persons only were entrusted with the liberty, for whom the church herself may safely be responsive, — that is, men learned and pious; and that the other part, the *vulgus cleri*, should instruct the people out of the fountains of the church and the public stock, till by so long exercise and discipline in the schools of the Prophets they may also be intrusted to minister of their own unto the people. This I am sure was the practice of the Primitive Church."

"I am convinced," said Dr. Johnson, "that I ought to be at Divine Service more frequently than I am; but the provocations given by ignorant and affected preachers too often disturb the mental calm which otherwise would succeed to prayer. I am apt to whisper to myself on such occasions, 'How can this illiterate fellow dream of fixing attention, after we have been listening to the sublimest truths, conveyed in the most chaste and exalted language, throughout a liturgy which must be regarded as the genuine offspring of piety impregnated by wisdom!'" — "Take notice, however," he adds, "though I make this confession respecting myself, I do not mean to recommend the fastidiousness that sometimes leads me to exchange congregational for solitary worship."

The saintly Herbert says,

"Judge not the Preacher, for he is thy Judge;
If thou mislike him thou conceiv'st him not.
God calleth preaching folly. Do not grudge
To pick out treasures from an earthen pot.
The worst speak something good. If all want sense,
God takes a text and preacheth patience.

He that gets patience and the blessing which
Preachers conclude with, hath not lost his pains."

This sort of patience was all that Daniel could have derived from the discourses of the poor curate; and it was a lesson of which his meek and benign temper stood in no need. Nature had endowed him with this virtue, and this Sunday's discipline exercised without strengthening it. While he was, in the phrase of the Religious Public, *sitting under* the preacher, he obeyed to a certain extent George Herbert's precept, — that is, he obeyed it as he did other laws with the existence of which he was unacquainted, —

Let vain or busy thoughts have there no part;
Bring not thy plough, thy plots, thy pleasure thither.

Pleasure made no part of his speculations at any time. Plots he had none. For the Plough, — it was what he never followed in fancy, patiently as he plodded after the furrow in his own vocation. And then for worldly thoughts they were not likely in that place to enter a mind which never at any time entertained them. But to that sort of thought (if thought it may be called) which cometh as it listeth, and which when the mind is at ease and the body in health, is the forerunner and usher of sleep, he certainly gave way. The curate's voice passed over his ear like the sound of the brook with which it blended, and it conveyed to him as little meaning and less feeling. During the sermon, therefore, he retired into himself, with as much or as little edification as a Quaker finds at a silent meeting.

It happened also that of the few clergy within the very narrow circle in which Daniel moved, some were in no good repute for their conduct, and none displayed either that zeal in the discharge of their pastoral functions, or that earnestness and ability in performing the service of the Church, which are necessary for commanding the respect and securing the affections of the parishioners. The clerical profession had never presented itself to him in its best, which is really its true light; and for that cause he would never have thought of it for the boy, even if the means of putting him forward in this path had been easier and more obvious than they were. And for the dissenting ministry, Daniel liked not the name of a Nonconformist. The Puritans had left behind them an ill savour in his part of the country, as they had done every where else; and the extravagances of the primitive Quakers, which during his childhood were fresh in remembrance, had not yet been forgotten.

It was well remembered in those parts that the Vicar of Kirkby Lonsdale, through the malignity of some of his puritanical parishioners, had been taken out of his bed — from his wife who was then big with child — and hurried away to Lancaster jail, where he was imprisoned three years for no other offence than that of fidelity to his Church and his King. And that the man who was a chief instigator of this persecution, and had enriched himself by the spoil of his neighbour's goods, though he flourished for awhile, bought a field and built a fine house, came to poverty at last, and died in prison, having for some time received his daily food there from the table of one of this very Vicar's sons. It was well remembered also that, in a parish of the adjoining county-palatine, the puritanical party had set fire in the night to the Rector's barns, stable, and parsonage; and that he and his wife and children had only as it were by miracle escaped from the flames.

William Dove had also among his traditional stores some stories of a stranger kind concerning the Quakers, these parts of the North having been a great scene of their vagaries in their early days. He used to relate how one of them went into the church at Brough, during the reign of the Puritans, with a white sheet about his body, and a rope about his neck, to prophesy before the people and their Whig Priest (as he called him) that the surplice which was then prohibited should again come into use, and that the Gallows should have its due! And how when their ringleader, George Fox, was put in prison at Carlisle, the wife of Justice Benson would eat no meat unless she partook it with him at the bars of his dungeon, declaring she was moved to do this; wherefore it was supposed he had bewitched her. And not without reason; for when this old George went, as he often did, into the Church to disturb the people, and they thrust him out, and fell upon him and beat him, sparing neither sticks nor stones if they came to hand, he was presently, for all that they had done to him, as sound and as fresh as if nothing had touched him; and when they tried to kill him, they could not take away his life! And how this old George rode a great black horse, upon which he was seen in the course of the same hour at two places, threescore miles distant from each other! And how some of the women who followed this old George used to strip off all their clothes, and in that plight go into the church at service time on the Sunday, to bear testimony against the pomps and vanities of the world; "and to be sure," said William, "they must have been witched, or they never would have done this." "Lord deliver us!" said Dinah, "to be sure they must!" — "To be sure they must, Lord bless us all!" said Haggy.

CHAPTER XXVII. P. I.

A PASSAGE IN PROCOPIUS IMPROVED. A STORY CONCERNING URIM AND THUMMIM; AND THE ELDER DANIEL'S OPINION OF THE PROFESSION OF THE LAW.

> Here is Domine Picklock,
> My man of Law, sollicits all my causes,
> Follows my business, makes and compounds my quarrels
> Between my tenants and me; sows all my strifes
> And reaps them too, troubles the country for me,
> And vexes any neighbour that I please. BEN JONSON.

AMONG the people who were converted to the Christian faith during the sixth century were two tribes or nations called the Lazi and the Zani. Methinks it had been better if they had been left unconverted; for they have multiplied prodigiously among us, so that between the Lazy Christians and the Zany ones, Christianity has grievously suffered.

It was one of the Zany tribe whom Guy once heard explaining to his congregation what was meant by Urim and Thummim, and in technical phrase *improving* the text. Urim and Thummim, he said, were two precious stones, or rather stones above all price, the Hebrew names of which have been interpreted to signify Light and Perfection, or Doctrine and Judgment, (which Luther prefers in his Bible, and in which some of the northern versions have followed him,) or the Shining and the Perfect, or Manifestation and Truth, the words in the original being capable of any or all of these significations. They were set in the High Priest's breast-plate of judgment; and when he consulted them upon any special occasion to discover the will of God, they displayed an extraordinary brilliancy if the matter which was referred to this trial were pleasing to the Lord Jehovah, but they gave no lustre if it were disapproved. "My Brethren," said the Preacher, "this is what learned Expositors, Jewish and Christian, tell me concerning these two precious stones. The stones themselves are lost. But, my Christian Brethren, we need them not, for we have a surer means of consulting and discovering the will of God; and still it is by Urim and Thummim, if we alter only a single letter in one of those mysterious words. Take your Bible, my brethren; *use him and thumb him — use him and thumb him well,* — and you will discover the will of God as surely as ever the High Priest did by the stones in his breast-plate!"

What Daniel saw of the Lazi, and what he heard of the Zani, prevented him from ever forming a wish to educate his son for a North country cure, which would have been all the preferment that lay within his view. And yet, if any person to whose judgment he deferred, had reminded him that Bishop Latimer had risen from as humble an origin, it might have awakened in him a feeling of ambition for the boy, not inconsistent with his own philosophy.

But no suggestions could ever have induced Daniel to choose for him the profession of the Law. The very name of Lawyer was to him a word of evil acceptation. Montaigne has a pleasant story of a little boy who when his mother had lost a lawsuit, which he had always heard her speak of as a perpetual cause of trouble, ran up to her in great glee to tell her of the loss as a matter for congratulation and joy; the poor child thought it was like losing a cough, or any other bodily ailment. Daniel entertained the same sort of opinion concerning all leg l proceedings. He knew that laws were necessary evils; but he thought they were much greater evils than there was any necessity that they should be; and believing this to be occasioned by those who were engaged in the trade of administering them, he looked upon lawyers as the greatest pests in the country —

> Because, their end being merely avarice,
> Winds up their wits to such a nimble strain
> As helps to blind the Judge, not give him eyes.*

He had once been in the Courts at Lancaster, having been called upon as witness in a civil suit, and the manner in which he was cross-examined there by one of those "young spruce Lawyers," whom Donne has so happily characterised as being

> —— "all impudence and tongue"

had confirmed him in this prejudice. What he saw of the proceedings that day induced him to agree with Beaumont and Fletcher, that

> Justice was a Cheese-monger, a mere cheese-monger,
> Weighed nothing to the world but mites and maggots
> And a main stink; Law, like a horse-courser,
> Her rules and precepts hung with gauds and ribbands,
> And pampered up to cozen him that bought her,
> When she herself was hackney, lame and founder'd.†

His was too simple and sincere an understanding to admire in any other sense than that of wondering at them —

---

* Lord Brooke. † Women Pleased.

Men of that large profession that can speak
To every cause, and things mere contraries,
Till they are hoarse again, yet all be law!
That with most quick agility can turn
And re-return; can make knots and undo them,
Give forked counsel, take provoking gold
On either hand, and put it up. These men
He knew would thrive; —*

but far was he from wishing that a son of his should thrive by such a perversion of his intellectual powers, and such a corruption of his moral nature.

On the other hand he felt a degree of respect amounting almost to reverence for the healing art, which is connected with so many mysteries of art and nature. And therefore when an opportunity offered of placing his son with a respectable practitioner, who he had every reason for believing would behave toward him with careful and prudent kindness, his entire approbation was given to the youth's own choice.

CHAPTER XXVIII.

PETER HOPKINS. EFFECTS OF TIME AND CHANGE. DESCRIPTION OF HIS DWELLING-HOUSE.

Combien de changemens depuis que suis au monde,
Qui n'est qu'un point du tems! PASQUIER.

PETER HOPKINS was a person who might have suffered death by the laws of Solon, if that code had been established in this country; for though he lived in the reigns of George I. and George II., he was neither Whig nor Tory, Hanoverian nor Jacobite. When he drank the King's health with any of his neighbours, he never troubled himself with considering which King was intended, nor to which side of the water their good wishes were directed. Under George or Charles he would have been the same quiet subject, never busying himself with a thought about political matters, and having no other wish concerning them than that they might remain as they were,—so far he was a Hanoverian, and no farther. There was something of the same temper in his religion; he was a sincere Christian, and had he been born to attendance at the Mass or the Meeting House would have been equally sincere in his attachment to either of those extremes: for his whole mind was in his profession. He was learned in its history; fond of its theories; and skilful in its practice, in which he trusted little to theory and much to experience.

Both he and his wife were at this time well stricken in years; they had no children, and no near kindred on either side; and being both kind-hearted people, the liking which they soon entertained toward Daniel for his docility, his simplicity of heart, his obliging temper, his original cast of mind, and his never-failing good-humour, ripened into a settled affection.

Hopkins lived next door to the Mansion House, which edifice was begun a few years after Daniel went to live with him. There is a view of the Mansion House in Dr. Miller's History of Doncaster, and in that print the dwelling in question is included. It had undergone no other alteration at the time this view was taken than that of having had its casements replaced by sash windows, an improvement which had been made by our Doctor, when the frame-work of the casements had become incapable of repair. The gilt pestle and mortar also had been removed from its place above the door. Internally the change had been greater; for the same business not being continued there after the Doctor's decease, the shop had been converted into a sitting room, and the very odour of medicine had passed away. But I will not allow myself to dwell upon this melancholy subject. The world is full of mutations; and there is hardly any that does not bring with it some regret at the time,—and alas, more in the retrospect! I have lived to see the American Colonies separated from Great Britain, the Kingdom of Poland extinguished, the Republic of Venice destroyed, its territory seized by one Usurper, delivered over in exchange to another, and the transfer sanctioned and con-

---

* BEN JONSON.

firmed by all the Powers of Europe in Congress assembled! I have seen Heaven knows how many little Principalities and States, proud of their independence, and happy in the privileges connected with it, swallowed up by the Austrian or the Prussian Eagle, or thrown to the Belgic Lion, as his share in the division of the spoils. I have seen constitutions spring up like mushrooms and kicked down as easily. I have seen the rise and fall of Napoleon.

I have seen Cedars fall
And in their room a mushroom grow;
I have seen Comets, threatening all,
Vanish themselves; *

wherefore then should I lament over what time and mutability have done to a private dwelling-house in Doncaster?

It was an old house, which when it was built had been one of the best in Doncaster; and even after the great improvements which have changed the appearance of the town, had an air of antiquated respectability about it. Had it been near the church it would have been taken for the Vicarage; standing where it did, its physiognomy was such that you might have guessed it was the Doctor's house, even if the pestle and mortar had not been there as his insignia. There were eight windows and two doors in front. It consisted of two stories, and was oddly built, the middle part having, something in the Scotch manner, the form of a gable end towards the street. Behind this was a single chimney, tall, and shaped like a pillar. In windy nights the Doctor was so often consulted by Mrs. Dove concerning the stability of that chimney, that he accounted it the plague of his life. But it was one of those evils which could not be removed without bringing on a worse, the alternative being whether there should be a tall chimney, or a smoky house. And after the mansion house was erected, there was one wind which, in spite of the chimney's elevation, drove the smoke down,—so inconvenient is it sometimes to be fixed near a great neighbour.

This unfortunate chimney, being in the middle of the house, served for four apartments; the Doctor's study and his bedchamber on the upper floor, the kitchen and the best parlour on the lower,—that parlour, yes, Reader, that very parlour wherein, as thou canst not have forgotten, Mrs. Dove was making tea for the Doctor on that ever memorable afternoon with which our history begins.

* Habington.

CHAPTER XXIX. P. I.

A HINT OF REMINISCENCE TO THE READER. THE CLOCK OF ST. GEORGE'S. A WORD IN HONOUR OF ARCHDEACON MARKHAM.

There is a ripe season for every thing, and if you slip that or anticipate it, you dim the grace of the matter be it never so good. As we say by way of Proverb that an hasty birth brings forth blind whelps, so a good tale tumbled out before the time is ripe for it, is ungrateful to the hearer. Bishop Hackett.

The judicious reader will now have perceived that in the progress of this narrative,—which may be truly said to

—— bear
A music in the ordered history
It lays before us,——

we have arrived at that point which determines the scene and acquaints him with the local habitation of the Doctor. He will perceive also that in our method of narration, nothing has been inartificially anticipated; that, there have been no premature disclosures, no precipitation, no hurry, or impatience on my part; and that, on the other hand, there has been no unnecessary delay, but that we have regularly and naturally come to this development. The author who undertakes a task like mine,

— must nombre al the hole cyrcumstaunce
Of hys matter with brevyacion,

as an old Poet * says of the professors of the rhyming art, and must moreover be careful

That he walke not by longe continuance
The perambulate way,

* Hawe's "Pastime of Pleasure."

as I have been, O Reader! and as it is my fixed intention still to be. Thou knowest, gentle Reader, that I have never wearied thee with idle and worthless words; thou knowest that the old comic writer spake truly when he said, that the man who speaks little says too much, if he says what is not to the point; but that he who speaks well and wisely, will never be accused of speaking at too great length,

> Τὸν μὴ λέγοντα τῶν δεόντων μηδὲ ἓν
> Μακρὸν νόμιζε, κἂν δύ' εἴπῃ συλλαβάς.
> Τὸν δ' εὖ λέγοντα, μὴ νόμιζ' εἶναι μακρὸν,
> Μηδ' ἂν σφόδρ' εἴπῃ πολλὰ, καὶ πολὺν χρόνον.*

My good Readers will remember that, as was duly noticed in our first chapter P I. the clock of St. George's had just struck five, when Mrs. Dove was pouring out the seventh cup of tea for her husband, and when our history opens. I have some observations to make concerning both the tea and the tea service, which will clear the Doctor from any imputation of intemperance in his use of that most pleasant, salutiferous and domesticising beverage: but it would disturb the method of my narration were they to be introduced in this place. Here I have something to relate about the Clock. Some forty or fifty years ago a Butcher, being one of the Churchwardens of the year, and fancying himself in that capacity invested with full power to alter and improve any thing in or about the Church, thought proper to change the position of the clock, and, accordingly, had it removed to the highest part of the tower, immediately under the battlements. Much beautiful Gothic work was cut away to make room for the three dials, which he placed on three sides of this fine tower; and when he was asked what had induced him thus doubly to disfigure the edifice, by misplacing the dials, and destroying so much of the ornamental part, the great and greasy killcow answered that by fixing the dials so high, he could now stand at his own shop-door and see what it was o'clock! That convenience this arrant churchwarden had the satisfaction of enjoying for several years, there being no authority that could call him to account for the insolent mischief he had done. But Archdeacon Markham (to his praise be it spoken), at the end of the last century, prevailed on the then churchwardens to remove two of the dials, and restore the architectural ornaments which had been defaced.

This was the clock which, with few intervals, measured out by hours the life of Daniel Dove from the seventeenth year of his age, when he first set up his rest within its sound.

Perhaps of all the works of man sun-dials and church-clocks are those which have conveyed most feeling to the human heart; the clock more than the sun-dial, because it speaks to the ear as well as to the eye, and by night as well as by day. Our forefathers understood this, and, therefore, they not only gave a Tongue to Time *, but provided that he should speak often to us, and remind us that the hours are passing. Their quarter-boys and their chimes were designed for this moral purpose as much as the memento which is so commonly seen upon an old clock-face, — and so seldom upon a new one. I never hear chimes that they do not remind me of those which were formerly the first sounds I heard in the morning, which used to quicken my step on my way to school, and which announced my release from it, when the same tune methought had always a merrier import. When I remember their tones, life seems to me like a dream, and a train of recollections arises, which, if it were allowed to have its course, would end in tears.

---

* Philemon.

* "The bell strikes one. We take no note of time
But from its loss. To give it then a tongue
Is wise in man."
Young's *Night Thoughts*. Night I.

CHAPTER XXX. P. I.

THE OLD BELLS RUNG TO A NEW TUNE.

If the bell have any sides the clapper will find 'em.
BEN JONSON.

THAT same St. George's Church has a peal of eight tunable bells, in the key of E. b. the first bell weighing seven hundred, one quarter, and fourteen pounds.

Tra tutte quante le musiche humane,
O Signor mio gentil, tra le più care
Gioje del mondo, è 'l suon delle campane ;
Don don don don don don, che ve ne pare ? *

They were not christened, because they were not Roman Catholic bells; for in Roman Catholic countries church bells are christened with the intention of causing them to be held in greater reverence,—

— però ordinò n'un consistoro
Un certo di quei buon papi all' antica,
Che non ci lavoravan di straforo,
Che la campana si, si benedica,
Poi si battezzi, e se le ponga il nome,
Prima che' in campanil l' ufizio dica.
Gli organi, ch' anco lor san sì ben come
Si dica il vespro, e le messe cantate,
Non hanno questo honor sopra le chiome.
Che le lor canne non son battezzate,
Ne' nome ha l' una Pier, l' altra Maria
*Come hanno le campane prelibate.**

The bells of St. George's, Doncaster, I say, were not christened, because they were Protestant bells; for distinction's sake, however, we will name them as the bells stand in the dirge of that unfortunate Cat whom Johnny Green threw into the well.

But it will be better to exhibit their relative weights in figures, so that they may be seen synoptically. Thus then;—

	Cwt.	qr.	lb.
Bim the first	7	1	14
Bim the second	8	0	18
Bim the third	8	2	6
Bim the fourth	10	3	15
Bim the fifth	13	1	0
Bim the sixth	15	2	16
Bom - -	22	1	0
Bell - -	29	1	20

* AGNOLO FIRENZUOLA.

I cannot but admit that these appellations are not so stately in appearance as those of the peal which the Bishop of Chalons recently baptized, and called a "happy and holy family" in the edifying discourse that he delivered upon the occasion. The first of these was called Marie, to which—or to whom—the Duke and Duchess of Danderville (so the newspapers give this name) stood sponsors. "It is you, Marie," said the Bishop, "who will have the honour to announce the festivals, and proclaim the glory of the Lord! You appear among us under the most happy auspices, presented by those respectable and illustrious hands to which the practices of piety have been so long familiar. And you, Anne," he pursued, addressing the second bell,—"an object worthy of the zeal and piety of our first magistrate (the Prefect), and of her who so nobly shares his solicitude,—you shall be charged with the same employment. Your voice shall be joined to Marie's upon important occasions. Ah! what touching lessons will you not give in imitation of her whose name you bear, and whom we reverence as the purest of Virgins! You, also, Deodate, will take part in this concert, you whom an angel, a new-born infant, has conjointly with me consecrated to the Lord! Speak, Deodate! and let us hear your marvellous accents." This Angel and Godmother, in whose name the third bell was given, was Mademoiselle Deodate Boisset, then in the second month of her age, daughter of Viscount Boisset. "And you, Stephanie, crowned with glory," continued the orator, in learned allusion to the Greek word στέφανος, "you are not less worthy to mingle your accents with the melody of your sisters. And you, lastly, Seraphine and Pudentienne, you will raise your voices in this touching concert, happy all of you in having been presented to the benedictions of the Church, by these noble and generous souls, so praiseworthy for the liveliness of their faith, and the holiness of their example." And then the Bishop concluded by calling upon the congregation to join with him in prayer that the Almighty would be pleased to preserve from all accidents this "happy and holy family of the bells."

We have no such sermons from our Bishops! The whole ceremony must have been as useful to the bells as it was edifying to the people.

Were I called upon to act as sponsor upon such an occasion, I would name my bell Peter Bell, in honour of Mr. Wordsworth. There has been a bull so called, and a bull it was of great merit. But if it were the great bell, then it should be called Andrew, in honour of Dr. Bell; and that bell should call the children to school.

There are, I believe, only two bells in England which are known by their christian names, and they are both called Tom; but Great Tom of Oxford, which happens to be much the smaller of the two, was christened in the feminine gender, being called Mary, in the spirit of catholic and courtly adulation at the commencement of the bloody Queen's reign. Tresham, the Vice-Chancellor, performed the ceremony, and his exclamation, when it first summoned him to mass, has been recorded: — "O delicate and sweet harmony! O beautiful Mary! how musically she sounds! how strangely she pleaseth my ear!"

In spite of this christening, the object of Dr. Tresham's admiration is as decidedly a Tom-Bell as the Puss in Boots who appeared at a Masquerade (Theodore Hook remembers when and where) was a Tom Cat. Often as the said Tom-Bell has been mentioned, there is but one other anecdote recorded of him; it occurred on Thursday the thirteenth day of March, 1806, and was thus described in a letter written two hours after the event: — "An odd thing happened to-day, about half-past four, Tom suddenly went mad; he began striking as fast as he could about twenty times. Every body went out doubting whether there was an earthquake, or whether the Dean was dead, or the College on fire. However, nothing was the matter but that Tom was taken ill in his bowels: in other words, something had happened to the works, but it was not of any serious consequence, for he has struck six as well as ever, and bids fair to toll 101 to-night as well as he did before the attack."

This was written by a youth of great natural endowments, rare acquirements, playful temper, and affectionate heart. If his days had been prolonged, his happy industry, his inoffensive wit, his sound judgement and his moral worth, favoured as they were by all favourable circumstances, must have raised him to distinction; and the name of Barrè Roberts, which is now known only in the little circle of his own and his father's friends, would have had its place with those who have deserved well of their kind and reflected honour upon their country.

But I return to a subject, which would have interested him in his antiquarian pursuits, — for he loved to wander among the Ruins of Time. We will return therefore to that ceremony of christening Church Bells, which, with other practices of the Holy Roman Catholic and Apostolic Church, has been revived in France.

Bells, say those Theologians in *issimi* who have gravely written upon this grave matter, — Bells, say they, are not actually baptized with that baptism which is administered for the remission of sins; but they are said to be christened because the same ceremonies which are observed in christening children are also observed in consecrating them, such as the washing, the anointing, and the imposing a name; all which, however, may more strictly be said to represent the signs and symbols of baptism than they may be called baptism itself.

Nothing can be more candid! Bells are not baptized for the remission of sins, because the original sin of a bell would be a flaw in the metal, or a defect in the tone, neither of which the Priest undertakes to remove. There was however a previous ceremony of blessing the furnace when the bells were cast within the precincts of a monastery, as they most frequently were in former times, and this may have been intended for the prevention of such defects. The Brethren stood round the furnace ranged in processional order, sang the 150th Psalm, and then after certain prayers blessed the molten metal, and called upon the Lord to infuse into it his grace and overshadow it with his power, for the honour of the Saint to whom the bell was to be dedicated and whose name it was to bear.

When the time of christening came, the officiating Priest and his assistant named every bell five times, as a sort of prelude, for some unexplained reason which may perhaps be as significant and mystical as the other parts of the ceremony. He then blessed the water in two vessels which were prepared for the service. Dipping a clean linen cloth in one of these vessels, he washed the bell within and without, the bell being suspended over a vessel wider in circumference than the bell's mouth, in order that no drop of the water employed in this washing might fall to the ground; for the water was holy. Certain psalms were said or sung (they were the 96th and the four last in the psalter) during this part of the ceremony and while the officiating Priest prepared the water in the second vessel: this he did by sprinkling salt in it, and putting holy oil upon it, either with his thumb, or with a stick; if the thumb were used, it was to be cleaned immediately by rubbing it well with salt over the same water. Then he dipt another clean cloth in this oiled and salted water, and again washed the bell within and without: after the service the cloths were burnt lest they should be profaned by other uses. The bell was then authentically named. Then it was anointed with chrism in the form of a cross four times on the broadest part of the outside, thrice on the smaller part, and four times on the inside, those parts being anointed with most care against which the clapper was to strike. After this the name was again given. Myrrh and frankincense were then brought, the bell was incensed while part of a psalm was recited, and the bell was authentically named a third time; after which the priest carefully wiped the chrism from the bell with tow, and the tow was immediately burnt in the censer. Next the Priest struck each bell thrice with its clapper, and named it again at every stroke; every one of the assistants in like manner struck it and named it once. The bells were then carefully covered each with a cloth and immediately hoisted that they might not be contaminated by any irreverent touch. The Priest concluded by explaining to the congregation, if he thought proper, the reason for this ceremony of christening the bells, which was that they might act as preservatives against thunder and lightning, and hail and wind, and storms of every kind, and moreover that they might drive away evil Spirits. To these and their other virtues the Bishop of Chalons alluded in his late truly Gallican and Roman Catholic discourse. "The Bells," said he, "placed like sentinels on the towers, watch over us and turn away from us the temptations of the enemy of our salvation, as well as storms and tempests. They speak and pray for us in our troubles; they inform heaven of the necessities of the earth."

Now were this edifying part of the Roman Catholic ritual to be re-introduced in the British dominions, — as it very possibly may be now that Lord Peter has appeared in his robes before the King, and been introduced by his title, — the opportunity would no doubt be taken by the Bishop or Jesuit who might direct the proceedings, of complimenting the friends of their cause by naming the first "holy and happy family" after them. And to commemorate the extraordinary union of sentiment which that cause has brought about between persons not otherwise remarkable for any similitude of feelings or opinions, they might unite two or more names in one bell (as is frequently done in the human subject), and thus with a peculiar felicity of compliment show who and who upon this great and memorable occasion have *pulled together*. In such a case the names selected for a peal of eight tunable bells might run thus: —

Bim 1st. — Canning O'Connel.
Bim 2d. — Plunkett Shiel.
Bim 3d. — Augustus Frederick Cobbett.

Bim 4th. — Williams Wynn Burdett Waithman.
Bim 5th. — Grenville Wood.
Bim 6th. — Palmerston Hume.
Bom — Lawless Brougham.
Bell — Lord King, *per se*;

— alone *par excellence*, as the thickest and thinnest friend of the cause, and moreover because

None but himself can be his parallel;

and last in order because the base note accords best with him; and because for the decorum and dignity with which he has at all times treated the Bishops, the clergy and the subject of religion, he must be allowed to bear the bell not from his compeers alone but from all his contemporaries.

CHAPTER XXXI. P. I.

MORE CONCERNING BELLS.

Lord, ringing changes all our bells hath marr'd;
Jangled they have and jarr'd
So long, they're out of tune, and out of frame;
They seem not now the same.
Put them in frame anew, and once begin
To tune them so, that they may chime all in!

HERBERT.

THERE are more mysteries in a peal of bells than were touched upon by the Bishop of Chalons in his sermon. There are plain bob-triples, bob-majors, bob-majors reversed, double bob-majors, and grandsire-bob-cators, and there is a Bob-maximus. Who Bob was, and whether he were Bob Major, or Major Bob, that is whether Major were his name or his rank, and if his rank, to what service he belonged, are questions which inexorable Oblivion will not answer, however earnestly adjured. And there is no Witch of Endor who will call up Bob from the grave to answer them himself. But there are facts in the history of bell-ringing which Oblivion has not yet made her own, and one of them is that the greatest performance ever completed by one person in the world was that of Mr. Samuel Thurston at the New Theatre Public House in the City of Norwich, on Saturday evening, July 1, 1809, when he struck all these intricate short peals, the first four upon a set of eight musical hand-bells, the last on a peal of ten.

But a performance upon hand-bells when compared to bell-ringing is even less than a review in comparison with a battle. Strength of arm as well as skill is required for managing a bell-rope. Samuel Thurston's peal of plain bob-triples was "nobly brought round" in two minutes and three quarters, and his grandsire-bob-cators were as nobly finished in five minutes and fourteen seconds. The reader shall now see what real bell-ringing is.

The year 1796 was remarkable for the performance of great exploits in this manly and English art, — for to England the art is said to be peculiar, the cheerful carrillons of the continent being played by keys. In that year, and in the month of August, the Westmoreland youths rang a complete peal of 5040 grandsire-triples in St. Mary's Church, Kendal, being the whole number of changes on seven bells. The peal was divided into ten parts, or courses of 504 each; the bobs were called by the sixth, a lead single was made in the middle of the peal, and another at the conclusion, which brought the bells home. Distinct leads and exact divisions were observed throughout the whole, and the performance was completed in three hours and twenty minutes. A like performance took place in the same month at Kidderminster in three hours and fourteen minutes. Stephen Hill composed and called the peal, it was conducted through with one single, which was brought to the 4984th change, viz. 1,267,453. This was allowed by those who were conversant in the art to exceed any peal ever yet rung in this kingdom by that method.

Paulo majora canamus. The Society of Cambridge youths that same year rang, in the Church of St. Mary the Great, a true and complete peal of Bob-maximus in five hours and five minutes. This consisted of 6600 changes, and for regularity of striking and harmony throughout the peal was allowed by competent judges to be a very masterly performance. In point of time the striking was to such a nicety that in each thousand changes the time did not vary one sixteenth of a minute, and the compass of the last thousand was exactly equal to the first.

Eight Birmingham youths (some of them were under twenty years of age) attempted a greater exploit; they ventured upon a complete peal of 15,120 bob-major. They failed indeed, *magnis tamen ausis*. For after they had rang upwards of eight hours and a half, they found themselves so much fatigued that they desired the caller would take the first opportunity to bring the bells home. This he soon did by omitting a bob, and so brought them round, thus making a peal of 14,224 changes in eight hours and forty-five minutes; the longest which was ever rung in that part of the country, or perhaps any where else.

In that same year died Mr. Patrick, the celebrated composer of church-bell music, and senior of the Society of Cumberland Youths, — an Hibernian sort of distinction for one in middle or later life. He is the same person whose name was well known in the scientific world as a maker of barometers; and he it was who composed the whole peal of Stedman's triples, 5040 changes, (which his obituarist says had till then been deemed impracticable, and for the discovery of which he received a premium of 50*l.* offered for that purpose by the Norwich amateurs of the art,) "his productions of real double and treble bob-royal being a standing monument of his unparalleled and superlative merits." This Mr. Patrick was interred on the afternoon of Sunday, June 26, in the churchyard of St. Leonard, Shoreditch; the corpse was followed to the grave by all the Ringing Societies in London and its environs, each sounding hand-bells with muffled clappers, the church bells at the same time ringing a dead peal:

'Ως οἵγ' ἀμφίεπον τάφον Πατρίκος βομβοδάμοιο.

James Ogden was interred with honours of the same kind at Ashton-under-Line, in the year of this present writing, 1827. His remains were borne to the grave by the ringers of St. Michael's Tower in that town, with whom he had rung the tenor bell for more than fifty years, and with whom he performed "the unprecedented feat" of ringing five thousand on that bell (which weighed 28 cwt.) in his sixty-seventh year. After the funeral his old companions rang a dead peal for him of 828 changes, that being the number of the months of his life. Such in England are the funeral honours of the Βέλτιστοι.

It would take ninety-one years to ring the changes upon twelve bells, at the rate of two strokes to a second; the changes upon fourteen could not be rung through at the same rate in less than 16,575 years; and upon four and twenty they would require more than 117,000 billions of years.

Great then are the mysteries of bell-ringing! And this may be said in its praise, that of all devices which men have sought out for obtaining distinction by making a noise in the world, it is the most harmless.*

CHAPTER XXXII. P. I.

AN INTRODUCTION TO CERTAIN PRELIMINARIES ESSENTIAL TO THE PROGRESS OF THIS WORK.

Mas demos ya el asiento en lo importante,
Que el tiempo huye del mundo por la posta.
BALBUENA.

THE subject of these memoirs heard the bells of St. George's ring for the battles of Dettingen and Culloden; for Commodore Anson's return and Admiral Hawke's victory; for the conquest of Quebec; for other victories, important in their day, though in the retro-

---

* Some readers may not be displeased with these old lines.

TINTINNABULUM SONAT!
Laudo Deum Verum, plebem voco, congrego clerum;
Defunctos ploro, pestem fugo, festa decoro.

spect they may seem to have produced little effect; and for more than one Peace; for the going out of the Old Style, and for the coming in of the New; for the accession, marriage, and coronation of George III.; for the birth of George IV.; and that of all his royal brethren and sisters; — and what was to him a subject of nearer and dearer interest than any of these events, — for his own wedding.

What said those bells to him that happy day? for that bells can convey articulate sounds to those who have the gift of interpreting their language, Whittington, Lord Mayor of London Town, knew by fortunate experience.

So did a certain Father Confessor in the Netherlands, whom a buxom widow consulted upon the perilous question whether she should marry a second husband, or continue in widowed blessedness. The prudent Priest deemed it too delicate a point for him to decide; so he directed her to attend to the bells of her church when next they chimed — (they were but three in number) — and bring him word what she thought they said; and he exhorted her to pray in the mean time earnestly for grace to understand them rightly, and in the sense that might be most for her welfare here and hereafter, as he on his part would pray for her. — She listened with mouth and ears the first time that the bells struck up; and the more she listened, the more plainly they said "*Nempt een man, Nempt een man!* — Take a Spouse, Take a Spouse!" "Aye, Daughter!" said the Confessor, when she returned to him with her report, "if the bells have said so, so say I; and not I alone, but the Apostle also, and the Spirit who through that Apostle hath told us when it is best for us to marry!" Reader, thou mayest thank the Leonine poet Gummarus Van Craen for this good story.

What said the Bells of Doncaster to our dear Doctor on that happy morning which made him a whole man by uniting to him the rib that he till then had wanted? They said to him as distinctly as they spoke to Whittington, and to the Flemish Widow, —

Daniel Dove brings Deborah home.
Daniel Dove brings Deborah home.

But whither am I hurrying? It was not till the year 1761 that that happy union was effected; and the fourteen years whose course of events I have reluctantly, yet of necessity, pretermitted, bring us only to 1748, in which year the Peace of Aix-la-Chapelle was made. Peter Hopkins and Mrs. Hopkins were then both living, and Daniel had not attained to the honours of his diploma. Before we come to the day on which the bells rang that joyful peal, I must enter into some details for the purpose of showing how he became qualified for his degree, and how he was enabled to take it; and it will be necessary therefore to say something of the opportunities of instruction which he enjoyed under Hopkins, and of the state of society in Doncaster at that time. And preliminary to, as preparatory for all this, some account is to be given of Doncaster itself.

Reader, you may skip this preliminary account if you please, but it will be to your loss if you do! You perhaps may be one of those persons who can travel from Dan to Beersheba, and neither make inquiry concerning, nor take notice of, any thing on the way; but, thank Heaven, I cannot pass through Doncaster in any such mood of mind. If, however, thou belongest to a better class, then may I promise that in what is here to follow thou wilt find something to recompense thee for the little time thou wilt employ in reading it, were that time more than it will be, or more valuable than it is. For I shall assuredly either tell thee of something which thou didst not know before (and let me observe by the bye that I never obtained any information of any kind which did not on some occasion or other prove available) — or I shall waken up to pleasurable consciousness thy napping knowledge. Snuff the candles therefore, if it be candlelight, and they require it (I hope, for thine eyes' sake, thou art not reading by a lamp!) — stir the fire, if it be winter, and it be prudent to refresh it with the poker; and then comfortably begin a new chapter:

*Faciam ut hujus loci semper memineris.**

CHAPTER XXXIII. P. I.

DONCASTRIANA. THE RIVER DON.

Rivers from bubbling springs
Have rise at first; and great from abject things.
MIDDLETON.

How would it have astonished Peter Hopkins if some one gifted with the faculty of second-sight had foretold to him that, at the sale of Pews in a new Church at Doncaster, eighteen of those Pews should produce upwards of sixteen hundred pounds, and that one of them should be bought at the price of £138, — a sum for which, in his days, lands enough might have been purchased to have qualified three men as Yorkshire Freeholders! How would it have surprised him to have been told that Doncaster races would become the greatest meeting in the North of England; that Princes would attend them, and more money would annually be won and lost there than might in old times have sufficed for a King's ransom! But the Doncaster of George the Fourth's reign is not more like the Doncaster of George the Second's, than George the Fourth himself, in manners, habit, character, and person is like his royal Great Grandfather; — not more like than to the Doncaster of the United States, if such a place there be there; or to the Doncaster that may be in New South Wales, Van Diemen's or Swan-river-land. It was a place of considerable importance when young Daniel first became an inhabitant of it; but it was very far from having attained all the advantages arising from its well-endowed corporation, its race-ground, and its position on the great north road.

It is beyond a doubt that Doncaster may be identified with the Danum of Antoninus and the Notitia, the Caer Daun of Nennius, and the Dona-cester of the Saxons; whether it were the Campo-Donum of Bede, — a royal residence of the Northumbrian Kings, where Paulinus the Romish Apostle of Northumbria built a Church, which, with the town itself, was burnt by the Welsh King Cadwallon, and his Saxon Ally the Pagan Penda, after a battle in which Edwin fell, — is not so certain: antiquaries differ upon this point, but they who maintain the affirmative appear to have the strongest case. In the charter granted to it by Richard Cœur de Lion the town is called Danecastre.

The name indicates that it was a Roman Station on the river Dan, Don or Dun, "so called," says Camden, "because 'tis carried in a low deep channel, for that is the signification of the British word Dan." I thank Dr. Prichard for telling me what it was not possible for Camden to know, — that Don in the language of the Ossetes, a Caucassian tribe, means water; and that in a country so remote as New Guinea, Dan has the same meaning. Our Doctor loved the river for its name's sake; and the better because the river Dove falls into it. Don however, though not without some sacrifice of feeling, he was content to call it, in conformity to the established usage. A more satisfactory reason to him would have been that of preserving the identity of name with the Don of Aberdeenshire and of the Cossacks, and the relationship in etymology with the Donau; but that the original pronunciation, which was, as he deemed, perverted in that latter name, was found in Danube; and that by calling his own river Don it ceased to be homonymous with that Dan which adds its waters and its name to the Jor.

* TERENCE

But the Yorkshire Don might be liked also for its own sake. Hear how its course is described in old prose and older verse! "The River Don or Dun," says Dodsworth in his Yorkshire collections, "riseth in the upper part of Pennystone parish, near Lady's Cross—(which may be called our Apennines, because the rain-water that falleth sheddeth from sea to sea)—cometh to Birchworth, so to Pennystone, thence to Boleterstone by Medop, leaveth Wharncliffe Chase (stored with roebucks, which are decayed since the great frost) on the north (belonging to Sir Francis Wortley, where he hath great ironworks. The said Wharncliffe affordeth two hundred dozen of coal for ever to his said works. In this Chase he had red and fallow deer and roes), and leaveth Bethuns, a Chase and Tower of the Earl of Salop, on the south side. By Wortley to Waddsley, where in times past Everingham of Stainber had a park, now disparked; thence to Sheffield, and washeth the castle wall; keepeth its course to Attercliffe, where is an iron forge of the Earl of Salop; from thence to Winkebank, Kymberworth and Eccles, where it entertaineth the Rother; cometh presently to Rotherham, thence to Aldwark Hall, the Fitzwilliams' ancient possession; then to Thriberg Park, the seat of Reresbyes Knights; then to Mexborough, where hath been a Castle; then to Conisborough Park and Castle of the Earls of Warrens, where there is a place called Horsas Tomb; from thence to Sprotebrough, the ancient seat of the famous family of Fitzwilliam, who have flourished since the Conquest; thence by Newton to Donecastre, Wheatley, and Kirk Sandal, to Barnby-Dunn; by Bramwith and Stainforth to Fishlake; thence to Turnbrig, a port town serving indifferently for all the west parts, where he pays his tribute to the Ayre."

Hear Michael Drayton next, who being as determined a personificator as Darwin himself, makes "the wide West Riding" thus address her favourite River Don:

Thou first of all my floods, whose banks do bound my south
And offerest up thy stream to mighty Humber's mouth;
Of yew and climbing elm that crown'd with many a spray,
From thy clear fountain first thro' many a mead dost play,
Till Rother, whence the name of Rotherham first begun,
At that her christened town doth lose her in my Don;
Which proud of her recourse, towards Doncaster doth drive,
Her great and chiefest town, the name that doth derive
From Don's near bordering banks; when holding on her race,
She, dancing in and out, indenteth Hatfield Chase,
Whose bravery hourly adds new honors to her bank:
When Sherwood sends her in slow Iddle that, made rank
With her profuse excess, she largely it bestows
On Marshland, whose swoln womb with such abundance flows,
As that her battening breast her fatlings sooner feeds,
And with more lavish waste than oft the grazier needs;
Whose soil, as some reports, that be her borderers, note,
With water under earth undoubtedly doth float,
For when the waters rise, it risen doth remain
High, while the floods are high, and when they fall again,
It falleth: but at last when as my lively Don
Along by Marshland side her lusty course hath run,
The little wandering Trent, won by the loud report
Of the magnific state and height of Humber's court,
Draws on to meet with Don, at her approach to Aire.

Seldon's rich commentary does not extend to that part of the Polyolbion in which these lines occur, but a comment upon the supposed rising and falling of the Marshland with the waters is supplied by Camden. "The Don," he says, after it has passed Hatfield Chase, "divides itself, one stream running towards the river Idel, which comes out of Nottinghamshire, the other towards the river Aire; in both which they continue till they meet again, and fall into the Æstuary of Humber. Within the island, or that piece of ground encompassed by the branches of these two rivers, are Dikemarsh, and Marshland, fenny tracts, or rather river-islands, about fifteen miles round, which produce a very green rank grass, and are as it were set round with little villages. Some of the inhabitants imagine the whole island floats upon the water; and that sometimes when the waters are increased 'tis raised higher; just like what Pomponius Mela tells us of the Isle of Autrum in Gaul." Upon this passage Bishop Gibson remarks, "As to what our author observes of the ground being heaved up, Dr. Johnston affirms he has spoke with several old men, who told him that the turf-moor between Thorne and Gowle was so much higher before the draining, especially in winter time, than it is now, that before they could see little of the church steeple, whereas now they can see the church-yard wall."

The poet might linger willingly with Ebenezer Elliott amid

——rock, vale and wood,—
Haunts of his early days, and still loved well,—
And where the sun, o'er purple moorlands wide,
Gilds Wharncliffe's oaks, while Don is dark below;
And where the blackbird sings on Rother's side,
And where Time spares the age of Conisbro';

but we must proceed with good matter-of-fact prose.

The river has been made navigable to Tinsley, within three miles of Sheffield, and by this means Sheffield, Rotherham and Doncaster carry on a constant intercourse with Hull. A cut was made for draining that part of Hatfield Chase called the Levels, by an adventurous Hollander, Cornelius Vermuyden by name, in the beginning of Charles the First's reign. Some two hundred families of French and Walloon refugees were induced to colonise there at that time. They were forcibly interrupted in their peaceful and useful undertaking by the ignorant people of the country, who were instigated and even led on by certain of the neighbouring gentry, as ignorant as themselves; but the Government was then strong enough to protect them; they brought about twenty-four thousand acres into cultivation, and many of their descendants are still settled upon the ground which was thus reclaimed. Into this new cut, which is at this day called the Dutch river, the Don was turned, its former course having been through Eastoft; but the navigation which has since proved so beneficial to the country, and toward which this was the first great measure, produced at first a plentiful crop of lawsuits, and one of the many pamphlets which this litigation called forth bears as an alias in its title, "the Devil upon Don."

Many vestiges of former cultivation were discovered when this cut was made,—such (according to Gibson's information) as gates, ladders, hammers, and shoes. The land was observed in some places to lie in ridges and furrows, as if it had been ploughed; and oaks and fir trees were frequently dug up, some of which were found lying along, with their roots still fastened; others, as if cut or burnt, and severed from the ground. Roots were long to be seen in the great cut, some very large and standing upright, others with an inclination toward the east.

About the year 1665 the body of a man was found in a turf-pit, some four yards deep, lying with his head toward the north. The hair and nails were not decayed, and the skin was like tanned leather; but it had lain so long there that the bones had become spongy.

CHAPTER XXXIV. P. I.

MORAL INTEREST OF TOPOGRAPHICAL WORKS. LOCAL ATTACHMENT.

Let none our Author rudely blame
Who from the story has thus long digrest;
But for his righteous pains may his fair fame
For ever travel, whilst his ashes rest.
SIR WILLIAM DAVENANT.

READER, if thou carest little or nothing for the Yorkshire river Don and for the town of Doncaster, and for the circumstances connected with it, I am sorry for thee. My venerable friend the Doctor was of a different disposition. He was one who loved, like Southey,

——uncontrolled, as in a dream
To muse upon the course of human things;
Exploring sometimes the remotest springs,
Far as tradition lends one guiding gleam;
Or following upon Thought's audacious wings
Into Futurity the endless stream.

He could not only find

——tongues in trees, books in the running brooks,
Sermons in stones, and good in every thing,—*

but endeavoured to find all he could in them, and for that reason delighted to inquire into the history of places and of things, and to understand their past as well as their present state. The revolutions of a mansion house within his circuit were as interesting to him as those of the Mogul Empire; and he had as much satisfaction in being acquainted with the windings of a brook from its springs

* SHAKESPEARE.

to the place where it fell into the Don, as he could have felt in knowing that the sources of the Nile had been explored, or the course and termination of the Niger.

Hear, Reader, what a journalist says upon rivers in the newest and most approved style of critical and periodical eloquence! He says, and he regarded himself no doubt with no small complacency while so saying,

"An acquaintance with" Rivers "well deserves to be erected into a distinct science. We hail *Potamology* with a cordial greeting, and welcome it to our studies, parlours, schools, reading-rooms, lecture-rooms, mechanics' institutes and universities. There is no end to the interest which Rivers excite. They may be considered physically, geographically, historically, politically, commercially, mathematically, poetically, pictorially, morally, and even religiously — in the world's anatomy they are its veins, as the primitive mountains, those mighty structures of granite, are its bones; they minister to the fertility of the earth, the purity of the air, and the health of mankind. They mark out nature's kingdoms and provinces, and are the physical dividers and subdividers of continents. They welcome the bold discoverer into the heart of the country, to whose coast the sea has borne his adventurous bark. The richest freights have floated on their bosoms, and the bloodiest battles have been fought upon their banks. They move the wheels of cotton mills by their mechanical power, and madden the souls of poets and painters by their picturesque splendour. They make scenery and are scenery, and land yields no landscape without water. They are the best vehicle for the transit of the goods of the merchant, and for the illustration of the maxims of the moralist. The figure is so familiar, that we scarcely detect a metaphor when the stream of life and the course of time flow on into the ocean of Eternity."

Hear, hear, oh hear!

Udite —
Fiumi correnti, e rive, —
E voi — fontane vive! *

* Giusto de' Conte.

Yet the person who wrote this was neither deficient in feeling, nor in power; it is the epidemic vice prevailing in an age of journals that has infected him. They who frame their style *ad captandum* fall into this vein, and as immediate effect is their object they are wise in their generation. The public to which they address themselves are attracted by it, as flies swarm about treacle.

We are advanced from the Age of Reason to the Age of Intellect, and this is the current eloquence of that age! — let us get into an atmosphere of common sense.

Topographical pursuits, my Doctor used to say, tend to preserve and promote the civilisation of which they are a consequence and a proof. They have always prospered in prosperous countries, and flourished most in flourishing times, when there have been persons enough of opulence to encourage such studies, and of leisure to engage in them. Italy and the Low Countries therefore took the lead in this branch of literature; the Spaniards and Portuguese cultivated it in their better days; and beginning among ourselves with Henry VIII. it has been continued with increasing zeal down to the present time.

Whatever strengthens our local attachments is favourable both to individual and national character. Our home, — our birth place, — our native land, — think for awhile what the virtues are which arise out of the feelings connected with these words; and if thou hast any intellectual eyes thou wilt then perceive the connection between topography and patriotism.

Show me a man who cares no more for one place than another, and I will show you in that same person one who loves nothing but himself. Beware of those who are homeless by choice! You have no hold on a human being whose affections are without a tap-root. The laws recognise this truth in the privileges which they confer upon freeholders; and public opinion acknowledges it also, in the confidence which it reposes upon those who have what is called a stake in the country. Vagabond and rogue are convertible terms; and with how much propriety any one may understand who knows what are the habits of the wandering classes, such as gypsies, tinkers, and potters.

The feeling of local attachment was possessed by Daniel Dove in the highest degree. Spurzheim and the crazyologists would have found out a bump on his head for its local habitation; — letting that quackery pass, it is enough for me to know that he derived this feeling from his birth as a mountaineer, and that he had also a right to it by inheritance, as one whose ancestors had from time immemorial dwelt upon the same estate. Smile not contemptuously at that word, ye whose domains extend over more square miles than there were square roods upon his patrimony! To have held that little patrimony unimpaired, as well as unenlarged, through so many generations, implies more contentment, more happiness, and a more uniform course of steadiness and good conduct, than could be found in the proudest of your genealogies!

The most sacred spot upon earth to him was his father's hearth-stead. Rhine, Rhone, Danube, Thames or Tyber, the mighty Ganges or the mightier Maranon, even Jordan itself, affected his imagination less than the Greta, or Wease as he was wont to call it, of his native fields; whose sounds in his boyhood were the first which he heard at morning and the last at night, and during so many peaceful and happy years made as it were an accompaniment to his solitary musings, as he walked between his father's house and his schoolmaster's, to and fro.

Next to that wild river Wease whose visible course was as delightful to the eye and ear, as its subterranean one was to the imagination, he loved the Don. He was not one of those refined persons who like to lessen their admiration of one object by comparing it with another. It entered as little into his mind to depreciate the Don because it was not a mountain stream, as it did into Corporal Trim's or Uncle Toby's to think the worse of Bohemia because it has no sea coast. What if it had no falls, no rapids or resting-places, no basins whose pellucid water might tempt Diana and the Oreades to bathe in it; instead of these the Don had beauties of its own, and utilities which give to such beauties when combined with them an additional charm. There was not a more pleasing object in the landscape to his eyes than the broad sail of a barge slowly moving between the trees, and bearing into the interior of England the produce of the Baltic, and of the East and West.

The place in the world which he loved best was Ingleton, because in that little peaceful village, as in his childhood it was, he had once known every body and every body had known him; and all his recollections of it were pleasurable, till time cast over them a softening but a pensive hue. But next to Ingleton he loved Doncaster.

And wherefore did he thus like Doncaster? For a better reason than the epigrammatist could give for not liking Dr. Fell, though perhaps many persons have no better than that epigrammatist had in this case, for most of their likings and dislikings. He liked it because he must have been a very unreasonable man if he had not been thankful that his lot had fallen there — because he was useful and respected there, contented, prosperous, happy; finally because it is a very likeable place, being one of the most comfortable towns in England: for it is clean, spacious, in a salubrious situation, well-built, well-governed, has no manufactures, few poor, a greater proportion of inhabitants who are not engaged in any trade or calling, than perhaps any other town in the kingdom, and moreover it sends no members to parliament.

INTERCHAPTER III.

THE AUTHOR QUESTIONS THE PROPRIETY OF PERSONIFYING CIRCUMSTANCE. DENIES THE UNITY AND INDIVISIBILITY OF THE PUBLIC, AND MAY EVEN BE SUSPECTED OF DOUBTING ITS OMNISCIENCE AND ITS INFALLIBILITY.

Ha forse
Testa la plebe, ove si chiuda in vece
Di senno, altro che nebbia? o forma voce
Chi sta più saggia, che un bebù d'armento?
CHIABRERA.

"WHAT a kind of Being is circumstance!"

says Horace Walpole in his atrocious tragedy of the Mysterious Mother.—A very odd kind of Being indeed. In the course of my reading I remember but three Beings equally remarkable,—as personified in prose and verse. Social-Tie was one; Catastrophe another; and Inoculation, heavenly Maid! the third.

But of all ideal Beings the most extraordinary is that which we call the Public. The Public and Transubstantiation I hold to be the two greatest mysteries in or out of nature. And there are certain points of resemblance between them.—For as the Priest creates the one mystery, so the author, or other appellant to the said Public, creates the other, and both bow down in worship, real or simulated, before the Idol of their own creation. And as every fragment of the wafer, break it into as many as you may, contains in itself the whole entire mystery of transubstantiation, just in the same manner every fractional part of the Public assumes to itself the powers, privileges and prerogatives of the whole, as virtually, potentially and indefeasably its own. Nay, every individual who deems himself a constituent member of the said Public arrogates them also, and when he professes to be acting *pro bono publico*, the words mean with him all the good he can possibly get for himself.

The old and famous illustration of Hermes may be in part applied to the Public; it is a circle of which the centre is every where: in part I say, for its circumference is defined. It is bounded by language, and has many intercircles. It is indeed a confused multiciplity of circles intersecting each other, perpetually in motion and in change. Every man is the centre of some circle, and yet involved in others; he who is not sometimes made giddy by their movements, has a strong head; and he who is not sometimes thrown off his balance by them, stands well upon his legs.

Again, the Public is like a nest of patent coffins packed for exportation, one within another. There are Publics of all sizes, from the *genus generalissimum*, the great general universal Public, whom London is not large enough to hold, to the *species specialissima*, the little Thinking Public, which may find room in a nutshell.

There is the fashionable Public, and the Religious Public, and the Play-going Public, and the Sporting Public, and the Commercial Public, and the Literary Public, and the Reading Public, and heaven knows how many Publics more. They call themselves Worlds sometimes,—as if a certain number of worldlings made a World!

He who pays his homage to any or all of these Publics, is a Publican and a Sinner.

"*Nunquam valui populo placere; nam quæ ego scio non probat populus; quæ probat populus, ego nescio.*" *
"*Bene et ille, quisquis fuit, (ambigitur enim de auctore.) cum quæreretur ab illo, quo tanta diligentia artis spectaret ad paucissimos perventuræ? Satis sunt, inquit, mihi pauci; satis est unus; satis est nullus.*" *

CHAPTER XXXV. P. I.

DONCASTRIANA. POTTERIC CARR. SOMETHING CONCERNING THE MEANS OF EMPLOYING THE POOR, AND BETTERING THEIR CONDITION.

Why should I sowen draf out of my fist,
When I may sowen wheat, if that me list?
CHAUCER.

DONCASTER is built upon a peninsula, or ridge of land, about a mile across, having a gentle slope from east to west, and bounded on the west by the river; this ridge is composed of three strata, to wit,—of the alluvial soil deposited by the river in former ages, and of limestone on the north and west; and of sandstone to the south and east. To the south of this neck of land lies a tract called Potteric Carr, which is much below the level of the river, and was a morass, or range of fens, when our Doctor first took up his abode in Doncaster. This tract extends about four miles in length and nearly three in breadth, and the security which it afforded against an attack on that side, while the river protected the peninsula by its

** SENECA, 2, 79.

semicircular bend on the other, was evidently one reason why the Romans fixed upon the site of Doncaster for a station. In Brockett's Glossary of North-Country words, Carr is interpreted to mean "flat marshy land; a pool or lake;" but the etymology of the word is yet to be discovered.

These fens were drained and enclosed pursuant to an act of Parliament which was obtained for that purpose in the year 1766. Three principal drains were then cut, fourteen feet wide, and about four miles long, into which the water was conducted from every part of the Carr, southward, to the little river Torne, at Rossington Bridge, whence it flows into the Trent. Before these drainings the ground was liable to frequent inundations, and about the centre there was a decoy for wild ducks: there is still a deep water there of considerable extent, in which very large pike and eels are found. The soil, which was so boggy at first that horses were lost when attempting to drink at the drains, has been brought into good cultivation (as all such ground may be) to the great improvement of the district; for till this improvement was effected intermittent fevers and sore throats were prevalent there, and they have ceased from the time that the land was drained. The most unhealthy season now is the Spring, when cold winds from the North and North East usually prevail during some six weeks; at other times Doncaster is considered to be a healthy place. It has been observed that when endemic diseases arrive there, they uniformly come from the south; and that the state of the weather may be foretold from a knowledge of what it has been at a given time in London, making an allowance of about three days, for the chance of winds. Here, as in all places which lie upon a great and frequented road, the transmission of diseases has been greatly facilitated by the increase of travelling.

But before we leave Potteric Carr, let us try, reader, whether we cannot improve it in another way, that is, in the dissenting and so-called evangelical sense of the word, in which sense the battle of Trafalgar was improved, in a sermon by the Reverend John Evans. Gentle Reader, let you and I in like manner endeavour to improve this enclosure of the Carr.

Four thousand acres of bog whereof that Carr consisted, and upon which common sand, coal ashes, and the scrapings of a limestone road were found the best manure, produce now good crops of grain, and excellent pasturage.

There are said to be in England and Wales at this time 3,984,000 acres of uncultivated but cultivable ground; 5,950,000 in Scotland; 4,900,000 in Ireland; 166,000 in the smaller British Islands. Crags, woods, and barren land are not included in this statement. Here are 15,000,000 acres, the worst of which is as good as the morass which has been reclaimed near Doncaster, and the far greater part very materially better.

I address myself now to any one of my readers who pays poor rates; but more especially to him who has any part in the disposal of those rates; and most especially to a clergyman, a magistrate, and a member of Parliament.

The money which is annually raised for poor-rates in England and Wales has for some years amounted to from five to six millions. With all this expenditure cases are continually occurring of death from starvation, either of hunger or cold, or both together; wretches are carried before the magistrates for the offence of lying in the streets or in unfinished houses, when they have not where to hide their heads; others have been found dead by the side of limekilns, or brickkilns, whither they had crept to save themselves from perishing for cold; and untold numbers die of the diseases produced by scanty and unwholesome food.

This money, moreover, is for the most part so applied, that they who have a rightful claim upon it, receive less than in justice, in humanity, and according to the intent of a law wisely and humanely enacted, ought to be their portion; while they who have only a legal claim upon it, that claim arising from an evil usage which has become prescriptive, receive pay, where justice, policy, and considerate humanity, and these very laws themselves, if rightly administered, would award restraint or punishment.

Thus it is in those parts of the United Kingdom, where a provision for the poor is directly raised by law. In Scotland the proportion of paupers is little less, and the evils attendant upon poverty are felt in an equal or nearly equal degree. In Ireland they exist to a far greater extent, and may truly be called terrible.

Is it fitting that this should be while there are fifteen millions of cultivable acres lying waste? Is it possible to conceive grosser improvidence in a nation, grosser folly, grosser ignorance of its duty and interest, or grosser neglect of both, than are manifested in the continuance and growth and increase of this enormous evil, when the means of checking it are so obvious, and that too by a process in which every step must produce direct and tangible good?

But while the Government is doing those things which it ought not to have done, and leaves undone those which it ought to do, let Parishes and Corporations do what is in their power for themselves. And bestir yourselves in this good work, ye who can! The supineness of the Government is no excuse for you. It is in the exertions of individuals that all national reformation must begin. Go to work cautiously, experimentally, patiently, charitably, and in faith! I am neither so enthusiastic as to suppose, nor so rash as to assert, that a cure may thus be found for the complicated evils arising from the condition of the labouring classes. But it is one of those remedial means by which much misery may be relieved, and much of that profligacy that arises from hopeless wretchedness be prevented. It is one of those means from which present relief may be obtained, and future good expected. It is the readiest way in which useful employment can be provided for the industrious poor. And if the land so appropriated should produce nothing more than is required for the support of those employed in cultivating it, and who must otherwise be partly or wholly supported by the poor-rates, such cultivation would, even then, be profitable to the public. Wherever there is heath, moor or fen,—which there is in every part of the Island,—there is work for the spade; employment and subsistence for man is to be found there, and room for him to encrease and multiply for generations.

Reader, if you doubt that bog and bad land may be profitably cultivated, go and look at Potteric Carr, (the members of both Houses who attend Doncaster Races, may spare an hour for this at the next meeting). If you desire to know in what manner the poor who are now helpless may be settled upon such land, so as immediately to earn their own maintenance, and in a short time to repay the first cost of their establishment, read the account of the Pauper Colonies in Holland; for there the experiment has been tried, and we have the benefit of their experience.

As for the whole race of Political Economists, our Malthusites, Benthamites, Utilitarians or Futilitarians, they are to the Government of this Country such counsellors as the magicians were to Pharaoh; whosoever listens to them has his heart hardened.—But they are no conjurors.

CHAPTER XXXVI. P. I.

REMARKS ON AN OPINION OF MR. CRABBE'S. TOPOGRAPHICAL POETRY. DRAYTON.

Do, pious marble, let thy readers know
What they and what their children owe
To Drayton's name, whose sacred dust
We recommend unto thy trust.
Protect his memory, and preserve his story;
Remain a lasting monument of his glory;
And when thy ruins shall disclaim
To be the Treasurer of his name,
His name that cannot fade, shall be
An everlasting monument to thee.

EPITAPH IN WESTMINSTER ABBEY.

THE Poet Crabbe has said that there subsists an utter repugnancy between the studies of topography and poetry. He must have intended by topography, when he said so, the mere definition of boundaries and specification of land-marks, such as are given in the advertisement of an estate for sale; and boys in certain parts of the country are taught to bear in mind by a remembrance in tail when the bounds of a parish are walked by the local authorities. Such topography indeed bears as little relation to poetry as a map or chart to a picture.

But if he had any wider meaning, it is evident, by the number of topographical poems, good, bad and indifferent, with which our language abounds, that Mr. Crabbe's predecessors in verse, and his contemporaries also, have differed greatly from him in opinion upon this point. The Poly-olbion, notwithstanding its common-place personifications and its inartificial transitions, which are as abrupt as those in the Metamorphoses and the Fasti, and not so graceful, is nevertheless a work as much to be valued by the students and lovers of English literature, as by the writers of local history. Drayton himself, whose great talents were deservedly esteemed by the ablest of his contemporaries in the richest age of English poetry, thought he could not be more worthily employed than in what he calls the Herculean task of this topographical poem; and in that belief he was encouraged by his friend and commentator Selden, to whose name the epithet of learned was in old times always and deservedly affixed. With how becoming a sense of its dignity and variety the Poet entered upon his subject, these lines may shew:

Thou powerful God of flames, in verse divinely great,
Touch my invention so with thy true genuine heat,
That high and noble things I slightly may not tell,
Nor light and idle toys my lines may vainly swell;
But as my subject serves so high or low to strain,
And to the varying earth so suit my varying strain,
That Nature in my work thou mayest thy power avow;
That as thou first found'st art, and didst her rules allow,
So I, to thine own self that gladly near would be,
May herein do the best in imitating thee.
As thou hast here a hill, a vale there, there a flood,
A mead here, there a heath, and now and then a wood,
These things so in my song I naturally may show
Now as the mountain high, then as the valley low;
Here fruitful as the mead; there as the heath be bare,
Then as the gloomy wood I may be rough, tho' rare.

I would not say of this Poet, as Kirkpatrick says of him, that when he

— his Albion sung
With their own praise the echoing vallies rung;
His bounding Muse o'er every mountain rode,
And every river warbled where he flowed;

but I may say that if instead of sending his Muse to ride over the mountains, and resting contented with her report, he had ridden or walked over them himself, his poem would better have deserved that praise for accuracy which has been bestowed upon it by critics who had themselves no knowledge which could enable them to say whether it were accurate or not. Camden was more diligent; he visited some of the remotest counties of which he wrote.

This is not said with any intention of detracting from Michael Drayton's fame: the most elaborate criticism could neither raise him above the station which he holds in English literature, nor degrade him from it. He is extolled not beyond the just measure of his deserts in his epitaph, which has been variously ascribed to Ben Jonson, to Randolph, and to Quarles, but with most probability to the former, who knew and admired and loved him.

He was a poet by nature, and carefully improved his talent; — one who sedulously laboured to deserve the approbation of such as were capable of appreciating, and cared nothing for the censures which others might pass upon him. "Like me that list," he says,

— my honest rhymes,
Nor care for critics, nor regard the times.

And though he is not a poet *virûm volitare per ora*, nor one of those whose better fortune it is to live in the hearts of their devoted admirers, yet what he deemed his greatest work will be preserved by its subject; some of his minor poems have merit enough in their execution to ensure their preservation, and no one who studies poetry as an art will think his time mis-spent in perusing the whole, — if he have any real love for the art which he is pursuing. The youth who enters upon that pursuit without a feeling of respect and gratitude for those elder poets, who by their labours have prepared the way for him, is not likely to produce any thing himself that will be held in remembrance by posterity.

CHAPTER XXXVII. P. I.

ANECDOTES OF PETER HEYLYN AND LIGHTFOOT, EXEMPLIFYING THAT GREAT KNOWLEDGE IS NOT ALWAYS APPLICABLE TO LITTLE THINGS: AND THAT AS CHARITY BEGINS AT HOME, SO IT MAY WITH EQUAL TRUTH SOMETIMES BE SAID THAT KNOWLEDGE ENDS THERE.

A scholar in his study knows the stars,
Their motion and their influence, which are fix'd,
And which are wandering; can decypher seas,
And give each several land his proper bounds:
But set him to the compass, he's to seek,
Where a plain pilot can direct his course
From hence unto both the Indies. HEYWOOD.

THERE was a Poet who wrote a descriptive poem, and then took a journey to see the scenes which he had described. Better late then never, he thought; and thought wisely in so thinking. Drayton was not likely to have acted thus upon after consideration, if in the first conception of his subject he did not feel sufficient ardour for such an undertaking. It would have required indeed a spirit of enterprise as unusual in those days as it is ordinary now. Many a long day's ride must he have taken over rough roads, and in wild countries; and many a weary step would it have cost him, and many a poor lodging must he have put up with at night, where he would have found poor fare, if not cold comfort. So he thought it enough, in many if not most parts, to travel by the map, and believed himself to have been sufficiently "punctual and exact in giving unto every province its peculiar bounds, in laying out their several landmarks, tracing the course of most of the principal rivers, and setting forth the situation and estate of the chiefest towns."

Peter Heylyn, who speaks thus of his own exactness in a work partaking enough of the same nature as the Poly-olbion to be remembered here, though it be in prose and upon a wider subject, tells a humorous anecdote of himself, in the preface to his Cosmography. "He that shall think this work imperfect," says he, "(though I confess it to be nothing but imperfections) for some deficiencies of this kind, may be likened to the country fellow, (in Aristophanes, if my memory fail not), who picked a great quarrel with the map because he could not find where his own farm stood. And such a country customer I did meet with once, a servant of my elder brother, sent by him with some horses to Oxford, to bring me and a friend of mine unto his house; who having lost his way as we passed through the forest of Whichwood, and not being able to recover any beaten track, did very earnestly entreat me to lead the way, till I had brought him past the woods to the open fields. Which when I had refused to do, as I had good reason, alledging that I had never been there before, and therefore that I could not tell which way to lead him; 'that's strange!' said he; 'I have heard my old master, your father, say that you made a book of all the world; and cannot you find your way out of the wood?'"

Peter Heylyn was one who fell on evil times, and on whom, in consequence, evil tongues have fallen. But he was an able, honest, brave man, who "stood to his tackling when he was tasted." And if thou hast not read his Survey of the State of France, Reader, thou hast not read one of our liveliest books of travels in its lighter parts; and one of the wisest and most replete with information that ever was written by a young man.

His more learned contemporary Lightfoot, who steered a safer but not so straight a course, met with an adventure not unlike that of Heylyn's in the forest; but the application which in the cosmographist's case was ridiculously made by an ignorant and simple man, was in this instance self-originated.

Lightfoot had promised to set forth as an accompaniment to his Harmony of the Evangelists, "A chorographical description of the land of Canaan, and those adjoining places, that we have occasion to look upon as we read the Gospels."—"I went on in that work," he says, "a good while, and that with much cheerfulness and content! for methought a Talmudical survey and history of the land of Canaan, (not omitting collections to be taken up out of the Scripture, and other writers,) as it would be new and rare, so it might not prove unwelcome nor unprofitable to those that delighted in such a subject."—It cost him as much pains to give the description as it would have done to travel thither; but says one of his Editors, "the unhappy chance that hindered the publishing this elaborate piece of his, which he had brought to pretty good perfection, was the edition of Doctor Fuller's Pisgah Sight; great pity it was that so good a book should have done so much harm; for that book, handling the same matters and preventing his, stopped his resolution of letting his labours on that subject see the light. Though he went a way altogether different from Dr. Fuller; and so both might have shown their face together in the world; and the younger sister, if we may make comparisons, might have proved the fairer of the two."

It is pleasant to see how liberally and equitably both Lightfoot and Fuller speak upon this matter; — "But at last, says the former, I understood that another workman, a far better artist than myself, had the description of the Land of Israel, not only in hand, but even in the press; and was so far got before me in that travel that he was almost at his journey's end, when I was but little more than setting out. It was grievous to me to have lost my labour, if I should now sit down; and yet I thought it wisdom not to lose more in proceeding farther, when one on the same subject, and of far more abilities in it, had got the start so far before me.

"And although I supposed, and at last was assured, even by that Author himself (my very learned and worthy friend) that we should not thrust nor hinder one another any whit at all, though we both went at once in the perambulation of that land, because he had not meddled with that Rabbinic way that I had gone; yet, when I considered what it was to glean after so clean a reaper, and how rough a Talmudical pencil would seem after so fine a pen, I resolved to sit down, and to stir no more in that matter, till time and occasion did show me more encouragement thereunto, than as yet I saw. And thus was my promise fallen to the ground, not by any carelessness or forgetfulness of mine, but by the happy prevention of another hand, by whom the work is likely to be better done. Yet was I unwilling to suffer my word utterly to come to nothing at all, though I might evade my promise by this fair excuse: but I was desirous to pay the reader something in pursuance of it, though it were not in this very same coin, nor the very same sum, that I had undertaken. Hereupon I turned my thoughts and my endeavours to a description of the Temple after the same manner, and from the same authors, that I had intended to have described the Land; and that the rather, not only that I might do some thing towards making good my promise; but also, that by a trial in a work of this nature of a lesser bulk, I might take some pattern and assay how the other, which would prove of a far larger pains and volume, would be accepted, if I should again venture upon it."

Lightfoot was sincere in the commendation which he bestowed upon Fuller's diligence, and his felicitous way of writing. And Fuller on his part rendered justice in the same spirit to Lightfoot's well known and peculiar erudition. "Far be it from me," he says, "that our pens should fall out, like the herdsmen of Lot and Abraham, the land not being able to bear them both, that they might dwell together. No such want of room in this subject, being of such latitude and receipt, that both we and hundreds more, busied together therein, may severally lose ourselves in a subject of such capacity. The rather, because we embrace several courses in this our description; it being my desire and delight, to stick only to the written word of God, whilst my worthy friend takes in the choicest Rabbinical and Talmudical relations, being so well seen in these studies, that it is questionable whether his skill or my ignorance be the greater therein."

Now then—(for now and then go thus lovingly together, in familiar English)—after these preliminaries, the learned Lightfoot, who at seven years of age, it is said, could not only read fluently the biblical Hebrew, but readily converse in it, may tell his own story.

"Here by the way," he says, "I cannot but mention, and I think I can never forget, a handsome and deserved check that mine own heart, meeting with a special occasion, did give me, upon the laying down of the other task, and the undertaking of this, for my daring to enter either upon the one or the other. That very day wherein I first set pen to paper to draw up the description of the Temple, having but immediately before laid aside my thoughts of the description of the Land, I was necessarily called out, towards the evening, to go to view a piece of ground of mine own, concerning which some litigiousness was emerging, and about to grow. The field was but a mile from my constant residence and habitation, and it had been in mine owning divers years together; and yet till that very time, had I never seen it, nor looked after it, nor so much as knew whereabout it lay. It was very unlikely I should find it out myself, being so utterly ignorant of its situation; yet because I desired to walk alone, for the enjoying of my thoughts upon that task that I had newly taken in hand, I took some direction which way to go, and would venture to find out the field myself alone. I had not gone far, but I was at a loss; and whether I went right or wrong I could not tell; and if right thither, yet I knew not how to do so farther; and if wrong, I knew not which way would prove the right, and so in seeking my ground I had lost myself. Here my heart could not but take me to task; and, reflecting upon what my studies were then, and had lately been upon, it could not but call me fool; and methought it spake as true to me, as ever it had done in all my life,—but only when it called me sinner. A fool that was so studious, and had been so searching about things remote, and that so little concerned my interest,—and yet was so neglective of what was near me, both in place, and in my particular concernment! And a fool again, who went about to describe to others, places and buildings that lay so many hundred miles off, as from hence to Canaan, and under so many hundred years' ruins,—and yet was not able to know, or find the way to a field of mine own, that lay so near me!

"I could not but acknowledge this reproof to be both seasonable, and seasoned both with truth and reason; and it so far prevailed with me, that it not only put me upon a resolution to lay by that work that I had newly taken in hand that morning, but also to be wiser in my bookishness for the time to come, than for it, and through it, to neglect and sink my estate as I had done. And yet within a little time after, I know not how, I was fallen to the same studies and studiousness again,—had got my laid-up task into my hands again before I was aware,—and was come to a determination to go on in that work, because I had my notes and collections ready by me as materials for it; and when that was done, then to think of the advice that my heart had given me, and to look to mine own business.

"So I drew up the description of the Temple itself, and with it the History of the Temple-service."

Lightfoot's heart was wise when it admonished him of humility; but it was full of deceit when it read him a lesson of worldly wisdom, for which his conscience and his better mind would have said to him "Thou Fool!" if he had followed it.

CHAPTER XXXVIII.

THE READER IS LED TO INFER THAT A TRAVELLER WHO STOPS UPON THE WAY TO SKETCH, BOTANISE, ENTOMOLOGISE, OR MINERALOGISE, TRAVELS WITH MORE PLEASURE AND PROFIT TO HIMSELF THAN IF HE WERE IN THE MAIL COACH.

Non servio materiæ sed indulgeo; quam quo ducit sequendum est, non quo invitat. SENECA.

FEAR not, my patient reader, that I should lose myself and bewilder you, either in the Holy land, or Whichwood forest, or in the wide fields of the Poly-olbion, or in Potteric Carr, or in any part of the country about Doncaster, most fortunate of English towns for circumstances which I have already stated and henceforth to be the most illustrious, as having been the place where my never-to-be-forgotten Philosopher and friend passed the greater part of his innocent and useful and happy life. Good patient reader, you may confide in me as in one who always knows his whereabout, and whom the Goddess Upibilia will keep in the right way.

In treating of that flourishing and every way fortunate town, I have not gone back to visionary times, like the author who wrote a description and drew a map of Anglesea as it was before the flood. Nor have I touched upon the ages when hyenas prowled over what is now Doncaster race-ground, and great lizards, huge as crocodiles, but with long necks and short tails, took their pleasure in Potteric Carr. I have not called upon thee, gentle and obsequious reader, to accompany me into a Præadamite world, nor even into the antediluvian one. We began with the earliest mention of Doncaster, — no earlier; and shall carry our summary notices of its history to the Doctor's time, — no later. And if sometimes the facts on which I may touch should call forth thoughts, and those thoughts remind me of other facts, anecdotes leading to reflection, and reflection producing more anecdotes, thy pleasure will be consulted in all this, my good and patient reader, and thy profit also as much as mine; nay, more in truth, for I might think upon all these things in silence, and spare myself the trouble of relating them.

> O Reader, had you in your mind
> Such stores as silent thought can bring,
> O gentle Reader, you would find
> A Tale in every thing! *

I might muse upon these things and let the hours pass by unheeded as the waters of a river in their endless course. And thus I might live in other years, — with those who are departed, in a world of my own, by force of recollection; — or by virtue of sure hope in that world which is their's now, and to which I shall, ere long, be promoted.

For thy pleasure, Reader, and for thy improvement, I take upon myself the pains of thus materialising my spiritual stores. Alas! their earthly uses would perish with me unless they were thus embodied!

"The age of a cultivated mind," says an eloquent and wise and thoughtful author, "is often more complacent and even more luxurious, than the youth. It is the reward of the due use of the endowments bestowed by nature: while they who in youth have made no provision for age, are left like an unsheltered tree, stripped of its leaves and its branches, shaking and withering before the cold blasts of winter.

"In truth, nothing is so happy to itself, and so attractive to others, as a genuine and ripened imagination, that knows its own powers, and throws forth its treasures with frankness and fearlessness. The more it produces, the more capable it becomes of production; the creative faculty grows by indulgence; and the more it combines, the more means and varieties of combinations it discovers.

"When death comes to destroy that mysterious and magical union of capacities and acquirements which has brought a noble genius to this point of power, how frightful and lamentable is the effect of the stroke that stops the current which was wont to

* WORDSWORTH.

put this mighty formation into activity! Perhaps the incomprehensible Spirit may have acted in conjunction with its corporeal adherents to the last. Then in one moment, what darkness and destruction follows a single gasp of breath!" *

This fine passage is as consolatory in its former part, as it is gloomy at the conclusion; and it is gloomy there, because the view which is there taken is imperfect. Our thoughts, our reminiscences, our intellectual acquirements, die with us to this world,—but to this world only. If they are what they ought to be, they are treasures which we lay up for Heaven. That which is of the earth, earthy, perishes with wealth, rank, honours, authority, and other earthly and perishable things; but nothing that is worth retaining can be lost. When Ovid says, in Ben Jonson's play,—

> We pour out our affections with our blood,
> And with our blood's affections fade our loves,

the dramatist makes the Roman Poet speak like a sensualist, as he was, and the philosophy is as false as it is foul. Affections well placed and dutifully cherished; friendships happily formed and faithfully maintained; knowledge acquired with worthy intent, and intellectual powers that have been diligently improved as the talents which our Lord and Master has committed to our keeping: these will accompany us into another state of existence, as surely as the soul in that state retains its identity and its consciousness.

INTERCHAPTER IV.

ETYMOLOGICAL DISCOVERIES CONCERNING THE REMAINS OF VARIOUS TRIBES OR FAMILIES MENTIONED IN SCRIPTURAL HISTORY.

> All things are big with jest; nothing that's plain
> But may be witty if thou hast the vein. HERBERT.

THAT the lost Ten Tribes of Israel may be found in London, is a discovery which any person may suppose he has made, when he walks for the first time from the city to Wapping. That the tribes of Judah and Benjamin flourish there is known to all mankind; and from them have sprung the Scripites, and the Omniumites, and the Threepercentites.

But it is not so well known that many other tribes noticed in the Old Testament are to be found in this Island of Great Britain.

There are the Hittites, who excel in one branch of gymnastics. And there are the Amorites, who are to be found in town and country; and there are the Gadites, who frequent watering places, and take picturesque tours.

Among the Gadites I shall have some of my best readers, who, being in good humour with themselves and with every thing else, except on a rainy day, will even then be in good humour with me. There will be Amorites in their company; and among the Amorites, too, there will be some, who, in the overflowing of their love, will have some liking to spare for the Doctor and his faithful memorialist.

The Poets, those especially who deal in erotics, lyrics, sentimentals or sonnets, are the Ah-oh-ites.

The gentlemen who speculate in chapels are the Puh-ites.

The chief seat of the Simeonites is at Cambridge; but they are spread over the land. So are the Man-ass-ites, of whom the finest specimens are to be seen in St. James's-Street, at the fashionable time of day for exhibiting the dress and the person upon the pavement.

The free-masons are of the family of the Jachinites.

The female Haggites are to be seen in low life wheeling barrows, and in high life seated at card tables.

The Shuhamites are the cordwainers.

The Teamanites attend the sales of the East India Company.

Sir James Mackintosh, and Sir James Scarlett, and Sir James Graham, belong to the Jim-nites.

Who are the Gazathites if the people of

---

* SIR EGERTON BRYDGES.

London are not, where any thing is to be seen? All of them are Gettites when they can, all would be Havites if they could.

The journalists should be Geshurites, if they answered to their profession: instead of this they generally turn out to be Geshu-wrongs.

There are, however, three Tribes in England, not named in the Old Testament, who considerably outnumber all the rest. These are the High Vulgarites, who are the children of Rahank and Phashan; the Middle Vulgarites, who are the children of Mammon and Terade, and the Low Vulgarites, who are the children of Tahag, Rahag, and Bohobtay-il.

With the Low Vulgarites I have no concern, but with the other two tribes, much. Well it is that some of those who are *fruges consumere nati*, think it proper that they should consume books also: if they did not, what a miserable creature wouldst thou be, Henry Colburn, who art their Bookseller! I myself have that kind of respect for the consumers which we ought to feel for every thing useful. If not the salt of the earth they are its manure, without which it could not produce so abundantly.

CHAPTER XXXIX.

A CHAPTER FOR THE INFORMATION OF THOSE WHO MAY VISIT DONCASTER, AND ESPECIALLY OF THOSE WHO FREQUENT THE RACES THERE.

> My good Lord, there is a Corporation,
> A body, — a kind of body. MIDDLETON.

WELL, reader, I have told thee something concerning the topography of Doncaster: and now in due order, and as in duty bound, will I give thee a sketch of its history; "*summa sequar fastigia rerum*," with becoming brevity, according to my custom, and in conformity with the design of this book. The Nobility and Gentry who attend the races there, will find it very agreeable to be well acquainted with every thing relating to the place; and I particularly invite their attention to that part of the present chapter which concerns the Doncaster charters, because as a wise and ancient author hath said, *turpe est homini nobili ejus civitatis in quâ versetur, jus ignorare*, which may be thus applied, that every gentleman who frequents Doncaster races ought to know the form and history of its corporation.

In Edward the Confessor's reign, the soccage part of Doncaster and of some adjoining townships was under the manor of Hexthorp, though in the topsy-turveying course of time Hexthorp has become part of the soke of Doncaster. Earl Tostig was the Lord of that manor, one of Earl Godwin's sons, and one who holds, like his father, no honourable place in the records of those times, but who in the last scene of his life displayed a heroism that may well redeem his name. The manor being two miles and a half long, and one and a half broad, was valued at eighteen pounds yearly rent; but when Doomsday book was compiled that rent had decreased one third. It had then been given by the Conqueror to his half-brother Robert Earl of Montaigne in Normandy, and of Cornwall in England. The said Earl was a lay-pluralist of the first magnitude, and had no fewer than seven hundred and fifty manors bestowed upon him as his allotment of the conquered kingdom. He granted the lordship and soke of Doncaster with many other possessions to Nigel de Fossard, which Nigel is believed to have been the Saxon noble who at the time of the conquest held these same possessions under the crown.

The Fossard family ended in an heiress in Cœur-de-Lion's reign; and the only daughter of that heiress was given in marriage by John Lackland to Peter de Malolieu or Maulay, as a reward for his part in the murder of Prince Arthur. Peter de Maulay bore, as such a service richly deserved, an ill name in the nation, being moreover a favourite of King John's, and believed to be one of his evil counsellors as well as of his wicked instruments: but the name was in good odour with his descendants, and was borne accordingly by eight Peters in succession. The eighth had no male issue; he left two daughters, and daughters are said by Fuller to be "silent strings, sending no sound to posterity, but losing their own surnames in their matches." Ralph Salvayne or Salvin, a descendant of the younger coheiress, in the reign of James I., claimed the Lordship of Doncaster; and William his son after a long suit with the Corporation, resigned his claim for a large sum of money.

The Burgesses had obtained their Charter from Richard I., in the fifth year of his reign, that king confirming to them their Soke, and Town or Village of Danecastre, to hold of him and his heirs, by the ancient rent, and over and above that rent, by an annual payment at the same time of twenty-five marks of silver. For this grant the Burgesses gave the king fifty marks of silver, and were thereby entitled to hold their Soke and Town "effectually and peaceably, freely and quietly, fully and honourably, with all the liberties and free customs to the same appertaining, so that none hereupon might them disturb." This charter, with all and singular the things therein contained, was ratified and confirmed by Richard II., to his beloved the then Burgesses of the aforesaid Town.

The Burgesses fearing that they might be molested in the enjoyment of these their liberties and free customs, through defect of a declaration and specification of the same, petitioned Edward IV., in the seventh year of his reign, that he would graciously condescend those liberties and free customs, under specifical declaration and express terms, to them and their heirs and successors, incorporating them, and making them persons fit and capable, with perpetual succession. Accordingly the king granted that Doncaster should be a free borough, and that the burgesses, tenants, resiants, and inhabitants and their successors, should be free burgesses and might have a Gild Merchant, and continue to have the same liberties and free customs, as they and their predecessors had theretofore reasonably used and enjoyed. And that they from thenceforth might be, in reality and name, one body and one perpetual community; and every year choose out of themselves one fit person to be the Mayor, and two other fit persons for the Serjeants at Mace, of the same town, within the same town dwelling, to rule and govern the community aforesaid, for ever. And further of his more abundant grace the king granted that the cognizance of all manner of pleas of debt, trespass, covenant, and all manner of other causes and contracts whatsoever within the same borough, should be holden before the Mayor. He granted also to the corporation the power of attachment for debt, by their Serjeants at Mace; and of his abundant grace that the Mayor should hold and exercise the office of Coroner also, during his year; and should be also a Justice and Keeper of the King's peace within the said borough. And he granted them of his same abundant grace the right of having a Fair at the said Borough every year upon the vigil, and upon the feast, and upon the morrow of the Annunciation of the Blessed Virgin Mary, to be held, and for the same three days to continue, with all liberties and free customs to this sort of fair appertaining, unless that fair should be to the detriment of the neighbouring fairs.

There appear to this Charter among others as witnesses, the memorable names of "our dearest brothers, George of Clarence, and Richard of Gloucester, Dukes; Richard Wydeville de Ryvers, our Treasurer of England, Earl; and our beloved and faithful William Hastynges de Hastynges, Chamberlain of our Household, and Anthony Wydevile de Scales, Knights. The charter is moreover decorated with the armorial bearings of the Corporation, a Lion sejeant, upon a cushion powdered ermine, holding in his paws and legs a banner with the castle thereon depicted, and this motto, *Son Comfort et Liesse*, his Comfort and Joy.

Henry VII. enlarged the charter, giving of his special grace, to the Mayor and Community all and singular the messuages, marshes, lands, tenements, rents, reversions and services, advowsons of churches, chantries and chapels, possessions and all hereditaments whatsoever within the Lordship and its dependencies, "with the court-leets, view-of-frank-pledges-courts, waters, mills, entry and discharge of waters, fairs, markets, tolls, picages, stallages, pontages, passages, and all and singular profits, commodities and emoluments whatsoever within that lordship and its precincts to the King, his heirs and successors howsoever appertaining, or lately belonging. And all and singular the issues, revenues, and profits of the aforesaid courts, view of frank pledge, waters, mills, fairs, markets, tolls, picages, stallages, pontages, passages, and the rest of the premises in what manner so ever accruing or arising." For this the Mayor and Community were to pay into the Exchequer yearly in equal portions, at the feasts of St. Michael the Archangel, and Easter, without fee, or any other charge, the sum of seventy and four pounds, thirteen shillings eleven pence and a halfpenny. Further of his more extensive grace, he granted them to hold twice in every year a leet or view of frank pledge; and that they might have the superintendency of the assize of bread and ale, and other victuals vendible whatsoever, and the correction and punishment of the same, and all and whatsoever, which to a leet or view of frank pledge appertaineth, or ought to appertain. And that they might have all issues and profits and perquisites, fines, penalties, redemptions, forfeitures, and amerciaments in all and singular these kind of leets, or frank pledge to be forfeited, or assessed, or imposed; and moreover wayf, strayf, infang-thief, and outfang-thief; and the goods and chattels of all and singular felons, and the goods of fugitives, convicts and attainted, and the goods and chattels of outlaws and waived; and the wreck of sea when it should happen, and goods and chattels whatsoever confiscated within the manor, lordship, soke, towns, villages, and the rest of the premises of the precincts of the same, and of every of them found, or to be found for ever."

In what way any wreck of sea could be thrown upon any part of the Doncastrian jurisdiction is a question which might have occasioned a curious discussion between Corporal Trim and his good master. How it could happen I cannot comprehend, unless "the fatal Welland," according to old saw,

> ——— which God forbid!
> Should drown all Holland with his excrement.*

Nor indeed do I see how it could happen then, unless Humber should at the same time drown all Lindsey, and the whole of the Yorkshire plain, and Trent bear a part also with all his thirty tributary streams, and the plain land of all the midland counties be once more flooded, "as it was in the days of Noah." But if the official person who drew up this charter of Henry the Seventh contemplated any such contingency, he must have been a whimsical person; and moreover an unreasonable one not to have considered that Doncaster itself must be destroyed by such a catastrophe, and consequently that its corporation even then could derive no benefit from wreck at sea.

Further of his more abundant grace King Henry granted to the Mayor and Community that they might hold two markets in the week for ever, to wit every Tuesday and every Saturday; and that they might hold a second fair, which was to be upon the vigil, and upon the day of St. James the Apostle, and upon the morrow of the day immediately following to continue: and that they might choose a Recorder; and hold a weekly court in their Guild Hall, which court should be a Court of Record: and that the Recorder and three of the Aldermen should be Justices as well as the Mayor, and that they might have a gaol within the precincts of their town.

Henry VIII. confirmed this his father's charter, and Elizabeth that her father's confirmation. In the next reign when the corporation, after having "endured the charge of many great and tedious suits," had compounded with Ralph Salvin for what they called his pretended title, they petitioned the King that he would be pleased to accept from them a surrender of their estates, together with an assurance of Salvin's title, and then graciously assure and convey the

* Spenser.

said manors and premises to them and their successors, so to secure them against any farther litigation.

This accordingly was done. In the fourth year after the Restoration the Mayor, Aldermen and Burgesses petitioned for a ratification of their existing privileges and for an enlargement of them, which Charles II. granted, "the borough being an ancient and populous borough, and he being desirous that for the time to come, for ever, one certain and invariable method might be had of, for, and in the preservation of our peace, and in the rule and governance of the same borough, and of our people in the same inhabiting, and of others resorting thither; and that that borough in succeeding times, might be, and remain a borough of harmony and peace, to the fear and terror of the wicked, and for the support and reward of the good." Wherefore he the King of his special grace, certain knowledge and mere motion, willed, granted, constituted, declared and confirmed, and by his then presents did will, grant, constitute, declare and confirm, that Doncaster should be, and continue for ever, a free borough itself; and that the Mayor and community, or commonalty thereof, should be one body corporate and politic in reality, deed and name, by the name of Mayor, Aldermen and Burgesses of the borough of Doncaster in the County of York, and by that name be capacitated and enabled to plead, and to be impleaded, answer and be answered; defend and be defended; and to have, purchase, receive, possess, give, grant and demise."

This body corporate and politic, which was to have perpetual succession, was by the Charter appointed to consist of one Mayor, twelve Aldermen, and twenty-four capital Burgesses, the Aldermen to be "of the better and more excellent inhabitants of the borough," and the capital Burgesses of the better, more reputable and discreet, and these latter were to be "for ever in perpetual future times, the Common Council of the borough." The three Estates of the Borough as they may be called, in court or convocation gathered together and assembled, were invested with full authority, power, and ability of granting, constituting, ordaining, making, and rendering firm, from time to time, such kind of laws, institutes, bye-laws, ordinances, and constitutions, which to them, or the greater part of them, shall seem to be, according to their sound understandings, good, salutary, profitable, honest, or honourable, and necessary for the good rule and governance of the Mayor, Aldermen, and Burgesses, and of all and singular, and other the inhabitants of the borough aforesaid; and of all the officers, ministers, artificers, and resiants whatsoever within the borough aforesaid, for the time being; and for the declaring in what manner and form, the aforesaid Mayor, Aldermen, and Burgesses, and all and singular other the ministers, officers, artificers, inhabitants, and resiants of the borough aforesaid, and their factors or agents, servants and apprentices, in their offices, callings, mysteries, artifices, and businesses, within the borough aforesaid, and the liberties of the same for the time being, shall have, behave, and use themselves, and otherwise for the more ultimate public good, common utility and good regimen of the borough aforesaid." And for the victualling of the borough, and for the better preservation, governance, disposing, letting, and demising of the lands, tenements, possessions, revenues, and hereditaments, vested in their body corporate, they had power to ordain and enforce such punishments, penalties, inflictions, and imprisonments of the body, or by fines and amerciaments, or by both of them, against and upon all delinquents and offenders against these their laws as might to them seem necessary, so that nevertheless this kind of laws, ordinances, institutions, and constitutions, be not repugnant, nor contrary to the laws and statutes of the kingdom.

Persons refusing to accept the office of Mayor, Alderman, Capital Burgess, or any other inferior office of the borough, except the Recorders, might be committed to gaol, till they consented to serve, or fined at the discretion of the Corporation, and held fast in their gaol till the fine was paid.

This Charter also empowered the Corporation to keep a fair on the Saturday before Easter, and thenceforth on every alternate Saturday until the feast of St. Andrew, for cattle, and to hold at such times a court of pie-powder.

James II. confirmed the corporation in all their rights and privileges, and by the Charter of Charles II., thus confirmed, Doncaster is governed at this day.

It was during the mayoralty of Thomas Pheasant that Daniel Dove took up his abode in Doncaster.

CHAPTER XL. P. I.

REMARKS ON THE ART OF VERBOSITY. A RULE OF COCCEIUS, AND ITS APPLICATION TO THE LANGUAGE AND PRACTICE OF THE LAW.

If they which employ their labour and travail about the public administration of justice, follow it only as a trade, with unquenchable and unconscionable thirst of gain, being not in heart persuaded that justice is God's own work, and themselves his agents in this business, — the sentence of right, God's own verdict, and themselves his priests to deliver it; formalities of justice do but serve to smother right, and that which was necessarily ordained for the common good, is through shameful abuse made the cause of common misery. HOOKER.

READER, thou mayest perhaps have thought me at times disposed to be circumambagious in my manner of narration. But now, having cast thine eyes over the Doncaster charters, even in the abridged form in which I have considerately presented them, thou knowest what a round-about style is when amplified with all possible varieties of professional tautology.

You may hear it exemplified to a certain degree, in most sermons of the current standard, whether composed by those who inflict them upon their congregation, or purchased ready made and warranted orthodox as well as original. In a still greater degree you may hear it in the extempore prayers of any meeting-house, and in those with which the so-called Evangelical Clergymen of the Establishment think proper sometimes to prologize and epilogize their grievous discourses. But in tautology the Lawyers beat the Divines hollow.

Cocceius laid it down as a fundamental rule of interpretation in theology, that the words and phrases of scripture are to be understood in every sense of which they are susceptible; that is, that they actually signify every thing that they can possibly signify. The Lawyers carry this rule farther in their profession than the Leyden Professor did in his: they deduce from words not only every thing that they can possibly signify, but sometimes a great deal more; and sometimes they make them bear a signification precisely opposite to what they were intended to express.

That crafty politician who said the use of language is to conceal our thoughts, did not go farther in his theory, than the members of the legal profession in their practice; as every deed which comes from their hands may testify, and every Court of Law bears record. You employ them to express your meaning in a deed of conveyance, a marriage settlement, or a will; and they so smother it with words, so envelope it with technicalities, so bury it beneath redundancies of speech, that any meaning which is sought for may be picked out, to the confusion of that which you intended. Something at length comes to be contested: you go to a Court of Law to demand your right; or you are summoned into one to defend it. You ask for justice, and you receive a nice distinction — a forced construction, — a verbal criticism. By such means you are defeated and plundered in a civil cause; and in a criminal one a slip of the pen in the indictment brings off the criminal scot free. As if slips of the pen in such cases were always accidental! But because Judges are incorruptible (as, blessed be God, they still are in this most corrupt nation), and because Barristers are not to be suspected of ever intentionally betraying the cause which they are fee'd to defend, it is taken for granted that the same incorruptibility, and the same principled integrity, or gentlemanly sense of honour which sometimes is its substitute, are to be found among all those persons who pass their miserable lives in quill-driving, day after day, from morning till night, at a scrivener's desk, or in an attorney's office!

CHAPTER XLI. P. I.

REVENUE OF THE CORPORATION OF DONCASTER WELL APPLIED.

Play not for gain but sport: who plays for more
Than he can lose with pleasure, stakes his heart;
Perhaps his wife's too, and whom she hath bore.

HERBERT.

Well, gentle Reader, we have made our way through the Charters, and seen that the Borough of Doncaster is, as it may be called, an *imperium in imperio* — or *regnum*, or rather, if there were such word, *regnulum, in regno* — (such a word there ought to be, and very probably was, and most certainly would be if the Latin were a living language) — a little kingdom in itself, modelled not unhappily after the form of that greater one whereof it is a part; differing from it, for reasons so evident that it would be a mere waste of words and time to explain them, — in being an elective instead of an hereditary monarchy, and also because the monarchy is held only for a year, not for life; and differing in this respect likewise, that its three estates are analogous to the vulgar and mistaken notion of the English constitution, not to what that constitution is, as transmitted to us by our fathers.

We have seen that its Mayor (or Monarch), its twelve Aldermen (or House of Lords), all being of the better and more excellent inhabitants, and its four-and-twenty capital Burgesses (or House of Commons,) all of the better, more reputable and discreet Doncastrians, constitute one body corporate and politic in reality, deed, and name, to the fear and terror of the wicked, and for the support and reward of the good; and that the municipal government has been thus constituted expressly to the end that Doncaster might remain for ever a borough of harmony and peace: to the better effecting of which most excellent intent, a circumstance which has already been adverted to, contributes greatly, to wit, that Doncaster sends no members to Parliament.

Great are the mysteries of Corporations; and great the good of them when they are so constituted, and act upon such principles as that of Doncaster.

There is an old Song which says —

Oh London is a gallant town
A most renowned city;
'Tis governed by the scarlet gown,
Indeed, the more's the pity.

The two latter verses could never be applied to Doncaster. In the middle of the last century the revenues of the Corporation did not exceed 1500*l.* a-year: at the beginning of this they had increased to nearly 6000*l.*, and this income was principally expended, as it ought to be, for the benefit of the Town. The public buildings have been erected from these funds; and liberal donations made from them to the Dispensary and other eleemosynary institutions. There is no constable-assessment, none for paving and lighting the street; these expenses are defrayed by the corporation, and families are supplied with river water chiefly at its expense.

Whether this body corporate should be commended or condemned for encouraging the horse-races, by building a grand stand upon the course, and giving annually a plate of the value of fifty pounds, to be run for, and two sums of twenty guineas each toward the stakes, is a question which will be answered by every one according to his estimate of right and wrong. Gentlemen of the Turf will approve highly of their conduct, so will those Gentlemen whose characteristics are either light fingers or black legs. Put it to the vote in Doncaster, and there will be few voices against them: take the sense of the nation upon it by universal suffrage, and there would be a triumphant majority in their favour.

In this, and alas! in too many other cases, *vox populi est vox diaboli.*

A greater number of families are said to

meet each other at Doncaster races, than at any other meeting of the same kind in England. That such an assemblage contributes greatly to the gaiety and prosperity of the town itself, and of the country round about, is not to be disputed. But horse races excite evil desires, call forth evil passions, encourage evil propensities, lead the innocent into temptation, and give opportunities to the wicked. And the good which arises from such amusements, either as mere amusement — (which is in itself unequivocally a good when altogether innocent), — or by circulating money in the neighbourhood, — or by tending to keep up an excellent breed of horses, for purposes of direct utility, — these consequences are as dust in the balance, when compared with the guilt and misery that arise from gambling.

Lord Exeter and the Duke of Grafton may, perhaps, be of a different opinion. So should Mr. Gully, whom Pindar may seem to have prophetically panegyrised as

——'Ολυμπιονίκαν
"Ανδρα, — πὺξ ἀρετὰν
Εὑρόντα.*

That gentleman, indeed, may, with great propriety, congratulate himself upon his knowledge of what is called the world, and the ability with which he has turned it to a good practical account. But Lord Burleigh, methinks, would shake his head in the ante-chamber of Heaven if he could read there the following paragraph from a Sunday Newspaper.

"Pleasures and Profits of the Turf. — We stated in a former number that Lord Exeter's turf-profits were, for the previous season, 26,000*l.*, this was intended to include bets. But we have now before us a correct and consecutive account of the Duke of Grafton's winnings, from 1811 to 1829 inclusive, taking in merely the value of the stakes for which the horses ran, and which amounts to no less a sum than 99,211*l.* 3*s.* 4*d.*, or somewhat more than 5000*l.* per annum. This, even giving in a good round sum for training and outlay, will leave a sufficiently pleasant balance in hand; to say nothing of the betting book, not often, we believe, light in figures. His Grace's greatest winnings were in 1822 and 1825: in the former of these years they amounted to 11,364*l.* 5*s.* — in the latter, 12,668*l.* 16*s.* 8*d.*"

It is to be hoped that the Duke has with his crest and coronet his motto also upon the covers of his racing and betting books, and upon his prize plates and cups:

Et Decus et Pretium Recti.

Before we pass from the Race-ground, let me repeat to the reader a wish of Horace Walpole's that "some attempt were made to ennoble our horse-races, by associating better arts with the courses, as by contributing for odes, the best of which should be rewarded by medals. Our nobility," says he, "would find their vanity gratified; for, as the pedigrees of their steeds would soon grow tiresome, their own genealogies would replace them, and, in the mean time, poetry and medals would be improved. Their lordships would have judgment enough to know if the horse (which should be the impression on one side) were not well executed; and, as I hold that there is no being more difficult to draw well than a horse, no bad artist could be employed. Such a beginning would lead farther; and the cup or plate for the prize might rise into beautiful vases."

Pity that the hint has not been taken, and an auxiliary sporting society formed for promoting the education of Pindars and Benvenuto Cellinis!

INTERCHAPTER V.

WHEREIN THE AUTHOR MAKES KNOWN HIS GOOD INTENTIONS TO ALL READERS, AND OFFERS GOOD ADVICE TO SOME OF THEM.

I can write, and talk too, as soft as other men *with submission to better judgements, — and I leave it to you Gentlemen. I am but one, and I always distrust myself. I only hint my thoughts: You'll please to consider whether you will not think that it may seem to deserve your consideration.* — This is a taking way of speaking. But much good may do them that use it! Asgill.

Reader, my compliments to you!

This is a form of courtesy which the Turks

---

* Olymp. vii. 162.

use in their compositions, and being so courteous a form, I have here adopted it. Why not? Turks though they are, we learnt inoculation from them, and the use of coffee; and hitherto we have taught them nothing but the use of tobacco in return.

Reader, my compliments to you!

Why is it that we hear no more of Gentle Readers? Is it that having become critical in this age of Magazines and Reviews, they have ceased to be gentle? But all are not critical;

The baleful dregs
Of these late ages, — that Circæan draught
Of servitude and folly, have not yet, —
Yet have not so dishonour'd, so deform'd
The native judgement of the human soul.*

In thus applying these lines I mean the servitude to which any rational man degrades his intellect, when he submits to receive an opinion from the dictation of another, upon a point whereon he is just as capable of judging for himself; — the intellectual servitude of being told by Mr. A. B. or C. whether he is to like a book or not, — or why he is to like it: and the folly of supposing that the man who writes anonymously, is on that very account entitled to more credit for judgment, erudition, and integrity, than the author who comes forwar in his own person, and stakes his character upon what he advances.

All Readers, however, — thank Heaven, and what is left among us of that best and rarest of all senses called Common Sense, — all Readers, however, are not critical. There are still some who are willing to be pleased, and thankful for being pleased; and who do not think it necessary that they should be able to *parse* their pleasure, like a lesson, and give a rule or a reason why they are pleased, or why they ought not to be pleased. There are still readers who have never read an Essay upon Taste; — and if they take my advice they never will; for they can no more improve their taste by so doing, than they could improve their appetite or their digestion by studying a cookery-book.

I have something to say to all classes of Readers: and, therefore, having thus begun to speak of one, with that class I will proceed. It is to the youthful part of my lectors — (why not lectors as well as auditors?) it is *virginibus puerisque* that I now address myself. Young Readers, you whose hearts are open, whose understandings are not yet hardened, and whose feelings are neither exhausted nor encrusted by the world, take from me a better rule than any professors of criticism will teach you!

Would you know whether the tendency of a book is good or evil, examine in what state of mind you lay it down. Has it induced you to suspect that what you have been accustomed to think unlawful may after all be innocent, and that that may be harmless which you have hitherto been taught to think dangerous? Has it tended to make you dissatisfied and impatient under the control of others; and disposed you to relax in that self-government, without which both the laws of God and man tell us there can be no virtue — and consequently no happiness? Has it attempted to abate your admiration and reverence for what is great and good, and to diminish in you the love of your country and your fellow-creatures? Has it addressed itself to your pride, your vanity, your selfishness, or any other of your evil propensities? Has it defiled the imagination with what is loathsome, and shocked the heart with what is monstrous? Has it disturbed the sense of right and wrong which the Creator has implanted in the human soul? If so — if you are conscious of all or any of these effects, — or if, having escaped from all, you have felt that such were the effects it was intended to produce, throw the book in the fire, whatever name it may bear in the title-page! Throw it in the fire, young man, though it should have been the gift of a friend! — young lady, away with the whole set, though it should be the prominent furniture of a rosewood bookcase!

* Akenside.

CHAPTER XLII. P. I.

DONCASTER CHURCH. THE RECTORIAL TITHES SECURED BY ARCHBISHOP SHARP FOR HIS OWN FAMILY.

Say, ancient edifice, thyself with years
Grown grey, how long upon the hill has stood
Thy weather-braving tower, and silent mark'd
The human leaf in constant bud and fall?
The generations of deciduous man,
How often hast thou seen them pass away!

HURDIS.

The ecclesiastical history of Doncaster is not so much to the credit of all whom it concerns, as the municipal. Nigel Fossard, in the year 1100, granted the advowson of its church to St. Mary's Abbey, York; and it was for rather more than two hundred years a rectory of two medieties, served by two resident rectors whom the Abbey appointed. In 1303, Archbishop Corbridge appropriated it to the abbey, and ordained it a perpetual vicarage. Fifty marks a year out of the profits of the rectory were then allowed for the Vicar's support, and he held the house and garden also which had formerly appertained to one of the Rectors. When, upon the dissolution of the monasteries, it fell to the crown, Henry VIII. gave it with other monastic impropriations to Archbishop Holgate, as some compensation for the valuable manors which he made the see of York alienate to himself. The church of Doncaster gained nothing by this transfer. The rectory was secured by Archbishop Sharp for his own family. At the beginning of the present century it was worth from 1000*l.* to 1200*l.* a year, while the Vicar had only an annual income of 80*l.* charged upon that rectory, and 20*l.* charged upon a certain estate. He had no tithes, no Easter offerings, and no other glebe than the churchyard, and an orchard attached to the vicarage: and he had to pay a curate to do the duty at Loversall church.

There is one remarkable epitaph in this church upon a monument of the altar form, placed just behind the reading-desk.

How, how, who is here?
I Robin of Doncaster, and Margaret my fere.
That I spent, that I had;
That I gave, that I have;
That I left, that I lost. A. D. 1579.
Quoth Robertus Byrkes who in this world did reign
Threescore years and seven, and yet lived not one.

Robin of Doncaster, as he is now familiarly called by persons connected, or acquainted with the church, is remembered only by this record which he has left of himself: perhaps the tomb was spared for the singularity of the epitaph, when prouder monuments in the same church were despoiled. He seems to have been one who, thinking little of any thing beyond the affairs of this world till the last year of his pilgrimage, lived during that year a new life. It may also be inferred that his property was inherited by persons to whom he was bound by no other ties than those of cold affinity; for if he had felt any concern for their welfare, he would not have considered those possessions as lost which were left to them.

Perhaps a farther inference may be fai ly drawn, that though the deceased had stood in this uncomfortable relation to his heirs-at-law, he was too just a man to set aside the course of succession which the law appointed. They who think that in the testamentary disposal of their property they have a right to do whatever it is legally in their power to do, may find themselves wofully mistaken when they come to render their account. Nothing but the weightiest moral considerations can justify any one in depriving another of that which the law of the land would otherwise in its due course have assigned him. But rights of descent cease to be held sacred in public opinion in proportion as men consider themselves exempt from all duty to their forefathers; and that is in proportion as principles become sophisticated, and society more and more corrupt.

St. George's is the only church in Doncaster, a town which in the year 1800 contained 1246 houses, 5697 souls: twenty years afterwards the houses had increased to 1729, and the inhabitants to 8544. The state having made no other provision for the religious instruction of the townspeople than one church, one vicar, and one curate — if the vicar, from other revenues than those of his vicarage, can afford to keep one — the far greater part of the inhabitants are left to be absenters by necessity, or dissenters by choice. It was the boast of the corporation in an address to Charles II. that they had not "one factious seditious person" in their town, "being all true sons of the Church of England and loyal subjects;" and that "in the height of all the late troubles and confusion (that is, during the civil wars and the commonwealth, — which might more truly have been called the common-woe) they never had any conventicle amongst them, the nurseries and seed plots of sedition and rebellion." — There are conventicles there now of every denomination. And this has been occasioned by the great sin of omission in the Government, and the great sin of commission in that Prelate who appropriated the property of the church to his own family.

Hollis Pigot was Vicar when Daniel Dove began to reside in Doncaster; and Mr. Fawkes was his Curate.

CHAPTER XLIII. P. I.

ANTIQUITIES OF DONCASTER. THE DEÆ MATRES. SAXON FONT. THE CASTLE. THE HALL CROSS.

> *Vieux monuments, —*
> *Las, peu à peu cendre vous devenez,*
> *Fable du peuple et publiques rapines!*
> *Et bien qu'au Temps pour un temps facent guerre*
> *Les bastimens, si est ce que le Temps*
> *Œuvres et noms finablement atterre.*
>
> JOACHIM DU BELLAY.

THE oldest monument in Doncaster is a Roman altar, which was discovered in the year 1781, in digging a cellar six feet deep, in St. Sepulchre's gate. An antiquary of Ferrybridge congratulated the corporation "on the great honour resulting therefrom."

Was it a great honour to Doncaster, — meaning by Doncaster its Mayor, its Aldermen, its capital burgesses, and its whole people, — was it, I say, an honour, a great honour to it, and these, and each and all of these, that this altar should have been discovered? Did the corporation consider it to be so? Ought it to be so considered? Did they feel that pleasurable though feverish excitement at the discovery which is felt by the fortunate man at the moment when his deserts have obtained their honourable meed? Richard Staveley was Mayor that year: Was it an honour to him and his mayoralty as it was to King Ferdinand of Spain that, when he was King, Christopher Columbus discovered the New World, — or to Queen Elizabeth, that Shakespeare flourished under her reign? Was he famous for it, as old Mr. Bramton Gurdon of Assington in Suffolk was famous, about the year 1627, for having three sons parliament men? If he was thus famous, did he "blush to find it fame," or smile that it should be accounted so? What is fame? what is honour? But I say no more. "He that hath knowledge spareth his words; and he that shutteth his lips is esteemed a man of understanding."

It is a votive altar, dedicated to the *Deæ Matres*, with this inscription:

MATRIBUS
M. NAN-
TONIUS.
ORBIOTAL.
VOTUM. SOLVIT. LUBENS. MERITO.

and it is curious because it is only the third altar dedicated to those Goddesses which has yet been found: the other two were also found in the North of England, one at Binchester near Durham, the other at Ribchester in Lancashire.

Next in antiquity to this Roman altar, is a Saxon font in the church; its date, which is now obliterated, is said to have been A. D. 1061.

Not a wreck remains of any thing that existed in Doncaster between the time when Orbiotal erected his altar to the local Goddesses, and when the baptismal font was made: nor the name of a single individual; nor memorial, nor tradition of a single event.

There was a castle there, the dykes of which might partly be seen in Leland's time, and the foundation of part of the walls,—nothing more, so long even then had it been demolished. In the area where it stood the church was built, and Leland thought that great part of the ruins of one building were used for the foundations of the other, and for filling up its walls. It is not known at what time the church was founded. There was formerly a stone built into its east end, with the date of A. D. 1071; but this may more probably have been originally placed in the castle than the church. Different parts of the building are of different ages, and the beautiful tower is supposed to be of Henry the Third's age.

The Hall Cross, as it is now called, bore this inscription:

ICEST : EST : LACRUICE : OTE : D : TILLI : A : KI : ALME : DEU : EN : FACE : MERCI : AM :

There can be little doubt that this Otto de Tilli is the same person whose name appears as a witness to several grants about the middle of the twelfth century, and who was Seneschal to the Earl of Conisborough. It stood uninjured till the Great Rebellion, when the Earl of Manchester's army, on their way from the South to the siege of York in the year 1644, chose to do the Lord service by defacing it. "And the said Earl of Manchester's men, endeavouring to pull the whole shank down, got a smith's forge-hammer and broke off the four corner crosses; and then fastened ropes to the middle cross, which was stronger and higher, thinking by that to pull the whole shank down. But a stone breaking off, and falling upon one of the men's legs, which was nearest it, and breaking his leg, they troubled themselves no more about it." This account, with a drawing of the cross in its former state, was in Fairfax's collection of antiquities, and came afterwards into Thoresby's possession. The Antiquarian Society published an engraving of it by that excellent and upright artist Vertue, of whom it is recorded that he never would engrave a fictitious portrait. The pillar was composed of five columns, a large one in the middle, and four smaller ones around it, answering pretty nearly to the cardinal points: each column was surmounted by a cross, that in the middle being the highest and proportionally large. There were numeral figures on the south face, near the top, which seem to have been intended for a dial; the circumference of the pillar was eleven feet seven, the height eighteen feet.

William Paterson, in the year of his mayoralty, 1678, "beautified it with four dials, ball and fane:" in 1792, when Henry Heaton was Mayor, it was taken down, because of its decayed state, and a new one of the same form was erected by the road-side, a furlong to the south of its former site, on Hop-cross hill. This was better than destroying the cross; and as either renovation or demolition had become necessary, the Corporation are to be commended for what they did. But it is no longer the same cross, nor on the same site which had once been consecrated, and where many a passing prayer had been breathed in simplicity and sincerity of heart.

What signifies the change? Both place and monument had long been desecrated. As little religious feeling was excited by it as would have been by the altar to the *Deæ Matres* if it had stood there. And of the hundreds of travellers who daily pass it, in or outside of stage coaches, in their own carriages, on horseback, or on foot; and of the thousands who flock thither during the races; and of the inhabitants of Doncaster itself, not a single soul cares whether it be the original cross or not, nor where it was originally erected, nor when, nor wherefore, nor by whom!

"I wish I did not!" said Dr. Dove, when some one advanced this consideration with the intent of reconciling him to the change. "I am an old man," said he, "and in age we dislike all change as naturally, and therefore, no doubt, as fitly, as in youth we desire it. The youthful generation, in their ardour for improvement and their love of novelty, strive to demolish what ought religiously to be preserved; the elders, in their caution and their fear, endeavour to uphold what has become useless, and even injurious. Thus, in the order of Providence, we have both the necessary impulse and the needful check.

"But I miss the old cross from its old place. More than fifty years had I known it there; and if fifty years' acquaintance did not give us some regard even for stocks and stones, we must be stocks and stones ourselves."

CHAPTER XLIV. P. I.

HISTORICAL CIRCUMSTANCES CONNECTED WITH DONCASTER. THOMAS, EARL OF LANCASTER. EDWARD IV. ASKE'S INSURRECTION. ILLUSTRIOUS VISITORS. JAMES I. BARNABEE. CHARLES I. CHURCH LIBRARY.

They unto whom we shall appear tedious, are in no wise injured by us, because it is in their own hands to spare that labour which they are not willing to endure.

HOOKER.

NOTHING more than the scanty notices which have already been mentioned is recorded concerning the history of Doncaster, till King John ordered it "to be enclosed with hertstone and pale, according as the ditch required; and that a light brecost or barbican should be made upon the bridge, to defend the town if need should be." The bridge was then of wood; in the following reign the townsmen "gave aid to make a stone bridge there:" in that reign a hospital for sick and leprous people was built there, the priories of St. James and St. Nicholas founded, a Dominican convent, and a Franciscan one. Henry III. slept there on his way to York. In the 23d year of Edward I. the borough was first summoned to send members to Parliament, from which burthen, as it was then considered, it was relieved in the ensuing year.

In 1321, Thomas Earl of Lancaster held a council here with other discontented Barons against Edward II.; in its results it brought many of them to an untimely death, and Lancaster himself suffered by the axe at Pomfret, as much in revenge for Gaveston, as for this rebellion. "In this sort," says an old chronicler, "came the mighty Earl of Lancaster to his end, being the greatest Peer in this realm, and one of the mightiest Earls in Christendom: for when he began to levy war against the King, he was possessed of five earldoms, Lancaster, Lincoln, Salisbury, Leicester, and Derby, beside other seigniories, lands, and possessions, great to his advancement in honour and puissance. But all this was limited within prescription of time, which being expired both honour and puissances were cut off with dishonour and death; for (O miserable state!)

Invida fatorum series, summisque negatum
Stare diu.

"But now touching the foresaid Earl of Lancaster, great strife rose afterwards amongst the people, whether he ought to be reputed for a saint, or no. Some held that he ought to be no less esteemed, for that he did many alms-deeds in his lifetime, honoured men of religion, and maintained a true quarrel till his life's end. Also his enemies continued not long after, but came to evil ends. Others conceived another opinion of him, alleging that he favoured not his wife, but lived in spouse-breach, defiling a great number of damsels and gentlewomen. If any offended him, he slew him shortly after in his wrathful mood. Apostates and other evil doers he maintained, and would not suffer them to be punished by due order of law. All his doings he used to commit to one of his secretaries, and took no heed himself thereof; and as for the manner of his death, he fled shamefully in the fight, and was taken and put to death against his will; yet by reason of certain miracles which were said to be done near the place both where he suffered and where he was buried, caused many to think he was a Saint. Howbeit, at length by the King's commandment, the church doors of the Priory where he was buried were shut and closed, so that no man might be suffered to come to the tomb to bring any offerings, or to do any other kind of devotion to the same. Also the hill where he suffered was kept by certain

Gascoigners appointed by the Lord Hugh Spenser his son, then lying at Pomfret, to the end that no people should come and make their prayers there in worship of the said Earl, whom they took verily for a martyr."

The next confederacy at Doncaster was more successful, though it led eventually to bloodier consequences. Bolingbroke, after landing at Ravensburg, was met here by Northumberland, Hotspur, Westmorland, and others, who engaged with him there, some of them probably not knowing how far his ambitious views extended, and who afterwards became the victims of their own turbulent policy. The Dragon's teeth which were then sown produced a plentiful harvest threescore years afterwards, when more than six-and-thirty thousand Englishmen fell by each other's hands at Towton, between this town and York. Edward IV. beheaded Sir Robert Willis and Sir Ralph Grey here, whom he had taken in the rout of Lose-coat field; and when he mustered his people here to march against Warwick and Clarence, whose intentions began then to be discovered, "it was said that never was seen in England so many goodly men and so well arranged in a field." Afterwards he passed through Doncaster when he returned from exile, on the way to his crowning victory at Barnet.

Richard III. also passed through this place on the way to York, where he was crowned. In Henry VIII.'s reign it became the actual seat of war, and a battle would have been fought there, if the Don had not, by its sudden rising, twice prevented Aske and his army of insurgents from attacking the Duke of Norfolk, with so superior a force that success would have been almost certain, and the triumph of the popish party a probable result. Here Norfolk, profiting by that delay, treated with the insurgents, and finally, by offering them a free pardon, and engaging that a free Parliament should be held in the North, induced them to disperse.

In 1538 John Grigge, the Mayor, lost a thumb in an affray at Marshgate, and next year the Prior of Doncaster was hanged for treason. In 1551 the town was visited by the plague: in that of 1582, 908 persons died here.

The next noticeable circumstance in the annals of Doncaster is, that James I. lodged there, at the sign of the Sun and Bear, on his way from Scotland to take possession of the Crown of England.

The maypole in the market-place was taken down in 1634, and the market cross erected there in its place. But the removal of the maypole seems to have been no proof of any improved state of morals in the town; for Barnabee, the illustrious potator, saw there the most unbecoming sight that he met with in all his travels. On his second visit the frail Levite was dead; and I will not pick out a name from the succession of Vicars which might suit the time of the poem, because, though Doncaster was the scene, it does not follow that the Vicar was the actor; and whoever he may have been, his name can be no object of legitimate curiosity, though Barnabee's justly was, till it was with so much ingenuity determined by Mr. Haslewood.

When the army which had been raised against the Scots was disbanded, Charles I. dined there at the house of Lady Carlingford, and a pear tree, which he is said to have planted, is now standing there in Mr. Maw's garden. Charles was there again in 1644, and attended service in the church. And from a house in the butter market it was that Morris with two companions attempted to carry off the parliamentary commander Rainsborough at noon-day, and failing in the attempt, killed him upon the spot.

A Church Library was founded here by the contributions of the clergy and gentry of the surrounding country in 1726. A chamber over the church porch was appropriated for the books, with the Archbishop's licence; and there was one curate of this town whose love of reading was so great, that he not only passed his days in this library, but had a bed fixed there, and spent his nights there also.

In 1731 all the streets were new paved, and the sign-posts taken down; and in 1739,

Daniel Dove, in remembrance of whom these volumes are composed, came to reside in Doncaster.

CHAPTER XLV. P. I.

CONCERNING THE WORTHIES, OR GOOD MEN, WHO WERE NATIVES OF DONCASTER OR OTHERWISE CONNECTED WITH THAT TOWN.

Vir bonus est quis?
TERENCE.

LET good old Fuller answer the well-known question which is conveyed in the motto to this chapter. "And here," he says, "be it remembered, that the same epithet in several places accepts sundry interpretations. He is called a Good Man in common discourse, who is not dignified with gentility; a Good Man upon the Exchange, who hath a responsible estate; a Good Man in a Camp, who is a tall man of his arms; a Good Man in the Church, who is pious and devout in his conversation. Thus, whatever is fixed therein in other relations, that person is a Good Man in history, whose character affords such matter as may please the palate of an ingenuous reader."

Two other significations may be added which Fuller has not pretermitted, because he could not include them, they being relatively to him, of posthumous birth. A Good Man upon State trials, or in certain Committees which it might not be discreet to designate, is one who will give his verdict without any regard to his oath in the first case or to the evidence in both. And in the language of the Pugilists it signifies one who can bear a great deal of beating: Hal Pierce, the Game Chicken and unrivalled glory of the ring, pronounced this eulogium upon Mr. Gully, the present honourable member for Pontefract, when he was asked for a candid opinion of his professional merits:—"Sir, he was the very Best Man as ever I had."

Among the Good Men, in Fuller's acceptation of the term, who have been in any way connected with Doncaster, the first in renown as well as in point of time, is Robin Hood. Many men talk of him who never shot in his bow; but many think of him when they drink at his Well, which is at Skelbroke by the way-side, about six miles from Doncaster on the York road. There is a small inn near with Robin Hood for its sign. This country has produced no other hero whose popularity has endured so long. The Duke of Marlborough, the Duke of Cumberland, and the Marquis of Granby have flourished upon sign-posts, and have faded there; so have their compeers Prince Eugene and Prince Ferdinand. Rodney and Nelson are fading; and the time is not far distant when Wellington also will have had his day. But while England shall be England, Robin Hood will be a popular name.*

Near Robin Hood's Well, and nearer to Doncaster, the Hermit of Hampole resided, at the place from which he was so called, "where living he was honoured, and dead was buried and sainted." Richard Role, however, for that was his name, was no otherwise sainted than by common opinion in those parts. He died in 1349, and is the oldest of our known Poets. His writings, both in verse and prose, which are of considerable extent, ought to be published at the expense of some national institution.

In the next generation John Marse, who was born in a neighbouring village of that name, flourished in the Carmelite Convent at Doncaster, and obtained great celebrity in his time for writing against—a far greater than himself—John Wickliffe.

It is believed that Sir Martin Frobisher was born at Doncaster, and that his father was Mayor of that place. "I note this the rather," says Fuller, "because learned Mr. Carpenter, in his Geography, recounts him among the famous men of Devonshire; but why should Devonshire, which hath a flock of Worthies of her own, take a lamb from another country." This brave seaman, when he left his property to a kinsman who was

---

* "And there they live like the old ROBIN HOOD OF ENGLAND." AS YOU LIKE IT.

very likely to dissipate it, said, "it was gotten at sea, and would never thrive long at land."

Lord Molesworth having purchased the estate at Edlington, four miles from Doncaster, formerly the property of Sir Edward Stanhope, resided there occasionally in the old mansion, during the latter part of his life. His Account of Denmark is a book which may always be read with profit. The Danish Ambassador complained of it to King William, and hinted that if one of his Danish Majesty's subjects had taken such liberties with the King of England, his master would, upon complaint, have taken off the author's head. "That I cannot do," replied William; "but if you please I will tell him what you say, and he shall put it into the next edition of his book."

Other remarkable persons who were connected with Doncaster, and were contemporaries with Dr. Dove, will be noticed in due time. Here I shall only mention two who have distinguished themselves since his day (alas!) and since I took my leave of a place endeared to me by so many recollections. Mr. Bingley, well known for his popular works upon Natural History, and Mr. Henry Lister Maw, the adventurous naval officer who was the first Englishman that ever came down the great river Amazons, are both natives of this town. I know not whether the Doncaster Maws are of Hibernian descent; but the name of M'Coghlan is in Ireland beautified and abbreviated into Maw; the M'Coghlan, or head of the family, was called the Maw; and a district of King's County was known within the memory of persons now living by the appellation of the Maw's County.

For myself, I am behind a veil which is not to be withdrawn: nevertheless I may say, without consideration of myself, that in Doncaster both because of the principal scene and of the subject of this work

HONOS ERIT HUIC QUOQUE TOMO.

INTERCHAPTER VI.

CONTINGENT CAUSES. PERSONAL CONSIDERATIONS INDUCED BY REFLECTING ON THEM. THE AUTHOR TREMBLES FOR THE PAST.

Vereis que no hay lazada desasida
De nudo y de pendencia soberana;
Ni á poder trastornar la orden del cielo
Las fuerzas llegan, ni el saber del suelo.

BALBUENA.

"THERE is no action of man in this life," says Thomas of Malmesbury, "which is not the beginning of so long a chain of consequences, as that no human providence is high enough to give us a prospect to the end." The chain of causes, however, is as long as the chain of consequences,—peradventure longer; and when I think of the causes which have combined to procreate this book, and the consequences which of necessity it must produce, I am lost in admiration.

How many accidents might for ever have impossibilitated the existence of this incomparable work! If, for instance, I the Unknown had been born in any other part of the world than in the British dominions; or in any other age than one so near the time in which the venerable subject of these memoirs flourished; or in any other place than where these localities could have been learned, and all these personalities were remembered; or if I had not counted it among my felicities like the philosopher of old, and the Polish Jews of this day, (who thank God for it in their ritual), to have been born a male instead of a female; or if I had been born too poor to obtain the blessings of education, or too rich to profit by them: or if I had not been born at all. If, indeed, in the course of six thousand years which have elapsed since the present race of intellectual inhabitants were placed upon this terraqueous globe, any chance had broken off one marriage among my innumerable married progenitors, or thwarted the courtship of those my equally innumerable ancestors who lived before that ceremony was instituted, or in countries where it was not known, — where, or how would my immortal part have existed at this time, or in what shape would these bodily elements have been compounded with which it is invested? A single miscarriage among my millions of grandmothers might have cut off the entail of my mortal being!

Quid non evertit primordia frivola vitæ ?
Nec mirum, vita est integra pene nihil.
Nunc perit, ah ! tenui pereuntis odore lucernæ,
Et fumum hunc funus fortior ille fugat.
Totum aquilis Cæsar rapidis circumvolet orbem,
Collegamque sibi vix ferat esse Jovem.
Quantula res quantos potuisset inepta triumphos,
Et magnum nasci vel prohibere Deum!
Exhæredasset moriente lucernula flammâ
Tot dominis mundum numinibusque novis.
Tu quoque tantilli, juvenis Pellæe, perisses,
(Quam gratus terris ille fuisset odor !)
Tu tantùm unius qui pauper regulus orbis,
Et prope privatus visus es esse tibi.
Nec tu tantùm, idem potuisset tollere casus
Teque, Jovis fili, Bucephalumque tuum :
Dormitorque urbem malè delevisset agaso
*Bucephalam è vestris, Indica Fata, libris.**

The snuff of a candle, — a fall, — a fright, — nay, even a fit of anger! Such things are happening daily, — yea, hourly, upon this peopled earth. One such mishap among so many millions of cases, millions ten million times told, centillions multiplied beyond the vocabulary of numeration, and ascending to ψαμμακόσια, — which word having been coined by a certain Alexis (perhaps no otherwise remembered) and latinised *arenaginta* by Erasmus, is now Anglicised *sandillions* by me; — one such among them all! — I tremble to think of it!

Again. How often has it depended upon political events! If the Moors had defeated Charles Martel; if William instead of Harold had fallen in the Battle of Hastings; if bloody Queen Mary had left a child; or if blessed Queen Mary had not married the Prince of Orange! In the first case the English might now have been Musselmen; in the second they would have continued to use the Saxon tongue, and in either of those cases the Ego could not have existed; for if Arabian blood were put in, or Norman taken out, the whole chain of succession would have been altered. The two latter cases, perhaps, might not have affected the bodily existence of the Ego; but the first might have entailed upon him the curse of Popery, and the second, if it had not subjected him to the same curse, would have made him the subject of a despotic government. In neither case could he have been capable of excogitating lucubrations, such as this high history contains: for either of these misfortunes would have emasculated his mind, unipsefying and unegofying the *Ipsissimus Ego*.

Another chance must be mentioned. One of my ancestors was, as the phrase is, out in a certain rebellion. His heart led him into the field and his heels got him out of it. Had he been less nimble, — or had he been taken and hanged, and hanged he would have been if taken, — there would have been no Ego at this day, no history of Dr. Daniel Dove. The Doctor would have been like the heroes who lived before Agamemnon, and his immortaliser would never have lived at all.

* Cowley.

CHAPTER XLVI. P. I.

DANIEL DOVE'S ARRIVAL AT DONCASTER. THE ORGAN IN SAINT GEORGE'S CHURCH. THE PULPIT. MRS. NEALE'S BENEFACTION.

Non ulla Musis pagina gratior
Quam quæ severis ludicra jungere
Novit, fatigatamque nugis
Utilibus recreare mentem.

Dr. Johnson.

It was in the Mayoralty of Thomas Pheasant (as has already been said) and in the year of our Lord 1739, that Daniel Dove the younger, having then entered upon his seventeenth year, first entered the town of Doncaster, and was there delivered by his excellent father to the care of Peter Hopkins. They loved each other so dearly, that this, which was the first day of their separation, was to both the unhappiest of their lives.

The great frost commenced in the winter of that year; and with the many longing lingering thoughts which Daniel cast towards his home, a wish was mingled that he could see the frozen waterfall in Weathercote Cave.

It was a remarkable era in Doncaster also, because the Organ was that year erected, at the cost of five hundred guineas, raised by voluntary subscription among the parishioners. Harris and Byfield were the builders, and it is still esteemed one of the best in the kingdom. When it was opened, the then curate, Mr. Fawkes, preached a sermon for the occasion, in which, after having rhetorised in praise of sacred music, and touched upon the cornet, flute, harp, sackbut, psaltery, dulcimer and all kinds of instruments, he turned to the organ and apostrophised it thus; — "But O what — O what — what shall I call *thee* by? thou divine Box of sounds!"

That right old worthy Francis Quarles of quaint memory, — and the more to be remembered for his quaintness, — knew how to *improve* an organ somewhat better than Mr. Fawkes. His poem upon one is the first in his Divine Fancies, and whether he would have it ranked among Epigrams, Meditations, or Observations, perhaps he could not himself tell. The Reader may class it as he pleases.

Observe this Organ: mark but how it goes!
'Tis not the hand alone of him that blows
The unseen bellows, nor the hand that plays
Upon the apparent note-dividing keys,
That makes these well-composed airs appear
Before the high tribunal of thine ear.
They both concur; each acts his several part;
Th' one gives it breath, the other lends it art.
Man is this Organ; to whose every action
Heaven gives a breath, (a breath without coaction,)
Without which blast we cannot act at all;
Without which Breath the Universe must fall
To the first nothing it was made of — seeing
In Him we live, we move, we have our being.
Thus filled with His diviner breath, and back't
With His first power, we touch the keys and act:
He blows the bellows: as we thrive in skill,
Our actions prove, like music, good or ill.

The question whether instrumental music may lawfully be introduced into the worship of God in the Churches of the New Testament, has been considered by Cotton Mather and answered to his own satisfaction and that of his contemporary countrymen and their fellow puritans, in his "Historical Remarks upon the discipline practised in the Churches of New England." — "The Instrumental Music used in the old Church of Israel," he says, "was an Institution of God; it was the Commandment of the Lord by the Prophets; and the Instruments are called God's Instruments, and Instruments of the Lord. Now there is not one word of Institution in the New Testament for Instrumental Music in the Worship of God. And because the holy God rejects all he does not command in his worship, he now therefore in effect says to us, *I will not hear the melody of thy Organs.* But, on the other hand, the rule given doth abundantly intimate that no voice is now heard in the Church but what is significant, and edifying by signification; which the voice of Instruments is not."

Worse logic than this and weaker reasoning no one would wish to meet with in the controversial writings of a writer from whose opinions he differs most widely. The Remarks form part of that extraordinary and highly interesting work the *Magnalia Christi Americana.* Cotton Mather is such an author as Fuller would have been if the old English Worthy, instead of having been from a child trained up in the way he should go, had been calvinisticated till the milk of human kindness with which his heart was always ready to overflow had turned sour.

"Though Instrumental Music," he proceeds to say, "were admitted and appointed in the worship of God under the Old Testament, yet we do not find it practised in the Synagogue of the Jews, but only in the Temple. It thence appears to have been a part of the ceremonial Pedagogy which is now abolished; nor can any say it was a part of moral worship. And whereas the common usage now hath confined Instrumental Music to Cathedrals, it seems therein too much to Judaise, — which to do is a part of the Anti-Christian Apostacy, — as well as to Paganise. — If we admit Instrumental Music in the worship of God, how can we resist the imposition of all the instruments used among the ancient Jews? Yea, Dancing as well as playing, and several other Judaic actions?"

During the short but active reign of the Puritans in England, they acted upon this preposterous opinion, and sold the Church organs, without being scrupulous concerning the uses to which they might be applied. A writer of that age, speaking of the prevalence of drunkenness, as a national vice, says, "that nothing may be wanting to the height of luxury and impiety of this abomination, they have translated the organs out of the Churches to set them up in taverns, chaunting their dithyrambics and bestial bacchanalias to the tune of those instruments which were wont to assist them in the celebration of God's praises, and regulate the voices of the worst singers in the world, — which are the English in their churches at present."

It cannot be supposed that the Organs which were thus disposed of, were instruments of any great cost or value. An old pair of Organs,—(for that was the customary mode of expression, meaning a set, — and in like manner a pair of cards, for a pack;) — an old pair of this kind belonging to Lambeth Church was sold in 1565 for 1*l.* 10*s.* Church Organs, therefore, even if they had not been at a revolutionary price, would be within the purchase of an ordinary vintner. "In country parish Churches," says Mr. Denne the Antiquary, "even where the district was small, there was often a choir of singers, for whom forms, desks and books were provided; and they probably most of them had benefactors who supplied them with a pair of organs that might more properly have been termed a box of whistles. To the best of my recollection there were in the chapels of some of the Colleges in Cambridge very, very, indifferent instruments. That of the chapel belonging to our old house was removed before I was admitted."

The use of the organ has occasioned a great commotion, if not a schism, among the methodists of late. Yet our holy Herbert could call Church music the "sweetest of sweets;" and describe himself when listening to it, as disengaged from the body, and "rising and falling with its wings."

Harris, the chief builder of the Doncaster Organ, was a contemporary and rival of Father Smith, famous among Organists. Each built one for the Temple Church, and Father Smith's had most votes in its favour.* The peculiarity of the Doncaster Organ, which was Harris's masterpiece, is, its having, in the great organ, two trumpets and a clarion, throughout the whole compass; and these stops are so excellent, that a celebrated musician said every pipe in them was worth its weight in silver.

Our Doctor dated from that year, in his own recollections, as the great era of his life. It served also for many of the Doncastrians, as a date to which they carried back their computations, till the generation which remembered the erecting of the organ was extinct.

This was the age of Church improvement in Doncaster, — meaning here by Church, the material structure. Just thirty years before, the Church had been beautified and the ceiling painted, too probably to the disfigurement of works of a better architectural age. In 1721 the old peal of five bells was replaced with eight new ones, of new metal, heretofore spoken of. In 1723 the church floor and church-yard, which had both been unlevelled by Death's levelling course, were levelled anew, and new rails were placed to the altar. Two years later the Corporation gave the new Clock, and it was fixed to strike on the watch bell, — that clock which numbered the hours of Daniel Dove's life from the age of seventeen till that of seventy. In 1736 the west gallery was put up, and in 1741, ten years after the organ, a new pulpit, but not in the old style; for pulpits, which are among the finest works of art in Brabant and Flanders, had degenerated in England, and in other protestant countries.

* See Lord Campbell's Lives of the Chancellors, vol. iii. p. 591. He states that Judge Jeffreys decided in favour of Smith's, and that Harris's went to Wolverhampton. I have often heard it there, and he who played on it had Music in his soul. If I recollect aright, his name was Rudge.

This probably was owing, in our own country, as much to the prevalence of puritanism, as to the general depravation of taste. It was for their beauty or their splendour that the early Quakers inveighed with such vehemence against pulpits, "many of which places," saith George Keith in his quaking days, "as we see in England and many other countries, have a great deal of superfluity, and vain and superfluous labour and pains of carving, painting and varnishing upon them, together with your cloth and velvet cushion in many places; because of which, and not for the height of them above the ground, we call them Chief Places. But as for a commodious place above the ground whereon to stand when one doth speak in an assembly, it was never condemned by our friends, who also have places whereupon to stand, when to minister, as they had under the Law." *

In 1743 a marble Communion Table was placed in the Church, and—(passing forward more rapidly than the regular march of this narration, in order to present these ecclesiastical matters without interruption,)—a set of chimes were fixed in 1754—merry be the memory of those by whom this good work was effected! The north and south galleries were re-built in 1765; and in 1767 the church was white-washed, a new reading-desk put up, the pulpit removed to what was deemed a more convenient station, and Mrs. Neale gave a velvet embroidered cover and cushion for it,—for which her name is enrolled among the benefactors of St. George's Church.

That velvet which, when I remember it, had lost the bloom of its complexion, will hardly have been preserved till now even by the dyer's renovating aid: and its embroidery has long since passed through the goldsmith's crucible. *Sic transit* excites a more melancholy feeling in me when a recollection like this arises in my mind, than even the "forlorn *hic jacet*" of a neglected tombstone. Indeed such is the softening effect of time upon those who have not been rendered obdurate and insensible by the world and the world's law, that I do not now call to mind without some emotion even that pulpit, to which I certainly bore no good will in early life, when it was my fortune to hear from it so many somniferous discourses; and to bear away from it, upon pain of displeasure in those whose displeasure to me was painful, so many texts, chapter and verse, few or none of which had been improved to my advantage. "Public sermons"—(hear! hear! for Martin Luther speaketh!)—"public sermons do very little edify children, who observe and learn but little thereby. It is more needful that they be taught and well instructed with diligence in schools; and at home that they be orderly heard and examined in what they have learned. This way profiteth much; it is indeed very wearisome, but it is very necessary." May I not then confess that no turn of expression however felicitous—no collocation of words however emphatic and beautiful—no other sentences whatsoever, although rounded, or pointed for effect with the most consummate skill, have ever given me so much delight, as those dear phrases which are employed in winding up a sermon, when it is brought to its long-wished-for close.

It is not always, nor necessarily thus; nor ever would be so if these things were ordered as they might and ought to be. Hugh Latimer, Bishop Taylor, Robert South, John Wesley, Robert Hall, Bishop Jebb, Bishop Heber, Christopher Benson, your hearers felt no such tedium! when you reached that period it was to them like the cessation of a strain of music, which while it lasted had rendered them insensible to the lapse of time.

"I would not," said Luther, "have preachers torment their hearers and detain them with long and tedious preaching."

* "By his order, the Reading-Pew and Pulpit"—(of the Church of *Layton Ecclesia* in the County of *Huntingdon*)—"were a little distant from each other, and both of an equal height, for he would often say, *They should neither have a precedency or priority of the other; but that Prayer and Preaching, being equally useful, might agree like brethren, and have an equal honour and estimation.*"
ISAAC WALTON'S LIFE OF MR. GEORGE HERBERT.

CHAPTER XLVII.

DONCASTRIANA. GUY'S DEATH. SEARCH FOR HIS TOMBSTONE IN INGLETON CHURCH-YARD.

> Go to the dull church-yard, and see
> Those hillocks of mortality,
> Where proudest man is only found
> By a small hillock in the ground.
>
> TIXALL POETRY.

THE first years of Daniel's abode in Doncaster were distinguished by many events of local memorability. The old Friar's bridge was taken down, and a new one with one large arch built in its stead. Turnpikes were erected on the roads to Saltsbrook and to Tadcaster; and in 1742 Lord Semple's regiment of Highlanders marched through the town, being the first soldiers without breeches who had ever been seen there since breeches were in use. In 1746 the Mansion House was begun, next door to Peter Hopkins's, and by no means to his comfort while the work was going on, nor indeed after it was completed, its effect upon his chimneys having heretofore been noticed. The building was interrupted by the rebellion. An army of six thousand English and Hessians was then encamped upon Wheatley Hills; and a Hessian general dying there, was buried in St. George's Church; from whence his leaden coffin was stolen by the grave-digger.

Daniel had then completed his twenty-second year. Every summer he paid a month's visit to his parents; and those were happy days, not the less so to all parties because his second home had become almost as dear to him as his first. Guy did not live to see the progress of his pupil; he died a few months after the lad had been placed at Doncaster, and the delight of Daniel's first return was overclouded by this loss. It was a severe one to the elder Daniel, who lost in the Schoolmaster his only intellectual companion.

I have sought in vain for Richard Guy's tombstone in Ingleton church-yard.* That there is one there can hardly, I think, be doubted; for if he left no relations who regarded him, nor perhaps effects enough of his own to defray this last posthumous and not necessary expense; and if Thomas Gent of York, who published the old poem of Flodden Field from his transcript, after his death, thought he required no other monument; Daniel was not likely to omit this last tribute of respect and affection to his friend. But the church-yard, which, when his mortal remains were deposited there, accorded well with its romantic site, on a little eminence above the roaring torrent, and with the then retired character of the village, and with the solemn use to which it was consecrated, is now a thickly-peopled burial-ground. Since their time, manufactures have been established in Ingleton, and though eventually they proved unsuccessful, and were consequently abandoned, yet they continued long enough in work largely to increase the population of the church-yard. Amid so many tombs the stone which marked poor Guy's resting-place might escape even a more diligent search than mine. Nearly a century has elapsed since it was set up: in the course of that time its inscription not having been re-touched, must have become illegible to all but an antiquary's poring and practised eyes; and perhaps to them also unless aided by his tracing tact, and by the conjectural supply of connecting words, syllables, or letters; indeed, the stone itself has probably become half interred, as the earth around it has been disturbed and raised. Time corrodes our epitaphs, and buries our very tombstones.

Returning pensively from my unsuccessful search in the church-yard, to the little inn at Ingleton, I found there, upon a sampler, worked in 1824 by Elizabeth Brown, aged 9, and framed as an ornament for the room which I occupied, some lines in as moral a strain of verse as any which I had that day perused among the tombs. And I transcribed them for preservation, thinking it not improbable that they had been originally composed by Richard Guy, for the use of his female scholars, and handed down for a

* "Grave-stones tell truth scarce forty years."
SIR T. BROWNE'S HYDRIATAPHIA.

like purpose, from one generation to another. This may be only a fond imagination, and perhaps it might not have occurred to me at another time; but many compositions have been ascribed in modern as well as ancient times, and indeed daily are so, to more celebrated persons, upon less likely grounds. These are the verses:

> Jesus permit thy gracious name to stand
> As the first effort of an infant's hand;
> And as her fingers on the sampler move,
> Engage her tender heart to seek thy love;
> With thy dear children may she have a part,
> And write thy name thyself upon her heart.

CHAPTER XLVIII.

A FATHER'S MISGIVINGS CONCERNING HIS SON'S DESTINATION. PETER HOPKINS'S GENEROSITY. DANIEL IS SENT ABROAD TO GRADUATE IN MEDICINE.

> Heaven is the magazine wherein He puts
> Both good and evil; Prayer's the key that shuts
> And opens this great treasure: 'tis a key
> Whose wards are Faith and Hope and Charity.
> Wouldst thou prevent a judgment due to sin?
> Turn but the key, and thou may'st lock it in.
> Or wouldst thou have a blessing fall upon thee?
> Open the door, and it will shower on thee!
>
> QUARLES.

THE elder Daniel saw in the marked improvement of his son at every yearly visit more and more cause to be satisfied with himself for having given him such a destination, and to thank Providence that the youth was placed with a master whose kindness and religious care of him might truly be called fatherly. There was but one consideration which sometimes interfered with that satisfaction, and brought with it a sense of uneasiness. The Doves, from time immemorial, had belonged to the soil as fixedly as the soil had belonged to them. Generation after generation they had moved in the same contracted sphere, their wants and wishes being circumscribed alike within their own few hereditary acres. Pride, under whatever form it may show itself, is of the Devil; and though Family Pride may not be its most odious manifestation, even that child bears a sufficiently ugly likeness of its father. But Family Feeling is a very different thing, and may exist as strongly in humble as in high life. Naboth was as much attached to the vineyard, the inheritance of his fathers, as Ahab could be to the throne which had been the prize, and the reward, or punishment, of his father Omri's ambition.

This feeling sometimes induced a doubt in Daniel whether affection for his son had not made him overlook his duty to his forefathers; — whether the fixtures of the land are not happier, and less in the way of evil, than the moveables: — whether he had done right in removing the lad from that station of life in which he was born, in which it had pleased God to place him; divorcing him, as it were, from his paternal soil, and cutting off the entail of that sure independence, that safe contentment, which his ancestors had obtained and preserved for him, and transmitted to his care to be in like manner by him preserved and handed down. The latent poetry which there was in the old man's heart made him sometimes feel as if the fields and the brook, and the hearth and the graves, reproached him for having done this! But then he took shelter in the reflection that he had consulted the boy's true welfare, by giving him opportunities of storing and enlarging his mind; that he had placed him in the way of intellectual advancement, where he might improve the talents which were committed to his charge, both for his own benefit and for that of his fellow-creatures. Certain he was that whether he had acted wisely or not, he had meant well. He was conscious that his determination had not been made without much and anxious deliberation, nor without much and earnest prayer; hitherto, he saw, that the blessing which he prayed for had followed it, and he endeavoured to make his heart rest in thankful and pious hope that that blessing would be continued. "Wouldst thou know," says Quarles, "the lawfulness of the action which thou desirest to undertake, let thy devotion recommend it to divine blessing. If it be lawful thou shalt perceive thy heart encouraged by thy prayer; if unlawful, thou shalt find thy prayer discouraged by thy heart. That action is not warrantable which either blushes to beg a blessing, or, having succeeded, dares not present a thanksgiving." Daniel might safely put his conduct to this test; and to this test, in fact, his own healthy and uncorrupted sense of religion led him, though probably he had never read these golden words of Quarles the Emblemist.

It was, therefore, with no ordinary delight that our good Daniel received a letter from his son, asking permission to go to Leyden, in conformity with his Master's wishes, and there prosecute his studies long enough to graduate as a Doctor in medicine. Mr. Hopkins, he said, would generously take upon himself the whole expense, having adopted him as his successor, and almost as a son; for as such he was treated in all respects, both by him and by his mistress, who was one of the best of women. And, indeed, it appeared that Mr. Hopkins had long entertained this intention, by the care which he had taken to make him keep up and improve the knowledge of Latin which he had acquired under Mr. Guy.

The father's consent, as might be supposed, was thankfully given; and accordingly Daniel Dove, in the twenty-third year of his age, embarked from Kingston-upon-Hull for Rotterdam, well provided by the care and kindness of his benevolent master with letters of introduction and of credit; and still better provided with those religious principles which, though they cannot ensure prosperity in this world, ensure to us things of infinitely greater moment,—good conduct, peace of mind, and the everlasting reward of the righteous.

CHAPTER XLIX.

CONCERNING THE INTEREST WHICH DANIEL THE ELDER TOOK IN THE DUTCH WAR, AND MORE ESPECIALLY IN THE SIEGE AND PROVIDENTIAL DELIVERY OF LEYDEN.

Glory to Thee in thine omnipotence,
O Lord who art our shield and our defence,
And dost dispense,
As seemeth best to thine unerring will,
(Which passeth mortal sense)
The lot of Victory still;
Edging sometimes with might the sword unjust;
And bowing to the dust
The rightful cause, that so such seeming ill
May thine appointed purposes fulfil;
Sometimes, as in this late auspicious hour
For which our hymns we raise,
Making the wicked feel thy present power;
Glory to thee and praise,
Almighty God, by whom our strength was given!
Glory to Thee, O Lord of Earth and Heaven!
SOUTHEY.

THERE were two portions of history with which the elder Daniel was better acquainted than most men,—that of Edward the Third's reign, and that of the Wars in the Netherlands down to the year 1608. Upon both subjects he was *homo unius libri;* such a man is proverbially formidable at his own weapon; and the book with which Johnson immortalised Osborne the bookseller, by knocking him down with it, was not a more formidable folio than either of those from which Daniel derived this knowledge.

Now of all the events in the wars of the Low Countries, there was none which had so strongly affected his imagination as the siege of Leyden. The patient fortitude of the besieged, and their deliverance, less by the exertions of man, (though no human exertions were omitted,) than by the special mercy of Him whom the elements obey, and in whom they had put their trust, were in the strong and pious mind of Daniel, things of more touching interest than the tragedy of Haarlem, or the wonders of military science and of courage displayed at the siege of Antwerp. Who indeed could forget the fierce answer of the Leydeners when they were, for the last time, summoned to surrender, that the men of Leyden would never surrender while they had one arm left to eat, and another to fight with! And the not less terrible reply of the Burgemeester Pieter Adriaanzoon Vander Werf, to some of the townsmen when they represented to him the extremity of famine to which they were reduced; "I have sworn to defend this city," he made answer, "and by God's help I mean to keep that oath! but if my death can help ye men, here is my body! cut it in pieces, and share it among ye as far as it will go." And who without partaking in the hopes and fears of the contest, almost as if it were still at issue, can peruse the details of that *amphibious* battle (if such an expression may be allowed) upon the inundated country, when, in the extremity of their distress, and at a time when the Spaniards said that it was as impossible for the Hollanders to save Leyden from their power, as it was for them to pluck the stars from heaven, "a great south wind, which they might truly say came from the grace of God," set in with such a spring tide, that in the course of eight-and-forty hours, the inundation rose half a foot, thus rendering the fields just passable for the flat-bottomed boats which had been provided for that service! A naval battle, among the trees; where the besieged, though it was fought within two miles of their walls, could see nothing because of the foliage; and amid such a labyrinth of dykes, ditches, rivers and fortifications, that when the besiegers retired from their palisades and sconces, the conquerors were not aware of their own success, nor the besieged of their deliverance!

"In this delivery," says the historian, "and in every particular of the enterprise, doubtless all must be attributed to the mere providence of God, neither can man challenge any glory therein; for without a miracle all the endeavours of the Protestants had been as wind. But God who is always good, would not give way to the cruelties wherewith the Spaniards threatened this town, with all the insolencies whereof they make profession in the taking of towns (although they be by composition) without any respect of humanity or honesty. And there is not any man but will confess with me, if he be not some atheist, or epicure, (who maintain that all things come by chance,) that this delivery is a work which belongs only unto God. For if the Spaniards had battered the town but with four cannons only, they had carried it, the people being so weakened with famine, as they could not endure any longer: besides a part of them were ill affected, and very many of their best men were dead of the plague. And for another testimony that it was God only who wrought, the town was no sooner delivered, but the wind which was south-west, and had driven the water out of the sea into the country, turned to north-east, and did drive it back again into the sea, as if the south-west wind had blown those three days only to that effect; wherefore they might well say that both the winds and the sea had fought for the town of Leyden. And as for the resolution of the States of Holland to drown the country, and to do that which they and their Prince, together with all the commanders, captains and soldiers of the army shewed in this sea-course, together with the constancy and resolution of the besieged to defend themselves, notwithstanding so many miseries which they suffered, and so many promises and threats which were made unto them, all in like sort proceeded from a divine instinct."

In the spirit of thoughtful feeling that this passage breathes, was the whole history of that tremendous struggle perused by the elder Daniel; and Daniel the son was so deeply imbued with the same feeling, that if he had lived till the time of the Peninsular War, he would have looked upon the condition to which Spain was reduced, as a consequence of its former tyranny, and as an awful proof how surely, soon or late, the sins of the fathers are visited upon the children.

Oh that all history were regarded in this spirit! "Even such as are in faith most strong, of zeal most ardent, should not," says one of the best and wisest of Theologians, "much mispend their time in comparing the degenerate fictions, or historical relations of times ancient or modern, with the everlasting truth. For though this method could not add much increase either to their faith or zeal, yet would it doubtless much avail for working placid and mild affections. The very penmen of Sacred Writ themselves were taught patience, and instructed in the ways of God's providence, by their experience of such events as the course of time is never barren of; not always related by canonical authors, nor immediately testified by the Spirit; but ofttimes believed upon a moral certainty, or such a resolution of circumstances concurrent into the first cause or disposer of all affairs as we might make of modern accidents, were we otherwise partakers of the Spirit, or would we mind heavenly matters as much as earthly."

CHAPTER L. P. I.

VOYAGE TO ROTTERDAM AND LEYDEN. THE AUTHOR CANNOT TARRY TO DESCRIBE THAT CITY. WHAT HAPPENED THERE TO DANIEL DOVE.

He took great content, exceeding delight in that his voyage. As who doth not that shall attempt the like ?—For peregrination charms our senses with such unspeakable and sweet variety, that some count him unhappy that never travelled, a kind of prisoner, and pity his case that from his cradle to his old age he beholds the same still; still, still, the same, the same! BURTON.

"WHY did Dan remain in ships?" says Deborah the Prophetess in that noble song, which, if it had been composed in Greek instead of Hebrew, would have made Pindar hide his diminished head, or taught him a loftier strain than even he has reached in his eagle flights—"Why did Dan remain in ships?" said the Prophetess. Our Daniel during his rough passage from the Humber to the Maese, thought that nothing should make him do so. Yet when all danger, real or imaginary, was over, upon that deep

Where Proteus' herds and Neptune's orcs do keep,
Where all is ploughed, yet still the pasture's green,
The ways are found, and yet no paths are seen:—"*

when all the discomforts and positive sufferings of the voyage were at an end; and when the ship,—

Quitting her fairly of the injurious sea †,

had entered the smooth waters of that stately river, and was gliding

Into the bosom of her quiet quay †;

he felt that the delight of setting foot on shore after a sea voyage, and that too the shore of a foreign country, for the first time, is one of the few pleasures which exceed any expectation that can be formed of them.

He used to speak of his landing, on a fine autumnal noon, in the well-wooded and well-watered city of Rotterdam, and of his journey along what he called the high-turnpike canal from thence to Leyden, as some of the pleasantest recollections of his life. Nothing, he said, was wanting to his enjoyment, but that there should have been some one to have partaken it with him in an equal degree. But the feeling that he was alone in a foreign land sate lightly on him, and did not continue long,—young as he was, with life and hope before him, healthful of body and of mind, cheerful as the natural consequence of that health corporeal and mental, and having always much to notice and enough to do—the one being an indispensable condition of happiness, the other a source of pleasure as long as it lasts; and where there is a quick eye and an inquiring mind, the longest residence abroad is hardly long enough to exhaust it.

No day in Daniel's life had ever passed in such constant and pleasurable excitement as that on which he made his passage from Rotterdam to Leyden, and took possession of the lodgings which Peter Hopkins's correspondent had engaged for him. His reception was such as instantly to make him feel that he was placed with worthy people. The little apprehensions, rather than anxieties, which the novelty of his situation occasioned, the sight of strange faces with which he was to be domesticated, and the sound of a strange language, to which, harsh and uninviting as it seemed, his ear and speech

* B. JONSON: Neptune's Triumph.

† QUARLES.

must learn to accustom themselves, did not disquiet his first night's rest. And having fallen asleep, notwithstanding the new position to which a Dutch bolster constrained him, he was not disturbed by the storks,

—all night
Beating the air with their obstreperous beaks,

(for with Ben Jonson's leave, this may much more appropriately be said of them than of the ravens), nor by the watchmen's rappers, or clap-sticks, which seem to have been invented in emulous imitation of the stork's instrumental performance.

But you and I, Reader, can afford to make no tarriance in Leyden. I cannot remain with you here till you could see the Rector Magnificus in his magnificence. I cannot accompany you to the monument of that rash Baron who set the crown of Bohemia in evil hour upon the Elector Palatine's unlucky head. I cannot take you to the graves of Boerhaave and of Scaliger. I cannot go with you into that library of which Heinsius said, when he was Librarian there, "I no sooner set foot in it and fasten the door, but I shut out ambition, love, and all those vices of which idleness is the mother and ignorance the nurse; and in the very lap of Eternity, among so many illustrious souls, I take my seat, with so lofty a spirit that I then pity the great who know nothing of such happiness." —*Plerunque in quâ simulac pedem posui, foribus pessulum abdo, ambitionem autem, amorem, libidinem, &c. excludo, quorum parens est ignavia, imperitia nutrix; et in ipso æternitatis gremio, inter tot illustres animas sedem mihi sumo, cum ingenti quidem animo, ut subinde magnatum me misereat qui felicitatem hanc ignorant!* I cannot walk with you round the ramparts, from which wide-circling and well-shaded promenade you might look down upon a large part of the more than two thousand gardens which a century ago surrounded this most horticultural city of a horticultural province, the garden, as it was called, of Holland, that is of the land of Gardeners. I cannot even go up the Burgt with you, though it be pretended that the Hengist of Anglo-Saxon history erected it; nor can I stop at the entrance of that odd place, for you to admire (as you could not but admire) the Lion of the United Provinces, who stands there erect and rampant in menacing attitude, grinning horribly a ghastly smile, his eyes truculent, his tail in full elevation, and in action correspondent to his motto *Pugno pro Patria*, wielding a drawn sword in his dreadful right paw.

Dear Reader, we cannot afford time for going to Oegstgeest, though the first Church in Holland is said to have been founded there by St. Willebord, and its burial-ground is the Campo Santo of the Dutch Roman Catholics, as Bunhill Fields of the English Dissenters. Nor can I accompany thee to Noortwyck and describe to thee its fish-ponds, its parterres, the arabesque carpet-work of its box, and the espalier walls or hedges, with the busts which were set in the archways, such as they existed when our Doctor, in his antedoctorial age, was a student at Leyden, having been kept up till that time in their old fashion by the representatives of Janus Dousa. We cannot, dear Reader, tarry to visit the gardens in that same pleasant village from which the neighbouring cities are supplied with medicinal plants; where beds of ranunculuses afford, when in blossom, a spectacle which no exhibition of art could rival in splendour and in beauty; and from whence rose leaves are exported to Turkey, there to have their essential oil extracted for Mahometan luxury.

We must not go to see the sluices of the Rhine, which Daniel never saw, because in his time the Rhine had no outlet through these Downs. We cannot walk upon the shore at Katwyck, where it was formerly a piece of Dutch courtship for the wooer to take his mistress in his arms, carry her into the sea till he was more than knee deep, set her down upon her feet, and then bearing her out again, roll her over and over upon the sand-hills by way of drying her. We have no time for visiting that scene of the Batavian Arcadia. No, reader, I cannot tarry to show thee the curiosities of Leyden, nor to talk over its *memorabilia*, nor to visit the pleasant parts of the surrounding country: though Gerard Goris says, that *comme la Ville de Leide, entourée par les plaisants villages de Soeterwoude, Stompvic, Wilsveen, Tedingerbroek, Oegstgeest, Leiderdorp et Vennep, est la Cêntre et la Delice de toute Hollande, ainsi la Campagne à l'entour de cette celèbre Ville est comme un autre Eden ou Jardin de plaisance, qui avec ses beaux attraits tellement transporte l'attention du spectateur qu'il se trouve contraint, comme par un ravissment d'esprit, de confesser qu'il n'a jamais veu pais au monde, ou l'art et la nature si bien ont pris leurs mesures pour aporter et entremêler tout ce qui peut servir à l'aise, à la recreation, et au profit.*

No, Reader, we must not linger here,

> *Hier, waar in Hollands heerlijkste oorden*
> *De lieve Lente zoeter lacht,*
> *Het schroeiend Zud, het grijnzend Noorden*
> *Zijn' gloed en strenge kou verzacht;*
> *Waar nijverheid en blij genoegen,*
> *Waar stilte en vlijt zich samenvoegen.**

We must return to Doncaster. It would not be convenient for me to enter minutely, even if my materials were sufficient for that purpose, into the course of our student's life, from the time when he was entered among the Greenies of this famous University; nor to describe the ceremonies which were used at his *ungreening*, by his associates; nor the academical ones with which, at the termination of his regular terms, his degree in medicine was conferred. I can only tell thee that, during his residence at Leyden, he learned with exemplary diligence whatever he was expected to learn there, and by the industrious use of good opportunities a great deal more.

But,—he fell in love with a Burgemeester's Daughter.

* Leyden's Ramp.

CHAPTER LI.

ARMS OF LEYDEN. DANIEL DOVE, M.D. A LOVE STORY, STRANGE BUT TRUE.

> *Oye el extraño caso, advierte y siente;*
> *Suceso es raro, mas verdad ha sido.*
>
> Balbuena.

The arms of Leyden are two cross keys, gules in a field argent; and having been entrusted with the power of those keys to bind and to loose,—and, moreover, to bleed and to blister, to administer at his discretion pills, potions, and powders, and employ the whole artillery of the pharmacopœia,—Daniel returned to Doncaster. The papal keys convey no such general power as the keys of Leyden: they give authority over the conscience and the soul; now it is not every man that has a conscience, or that chooses to keep one; and as for souls, if it were not an article of faith to believe otherwise,—one might conclude that the greater part of mankind had none, from the utter disregard of them which is manifested in the whole course of their dealings with each other. But bodily diseases are among the afflictions which flesh is heir to; and we are not more surely *fruges consumere nati*, than we are born to consume physic also, greatly to the benefit of that profession in which Daniel Dove had now obtained his commission.

But though he was now M.D. in due form, and entitled to the insignia of the professional wig, the muff, and the gold-headed cane, it was not Mr. Hopkins's intention that he should assume his title, and commence practice as a physician. This would have been an unpromising adventure; whereas, on the other hand, the consideration which a regular education at Leyden, then the most flourishing school of medicine, would obtain for him in the vicinity, was a sure advantage. Hopkins could now present him as a person thoroughly qualified to be his successor: and if at any future time Dove should think proper to retire from the more laborious parts of his calling, and take up his rank, it would be in his power to do so.

But one part of my Readers are, I suspect, at this time a little impatient to know something about the Burgemeester's Daughter; and I, because of the

> —— allegiance and fast fealty
> Which I do owe unto all womankind *,

am bound to satisfy their natural and be-

* Spenser.

coming curiosity. Not, however, in this place; for though love has its bitters, I never will mix it up in the same chapter with physic. Daniel's passion for the Burgemeester's Daughter must be treated of in a chapter by itself, this being a mark of respect due to the subject, to her beauty, and to the dignity of Mynheer, her Wel Edel, Groot, Hoogh-Achtbaer father.

First, however, I must dispose of an objection.

There may be readers who, though they can understand why a lady instead of telling her love, should

> —— let concealment like a worm in the bud
> Feed on her damask cheek,

will think it absurd to believe that any man should fix his affections as Daniel did upon the Burgemeester's Daughter, on a person whom he had no hopes of obtaining, and with whom, as will presently appear, he never interchanged a word. I cannot help their incredulity. But if they will not believe me they may perhaps believe the newspapers, which, about the year 1810, related the following case in point.

"A short time since a curious circumstance happened. The Rector of St. Martin's parish was sent for to pray by a gentleman of the name of Wright, who lodged in St. James's Street, Pimlico. A few days afterwards Mr. Wright's solicitor called on the Rector, to inform him that Mr. Wright was dead, and had made a codicil to his will wherein he had left him 1000*l.*, and Mr. Abbott, the Speaker of the House of Commons, 2000*l.*, and all his personal property and estates, deer-park and fisheries, &c. to Lady Frances Bruce Brudenell, daughter of the Earl of Ailesbury. Upon the Rector's going to Lord Ailesbury's to inform her Ladyship, the house-steward said she was married to Sir Henry Wilson of Chelsea Park, but he would go to her Ladyship and inform her of the matter. Lady Frances said she did not know any such person as Mr. Wright, but desired the Steward to go to the Rector to get the whole particulars, and say she would wait on him the next day: she did so, and found to her great astonishment that the whole was true. She afterwards went to St. James's Street, and saw Mr. Wright in his coffin; and then she recollected him, as having been a great annoyance to her many years ago at the Opera House, where he had a box next to hers: he never spoke to her, but was continually watching her, look wherever she would, till at length she was under the necessity of requesting her friends to procure another box. The estates are from 20 to 30,000*l.* a-year. Lady Frances intends putting all her family into mourning out of respect."

Whether such a bequest ought to have been held good in law, and if so, whether it ought in conscience to have been accepted, are points upon which I should probably differ both from the Lord Chancellor, and the Lady Legatee.

CHAPTER LII.

SHOWING HOW THE YOUNG STUDENT FELL IN LOVE — AND HOW HE MADE THE BEST USE OF HIS MISFORTUNE.

> *Il creder, donne vaghe, è cortesia,*
> *Quando colui che scrive o che favella,*
> *Possa essere sospetto di bugia,*
> *Per dir qualcosa troppo rara e bella.*
> *Dunque chi ascolta questa istoria mea*
> *E non la crede frottola o novella*
> *Ma cosa vera — come ella è di fatto,*
> *Fa che di lui mi chiami soddisfatto.*
>
> *E pure che mi diate piena fede,*
> *De la dubbiezza altrui poco mi cale.*
>
> RICCIARDETTO.

DEAR Ladies, I can neither tell you the name of the Burgemeester's Daughter, nor of the Burgemeester himself. If I ever heard them they have escaped my recollection. The Doctor used to say his love for her was in two respects like the small-pox; for he took it by inoculation, and having taken it, he was secured from ever having the disease in a [illegible] dangerous form

The case was a very singular one. Had it not been so it is probable I should never have been made acquainted with it. Most men seem to consider their unsuccessful love, when it is over, as a folly which they neither like to speak of, nor to remember.

Daniel Dove never was introduced to the Burgemeester's Daughter, never was in company with her, and, as already has been intimated, never spoke to her. As for any hope of ever by any possibility obtaining a return of his affection, a devout Roman Catholic might upon much better grounds hope that Saint Ursula, or any of her Eleven Thousand Virgins would come from her place in Heaven to reward his devotion with a kiss. The gulph between Dives and Lazarus was not more insuperable than the distance between such an English Greeny at Leyden and a Burgemeester's Daughter.

Here, therefore, dear Ladies, you cannot look to read of

> *Le speranze, gli affetti,*
> *La data fe', le tenerezze, i primi*
> *Scambievoli sospiri, i primi sguardi.**

Nor will it be possible for me to give you

> *—l'idea di quel volto*
> *Dove apprese il suo core*
> *La prima volta a sospirar d'amore.**

This I cannot do; for I never saw her picture, nor heard her features described. And most likely if I had seen her herself, in her youth and beauty, the most accurate description that words could convey might be just as like Fair Rosamond, Helen, Rachael, or Eve. Suffice it to say that she was confessedly the beauty of that city, and of those parts.

But it was not for the fame of her beauty that Daniel fell in love with her: so little was there of this kind of romance in his nature, that report never raised in him the slightest desire of seeing her. Her beauty was no more than Hecuba's to him, till he saw it. But it so happened that having once seen it, he saw it frequently, at leisure, and always to the best advantage: "and so," said he, "I received the disease by inoculation."

Thus it was. There was at Leyden an English Presbyterian Kirk for the use of the English students, and any other persons who might choose to frequent it. Daniel felt the want there of that Liturgy in the use of which he had been trained up: and finding nothing which could attract him to that place of worship except the use of his own language,—which, moreover, was not used by the preacher in any way to his edification,—he listened willingly to the advice of the good man with whom he boarded, and this was, that, as soon as he had acquired a slight knowledge of the Dutch tongue, he should, as a means of improving himself in it, accompany the family to their parish church. Now this happened to be the very church which the Burgemeester and his family attended: and if the allotment of pews in that church had been laid out by Cupid himself, with the fore-purpose of catching Daniel as in a pitfall, his position there in relation to the Burgemeester's Daughter could not have been more exactly fixed.

"God forgive me!" said he; "for every Sunday while she was worshipping her Maker, I used to worship her."

But the folly went no farther than this; it led him into no act of absurdity, for he kept it to himself; and he even turned it to some advantage, or rather it shaped for itself a useful direction, in this way: having frequent and unobserved opportunity of observing her lovely face, the countenance became fixed so perfectly in his mind, that even after the lapse of forty years, he was sure, he said, that if he had possessed a painter's art, he could have produced her likeness. And having her beauty thus impressed upon his imagination, any other appeared to him only as a foil to it, during that part of his life when he was so circumstanced that it would have been an act of imprudence for him to run in love.

I smile to think how many of my readers, when they are reading this chapter aloud in a domestic circle, will *bring up* at the expression of *running in love;*—like a stage-coachman, who, driving at the smooth and steady pace of nine miles an hour on a macadamised road, comes upon some accidental obstruction only just in time to check the horses.

Amorosa who flies into love; and Ama-

* Metasia.

tura who flutters as if she were about to do the same; and Amoretta who dances into it, (poor creatures, God help them all three!) and Amanda,—Heaven bless her!—who will be led to it gently and leisurely along the path of discretion, they all make a sudden stop at the words.

CHAPTER LIII. P. I.

OF THE VARIOUS WAYS OF GETTING IN LOVE. A CHAPTER CONTAINING SOME USEFUL OBSERVATIONS, AND SOME BEAUTIFUL POETRY.

Let cavillers know, that as the Lord John answered the Queen in that Italian Guazzo, an old, a grave discreet man is fittest to discourse of love-matters; because he hath likely more experience, observed more, hath a more staid judgement, can better discern, resolve, discuss, advise, give better cautions and more solid precepts, better inform his auditors in such a subject, and, by reason of his riper years, sooner divert. BURTON.

SLIPS of the tongue are sometimes found very inconvenient by those persons who, owing to some unlucky want of correspondence between their wits and their utterance, say one thing when they mean to say another, or bolt out something which the slightest degree of forethought would have kept unsaid. But more serious mischief arises from that misuse of words which occurs in all inaccurate writers. Many are the men, who merely for want of understanding what they say, have blundered into heresies and erroneous assertions of every kind, which they have afterwards passionately and pertinaciously defended, till they have established themselves in the profession, if not in the belief, of some pernicious doctrine or opinion, to their own great injury and that of their deluded followers, and of the commonwealth.

There may be an opposite fault; for indeed upon the agathokakological globe there are opposite qualities always to be found in parallel degrees, north and south of the equator.

A man may dwell upon words till he becomes at length a mere precisian in speech. He may think of their meaning till he loses sight of all meaning, and they appear as dark and mysterious to him as chaos and outer night. "Death! Grave!" exclaims Goethe's suicide, "I understand not the words!" and so he who looks for its quintessence might exclaim of every word in the dictionary.

They who cannot swim should be contented with wading in the shallows: they who can may take to the deep water, no matter how deep, so it be clear. But let no one dive in the mud.

I said that Daniel fell in love with the Burgemeester's Daughter, and I made use of the usual expression because there it was the most appropriate: for the thing was accidental. He himself could not have been more surprised if, missing his way in a fog, and supposing himself to be in the Breedestraat of Leyden, where there is no canal, he had fallen into the water;—nor would he have been more completely over head and ears at once.

A man falls in love, just as he falls down stairs. It is an accident,—perhaps, and very probably a misfortune; something which he neither intended, nor foresaw, nor apprehended. But when he runs in love it is as when he runs in debt; it is done knowingly and intentionally; and very often rashly, and foolishly, even if not ridiculously, miserably, and ruinously.

Marriages that are made up at watering-places are mostly of this running sort; and there may be reason to think that they are even less likely to lead to—I will not say happiness, but to a very humble degree of contentment,—than those which are a plain business of bargain and sale; for into these latter a certain degree of prudence enters on both sides. But there is a distinction to be made here: the man who is married for mere worldly motives, without a spark of affection on the woman's part, may nevertheless get, in every worldly sense of the word, a good wife; and while English women continue to be what, thank Heaven they are, he is likely to do so: but when a woman is married for the sake of her fortune, the case is altered, and the chances are five hundred to one that she marries a villain, or at best a scoundrel.

Falling in love and running in love are both, as every body knows, common enough; and yet less so than what I shall call catching love. Where the love itself is imprudent, that is to say, where there is some just prudential cause or impediment why the two parties should not be joined together in holy matrimony, there is generally some degree of culpable imprudence in catching it, because the danger is always to be apprehended, and may in most cases be avoided. But sometimes the circumstances may be such as leave no room for censure, even when there may be most cause for compassion; and under such circumstances our friend, though the remembrance of the Burgemeester's daughter was too vivid in his imagination for him ever to run in love, or at that time deliberately to walk into it, as he afterwards did,—under such circumstances, I say, he took a severe affection of this kind. The story is a melancholy one, and I shall relate it not in this place.

The rarest, and surely the happiest marriages, are between those who have grown in love. Take the description of such a love in its rise and progress, ye thousands and tens of thousands who have what is called a taste for poetry,—take it in the sweet words of one of the sweetest and tenderest of English Poets; and if ye doubt upon the strength of my opinion whether Daniel deserves such praise, ask Leigh Hunt, or the Laureate, or Wordsworth, or Charles Lamb.

Ah! I remember well (and how can I
But evermore remember well) when first
Our flame began, when scarce we knew what was
The flame we felt; when as we sat and sighed
And looked upon each other, and conceived
Not what we ailed,—yet something we did ail;
And yet were well, and yet we were not well,
And what was our disease we could not tell.
Then would we kiss, then sigh, then look: and thus
In that first garden of our simpleness
We spent our childhood. But when years began
To reap the fruit of knowledge, ah how then
Would she with graver looks, with sweet stern brow,
Check my presumption and my forwardness;
Yet still would give me flowers, still would me show
What she would have me, yet not have me know.

Take also the passage that presently follows this; it alludes to a game which has long been obsolete,—but some fair reader I doubt not will remember the lines when she dances next.

And when in sport with other company
Of nymphs and shepherds we have met abroad,
How would she steal a look, and watch mine eye
Which way it went? And when at Barley-break
It came unto my turn to rescue her,
With what an earnest, swift and nimble pace
Would her affection make her feet to run,
And further run than to my hand! her race
Had no stop but my bosom, where no end.
And when we were to break again, how late
And loth her trembling hand would part with mine;
And with how slow a pace would she set forth
To meet the encountering party who contends
To attain her, scarce affording him her fingers' ends!*

CHAPTER LIV. P. I.

MORE CONCERNING LOVE AND MARRIAGE, AND MARRIAGE WITHOUT LOVE.

Nay, Cupid, pitch thy trammel where thou please,
Thou canst not fail to catch such fish as these.
QUARLES.

WHETHER chance or choice have most to do in the weighty concerns of love and matrimony, is as difficult a question, as whether chance or skill have most influence upon a game at backgammon. Both enter into the constitution of the game; and choice will always have some little to do with love, though so many other operating motives may be combined with it, that it sometimes bears a very insignificant part: but from marriage it is too frequently precluded on the one side, unwilling consent, and submission to painful circumstances supplying its place; and there is one sect of Christians (the Moravians), who, where they hold to the rigour of their institute, preclude it on both sides. They marry by lot; and if divorces ever take place among them, the scandal has not been divulged to the profaner world.

Choice, however, is exercised among all other Christians; or where not exercised, it is presumed by a fiction of law or of divinity, call it which you will. The husband even insists upon it in China where the pig is bought in a poke; for when pigsnie arrives and the

* HYMEN'S TRIUMPH.

purchaser opens the close sedan chair in which she has been conveyed to his house, if he does not like her looks at first sight, he shuts her up again and sends her back.

But when a bachelor who has no particular attachment, makes up his mind to take unto himself a wife, for those reasons to which Uncle Toby referred the Widow Wadman as being to be found in the Book of Common Prayer, how then to choose is a matter of much more difficulty, than one who has never considered it could suppose. It would not be paradoxical to assert that in the sort of choice which such a person makes, chance has a much greater part than either affection or judgment. To set about seeking a wife is like seeking one's fortune, and the probability of finding a good one in such a quest is less, though poor enough, Heaven knows, in both cases.

The bard has sung, God never form'd a soul
 Without its own peculiar mate, to meet
Its wandering half, when ripe to crown the whole
 Bright plan of bliss, most heavenly, most compleat!

But thousand evil things there are that hate
 To look on happiness; these hurt, impede,
And leagued with time, space, circumstance and fate,
 Keep kindred heart from heart, to pine and pant and bleed.

And as the dove to far Palmyra flying,
 From where her native founts of Antioch beam,
Weary, exhausted, longing, panting, sighing,
 Lights sadly at the desert's bitter stream;

So many a soul o'er life's drear desert faring,
 Love's pure congenial spring unfound, unquaff'd,
Suffers, recoils, then thirsty and despairing
 Of what it would, descends and sips the nearest draught.*

So sings Maria del Occidente, the most impassioned and most imaginative of all poetesses.

According to the new revelation of the Saint Simonians, every individual human being has had a fitting mate created, the one and only woman for every individual man, and the one and only man for every individual woman; and unless the persons so made, fitted and intended for each other, meet and are joined together in matrimonial bonds, there can be no perfect marriage for either, that harmonious union for which they were designed being frustrated for both. Read the words of the Chief of the New Hierarchy himself, Father Bazard: *Il n'y a sur la terre pour chaque homme qu'une seule femme, et pour chaque femme qu'un seul homme, qui soient destinés à former dans le mariage l'union harmonique du couple. — Grâce aux lumieres de cette revelation, les individus les plus avancés peuvent aussi dès aujourd'hui sentir et former le lien qui doit les unir dans le mariage.*

But if Sinner Simon and his disciples, — (most assuredly they ought to be unsainted!) — were right in this doctrine, happy marriages would be far more uncommon than they are; the man might with better likelihood of finding it look for a needle in a bottle of hay, than seek for his other half in this wide world; and the woman's chance would be so immeasurably less, that no intelligible form of figures could express her fraction of it.

The man who gets in love because he has determined to marry, instead of marrying because he is in love, goes about to private parties and to public places in search of a wife; and there he is attracted by a woman's appearance, and the figure which she makes in public, not by her amiable deportment, her domestic qualities and her good report. Watering-places might with equal propriety be called fishing places, because they are frequented by female anglers, who are in quest of such prey, the elder for their daughters, the younger for themselves. But it is a dangerous sport, for the fair Piscatrix is not more likely to catch a bonito, or a dorado, than she is to be caught by a shark.

Thomas Day, not old Thomas Day of the old glee, nor the young Thomas Day either, — a father and son whose names are married to immortal music, — but the Thomas Day who wrote Sandford and Merton, and who had a heart which generally led him right, and a head which as generally led him wrong; that Thomas Day thought that the best way of obtaining a wife to his mind, was to breed one up for himself. So he selected two little orphan girls from a charity school, with the intention of marrying in

* Zophiel.

due time the one whom he should like best. Of course such proper securities as could alone justify the managers of the charity in consenting to so uncommon a transaction, were required and given. The experiment succeeded in every thing—except its specific object; for he found at last that love was not a thing thus to be bespoken on either side; and his Lucretia and Sabrina, as he named them, grew up to be good wives for other men. I do not know whether the life of Thomas Day has yet found its appropriate place in the Wonderful Magazine, or in the collection entitled Eccentric Biography,—but the Reader may find it livelily related in Miss Seward's Life of Darwin.

The experiment of breeding a wife is not likely to be repeated. None but a most determined theorist would attempt it; and to carry it into effect would require considerable means of fortune, not to mention a more than ordinary share of patience: after which there must needs be a greater disparity of years than can be approved in theory upon any due consideration of human nature, and any reasonable estimate of the chances of human life.

CHAPTER LV. P. I.

THE AUTHOR'S LAST VISIT TO DONCASTER.

Fuere quondam hæc sed fuere;
Nunc ubi sint, rogitas? Id annos
Scire hos oportet scilicet. O bonæ
Musæ, O Lepôres—O Charites meræ!
O gaudia offuscata nullis
Litibus! O sine nube soles!

JANUS DOUZA.

I HAVE more to say, dear Ladies, upon that which to you is, and ought to be, the most interesting of all worldly subjects, matrimony, and the various ways by which it is brought about; but this is not the place for saying it. The Doctor is not at this time thinking of a wife: his heart can no more be taken so long as it retains the lively image of the Burgemeester's Daughter, than Troy-town while the Palladium was safe.

Imagine him, therefore, in the year of our Lord 1747, and in the twenty-sixth year of his age, returned to Doncaster, with the Burgemeester's Daughter, seated like the Lady in the Lobster, in his inmost breast; with physic in his head and at his fingers' ends; and with an appetite for knowledge which had long been feeding voraciously, digesting well, and increasing in its growth by what it fed on. Imagine him returned to Doncaster, and welcomed once more as a son by the worthy old Peter Hopkins and his good wife, in that comfortable habitation which I have heretofore described, and of which (as was at the same time stated) you may see a faithful representation in Miller's History of that good town; a faithful representation, I say, of what it was in 1804; the drawing was by Frederic Nash; and Edward Shirt made a shift to engrave it; the house had then undergone some alterations since the days when I frequented it; and now!—

Of all things in this our mortal pilgrimage one of the most joyful is the returning home after an absence which has been long enough to make the heart yearn with hope, and not sicken with it, and then to find when you arrive there that all is well. But the most purely painful of all painful things is to visit after a long, long interval of time the place which was once our home;—the most purely painful, because it is unmixed with fear, anxiety, disappointment, or any other emotion but what belongs to the sense of time and change, then pressing upon us with its whole unalleviated weight.

It was my fortune to leave Doncaster early in life, and, having passed *per varios casus*, and through as large a proportion of good and evil in my humble sphere, as the pious Æneas, though not exactly *per tot discrimina rerum*, not to see it again till after an absence of more than forty years, when my way happened to lie through that town. I should never have had heart purposely to visit it, for that would have been seeking sorrow; but to have made a circuit for the sake of avoiding the place would have been an act of weakness; and no man who has a proper degree of self-respect will do any thing of which he might justly feel ashamed.

It was evening, and late in autumn, when I entered Doncaster, and alighted at the Old Angel Inn. "The *Old* Angel!" said I to my fellow-traveller; "you see that even Angels on earth grow old!"

My companion knew how deeply I had been indebted to Dr. Dove, and with what affection I cherished his memory. We presently sallied forth to look at his former habitation. Totally unknown as I now am in Doncaster, (where there is probably not one living soul who remembers either me, or my very name,) I had determined to knock at the door, at a suitable hour on the morrow, and ask permission to enter the house in which I had passed so many happy and memorable hours, long ago. My age and appearance, I thought, might justify this liberty; and I intended also to go into the garden and see if any of the fruit trees were remaining, which my venerable friend had planted, and from which I had so often plucked and ate.

When we came there, there was nothing by which I could have recognised the spot, had it not been for the Mansion House that immediately adjoined it. Half of its site had been levelled to make room for a street or road which had been recently opened. Not a vestige remained of the garden behind. The remaining part of the house had been re-built; and when I read the name of R. Dennison on the door, it was something consolatory to see that the door itself was not the same which had so often opened to admit me.

Upon returning to the spot on the following morning I perceived that the part which had been re-built is employed as some sort of official appendage to the Mansion House; and on the naked side-wall now open to the new street, or road, I observed most distinctly where the old tall chimney had stood, and the outline of the old pointed roof. These were the only vestiges that remained; they could have no possible interest in any eyes but mine, which were likely never to behold them again; and indeed it was evident that they would soon be effaced as a deformity, and the naked side-wall smoothed over with plaster. But they will not be effaced from my memory, for they were the last traces of that dwelling which is the *Kebla* of my retrospective day-dreams, the *Sanctum Sanctorum* of my dearest recollections; and, like an apparition from the dead, once seen, they were never to be forgotten.

CHAPTER LVI. P. I.

A TRUCE WITH MELANCHOLY. GENTLEMEN SUCH AS THEY WERE IN THE YEAR OF OUR LORD 1747. A HINT TO YOUNG LADIES CONCERNING THEIR GREAT-GRANDMOTHERS.

> Fashions that are now called new,
> Have been worn by more than you;
> Elder times have used the same,
> Though these new ones get the name.
>
> MIDDLETON.

Well might Ben Jonson call bell-ringing "the poetry of steeples!" It is a poetry which in some heart or other is always sure to move an accordant key; and there is not much of the poetry, so called by courtesy because it bears the appearance of verse, of which this can be said with equal truth. Doncaster since I was one of its inhabitants had been so greatly changed, — (improved I ought to say, for its outward changes had really been improvements,) — that there was nothing but my own recollections to carry me back into the past, till the clock of St. George's struck nine, on the evening of our arrival, and its chimes began to measure out the same time in the same tones which I used to hear as regularly as the hours came round, forty long years ago.

Enough of this! My visit to Doncaster was incidentally introduced by the comparison which I could not choose but make between such a return, and that of the Student from Leyden. We must now revert to the point from whence I strayed, and go farther back than the forty years over which the chimes, as if with magic, had transported me. We must go back to the year 1747, when gentlemen wore sky-blue coats, with silver button holes and huge cuffs extending more than half way from the middle of the hand to the elbow, short breeches just reaching to the silver garters at the knee, and embroidered waistcoats with long flaps which came almost as low. Were I to describe Daniel Dove in the wig which he then wore, and which observed a modest mean between the bush of the Apothecary and the consequential foretop of the Physician with its depending knots, fore and aft; were I to describe him in a sober suit of brown or snuff-coloured dittos, such as beseemed his profession, but with cuffs of the dimensions, waistcoat-flaps of the length, and breeches of the brevity before mentioned; Amorosa and Amatura and Amoretta would exclaim that love ought never to be named in connection with such a figure,—Amabilis, sweet girl, in the very bloom of innocence and opening youth, would declare she never could love such a creature, and Amanda herself would smile, not contemptuously, nor at her idea of the man, but at the mutability of fashion. Smile if you will, young Ladies! your great-grandmothers wore large hoops, peaked stomachers, and modesty-bits *; their riding-habits and waistcoats were trimmed with silver, and they had very gentleman-like perukes for riding in, as well as gentleman-like cocked hats. Yet, young Ladies, they were as gay and giddy in their time as you are now; they were as attractive and as lovely; they were not less ready than you are to laugh at the fashions of those who had gone before them; they were wooed and won by gentlemen in short breeches, long flapped waistcoats, large cuffs, and tie-wigs; and the wooing and winning proceeded much in the same manner as it had done in the generations before them, as the same agreeable part of this world's business proceeds among yourselves, and as it will proceed when you will be as little thought of by your great-grand-daughters as your great-grand-mothers are at this time by you. What care you for your great-grand-mothers!

The law of entails sufficiently proves that our care for our posterity is carried far, sometimes indeed beyond what is reasonable and just. On the other hand, it is certain that the sense of relationship in the ascending line produces in general little other feeling than that of pride in the haughty and high-born. That it should be so to a certain degree, is in the order of nature and for the general good: but that in our selfish state of society this indifference for our ancestors is greater than the order of nature would of itself produce, may be concluded from the very different feeling which prevailed among some of the ancients, and still prevails in other parts of the world.

He who said that he did not see why he should be expected to do any thing for Posterity, when Posterity had done nothing for him, might be deemed to have shown as much worthlessness as wit in this saying, if it were any thing more than the sportive sally of a light-hearted man. Yet one who "keeps his heart with all diligence," knowing that "out of it are the issues of life," will take heed never lightly to entertain a thought that seems to make light of a duty,—still less will he give it utterance. We owe much to Posterity, nothing less than all that we have received from our Forefathers. And for myself I should be unwilling to believe that nothing is due from us to our ancestors. If I did not acquire this feeling from the person who is the subject of these volumes, it was at least confirmed by him. He used to say that one of the gratifications which he promised himself after death, was that of becoming acquainted with all his progenitors, in order, degree above degree, up to Noah, and from him up to our first parents. "But," said he, "though I mean to proceed regularly step by step, curiosity will make me in one instance trespass upon this proper arrangement, and I shall take the earliest opportunity of paying my respects to Adam and Eve."

* Probably the same as the Modesty-piece. Johnson quotes the following from the Guardian. "A narrow lace which runs along the upper part of the stays before, being a part of the tucker, is called the *Modesty-piece*." —*in v.*

CHAPTER LVII. P. I.

AN ATTEMPT IS MADE TO REMOVE THE UNPLEASANT IMPRESSION PRODUCED UPON THE LADIES BY THE DOCTOR'S TIE-WIG AND HIS SUIT OF SNUFF-COLOURED DITTOS.

So full of shapes is fancy
That it alone is high fantastical.
TWELFTH NIGHT.

I MUST not allow the feminine part of my readers to suppose that the Doctor, when in his prime of life, was not a very likeable person in appearance, as well as in every thing else, although he wore what, in the middle of the last century, was the costume of a respectable country practitioner in medicine. Though at Leyden he could only look at a Burgemeester's daughter as a cat may look at a King, there was not a Mayor or Alderman's daughter in Doncaster who would have thought herself disparaged if he had fixed his eyes upon her, and made her a proffer of his hand.

Yet, as in the opinion of many dress "makes the man," and any thing which departs widely from the standard of dress, "the fellow," I must endeavour to give those young Ladies who are influenced more than they ought to be, and perhaps more than they are aware, by such an opinion, a more favourable notion of the Doctor's appearance, than they are likely to have if they bring him before their eyes in the fashion of his times. It will not assist this intention on my part, if I request you to look at him as you would look at a friend who was dressed in such a costume for a masquerade or a fancy ball; for your friend would expect and wish to be laughed at, having assumed the dress for that benevolent purpose. Well, then, let us take off the aforesaid sad snuff-colour coat with broad deep cuffs, still the waistcoat with its long flaps, and the breeches that barely reach to the knee, will provoke your merriment. We must not proceed farther in undressing him; and if I conceal these under a loose morning gown of green damask, the insuperable perriwig would still remain.

Let me then present him to your imagination, setting forth on horseback in that sort of weather which no man encounters voluntarily, but which men of his profession who practise in the Country are called upon to face at all seasons and all hours. Look at him in a great coat of the closest texture that the looms of Leeds could furnish,—one of those dreadnoughts, the utility of which sets fashion at defiance. You will not observe his boot-stockings coming high above the knees; the coat covers them; and if it did not, you would be far from despising them now. His tie-wig is all but hidden under a hat, the brim of which is broad enough to answer in some degree the use of an umbrella. Look at him now, about to set off on some case of emergency; with haste in his expressive eyes, and a cast of thoughtful anxiety over one of the most benignant countenances that Nature ever impressed with the characters of good humour and good sense!

Was he, then, so handsome? you say. Nay, Ladies, I know not whether you would have called him so; for, among the things which were too wonderful for him, yea, which he knew not, I suspect that Solomon might have included a woman's notion of handsomeness in man.

CHAPTER LVIII. P. I.

CONCERNING THE PORTRAIT OF DOCTOR DANIEL DOVE.

The sure traveller,
Though he alight sometimes still goeth on.
HERBERT.

THERE is no portrait of Dr. Daniel Dove.

And there Horrebow, the Natural Historian of Iceland,—if Horrebow had been his biographer—would have ended this chapter.*

---

* The author of the Doctor, &c.; had evidently in view the end of the Laureate's Second Letter in his Vindiciæ Eccles. Anglic. "And with this I conclude a letter which may remind the reader of the Chapter concerning Owls in Horrebow's Natural History of Iceland."

"Here perchance,"—(observe, Reader, I am speaking now in the words of the Lord Keeper, Sir Nicholas Bacon,)—"here perchance a question would be asked—(and yet I do marvel to hear a question made of so plain a matter,)—what should be the cause of this? If it were asked,"—(still the Lord Keeper speaketh) "thus I mean to answer: That I think no man so blind but seeth it, no man so deaf but heareth it, nor no man so ignorant but understandeth it." "*Il y a des demandes si sottes qu'on ne les sçauroit resoudre par autre moyen que par la moquerie et les absurdities; afin qu'une sottise pousse l'autre.*"*

But some reader may ask what have I answered here, or rather what have I brought forward the great authority of the Lord Keeper Sir Nicholas Bacon and the arch-vituperator P. Garasse, to answer for me? Do I take it for granted that the cause wherefore there is no portrait of Dr. Daniel Dove should be thus apparent? or the reason why, there being no such portrait, Horrebow should simply have said so, and having so said, end therewith the chapter which he had commenced upon the subject.

O, gentle reader, you who ask this pertinent question,—I entirely agree with you! there is nothing more desirable in composition than perspicuity; and in perspicuity precision is implied. Of the Author who has attained it in his style, it may indeed be said, *omne tulit punctum*, so far as relates to style; for all other graces, those only excepted which only genius can impart, will necessarily follow. Nothing is so desirable, and yet it should seem that nothing is so difficult. He who thinks least about it when he is engaged in composition will be most likely to attain it, for no man ever attained it by labouring for it. Read all the treatises upon composition that ever were composed, and you will find nothing which conveys so much useful instruction as the account given by John Wesley of his own way of writing. "I never think of my style," says he; "but just set down the words that come first. Only when I transcribe any thing for the press, then I think it my duty to see that every phrase be clear, pure and proper: conciseness, which is now as it were natural to me, brings *quantum sufficit* of strength. If after all I observe any stiff expression, I throw it out neck and shoulders." Let your words take their course freely; they will then dispose themselves in their natural order, and make your meaning plain:—that is, Mr. Author, supposing you have a meaning; and that it is not an insidious, and for that reason, a covert one. With all the head-work that there is in these volumes, and all the heart-work too, I have not bitten my nails over a single sentence which they contain. I do not say that my hand has not sometimes been passed across my brow; nor that the fingers of my left hand have not played with the hair upon my forehead,—like Thalaba's with the grass that grew beside Oneiza's tomb.

No people have pretended to so much precision in their language as the Turks. They have not only verbs active, passive, transitive, and reciprocal, but also verbs cooperative, verbs meditative, verbs frequentative, verbs negative, and verbs impossible; and, moreover, they have what are called verbs of opinion, and verbs of knowledge. The latter are used when the speaker means it to be understood that he speaks of his own sure knowledge, and is absolutely certain of what he asserts; the former when he advances it only as what he thinks likely, or believes upon the testimony of others.

Now in the Turkish language the word whereon both the meaning and the construction of the sentence depend, is placed at the end of a sentence, which extends not unfrequently to ten, fifteen, or twenty lines. What, therefore, they might gain in accuracy by this nice distinction of verbs must be more than counterbalanced by the ambiguity consequent upon long-windedness. And, notwithstanding their conscientious moods, they are not more remarkable for veracity than their neighbours who, in ancient times, made so much use of the indefinite tenses, and were said to be always liars.

* Garasse.

We have a sect in our own country who profess to use a strict and sincere plainness of speech; they call their dialect *the plain language*, and yet they are notorious for making a studied precision in their words answer all the purposes of equivocation.

CHAPTER LIX. P. I.

SHOWING WHAT THAT QUESTION WAS, WHICH WAS ANSWERED BEFORE IT WAS ASKED.

Chacun a son stile; le mien, comme vouz voyez, n'est pas laconique. ME. DE SEVIGNE'.

IN reporting progress upon the subject of the preceding chapter, it appears that the question asked concerning the question that was answered, was not itself answered in that chapter; so that it still remains to be explained what it was that was so obvious as to require no other answer than the answer that was there given; whether it was the reason why there is no portrait of Dr. Daniel Dove? or the reason why Horrebow, if he had been the author of this book, would simply have said that there was none, and have said nothing more about it?

The question which was answered related to Horrebow. He would have said nothing more about the matter, because he would have thought there was nothing more to say; or because he agreed with Britain's old rhyming Remembrancer, that although

> More might be said hereof to make a proof,
> Yet more to say were more than is enough.

But if there be readers who admire a style of such barren brevity, I must tell them in the words of Estienne Pasquier, that *je fais grande conscience d'alambiquer mon esprit en telle espece d'escrite pour leur complaire.* Do they take me for a Bottle-Conjurer that I am to compress myself into a quart, wine-merchants' measure, and be corked down? I must have "ample room and verge enough," — a large canvass such as Haydon requires, and as Rubens required before him. When I pour out nectar for my guests it must be into

> —— a bowl
> Large as my capacious soul.

It is true I might have contented myself with merely saying there is no portrait of my venerable friend; and the benevolent reader would have been satisfied with the information, while at the same time he wished there had been one, and perhaps involuntarily sighed at thinking there was not. But I have duties to perform; first to the memory of my most dear philosopher and friend; secondly, to myself; thirdly, to posterity, which in this matter I cannot conscientiously prefer either to myself or my friend; fourthly, to the benevolent reader who delighteth in this book, and consequently loveth me therefore, and whom therefore I love, though, notwithstanding here is love for love between us, we know not each other now, and never shall! fourthly, I say to the benevolent reader, or rather readers, *utriusque generis;* and, fifthly, to the Public for the time being. "England expects every man to do his duty;" and England's expectation would not be disappointed if every Englishman were to perform his as faithfully and fully as I will do mine. Mark me, Reader, it is only of my duties to England, and to the parties above-mentioned that I speak; other duties I am accountable for elsewhere. God forbid that I should ever speak of them in this strain, or ever think of them otherwise than in humility and fear!

CHAPTER LX. P. I.

SHOWING CAUSE WHY THE QUESTION WHICH WAS NOT ASKED OUGHT TO BE ANSWERED.

> Nay in troth I talk but coarsely,
> But I hold it comfortable for the understanding.
> BEAUMONT AND FLETCHER.

"WHAT, more buffoonery!" says the Honourable Fastidious Feeble-wit, who condescends to act occasionally as Small Critic to the Court Journal: — "what, still more of this buffoonery!"

"Yes, Sir, — *vous ne recevrez de moy, sur le commencement et milieu de celuy-cy mien chapitre que bouffonnerie; et toutesfois bouffonnerie qui porte quant à soy une philosophie et* *contemplation générale de la vanité de ce monde.*" *

"More absurdities still!" says Lord Make-motion Ganderman, "more and more absurdities!"

"Ay, my Lord!" as the Gracioso says in one of Calderon's Plays,

> *¿ sino digo lo que quiero,*
> *de que me sirve ser loco?*

"Ay, my Lord!" as the old Spaniard says in his national poesy, "*mas, y mas, y mas, y mas,*" more, and more, and more, and more. You may live to learn what vaunted maxims of your political philosophy are nothing else than absurdities in masquerade; what old and exploded follies there are, which with a little vamping and varnishing pass for new and wonderful discoveries;

> What a world of businesses
> Which by interpretation are mere nothings! †

This you may live to learn. As for my absurdities, they may seem very much beneath your sapience; but when I say *hæ nugæ seria ducunt*, (for a trite quotation when well-set is as good as one that will be new to every body,) let me add, my Lord, that it will be well both for you and your country, if your practical absurdities do not draw after them consequences of a very different dye!

No, my Lord, as well as Ay, my Lord!

> Never made man of woman born
> Of a bullock's tail, a blowing-horn;
> Nor can an ass's hide disguise
> A lion, if he ramp and rise.‡

"More fooling," exclaims Dr. Dense: he takes off his spectacles, lays them on the table beside him, with a look of despair, and applies to the snuff-box for consolation. It is a capacious box, and the Doctor's servant takes care that his master shall never find in it a deficiency of the best rappee. "More fooling!" says that worthy Doctor.

Fooling, say you, my learned Dr. Dense? Chiabrera will tell you

> —— *che non è ria*
> *Una gentil follia,*—

my erudite and good Doctor;

> But do you know what fooling is? true fooling,—
> The circumstances that belong unto it?
> For every idle knave that shews his teeth,
> Wants, and would live, can juggle, tumble, fiddle,
> Make a dog-face, or can abuse his fellow,
> Is not a fool at first dash.§

It is easy to talk of fooling and of folly, *mais d'en savoir les ordres, les rangs, les distinctions; de connoître ces différences délicates qu'il y a de Folie à Folie; les affinités et les alliances qui se trouvent entre la Sagesse et cette même Folie*, as Saint Evremond says; to know this is not under every one's nightcap; and perhaps, my learned Doctor, may not be under your wig, orthodox and in full buckle as it is.

The Doctor is all astonishment, and almost begins to doubt whether I am fooling in earnest. Ay, Doctor! you meet in this world with false mirth as often as with false gravity; the grinning hypocrite is not a more uncommon character than the groaning one. As much light discourse comes from a heavy heart, as from a hollow one; and from a full mind as from an empty head. "Levity," says Mr. Danby, "is sometimes a refuge from the gloom of seriousness. A man may whistle 'for want of thought,' or from having too much of it."

"Poor creature!" says the Reverend Philocalvin Frybabe. "Poor creature! little does he think what an account he must one day render for every idle word!"

And what account, odious man, if thou art a hypocrite, and hardly less odious if thou art sincere in thine abominable creed, —what account wilt thou render for thine extempore prayers and thy set discourses? My words, idle as thou mayest deem them, will never stupify the intellect, nor harden the heart, nor besot the conscience like an opiate drug!

"Such facetiousness," saith Barrow, "is not unreasonable or unlawful which ministereth harmless divertisement and delight to conversation; harmless, I say, that is, not entrenching upon piety, not infringing charity or justice, not disturbing peace. For Christianity is not so tetrical, so harsh, so

* Pasquier. † Beaumont and Fletcher. ‡ Peele.

§ Beaumont and Fletcher.

envious as to bar us continually from innocent, much less from wholesome and useful pleasure, such as human life doth need or require. And if jocular discourse may serve to good purposes of this kind; if it may be apt to raise our drooping spirits, to allay our irksome cares, to whet our blunted industry, to recreate our minds, being tired and cloyed with graver occupations; if it may breed alacrity, or maintain good-humour among us; if it may conduce to sweeten conversation and endear society, then is it not inconvenient, or unprofitable. If for those ends we may use other recreations, employing on them our ears and eyes, our hands and feet, our other instruments of sense and motion; why may we not as well to them accommodate our organs of speech and interior sense? Why should those games which excite our wit and fancies be less reasonable than those whereby our grosser parts and faculties are exercised? yea, why are not those more reasonable, since they are performed in a manly way, and have in them a smack of reason; seeing also they may be so managed, as not only to divert and please, but to improve and profit the mind, rousing and quickening it, yea, sometimes enlightening and instructing it, by good sense conveyed in jocular expression."

But think not that in thus producing the authority of one of the wisest and best of men, I offer any apology for my levities to your Gravityships! they need it not and you deserve it not.

Questi —
Son fatti per dar pasto a gl' ignoranti;
Ma voi ch' avete gl' intelletti sani,
Mirate la dottrina che s'asconde
Sotto queste coperte alte e profonde.

Le cose belle, e preziose, e care,
Saporite, soavi e dilicate,
Scoperte in man non si debbon portare
*Perchè da' porci non sieno imbrattate.**

Gentlemen, you have made me break the word of promise both to the eye and ear. I began this chapter with the intention of showing to the reader's entire satisfaction, why the question which was not asked, ought to be answered; and now another chapter must be appropriated to that matter! Many things happen between the cup and the lip, and between the beginning of a chapter and the conclusion thereof.

CHAPTER LXI. P. I.

WHEREIN THE QUESTION IS ANSWERED WHICH OUGHT TO HAVE BEEN ASKED.

Ajutami, tu penna, et calamaio,
Ch' io hò tra mano una materia asciutta.
MATTIO FRANZESI.

WHEREFORE there is no portrait of my excellent friend, is a question which ought to be answered, because the solution will exhibit something of what in the words of the old drinking song he used to call his "poor way of thinking." And it is a question which may well be asked, seeing that in the circle wherein he moved, there were some persons of liberal habits and feelings as well as liberal fortune, who enjoyed his peculiarities, placed the fullest reliance upon his professional skill, appreciated most highly his moral and intellectual character, and were indeed personally attached to him in no ordinary degree.

For another reason also ought this question to be resolved; a reason which whatever the reader may think, has the more weight with me, because it nearly concerns myself. "There is indeed," says the Philosopher of Bemerton, "a near relation between seriousness and wisdom, and one is a most excellent friend to the other. A man of a serious, sedate and considerate temper, as he is always in a ready disposition for meditation, (the best improvement both of knowledge and manners,) so he thinks without disturbance, enters not upon another notion till he is master of the first, and so makes clean work with it: — whereas a man of a loose, volatile and shattered humour, thinks only by fits and starts, now and then in a morning interval, when the serious mood comes upon him;

* ORLANDO INNAMORATO.

and even then too, let but the least trifle cross his way, and his desultorious fancy presently takes the scent, leaves the unfinished and half-mangled notion, and skips away in pursuit of the new game." Reader, it must be my care not to come under this condemnation; and therefore I must follow to the end the subject which is before me: *quare autem nobis — dicendum videtur, ne temere secuti putemur; et breviter dicendum, ne in hujusmodi rebus diutius, quam ratio præcipiendi postulet commoremur.**

Mr. Copley of Netherhall was particularly desirous of possessing this so-much-by-us-now-desiderated likeness, and would have invited an Artist from London, if the Doctor could have been prevailed upon to sit for it; but to this no persuasions could induce him. He never assigned a reason for this determination, and indeed always evaded the subject when it was introduced, letting it at the same time plainly be perceived that he was averse to it, and wished not to be so pressed as to draw from him a direct refusal. But once when the desire had been urged with some seriousness, he replied that he was the last of his race, and if he were to be the first who had his portrait taken, well might they who looked at it exclaim with Solomon, "Vanity of vanities!"

In that thought indeed it was that the root of his objection lay. *Pauli in domo, præter se nemo superest*, is one of the most melancholy reflections to which Paulus Æmilius gave utterance in that speech of his which is recorded by Livy. The speedy extinction of his family in his own person was often in the Doctor's mind; and he would sometimes touch upon it when, in his moods of autumnal feeling, he was conversing with those persons whom he had received into his heart of hearts. Unworthy as I was, it was my privilege and happiness to be one of them; and at such times his deepest feelings could not have been expressed more unreservedly, if he had given them utterance in poetry or in prayer.

Blessed as he had been in all other things to the extent of his wishes, it would be unreasonable in him, he said, to look upon this as a misfortune; so to repine would indicate little sense of gratitude to that bountiful Providence which had so eminently favoured him; little also of religious acquiescence in its will. It was not by any sore calamity nor series of afflictions that the extinction of his family had been brought on; the diminution had been gradual, as if to show that their uses upon earth were done. His grandfather had only had two children; his parents but one, and that one was now *ultimus suorum.* They had ever been a family in good repute, walking inoffensively towards all men, uprightly with their neighbours, and humbly with their God; and perhaps this extinction was their reward. For what Solon said of individuals, that no one could truly be called happy till his life had terminated in a happy death, holds equally true of families.

Perhaps, too, this timely extinction was ordained in mercy, to avert consequences which might else so probably have arisen from his forsaking the station in which he was born; a lowly, but safe station, exposed to fewer dangers, trials, or temptations, than any other in this age or country, with which he was enabled to compare it. The sentiment with which Sanazzaro concludes his Arcadia was often in his mind, not as derived from that famous author, but self-originated: *per cosa vera ed indubitata tener ti puoi, che chi più di nascoso e più lontano dalla moltitudine vive, miglior vive; e colui trà mortali si può con più verità chiamar beato, che senza invidia delle altrui grandezze, con modesto animo della sua fortuna si contenta.* His father had removed him from that station; he would not say unwisely, for his father was a wise and good man, if ever man deserved to be so called; and he could not say unhappily; for assuredly he knew that all the blessings which had earnestly been prayed for, had attended the determination. Through that blessing he had obtained the whole benefit which his father desired for him, and had escaped evils which perhaps had not been fully apprehended. His in-

* Cicero.

tellectual part had received all the improvement of which it was capable, and his moral nature had sustained no injury in the process; nor had his faith been shaken, but stood firm, resting upon a sure foundation. But the entail of humble safety had been, as it were, cut off; the birth-right—so to speak—had been renounced. His children, if God had given him children, must have mingled in the world, there to shape for themselves their lot of good or evil; and he knew enough of the world to know how manifold and how insidious are the dangers, which, in all its paths, beset us. He never could have been to them what his father had been to him;—that was impossible. They could have had none of those hallowing influences both of society and solitude to act upon them, which had imbued his heart betimes, and impressed upon his youthful mind a character that no after circumstances could corrupt. They must inevitably have been exposed to more danger, and could not have been so well armed against it. That consideration reconciled him to being childless. God, who knew what was best for him, had ordained that it should be so; and he did not, and ought not, to regret, that having been the most cultivated of his race, and so far the happiest, it was decreed that he should be the last. God's will is best.

Ὣς ἔφατ' εὐχόμενος; for with some aspiration of piety he usually concluded his more serious discourse, either giving it utterance, or with a silent motion of the lips, which the expression of his countenance, as well as the tenour of what had gone before, rendered intelligible to those who knew him as I did.

CHAPTER LXII.

IN WHICH IS RELATED THE DISCOVERY OF A CERTAIN PORTRAIT AT DONCASTER.

Call in the Barber! If the tale be long
He'll cut it short, I trust. MIDDLETON.

HERE I must relate a circumstance which occurred during the few hours of my last, and by me ever-to-be-remembered visit to Doncaster. As we were on the way from the Old Angel Inn to the Mansion House, adjoining which stood, or to speak more accurately had stood, the Kebla to which the steps of my pilgrimage were bent, we were attracted by a small but picturesque group in a shaving-shop, exhibited in strong relief by the light of a blazing fire, and of some glaring lamps. It was late in autumn and on a Saturday evening, at which time those persons in humble life, who cannot shave themselves, and whose sense of religion leads them to think that what may be done on the Saturday night ought not to be put off till the Sunday morning, settle their weekly account with their beards. There was not story enough in the scene to have supplied Wilkie with a subject for his admirable genius to work upon, but he would certainly have sketched the group if he had seen it as we did. Stopping for a minute, at civil distance from the door, we observed a picture over the fire-place, and it seemed so remarkable that we asked permission to go in and look at it more nearly. It was an unfinished portrait, evidently of no common person, and by no common hand; and as evidently it had been painted many years ago. The head was so nearly finished that nothing seemed wanting to complete the likeness; the breast and shoulders were faintly sketched in a sort of whitewash which gave them the appearance of being covered with a cloth. Upon asking the master of the shop if he could tell us whose portrait it was, Mambrino, who seemed to be a good-natured fellow, and was pleased at our making the inquiry, replied that it had been in his possession many years, before he knew himself. A friend of his had made him a present of it, because, he said, the gentleman looked by his dress as if he was just ready to be shaved, and had an apron under his chin; and therefore his shop was the properest place for it. One day, however, the picture attracted the notice of a passing stranger, as it had done ours, and he recognised it for a portrait of Garrick. It certainly was so; and any one who knows Garrick's face may satisfy himself of this when he happens to be in Doncaster. Mambrino's shop is not far from the Old Angel, and on the same side of the street.

My companion told me that when we entered the shop he had begun to hope it might prove to be a portrait of my old friend: he seemed even to be disappointed that we had not fallen upon such a discovery, supposing that it would have gratified me beyond measure. But upon considering in my own mind if this would have been the case, two questions presented themselves. The first was, whether knowing as I did that the Doctor never sate for his portrait, and knowing also confidentially the reason why he never could be persuaded to do so, or rather the feeling which possessed him on that subject,—knowing these things, I say, the first question was, whether if a stolen likeness had been discovered, I ought to have rejoiced in the discovery. For as I certainly should have endeavoured to purchase the picture, I should then have had to decide whether or not it was my duty to destroy it; for which,—or, on the other hand, for preserving it,—so many strong reasons and so many refined ones, might have been produced, *pro* and *con*, that I could not have done either one or the other, without distrusting the justice of my own determination: if I preserved it, I should continually be self-accused for doing wrong; if I destroyed it, self-reproaches would pursue me for having done what was irretrievable; so that while I lived I should never have been out of my own Court of Conscience. And let me tell you, Reader, that to be impleaded in that Court is even worse than being brought into the Court of Chancery.

Secondly, the more curious question occurred, whether if there had been a portrait of Dr. Dove, it would have been like him.

"That," says Mr. Everydayman, "is as it might happen."

"Pardon me, Sir; my question does not regard happening. Chance has nothing to do with the matter. The thing queried is whether it could or could not have been."

And before I proceed to consider that question, I shall take the counsel which Catwg the Wise gave to his pupil Taliesin; and which by these presents I recommend to every reader who may be disposed to consider himself for the time being as mine:

"Think before thou speakest;
First, what thou shalt speak;
Secondly, why thou shouldest speak;
Thirdly, to whom thou mayest have to speak;
Fourthly, about whom (or what) thou art to speak;
Fifthly, what will come from what thou mayest speak;
Sixthly, what may be the benefit from what thou shalt speak;
Seventhly, who may be listening to what thou shalt speak.

Put thy word on thy fingers' ends before thou speakest it, and turn it these seven ways before thou speakest it; and there will never come any harm from what thou shalt say!

Catwg the Wise delivered this counsel to Taliesin, Chief of Bards, in giving him his blessing."

CHAPTER LXIII.

A DISCUSSION CONCERNING THE QUESTION LAST PROPOSED.

Questo è bene un de' più profondi passi
Che noi habbiamo ancora oggi tentato;
E non è mica da huomini bassi.

AGNOLO FIRENZUOLA.

GOOD and satisfactory likenesses may, beyond all doubt, be taken of Mr. Everydayman himself, and indeed of most persons: and were it otherwise, portrait-painting would be a worse profession than it is, though too many an unfortunate artist has reason bitterly to regret that he possessed the talents which tempted him to engage in it. There are few faces of which even a mediocre painter cannot produce what is called a staring likeness, and Sir Thomas Lawrence a handsome one;

Sir Thomas is the painter who pleases every body!

But there are some few faces with which no artist can succeed so as to please himself, (if he has a true feeling for his own art,) or to content those persons who are best acquainted with the living countenance. This is the case where the character predominates over the features, and that character itself is one in which many and seemingly opposite qualities are compounded. Garrick in Abel Drugger, Garrick in Sir John Brute, and Garrick in King Lear, presented three faces as different as were the parts which he personated; yet the portraits which have been published of him in those parts may be identified by the same marked features, which, flexible as they were rendered by his histrionic power, still under all changes retained their strength and their peculiarity. But where the same flexibility exists and the features are not so peculiar or prominent, the character is then given by what is fleeting, not by what is fixed; and it is more difficult to hit a likeness of this kind than to paint a rainbow.

Now I cannot but think that the Doctor's countenance was of this kind. I can call it to mind as vividly as it appears to me in dreams; but I could impart no notion of it by description. Words cannot delineate a single feature of his face,—such words at least as my knowledge enables me to use. A sculptor, if he had measured it, might have given you technically the relative proportions of his face in all its parts: a painter might describe the facial angle, and how the eyes were set, and if they were well-slit, and how the lips were formed, and whether the chin was in the just mean between rueful length and spectatorial brevity; and whether he could have passed over Strasburgh Bridge* without hearing any observations made upon his nose. My own opinion is that the sentinel would have had something to say upon that subject; and if he had been a Protestant Soldier (which, if an Alsacian, he was likely to be) and accustomed to read the Bible, he might have been reminded by it of the Tower of Lebanon, looking towards Damascus; for, as an Italian Poet says,

> —— *in prospettiva*
> *Ne mostra un barbacane sforacchiato.**

I might venture also to apply to the Doctor's nose that safe generality by which Alcina's is described in the Orlando Furioso.

> *Quindi il naso, per mezzo il viso scende,*
> *Che non trova l'invidia ove l'emende.*

But farther than this, which amounts to no more than a doubtful opinion and a faint adumbration, I can say nothing that would assist any reader to form an idea at once definite and just of any part of the Doctor's face. I cannot even positively say what was the colour of his eyes. I only know that mirth sparkled in them, scorn flashed from them, thought beamed in them, benevolence glistened in them; that they were easily moved to smiles, easily to tears. No barometer ever indicated more faithfully the changes of the atmosphere than his countenance corresponded to the emotions of his mind; but with a mind which might truly be said to have been

> —— so various, that it seemed to be
> Not one, but all mankind's epitome,

thus various, not in its principles, or passions, or pursuits, but in its inquiries, and fancies, and speculations, and so alert that nothing seemed to escape its ever watchful and active apprehension,—with such a mind the countenance that was its faithful index was perpetually varying: its likeness, therefore, at any one moment could but represent a fraction of the character which identified it, and which left upon you an indescribable and inimitable impression resulting from its totality, though, in its totality, it never was and never could be seen.

Have I made myself understood?

I mean to say that the ideal face of any one to whom we are strongly and tenderly attached,—that face which is enshrined in our heart of hearts and which comes to us in dreams long after it has mouldered in the

* He hath a long nose with a bending ridge;
It might be worthy of notice on Strasburg Bridge.
ROBERT THE RHYMER'S, &c.

* MATTIO FRANZESI.

grave,—that face is not the exact mechanical countenance of the beloved person, not the countenance that we ever actually behold, but its abstract, its idealisation, or rather, its realisation; the spirit of the countenance, its essence and its life. And the finer the character, and the more various its intellectual powers, the more must this true εἴδωλον differ from the most faithful likeness that a painter or a sculptor can produce.

Therefore I conclude that if there had been a portrait of Dr. Daniel Dove, it could not have been like him, for it was as impossible to paint the character which constituted the identity of his countenance, as to paint the flavour of an apple, or the fragrance of a rose.

CHAPTER LXIV.

DEFENCE OF PORTRAIT-PAINTING. A SYSTEM OF MORAL COSMETICS RECOMMENDED TO THE LADIES. GWILLIM. SIR T. LAWRENCE. GEORGE WITHER. APPLICATION TO THE SUBJECT OF THIS WORK.

Pingitur in tabulis formæ peritura venustas,
Vivat ut in tabulis, quod perit in facie.

OWEN.

THE reader will mistake me greatly if he supposes that in showing why it was impossible there should be a good portrait of Dr. Daniel Dove, I meant to depreciate the art of portrait-painting. I have a very high respect for that art, and no person can be more sincerely persuaded of its moral uses. The great number of portraits in the annual exhibitions of our Royal Academy is so far from displeasing me that I have always regarded it as a symptom of wholesome feeling in the nation,—an unequivocal proof that the domestic and social affections are still existing among us in their proper strength, and cherished as they ought to be. And when I have heard at any time observations of the would-be-witty kind upon the vanity of those who allow their portraits thus to be hung up for public view, I have generally perceived that the remark implied a much greater degree of conceit in the speaker. As for allowing the portrait to be exhibited, that is no more than an act of justice to the artist, who has no other means of making his abilities known so well, and of forwarding himself in his profession. If we look round the rooms at Somerset House, and observe how large a proportion of the portraits represent children, the old, and persons in middle life, we shall see that very few indeed are those which can have been painted, or exhibited for the gratification of personal vanity.

Sir Thomas Lawrence ministers largely to self-admiration: and yet a few years ripen even the most flattering of his portraits into moral pictures:

Perchè, donne mie care, la beltà
Ha l' ali al capo, a le spalle ed a' piè:
E vola si, che non si scorge più
*Vestigio alcun ne' visi, dove fù.**

Helen in her old age, looking at herself in a mirror, is a subject which old sonnetteers were fond of borrowing from the Greek Anthology. Young Ladies! you who have sate to Sir Thomas, or any artist of his school, I will tell you how your portraits may be rendered more useful monitors to you in your progress through life than the mirror was to Helen, and how you may derive more satisfaction from them when you are grown old. Without supposing that you actually "called up a look" for the painter's use, I may be certain that none of you during the times of sitting permitted any feeling of ill-humour to cast a shade over your countenance; and that if you were not conscious of endeavouring to put on your best looks for the occasion, the painter was desirous of catching them, and would catch the best he could. The most thoughtless of you need not be told that you cannot retain the charms of youthful beauty, but you may retain the charm of an amiable expression through life: never allow yourselves to be seen with a worse than you wore for the painter! Whenever you feel ill-tempered, remember that you look ugly; and be assured that every emotion of fretfulness, of ill-humour, of anger, of irritability, of impatience, of pride, haughtiness,

---

* RICCIARDETTO.

envy, or malice, any unkind, any uncharitable, any ungenerous feeling, lessens the likeness to your picture, and not only deforms you while it lasts, but leaves its trace behind; for the effect of the passions upon the face is more rapid and more certain than that of time.

"His counsel," says Gwillim the Pursuivant, "was very behoveful, who advised all gentlewomen often to look on glasses, that so, if they saw themselves beautiful, they might be stirred up to make their minds as fair by virtue as their faces were by nature; but if deformed, they might make amends for their outward deformity, with their intern pulchritude and gracious qualities. And those that are proud of their beauty should consider that their own hue is as brittle as the glass wherein they see it; and that they carry on their shoulders nothing but a skull wrapt in skin which one day will be loathsome to be looked on."

The conclusion of this passage accorded not with the Doctor's feelings. He thought that whatever tended to connect frightful and loathsome associations with the solemn and wholesome contemplation of mortality, ought to be avoided as injudicious and injurious. So too with regard to age: if it is dark and unlovely "the fault," he used to say, "is generally our own; Nature may indeed make it an object of compassion, but not of dislike, unless we ourselves render it so. It is not of necessity that we grow ugly as well as old." Donne says

No spring, nor summer's beauty hath such grace
As I have seen in one autumnal face;

he was probably speaking of his wife, for Donne was happy in his marriage, as he deserved to be. There is a beauty which, as the Duchess of Newcastle said of her mother's, is "beyond the reach of time;" that beauty depends upon the mind, upon the temper,— Young Ladies, upon yourselves!

George Wither wrote under the best of his portraits,

What I WAS, is passed by;
What I AM, away doth fly;
What I SHALL BE, none do see;
Yet in THAT my beauties be.

He commenced also a Meditation upon that portrait in these impressive lines:

When I behold my Picture and perceive
How vain it is our Portraitures to leave
In lines and shadows, (which make shews to-day
Of that which will to-morrow fade away,)
And think what mean resemblances at best
Are by mechanic instruments exprest,
I thought it better much to leave behind me,
Some draught, in which my living friends might find me,
The same I am, in that which will remain
Till all is ruined and repaired again.

In the same poem he says,

A Picture, though with most exactness made,
Is nothing but the shadow of a shade.
For even our living bodies, (though they seem
To others more, or more in our esteem,)
Are but the shadow of that Real Being,
Which doth extend beyond the fleshly seeing,
And cannot be discerned, until we rise
Immortal objects for immortal eyes.

Like most men, George Wither, as he grew more selfish, was tolerably successful in deceiving himself as to his own motives and state of mind. If ever there was an honest enthusiast, he had been one; afterwards he feathered his nest with the spoils of the Loyalists and of the Bishops; and during this prosperous part of his turbulent life there must have been times when the remembrance of his former self brought with it more melancholy and more awful thoughts than the sight of his own youthful portrait, in its fantastic garb, or of that more sober resemblance upon which his meditation was composed.

Such a portraiture of the inner or real being as Wither in his better mind wished to leave in his works, for those who knew and loved him, such a portraiture am I endeavouring to compose of Dr. Dove, wherein the world may see what he was, and so become acquainted with his intellectual lineaments, and with those peculiarities, which, forming as it were the idiosyncrasy of his moral constitution, contributed in no small degree to those ever-varying lights and shades of character and feeling in his living countenance, which, I believe, would have baffled the best painter's art.

Poi voi sapete quanto egli è dabbene,
Com' ha giudizio, ingegno, e discrezione
*Come conosce il vero, il bello, e 'l bene.**

* BERNI.

CHAPTER LXV.

SOCIETY OF A COUNTRY TOWN. SUCH A TOWN A MORE FAVOURABLE HABITAT FOR SUCH A PERSON AS DR. DOVE THAN LONDON WOULD HAVE BEEN.

Be then thine own home, and in thyself dwell;
Inn any where;
And seeing the snail, which every where doth roam,
Carrying his own home still, still is at home,
Follow (for he is easy paced) this snail;
Be thine own Palace, or the World's thy jail.
DONNE.

SUCH then as Daniel Dove was in the twenty-sixth year of his age we are now to consider him, settled at Doncaster, and with his way of life chosen, for better for worse, in all respects; except, as my female readers will remember, that he was neither married, nor engaged, nor likely to be so.

One of the things for which he used to thank God was that the world had not been all before him where to choose, either as to calling or place, but that both had been well chosen for him. To choose upon such just motives as can leave no rational cause for after repentance requires riper judgment than ought to be expected at the age when the choice is to be made; it is best for us therefore at a time of life when, though perhaps we might choose well, it is impossible that we could choose wisely, to acquiesce in the determination of others, who have knowledge and experience to direct them. Far happier are they who always know what they are to do, than they who have to determine what they will do.

Bisogna far quel che si deve fare,
*E non gia tutto quello che si vuole.**

Thus he was accustomed to think upon this subject.

But was he well placed at Doncaster?

It matters not where those men are placed, who, as South says, "have souls so dull and stupid as to serve for little else but to keep their bodies from putrefaction." Ordinary people, whether their lot be cast in town or country, in the metropolis or in a village, will go on in the ordinary way, conforming their habits to those of the place. It matters nothing more to those who live less in the little world about them, than in a world of their own, with the whole powers of the head and of the heart too (if they have one) intently fixed upon some favourite pursuit:— if they have a heart I say, for it sometimes happens that where there is an excellent head, the heart is nothing more than a piece of hard flesh. In this respect, the highest and the meanest intellects are, in a certain sense, alike self-sufficient; that is, they are so far independent of adventitious aid, that they derive little advantage from society and suffer nothing from the want of it. But there are others for whose mental improvement, or at least mental enjoyment, collision, and sympathy, and external excitement seem almost indispensable. Just as large towns are the only places in which first-rate workmen in any handicraft business can find employment, so men of letters and of science generally appear to think that nowhere but in a metropolis can they find the opportunities which they desire of improvement or of display. These persons are wise in their generation, but they are not children of light.

Among such persons it may perhaps be thought that our friend should be classed; and it cannot be doubted that, in a more conspicuous field of action, he might have distinguished himself, and obtained a splendid fortune. But for distinction he never entertained the slightest desire, and with the goods of fortune which had fallen to his share he was perfectly contented. But was he favourably situated for his intellectual advancement?—which, if such an inquiry had come before him concerning any other person, is what he would have considered to be the question-issimus. I answer without the slightest hesitation, that he was.

In London he might have mounted a Physician's wig, have ridden in his carriage, have attained the honours of the College, and added F.R.S. to his professional initials. He might, if Fortune opening her eyes had chosen to favour desert, have become Sir

* PANANTI.

Daniel Dove, Bart., Physician to his Majesty. But he would then have been a very different person from the Dr. Dove of Doncaster, whose memory will be transmitted to posterity in these volumes, and he would have been much less worthy of being remembered. The course of such a life would have left him no leisure for himself; and metropolitan society, in rubbing off the singularities of his character, would just in the same degree have taken from its strength.

It is a pretty general opinion that no society can be so bad as that of a small country town; and certain it is that such towns offer little or no choice. You must take what they have and make the best of it. But there are not many persons to whom circumstances allow much latitude of choice anywhere, except in those public places, as they are called, where the idle and the dissipated, like birds of a feather, flock together. In any settled place of residence men are circumscribed by station and opportunities, and just as much in the capital as in a provincial town. No one will be disposed to regret this, if he observes, where men have most power of choosing their society, how little benefit is derived from it, or, in other words, with how little wisdom it is used.

After all, the common varieties of human character will be found distributed in much the same proportion everywhere, and in most places there will be a sprinkling of the uncommon ones. Everywhere you may find the selfish and the sensual, the carking and the careful, the cunning and the credulous, the worldling and the reckless. But kind hearts are also everywhere to be found, right intentions, sober minds, and private virtues,—for the sake of which let us hope that God may continue to spare this hitherto highly-favoured nation, notwithstanding the fearful amount of our public and manifold offences.

The society then of Doncaster, in the middle of the last century, was like that of any other country town which was neither the seat of manufactures, nor of a Bishop's see; in either of which more information of a peculiar kind would have been found,—more active minds, or more cultivated ones. There was enough of those eccentricities for which the English above all other people are remarkable, those aberrations of intellect which just fail to constitute legal insanity, and which, according to their degree, excite amusement, or compassion. Nor was the town without its full share of talents; these there was little to foster and encourage, but happily there was nothing to pervert and stimulate them to a premature and mischievous activity.

In one respect it more resembled an episcopal than a trading city. The four kings and their respective suits of red and black were not upon more frequent service in the precincts of a cathedral, than in the good town of Doncaster. A stranger who had been invited to spend the evening with a family there, to which he had been introduced, was asked by the master of the house to take a card as a matter of course; upon his replying that he did not play at cards, the company looked at him with astonishment, and his host exclaimed—"What, Sir! not play at cards? the Lord help you!"

I will not say the Lord helped Daniel Dove, because there would be an air of irreverence in the expression, the case being one in which he, or any one, might help himself. He knew enough of all the games which were then in vogue to have played at them, if he had so thought good; and he would have been as willing, sometimes, in certain moods of mind, to have taken his seat at a card-table, in houses where card-playing did not form part of the regular business of life, as to have listened to a tune on the old-fashioned spinnet, or the then new-fashioned harpsichord. But that which as an occasional pastime he might have thought harmless and even wholesome, seemed to him something worse than folly when it was made a kill-time,—the serious occupation for which people were brought together,—the only one at which some of them ever appeared to give themselves the trouble of thinking. And seeing its effects upon the temper, and how nearly this habit was connected with a spirit of gambling, he thought that cards had not without reason been called the Devil's Books.

I shall not therefore introduce the reader to a Doncaster card-party, by way of showing him the society of the place. The Mrs. Shuffles, Mrs. Cuts, and Miss Dealems, the Mr. Tittles and Mrs. Tattles, the Humdrums and the Prateapaces, the Fribbles and the Feebles, the Perts and the Prims, the Littlewits and the Longtongues, the Heavyheads and the Broadbelows, are to be found everywhere.

"It is quite right," says one of the Guessers at Truth, "that there should be a heavy duty on cards: not only on moral grounds; not only because they act on a social party like a torpedo, silencing the merry voice and numbing the play of the features; not only to still the hunger of the public purse, which, reversing the qualities of Fortunatus's, is always empty, however much you may put into it; but also because every pack of cards is a malicious libel on courts, and on the world, seeing that the trumpery with number one at the head, is the best part of them; and that it gives kings and queens no other companions than knaves."

CHAPTER LXVI.

MR. COPLEY OF NETHERHALL. SOCIETY AT HIS HOUSE. DRUMMOND. BURGH. GRAY. MASON. MILLER THE ORGANIST AND HISTORIAN OF DONCASTER. HERSCHEL.

> All worldly joys go less
> To the one joy of doing kindnesses.
>
> HERBERT.

THERE was one house in Doncaster in which cards were never introduced; this house was Netherhall, the seat of Mr. Copley; and there Dr. Dove had the advantage of such society as was at that time very rarely, and is still not often, to be enjoyed anywhere.

The Copleys are one of the most ancient families in Doncaster: Robert Grosseteste, one of the most eminent of our English churchmen before the Reformation, was a branch from their stock. Robert Copley, who in the middle of the last century represented the family, was brought up at Westminster School, and while there took, what is very unusual for boys at Westminster or any other school to take, lessons in music. Dr. Crofts was his master, and made him, as has been said by a very competent judge, a very good performer in thorough-bass on the harpsichord. He attempted painting also, but not with equal success; the age of painting in this country had not then arrived.

Mr. Copley's income never exceeded twelve hundred a-year; but this which is still a liberal income, was then a large one, in the hands of a wise and prudent man. Netherhall was the resort of intellectual men, in whose company he delighted; and the poor were fed daily from his table. Drummond, afterwards Archbishop of York, was his frequent guest; so was Mason; so was Mason's friend Dr. Burgh; and Gray has sometimes been entertained there. One of the "strong names" of the King of Dahomey means, when interpreted, "wherever I rub, I leave my scent." In a better sense than belongs to this metaphorical boast of the power and the disposition to be terrible, it may be said of such men as Gray and Mason that wherever they have resided, or have been entertained as abiding guests, an odour of their memory remains. Who passes by the house at Streatham that was once Mrs. Thrale's without thinking of Dr. Johnson?

During many years Mr. Copley entertained himself and his friends with a weekly concert at Netherhall, he himself, Sir Brian Cooke and some of his family, and Dr. Miller the organist, and afterwards Historian of Doncaster, being performers. Miller, who was himself a remarkable person, had the fortune to introduce a more remarkable one to these concerts; it is an interesting anecdote in the history of that person, of Miller, and of Doncaster.

About the year 1760 as Miller was dining at Pontefract with the officers of the Durham militia, one of them, knowing his love of music, told him they had a young German in their band as a performer on the hautboy, who had only been a few months in England, and yet spoke English almost as well as a native, and who was also an excellent performer on the violin; the officer added, that if Miller would come into another room this German should entertain him with a solo. The invitation was gladly accepted, and Miller heard a solo of Giardini's executed in a manner that surprised him. He afterwards took an opportunity of having some private conversation with the young musician, and asked him whether he had engaged himself for any long period to the Durham militia. The answer was, "only from month to month." "Leave them then," said the organist, "and come and live with me. I am a single man, and think we shall be happy together; and doubtless your merit will soon entitle you to a more eligible situation." The offer was accepted as frankly as it was made: and the reader may imagine with what satisfaction Dr. Miller must have remembered this act of generous feeling, when he hears that this young German was Herschel the Astronomer.

"My humble mansion," says Miller, "consisted at that time but of two rooms. However, poor as I was, my cottage contained a small library of well-chosen books; and it must appear singular that a foreigner who had been so short a time in England should understand even the peculiarities of the language so well, as to fix upon Swift for his favourite author." He took an early opportunity of introducing his new friend at Mr. Copley's concerts; the first violin was resigned to him: and never, says the organist, had I heard the concertos of Corelli, Geminiani and Avison, or the overtures of Handel, performed more chastely, or more according to the original intention of the composers than by Mr. Herschel. I soon lost my companion: his fame was presently spread abroad; he had the offer of pupils, and was solicited to lead the public concerts both at Wakefield and Halifax. A new organ for the parish church of Halifax was built about this time, and Herschel was one of the seven candidates for the organist's place. They drew lots how they were to perform in succession. Herschel drew the third, the second fell to Mr., afterwards Dr., Wainwright of Manchester, whose finger was so rapid that old Snetzler, the organ-builder, ran about the church, exclaiming, *Te Tevel, te Tevel! he run over te keys like one cat; he will not give my piphes room for to shpeak.* "During Mr. Wainwright's performance," says Miller, "I was standing in the middle aisle with Herschel; what chance have you, said I, to follow this man?" He replied, "I don't know; I am sure fingers will not do." On which he ascended the organ loft, and produced from the organ so uncommon a fulness,—such a volume of slow solemn harmony, that I could by no means account for the effect. After this short extempore effusion, he finished with the old hundredth-psalm-tune, which he played better than his opponent. *Ay, ay,* cried old Snetzler, *tish is very goot, very goot indeet; I vil luf tish man, for he gives my piphes room for to shpeak.* Having afterwards asked Mr. Herschel by what means, in the beginning of his performance, he produced so uncommon an effect, he replied, "I told you fingers would not do!" and producing two pieces of lead from his waistcoat pocket, "one of these," said he, "I placed on the lowest key of the organ, and the other upon the octave above; thus by accommodating the harmony, I produced the effect of four hands instead of two."

CHAPTER LXVII.

A MYTHOLOGICAL STORY MORALISED.

Il faut mettre les fables en presse pour en tirer quelque suc de vérité.
GARASSE.

It is related of the great mythological personage Baly, that Veeshnoo, when he dispossessed him of his impious power, allowed him, in mitigation of his lot, to make his choice, whether he would go to the Swerga, and take five ignorant persons with him who were to be his everlasting companions there, or to Padalon and have five Pundits in his company. Baly preferred the good company with the bad quarters.

That that which is called good company has led many a man to a place which it is not considered decorous to mention before "ears polite," is a common, and, therefore, the more an awful truth. The Swerga and Padalon are the Hindoo Heaven and Hell; and if the Hindoo fable were not obviously intended to extol the merits of their Pundits, or learned men, as the missionary Ward explains the title, it might with much seeming likelihood bear this moral interpretation, that Baly retained the pride of knowledge even when convinced by the deprivation of his power that the pride of power was vanity, and in consequence drew upon himself a further punishment by his choice.

For although Baly, because of the righteousness with which he had used his power, was so far favoured by the Divinity whom he had offended, that he was not condemned to undergo any of those torments of which there was as rich an assortment and as choice a variety in Padalon, as ever monkish imagination revelled in devising, it was at the best a dreadful place of abode · and so it would appear if Turner were to paint a picture of its Diamond City from Southey's description. I say Turner, because, though the subject might seem more adapted to Martin's cast of mind, Turner's colouring would well represent the fiery streams and the sulphureous atmosphere; and that colouring being transferred from earthly landscapes to its proper place, his rich genius would have full scope for its appropriate display. Baly, no doubt, as a state prisoner who was to be treated with the highest consideration as well as with the utmost indulgence, would have all the accommodations that Yamen could afford him. There he and the Pundits might

> —— reason high
> Of Providence, foreknowledge, will, and fate,
> Fix'd fate, free will, foreknowledge absolute,
> And find no end, in wandering mazes lost.

They might argue there of good and evil,

> Of happiness and final misery,
> Passion and apathy, and glory and shame;

and such discourses possibly

> — with a pleasing sorcery might charm
> Pain for awhile and anguish, and excite
> Fallacious hope, or arm the obdured breast
> With stubborn patience as with triple steel.

But it would only be *for awhile* that they could be thus beguiled by it, for it is

> Vain wisdom all, and false philosophy!

it would be only for awhile, and they were there for a time which in prospect must appear all but endless. The Pundits would not thank him for bringing them there; Baly himself must continually wish he were breathing the heavenly air of the Swerga in the company of ignorant but happy associates, and he would regret his unwise choice even more bitterly than he remembered the glorious city wherein he had reigned in his magnificence.

He made a great mistake. If he had gone with the ignorant to Heaven he would have seen them happy there, and partaken their happiness, though they might not have been able to derive any gratification from his wisdom;—which said wisdom, peradventure, he himself when he was there might have discovered to be but foolishness. It is only in the company of the good that real enjoyment is to be found; any other society is hollow and heartless. You may be excited by the play of wit, by the collision of ambitious spirits, and by the brilliant exhibition of self-confident power; but the satisfaction ends with the scene. Far unlike this is the quiet confiding intercourse of sincere minds and friendly hearts, knowing, and loving, and esteeming each other; and such intercourse our philosopher enjoyed in Doncaster.

Edward Miller, the Organist, was a person very much after Daniel Dove's own heart. He was a warm-hearted, simple-hearted, right-hearted man: an enthusiast in his profession, yet not undervaluing, much less despising, other pursuits. The one Doctor knew as little of music as the other did of medicine; but Dr. Dove listened to Miller's performance with great pleasure, and Dr. Miller, when he was indisposed, took Dove's physic with perfect faith.

This musician was brother to William Miller, the bookseller, well known in the early part of the present century as a publisher of splendid works, to whose flourishing business in Albemarle Street the more flourishing John Murray succeeded. In the worldly sense of the word the musician was far less fortunate than the bibliopole, a doctorate in his own science being the height of the honours to which he attained, and the place of organist at Doncaster the height of the preferment. A higher station was once presented to his hopes. The Marquis of Rockingham applied in his behalf for the place of Master of his Majesty's band of musicians, then vacated by the death of Dr. Boyce; and the Duke of Manchester, who was at that time Lord Chamberlain, would have given it him if the King had not particularly desired him to bestow it on Mr. Stanley, the celebrated blind performer on the organ. Dr. Miller was more gratified by this proof of the Marquis's good-will towards him than disappointed at its failure. Had the application succeeded, he would not have written the History of Doncaster; nor would he have borne a part in a well-intended and judicious attempt at reforming our church psalmody, in which part of our church service reformation is greatly needed.* This meritorious attempt was made when George Hay Drummond, whose father had been Archbishop of York, was Vicar of Doncaster, having been presented to that vicarage in 1785, on the demise of Mr. Hatfield.

At that time the Parish Clerk used there, as in all other parish churches, to choose what psalm should be sung "to the praise and glory of God," and what portions of it; and considering himself as a much more important person in this department of his office than the organist, the only communication upon the subject which he held with Dr. Miller was to let him know what tune he must play, and how often he was to repeat it. "Strange absurdity!" says Miller. "How could the organist, placed in this degrading situation, properly perform his part of the church service? Not knowing the words, it was impossible for him to accommodate his music to the various sentiments contained in different stanzas, consequently his must be a mere random performance, and frequently producing improper effects." This, however, is what only a musician would feel; but it happened one Sunday that the clerk gave out some verses which were either ridiculously inapplicable to the day, or bore some accidental and ludicrous application, so that many of the congregation did not refrain from laughter. Mr. Drummond upon this, for he was zealously attentive to all the duties of his calling, said to Miller, "that in order to prevent any such occurrence in future he would make a selection of the best verses in each psalm, from the authorised version of Tate and Brady, and arrange them for every Sunday and festival throughout the year, provided he, the organist, who was perfectly qualified for such a task, would adapt them to proper music." To such a man as Miller this was the greatest gratification that could have been afforded; and it proved also to be the greatest service that was ever rendered to him in the course of his life; for, through Mr. Drummond's interest, the King and the Bishop patronised the work, and nearly five thousand copies were subscribed for, the list of subscribers being, it is believed, longer than had ever been obtained for any musical publication in this kingdom.

Strange to say, nothing of this kind had been attempted before; for the use of psalmody in our churches was originally no part of the service; but having, as it were, crept in, and been at first rather suffered than encouraged, and afterwards allowed and permitted only, not enjoined, no provision seems ever to have been made for its proper or even decent performance. And

* "It is sad to hear what whining, toting, yelling, or screeching there is in many country congregations, as if the people were affrighted or distracted." — *Thomas Mace's Music's Monument*, p. 3.

when an arrangement like this of Mr. Drummond's had been prepared, and Dr. Miller, with sound judgement, had adapted it, where that could be done, to the most popular of the old and venerable melodies which had been so long in possession, it may seem more strange that it should not have been brought into general use. This I say might be thought strange, if any instance of that supine and sinful negligence which permits the continuance of old and acknowledged defects in the church establishment, and church service, could be thought so.

Mr. Drummond had probably been led to think upon this subject by Mason's conversation, and by his Essays, historical and critical, on English Church Music. Mason who had a poet's ear and eye was ambitious of becoming both a musician and a painter. According to Miller he succeeded better in his musical than in his pictorial attempts, for he performed decently on the harpsichord; but in painting he never arrived even at a degree of mediocrity, and in music it was not possible to teach him the principles of composition, Miller and others having at his own desire attempted in vain to instruct him. Nevertheless, such a man, however superficial his knowledge of the art, could not but feel and reason justly upon its use and abuse in our Church Service; and he was for restricting the organist much in the same way that Drummond and Miller were for restraining the clerk. For after observing that what is called the voluntary requires an innate inventive faculty, which is certainly not the lot of many; and that the happy few who possess it will not at all times be able to restrain it within the bounds which reason and, in this case, religion would prescribe, he said, "it was to be wished therefore that in our established church extempore playing were as much discountenanced as extempore praying; and that the organist were as closely obliged in this solo and separate part of his office to keep to set forms, as the officiating minister; or as he himself is when accompanying the choir in an anthem, or a parochial congregation in a psalm." He would have indulged him, however, with a considerable quantity of these set forms, and have allowed him, if he approached in some degree to Rousseau's high character of a Preluder, "to descant on certain single grave texts which Tartini, Geminiani, Corelli or Handel would abundantly furnish, and which may be found at least of equal elegance and propriety in the Largo and Adagio movements of Haydn or Pleyel."

Whatever Miller may have thought of this proposal, there was a passage in Mason's Essay in favour of voluntaries which was in perfect accord with Dr. Dove's notions. "Prompt and as it were casual strains," says the Poet, "which do not fix the attention of the hearer, provided they are the produce of an original fancy, which scorns to debase itself by imitating common and trivial melodies, are of all others the best adapted to induce mental serenity. We in some sort listen to such music as we do to the pleasing murmur of a neighbouring brook, the whisper of the passing breeze, or the distant warblings of the lark and nightingale; and if agreeable natural voices have the power of soothing the contemplative mind, without interrupting its contemplations, simple musical effusions must assuredly have that power in a superior degree. All that is to be attended to by the organist is to preserve such pleasing simplicity; and this musical measures will ever have, if they are neither strongly accented, nor too regularly rhythmical. But when this is the case, they cease to soothe us, because they begin to affect us. Add to this that an air replete with short cadences and similar passages is apt to fix itself too strongly on the memory; whereas a merely melodious or harmonical movement glides, as it were, through the ear, awakens a transient pleasing sensation, but leaves behind it no lasting impression. Its effect ceases, when its impulse on the auditory nerve ceases;—an impulse strong enough to dispel from the mind *all eating care* (to use our great Poet's own expression), but in no sort to rouse or ruffle any of its faculties, save those only which attend truly devotional duty."

This passage agreed with some of the Doctor's peculiar notions. He felt the power of devotional music both in such preparatory strains as Mason has here described, and in the more exciting emotions of congregational psalmody. And being thus sensible of the religious uses which may be drawn from music, he was the more easily led to entertain certain speculations concerning its application in the treatment of diseases, as will be related hereafter.

CHAPTER LXVIII.

ECCENTRIC PERSONS, WHY APPARENTLY MORE COMMON IN ENGLAND THAN IN OTHER COUNTRIES. HARRY BINGLEY.

> Blest are those
> Whose blood and judgement are so well commingled,
> That they are not a pipe for Fortune's finger
> To sound what stop she please.
>
> HAMLET.

THERE is a reason why eccentricity of character seems to be much more frequent in England than in other countries.—

Here some reflective reader, methinks, interrupts me with—"seems, good Author."

"Ay, and it is!"

Have patience, good reader, and hear me to the end! There is a reason why it seems so; and the reason is, because all such eccentricities are recorded here in newspapers and magazines, so that none of them are lost; and the most remarkable are brought forward from time to time, in popular compilations. A collection of what is called Eccentric Biography is to form a portion of Mr. Murray's Family Library.

But eccentric characters probably are more frequent among us than among most other nations; and for this there are two causes. The first is to be found in that spirit of independence upon which the English pride themselves, and which produces a sort of Drawcansir-like bravery in men who are eccentrically inclined. It becomes a perverse sort of pleasure in them to act preposterously, for the sake of showing that they have a right to do as they please, and the courage to exercise that right, let the rest of the world think what it will of their conduct.

The other reason is that mad-houses very insufficiently supply the place of convents, and very ill also. It might almost be questioned whether convents do not well nigh make amends to humanity for their manifold mischiefs and abominations, by the relief which they afford as asylums for insanity, in so many of its forms and gradations. They afford a cure also in many of its stages, and precisely upon the same principle on which the treatment in mad-houses is founded: but oh! how differently is that principle applied! That passive obedience to another's will which in the one case is exacted by authority acting through fear, and oftentimes enforced by no scrupulous or tender means, is in the other required as a religious duty,—an act of virtue,—a voluntary and accepted sacrifice,—a good work which will be carried to the patient's account in the world to come. They who enter a convent are to have no will of their own there; they renounce it solemnly upon their admission; and when this abnegation is sincerely made, the chief mental cause of insanity is removed. For assuredly in most cases madness is more frequently a disease of the will than of the intellect. When Diabolus appeared before the town of Mansoul, and made his oration to the citizens at Ear-Gate, Lord Will-be-will was one of the first that was for consenting to his words, and letting him into the town.

We have no such asylums in which madness and fatuity receive every possible alleviation, while they are at the same time subjected to the continual restraint which their condition requires. They are wanted also for repentant sinners, who when they are awakened to a sense of their folly, and their guilt, and their danger, would fain find a place of religious retirement, wherein they might pass the remainder of their days in preparing for death. Lord Goring, the most profligate man of his age, who by his profligacy, as much as by his frequent misconduct, rendered irreparable injury to the cause which he intended to serve, retired to Spain after the ruin of that cause, and there ended his days as a Dominican Friar. If there be any record of him in the Chronicles of the Order, the account ought to be curious at least, if not edifying. But it is rather (for his own sake) to be hoped than supposed that he did not hate and despise the follies and the frauds of the fraternity into which he had entered more heartily than the pomps and vanities of the world which he had left.

On the other hand wherever convents are among the institutions of the land, not to speak of those poor creatures who are thrust into them against their will, or with only a mockery of freedom in the choice, — it must often happen that persons enter them in some fit of disappointment, or resentment, or grief, and find themselves, when the first bitterness of passion is past, imprisoned for life by their own rash, but irremediable act and deed. The woman, who, when untoward circumstances have prevented her from marrying the man she loves, marries one for whom she has no affection, is more likely (poor as her chance is) to find contentment and perhaps happiness, than if for the same cause she had thrown herself into a nunnery. Yet this latter is the course to which, if she were a Roman Catholic, her thoughts would perhaps preferably at first have turned, and to which they would probably be directed by her confessor.

Men who are weary of the ways of the world, or disgusted with them, have more licence, as well as more resources than women. If they do not enter upon some dangerous path of duty, or commence wanderers, they may choose for themselves an eccentric path, in which, if their habits are not such as expose them to insult, or if their means are sufficient to secure them against it, they are not likely to be molested, — provided they have no relations whose interest it may be to apply for a statute of lunacy against them.

A gentleman of this description well known in London towards the close of George the Second's reign by the name of Harry Bingley, came in the days of Dr. Dove to reside upon his estate in the parish of Bolton-upon-Derne near Doncaster. He had figured as an orator and politician in coffee-houses at the west end of the town, and enjoyed the sort of notoriety which it was then his ambition to obtain; but discovering with the Preacher that this was vanity and vexation of spirit, when it was either too late for him to enter upon domestic life, or his habits had unfitted him for it, he retired to his estate, which with the house upon it he had let to a farmer; in that house he occupied two rooms, and there indulged his humour as he had done in London, though it had now taken a very different direction.

"Cousin-german to Idleness," says Burton, is "*nimia solitudo*, too much solitariness. Divers are cast upon this rock for want of means; or out of a strong apprehension of some infirmity, disgrace, or through bashfulness, rudeness, simplicity, they cannot apply themselves to others' company. *Nullum solum infelici gratius solitudine, ubi nullus sit qui miseriam exprobret.* This enforced solitariness takes place and produceth his effect soonest in such as have spent their time, jovially peradventure, in all honest recreations, in good company, in some great family, or populous city; and are upon a sudden confined to a desert country cottage far off, restrained of their liberty and barred from their ordinary associates. Solitariness is very irksome to such, most tedious, and a sudden cause of great inconvenience."

The change in Bingley's life was as great and sudden as that which the Anatomist of Melancholy has here described; but it led to no bodily disease nor to any tangible malady. His property was worth about fourteen hundred a-year. He kept no servant, and no company; and he lived upon water-gruel and celery, except at harvest time, when he regaled himself with sparrow pies, made of the young birds just fledged, for which he paid the poor inhabitants who caught them two pence a-head. Probably he supposed that it was rendering the neighbourhood a service thus to rid it of what he considered both a nuisance and a delicacy. This was his only luxury; and his only business was to collect about a dozen boys and girls on Sundays, and hear them say their Catechism, and read a chapter in the New Testament, for which they received remuneration in the intelligible form of two pence each, but at the feasts and statutes, "most sweet guerdon, better than remuneration," in the shape of sixpence. He stood godfather for several poor people's children, they were baptized by his surname; when they were of proper age he used to put them out as apprentices, and in his will he left each of them an hundred guineas to be paid when they reached the age of twenty-five if they were married, but not till they married; and if they reached the age of fifty without marrying, the legacy was then forfeited. There were two children for whom he stood godfather, but whose parents did not choose that they should be named after him; he never took any notice of these children, nor did he bequeath them any thing; but to one of the others he left the greater part of his property.

This man used every week day to lock himself in the church and pace the aisles for two hours, from ten till twelve o'clock. An author, who, in his own peculiar and admirable way, is one of the most affecting writers of any age or country, has described with characteristic feeling the different effects produced upon certain minds by entering an empty or a crowded church. "In the latter," he says, "it is chance but some present human frailty,—an act of inattention on the part of some of the auditory,—or a trait of affectation, or worse, vain-glory on that of the preacher,—puts us by our best thoughts, disharmonising the place and the occasion. But wouldst thou know the beauty of holiness?—go alone on some week day, borrowing the keys of good master Sexton; traverse the cool aisles of some country church; think of the piety that has kneeled there,—the congregations old and young that have found consolation there,—the meek pastor,—the docile parishioners,—with no disturbing emotions, no cross conflicting comparisons, drink in the tranquillity of the place, till thou thyself become as fixed and motionless as the marble effigies that kneel and weep around thee!" *

Harry Bingley died in lodgings at Rotherham, whither he had removed when he felt himself ill, that he might save expense by being nearer a physician. According to his own direction his body was brought back from thence to the village, and interred in the churchyard; and he strictly enjoined that no breast-plate, handles, or any ornaments whatever should be affixed to his coffin, nor any gravestone placed to mark the spot where his remains were deposited.

Would or would not this godfather general have been happier in a convent or a hermitage, than he was in thus following his own humour? It was Dr. Dove's opinion that upon the whole he would; not that a conventual, and still less an eremital way of life would have been more rational, but because there would have been a worthier motive for choosing it; and if not a more reasonable hope, at least a firmer persuasion that it was the sure way to salvation.

That Harry Bingley's mind had taken a religious turn appeared by his choosing the church for his daily place of promenade. Meditation must have been as much his object as exercise, and of a kind which the place invited. It appeared also by the sort of Sunday-schooling which he gave the children, long before Sunday Schools,—whether for good or evil,—were instituted, or as the phrase is, invented by Robert Raikes of eccentric memory. (Patrons and Patronesses of Sunday Schools, be not offended if a doubt concerning their utility be here implied! The Doctor entertained such a doubt; and the why and the wherefore shall in due time be fairly stated.) But Bingley certainly came under the description of a humourist, rather than of a devotee or religious enthusiast; in fact, he bore that character. And the Doctor's knowledge of human nature led him to conclude that solitary humourists are far from being happy. You see them,

* The Last Essays of Elia.

as you see the blind, at their happiest times, when they have something to divert their thoughts. But in the humourist's course of life, there is a sort of defiance of the world and the world's law; indeed, any man who departs widely from its usages avows this; and it is, as it ought to be, an uneasy and uncomfortable feeling, wherever it is not sustained by a high state of excitement; and that state, if it be lasting, becomes madness. Such persons when left to themselves and to their own reflections, as they necessarily are for the greater part of their time, must often stand not only self-arraigned for folly, but self-condemned for it.

CHAPTER LXIX.

A MUSICAL RECLUSE AND HIS SISTER.

"Some proverb maker, I forget who, says, God hath given to some men wisdom and understanding, and to others the art of playing on the fiddle."

Professor PARK's Dogmas of the Constitution.

THE Doctor always spoke of Bingley as a melancholy example of strength of character misapplied. But he used to say that strength of character was far from implying strength of mind; and that strength of mind itself was no more a proof of sanity of mind, than strength of body was of bodily health. Both may coexist with mortal maladies, and both, when existing in any remarkable degree, may oftentimes be the cause of them.

Alas for man!
Exuberant health diseases him, frail worm!
And the slight bias of untoward chance
Makes his best virtues from the even line,
With fatal declination, swerve aside.*

There was another person within his circuit who had taken umbrage at the world, and withdrawn from it to enjoy, or rather solace himself according to his own humour in retirement; not in solitude, for he had a sister, who with true sisterly affection accommodated herself to his inclinations, and partook of his taste. This gentleman, whose name was Jonathan Staniforth, had taken out a patent for a ploughing machine, and had been deprived, unjustly as he deemed, of the profits which he had expected from it, by a lawsuit. Upon this real disappointment, aggravated by the sense, whether well or ill founded of injustice, he retired to his mansion in the village of Firbeck, about ten miles south of Doncaster, and there discarding all thoughts of mechanics, which had been his favourite pursuit, he devoted himself to the practice of music;—devoted is not too strong an expression. He had passed the middle of his life before the Doctor knew him; and it was not till some twenty years later that Miller became acquainted with them.

"I was introduced," says the Organist, "into a room where was sitting a thin old Gentleman, upwards of seventy years of age, playing on the violin. He had a long time lived sequestered from the world, and dedicated not less than eight hours a-day to the practice of music. His shrunk shanks were twisted in a peculiar form, by the constant posture in which he sate; and so indifferent was he about the goodness of his instrument, that, to my astonishment, he always played on a common Dutch fiddle, the original price of which could not be more than half a guinea; the strings were bad, and the whole instrument dirty and covered with resin. With this humble companion he used to work hard every morning on the old solos of Vivaldi, Tessarini, Corelli, and other ancient composers. The evening was reserved for mere amusement, in accompanying an ancient sister, who sung most of the favourite songs from Handel's old Italian Operas, which he composed soon after his arrival in England. These Operas she had heard on their first representation in London; consequently her performance was to me an uncommon treat. I had an opportunity of comparing the different manner of singing in the beginning of the century, to that which I had been accustomed to hear. And indeed the style was so different, that, musically considered, it might truly be called a different language. None of the present embellishments or graces in music

* RODERICK.

were used, — no *appoggiatura*, — no unadorned sustaining, or swelling long notes; they were varbled by a continual tremulous accent from beginning to end; and when she arrived at the period of an air, the brother's violin became mute, and she, raising her eyes to the top of the room, and stretching out her throat, executed her extempore cadence in a succession of notes perfectly original, and concluded with a long shake something like the bleating of a lamb."

Miller's feelings during this visit were so wholly professional, that in describing this brother and sister forty years afterwards, he appears not to have been sensible in how affecting a situation they were placed. Crabbe would have treated these characters finely had they fallen in his way. And so Chancey Hare Townsend could treat them, who has imitated Crabbe with such singular skill, and who has moreover music in his soul and could give the picture the soft touches which it requires.

I must not omit to say that Mr. Staniforth and his sister were benevolent, hospitable, sensible, worthy persons. Thinkest thou, reader, that they gave no proof of good sense in thus passing their lives? Look round the circle of thine acquaintance, and ask thyself how many of those whose time is at their own disposal, dispose of it more wisely,—that is to say, more beneficially to others, or more satisfactorily to themselves? The sister fulfilled her proper duties in her proper place, and the brother in contributing to her comfort performed his; to each other they were, as their circumstances required them to be, all in all; they were kind to their poor neighbours, and they were perfectly inoffensive towards the rest of the world. — They who are wise unto salvation, know feelingly, when they have done best, that their best works are worth nothing; but they who are conscious that they have lived inoffensively may have in that consciousness a reasonable ground of comfort.

The Apostle enjoins us to "eschew evil and do good." To do good is not in every one's power; and many who think they are doing it, may be grievously deceived for lack of judgment, and be doing evil the while instead, with the best intentions, but with sad consequences to others, and eventual sorrow for themselves. But it is in every one's power to eschew evil, so far as never to do wilful harm; and if we were all careful never unnecessarily to distress or disquiet those who are committed to our charge, or who must be affected by our conduct, — if we made it a point of conscience never to disturb the peace, or diminish the happiness of others, — the mass of moral evil by which we are surrounded would speedily be diminished, and with it no inconsiderable portion of those physical ones would be removed, which are the natural consequence and righteous punishment of our misdeeds.

CHAPTER LXX.

SHOWING THAT ANY HONEST OCCUPATION IS BETTER THAN NONE, BUT THAT OCCUPATIONS WHICH ARE DEEMED HONOURABLE ARE NOT ALWAYS HONEST.

J'ai peine à concevoir pourquoi le plûpart des hommes ont une si forte envie d'être heureux, et une si grande incapacité pour le devenir.

VOYAGES DE MILORD CETON.

"HAPPY," said Dr. Dove, "is the man who, having his whole time thrown upon his hands, makes no worse use of it than to practise eight hours a-day upon a bad fiddle." It was a sure evidence, he insisted, that Mr. Staniforth's frame of mind was harmonious; the mental organ was in perfect repair, though the strings of the material instrument jarred; and he enjoyed the scientific delight which Handel's composition gave him abstractedly, in its purity and essence.

"There can now," says an American preacher *, "be no doubt of this truth because there have been so many proofs of it that the man who retires completely from business, who is resolved to do nothing but enjoy himself, never attains the end at which

* FREEMAN's Eighteen Sermons.

he aims. If it is not mixed with other ingredients, no cup is so insipid, and at the same time so unhealthful, as the cup of pleasure. When the whole enjoyment of the day is to eat, and drink, and sleep, and talk, and visit, life becomes a burden too heavy to be supported by a feeble old man, and he soon sinks into the arms of spleen, or falls into the jaws of death."

Alas! it is neither so easy a thing, nor so agreeable a one as men commonly expect, to dispose of leisure when they retire from the business of the world. Their old occupations cling to them, even when they hope that they have emancipated themselves.

Go to any sea-port town and you will see that the Sea-captain who has retired upon his well-earned savings, sets up a weathercock in full view from his windows, and watches the variations of the wind as duly as when he was at sea, though no longer with the same anxiety.

Every one knows the story of the Tallow Chandler, who, having amassed a fortune, disposed of his business, and taken a house in the country, not far from London, that he might enjoy himself, after a few months trial of a holiday life, requested permission of his successor to come into town, and assist him on melting days. I have heard of one who kept a retail spirit-shop, and having in like manner retired from trade, used to employ himself by having one puncheon filled with water, and measuring it off by pints into another. I have heard also of a butcher in a small country town, who some little time after he had left off business, informed his old customers that he meant to kill a lamb once a week, just for his amusement.

There is no way of life to which the generality of men cannot conform themselves; and it seems as if the more repugnance they may at first have had to overcome, the better at last they like the occupation. They grow insensible to the loudest and most discordant sounds, or remain only so far sensible of them, that the cessation will awaken them from sleep. The most offensive smells become pleasurable to them in time, even those which are produced by the most offensive substances. The temperature of a glass-house is not only tolerable but agreeable to those who have their fiery occupation there. Wisely and mercifully was this power of adaptation implanted in us for our good; but in our imperfect and diseased society it is grievously perverted. We make the greater part of the evil circumstances in which we are placed; and then we fit ourselves for those circumstances by a process of systematic degradation, the effect of which most people see in the classes below them, though they may not be conscious that it is operating in a different manner, but with equal force, upon themselves.

For there is but too much cause to conclude that our moral sense is more easily blunted than our physical sensations. Roman Ladies delighted in seeing the gladiators bleed and die in the public theatre. Spanish Ladies at this day clap their hands in exultation at spectacles which make English Soldiers sicken and turn away. The most upright Lawyer acquires a sort of Swiss conscience for professional use; he is soon taught that considerations of right and wrong have nothing to do with his brief, and that his business is to do the best he can for his client, however bad the case. If this went no farther than to save a criminal from punishment, it might be defensible on the ground of humanity and of charitable hope. But to plead with the whole force of an artful mind in furtherance of a vexatious and malicious suit, — and to resist a rightful claim with all the devices of legal subtlety, and all the technicalities of legal craft, — I know not how he who considers this to be his duty towards his client, can reconcile it with his duty towards his neighbour; or how he thinks it will appear in the account he must one day render to the Lord for the talents which have been committed to his charge.

There are persons indeed who have so far outgrown their catechism as to believe that their only duty is to themselves; and who in the march of intellect have arrived at the convenient conclusion that there is no account to be rendered after death. But they would resent any imputation upon their honour or their courage as an offence not to be forgiven; and it is difficult therefore to understand how even such persons can undertake to plead the cause of a scoundrel in cases of seduction, — how they can think that the acceptance of a dirty fee is to justify them for cross-examining an injured and unhappy woman with the cruel wantonness of unmanly insult, bruising the broken reed, and treating her as if she were as totally devoid of shame, as they themselves of decency and of humanity. That men should act thus and be perfectly unconscious the while that they are acting a cowardly and rascally part, — and that society should not punish them for it by looking upon them as men who have lost their caste, would be surprising if we did not too plainly see to what a degree the moral sense, not only of individuals, but of a whole community, may be corrupted.

Physiologists have observed that men and dogs are the only creatures whose nature can accommodate itself to every climate, from the burning sands of the desert to the shores and islands of the frozen ocean. And it is not in their physical nature alone that this power of accommodation is found. Dogs who beyond all reasonable question have a sense of duty, and fidelity, and affection, towards their human associates, — a sense altogether distinct from fear and selfishness, — who will rush upon any danger at their master's bidding, and die broken-hearted beside his body, or upon his grave, — dogs, I say, who have this capacity of virtue, have nevertheless been trained to act with robbers against the traveller, and to hunt down human beings and devour them. But depravity sinks deeper than this in man; for the dog when thus deteriorated acts against no law, natural or revealed, no moral sense; he has no power of comparing good and evil and choosing between them, but may be trained to either, and in either is performing his intelligible duty of obedience.

CHAPTER LXXI.

TRANSITION IN OUR NARRATIVE PREPARATORY TO A CHANGE IN THE DOCTOR'S LIFE. A SAD STORY SUPPRESSED. THE AUTHOR PROTESTS AGAINST PLAYING WITH THE FEELINGS OF HIS READERS. ALL ARE NOT MERRY THAT SEEM MIRTHFUL. THE SCAFFOLD A STAGE. DON RODRIGO CALDERON. THISTLEWOOD. THE WORLD A MASQUERADE, BUT THE DOCTOR ALWAYS IN HIS OWN CHARACTER.

This breaks no rule of order.
If order were infringed then should I flee
From my chief purpose and my mark should miss.
Order is Nature's beauty, and the way
To Order is by rules that Art hath found.

GWILLIM.

THE question "Who was the Doctor?" has now, methinks, been answered, though not fully, yet sufficiently for the present stage of our memorials, while he is still a bachelor, a single man, an imperfect individual, half only of the whole being which by the laws of nature, and of Christian polity, it was designed that man should become.

The next question therefore that presents itself for consideration relates to that other, and as he sometimes called it better half, which upon the union of the two moieties made him a whole man. — Who was Mrs. Dove?

The reader has been informed how my friend in his early manhood, when about-to-be-a-Doctor, fell in love. Upon that part of his history I have related all that he communicated, which was all that could by me be known, and probably all there was to know. From that time he never fell in love again; nor did he ever run into it; but as was formerly intimated, he once caught the affection. The history of this attachment I heard from others; he had suffered too deeply ever to speak of it himself; and having maturely considered the matter I have determined not to relate the circumstances. Suffice it to say that he might at the same time have caught from the same person an insidious and mortal disease, if his constitution had been as susceptible of the one contagion, as his heart was of the other. The tale is too painful to be told. There are authors enough in the world who delight in drawing tears; there will always be young readers enough who are not unwilling to shed them; and perhaps it may be wholesome for the young and happy upon whose tears there is no other call.

Not that the author is to be admired, or even excused, who draws too largely upon our lachrymal glands. The pathetic is a string which may be touched by an unskilful hand, and which has often been played upon by an unfeeling one.

For my own part, I wish neither to make my readers laugh nor weep. It is enough for me, if I may sometimes bring a gleam of sunshine upon thy brow, Pensoso; and a watery one over thy sight, Buonallegro; a smile upon Penserosa's lips, a dimple in Amanda's cheek, and some quiet tears, Sophronia, into those mild eyes, which have shed so many scalding ones! When my subject leads me to distressful scenes, it will, as Southey says, not be

> — my purpose e'er to entertain
> The heart with useless grief; but, as I may,
> Blend in my calm and meditative strain
> Consolatory thoughts, the balm for real pain.*

The maxim that an author who desires to make us weep must be affected himself by what he writes, is too trite to be repeated in its original language. Both authors and actors, however, can produce this effect without eliciting a spark of feeling from their own hearts; and what perhaps may be deemed more remarkable, they can with the same success excite merriment in others, without partaking of it in the slightest degree themselves. No man ever made his contemporaries laugh more heartily than Scarron, whose bodily sufferings were such that he wished for himself

> — *à toute heure*
> *Ou la mort, ou santé meilleure:*

And who describes himself in his epistle to Sarazin, as

> *Un Pauvret*
> *Très-maigret;*
> *Au col tors,*
> *Dont le corps*
> *Tout tortu,*
> *Tout bossu,*
> *Suranné,*
> *Décharné,*
> *Est réduit*
> *Jour et nuit*
> *A souffrir*
> *Sans guerir*
> *Des tourmens*
> *Véhémens.*

It may be said perhaps that Scarron's disposition was eminently cheerful, and that by indulging in buffoonery he produced in himself a pleasurable excitement, not unlike that which others seek from strong liquors, or from opium; and therefore that his example tends to invalidate the assertion in support of which it was adduced. This is a plausible objection; and I am far from undervaluing the philosophy of Pantagruelism, and from denying that its effects may, and are likely to be as salutary as any that were ever produced by the proud doctrines of the Porch. But I question Scarron's right to the appellation of a Pantagruelist; his humour had neither the height nor the depth of that philosophy.

There is a well-known anecdote of a physician, who being called in to an unknown patient, found him suffering under the deepest depression of mind, without any discoverable disease, or other assignable cause. The physician advised him to seek for cheerful objects, and recommended him especially to go to the theatre and see a famous actor then in the meridian of his powers, whose comic talents were unrivalled. Alas! the comedian who kept crowded theatres in a roar was this poor hypochondriac himself!

The state of mind in which such men play their part, whether as authors or actors, was confessed in a letter written from Yarmouth Gaol to the Doctor's friend Miller, by a then well-known performer in this line, George Alexander Stevens. He wrote to describe his distress in prison, and to request that Miller would endeavour to make a small collection for him, some night at a

* Tale of PARAGUAY.

concert; and he told his sad tale sportively. But breaking off that strain he said; "You may think I can have no sense, that while I am thus wretched I should offer at ridicule! But, Sir, people constituted like me, with a disproportionate levity of spirits, are always most merry when they are most miserable; and quicken like the eyes of the consumptive, which are always brightest the nearer a patient approaches to dissolution."

It is one thing to jest, it is another to be mirthful. Sir Thomas More jested as he ascended the scaffold. In cases of violent death, and especially upon an unjust sentence, this is not surprising; because the sufferer has not been weakened by a wasting malady, and is in a state of high mental excitement and exertion. But even when dissolution comes in the course of nature, there are instances of men who have died with a jest upon their lips. Garci Sanchez de Badajoz when he was at the point of death desired that he might be dressed in the habit of St. Francis; this was accordingly done, and over the Franciscan frock they put on his habit of Santiago, for he was a knight of that order. It was a point of devotion with him to wear the one dress, a point of honour to wear the other; but looking at himself in this double attire, he said to those who surrounded his death-bed, "The Lord will say to me presently, my friend Garci Sanchez, you come very well wrapt up! (*muy arropado*) and I shall reply, Lord, it is no wonder, for it was winter when I set off."

The author who relates this anecdote remarks that *o morrer com graça he muyto bom, e com graças he muyto mão:* the observation is good but untranslateable, because it plays upon the word which means grace as well as wit. The anecdote itself is an example of the ruling humour "strong in death;" perhaps also of that pride or vanity, call it which we will, which so often, when mind and body have not yielded to natural decay, or been broken down by suffering, clings to the last in those whom it has strongly possessed. Don Rodrigo Calderon, whose fall and exemplary contrition served as a favourite topic for the poets of his day, wore a Franciscan habit at his execution, as an outward and visible sign of penitence and humiliation; as he ascended the scaffold, he lifted the skirts of the habit with such an air that his attendant confessor thought it necessary to reprove him for such an instance of ill-timed regard to his appearance. Don Rodrigo excused himself by saying that he had all his life carried himself gracefully!

The author by whom this is related calls it an instance of illustrious hypocrisy. In my judgment the Father Confessor who gave occasion for it deserves a censure far more than the penitent sufferer. The movement beyond all doubt was purely habitual, as much so as the act of lifting his feet to ascend the steps of the scaffold; but the undeserved reproof made him feel how curiously whatever he did was remarked; and that consciousness reminded him that he had a part to support, when his whole thoughts would otherwise have been far differently directed.

A personage in one of Webster's Plays says,

> I knew a man that was to lose his head
> Feed with an excellent good appetite
> To strengthen his heart scarce half an hour before,
> And if he did, it only was to speak.

Probably the dramatist alluded to some well known fact which was at that time of recent occurrence. When the desperate and atrocious traitor Thistlewood was on the scaffold, his demeanour was that of a man who was resolved boldly to meet the fate he had deserved; in the few words which were exchanged between him and his fellow criminals he observed, that the grand question whether or not the soul was immortal would soon be solved for them. No expression of hope escaped him, no breathing of repentance; no spark of grace appeared. Yet (it is a fact, which whether it be more consolatory or awful, ought to be known,) on the night after the sentence, and preceding his execution, while he supposed that the person who was appointed to watch him in his cell, was asleep, this miserable man was seen by that person repeatedly to rise upon his knees, and heard repeatedly calling upon Christ his

Saviour to have mercy upon him, and to forgive him his sins!

All men and women are verily, as Shakspeare has said of them, merely players,—when we see them upon the stage of the world; that is, when they are seen any where except in the freedom and undressed intimacy of private life. There is a wide difference indeed in the performers, as there is at a masquerade between those who assume a character, and those who wear dominoes; some play off the agreeable, or the disagreeable for the sake of attracting notice; others retire as it were into themselves; but you can judge as little of the one as of the other. It is even possible to be acquainted with a man long and familiarly, and as we may suppose intimately, and yet not to know him thoroughly or well. There may be parts of his character with which we have never come in contact, — recesses which have never been opened to us,—springs upon which we have never touched. Many there are who can keep their vices secret; would that all bad men had sense and shame enough to do so, or were compelled to it by the fear of public opinion! Shame of a very different nature, — a moral shamefacedness, — which, if not itself an instinctive virtue, is near akin to one, makes those who are endowed with the best and highest feelings, conceal them from all common eyes; and for our performance of religious duties, — our manifestations of piety, — we have been warned that what of this kind is done to be seen of men, will not be rewarded openly before men and angels at the last.

If I knew my venerable friend better than I ever knew any other man, it was because he was in many respects unlike other men, and in few points more unlike them than in this, that he always appeared what he was, — neither better nor worse. With a discursive intellect and a fantastic imagination, he retained his simplicity of heart. He had kept that heart unspotted from the world; his father's blessing was upon him, and he prized it beyond all that the world could have bestowed. Crowe says of us,

> Our better mind
> Is as a Sunday's garment, then put on
> When we have nought to do; but at our work
> We wear a worse for thrift!

It was not so with him; his better mind was not as a garment to be put on and off at pleasure; it was like its plumage to a bird, its beauty and its fragrance to a flower, except that it was not liable to be ruffled, nor to fade, nor to exhale and pass away. His mind was like a peacock always in full attire; it was only at times indeed, (to pursue the similitude,) that he expanded and displayed it; but its richness and variety never could be concealed from those who had eyes to see them.

> — His sweetest mind
> 'Twixt mildness tempered and low courtesy,
> Could leave as soon to be, as not be kind.
> Churlish despite ne'er looked from his calm eye,
> Much less commanded in his gentle heart;
> To baser men fair looks he would impart;
> Nor could he cloak ill thoughts in complimental art.*

What he was in boyhood has been seen, and something also of his manlier years; but as yet little of the ripe fruits of his intellectual autumn have been set before the readers. No such banquet was promised them as that with which they are to be regaled. "The booksellers," says Somner the antiquary, in an unpublished letter to Dugdale, "affect a great deal of title as advantageous for the sale; but judicious men dislike it, as savouring of too much ostentation, and suspecting the wine is not good where so much bush is hung out." Somebody, I forget who, wrote a book upon the titles of books, regarding the title as a most important part of the composition. The bookseller's fashion of which Somner speaks has long been obsolete; mine is a brief title promising little, but intending much. It specifies only the Doctor; but his gravities and his levities, his opinions of men and things, his speculations moral and political, physical and spiritual, his philosophy and his religion, each blending with each, and all with all, these are comprised in the &c. of my title-page, — these and his Pantagruelism to boot. When I meditate upon these I may exclaim with the poet: —

* Phineas Fletcher.

Mnemosyne hath kiss'd the kingly Jove,
And entertained a feast within my brain.*

These I shall produce for the entertainment of the idle reader, and for the recreation of the busy one; for the amusement of the young, and the contentment of the old; for the pleasure of the wise, and the approbation of the good; and these when produced will be the monument of Daniel Dove. Of such a man it may indeed be said that he

Is his own marble; and his merit can
Cut him to any figure, and express
More art than Death's Cathedral palaces,
Where royal ashes keep their court! †

Some of my contemporaries may remember a story once current at Cambridge, of a luckless undergraduate, who being examined for his degree, and failing in every subject upon which he was tried, complained that he had not been questioned upon the things which he knew. Upon which the examining master, moved less to compassion by the impenetrable dulness of the man than to anger by his unreasonable complaint, tore off about an inch of paper, and pushing it towards him, desired him to write upon that all he knew!

And yet bulky books are composed, or compiled by men who know as little as this poor empty individual. Tracts, and treatises, and tomes, may be, and are written by persons, to whom the smallest square sheet of delicate note paper, rose-coloured, or green, or blue, with its embossed border, manufactured expressly for ladies' fingers and crow-quills, would afford ample room, and verge enough, for expounding the sum total of their knowledge upon the subject whereon they undertake to enlighten the public.

Were it possible for me to pour out all that I have taken in from him, of whose accumulated stores I, alas! am now the sole living depository, I know not to what extent the precious reminiscences might run.

Per sua gratia singulare
Par ch' io habbi nel capo una seguenza,
Una fontana, un fiume, un lago, un mare,
Id est un pantanaccio d'eloquenza. ‡

Sidronius Hosschius has supplied me with a simile for this stream of recollections.

Æstuat et cursu nunquam cessante laborat
Eridanus, fessis irrequietus aquis;
Spumeus it, fervensque, undamque supervenit unda;
Hæc illam, sed et hanc non minus ista premit.
Volvitur, et volvit pariter, motuque perenni
Truditur à fluctu posteriore prior.

As I shall proceed

Excipiet curam nova cura, laborque laborem,
Nec minus exhausto quod superabit erit.

But for stores which in this way have been received, the best compacted memory is like a sieve; more of necessity slips through than stops upon the way; and well is it, if that which is of most value be what remains behind. I have pledged myself, therefore, to no more than I can perform; and this the reader shall have within reasonable limits, and in due time, provided the performance be not prevented by any of the evils incident to human life.

At present, my business is to answer the question "Who was Mrs. Dove?"

CHAPTER LXXII.

IN WHICH THE FOURTH OF THE QUESTIONS PROPOSED IN CHAPTER II. P. I. IS BEGUN TO BE ANSWERED; SOME OBSERVATIONS UPON ANCESTRY ARE INTRODUCED, AND THE READER IS INFORMED WHY THE AUTHOR DOES NOT WEAR A CAP AND BELLS.

Boast not the titles of your ancestors,
Brave youths! they're their possessions, none of yours.
When your own virtues equall'd have their names,
'Twill be but fair to lean upon their fames,
For they are strong supporters; but till then
The greatest are but growing gentlemen.

BEN JONSON.

WHO was Mrs. Dove?

A woman of the oldest family in this or any other kingdom, for she was beyond all doubt a legitimate descendant of Adam.

---

* ROBERT GREEN. † MIDDLETON. ‡ MATTEO FRANZESI.

Her husband perhaps might have rather said that she was a daughter of Eve. But he would have said it with a smile of playfulness, not of scorn.

To trace her descent somewhat lower, and bring it nearer to the stock of the Courtenays, the Howards, the Manriques, the Bourbons and Thundertentronks, she was a descendant of Noah, and of his eldest son Japhet. She was allied to Ham, however, in another way, besides this remote niece-ship.

As how I pray you, Sir?

Her maiden name was Bacon.

Grave Sir, be not disconcerted. I hope you have no antipathy to such things: or at least that they do not act upon you, as the notes of a bagpipe are said to act upon certain persons whose unfortunate idiosyncrasy exposes them to very unpleasant effects from the sound.

Mr. Critickin,—for as there is a diminutive for cat, so should there be for critic,—I defy you! Before I can be afraid of your claws, you must leave off biting your nails.

I have something better to say to the Reader, who follows wherever I lead up and down, high and low, to the hill and to the valley, contented with his guide, and enjoying the prospect which I show him in all its parts, in the detail and in the whole, in the foreground and home scene, as well as in the Pisgah view. I will tell him before the chapter is finished, why I do not wear a cap and bells.

To you, my Lady, who may imagine that Miss Bacon was not of a good family, (Lord Verulam's line, as you very properly remark, being extinct,) I beg leave to observe that she was certainly a cousin of your own; somewhere within the tenth and twentieth degrees, if not nearer. And this I proceed to prove.

Every person has two immediate parents, four ancestors in the second degree, eight in the third, and so the pedigree ascends, doubling at every step, till in the twentieth generation, he has no fewer than one million, thirty thousand, eight hundred and ninety-six

Great, great, great,
great, great, great,
great, great, great,
great, great, great,
great, great, great,
great, great, great,

grandfathers and grandmothers. Therefore, my Lady, I conceive it to be absolutely certain, that under the Plantagenets, if not in the time of the Tudors, some of your ancestors must have been equally ancestors of Miss Deborah Bacon.

"At the conquest," says Sir Richard Phillips, "the ancestry of every one of the English people was the whole population of England; while on the other hand, every one having children at that time, was the direct progenitor of the whole of the living race."

The reflecting reader sees at once that it must be so. *Plato ait, Neminem regem non ex servis esse oriendum, neminem non servum ex regibus. Omnia ista longa varietas miscuit, et sursum deorsum fortuna versavit. Quis ergo generosus? ad virtutem bene à natura compositus. Hoc unum est intuendum: alioqui, si ad vetera revocas, nemo non inde est, ante quod nihil est.** And the erudite Ihre in the *Proemium* to his invaluable Glossary, says, *ut aliquoto cognationis gradu, sed per monumentorum defectum hodie inexplicabile, omnes homines inter se connexi sunt.*

Now then to the gentle reader. The reason why I do not wear a cap and bells is this.

There are male caps of five kinds which are worn at present in this kingdom; to wit, the military cap, the collegiate cap, the jockey cap, the travelling cap, and the night cap. Observe, reader, I said *kinds*, that is to say in scientific language *genera*,—for the *species* and varieties are numerous, especially in the former *genus*.

I am not a soldier; and having long been weaned from Alma Mater, of course have left off my college cap. The gentlemen of the —— hunt would object to my going

* SENECA.

out with the bells on: it would be likely to frighten their horses; and were I to attempt it, it might involve me in unpleasant disputes, which might possibly lead to more unpleasant consequences. To my travelling cap the bells would be an inconvenient appendage; nor would they be a whit more comfortable upon my night-cap. Besides, my wife might object to them.

It follows that if I would wear a cap and bells, I must have a cap made on purpose. But this would be rendering myself singular; and of all things a wise man will most avoid any ostentatious appearance of singularity.

Now I am certainly not singular in playing the fool without one.

And indeed if I possessed such a cap, it would not be proper to wear it in this part of my history.

CHAPTER LXXIII.

RASH MARRIAGES. AN EARLY WIDOWHOOD. AFFLICTION RENDERED A BLESSING TO THE SUFFERERS; AND TWO ORPHANS LEFT, THOUGH NOT DESTITUTE, YET FRIENDLESS.

> Love built a stately house; where Fortune came,
> And spinning fancies, she was heard to say
> That her fine cobwebs did support the frame;
> Whereas they were supported by the same.
> But Wisdom quickly swept them all away.
>
> HERBERT.

MRS. Dove was the only child of a clergyman who held a small vicarage in the West Riding. Leonard Bacon, her father, had been left an orphan in early youth. He had some wealthy relations by whose contributions he was placed at an endowed grammar-school in the country, and having through their influence gained a scholarship to which his own deserts might have entitled him, they continued to assist him—sparingly enough indeed—at the University, till he succeeded to a fellowship. Leonard was made of Nature's finest clay, and Nature had tempered it with the choicest dews of heaven.

He had a female cousin about three years younger than himself, and in like manner an orphan, equally destitute, but far more forlorn. Man hath a fleece about him which enables him to bear the buffetings of the storm;—but woman when young, and lovely, and poor, is as a shorn lamb for which the wind has not been tempered.

Leonard's father and Margaret's had been bosom friends. They were subalterns in the same regiment, and being for a long time stationed at Salisbury, had become intimate at the house of Mr. Trewbody, a gentleman of one of the oldest families in Wiltshire. Mr. Trewbody had three daughters. Melicent, the eldest, was a celebrated beauty, and the knowledge of this had not tended to improve a detestable temper. The two youngest, Deborah and Margaret, were lively, good-natured, thoughtless, and attractive. They danced with the two Lieutenants, played to them on the spinnet, sung with them and laughed with them,—till this mirthful intercourse became serious, and knowing that it would be impossible to obtain their father's consent, they married the men of their hearts without it. Palmer and Bacon were both without fortune, and without any other means of subsistence than their commissions. For four years they were as happy as love could make them; at the end of that time Palmer was seized with an infectious fever. Deborah was then far advanced in pregnancy, and no solicitations could induce Bacon to keep from his friend's bed-side. The disease proved fatal; it communicated to Bacon and his wife; the former only survived his friend ten days, and he and Deborah were then laid in the same grave. They left an only boy of three years old, and in less than a month the widow Palmer was delivered of a daughter.

In the first impulse of anger at the flight of his daughters, and the degradation of his family, (for Bacon was the son of a tradesman, and Palmer was nobody knew who,) Mr. Trewbody had made his will, and left the whole sum, which he had designed for his three daughters, to the eldest. Whether the situation of Margaret and the two orphans might have touched him is, perhaps, doubtful,—for the family were either light-hearted or hard-hearted, and his heart was of the hard sort; but he died suddenly a few months before his sons-in-law. The only son, Trewman Trewbody, Esq., a Wiltshire fox-hunter, like his father, succeeded to the estate; and as he and his eldest sister hated each other cordially, Miss Melicent left the manor-house, and established herself in the Close at Salisbury, where she lived in that style which a portion of 6000*l.* enabled her in those days to support.

The circumstance which might appear so greatly to have aggravated Mrs. Palmer's distress, if such distress be capable of aggravation, prevented her perhaps from eventually sinking under it. If the birth of her child was no alleviation of her sorrow, it brought with it new feelings, new duties, new cause for exertion, and new strength for it. She wrote to Melicent and to her brother, simply stating her own destitute situation, and that of the orphan Leonard; she believed that their pride would not suffer them either to let her starve or go to the parish for support, and in this she was not disappointed. An answer was returned by Miss Trewbody, informing her that she had nobody to thank but herself for her misfortunes; but, that notwithstanding the disgrace which she had brought upon the family, she might expect an annual allowance of ten pounds from the writer, and a like sum from her brother; upon this she must retire into some obscure part of the country, and pray God to forgive her for the offence she had committed in marrying beneath her birth and against her father's consent.

Mrs. Palmer had also written to the friends of Lieutenant Bacon,—her own husband had none who could assist her. She expressed her willingness and her anxiety to have the care of her sister's orphan, but represented her forlorn state. They behaved more liberally than her own kin had done, and promised five pounds a-year as long as the boy should require it. With this and her pension she took a cottage in a retired village. Grief had acted upon her heart like the rod of Moses upon the rock in the desert; it had opened it, and the well-spring of piety had gushed forth. Affliction made her religious, and religion brought with it consolation, and comfort, and joy. Leonard became as dear to her as Margaret. The sense of duty educed a pleasure from every privation to which she subjected herself for the sake of economy; and in endeavouring to fulfil her duties in that state of life to which it had pleased God to call her, she was happier than she had ever been in her father's house, and not less so than in her marriage state. Her happiness indeed was different in kind, but it was higher in degree. For the sake of these dear children she was contented to live, and even prayed for life; while, if it had respected herself only, Death had become to her rather an object of desire than of dread. In this manner she lived seven years after the loss of her husband, and was then carried off by an acute disease, to the irreparable loss of the orphans who were thus orphaned indeed.

CHAPTER LXXIV.

A LADY DESCRIBED WHOSE SINGLE LIFE WAS NO BLESSEDNESS EITHER TO HERSELF OR OTHERS. A VERACIOUS EPITAPH AND AN APPROPRIATE MONUMENT.

Beauty! my Lord,—'tis the worst part of woman!
A weak poor thing, assaulted every hour
By creeping minutes of defacing time;
A superficies which each breath of care
Blasts off; and every humorous stream of grief
Which flows from forth these fountains of our eyes,
Washeth away, as rain doth winter's snow.

GOFF.

MISS TREWBODY behaved with perfect propriety upon the news of her sister's death. She closed her front windows for two days; received no visitors for a week; was much indisposed, but resigned to the will of Providence, in reply to messages of condolence; put her servants in mourning, and sent for Margaret that she might do her duty to her sister's child by breeding her up under her own eye. Poor Margaret was transferred from the stone floor of her mother's cottage to the Turkey carpet of her aunt's parlour. She was too young to comprehend at once the whole evil of the exchange; but she learned to feel and understand it during years of bitter dependence, unalleviated by any hope, except that of one day seeing Leonard, the only creature on earth whom she remembered with affection.

Seven years elapsed, and during all those years Leonard was left to pass his holidays, summer and winter, at the grammar-school where he had been placed at Mrs. Palmer's death: for although the master regularly transmitted with his half-yearly bill the most favourable accounts of his disposition and general conduct, as well as of his progress in learning, no wish to see the boy had ever arisen in the hearts of his nearest relations; and no feeling of kindness, or sense of decent humanity, had ever induced either the fox-hunter Trewman or Melicent his sister, to invite him for Midsummer or Christmas. At length in the seventh year a letter announced that his school-education had been completed, and that he was elected to a scholarship at ——— College, Oxford, which scholarship would entitle him to a fellowship in due course of time: in the intervening years some little assistance from his *liberal benefactors* would be required; and the liberality of those *kind friends* would be well bestowed upon a youth who bade so fair to do honour to himself, and to reflect *no disgrace upon his honourable connections.* The head of the family promised his part, with an ungracious expression of satisfaction at thinking that "thank God, there would soon be an end of these demands upon him." Miss Trewbody signified her assent in the same amiable and religious spirit. However much her sister had disgraced her family, she replied, "please God it should never be said that she refused to do her duty."

The whole sum which these wealthy relations contributed was not very heavy,—an annual ten pounds each: but they contrived to make their nephew feel the weight of every separate portion. The Squire's half came always with a brief note desiring that the receipt of the enclosed sum might be acknowledged without delay,—not a word of kindness or courtesy accompanied it: and Miss Trewbody never failed to administer with her remittance a few edifying remarks upon the folly of his mother in marrying beneath herself; and the improper conduct of his father in connecting himself with a woman of family, against the consent of her relations, the consequence of which was that he had left a child dependant upon those relations for support. Leonard received these pleasant preparations of charity only at distant intervals, when he regularly expected them, with his half-yearly allowance. But Margaret meantime was dieted upon the food of bitterness, without one circumstance to relieve the misery of her situation.

At the time, of which I am now speaking, Miss Trewbody was a maiden lady of forty-seven, in the highest state of preservation. The whole business of her life had been to take care of a fine person, and in this she had succeeded admirably. Her library consisted of two books; Nelson's Festivals and Fasts was one, the other was "the Queen's Cabinet unlocked;" and there was not a cosmetic in the latter which she had not faithfully prepared. Thus by means, as she believed, of distilled waters of various kinds, May-dew and butter-milk, her skin retained its beautiful texture still, and much of its smoothness; and she knew at times how to give it the appearance of that brilliancy which it had lost. But that was a profound secret. Miss Trewbody, remembering the example of Jezebel, always felt conscious that she was committing a sin when she took the rouge-box in her hand, and generally ejaculated in a low voice, the Lord forgive me! when she laid it down: but looking in the glass at the same time, she indulged a hope that the nature of the temptation might be considered as an excuse for the transgression. Her other great business was to observe with the utmost precision all the punctilios of her situation in life; and the time which was not devoted to one or other of these worthy occupations, was employed in scolding her servants, and tormenting her niece. This employment, for it was so habitual that it deserved that name, agreed excellently with her constitution. She was troubled with no acrid humours, no fits of bile, no diseases of the spleen, no vapours or hysterics. The morbid matter was all collected in her temper, and found a regular vent at her tongue. This kept the lungs in vigorous health; nay, it even seemed to supply the place of wholesome exercise, and to stimulate the system like a perpetual blister, with this peculiar advantage, that instead of an inconvenience it was a pleasure to herself, and all the annoyance was to her dependents.

Miss Trewbody lies buried in the Cathedral at Salisbury, where a monument was erected to her memory worthy of remembrance itself for its appropriate inscription and accompaniments. The epitaph recorded her as a woman eminently pious, virtuous, and charitable, who lived universally respected, and died sincerely lamented by all who had the happiness of knowing her. This inscription was upon a marble shield supported by two Cupids, who bent their heads over the edge, with marble tears larger than grey pease, and something of the same colour, upon their cheeks. These were the only tears which her death occasioned, and the only Cupids with whom she had ever any concern.

CHAPTER LXXV.

A SCENE WHICH WILL PUT SOME OF THOSE READERS WHO HAVE BEEN MOST IMPATIENT WITH THE AUTHOR, IN THE BEST HUMOUR WITH HIM.

There is no argument of more antiquity and elegancy than is the matter of Love; for it seems to be as old as the world, and to bear date from the first time that man and woman was: therefore in this, as in the finest metal, the freshest wits have in all ages shown their best workmanship. ROBERT WILMOT.

WHEN Leonard had resided three years at Oxford, one of his college-friends invited him to pass the long vacation at his father's house, which happened to be within an easy ride of Salisbury. One morning, therefore, he rode to that city, rung at Miss Trewbody's door, and having sent in his name, was admitted into the parlour, where there was no one to receive him, while Miss Trewbody adjusted her head-dress at the toilette, before she made her appearance. Her feelings while she was thus employed were not of the pleasantest kind toward this unexpected guest; and she was prepared to accost him with a reproof for his extravagance in undertaking so long a journey, and with some mortifying questions concerning the business which brought him there. But this amiable intention was put to flight, when Leonard, as soon as she entered the room, informed her that having accepted an invitation into that neighbourhood, from his friend and fellow-collegian, the son of Sir Lambert Bowles, he had taken the earliest opportunity of coming to pay his respects to her, and acknowledging his obligations, as bound alike by duty and inclination. The name of Sir Lambert Bowles acted upon Miss Trewbody like a charm: and its mollifying effect was not a little aided by the tone of her nephew's address, and the sight of a fine youth in the first bloom of manhood, whose appearance and manners were such that she could not be surprised at the introduction he had obtained into one of the first families in the county. The scowl, therefore, which she brought into the room upon her brow, passed instantly away, and was succeeded by so gracious an aspect, that Leonard, if he had not divined the cause, might have mistaken this gleam of sunshine for fair weather.

A cause which Miss Trewbody could not possibly suspect had rendered her nephew's address thus conciliatory. Had he expected to see no other person in that house, the visit would have been performed as an irksome obligation, and his manner would have appeared as cold and formal as the reception which he anticipated. But Leonard had not forgotten the playmate and companion with whom the happy years of his childhood had been passed. Young as he was at their separation, his character had taken its stamp during those peaceful years, and the impression which it then received was indelible. Hitherto hope had never been to him so delightful as memory. His thoughts wandered back into the past more frequently than they took flight into the future; and the favourite form which his imagination called up was that of the sweet child, who in winter partook his bench in the chimney corner, and in summer sate with him in the porch, and strung the fallen blossoms of jessamine upon stalks of grass. The snowdrop and the crocus reminded him of their little garden, the primrose of their sunny orchard-bank, and the blue bells and the cowslip of the fields, wherein they were allowed to run wild, and gather them in the merry month of May. Such as she then was he saw her frequently in sleep, with her blue eyes, and rosy cheeks, and flaxen curls: and in his day-dreams he sometimes pictured her to himself such as he supposed she now might be, and dressed up the image with all the magic of ideal beauty. His heart, therefore, was at his lips when he inquired for his cousin. It was not without something like fear, and an apprehension of disappointment, that he awaited her appearance; and he was secretly condemning himself for the romantic folly which he had encouraged, when the door opened, and a creature came in, —less radiant, indeed, but more winning than his fancy had created, for the loveliness of earth and reality was about her.

"Margaret," said Miss Trewbody, "do you remember your cousin Leonard?"

Before she could answer, Leonard had taken her hand. "'Tis a long while, Margaret, since we parted!—ten years!—But I have not forgotten the parting, — nor the blessed days of our childhood."

She stood trembling like an aspen leaf, and looked wistfully in his face for a moment, then hung down her head, without power to utter a word in reply. But he felt her tears fall fast upon his hand, and felt also that she returned its pressure.

Leonard had some difficulty to command himself, so as to bear a part in conversation with his aunt, and keep his eyes and his thoughts from wandering. He accepted, however, her invitation to stay and dine with her with undissembled satisfaction, and the pleasure was not a little heightened when she left the room to give some necessary orders in consequence. Margaret still sate trembling and in silence. He took her hand, pressed it to his lips, and said in a low earnest voice, "dear dear Margaret!" She raised her eyes, and fixing them upon him with one of those looks the perfect remembrance of which can never be effaced from the heart to which they have been addressed, replied in a lower but not less earnest tone, "dear Leonard!" and from that moment their lot was sealed for time and for eternity.

CHAPTER LXXVI.

A STORY CONCERNING CUPID WHICH NOT ONE READER IN TEN THOUSAND HAS EVER HEARD BEFORE; A DEFENCE OF LOVE WHICH WILL BE VERY SATISFACTORY TO THE LADIES.

> They do lie,
> Lie grossly who say Love is blind, — by him
> And Heaven they lie! he has a sight can pierce
> Thro' ivory, as clear as it were horn,
> And reach his object.
>
> BEAUMONT and FLETCHER.

THE Stoics who called our good affections eupathies, did not manage those affections as well as they understood them. They kept them under too severe a discipline, and erroneously believed that the best way to strengthen the heart was by hardening it. The Monks carried this error to its utmost extent, falling indeed into the impious absurdity that our eupathies are sinful in themselves. The Monks have been called the Stoics of Christianity; but the philosophy of the Cloister can no more bear comparison with that of the Porch, than Stoicism itself with Christianity pure and undefiled. Van Helmont compares even the Franciscans with the Stoics; *paucis mutatis*, he says, *videbam Capucinum esse Stoicum Christianum.* He might have found a closer parallel for them in the Cynics both for their filth and their extravagance. And here I will relate a Rabbinical tradition.

On a time the chiefs of the Synagogue, being mighty in prayer, obtained of the Lord that the Evil Spirit who had seduced the Jews to commit idolatry, and had brought other nations against them to overthrow their city and destroy the Temple, should be delivered into their hands for punishment; when by advice of Zechariah the prophet they put him in a leaden vessel, and secured him there with a weight of lead upon his face. By this sort of *peine forte et dure*, they laid him so effectually that he has never appeared since. Pursuing then their supplications while the ear of Heaven was open, they entreated that another Evil Spirit, by whom the people had continually been led astray, might in like manner be put into their power. This prayer also was granted; and the Demon with whom Poets, Lovers, and Ladies are familiar, by his heathen name of Cupid, was delivered up to them.

> ———*folle per lui*
> *Tutto il mondo si fa. Perisca Amore,*
> *E saggio ognun sarà.**

The prophet Zechariah warned them not to be too hasty in putting him to death, for fear of the consequences;

> ——You shall see
> A fine confusion in the country; mark it!

But the prophet's counsel was as vain as the wise courtier's in Beaumont and Fletcher's tragedy, who remonstrated against the decree for demolishing Cupid's altars. They disregarded his advice; because they were determined upon destroying the enemy now that they had him in their power; and they bound their prisoner fast in chains, while they deliberated by what death he should die. These deliberations lasted three days; on the third day it happened that a new-laid egg was wanted for a sick person, and behold! no such thing was to be found throughout the kingdom of Israel, for since this Evil Spirit was in durance, not an egg had been laid; and it appeared upon inquiry, that the whole course of kind was suspended. The chiefs of the Synagogue perceived then that not without reason Zechariah had warned them; they saw that if they put their prisoner to death the world must come to an end; and therefore they contented themselves with putting out his eyes, that he might not see to do so much mischief, and let him go.

Thus it was that Cupid became blind,— a fact unknown to the Greek and Roman Poets and to all the rhymesters who have succeeded them.

The Rabbis are coarse fablers. Take away love, and not physical nature only, but the heart of the moral world would be palsied:

> This is the salt unto Humanity
> And keeps it sweet.*

> *Senza di lui*
> *Che diverrian le sfere,*
> *Il mar, la terra? Alla sua chiara face*
> *Si coloran le stelle; ordine e lume*
> *Ei lor ministra; egli mantiene in pace*
> *Gli' elemente discordi; unisce insieme*
> *Gli opposti eccessi; e con eterno giro,*
> *Che sembra caso, ed è saper profondo,*
> *Forma, scompone, e riproduce il mondo.*†

It is with this passion as with the Amreeta in Southey's Hindoo tale, the most original of his poems; its effects are beneficial or malignant according to the subject on which it acts. In this respect Love may also be likened to the Sun, under whose influence one plant elaborates nutriment for man, and another poison; and which, while it draws up pestilence from the marsh and jungle, and sets the simoom in motion over the desert, diffuses light, life, and happiness over the healthy and cultivated regions of the earth.

It acts terribly upon Poets. Poor creatures, nothing in the whole details of the Ten Persecutions, or the history of the Spanish Inquisition, is more shocking than what they have suffered from Love, according to the statements which they have given of their own sufferings. They have endured scorching, frying, roasting, burning, sometimes by a slow fire, sometimes by a quick one; and melting, — and this too from a fire,

* METASTASIO.

* BEAUMONT and FLETCHER. † METASTASIO.

which, while it thus affects the heart and liver, raises not a blister upon the skin; resembling in this respect that penal fire which certain theological writers describe as being more intense because it is invisible,—existing not in form, but in essence, and acting therefore upon spirit as material and visible fire acts upon the body. Sometimes they have undergone from the same cause all the horrors of freezing and petrifaction. Very frequently the brain is affected; and one peculiar symptom of the insanity arising from this cause, is that the patients are sensible of it, and appear to boast of their misfortune.

Hear how it operated upon Lord Brooke, who is called the most thoughtful of poets, by the most bookful of Laureates. The said Lord Brooke in his love, and in his thoughtfulness, confesseth thus;

I sigh; I sorrow; *I do play the fool!*

Hear how the grave—the learned Pasquier describes its terrible effects upon himself!

Jà je sens en mes os une flamme nouvelle
Qui me mine, qui m'ard, qui brusle ma möuelle.

Hear its worse moral consequences, which Euphues avowed in his wicked days! "He that cannot dissemble in love is not worthy to live. I am of this mind, that both might and malice, deceit and treachery, all perjury and impiety, may lawfully be committed in love, which is lawless."

Hear too how Ben Jonson makes the Lady Frampul express her feelings!

My fires and fears are met: I burn and freeze;
My liver's one great coal, my heart shrunk up
With all the fibres; and the mass of blood
Within me is a standing lake of fire,
Curl'd with the cold wind of my gelid sighs,
That drive a drift of sleet through all my body
And shoot a February through my veins.

And hear how Artemidorus, not the oneirologist, but the great philosopher at the Court of the Emperor Sferamond, describes the appearances which he had observed in dissecting some of those unfortunate persons, who had died of love:—*Quant à mon regard*, says he, *j'en ay veu faire anatomie de quelques uns qui estoient morts de cette maladie, qui avoient leurs entrailles toutes retirées, leur pauvre cœur tout buslé, leur foye toute enfumé, leurs poulmons tout rostis, les ventricules de leurs cerveaux tous endommagez; et je croy que leur pauvre ame étoit cuite et arse à petite feu, pour la vehemence et excessif chaleur et ardeur inextinguible qu'ils enduroient lors que la fievre d'amour les avoit surprins.**

But the most awful description of its dangerous operation upon persons of his own class is given by the Prince of the French Poets, not undeservedly so called in his own times. Describing the effect of love upon himself when he is in the presence of his mistress, Ronsard says,

Tant s'en faut que je sois alors maistre de moy,
Que je n'rois les Dieux, et trahirois mon Roy,
Je vendrois mon pay, je meurtrirois mon père;
Telle rage me tient après que j'ay tasté
A longs traits amoureux de la poison amère
Qui sort de ces beaux yeux dont je suis enchanté.

Mercy on us! neither Petrarch, nor poor Abel Shufflebottom himself, was so far gone as this!

In a diseased heart it loses its nature, and combining with the morbid affection which it finds, produces a new disease.

When it gets into an empty heart, it works there like quicksilver in an apple dumpling, while the astonished cook, ignorant of the roguery which has been played her, thinks that there is not Death, but the Devil in the pot.

In a full heart, which is tantamount to saying a virtuous one, (for in every other, conscience keeps a void place for itself, and the hollow is always felt,) it is sedative, sanative, and preservative: a drop of the true elixir, no mithridate so effectual against the infection of vice.

How then did this passion act upon Leonard and Margaret? In a manner which you will not find described in any of Mr. Thomas Moore's poems; and which Lord Byron is as incapable of understanding, or even believing in another, as he is of feeling it in himself.

* Amadis de Gaule. Liv. 23.

CHAPTER LXXVII.

MORE CONCERNING LOVE AND THE DREAM OF LIFE.

Happy the bonds that hold ye;
Sure they be sweeter far than liberty.
There is no blessedness but in such bondage;
Happy that happy chain; such links are heavenly.
BEAUMONT and FLETCHER.

I WILL not describe the subsequent interviews between Leonard and his cousin, short and broken but precious as they were; nor that parting one in which hands were plighted, with the sure and certain knowledge that hearts had been interchanged. Remembrance will enable some of my readers to portray the scene, and then perhaps a sigh may be heaved for the days that are gone: Hope will picture it to others, — and with them the sigh will be for the days that are to come.

There was not that indefinite deferment of hope in this case at which the heart sickens. Leonard had been bred up in poverty from his childhood; a parsimonious allowance, grudgingly bestowed, had contributed to keep him frugal at College, by calling forth a pardonable if not a commendable sense of pride in aid of a worthier principle. He knew that he could rely upon himself for frugality, industry, and a cheerful as well as a contented mind. He had seen the miserable state of bondage in which Margaret existed with her Aunt, and his resolution was made to deliver her from that bondage as soon as he could obtain the smallest benefice on which it was possible for them to subsist. They agreed to live rigorously within their means, however poor, and put their trust in Providence. They could not be deceived in each other, for they had grown up together; and they knew that they were not deceived in themselves. Their love had the freshness of youth, but prudence and forethought were not wanting; the resolution which they had taken brought with it peace of mind, and no misgiving was felt in either heart when they prayed for a blessing upon their purpose. In reality it had already brought a blessing with it; and this they felt; for love, when it deserves that name, produces in us what may be called a regeneration of its own, — a second birth, — dimly, but yet in some degree, resembling that which is effected by Divine Love when its redeeming work is accomplished in the soul.

Leonard returned to Oxford happier than all this world's wealth or this world's honours could have made him. He had now a definite and attainable hope, — an object in life which gave to life itself a value. For Margaret, the world no longer seemed to her like the same earth which she had till then inhabited. Hitherto she had felt herself a forlorn and solitary creature, without a friend; and the sweet sounds and pleasant objects of nature had imparted as little cheerfulness to her as to the debtor who sees green fields in sunshine from his prison, and hears the lark singing at liberty. Her heart was open now to all the exhilarating and all the softening influences of birds, fields, flowers, vernal suns, and melodious streams. She was subject to the same daily and hourly exercise of meekness, patience, and humility; but the trial was no longer painful; with love in her heart, and hope and sunshine in her prospect, she found even a pleasure in contrasting her present condition with that which was in store for her.

In these our days every young lady holds the pen of a ready writer, and words flow from it as fast as it can indent its zigzag lines, according to the reformed system of writing, — which said system improves handwritings by making them all alike and all illegible. At that time women wrote better and spelt worse: but letter writing was not one of their accomplishments. It had not yet become one of the general pleasures and luxuries of life, — perhaps the greatest gratification which the progress of civilisation has given us. There was then no mail coach to waft a sigh across the country at the rate of eight miles an hour. Letters came slowly and with long intervals between; but when they came, the happiness which they imparted to Leonard and Margaret lasted during the interval, however long. To Leonard it was as an exhilarant and a cordial which rejoiced and strengthened him. He trod the earth with a lighter and more elated movement on the day when he received a letter from Margaret, as if he felt himself invested with an importance which he had never possessed till the happiness of another human being was inseparably associated with his own;

> So proud a thing it was for him to wear
> Love's golden chain,
> With which it is best freedom to be bound.*

Happy, indeed, if there be happiness on earth, as that same sweet poet says, is he,

> Who love enjoys, and placed hath his mind
> Where fairest virtues fairest beauties grace,
> Then in himself such store of worth doth find
> That he deserves to find so good a place.*

This was Leonard's case; and when he kissed the paper, which her hand had pressed, it was with a consciousness of the strength and sincerity of his affection, which at once rejoiced and fortified his heart. To Margaret his letters were like summer dew upon the herb that thirsts for such refreshment. Whenever they arrived, a head-ache became the cause or pretext for retiring earlier than usual to her chamber, that she might weep and dream over the precious lines: —

> True gentle love is like the summer dew,
> Which falls around when all is still and hush;
> And falls unseen until its bright drops strew
> With odours, herb and flower, and bank and bush.
> O love! — when womanhood is in the flush,
> And man's a young and an unspotted thing,
> His first-breathed word, and her half-conscious blush,
> Are fair as light in heaven, or flowers in spring.†

INTERCHAPTER VII.

OBSOLETE ANTICIPATIONS; BEING A LEAF OUT OF AN OLD ALMANAC, WHICH, LIKE OTHER OLD ALMANACS, THOUGH OUT OF DATE IS NOT OUT OF USE.

> If
> You play before me, I shall often look on you,
> I give you that warning beforehand.
> Take it not ill, my masters, I shall laugh at you,
> And truly when I am least offended with you;
> It is my humour. MIDDLETON.

WHEN St. Thomas Aquinas was asked in what manner a man might best become learned, he answered, "by reading one book;" "meaning," says Bishop Taylor, "that an understanding entertained with several objects is intent upon neither, and profits not." Lord Holland's poet, the prolific Lope de Vega, tells us to the same purport:

> *Que es estudiante notable*
> *El que lo es de un libro solo.*
> *Que quando no estavan llenos*
> *De tantos libros agenos,*
> *Como van dexando atras,*
> *Sabian los hombres mas*
> *Porque estudiavan en menos.*

The *homo unius libri* is indeed proverbially formidable to all conversational figurantes. Like your sharp-shooter, he knows his piece perfectly, and is sure of his shot. I would, therefore, modestly insinuate to the reader what infinite advantages would be possessed by that fortunate person who shall be the *homo hujus libri.*

According to the Lawyers the King's eldest son is for certain purposes of full age as soon as he is born, — great being the mysteries of Law! I will not assume that in like manner *hic liber* is at once to acquire maturity of fame; for fame, like the oak, is not the product of a single generation; and a new book in its reputation is but as an acorn, the full growth of which can be known only by posterity. The Doctor will not make so great a sensation upon its first appearance as Mr. Southey's Wat Tyler, or the first two Cantos of Don Juan; still less will it be talked of so universally as the murder of Mr. Weire. Talked of, however, it will be widely, largely, loudly and *lengthily* talked of: lauded and vituperated, vilified and extolled, heartily abused, and no less heartily admired.

Thus much is quite certain, that before it has been published a week, eight persons will be named as having written it; and these eight positive lies will be affirmed each as positive truths on positive knowledge.

Within the month Mr. Woodbee will write to one Marquis, one Earl, two Bishops, and two Reviewers-Major, assuring them that he is *not* the Author. Mr. Sligo will cautiously avoid making any such declaration, and will take occasion significantly to remark

* DRUMMOND. † ALLAN CUNNINGHAM.

upon the exceeding impropriety of saying to any person that a work which has been published anonymously is supposed to be his. He will observe also, that it is altogether unwarrantable to ask any one, under such circumstances, whether the report be true. Mr. Blueman's opinion of the book will be asked by four-and-twenty female correspondents, all of the order of the stocking.

Professor Wilson will give it his hearty praise. Sir Walter Scott will deny that he has any hand in it. Mr. Coleridge will smile if he is asked the question. If it be proposed to Sir Humphry Davy he will smile too, and perhaps blush also. The Laureate will observe a careless silence; Mr. Wordsworth a dignified one. And Professor Porson, if he were not gone where his Greek is of no use to him, would accept credit for it, though he would not claim it.

The Opium-Eater, while he peruses it, will doubt whether there is a book in his hand, or whether he be not in a dream of intellectual delight.

"My little more than nothing" Jeffrey the second—(for of the small Jeffreys, Jeffrey Hudson must always be the first)—will look less when he pops upon his own name in its pages. Sir Jeffrey Dunstan is Jeffrey the third: he must have been placed second in right of seniority, had it not been for the profound respect with which I regard the University of Glasgow. The Rector of Glasgow takes precedence of the Mayor of Garratt.

And what will the Reviewers do? I speak not of those who come to their office, (for such there are, though few,) like Judges to the bench, stored with all competent knowledge and in an equitable mind; prejudging nothing, however much they may foreknow; and who give their sentence without regard to persons, upon the merits of the case; but the aspirants and wranglers at the bar, the dribblers and the spit-fires, (there are of both sorts;)—the puppies who bite for the pleasure which they feel in exercising their teeth, and the dogs whose gratification consists in their knowledge of the pain and injury that they inflict;—the creepers of literature, who suck their food, like the ivy, from what they strangulate and kill; they who have a party to serve, or an opponent to run down; what opinion will they pronounce in their utter ignorance of the author? They cannot play without a bias in their bowls!—Ay, there's the rub!

Ha ha, ha ha! this World doth pass
Most merrily, I'll be sworn,
For many an honest Indian Ass
Goes for a Unicorn.
Farra diddle dyno,
This is idle fyno!
Tygh hygh, tygh hygh! O sweet delight!
He tickles this age that can
Call Tullia's ape a marmasite,
And Leda's goose a swan.*

Then the discussion that this book will excite among blue stockings, and blue beards! The stir! the buzz! the bustle! The talk at tea tables in the country, and *conversazione* in town,—in Mr. Murray's room, at Mr. Longman's dinners, in Mr. Hatchard's shop,—at the Royal Institution,—at the Alfred, at the Admiralty, at Holland House! Have you seen it?—Do you understand it? Are you not disgusted with it?—Are you not provoked at it?—Are you not delighted with it? Whose is it? Whose can it be?

Is it Walter Scott's?—There is no Scotch in the book; and that hand is never to be mistaken in its masterly strokes. Is it Lord Byron's?—Lord Byron's! Why the Author fears God, honours the King, and loves his country and his kind. Is it by Little Moore?—If it were, we should have sentimental lewdness, Irish patriotism, which is something very like British treason, and a plentiful spicing of personal insults to the Prince Regent. Is it the Laureate?—He lies buried under his own historical quartos! There is neither his mannerism, nor his moralism, nor his methodism. Is it Wordsworth?—What,—an Elephant cutting capers on the slack wire! Is it Coleridge?—The method indeed of the book might lead to such a suspicion,—but then it is intelligible throughout. Mr. A——?—there is Latin in it. Mr. B——?—there is

* British Bibliographer.

Greek in it. Mr. C——? — it is written in good English. Mr. Hazlitt? It contains no panegyric upon Bonaparte; no imitations of Charles Lamb; no plagiarisms from Mr. Coleridge's conversation; no abuse of that gentleman, Mr. Southey and Mr. Wordsworth, — and no repetitions of himself. Certainly, therefore, it is *not* Mr. Hazlitt's.

Is it Charles Lamb?

> Baa! Baa! good Sheep, have you any wool?
> Yes marry, that I have, three bags full.

Good Sheep I write here, in emendation of the nursery song; because nobody ought to call this Lamb a *black* one.

Comes it from the Admiralty? There indeed wit enough might be found and acuteness enough, and enough of sagacity, and enough of knowledge both of books and men; but when

> The Raven croaked as she sate at her meal
> And the Old Woman knew what he said, *—

the Old Woman knew also by the tone who said it.

Does it contain the knowledge, learning, wit, sprightliness, and good sense, which that distinguished patron of letters my Lord Puttiface Papinhead has so successfully concealed from the public and from all his most intimate acquaintance during his whole life?

Is it Theodore Hook with the learned assistance of his brother the Archdeacon?— A good guess that of the Hook: have an eye to it!

"I guess it is our Washington Irving," says the New Englander. The Virginian replies, "I reckon it may be;" and they agree that none of the Old Country Authors are worthy to be compared with him.

Is it Smith?

Which of the Smiths? for they are a numerous people. To say nothing of Black Smiths, White Smiths, Gold Smiths, and Silver Smiths, there is Sydney, who is Joke-Smith to the Edinburgh Review; and William, who is Motion Smith to the Dissenters Orthodox and Heterodox, in Parliament, having been elected to represent them, — to wit, the aforesaid Dissenters — by the citizens of Norwich. And there is *Cher Bobus* who works for nobody; and there is Horace and his brother James, who work in Colburn's forge at the sign of the Camel. You probably meant these brothers; they are clever fellows, with wit and humour as fluent as their ink; and to their praise be it spoken with no gall in it. But their wares are of a very different quality.

Is it the Author of Thinks I to myself? — "Think you so," says I to myself I. Or the Author of the Miseries of Human Life? George Colman? Wrangham, — unfrocked and in his lighter moods? Yorick of Dublin? Dr. Clarke? Dr. Busby? The Author of My Pocket Book? D'Israeli? Or that phenomenon of eloquence, the celebrated Irish Barrister, Counsellor Phillips? Or may it not be the joint composition of Sir Charles and Lady Morgan? he compounding the speculative, scientific, and erudite ingredients; she intermingling the lighter parts, and infusing her own grace, airiness, vivacity, and spirit through the whole. A well-aimed guess: for they would throw out opinions differing from their own, as ships in time of war hoist false colours; and thus they would enjoy the baffled curiosity of those wide circles of literature and fashion in which they move with such enviable distinction both at home and abroad.

Is it Mr. Mathurin? Is it Hans Busk? —

> Busk ye, busk ye, my bonny bonny bride,
> Busk ye, my winsome marrow!

Is it he who wrote of a World without Souls, and made the Velvet Cushion relate its adventures?

Is it Rogers? — The wit and the feeling of the book may fairly lead to such an ascription, if there be sarcasm enough to support it. So may the Pleasures of Memory which the Author has evidently enjoyed during the composition.

Is it Mr. Utinam? He would have written it, — if he could. — Is it Hookham Frere? He could have written it, — if he would. — Has Matthias taken up a new Pursuit in Literature? Or has William Bankes been trying the experiment whether he can im-

* Southey.

part as much amusement and instruction by writing, as in conversation?

Or is it some new genius "breaking out at once like the Irish Rebellion a hundred thousand strong?" Not one of the Planets, nor fixed stars of our Literary System, but a Comet as brilliant as it is eccentric in its course.

Away the dogs go, whining here, snuffing there, nosing in this place, pricking their ears in that, and now full-mouthed upon a false scent,—and now again all at fault.

Oh the delight of walking invisible among mankind!

"Whoever he be," says Father O'Faggot, "he is an audacious heretic." "A schoolmaster, by his learning," says Dr. Fullbottom Wigsby. The Bishop would take him for a Divine, if there were not sometimes a degree of levity in the book, which, though always innocent, is not altogether consistent with the gown. Sir Fingerfee Dolittle discovers evident marks of the medical profession. "He has manifestly been a traveller," says the General, "and lived in the World." The man of letters says it would not surprise him if it were the work of a learned Jew. Mr. Dullman sees nothing in the book to excite the smallest curiosity; he really does not understand it, and doubts whether the Author himself knew what he would be at. Mr. McDry declares, with a harsh Scotch accent, "It's just parfit nonsense."

INTERCHAPTER VIII.

A LEAF OUT OF THE NEW ALMANAC. THE AUTHOR THINKS CONSIDERATELY OF HIS COMMENTATORS; RUMINATES; RELATES AN ANECDOTE OF SIR THOMAS LAWRENCE; QUOTES SOME PYRAMIDAL STANZAS, WHICH ARE NOT THE WORSE FOR THEIR ARCHITECTURE, AND DELIVERS AN OPINION CONCERNING BURNS.

> To smell to a turf of fresh earth is wholesome for the body; no less are thoughts of mortality cordial to the Soul. *Earth thou art, to earth thou shalt return.*
>
> FULLER.

THE Commentators in the next millennium, and even in the next century, will, I foresee, have no little difficulty, in settling the chronology of this opus. I do not mean the time of its conception, the very day and hour of that happy event having been recorded in the seventh chapter, A. I.: nor the time of its birth, that, as has been registered in the weekly Literary Journals, having been in the second week of January, 1834. But at what intervening times certain of its Chapters and Interchapters were composed.

A similar difficulty has been found with the Psalms, the Odes of Horace, Shakespeare's Plays, and other writings sacred or profane, of such celebrity as to make the critical inquiry an object of reasonable curiosity, or of real moment.

They, however, who peruse the present volume while it is yet a new book, will at once have perceived that between the composition of the preceding Chapter and their perusal thereof, an interval as long as one of Nourjahad's judicial visitations of sleep must have elapsed. For many of the great performers who figured upon the theatre of public life when the anticipations in that Chapter were expressed, have made their exits; and others who are not there mentioned, have since that time made their entrances.

The children of that day have reached their stage of adolescence; the youth are now in mid life; the middle-aged have grown old, and the old have passed away. I say nothing of the political changes that have intervened. Who can bestow a thought upon the pantomime of politics, when his mind is fixed upon the tragedy of human life?

Robert Landor (a true poet like his great brother, if ever there was one) says finely in his Impious Banquet,

> There is a pause near death when men grow bold
> Toward all things else:

Before that awful pause, whenever the thought is brought home to us, we feel ourselves near enough to grow indifferent to them, and to perceive the vanity of all earthly pursuits, those only excepted which have the good of our fellow creatures for their object, and tend to our own spiritual improvement.

But this is entering upon a strain too serious for this place; though any reflection upon the lapse of time and the changes that steal on us in its silent course leads naturally to such thoughts.

Omnia paulatim consumit longior ætas,
Vivendoque simul morimur, rapimurque manendo.
Ipse mihi collatus enim non ille videbor;
Frons alia est, moresque alii, nova mentis imago,
*Voxque aliud mutata sonat.**

Sir Thomas Lawrence was told one day that he had made a portrait, which he was then finishing, ten years too young. "Well," he replied, "I have; and I see no reason why it should not be made so." There was this reason: ten years, if they bring with them only their ordinary portion of evil and of good, cannot pass over any one's head without leaving their moral as well as physical traces, especially if they have been years of active and intellectual life. The painter, therefore, who dips his brush in Medea's kettle, neither represents the countenance as it is, nor as it has been.

"And what does that signify?" Sir Thomas might ask in rejoinder.—What indeed! Little to any one at present, and nothing when the very few who are concerned in it shall have passed away,—except to the artist. The merits of his picture as a work of art are all that will then be considered; its fidelity as a likeness will be taken for granted, or be thought of as little consequence as in reality it then is.

Yet if Titian or Vandyke had painted upon such a principle, their portraits would not have been esteemed as they now are. We should not have felt the certainty which we now feel, that in looking at the pictures of the Emperor Charles V. and of Cortes; of King Charles the Martyr, and of Strafford, we see the veritable likeness and true character of those ever-memorable personages.

Think of the changes that any ten years in the course of human life produce in body and in mind, and in the face, which is in a certain degree the index of both. From thirty to forty is the decade during which the least outward and visible alteration takes place; and yet how perceptible is it even during that stage in every countenance that is composed of good flesh and blood! For I do not speak of those which look as if they had been hewn out of granite, cut out of a block, cast in bronze, or moulded either in wax, tallow, or paste.

Ten years!

Quarles in those Hieroglyphics of the Life of Man, which he presents to the Reader as an Egyptian dish dressed in the English fashion, symbolises it by the similitude of a taper divided into eight equal lengths, which are to burn for ten years each,—if the candle be not either wasted, or blown out by the wind, or snuffed out by an unskilful hand, or douted (to use a good old word) with an extinguisher, before it is burned down to the socket. The poem which accompanies the first print of the series begins thus, in pyramidal stanzas; such they were designed to be, but their form resembles that of an Aztecan or Mexican Cu, rather than of an Egyptian pyramid.

1.

Behold
How short a span
Was long enough of old
To measure out the life of man!
In those well-temper'd days, his time was then
Surveyed, cast up, and found but threescore years and ten.

2.

Alas
And what is that!
They come and slide and pass
Before my pen can tell thee what.
The posts of life are swift, which having run
Their seven short stages o'er, their short-liv'd task is done.

"I had an old grand-uncle," says Burns, "with whom my mother lived awhile in her girlish years. The good man was long blind ere he died, during which time his highest enjoyment was to sit down and cry, while my mother would sing the simple old song of the Life and Age of Man."

It is certain that this old song was in Burns's mind when he composed to the same cadence those well-known stanzas of which the burthen is that "man was made to mourn." But the old blind man's tears were tears of piety, not of regret; it was his

* Petrarch.

greatest enjoyment thus to listen and to weep; and his heart the while was not so much in the past, as his hopes were in the future. They were patient hopes; he knew in Whom he believed, and was awaiting his deliverance in God's good time. *Sunt homines qui cum patientiâ moriuntur; sunt autem quidam perfecti qui cum patientiâ vivunt.** Burns may perhaps have been conscious in his better hours (and he had many such), that he had inherited the feeling (if not the sober piety) which is so touchingly exemplified in this family anecdote;—that it was the main ingredient in the *athanasia* of his own incomparable effusions; and that without it he never could have been the moral, and therefore never the truly great poet that he eminently is.

INTERCHAPTER IX.

AN ILLUSTRATION FOR THE ASSISTANCE OF THE COMMENTATORS DRAWN FROM THE HISTORY OF THE KORAN. REMARKS WHICH ARE NOT INTENDED FOR MUSSELMEN, AND WHICH THE MISSIONARIES IN THE MEDITERRANEAN ARE ADVISED NOT TO TRANSLATE.

You will excuse me if I do not strictly confine myself to narration, but now and then intersperse such reflections as may offer while I am writing. JOHN NEWTON.

BUT the most illustrious exemplification of the difficulty which the Doctorean or Dovean commentators will experience in settling the chronology of these chapters, is to be found in the history of the Koran.

Mahommedan Doctors are agreed that the first part or parcel of their sacred book which was revealed to the prophet, consisted of what now stands as the first five verses of the ninety-sixth chapter; and that the chapter which ought to be the last of the whole hundred and fourteen, because it was the last which Mahommed delivered, is placed as the ninth in order.

The manner in which the book was originally produced, and afterwards put together, explains how this happened.

Whenever the Impostor found it convenient to issue a portion, one of his disciples wrote it, from his dictation, either upon palm-leaves or parchment, and these were put promiscuously into a chest. After his death Abubeker collected them into a volume, but with so little regard to any principle of order or connection, that the only rule which he is supposed to have followed was that of placing the longest chapters first.

Upon this M. Savary remarks, *ce bouleversement dans un ouvrage qui est un recueil de préceptes donnés dans différens temps et dont les premiers sont souvent abrogés par les suivans, y a jetté la plus grand confusion. On ne doit donc y chercher ni ordre ni suit.* And yet one of the chapters opens with the assertion that "a judicious order reigns in this book,"—according to Savary's version, which here follows those commentators who prefer this among the five interpretations which the words may bear.

Abubeker no doubt was of opinion that it was impossible to put the book together in any way that could detract from its value and its use. If he were, as there is every reason to think, a true believer, he would infer that the same divine power which revealed it piece-meal would preside over the arrangement, and that the earthly copy would thus miraculously be made a faithful transcript of the eternal and uncreated original.

If, on the other hand, he had been as audacious a knave as his son-in-law, the false prophet himself, he would have come with equal certainty to the same conclusion by a different process: for he would have known that if the separate portions, when they were taken out of the chest, had been shuffled and dealt like a pack of cards, they would have been just as well assorted as it was possible to assort them.

A north-country dame in days of old economy, when the tailor worked for women as well as men, delivered one of her nether garments to a professor of the sartorial art with these directions:

* ST. AUGUSTIN.

"Here Talleor, tak this petcut; thoo mun bin' me't, and thoo mun tap-bin' me't; thoo mun turn me't rangsid afoor, tapsid bottom, insid oot: thoo can do't, thoo mun do't, and thoo mun do't speedly."—Neither Bonaparte nor Wellington ever gave their orders on the field of battle with more precision, or more emphatic and authoritative conciseness.

Less contrivance was required for editing the Koran, than for renovating this petticoat: the Commander of the Faithful had only to stitch it together and bin' me't.

The fable is no doubt later than Abubeker's time that the first transcript of this book from its eternal and uncreated original in the very essence of the Deity, is on the Preserved Table, fast by the throne of God; on which Table all the divine decrees of things past, passing, and to come, are recorded. The size of the Table may be estimated by that of the Pen wherewith these things were written on it. The Great Pen was one of the first three created things; it is in length five hundred years' journey, and in breadth, eighty; and I suppose the rate of an Angel's travelling is intended, which considerably exceeds that of a rail-road, a race-horse, or a carrier-pigeon. A copy of the Koran, transcribed upon some celestial material from this original on the Preserved Table, bound in silk, and ornamented with gold and set with precious stones from Paradise, was shown to the Prophet by the Angel Gabriel, once a year, for his consolation, and twice during the last year of his life.

Far later is the legend transmitted by the Spanish Moor, Mahomet Rabadan, that Othman arranged the fragments and copied them in the Prophet's life-time; and that when this transcript was completed, Gabriel presented the Prophet with another copy of the whole, written by his own arch-angelic hand in heaven, whereby the greatest honour and most perfect satisfaction that could be given to man were imparted, and the most conclusive proof afforded of the fidelity with which Othman had executed his holy task. For when his copy was collated with the Angel's it was found to be so exact, "that not the least tittle was variated or omitted, but it seemed as if the same hand and pen had written them both," the only difference being in the size of the letters, and consequently of the two books, and in their legibility.

Gabriel's copy was contained in sixteen leaves, the size of a Damascus coin, not larger than an English shilling; and the strokes of the letters were so much finer than any human hair or any visible thread, that they are compared to the hairs of a serpent, which are so fine that no microscope has ever yet discovered them. They were plainly legible to all who were pure and undefiled; but no unclean person could discern a single syllable, nor could any pen ever be made fine enough to imitate such writing. The ink was of a rich purple, the cover of a bright chesnut colour. Mahommed continually carried this wonderful book about him in his bosom, and when he slept he had it always under his pillow or next his heart. After his decease it disappeared, nor though Othman and Ali diligently sought for it could it ever be found; it was believed, therefore, to have returned to the place from whence it came.

But this is a legend of later date; and learned Mahommedans would reject it not merely as being apocryphal, but as false.

Before I have done with the subject, let me here, on the competent authority of Major Edward Moore, inform the European reader, who may be ignorant of Arabic, that the name of the Arabian False Prophet is, in the language of his own country, written with four letters—M. H. M. D.—a character called *teshdid* over the medial M denoting that sound to be prolonged or doubled; so that Mahammad would better than any other spelling represent the current vernacular pronunciation.

Here let me observe by the way, that the work which the reader has now the privilege of perusing is as justly entitled to the name of the Koran as the so-called pseudo-bible itself, because the word signifies "*that which ought to be read;*" and, moreover, that like the Musselman's Koran, it might also be called Dhikr, which is, being interpreted, "*the Admonition*," because of the salutary instruction and advice which it is intended to convey.

> Take, if ye can, ye careless and supine,
> Counsel and caution from a voice like mine!
> Truths that the theorist could never reach,
> And observation taught me, I would teach.*

Having given the reader this timely intimation, I shall now explain in what my commentators will find a difficulty of the same kind as that which Abubeker would have had, if, in putting together the disorderly writings entrusted to his care, he had endeavoured to arrange them according to the order in which the several portions were produced.

When Mahommed wanted to establish an ordinance for his followers, or to take out a licence for himself for the breach of his own laws, as when he chose to have an extra allowance of wives, or coveted those of his neighbours, he used to promulgate a fragment of the Koran, revealed *pro re natâ*, that is to say in honest old English, *for the nonce*. It has been determined with sufficient accuracy at what times certain portions were composed, because the circumstances in his public or private history which rendered them necessary, or convenient, are known. And what has been done with these parts, might have been done with the whole, if due pains had been taken, at a time when persons were still living who knew when, and why, every separate portion had been,—as they believed,—revealed. This would have required more diligence than the first Caliph had either leisure or inclination to bestow, and perhaps more sagacity than he possessed; the task would have been difficult, but it was possible.

But my commentators will never be able to ascertain any thing more of the chronology of this Koran, than the dates of its conception, and of its birth-day, the interval between them having been more than twenty years.

* Cowper.

INTERCHAPTER X.

MORE ON THE FOREGOING SUBJECT. ELUCIDATION FROM HENRY MORE AND DOCTOR WATTS. AN INCIDENTAL OPINION UPON HORACE WALPOLE. THE STREAM OF THOUGHT "FLOWETH AT ITS OWN SWEET WILL." PICTURES AND BOOKS. A SAYING OF MR. PITT'S CONCERNING WILBERFORCE. THE AUTHOR EXPLAINS IN WHAT SENSE IT MIGHT BE SAID THAT HE SOMETIMES SHOOTS WITH A LONG BOW.

Vorrei, disse il Signor Gasparo Pallavicino, che voi ragionassi un poco piu minutamente di questo, che non fate; che en vero vi tenete molto al generale, et quasi ci mostrate le cose per transito. Il Cortegiano.

Henry More, in the Preface General to the collection of his philosophical writings, says to the reader, "if thy curiosity be forward to inquire what I have done in these new editions of my books, I am ready to inform thee that I have taken the same liberty in this Intellectual Garden of my own planting, that men usually take in their natural ones; which is, to set or pluck up, to transplant and inoculate, where and what they please. And therefore if I have rased out some things, (which yet are but very few) and transposed others, and interserted others, I hope I shall seem injurious to no man in ordering and cultivating this Philosophical Plantation of mine according to mine own humour and liking."

Except as to the rasing out, what our great Platonist has thus said for himself, may here be said for me. "Many things," as the happy old lutanist, Thomas Mace, says, "are good, yea, very good; but yet upon after-consideration we have met with the comparative, which is better; yea, and after that, with the superlative, (best of all), by adding to, or altering a little, the same good things."

During the years that this Opus has been in hand (and in head and heart also) nothing was expunged as if it had become obsolete because the persons therein alluded to had departed like shadows, or the subjects there touched on had grown out of date;

but much was introduced from time to time where it fitted best. Allusions occur in relation to facts which are many years younger than the body of the chapter in which they have been grafted, thus rendering it impossible for any critic, however acute, to determine the date of any one chapter by its contents.

What Watts has said of his own Treatise upon the Improvement of the Mind may therefore, with strict fidelity, be applied to this book, which I trust, O gentle Reader, thou wilt regard as specially conducive to the improvement of thine. "The work was composed at different times, and by slow degrees. Now and then indeed it spread itself into branches and leaves, like a plant in April, and advanced seven or eight pages in a week; and sometimes it lay by without growth, like a vegetable in the winter, and did not increase half so much in the revolution of a year. As thoughts occurred to me in reading or meditation, or in my notices of the various appearances of things among mankind, they were thrown under appropriate heads, and were, by degrees, reduced to such a method as the subject would admit. The language and dress of these sentiments is such as the present temper of mind dictated, whether it were grave or pleasant, severe or smiling. And a book which has been twenty years in writing may be indulged in some variety of style and manner, though I hope there will not be found any great difference of sentiment." With little transposition Watts's words have been made to suit my purpose; and when he afterwards speaks of "so many lines altered, so many things interlined, and so many paragraphs and pages here and there inserted," the circumstances which he mentions as having deceived him in computing the extent of his work, set forth the embarrassment which the commentators will find in settling the chronology of mine.

The difficulty would not be obviated were I, like Horace Walpole, — (though Heaven knows for no such motives as influenced that posthumous libeller,) — to leave a box containing the holograph manuscript of this Opus in safe custody, with an injunction that the seals should not be broken till the year of our Lord 2000. Nothing more than what has been here stated would appear in that inestimable manuscript. Whether I shall leave it as an heir-loom in my family, or have it deposited either in the public library of my Alma Mater, or that of my own College, or bequeath it as a last mark of affection to the town of Doncaster, concerns not the present reader. Nor does it concern him to know whether the till-then-undiscoverable name of the author will be disclosed at the opening of the seals. An adequate motive for placing the manuscript in safe custody is, that a standard would thus be secured for posterity whereby the always accumulating errors of the press might be corrected. For modern printers make more and greater blunders than the copyists of old.

In any of those works which posterity will not be "willing to let perish," how greatly would the interest be enhanced, if the whole history of its rise and progress were known, and amid what circumstances, and with what views, and in what state of mind, certain parts were composed. Sir Walter, than whom no man ever took more accurate measure of the public taste, knew this well; and posterity will always be grateful to him for having employed his declining years in communicating so much of the history of those works which obtained a wider and more rapid celebrity than any that ever preceded them, and perhaps than any that ever may follow them.

An author of the last generation, (I cannot call to mind who,) treated such an opinion with contempt, saying in his preface that "there his work was, and that as the Public were concerned with it only as it appeared before them, he should say nothing that would recal the blandishments of its childhood:" whether the book was one of which the maturity might just as well be forgotten as the nonage, I do not remember. But he must be little versed in bibliology who has not learnt that such reminiscences are not more agreeable to an author himself, than they are to his readers, (if he obtain any,) in after times; for every trifle that relates to the history of a favourite author, and of his works, then becomes precious.

Far be it for me to despise the relic-mongers of literature, or to condemn them, except when they bring to light things which ought to have been buried with the dead; like the Dumfries craniologists, who, when the grave of Burns was opened to receive the corpse of his wife, took that opportunity of *abstracting* the poet's skull that they might make a cast from it! Had these men forgotten the malediction which Shakespeare utters from his monument? And had they never read what Wordsworth says to such men in his Poet's epitaph—

Art thou one all eyes,
Philosopher! a fingering slave,
One that would peep and botanize
Upon his mother's grave?

Wrapt closely in thy sensual fleece,
O turn aside,—and take, I pray,
That he below may rest in peace,
Thy pin-point of a soul away!

O for an hour of Burns' for these men's sake! Were there a Witch of Endor in Scotland it would be an act of comparative piety in her to bring up his spirit; to stigmatise them in verses that would burn for ever would be a gratification for which he might think it worth while to be thus brought again upon earth.

But to the harmless relic-mongers we owe much; much to the Thomas Hearnes and John Nichols, the Isaac Reids and the Malones, the Haslewoods and Sir Egertons. Individually, I owe them much, and willingly take this opportunity of acknowledging the obligation. And let no one suppose that Sir Egerton is disparaged by being thus classed among the pioneers of literature. It is no disparagement for any man of letters, however great his endowments, and however extensive his erudition, to take part in those patient and humble labours by which honour is rendered to his predecessors, and information preserved for those who come after him.

But in every original work which lives and deserves to live, there must have been some charms which no editorial diligence can preserve, no critical sagacity recover. The pictures of the old masters suffer much when removed from the places for which they, and in which many of them were painted. It may happen that one which has been conveyed from a Spanish palace or monastery to the collection of Marshal Soult, or any other Plunder-Master-General in Napoleon's armies, and have passed from thence,—honestly as regards the purchaser,—to the hands of an English owner, may be hung at the same elevation as in its proper place, and in the same light. Still it loses much. The accompaniments are all of a different character; the air and odour of the place are different. There is not here the locality that consecrated it,—no longer the *religio loci*. Wealth cannot purchase these; power may violate and destroy, but it cannot transplant them. The picture in its new situation is seen with a different feeling, by those who have any true feeling for such things.

Literary works of imagination, fancy, or feeling, are liable to no injury of this kind; but in common with pictures they suffer a partial deterioration in even a short lapse of time. In such works as in pictures, there are often passages which once possessed a peculiar interest, personal and local, subordinate to the general interest. The painter introduced into an historical piece the portrait of his mistress, his wife, his child, his dog, his friend, or his faithful servant. The picture is not, as a work of art, the worse where these persons were not known, or when they are forgotten: but there was once a time when it excited on this account in very many beholders, a peculiar delight which it can never more impart.

So it is with certain books: and though there is perhaps little to regret in any thing that becomes obsolete, an author may be allowed to sigh over what he feels and knows to be evanescent.

Mr. Pitt used to say of Wilberforce that he was not so single minded in his speeches as might have been expected from the sincerity of his character, and as he would have been if he had been less dependant upon popular support. Those who knew him, and how he was connected, he said, could perceive that some things in his best speeches were intended to *tell* in such and such quarters,—upon Benjamin Sleek in one place, Isaac Drab in another, and Nehemiah Wilyman in a third.—Well would it be if no man ever looked askant with worse motives!

Observe, Reader, that I call him simply Wilberforce, because any common prefix would seem to disparage that name, especially if used by one who regarded him with admiration; and with respect, which is better than admiration, because it can be felt for those only whose virtues entitle them to it; and with kindliness, which is better than both, because it is called forth by those kindly qualities that are worth more than any talents, and without which a man, though he may be both great and good, never can be amiable. No one was ever blest with a larger portion of those gifts and graces which make up the measure of an amiable and happy man.

It will not be thought then that I have repeated with any disrespectful intention what was said of Wilberforce by Mr. Pitt. The observation was brought to mind while I was thinking how many passages in these volumes were composed with a double intention, one for the public and for posterity, the other private and personal, written with special pleasure on my part, *speciali gratiâ*, for the sake of certain individuals. Some of these, which are calculated for the meridian of Doncaster, the commentators may possibly, if they make due research, discover; but there are others which no ingenuity can detect. Their quintessence exhales when the private, which was in these cases the primary, intention has been fulfilled. Yet the consciousness of the emotions which those passages will excite, the recollections they will awaken, the surprise and the smile with which they will be received,—yea and the melancholy gratification,—even to tears,—which they will impart, has been one and not the least of the many pleasures which I have experienced while employed upon this work.

Πολλά μοι ὑπ' ἀγκῶ-
-νος ὠκέα βέλη
Ἔνδον ἐντὶ φαρέτρας
Φωνᾶντα συνετοῖσιν.*

But while thus declaring that these volumes contain much covert intention of this kind, I utterly disclaim all covert malevolence. My roving shafts are more harmless even than bird bolts, and can hurt none on whom they fall. The arrows with which I take aim carry tokens of remembrance and love, and may be likened to those by which intelligence has been conveyed into besieged places. Of such it is that I have been speaking. Others, indeed, I have in the quiver which are pointed and barbed.

ἐμοὶ μὲν ὦν Μοῖσα καρτερώ-
-τατον βέλος ἀλκᾷ τρέφει.*

When one of these is let fly, (with sure aim and never without just cause,) it has its address written on the shaft at full length, like that which Aster directed from the walls of Methone to Philip's right eye.

Or' c'est assez s' estre esgaré de son grand chemin: j'y retourne et le bats, et le trace comme devant.†

CHAPTER LXXVIII.

AMATORY POETRY NOT ALWAYS OF THE WISEST KIND. AN ATTEMPT TO CONVEY SOME NOTION OF ITS QUANTITY. TRUE LOVE, THOUGH NOT IN EVERY CASE THE BEST POET, THE BEST MORALIST ALWAYS.

El Amor es tan ingenioso, que en mi opinion, mas poetas ha hecho el solo, que la misma naturaleza.

PEREZ DE MONTALVAN.

I RETURN to the loves of Leonard and Margaret.

That poet asked little from his mistress, who entreated her to bestow upon him, not a whole look, for this would have been too great a mercy for a miserable lover, but part of a look, whether it came from the white of her eye, or the black, and if even that were too much, then he besought her only to seem to look at him:

* PINDAR. † BRANTOME.

Un guardo — un guardo? no, troppo pietate
E per misero Amante un guardo intero;
Solo un de' vostri raggi, occhi girate,
O parte del bel bianco, o del bel nero.
E se troppo vi par, non mi mirate;
Ma fate sol sembiante di mirarmi,
*Che nol potete far senza bearmi.**

This is a new thought in amatory poetry; and the difficulty of striking out a new thought in such poetry, is of all difficulties the greatest. Think of a look from the white of an eye! Even part of a look, however, is more than a lady will bestow upon one whom she does not favour; and more than one whom she favours will consent to part with. An Innamorato Furioso in one of Dryden's tragedies says:

I'll not one corner of a glance resign!

Poor Robert Greene, whose repentance has not been disregarded by just posterity, asked his mistress in his licentious days, to look upon him with one eye, (no doubt he meant a sheep's eye;) this also was a new thought; and he gave the reason for his request in this sonnet —

On women nature did bestow two eyes,
Like heaven's bright lamps, in matchless beauty shining,
Whose beams do soonest captivate the wise,
And wary heads, made rare by art's refining.
But why did nature, in her choice combining,
Plant two fair eyes within a beauteous face?
That they might favour two with equal grace.
Venus did soothe up Vulcan with one eye,
With the other granted Mars his wished glee.
If she did so whom Hymen did defy,
Think love no sin, but grant an eye to me!
In vain else nature gave two stars to thee.
If then two eyes may well two friends maintain,
Allow of two, and prove not nature vain.

Love, they say, invented the art of tracing likenesses, and thereby led the way to portrait painting. Some painters it has certainly made; whether it ever made a poet may be doubted: but there can be no doubt that under its inspiration more bad poetry has been produced than by any, or all other causes.

Hæc via jam cunctis nota est, hæc trita poetis
Materia, hanc omnis tractat ubique liber.†

As the most forward bud
Is eaten by the canker ere it blow,
Even so by Love the young and tender wit
Is turn'd to folly.‡

* Chiabrera. † Scauranus. ‡ Shakespeare.

Vanity, presumption, ambition, adulation, malice and folly, flatulent emptiness and ill-digested fulness, misdirected talent and misapplied devotion, wantonness and want, good motives, bad motives, and mixed motives have given birth to verses in such numberless numbers, that the great lake of Oblivion in which they have sunk, must long ago have been filled up, if there had been any bottom to it. But had it been so filled up, and a foundation thus laid, the quantity of love poems which have gone to the same place, would have made a pile there that would have been the eighth wonder of the world. It would have dwarfed the Pyramids. Pelion upon Ossa would have seemed but a type of it; and the Tower of Babel would not, even when that Tower was at its highest elevation, have overtopped it, though the old rhyme says that

Seven mile sank, and seven mile fell,
And seven mile still stand and ever shall.

Ce n'est que feu de leurs froids chaleurs,
Ce n'est qu' horreur de leurs feintes douleurs,
Ce n'est encor de leurs souspirs et pleurs,
Que vents, pluye, et orages:
Et bref, ce n'est à ouir leurs chansons,
De leurs amours, que flammes et glaçons,
Fleches, liens, et mille autres façons
De semblables outrages.

De voz beautez, ce n'est que tout fin or,
Perles, crystal, marbre, et ivoyre encor,
Et tout l'honneur de l'Indique thresor,
Fleurs, lis, œillets, et roses:
De voz doulceurs cë n'est que succre et miel,
De voz rigueures n'est qu' aloës, et fiel,
De voz esprits c'est tous ce que le ciel
Tient de graces encloses.

* * * *

Il n'y a roc, qui n'entende leurs voix,
Leurs piteux cris ont faict cent mille fois
Pleurer les monts, les plaines, et les bois,
Les antres et fonteines.
Bref, il n'y a ny solitaires lieux,
N'y lieux hantez, voyre mesmes les cieux,
Qui ça et là ne montrent à leurs yeux
L'image de leurs peines.

Cestuy-la porte en son cueur fluctueux
De l'Ocean les flots tumultueux,
Cestuy l'horreur des vents impetueux
Sortans de leur caverne:
L'un d'un Caucase, et Mongibel se plaingt,
L'autre en veillant plus de songes se peingt,
Qu'il n'en fut onq'en cest orme, qu'on feinct
En la fosse d'Averne.

Qui contrefaict ce Tantale mourant
Bruslé de soif au milieu d'un torrent,
Qui repaissant un aigle devorant,
S'accoustre en Promethee:

Et qui encor, par un plus chaste vœu,
En se bruslant, veult Hercule estre veu,
Mais qui se mue en eau, air, terre, et feu,
Comme uu second Protee.

L'un meurt de froid, et l'autre meurt de chauld;
L'un vole bas, et l'autre vole hault,
L'un est chetif, l'autre a ce qui luy fault;
L'un sur l'esprit se fonde,
L'autre s'arreste à la beauté du corps;
On ne vid onq' si horribles discords
En ce cahos, qui troubloit les accords
*Dont fut basty le monde.**

But, on the other hand, if love, simple love, is the worst of poets, that same simple love is beyond comparison the best of letter writers. In love poems conceits are distilled from the head; in love letters feelings flow from the heart; and feelings are never so feelingly uttered, affection never so affectionately expressed, truth never so truly spoken, as in such a correspondence. Oh, if the disposition which exists at such times were sustained through life, marriage would then be indeed the perfect union, the "excellent mystery" which our Father requires from those who enter into it, that it should be made; and which it might always be, under his blessing, were it not for the misconduct of one or the other party, or of both. If such a disposition were maintained, — "if the love of husbands and wives were grounded (as it then would be) in virtue and religion, it would make their lives a kind of heaven on earth; it would prevent all those contentions and brawlings which are the great plagues of families, and the lesser hell in passage to the greater." Let no reader think the worse of that sentence because it is taken from that good homely old book, the better for being homely, entitled the Whole Duty of Man.

I once met with a book in which a servant girl had written on a blank leaf, "*not much love after marriage, but a good deal before!*" In her station of life this is but too true; and in high stations also, and in all those intermediate grades where either the follies of the world, or its cares, exercise over us an unwholesome influence. But it is not so with well constituted minds in those favourable circumstances wherein the heart is neither corrupted by wealth, nor hardened by neediness. So far as the tendency of modern usages is to diminish the number of persons who are thus circumstanced, in that same proportion must the sum of happiness be diminished, and of those virtues which are the only safeguard of a nation. And that modern policy and modern manners have this tendency, must be apparent to every one who observes the course both of public and private life.

This girl had picked up a sad maxim from the experience of others; I hope it did not as a consequence make her bestow too much love before marriage herself, and meet with too little after it. I have said much of worthless verses upon this subject; take now, readers, some that may truly be called worthy of it. They are by the Manchester poet, Charles Swain.

1.

Love? — I will tell thee what it is to love!
It is to build with human thoughts a shrine,
Where Hope sits brooding like a beauteous dove;
Where Time seems young, and Life a thing divine.
All tastes, all pleasures, all desires combine
To consecrate this sanctuary of bliss.
Above, the stars in shroudless beauty shine;
Around, the streams their flowery margins kiss;
And if there's heaven on earth, that heaven is surely this!

2.

Yes, this is Love, the stedfast and the true,
The immortal glory which hath never set;
The best, the brightest boon the heart e'er knew:
Of all life's sweets the very sweetest yet!
Oh! who but can recall the eve they met
To breathe, in some green walk, their first young vow,
While summer flowers with moonlight dews were wet,
And winds sigh'd soft around the mountain's brow,
And all was rapture then which is but memory now!

The dream of life indeed can last with none of us, —

As if the thing beloved were all a Saint,
And every place she entered were a shrine: †

but it must be our own fault, when it has passed away, if the realities disappoint us: they are not "weary, stale, flat and unprofitable," unless we ourselves render them so. The preservation of the species is not the sole end for which love was implanted in the human heart; that end the Almighty might as easily have effected by other means: not so the development of our

* Joachim du Bellay.

† Gondibert.

moral nature, which is its higher purpose. The comic poet asserts that

Verum illud verbum est vulgo quod dici solet,
Omnes sibi esse melius malle, quam alteri: *

but this is not true in love. The lover never says

Heus proximus sum egomet mihi; *

He knows and understands the falsehood of the Greek adage,

φιλεῖ δ' ἑαυτοῦ πλεῖον οὐδεὶς οὐδένα·

and not lovers alone, but husbands and wives, and parents, feel that there are others who are dearer to them than themselves. Little do they know of human nature who speak of marriage as doubling our pleasures and dividing our griefs: it doubles, or more than doubles both.

CHAPTER LXXIX.

AN EARLY BEREAVEMENT. TRUE LOVE ITS OWN COMFORTER. A LONELY FATHER AND AN ONLY CHILD.

Read ye that run the aweful truth,
With which I charge my page;
A worm is in the bud of youth,
And at the root of age. COWPER.

LEONARD was not more than eight-and-twenty when he obtained a living, a few miles from Doncaster. He took his bride with him to the vicarage. The house was as humble as the benefice, which was worth less than £50 a-year; but it was soon made the neatest cottage in the country round, and upon a happier dwelling the sun never shone. A few acres of good glebe were attached to it; and the garden was large enough to afford healthful and pleasurable employment to its owners. The course of true love never ran more smoothly; but its course was short.

O how this spring of love resembleth
The uncertain glory of an April day,
Which now shows all the beauty of the sun,
And by and by a cloud takes all away! †

Little more than five years from the time of their marriage had elapsed, before a head-stone in the adjacent churchyard told where the remains of Margaret Bacon had been deposited in the 30th year of her age.

When the stupor and the agony of that bereavement had passed away, the very intensity of Leonard's affection became a source of consolation. Margaret had been to him a purely ideal object during the years of his youth; death had again rendered her such. Imagination had beautified and idolised her then; faith sanctified and glorified her now. She had been to him on earth all that he had fancied, all that he had hoped, all that he had desired. She would again be so in heaven. And this second union nothing could impede, nothing could interrupt, nothing could dissolve. He had only to keep himself worthy of it by cherishing her memory, hallowing his heart to it while he performed a parent's duty to their child; and so doing to await his own summons, which must one day come, which every day was brought nearer, and which any day might bring.

—— 'Tis the only discipline we are born for;
All studies else are but as circular lines,
And death the centre where they must all meet. ‡

The same feeling which from his childhood had refined Leonard's heart, keeping it pure and undefiled, had also corroborated the natural strength of his character, and made him firm of purpose. It was a saying of Bishop Andrewes that "good husbandry is good divinity;" "the truth whereof," says Fuller, "no wise man will deny." Frugality he had always practised as a needful virtue, and found that in an especial manner it brings with it its own reward. He now resolved upon scrupulously setting apart a fourth of his small income to make a provision for his child, in case of her surviving him, as in the natural course of things might be expected. If she should be removed before him, — for this was an event the possibility of which he always bore in mind, — he had resolved that whatever should have been accumulated with this intent, should be disposed of to some other pious purpose, —

---

* TERENCE. † SHAKESPEARE. ‡ MASSINGER.

N

for such, within the limits to which his poor means extended, he properly considered this. And having entered on this prudential course with a calm reliance upon Providence in case his hour should come before that purpose could be accomplished, he was without any earthly hope or fear, — those alone excepted, from which no parent can be free.

The child had been christened Deborah after her maternal grandmother, for whom Leonard ever gratefully retained a most affectionate and reverential remembrance. She was a healthy, happy creature in body and in mind; at first

> —— one of those little prating girls
> Of whom fond parents tell such tedious stories;*

afterwards, as she grew up, a favourite with the village school-mistress, and with the whole parish; docile, good-natured, lively and yet considerate, always gay as a lark and busy as a bee. One of the pensive pleasures in which Leonard indulged was to gaze on her unperceived, and trace the likeness to her mother.

> Oh Christ!
> How that which was the life's life of our being,
> Can pass away, and we recall it thus!†

That resemblance which was strong in childhood lessened as the child grew up; for Margaret's countenance had acquired a cast of meek melancholy during those years in which the bread of bitterness had been her portion; and when hope came to her, it was that "hope deferred" which takes from the cheek its bloom, even when the heart, instead of being made sick, is sustained by it. But no unhappy circumstances depressed the constitutional buoyancy of her daughter's spirits. Deborah brought into the world the happiest of all nature's endowments, an easy temper and a light heart. Resemblant therefore as the features were, the dissimilitude of expression was more apparent; and when Leonard contrasted in thought the sunshine of hilarity that lit up his daughter's face, with the sort of moonlight loveliness which had given a serene and saint-like character to her mother's, he wished to persuade himself that as the early translation of the one seemed to have been thus prefigured, the other might be destined to live for the happiness of others till a good old age, while length of years in their course should ripen her for heaven.

* Dryden. † Isaac Comnenus.

CHAPTER LXXX.

OBSERVATIONS WHICH SHOW THAT WHATEVER PRIDE MEN MAY TAKE IN THE APPELLATIONS THEY ACQUIRE IN THEIR PROGRESS THROUGH THE WORLD, THEIR DEAREST NAME DIES BEFORE THEM.

> —— Thus they who reach
> Grey hairs, die piecemeal.
> Southey.

The name of Leonard must now be dropped as we proceed. Some of the South-American tribes, among whom the Jesuits laboured with such exemplary zeal, and who take their personal appellations, (as most names were originally derived,) from beasts, birds, plants, and other visible objects, abolish upon the death of every individual the name by which he was called, and invent another for the thing from which it was taken, so that their language, owing to this curiously inconvenient custom, is in a state of continual change. An abolition almost as complete with regard to the person had taken place in the present instance. The name, Leonard, was consecrated to him by all his dearest and fondest recollections. He had been known by it on his mother's knees, and in the humble cottage of that aunt who had been to him a second mother and by the wife of his bosom, his first, last and only love. Margaret had never spoken to him, never thought of him, by any other name. From the hour of her death, no human voice ever addressed him by it again. He never heard himself so called, except in dreams. It existed only in the dead letter he signed it mechanically in the course of business, but it had ceased to be a living name.

Men willingly prefix a handle to their names, and tack on to them any two or more honorary letters of the alphabet as a tail; they drop their surnames for a dignity, and change them for an estate or a title. They are pleased to be Doctor'd and Professor'd; to be Captain'd, Major'd, Colonel'd, General'd, or Admiral'd;—to be Sir John'd, my-Lorded, or your-Graced. "You and I," says Cranmer in his Answer to Gardiner's book upon Transubstantiation—"you and I were delivered from our surnames when we were consecrated Bishops; sithence which time we have so commonly been used of all men to be called Bishops, you of Winchester, and I of Canterbury, that the most part of the people know not that your name is Gardiner, and mine Cranmer. And I pray God, that we being called to the name of Lords, have not forgotten our own baser estates, that once we were simple squires!"—But the emotion with which the most successful suitor of Fortune hears himself first addressed by a new and honourable title, conferred upon him for his public deserts, touches his heart less, (if that heart be sound at the core,) than when, after long absence, some one who is privileged so to use it, accosts him by his christian name,—that household name which he has never heard but from his nearest relations, and his old familiar friends. By this it is that we are known to all around us in childhood; it is used only by our parents and our nearest kin when that stage is passed; and as they drop off, it dies as to its oral uses with them.

It is because we are remembered more naturally in our family and paternal circles by our baptismal than our hereditary names, and remember ourselves more naturally by them, that the Roman Catholic, renouncing, upon a principle of perverted piety, all natural ties when he enters a convent and voluntarily dies to the world, assumes a new one. This is one manifestation of that intense selfishness which the law of monastic life inculcates, and affects to sanctify. Alas, there need no motives of erroneous religion to wean us from the ties of blood and of affection! They are weakened and dissolved by fatal circumstances and the ways of the world, too frequently and too soon.

"Our men of rank," said my friend one day when he was speaking upon this subject, "are not the only persons who go by different appellations in different parts of their lives. We all moult our names in the natural course of life. I was Dan in my father's house, and should still be so with my uncle William and Mr. Guy, if they were still living. Upon my removal to Doncaster, my master and mistress called me Daniel, and my acquaintance Dove. In Holland I was Mynheer Duif. Now I am the Doctor, and not among my patients only; friends, acquaintance, and strangers, address me by this appellation; even my wife calls me by no other name; and I shall never be any thing but the Doctor again,—till I am registered at my burial by the same names as at my christening."

CHAPTER LXXXI.

A QUESTION WHETHER LOVE SHOULD BE FAITHFUL TO THE DEAD. DOUBTS ADVANCED AND CASES STATED.

> O even in spite of death, yet still my choice,
> Oft with the inward all-beholding eye
> I think I see thee, and I hear thy voice!
>
> LORD STERLINE.

IN the once popular romance of Astrea the question *si Amour peut mourir par la mort de la chose aimée?* is debated in reference to the faithful shepherd, Tyrcis, who, having lost his mistress Cleon, (Cleon serving for a name feminine in French, as Stella has done in English,) and continuing constant to her memory, is persecuted by the pertinacious advances of Laonice. The sage shepherd, Sylvandre, before whom the point is argued, and to whom it is referred for judgment, delivers, to the great disappointment of the lady, the following sentence: *Qu'une Amour perissable n'est pas vray Amour; car il doit suivre le sujet qui luy à donné naissance. C'est pourquoy ceux qui ont aimé le corps seulement, doivent enclorre toutes les amours du corps dans le mesme tombeau ou il s'enserre: mais ceux qui outre cela ont aimé l'esprit, doivent avec leur Amour voler apres cet esprit aimé jusques au plus haut ciel, sans que les distances les puissent separer.*

The character of a constant mourner is sometimes introduced in romances of the earlier and nobler class; but it is rare in those works of fiction, and indeed it is not common in what has happily been called the romance of real life. Let me, however, restrict this assertion within its proper bounds. What is meant to be here asserted (and it is pertinent to this part of our story) is, that it is not common for any one who has been left a widow or widower, early in life, to remain so always out of pure affection to the memory of the dead, unmingled with any other consideration or cause. Such constancy can be found only where there is the union of a strong imagination and a strong heart,—which, perhaps, is a rare union; and if to these a strong mind be united, the effect would probably be different.

It is only in a strong imagination that the deceased object of affection can retain so firm a hold as never to be dispossessed from it by a living one; and when the imagination is thus possessed, unless the heart be strong, the heart itself, or the intellect, is likely to give way. A deep sense of religion would avert the latter alternative; but I will not say that it is any preservative against the former.

A most affecting instance of this kind is related by Dr. Uwins in his Treatise on Disorders of the Brain. A lady on the point of marriage, whose intended husband usually travelled by the stage-coach to visit her, went one day to meet him, and found instead of him an old friend, who came to announce to her the tidings of his sudden death. She uttered a scream, and piteously exclaimed—"he is dead!" But then all consciousness of the affliction that had befallen her ceased. "From that fatal moment," says the Author, "has this unfortunate female daily for fifty years, in all seasons, traversed the distance of a few miles to the spot where she expected her future husband to alight from the coach; and every day she utters in a plaintive tone, 'he is not come yet! I will return to-morrow!'"

There is a more remarkable case in which love, after it had long been apparently extinct, produced a like effect upon being accidentally revived. It is recorded in a Glasgow newspaper. An old man residing in the neighbourhood of that city found a miniature of his wife, taken in her youth. She had been dead many years, and he was a person of strictly sedate and religious habits; but the sight of this picture overcame him. From the time of its discovery till his death, which took place some months afterwards, he neglected all his ordinary duties and employments, and became in a manner imbecile, spending whole days without uttering a word, or manifesting the slightest interest in passing occurrences. The only one with whom he would hold any communication was a little grandchild, who strikingly resembled the portrait; to her he was perfectly docile; and a day or two before his death he gave her his purse, and strictly enjoined her to lay the picture beside him in his coffin,—a request which was accordingly fulfilled.

Mr. Newton, of Olney, says, that once in the West Indies, upon not receiving letters from his wife in England, he concluded that surely she was dead, and this apprehension affected him so much, that he was nearly sinking under it. "I felt," says he, "some severe symptoms of that mixture of pride and madness which is commonly called a broken heart; and indeed, I wonder that this case is not more common than it appears to be. How often do the potsherds of the earth presume to contend with their Maker! and what a wonder of mercy is it that they are not all broken!"

This is a stern opinion; and he who delivered it held stern tenets, though in his own disposition compassionate and tender. He was one who could project his feelings, and relieve himself in the effort. No husband ever loved his wife more passionately, nor with a more imaginative affection; the long and wasting disease by which she was consumed, affected him proportionably to this deep attachment; but immediately upon her death he roused himself, after the example of David, threw off his grief, and preached her funeral sermon. He ought to have known that this kind of strength and in this degree is given to very few of us,—that a heart may break, even though it be thoroughly resigned to the will of God, and acquiesces in it, and has a lively faith in God's mercies;—yea, that this very resignation, this entire acquiescence, this sure and certain hope, may even accelerate its breaking; and a soul thus chastened, thus purified, thus ripened for immortality, may unconsciously work out the deliverance which it ardently, but piously withal, desires.

What were the Doctor's thoughts upon this subject, and others connected with it, will appear in the proper place. It is touched upon here in relation to Leonard. His love for Margaret might be said to have begun with her life, and it lasted as long as his own. No thought of a second marriage even entered his mind; though in the case of another person, his calm views of human nature and of the course of life would have led him to advise it.

CHAPTER LXXXII.

THE DOCTOR IS INTRODUCED, BY THE SMALL-POX, TO HIS FUTURE WIFE.

> Long-waiting love doth entrance find
> Into the slow-believing mind.
>
> SYDNEY GODOLPHIN.

WHEN Deborah was about nineteen, the small-pox broke out in Doncaster, and soon spread over the surrounding country, occasioning everywhere a great mortality. At that time inoculation had very rarely been practised in the provinces; and the prejudice against it was so strong, that Mr. Bacon, though convinced in his own mind that the practice was not only lawful, but advisable, refrained from having his daughter inoculated till the disease appeared in his own parish. He had been induced to defer it during her childhood, partly because he was unwilling to offend the prejudices of his parishioners, which he hoped to overcome by persuasion and reasoning when time and opportunity might favour; still more because he thought it unjustifiable to introduce such a disease into his own house, with imminent risk of communicating it to others, which were otherwise in no danger, in which the same preparations would not be made, and where, consequently, the danger would be greater. But when the malady had shown itself in the parish, then he felt that his duty as a parent required him to take the best apparent means for the preservation of his child; and that as a pastor also it became him now in his own family to set an example to his parishioners.

Deborah, who had the most perfect reliance upon her father's judgment, and lived in entire accordance with his will in all things, readily consented; and seemed to regard the beneficial consequences of the experiment to others with hope, rather than to look with apprehension to it for herself. Mr. Bacon therefore went to Doncaster and called upon Dr. Dove. "I do not," said he, "ask whether you would advise me to have my daughter inoculated; where so great a risk is to be incurred, in the case of an only child, you might hesitate to advise it. But if you see nothing in her present state of health, or in her constitutional tendencies, which would render it more than ordinarily dangerous, it is her own wish and mine, after due consideration on my part, that she should be committed to your care,—putting our trust in Providence."

Hitherto there had been no acquaintance between Mr. Bacon and the Doctor, farther than that they knew each other by sight and by good report. This circumstance led to a growing intimacy. During the course of his attendance the Doctor fell in friendship with the father, and the father with him.

"Did he fall in love with his patient?"

"No, ladies."

You have already heard that he once fell in love, and how it happened. And you have also been informed that he caught love once, though I have not told you how, because it would have led me into too melancholy a tale. In this case he neither fell in love, nor caught it, nor ran into it, nor walked into it; nor was he overtaken in it, as a boon companion is in liquor, or a runaway in his flight. Yet there was love between the parties at last, and it was love for love, to the heart's content of both. How this came to pass will be related at the proper time and in the proper place.

For here let me set before the judicious Reader certain pertinent remarks by the pious and well-known author of a popular treatise upon the Right Use of Reason,—a treatise which has been much read to little purpose. That author observes, that "those writers and speakers, whose chief business is to amuse or delight, to allure, terrify, or persuade mankind, do not confine themselves to any natural order, but in a cryptical or hidden method, adapt every thing to their designed ends. Sometimes they omit those things which might injure their design, or grow tedious to their hearers, though they seem to have a necessary relation to the point in hand; sometimes they add those things which have no great reference to the subject, but are suited to allure or refresh the mind and the ear. They dilate sometimes, and flourish long upon little incidents, and they skip over, and but lightly touch the drier part of the theme.—They omit things essential which are not beautiful; they insert little needless circumstances and beautiful digressions: they invert times and actions, in order to place every thing in the most affecting light;—they place the first things last, and the last things first with wondrous art; and yet so manage it as to conceal their artifice, and lead the senses and passions of their hearers into a pleasing and powerful captivity."

CHAPTER LXXXIII.

THE AUTHOR REQUESTS THE READER NOT TO BE IMPATIENT. SHOWS FROM LORD SHAFTESBURY AT WHAT RATE A JUDICIOUS WRITER OUGHT TO PROCEED. DISCLAIMS PROLIXITY FOR HIMSELF, AND GIVES EXAMPLES OF IT IN A GERMAN PROFESSOR, A JEWISH RABBI, AND TWO COUNSELLORS, ENGLISH AND AMERICAN.

Pand. He that will have a cake out of the wheat, must tarry the grinding.
Troilus. Have I not tarried?
Pand. Ay, the grinding; but you must tarry the bolting.
Troilus. Have I not tarried?
Pand. Ay, the bolting; but you must tarry the leavening.
Troilus. Still have I tarried.
Pand. Ay, to the leavening: but here's yet in the word hereafter, the kneading, the making of the cake, the heating of the oven, and the baking; nay, you must stay the cooling too; or you may chance to burn your lips.

TROILUS AND CRESSIDA.

I passed over fourteen years of the Doctor's boyhood and adolescence, as it may be remembered was stated in the twenty-fifth Chapter; but I must not in like manner pass over the years that intervened between his first acquaintance with Deborah Bacon, and the happy day whereon the bells of St. George's welcomed her to Doncaster as his bride. It would be as inconsistent with my design to pretermit this latter portion of his life, as it would have been incompatible with my limits to have recorded the details of the former, worthy to be recorded as they were. If any of my readers should be impatient on this occasion, and think that I ought to have proceeded to the marriage without delay, or at least to the courtship, I must admonish them in the words of a Turkish saying, that "hurry comes from the Devil, and slow advancing from Allah."—"Needs must go when the Devil drives," says the proverb: but the Devil shall never drive me. I will take care never to go at such a rate, "as if haste had maimed speed by overrunning it at starting."

"The just composer of a legitimate piece," says Lord Shaftesbury, "is like an able traveller, who exactly measures his journey, considers his ground, premeditates his stages and intervals of relaxation and intention, to the very conclusion of his undertaking, that he happily arrives where he first proposed at setting out. He is not presently upon the spur, or in his full career, but walks his steed leisurely out of the stable, settles himself in his stirrups, and when fair road and season offer, puts on perhaps to a round trot, thence into a gallop, and after a while takes up. As down, or meadow, or shady lane present themselves, he accordingly suits his pace, favours his palfrey, and is sure not to bring him puffing, and in a heat, into his last inn."

Yes, Reader,

— matter needless, of importless burden *

may as little be expected to flow from the slit of my pen, as to "divide the lips" of wise Ulysses. On the other hand what is needful, what is weighty in its import, let who will be impatient, must not be left unsaid.

Varie fila a varie tele
Uopo mi son, che tutte ordire intendo.†

It is affirmed by the angelic Doctor, St. Thomas Aquinas, that of corporeal things the quantity is in proportion to the quality, that which is best being always in the same degree the greatest. "Thus in this our universe," he says, "the water is more than the earth, the air more than the water, the fire more than the air; the first heaven larger than the sphere of fire, the second than the first, the third than the second; and so they proceed increasing to the tenth sphere, and to the empyrean, which is, *inestimabilis et incomparabilis magnitudinis.*"

Upon the principle which this greatest of the schoolmen has assumed, I leave the reader to infer what would be the probable and proper extent of the present opus, were I to indulge my genius and render justice to the subject.

To make it exceed in length the histories of Sir Charles Grandison and of Clarissa Harlowe, or the bulkier romances of Calprenede and the Scuderys, it would not be necessary to handle it in the manner of a lawyer who, having no more argument than would lie in a nut-shell, wire-draws it and hammers at it, and hammers at it and wire-draws it, and then wire-draws it and hammers at it again, like a lecturer who is exhibiting the infinite ductility of gold.

"What a gift," says Fuller, "had John Halsebach, Professor at Vienna, in tediousness, who being to expound the Prophet Isaiah to his auditors, read twenty-one years on the first chapter, and yet finished it not!" Mercator, in the description of Austria in his Atlas, has made mention of this Arch-Emperor of the Spintexts.

If I had been in John Halsebach's place, my exposition of that first chapter would have been comprised in one lecture, of no hungry or sleepy duration. But if John Halsebach were in mine, he would have filled more volumes than Rees's Cyclopædia with his account of Daniel Dove.

And yet Rabbi Chananiah may contest the palm with the Vienna Professor. It is recorded of him that when he undertook to write a commentary upon part of the Prophet Ezekiel, he required the Jews to supply him with three hundred tons of oil for the use of his lamp, while he should be engaged in it.‡

It is well known upon one of the English circuits that a leading barrister once undertook to speak while an express went twenty miles to bring back a witness whom it was necessary to produce upon the trial. But what is this to the performance of an American counsellor, who upon a like emergency held the judge and the jury by their ears for three mortal days! He indeed was put to his wits' end for words wherewith to fill up the time; and he introduced so many truisms, and argued at the utmost length so many indisputable points, and expatiated so profusely upon so many trite ones, that Judge Marshal (the biographer of Wash-

* TROILUS AND CRESSIDA.

† ARIOSTO.

‡ "The Jews did not suffer this book, or at least the beginning of it, to be read by any who had not attained their thirtieth year; and restrictions were imposed upon Commentators who might be disposed to write upon it." — BISHOP GRAY'S *Key to the Old Testament*.

ington and the most patient of listeners,) was so far moved at last as to say, "Mr. Such a one! — (addressing him by his name in a deliberate tone of the mildest reprehension,) — there are some things with which the Court should be supposed to be acquainted."

I can say with Burton, *malo decem potius verba, decies repetita licet, abundare, quam unum desiderari.* "To say more than a man can say, I hold it not fit to be spoken: but to say what a man ought to say, — there," — with Simon the tanner of Queenborough, — "I leave you."

CHAPTER LXXXIV.

A LOOP DROPPED IN THE FOREGOING CHAPTER IS HERE TAKEN UP.

Enobarbus. Every time
Serves for the matter that is then born in it.
Lepidus. But small to greater matters must give way.
Enobarbus. Not if the small come first.
SHAKESPEARE.

IN the last chapter an illustration of tediousness was omitted, because it so happily exhibits the manner in which a stop may be put to a tedious discourse without incivility, that it deserves a chapter to itself.

When Madame de Stael resided at Copet, it was her custom to collect around her in the evening a circle of literati, the blue legs of Geneva, by some one of whom an essay, a disquisition, or a portion of a work in progress was frequently read aloud to entertain the rest. Professor Dragg's History of Religion had occupied on one of those evenings more time than was thought necessary, or convenient by the company, and especially by the lady of the chateau. It began at the beginning of the world, and did not pass to the Deluge with the rapidity which Dandin required from the pleader in Racine's comedy, who in like manner opened his case before the Creation. Age after age rolled away over the Professor's tongue, the course of which seemed to be interminable as that of the hand of the dial, while the clock struck the hour, and the quarter, and the half hour, and the third quarter, and then the whole hour again, and then again the quarters. "A tedious person," says Ben Jonson, "is one a man would leap a steeple from." Madame de Stael could tolerate nothing that was dry, except her father; but she could neither leap out of her own window, nor walk out of her own room, to escape from Professor Dragg. She looked wistfully round, and saw upon many a countenance an occasional and frequent movement about the lips, indicating that a yawn was at that moment painfully stifled in its birth. Dumont committed no such violence upon nature; he had resigned himself to sleep. The Professor went steadily on. Dumont slept audibly. The Professor was deaf to every sound but that of his own voice. Madame de Stael was in despair. The Professor coming to the end of an eloquent chapter declaimed with great force and vehemence the emphatic close, and prepared to begin the next. Just in that interstice of time, Dumont stirred and snorted. Madame de Stael seized the opportunity; she clapped her hands and ejaculated *Mon Dieu! Voyez Dumont! Il a dormi pendant deux siecles!* Dumont opened his eyes, and Professor Dragg closed his manuscript.

CHAPTER LXXXV.

THE DOCTOR'S CONTEMPORARIES AT LEYDEN. EARLY FRIENDSHIP. COWPER'S MELANCHOLY OBSERVATION THAT GOOD DISPOSITIONS ARE MORE LIKELY TO BE CORRUPTED THAN EVIL ONES TO BE CORRECTED. YOUTHFUL CONNECTIONS LOOSENED IN THE COMMON COURSE OF THINGS. A FINE FRAGMENT BY WALTER LANDOR.

Lass mich den Stunde gedenken, und jedes kleineren umstands.
Ach, wer ruft nicht so gern unwiederbringliches an!
Jenes süsse Gedränge der leichtesten irdischen Tage,
Ach, wer schätzt ihn genug, diesen vereilenden Werth!
Klein erscheinet es nun, doch ach! nicht kleinlich dem Herzen;
Macht die Liebe, die Kunst, jegliches Kleine doch gross.
GOETHE.

THE circumstances of my friend's boyhood and early youth, though singularly favourable to his peculiar cast of mind, in many or indeed most respects, were in this point disadvantageous, that they afforded him little or no opportunity of forming those early friendships which, when they are well formed, contribute so largely to our future happiness. Perhaps the greatest advantage of public education, as compared with private, is, that it presents more such opportunities than are ever met with in any subsequent stage of human life. And yet even then in friendship, as afterwards in love, we are for the most part less directed by choice than by what is called chance.

Daniel Dove never associated with so many persons of his own age at any other time as during his studies at Leyden. But he was a foreigner there, and this is almost as great an obstacle to friendship as to matrimony; and there were few English students among whom to choose. Dr. Brocklesby took his degree, and left the University the year before he entered it; Brocklesby was a person in whose society he might have delighted; but he was a cruel experimentalist, and the dispathy which this must have excited in our friend, whose love of science, ardent as it was, never overcame the sense of humanity, would have counteracted the attraction of any intellectual powers, however brilliant. Akenside, with whom in many respects he would have felt himself in unison, and by whose society he might have profited, graduated also there just before his time.

He had a contemporary more remarkable than either in his countryman John Wilkes, who was pursuing his studies there, not without some diligence, under the superintendence of a private tutor; and who obtained much notice for those lively and agreeable talents which were afterwards so flagrantly abused. But the strict and conscientious frugality which Dove observed, rendered it unfit for him to associate with one who had a liberal allowance, and expended it lavishly: and there was also a stronger impediment to any intimacy between them; for no talents however companionable, no qualities however engaging, could have induced him to associate with a man whose irreligion was of the worst kind, and who delighted in licentious conversation.

There was one of his countrymen indeed there (so far as a Scotchman may be called so) with whom he formed an acquaintance that might have ripened into intimacy, if their lots had fallen near to each other in after life. This was Thomas Dickson, a native of Dumfries; they attended the same lectures, and consorted on terms of friendly familiarity. But when their University course is completed, men separate, like stage-coach travellers, at the end of a journey, or fellow passengers in a ship when they reach their port. While Dove "pursued the noiseless tenor of his way" at Doncaster, Dickson tried his fortune in the metropolis, where he became Physician to the London Hospital, and a Fellow of the Royal Society. He died in the year 1784, and is said in his epitaph to have been "a man of singular probity, loyalty, and humanity; kind to his relations, beloved by all who knew him, learned and skilful in his profession. Unfeed by the poor, he lived to do good, and died a Christian believer." For awhile some intercourse between him and the Doctor had been kept up by letters; but the intervals in their correspondence became longer and longer as each grew more engaged in business; and new connexions gradually effaced an impression which had not been made early, nor had ever been very deep. The friendship that, with no intercourse to nourish it, keeps itself alive for years, must have strong roots in a good soil.

Cowper regarded these early connexions in an unfavourable and melancholy mood. "For my own part," says he, "I found such friendships, though warm enough in their commencement, surprisingly liable to extinction; and of seven or eight whom I had selected for intimates out of about three hundred, in ten years' time not one was left me. The truth is that there may be, and often is, an attachment of one boy to another, that looks very like a friendship; and while they are in circumstances that enable them mutually to oblige and to assist each other, promises well and bids fair to be lasting. But they are no sooner separated from each other, by entering into the world at large, than other connexions and new employments in which they no longer share together, efface the remembrance of what passed in earlier days, and they become strangers to each other for ever. Add to this, the *man* frequently differs so much from the *boy*, — his principles, manners, temper, and conduct, undergo so great an alteration, — that we no longer recognise in him our old play-fellow, but find him utterly unworthy and unfit for the place he once held in our affections." These sentiments he has also expressed in verse: —

— School-friendships are not always found,
Though fair in promise, permanent and sound;
The most disinterested and virtuous minds,
In early years connected, time unbinds;
New situations give a different cast
Of habit, inclination, temper, taste;
And he that seem'd our counterpart at first,
Soon shows the strong similitude reversed.
Young heads are giddy, and young hearts are warm,
And make mistakes for manhood to reform.
Boys are, at best, but pretty buds unblown,
Whose scent and hues are rather guessed than known;
Each dreams that each is just what he appears,
But learns his error in maturer years,
When disposition, like a sail unfurled,
Shows all its rents and patches to the world.

Disposition, however, is the one thing which undergoes no other change than that of growth in after life. The physical constitution, when any morbid principle is innate in it, rarely alters; the moral constitution — (except by a miracle of God's mercy) — never.

—'Ανθρώποις δ' ἀεὶ
'Ο μὲν πονηρὸς, οὐδὲν ἄλλο πλὴν κακός.*

" Believe, if you will," say the Persians, " that a mountain has removed from one place to another; but if you are told that a man has changed his nature, believe it not!"

The best of us have but too much cause for making it part of our daily prayer that we fall into no sin! But there is an original pravity which deserves to be so called in the darkest import of the term, — an inborn and incurable disease of the moral being, manifested as soon as it has strength to show itself; and wherever this is perceived in earliest youth, it may too surely be predicted what is to be expected when all control of discipline is removed. Of those that bring with them such a disposition into the world, it cannot be said that they fall into sin, because it is too manifest that they seek and pursue it as the bent of their nature. No wonder that wild theories have been devised to account for what is so mysterious, so awful, and yet so incontestable! Zephaniah Holwell, who will always be remembered for his sufferings in the Black Hole, wrote a strange book in which he endeavoured to prove that men were fallen angels, that is, that human bodies are the forms in which fallen angels are condemned to suffer for the sins which they have committed in their former state. Akin to this is the Jewish fancy, held by Josephus, as well as his less liberalised countrymen, that the souls of wicked men deceased got into the bodies of the living and possessed them; and by this agency they accounted for all diseases. Holwell's theory is no doubt as old as any part of the Oriental systems of philosophy and figments; it is one of the many vain attempts to account for that fallen nature of which every man who is sincere enough to look into his own heart, finds there what may too truly be called an indwelling witness. Something like the Jewish notion was held by John Wesley and Adam Clarke; and there are certain cases in which it is difficult not to admit it, especially when the question of the demoniacs is considered. Nor is there any thing that shocks us in supposing this to be possible for the body, and the mind also, as depending upon the bodily organs. — But that the moral being, the soul itself, the life of life, the immortal part, should appear, as so often it undoubtedly does, to be thus possessed, this indeed is of all mysterious things the darkest.

For a disposition thus evil in its nature it almost seems as if there could be no hope.

* Euripides.

On the other hand, there is no security in a good one, if the support of good principles (that is to say, of religion — of Christian faith —) be wanting. It may be soured by misfortunes, it may be corrupted by wealth, it may be blighted by neediness, it may lose "all its original brightness."

School friendships arise out of sympathy of disposition at an age when the natural disposition is under little control and less disguise; and there are reasons enough, of a less melancholy kind than Cowper contemplated, why so few of these blossoms set, and of those which afford a promise of fruit, why so small a proportion should bring it to maturity. "The amity that wisdom knits not folly may easily untie*;" and even when not thus dissolved, the mutual attachment which in boyhood is continually strengthened by similarity of circumstance and pursuits, dies a natural death in most cases when that similarity ceases. If one goes north in the intellectual bearings of his course in life, and the other south, they will at last be far as the poles asunder. If their pursuits are altogether different, and their opinions repugnant, in the first case they cease to think of each other with any warm interest; in the second, if they think of each other at all, it is with an uncomfortable feeling, and a painful sense of change.

The way in which too many ordinary minds are worsened by the mere course of time is finely delineated by Landor, in some verses which he designed as an imitation, not of a particular passage in a favourite Greek author, but of his manner and style of thought.

Friendship, in each successive stage of life,
As we approach him, varies to the view;
In youth he wears the face of Love himself,
Of Love without his arrows and his wings.
Soon afterwards with Bacchus and with Pan
Thou findest him; or hearest him resign,
To some dog-pastor, by the quiet fire,
With much good-will and jocular adieu,
His age-worn mule, or broken-hearted steed.
Fly not, as thou wert wont, to his embrace;
Lest, after one long yawning gaze, he swear
Thou art the best good fellow in the world,
But he had quite forgotten thee, by Jove!
Or laughter wag his newly bearded chin
At recollection of his childish hours.
But wouldst thou see, young man, his latest form,
When e'en this laughter, e'en this memory fails,
Look at yon fig-tree statue! golden once,
As all would deem it, rottenness falls out
At every little hole the worms have made;
And if thou triest to lift it up again
It breaks upon thee! Leave it! touch it not!
Its very lightness would encumber thee.
Come — thou hast seen it: 'tis enough; be gone!

The admirable writer who composed these verses in some melancholy mood, is said to be himself one of the most constant and affectionate of friends. It may indeed safely be affirmed, that generous minds, when they have once known each other, never can be alienated as long as both retain the characteristics which brought them into union. No distance of place, or lapse of time, can lessen the friendship of those who are thoroughly persuaded of each other's worth. There are even some broken attachments in friendship as well as in love which nothing can destroy, and it sometimes happens that we are not conscious of their strength till after the disruption.

There are a few persons known to me in years long past, but with whom I lived in no particular intimacy then, and have held no correspondence since, whom I could not now meet without an emotion of pleasure deep enough to partake of pain, and who, I doubt not, entertain for me feelings of the same kind and degree; whose eyes sparkle when they hear, and glisten sometimes when they speak of me; and who think of me as I do of them, with an affection that increases as we advance in years. This is because our moral and intellectual sympathies have strengthened; and because, though far asunder, we know that we are travelling the same road toward our resting place in heaven. "There is such a pleasure as this," says Cowper, "which would want explanation to some folks, being perhaps a mystery to those whose hearts are a mere muscle, and serve only for the purposes of an even circulation."

* SHAKESPEARE.

CHAPTER LXXXVI.

PETER HOPKINS. REASONS FOR SUPPOSING THAT HE WAS AS GOOD A PRACTITIONER AS ANY IN ENGLAND; THOUGH NOT THE BEST. THE FITTEST MASTER FOR DANIEL DOVE. HIS SKILL IN ASTROLOGY.

Que sea Medico mas grave
Quien mas aforismos sabe,
Bien puede ser.
Mas que no sea mas experto
El que mas huviere muerto,
No puede ser. GONGORA.

Of all the persons with whom Daniel Dove associated at Doncaster, the one who produced the most effect upon his mind was his master and benefactor, Peter Hopkins. The influence indeed which he exercised, insensibly as it were, upon his character, was little less than that whereby he directed and fixed the course of his fortune in life. A better professional teacher in his station could nowhere have been found; for there was not a more skilful practitioner in the Three Ridings, consequently not in England; consequently not in Christendom, and by a farther consequence not in the world. Fuller says of Yorkshire that "one may call, and justify it to be the best shire in England; and that not by the help of the general katachresis of *good* for *great*, (as a *good* blow, a *good* piece, &c.,) but in the proper acceptation thereof. If in Tully's Orations, all being excellent, that is adjudged *optima quæ longissima*, the best which is the longest; then by the same proportion, this Shire, partaking in goodness alike with others, must be allowed the best." Yorkshire therefore being the best county in England, as being the largest, of necessity it must have as good practitioners in medicine as are to be found in any other county; and there being no better practitioner than Peter Hopkins there, it would have been in vain to seek for a better elsewhere.

As good a one undoubtedly might have been found;

I trust there were within this realm
Five hundred as good as he,*

though there goes more to the making of a Peter Hopkins than of an Earl Percy. But I very much doubt (and this is one of the cases in which doubt scarcely differs a shade from disbelief) whether there could anywhere have been found another person whose peculiarities would have accorded so curiously with young Daniel's natural bent, and previous education. Hopkins had associated much with Guy, in the early part of their lives; (it was indeed through this connexion that the lad was placed at Doncaster); and, like Guy, he had tampered with the mystical sciences. He knew the theories, and views, and hopes

—— which set the Chymist on
To search that secret-natured stone,
Which the philosophers have told,
When found, turns all things into gold;
But being hunted and not caught,
Oh! sad reverse! turns gold to nought.†

This knowledge he had acquired, like his old friend, for its own sake,—for the pure love of speculation and curious inquiry,—not with the slightest intention of ever pursuing it for the desire of riches. He liked it, because it was mysterious; and he could listen with a half-believing mind to the legends (as they may be called) of those Adepts who from time to time have been heard of, living as erratic a life as the Wandering Jew; but with this difference, that they are under no curse, and that they may forego their immortality, if they do not choose to renew the lease of it, by taking a dose of the elixir in due time.

He could cast a nativity with as much exactness, according to the rules of art, as William Lilly, or Henry Coley, that Merlinus Anglicus Junior, upon whom Lilly's mantle descended; or the Vicar of Thornton in Buckinghamshire, William Bredon, a profound Divine, and "absolutely the most polite person for nativities in that age;" who being Sir Christopher Heydon's chaplain, had a hand in composing that Knight's Defence of Judicial Astrology; but withal

* CHEVY CHACE.

† ARBUTHNOT.

was so given over to tobacco and drink, that when he had no tobacco, he would cut the bell-ropes, and smoke them.

Peter Hopkins could erect a scheme either according to the method of Julius Firmicus, or of Aben-Ezra, or of Campanus, Alcabitius, or Porphyrius, "for so many ways are there of building these houses in the air;" and in that other called the Rational Way, which in a great degree superseded the rest, and which Johannes Muller, the great Regiomontanus, gave to the world in his Tables of Directions, drawn up at the Archbishop of Strigonia's request. He could talk of the fiery and the earthly Trigons, the aerial and the watery; and of that property of a triangle—(now no longer regarded at Cambridge)—whereby Sol and Jupiter, Luna and Venus, Saturn and Mercury, respectively become joint Trigonocrators, leaving Mars to rule over the watery Trigon alone. He knew the Twelve Houses as familiarly as he knew his own; the Horoscope, which is the House of Life, or more awfully to unlearned ears, *Domus Vitæ;* the House of Gain and the House of Fortune;—for Gain and Fortune no more keep house together in heaven, than either of them do with Wisdom, and Virtue, and Happiness on earth; the Hypogeum, or House of Patrimony, which is at the lowest part of heaven, the *Imum Cœli*, though it be in many respects a good house to be born in here below; the Houses of Children, of Sickness, of Marriage, and of Death; the House of Religion; the House of Honours, which, being the Mesouranema, is also called the Heart of Heaven; the Agathodemon, or House of Friends, and the Cacodemon, or House of Bondage. All these he knew, and their Consignificators, and their Chronocrators or Alfridarii, who give to these Consignificators a septennial dominion in succession.

He could ascertain the length of the planetary hour at any given time and place, anachronism being nowhere of greater consequence,—for if a degree be mistaken in the scheme, there is a year's error in the prognostication, and so in proportion for any inaccuracy more or less. Sir Christopher Heydon, the last great champion of this occult science, boasted of possessing a watch so exact in its movements, that it would give him with unerring precision not the minute only, but the very scruple of time. That erudite professor knew—

> *In quas Fortunæ leges quæque hora valeret;*
> *Quantaque quam parvi facerent discrimina motus.**

Peter Hopkins could have explained to a student in this art, how its astronomical part might be performed upon the celestial globe "with speed, ease, delight, and demonstration." He could have expatiated upon conjunctions and oppositions; have descanted upon the four Cardinal Houses; signs fixed, moveable, or common; signs human and signs bestial; semi-sextiles, sextiles, quintiles, quartiles, trediciles, trines, biquintiles and quincunxes; the ascension of the planets, and their declination; their dignities essential and accidental; their exaltation and retrogradation; till the hearer by understanding a little of the baseless theory, here and there, could have persuaded himself that he comprehended all the rest. And if it had been necessary to exact implicit and profound belief, by mysterious and horisonant terms, he could have amazed the listener with the Lords of Decanats, the Five Fortitudes, and the Head and Tail of the Dragon; and have astounded him by ringing changes upon Almugea, Cazimi, Hylech, Aphetes, Anacretes and Alcochodon.

"So far," says Fabian Withers, "are they distant from the true knowledge of physic which are ignorant of astrology, that they ought not rightly to be called physicians, but deceivers:—for it hath been many times experimented and proved, that that which many physicians could not cure or remedy with their greatest and strongest medicines, the astronomer hath brought to pass with one simple herb, by observing the moving of the signs.—There be certain evil times and years of a man's life, which are at every seven years' end. Wherefore if thou wilt prolong thy days, as often as thou comest to every seventh or ninth year (if

* Manilius.

thou givest any credit to Marsilius Ficinus, or Firmicus), diligently consult with an astronomer, from whence and by what means any peril or danger may happen, or come unto thee; then either go unto a physician, or use discretion and temperance, and by that means thou mayest defer and prolong thy natural life through the rules of astronomy, and the help of the physician. Neither be ashamed to inquire of the physician what is thy natural diet, and of the astronomer what star doth most support and favour thy life, and to see in what aspect he is with the moon."

That once eminent student in the mathematics and the celestial sciences, Henry Coley, who, as Merlin junior continued Lilly's Almanac, and published also his own yearly *Nuncius Sydereus*, or Starry Messenger,—the said Coley, whose portrait in a flowing wig and embroidered band, most unlike to Merlin, has made his Ephemeris in request among the Graingerites,—he tells us it is from considering the nature of the planets, together with their daily configurations, and the mixture of their rays or beams of light and heat, that astrologers deduce their judgment of what may *probably*, not *positively* happen: for Nature, he observes, works very abstrusely; and one person may be able to make a better discovery than another, whence arise diversities of opinion too often about the same thing. The physician knows that the same portion of either single or compound simples will not work upon all patients alike; so neither can the like portion and power of qualities stir up, or work always the same; but may sometimes receive either *intention* or *remission* according to the disposed aptness of the subject, the elements or elementary bodies not always admitting of their powers alike, or when they be overswayed by more potent and prevalent operations. For universal and particular causes do many times differ so as the one hinders the operation of the other; and Nature may sometimes be so abstrusely shut up, that what we see not may overpower and work beyond what we see."

Thus were these professors of a pseudo-science always provided with an excuse, however grossly their predictions might be contradicted by the event. It is a beautiful specimen of the ambiguity of the art that the same aspect threatened a hump-back or the loss of an eye; and that the same horoscope which prognosticated a crown and sceptre was held to be equally accomplished if the child were born to a fool's-cap, a bauble, and a suit of motley. "The right worshipful, and of singular learning in all sciences, Sir Thomas Smith, the flower in his time of the University of Cambridge," and to whom, more than to any other individual, both Universities are beholden; for when Parliament, in its blind zeal for ultra-reformation, had placed the Colleges, as well as the Religious Houses at the King's disposal, he, through Queen Katharine Par, prevailed upon Henry to preserve them, instead of dividing them also among the great court cormorants; and he it was who reserved for them the third part of their rents in corn, making that a law which had always been his practice when he was Provost of Eton:—this Sir Thomas used, as his grateful pupil Richard Eden has recorded, to call astrology *ingeniosissimam artem mentiendi*,—the most ingenious art of lying.

Ben Jonson's servant and pupil* has given some good comic examples of the way in which those who honestly endeavoured to read the stars might be deceived,—though when the stars condescended "to palter in a double sense" it was seldom in so good a humour.

—— One told a gentleman
His son should be a man-killer, and be hang'd for't;
Who after proved a great and rich physician,
And with great fame, in the University
Hang'd up in picture for a grave example!
—— Another schemist
Found that a squint-eyed boy should prove a notable
Pick-purse, and afterwards a most strong thief;
When he grew up to be a cunning lawyer,
And at last [illegible] Judge!

* Broome.

CHAPTER LXXXVII.

ASTROLOGY. ALMANACKS. PRISCILLIANISM RETAINED IN THEM TO THIS TIME.

I wander 'twixt the poles
And heavenly hinges, 'mongst eccentricals,
Centers, concentricks, circles, and epicycles.

ALBUMAZAR.

THE connexion between astrology and the art of medicine is not more firmly believed in Persia at this day, than it was among the English people during the age of almanack-makers. The column which contained the names of the saints for every day, as fully as they are still given in Roman Catholic almanacks, was less frequently consulted than those in which the aspects were set down, and the signs and the parts of the human body under their respective governance. Nor was any page in the book regarded with more implicit belief than that which represented the "Anatomy of Man's body as the parts thereof are governed by the twelve Constellations, or rather by the Moon as she passeth by them." In those representations man indeed was not more uglily than fearfully made, — as he stood erect and naked, spiculated by emitted influences from the said signs, like another St. Sebastian; or as he sate upon the globe placed like a butt for him, while they radiated their shafts of disease and pain.

Portentous as the Homo in the almanack is, he made a much more horrific appearance in the Margarita Philosophica, which is a Cyclopædia of the early part of the 16th century. There Homo stands, naked but not ashamed, upon the two Pisces, one foot upon each, the Fish being neither in air, nor water, nor upon earth, but self-suspended as it appears in the void. Aries has alighted with two feet on Homo's head, and has sent a shaft through the forehead into his brain. Taurus has quietly seated himself across his neck. The Gemini are riding astride a little below his right shoulder. The whole trunk is laid open, as if part of the old accursed punishment for high treason had been performed upon him. The Lion occupies the thorax as his proper domain, and the Crab is in possession of the abdomen. Sagittarius, volant in the void, has just let fly an arrow, which is on the way to his right arm. Capricornus breathes out a visible influence that penetrates both knees; Aquarius inflicts similar punctures upon both legs. Virgo fishes as it were at his intestines; Libra at the part affected by schoolmasters in their anger; and Scorpio takes the wickedest aim of all.

The progress of useful knowledge has in our own days at last banished this man from the almanack; at least from all annuals of that description that carry with them any appearance of respectability. If it has put an end to this gross superstition, it has done more than the Pope could do fourteen centuries ago, when he condemned it, as one of the pernicious errors of the Priscillianists.

In a letter to Turribius, Bishop of Astorga, concerning that heresy, Pope St. Leo the Great says: *Si universæ hæreses, quæ ante Priscilliani tempus exortæ sunt, diligentius retractentur, nullus pene invenitur error de quo non traxerit impietas ista contagium: quæ non contenta eorum recipere falsitates, qui ab Evangelio Christi sub Christi nomine deviarunt, tenebris se etiam paganitatis immersit, ut per magicarum artium prophana secreta, et mathematicorum vana mendacia, religionis fidem, morumque rationem in potestate dæmonum, et in affectu syderum collocarent. Quod si et credi liceat et doceri, nec virtutibus præmium, nec vitiis pœna debebitur, omniaque non solum humanarum legum, sed etiam divinarum constitutionum decreta solventur: quia neque de bonis, neque de malis actibus ullum poterit esse judicium, si in utramque partem fatalis necessitas motum mentis impellit, et quicquid ab hominibus agitur, non est hominum, sed astrorum. Ad hanc insaniam pertinet prodigiosa illa totius humani corporis per duodecim Cœli signa distinctio, ut diversis partibus diversæ præsideant potestates; et creatura, quam Deus ad imaginem suam fecit, in tantâ sit obligatione syderum, in quantâ est connectione membrorum.*

But invention has been as rare among heretics as among poets. The architect of the Priscillian heresy (the male heresy of that name, for there was a female one also) borrowed this superstition from the mathematicians, — as the Romans called the astrological impostors of those times. For this there is the direct testimony of Saint Augustine: *Astruunt etiam fatalibus stellis homines colligatos, ipsumque corpus nostrum secundum duodecim signa cœli esse compositum; sicut hi qui Mathematici vulgo appellantur, constituentes in capite Arietem, Taurum in cervice, Geminos in humeris, Cancrum in pectore, et cetera nominatim signa percurrentes ad plantas usque perveniunt, quas Piscibus tribuunt, quod ultimum signum ab Astrologis nuncupatur.*

These impostors derived this part of their craft from Egypt, where every month was supposed to be under the care of three Decans or Directors, for the import of the word must be found in the neighbouring language of the Hebrews and Syrians. There were thirty-six of these, each superintending ten days; and these Decans were believed to exercise the most extensive influence over the human frame. Astrological squares calculated upon this mythology are still in existence. St. Jerome called it the opprobrium of Egypt.

The medical superstition derived from this remote antiquity has continued down to the present generation in the English almanacks, is still continued in the popular almanacks of other countries, and prevails at this time throughout the whole Mahommedan and Eastern world. So deeply does error strike its roots, and so widely scatter its seeds; and so difficult is it to extirpate any error whatsoever, or any evil, which it is the interest of any class of men to maintain. And the rogues had much to say for themselves.

"Notwithstanding the abuses put upon the art of Astrology," said an eminent Professor, "doubtless some judgment may be made thereby what any native may be by nature prone or addicted to. For the aspects of the Planets among themselves, as also the Fixed Stars, 'tis more than supposed, may cause many strange effects in sublunary bodies, but especially in those that have been almost worn out with decrepit age, or debilitated with violent or tedious diseases; wherefore this knowledge may be requisite, and of excellent use to physicians and chirurgeons, &c., for old aches and most diseases do vary according to the change of the air and weather, and that proceeds from the motion of the heavens and aspects of the planets." — Who that has any old aches in his bones, — or has felt his corns shoot — but must acknowledge the truth that was brought forward here in support of an impudent system of imposture? The natural pride, and the natural piety of man, were both appealed to when he was told that the stars were appointed for signs and tokens, — that "the reason why God hath given him an upright countenance is, that he might converse with the celestial bodies, which are placed for his service as so many diamonds in an azure canopy of perpetuity," — and that astrologers had a large field to walk in, for "all the productions of Time were the subjects of their science, and there is nothing under the Sun but what is the birth of Time." There is no truth however pure, and however sacred, upon which falsehood cannot fasten, and engraft itself therein.

Laurence Humphrey, who was sufficiently known in Queen Elizabeth's days as one of the standard-bearers of the Nonconformists, but who, like many others, grew conformable in the end as he grew riper in experience and sager in judgment, — in his Optimates or Treatise concerning Nobility, which he composed for the use of that class and of the Gentry, observed how "this science above all others was so snatched at, so beloved, and even devoured by most persons of honour and worship, that they needed no excitement to it, but rather a bridle; no trumpeter to set them on, but a reprover to take them off from their heat. Many," he said, "had so trusted to it, that they almost distrusted God." He would not indeed wholly condemn the art, but the nobility should not have him a persuader nor an applauder of it; for there were already enough! In vain might a Bishop warn his hearers from the pulpit and from the press that "no soothsayer, no palterer, no judicial astrologer is able to tell any man the events of his life." Man is a dupeable animal. Quacks in medicine, quacks in religion, and quacks in politics know this, and act upon that knowledge. There is scarcely any one who may not, like a trout, be taken by tickling.

CHAPTER LXXXVIII.

AN INCIDENT WHICH BRINGS THE AUTHOR INTO A FORTUITOUS RESEMBLANCE WITH THE PATRIARCH OF THE PREDICANT FRIARS. DIFFERENCES BETWEEN THE FACT AND THE FABLE; AND AN APPLICATION WHICH, UNLIKE THOSE THAT ARE USUALLY APPENDED TO ESOP'S FABLES, THE READER IS LIKELY NEITHER TO SKIP NOR TO FORGET.

Diré aqui una maldad grande del Demonio.
PEDRO DE CIECA DE LEON.

WHILE I was writing that last chapter, a flea appeared upon the page before me, as there did once to St. Dominic.

But the circumstances in my case and in St. Dominic's were different.

For, in the first place I, as has already been said, was writing; but St. Dominic was reading.

Secondly, the flea which came upon my paper was a real flea, a flea of flea-flesh and blood, partly flea-blood and partly mine, which the said flea had flea-feloniously appropriated to himself by his own process of flea-botomy. That which appeared upon St. Dominic's book was the Devil in disguise

The intention with which the Devil abridged himself into so diminutive a form, was that he might distract the Saint's attention from his theological studies, by skipping upon the page, and perhaps provoke him to unsaintlike impatience by eluding his fingers.

But St. Dominic was not so to be deceived: he knew who the false flea was!

To punish him therefore for this diabolical intrusion, he laid upon him a holy spell whereby Flea Beelzebub was made to serve as a marker through the whole book. When Dominic, whether in the middle of a sentence or at the end, lifted his eyes from the page in meditation, Flea Beelzebub moved to the word at which the Saint had paused, — he moved not by his own diabolical will, but in obedience to an impulse which he had no power to resist; and there he remained, having as little power to remove, till the Saint's eye having returned to the book, and travelled farther, stopped at another passage. And thus St. Dominic used him through the volume, putting him moreover whenever he closed the book to the *peine forte et dure*.

When Dominic had finished the volume, he dismissed his marker. Had it been a heretic, instead of the Devil, the canonised founder of the Friars Predicant, and Patron Saint of the Inquisition, would not have let him off so easily.

Indeed I cannot but think that his lenity in this case was ill-placed. He should have dealt with that flea as I did with mine.

"How, Mr. Author, was that?"

"I dealt with it, Sir, as Agesilaus unceremoniously did with one victim upon the altar of Chalciœcious Pallas, at the same time that with all due ceremony he was sacrificing another. An ox was the premeditated and customary victim; the extemporaneous and extraordinary one was a six-footed 'small deer.' Plutarch thought the fact worthy of being recorded; and we may infer from it that the Spartans did not always comb their long hair so carefully as the Three Hundred did at Thermopylæ, when on the morning of that ever-glorious fight, they made themselves ready to die there in obedience to the institutions of their country. What the King of Lacedæmon did with his crawler, I did with my skipper;—I cracked it, Sir."

"And for what imaginable reason can you have thought fit to publish such an incident to the world?"

"For what reason, Sir?—why, that Hop-o'-my-thumb the critic may know what he has to expect, if I lay hold of him!"

CHAPTER LXXXIX.

A CHAPTER CHARACTERISTIC OF FRENCH ANTIQUARIES, FRENCH LADIES, FRENCH LAWYERS, FRENCH JUDGES, FRENCH LITERATURE, AND FRENCHNESS IN GENERAL.

Quid de pulicibus? vitæ salientia puncta.
COWLEY.

Now, Reader, having sent away the small Critic with a flea in his ear, I will tell you something concerning one of the curiosities of literature.

The most famous flea, for a real flea, that has yet been heard of, — for not even the King of the Fleas, who, as Dr. Clarke and his fellow traveller found to their cost, keeps his court at Tiberias, approaches it in celebrity, — nor the flea of that song, which Mephistopheles sung in the cellar at Leipzig, — that flea for whom the King ordered breeches and hose from his own tailor; who was made prime minister; and who, when he governed the realm, distinguished himself, like Earl Grey, by providing for all his relations: — the most illustrious, I say, of all fleas, — *pulicum facile princeps* — was that flea which I know not whether to call Mademoiselle des Roches's flea, or Pasquier's flea, or the flea of Poictiers.

In the year 1579, when the *Grands Jours*, or Great Assizes, were held at Poictiers under President de Harlay, Pasquier, who was one of the most celebrated advocates, most accomplished scholars, and most learned men in France, attended in the exercise of his profession. Calling there one day upon Madame des Roches and her daughter, Mademoiselle Catherine, whom he describes as *l'une des plus belles et sages de nostre France*, while he was conversing with the young lady he espied a flea, *parquée au beau milieu de son sein.*

Upon this Pasquier made such a speech as a Frenchman might be expected to make upon so felicitous an occasion, admiring the taste of the flea, envying its happiness, and marvelling at its boldness *de s'estre mise en si beau jour; parce que jaloux de son heur, peu s'en falloit,* he says, *que je ne misse la main sur elle, en deliberation de luy faire un mauvais tour; et bien luy prenoit qu'elle estoit en lieu de franchise!* This led to a *contention mignarde* between the young lady and the learned lawyer, who was then more than fifty years of age; *finalement, ayant esté l'autheur de la noise*, says Pasquier, *je luy dis que puisque ceste Puce avoit receu tant d'heur de se repaistre de son sang, et d'estre reciproquement honorée de nos propos, elle meritoit encores d'estre enchâssée dedans nos papiers, et que tres-volontiers je m'y employerois, si cette Dame vouloit de sa part faire le semblable; chose qu'elle m'accorda liberalement.* Each was in earnest, but each, according to the old Advocate, supposed the other to be in jest: both went to work upon this theme after the visit, and each finished a copy of verses about the same time, *tombants en quelques rencontres de mots les plus signalez pour le subject.* Pasquier thinking to surprise the lady, sent his poem to her as soon as he had transcribed it, on a Sunday morning, — the better the day the better being the deed; and the lady apprehending that they might have fallen upon some of the same thoughts, lest she should be suspected of borrowing what she knew to be her own, sent back the first draught of her verses by his messenger, not having had time to write them fairly out. *Heureuse, certes, rencontre et jouyssance de deux esprits, qui passe d'un long entrejet, toutes ces opinions follastres et vulgaires d'amour. Que si en cecy tu me permets d'y apporter quelque chose de mon jugement je te diray, qu'en l'un tu trouveras les discours d'une sage fille, en l'autre les discours d'un homme qui n'est pas trop fol; ayants l'un et l'autre par une bienseance des nos sexes joüé tels roolles que devions.*

The Demoiselle, after describing in her poem the feats of the flea, takes a hint from the resemblance in sound between *puce* and *pucelle*, and making an allegorical use of mythology, makes by that means a decorous allusion to the vulgar notion concerning the unclean circumstances by which fleas, as they say, are bred:

Puce, si ma plume estoit digne,
Je descrirois vostre origine ;
Et comment le plus grand des Dieux
Pour la terre quittant les cieux,
Vous fit naître, comme il me semble,
Orion et vous tout ensemble.

She proceeds to say that Pan became enamoured of this sister of Orion; that Diana, to preserve her from his pursuit, metamorphosed her into a flea (*en puce*), and that in this transformation nothing remained of her

Sinon
La crainte, l'adresse, et le nom.

Pasquier in his poem gave himself a pretty free scope in his imaginary pursuits of the flea, and in all the allusions to which its name would on such an occasion invite an old Frenchman. If the story had ended here, it would have been characteristic enough of French manners: *Or voy, je te prie*, says Pasquier, *quel fruict nous a produit cette belle altercation, ou pour mieux dire, symbolization de deux ames. Ces deux petits Jeux poëtiques commencerent à courir par les mains de plusieurs, et se trouverent si agreables, que sur leur modelle, quelques personnages de marque voulurent estre de la partie ; et s'employerent sur mesme subject à qui mieux mieux, les uns en Latin, les autres en François, et quelques-uns en l'une et l'autre langue : ayant chacun si bien exploité en son endroict, qu' à chacun doit demeurer la victoire.*

Among the distinguished persons who exercised their talents upon this worthy occasion, Brisson was one; that Brisson of whom Henri III. said that no king but himself could boast of so learned a subject; who lent the assistance of his great name and talents towards setting up the most lawless of all tyrannies, that of an insurrectionary government; and who suffered death under that tyranny, as the reward such men always (and righteously as concerns themselves, however iniquitous the sentence) receive from the miscreants with whom they have leagued. He began his poem much as a scholar might be expected to do, by alluding to the well-known pieces which had been composed upon somewhat similar subjects.

Fœlices meritò Mures Ranæque loquaces
Queis cæci vatis contigit ore cani :
Vivet et extento lepidus Passerculus ævo
Cantatus numeris, culte Catulle tuis.
Te quoque, parve Culex, nulla unquam muta silebit
Posteritas, docti suave Maronis opus.
Ausoniusque Pulex, dubius quem condidit auctor,
Canescet sæclis innumerabilibus.
Pictonici at Pulicis longè præclarior est sors,
Quem fovet in tepido casta puella sinu.
Fortunate Pulex nimium, tua si bona noris,
Alternis vatum nobilitate metris.

In the remainder of his poem Brisson takes the kind of range which, if the subject did not actually invite, it seemed at least to permit. He produced also four Latin epigrams against such persons as might censure him for such a production, and these, as well as the poem itself, were translated into French by Pasquier. This was necessary for the public, not for Madame des Roches, and her daughter, who were versed both in Latin and Greek. Among the numerous persons whom the Assizes had brought to Poictiers, whether as judges, advocates, suitors, or idlers, every one who could write a Latin or a French verse tried his skill upon this small subject. *Tout le Parnasse latin et françois du royaume*, says Titon du Tillet, *voulut prendre part a cette rare decouverte, sur tout apres avoir reconnu que la fille, quoique tres-sage, entendoit raillerie.* There is one Italian sonnet in the collection, one Spanish, and, according to the Abbé Goujet, there are some Greek verses, but in the republication of Pasquier's works these do not appear: they were probably omitted, as not being likely ever again to meet with readers. Some of the writers were men whose names would have been altogether forgotten if they had not been thus preserved; and others might as well have been forgotten for the value of any thing which they have left; but some were deservedly distinguished in their generation, and had won for themselves an honourable remembrance, which will not pass away. The President Harlay himself encouraged Pasquier by an eulogistic epigram, and no less a person than Joseph Scaliger figures in Catullian verse among the flea-poets.

The name of the Demoiselle des Roches afforded occasion for such allusions to the rocks of Parnassus as the dealers in commonplace poetry could not fail to profit by.

Nil rerum variat perennis ordo.
Et constant sibi Phœbus et sorores;
Nec Pulex modo tot simul Poetas,
Sed Parnassia fecit ipsa rupes, —
Rupes, aut Heliconia Hippocrene.

These verses were written by Pithou, to whose satirical talents his own age was greatly indebted for the part which he took in the Satyre Menippée; and to whose collections and serious researches his country will always remain so. Many others harped upon the same string; and Claude Binet, in one of his poems, compared the Lady to Rochelle, because all suitors had found her impregnable.

Nicolas Rapin, by way of varying the subject, wrote a poem in vituperation of the aforesaid flea, and called it *La Contrepuce.* He would rather, he said, write in praise of a less mentionable insect; which, however, he did mention; and, moreover, broadly explained, and in the coarsest terms, the Lady's allusion to Orion.

The flea having thus become the business, as well as the talk of Poictiers, some epigrams were sported upon the occasion.

Causidicos habuit vigilantes Curia; namque
Illis perpetuus tinnit in aure Pulex.

The name of Nicolas Rapinus is affixed to this; that of Raphael Gallodonius to the following.

Ad consultissimos Supremi Senatus Gallici Patronos, in Rupeæ Pulicem ludentes.

Abdita causarum si vis responsa referre,
Hos tam perspicuos consule Causidicos:
Qui juris callent apices, vestigia morsu
Metiri pulicum carmine certa sciunt.
Ecquid eos latuisse putas dum seria tractant,
Qui dum nugantur, tam bene parva canunt?

The President of the Parliament of Paris, Pierre de Soulfour, compared the flea to the Trojan horse, and introduced this gigantic compliment with a stroke of satire.

Quid Magni peperêre Dies? res mira canenda est,
Vera tamen; Pulicem progenuere brevem.
Quicquid id est, tamen est magnum; Magnisque Diebus
Non sine divino numine progenitum.
Ille utero potuit plures gestare poetas,
Quam tulit audaces techna Pelasga duces.
Tros equus heröes tantos non fudit ab alvo,
Dulcisonos vates quot tulit iste Pulex.

Pasquier was proud of what he had done in starting the flea, and of the numerous and distinguished persons who had been pleased to follow his example in poetising upon it; *pour memorial de laquelle*, he says, *jai voulu dresser ce trophée, qui est la publication de leurs vers.* So he collected all these verses in a small quarto volume, and published them in 1582, with this title — La Puce; *ou Jeux Poëtiques Francois et Latins: composez sur la Puce aux Grands Jours de Poictiers l'an* 1579: *dont Pasquier fut le premier motif.* He dedicated the volume to the President Harlay, in the following sonnet:

Pendant que du Harlay de Themis la lumiere,
Pour bannir de Poictou l'espouventable mal,
Exerçant la justice à tous de poids égal,
Restablessoit l'Astrée en sa chaire premiere;
Quelques nobles esprits, pour se donner carriere,
Voulourent exalter un petit animal,
Et luy coler aux flancs les aisles du cheval
Qui prend jusque au ciel sa course coutumiere.
Harlay, mon Achille, relasche tes esprits;
Sousguigne d'un bon œil tant soit peu ces escrits,
Il attendent de toy, ou la mort, ou la vie:
Si tu pers à les lire un seul point de ton temps,
Ils vivront immortels dans le temple des ans,
Malgré l'oubly, la mort, le mesdire et l'envie.

The original volume would have passed away with the generation to which it belonged, or if preserved, it would, like many others more worthy of preservation, have been found only in the cabinets of those who value books for their rarity rather than their intrinsic worth: this would have been its fate if it had not been comprised in the collective edition of Pasquier's works, which, as relating to his own times, to the antiquities of his country, and to French literature, are of the greatest importance. It was properly included there, not merely because it is characteristic of the nation, and of the age, but because it belongs to the history of the individual.

Here in England the Circuit always serves to sharpen the wits of those who are waiting, some of them hungrily, and but too many hopelessly, for practice; and as nowhere there is more talent running to seed than at the bar, epigrams circulate there as freely as opinions, — and much more harmlessly. But that the elders of the profession, and the judges, should take part in such levities as the *Jeux Poetiques* of Poictiers, would at all times have been as much out of character in England, as it would be still in character among our lighter-heeled, lighter-hearted, and lighter-headed neighbours. The same facility in composing Latin verse would not now be found at the French bar; but if a flea was started there, a full cry might as easily be raised after it, as it was at the *Grands Jours* held under the President Harlay; and they who joined in the cry would take exactly the same tone. You would find in their poetry just as much of what Pasquier calls *mignardise*, and just as little exertion of intellect in any other direction.

It is not language alone, all but all-powerful in this respect as language is, which makes the difference in whatever belongs to poetry, between the French and the English. We know how Donne has treated this very subject; and we know how Cleveland, and Randolph and Cowley would have treated it, licentiously indeed, but with such a profusion of fantastic thought, that a prodigality of talent would seem even greater than the abuse. In later times, if such a theme had presented itself, Darwin would have put the flea in a solar microscope, and painted the monster with surprising accuracy in the most elaborate rhymes: he would then have told of fleas which had been taken and tamed, and bound in chains, or yoked to carriages; and this he would have done in couplets so nicely turned, and so highly polished, that the poetical artist might seem to vie with the flea-tamer and carriage-builder in patience and in minute skill. Cowper would have passed with playful but melancholy grace

From gay to grave, from lively to severe,

and might have produced a second Task. And in our own days, Rogers would case the flea, like his own gnat, in imperishable amber. Leigh Hunt would luxuriate in a fairy poem, fanciful as Drayton's Nymphidia, or in the best style of Herrick. Charles Lamb would crack a joke upon the subject; but then he would lead his readers to think while he was amusing them, make them feel if they were capable of feeling, and perhaps leave them in tears. Southey would give us a strain of scornful satire and meditative playfulness in blank verse of the Elizabethan standard. Wordsworth, — no, Wordsworth would disdain the flea: but some imitator of Wordsworth would enshrine the flea in a Sonnet the thought and diction of which would be as proportionate to the subject matter, as the Great Pyramid is to the nameless one of the Pharaohs for whose tomb it was constructed. Oxford and Cambridge would produce Latin verses, good in their manner as the best of Pasquier's collection, and better in every thing else; they would give us Greek verses also, as many and as good. Landor would prove himself as recondite a Latinist as Scaliger, and a better poet; but his hendecasyllables* would not be so easily construed. Cruikshank would illustrate the whole collection with immortal designs, such as no other country, and no other man could produce. The flea would be introduced upon the stage in the next new Pantomime; Mr. Irving would discover it in the Apocalypse; and some preacher of Rowland Hill's school would improve it (as the phrase is) in a sermon, and exhort his congregation to *flee* from sin.

I say nothing of Mr. Moore, and the half dozen Lords who would *mignardise* the subject like so many Frenchmen. But how would Bernard Barton treat it? Perhaps Friend Barton will let us see in one of the next year's Annuals.

I must not leave the reader with an unfavourable opinion of the lady whose flea obtained such singular celebrity, and who *quoique tres sage entendoit raillerie*. Titon du Tillet intended nothing equivocal by that expression; and the tone which the Flea-poets took was in no degree derogatory to her, for the manners of the age permitted it. Les Dames des Roches, both mother and daugh-

* Landor's "Phaleuciorum Liber" was published at Pisa in 1820. It is appended to his "Idyllia Heroica Decem." The copy before me was his presentation copy to Southey, with corrections in his own handwriting.

ter, were remarkable and exemplary women; and there was a time when Poictiers derived as much glory from these blue ladies as from the Black Prince. The mother, after living most happily with her husband eight-and-twenty years, suffered greatly in her widowhood from vexatious lawsuits, difficult circumstances, and broken health; but she had great resources in herself, and in the dutiful attachment of Catherine, who was her only child, and whom she herself had nursed and educated; the society of that daughter enabled her to bear her afflictions, not only with patience but with cheerfulness. No solicitations could induce Catherine to marry; she refused offers which might in all other respects have been deemed eligible, because she would not be separated from her mother, from whom she said death itself could not divide her. And this was literally verified, for in 1587 they both died of the plague on the same day.

Both were women of great talents and great attainments. Their joint works in prose and verse were published in their life-time, and have been several times reprinted, but not since the year 1604. The poetry is said to be of little value; but the philosophical dialogues are praised as being neither deficient in genius nor in solidity, and as compositions which may still be perused with pleasure and advantage. This is the opinion of a benevolent and competent critic, the Abbé Goujet. I have never seen the book.

Before I skip back to the point from which my own flea and the Poictiers' flea have led me, I must tell a story of an English lady who under a similar circumstance was not so fortunate as Pasquier's accomplished friend. This lady, who lived in the country, and was about to have a large dinner party, was ambitious of making as great a display as her husband's establishment, a tolerably large one, could furnish: so that there might seem to be no lack of servants, a great lad, who had been employed only in farm work, was trimmed and dressed for the occasion, and ordered to take his stand behind his mistress's chair, with strict injunctions not to stir from the place, nor do any thing unless she directed him; the lady well knowing that although no footman could make a better appearance as a piece of still-life, some awkwardness would be inevitable, if he were put in motion. Accordingly Thomas, having thus been duly drilled and repeatedly enjoined, took his post at the head of the table behind his mistress, and for a while he found sufficient amusement in looking at the grand set-out, and staring at the guests: when he was weary of this, and of an inaction to which he was so little used, his eyes began to pry about nearer objects. It was at a time when our ladies followed the French fashion of having the back and shoulders under the name of the neck uncovered much lower than accords either with the English climate, or with old English notions; — a time when, as Landor expresses it, the usurped dominion of *neck* had extended from the ear downwards, almost to where mermaids become fish. This lady was in the height, or lowness of that fashion; and between her shoulder-blades, in the hollow of the back, not far from the confines where nakedness and clothing met, Thomas espied what Pasquier had seen upon the neck of Mademoiselle des Roches. The guests were too much engaged with the business and the courtesies of the table to see what must have been worth seeing, the transfiguration produced in Thomas's countenance by delight, when he saw so fine an opportunity of showing himself attentive, and making himself useful. The lady was too much occupied with her company to feel the flea; but to her horror she felt the great finger and thumb of Thomas upon her back, and to her greater horror heard him exclaim in exultation, to the still greater amusement of the party — *a vlea, a vlea! my lady, ecod I've caught 'en!*

CHAPTER XC.

WHEREIN THE CURIOUS READER MAY FIND SOME THINGS WHICH HE IS NOT LOOKING FOR, AND WHICH THE INCURIOUS ONE MAY SKIP IF HE PLEASES.

Voulant doncques satisfaire à la curiosité de touts bons compagnons, j'ay revolvé toutes les Pantarches des Cieux, calculé les quadrats de la Lune, crocheté tout ce que jamais penserent touts les Astrophiles, Hypernephelistes, Anemophylaces, Uranopetes et Omprophozes. RABELAIS.

A MINUTE's recollection will carry the reader back to the chapter whereon that accidental immolation took place, which was the means of introducing him to the *bas-bleus* of Poictiers. We were then engaged upon the connection which in Peter Hopkins's time still subsisted between astrology and the practice of medicine.

Court de Gebelin in his great hypothetical, fanciful, but withal ingenious, erudite, and instructive work, says that the almanack was one of the most illustrious and most useful efforts of genius of the first men, and that a complete history of it would be a precious canvass for the history of the human race, were it not that unfortunately many of the necessary materials have perished. *On peut assurer*, he says, *que sans almanach, les operations de l'agriculture seroient incertaines; que les travaux des champs ne se rencontreroient que per hazard dans les tems convenables: qui il n'y auroit ni fêtes ni assemblées publiques, et que la memoire des tems anciens ne seroit qu'un cahos.*

This is saying a little too much. But who is there that has not sometimes occasion to consult the almanack? Maximilian I. by neglecting to do this failed in an enterprise against Bruges. It had been concerted with his adherents in that turbulent city, that he should appear before it at a certain time, and they would be ready to rise in his behalf, and open the gates for him. He forgot that it was leap-year, and came a day too soon; and this error on his part cost many of the most zealous of his friends their lives. It is remarkable that neither the historian who relates this, nor the writers who have followed him, should have looked in the almanack to guard against any inaccuracy in the relation; for they have fixed the appointed day on the eve of St. Matthias, which being the 23d of February could not be put out of its course by leap-year.

This brings to my recollection a legal anecdote, that may serve in like manner to exemplify how necessary it is upon any important occasion to scrutinise the accuracy of a statement before it is taken upon trust. A fellow was tried (at the Old Bailey, if I remember rightly) for highway robbery, and the prosecutor swore positively to him, saying he had seen his face distinctly, for it was a bright moonlight night. The counsel for the prisoner cross-questioned the man, so as to make him repeat that assertion, and insist upon it. He then affirmed that this was a most important circumstance, and a most fortunate one for the prisoner at the bar: because the night on which the alleged robbery was said to have been committed was one in which there had been no moon; it was during the dark quarter! In proof of this he handed an almanack to the Bench, — and the prisoner was acquitted accordingly. The prosecutor, however, had stated every thing truly; and it was known afterwards that the almanack with which the counsel came provided had been prepared and printed for the occasion.

There is a pleasing passage in Sanazzaro's Arcadia, wherein he describes two large beechen tablets, suspended in the temple of Pan, one on each side of the altar, *scritte di rusticane lettere; le quali successivamente di tempo in tempo per molti anni conservate dai passati pastori, contenevano in se le antiche leggi, e gli ammaestramenti della pastorale vita: dalle quali tutto quello che fra le selve oggi se adopra, ebbe prima origine.* One of these tablets contained directions for the management of cattle. In the other *eran notati tutti i di dell' anno, e i varj mutamenti delle stagioni, e la inequalità delle notte e del giorno, insieme con la osservazione delle ore, non poco necessarie a viventi, e li non falsi pronostici delle tempestati : e quando il Sole con suo nascimento denunzia serenita, e quando pioggia, e quando venti, e quando grandini; e quali giorni son della luna fortunati, e quali infelici alle opre de' mortali : e che ciascuno in ciascuna ora dovesse fuggire, o seguitare, per non offendere le osservabili volonta degli Dii.*

It is very probable that Sanazzaro has transferred to his pastoral what may then have been the actual usage in more retired parts of the country, and that before the invention of printing rendered almanacks accessible to every one, a calendar, which served for agricultural as well as ecclesiastical purposes, was kept in every considerable church. Olaus Magnus says that the northern countrymen used to have a calendar cut upon their walking-sticks (*baculos annales*, he calls them); and that when they met at church from distant parts, they laid their heads together and made their computations. The origin of these wooden almanacks, which belong to our own antiquities, as well as to those of Scandinavia, is traced hypothetically to the heathen temple, authentically to the Church. It has been supposed that the Cimbri received the Julian calendar from Cæsar himself, after his conquest, as it is called, of Britain; and that it was cut in Runic characters for the use of the priests, upon the rocks, or huge stones, which composed their rude temples, till some one thought of copying it on wood and rendering it portable, for common use : — *donec tandem*, (are Wormius's words,) *ingenii rarâ dexteritate emersit ille, quisquis tandem fuerit, qui per lignea hæcce compendia, tam utile tamque necessarium negotium plebi communicandum duxit: cujus nomen si exstaret æquiore jure fastis hisce insereretur, quam multorum tituli, quos boni publici cura vix unquam tetigit.*

The introduction of the Julian calendar at that time is, however, nothing better than an antiquary's mere dream. At a later period the Germans, who had much more communication with the Romans than ever the Scandinavians had, divided the year into three seasons, if Tacitus was rightly informed; this being one consequence of the little regard which they paid to agriculture. *Hyems et ver et æstas intellectum ac vocabula habent; autumni perinde nomen ac bona ignorantur.*

Moreover, Wormius was assured, (and this was a fact which might well have been handed down by memory, and was not likely to have been recorded), that the wooden almanacks were originally copied from a written one in a very ancient manuscript preserved in the church at Drontheim. There is no proof that a pagan *Rimstoke* ever existed in those countries. The clergy had no interest in withholding this kind of knowledge from the people even in the darkest ages of papal tyranny and monkish imposture. But during the earlier idolatries of the Romans it seems to have been withheld; and it was against the will of the Senate that the Fasti were first divulged to the people by Cneius Flavius Scriba.

The carelessness of the Romans during many ages as to the divisions of time, seems scarcely compatible even with the low degree of civilisation which they had attained. We are told that when the Twelve Tables were formed, no other distinctions of the day than those of sunrise and sunset were known among them by name; that some time after they began to compute from noon to noon; and that for three hundred years they had nothing whereby to measure an hour, nor knew of any such denomination, *tamdiu populi Romani indiscreta lux fuit.* A brazen pillar, which marked the hour of noon by its shortest shadow, was the only means of measuring time, till, in the first Punic war, the Consul M. Valerius Messala brought thither a sun-dial from the spoils of Catana in Sicily. This was in the 477th year of the City; and by that dial the Romans went ninety-nine years without adapting it to the meridian of Rome. A better was then erected; but they were still without any guide in cloudy weather, till in the year 595 after the building of the City, Scipio Nasica introduced the water-clock, which is said to have been invented about eighty years before by Ctesibius of Alexandria.

When the Romans had begun to advance in civilisation, no people ever made a more rapid progress in all the arts and abuses which follow in its train. Astrology came with astronomy from the East, for science had speedily been converted into a craft, and in the age of the Cæsars the Egyptian professors of that craft were among the pests of Rome.

More than one Roman calendar is in existence, preserved by the durability of the material, which is a square block of marble. Each side contains three months, in parallel columns, headed by the appropriate signs of the zodiac. In these the astronomical information was given, with directions for the agricultural business of the month, and notices of the respective gods under whose tutelage the months were placed, and of the religious festivals in their course, with a warning to the husbandmen against neglecting those religious duties, upon the due performance of which the success of their labours depended.

Those learned authors who look in the Scriptures for what is not to be found there, and supply by conjectures whatever they wish to find, have not decided whether astronomy was part of Adam's infused knowledge, or whether it was acquired by him, and his son Seth; but from Seth they say it descended to Abraham, and he imparted it to the Egyptians. Whatever may be thought of this derivation, the Egyptian mind seems always to have pullulated with superstition, as the slime of their own Nile is said to have fermented into low and loathsome forms of miscreated life. The Rabbis say that ten measures of witchcraft were sent into the world, and Egypt got nine of them.

The Greeks are said to have learned from the Babylonians the twelve divisions of the day. The arrow-headed * inscriptions at Babylon are supposed by some of those who have bestowed most attention upon them to be calendars: and there can be little doubt that where the divisions of time were first scientifically observed, there the first calendar would be formed. In Egypt, however, it is that we hear of them first; and such resemblances exist between the Egyptian calendar, and the oldest of those which have been discovered in the north of Europe, that Court de Gebelin supposes they must have had a common origin, and in an age anterior to those Chaldeans whose astronomical observations ascended nineteen hundred years before the age of Alexander. This is too wild an assumption to be soberly maintained. What is common to both found its way to Scandinavia in far later times. Christianity was imported into those countries with all the corruptions which it had gathered in the East as well as in the West; and the Christian calendar brought with it as many superstitions of European growth, as there was room for inserting. There was room for many even upon the Norwegian staff.

The lineal descendant of that *rimstoke* was still in use in the middle of England at the close of the 17th century; though it was then, says Plot, a sort of antiquity so little known that it had hardly been heard of in the southern parts, and was understood but by few of the gentry in the northern. Clogg † was the English name, whether so called from the word log, because they were generally made of wood, and not so commonly of oak or fir as of box; or from the resemblance of the larger ones to the clogs, "wherewith we restrain the wild, extravagant, mischievous motions of some of our dogs," he knew not. There were some few of brass. Some were of convenient size for the pocket; and there were larger ones, which used to hang at one end of the mantle tree of the chimney for family use; as in Denmark the *rimstoke* was found in every respectable yeoman's house at the head of the table, or suspended from a beam. Plot minutely and carefully described these, and endeavoured, but not always with success,

* See the Paper of N. L. Westergaard on the Median Species of Arrow-headed Writing, in the *Mémoires de la Société Royale des Antiquaires du Nord*, 1844, p. 271., &c.

† The Icelandic is *Klokr*, — the Danish, *Klog*. On this point, see the *Specimen Calendarii Gentilis*, appended to the 3d vol. of the *Ædda Sæmundar hins Froda*, pp. 999—1124.

to explain some of the hieroglyphes or symbols by which the festivals were denoted; all which he had seen had only the Prime (or Golden Number) and the immovable feasts; the Prime, so called as indicating *primas lunas* through the year, our ancestors set in the margin of their calendars in characters of gold, — and thence its other name.

The rudest that has ever been discovered was found in pulling down part of a château in Bretagne. Its characters had so magical an appearance, that it would have been condemned by acclamation to the flames, if the Lord of the Chateau had not rescued it, thinking it was more likely to puzzle an antiquary than to raise the Devil. He sent it to Sainte-Palaye, and M. Lancelot succeeded in fully explaining it. Most barbarous as it was, there is reason for concluding that it was not older than the middle of the 17th century.

In Peter Hopkins's time the clogg was still found in farm houses. He remembered when a countryman had walked to the nearest large town, thirty miles distant, for the express purpose of seeing an almanack, the first that had been heard of in those parts. His inquiring neighbours crowded round the man on his return. "Well — well," said he, "I know not! it maffles and talks. But all I could make out is that Collop Monday falls on a Tuesday next year."

CHAPTER XCI.

THE AUTHOR DISPLAYS A LITTLE MORE OF SUCH READING AS IS SELDOM READ, AND SHOWS THAT LORD BYRON AND AN ESSEX WIDOW DIFFERED IN OPINION CONCERNING FRIDAY.

Si j'avois dispersé ceci en divers endroits de mon ouvrage, j'aurois évité la censure de ceux qui appelleront ce chapitre un fatras de petit recueils. Mais comme je cherche la commodité de mes lecteurs plutôt que la mienne, je veux bien au depens de cette censure, leur épargner la peine de rassembler ce que j'aurois dispersé. BAYLE.

THERE is no superstition, however harmless it may appear, and may indeed long continue to be, but has in it some latent evil. Much has arisen from the distinction of unlucky days, which may very innocently and naturally have originated, though it was afterwards dexterously applied by astrologers, and by the priests of false religions, to their own purposes. No one would willingly commence an important undertaking on the anniversary of a day which had brought to him some great and irreparable calamity. It would be indecent to fix upon St. Bartholomew's for a day of public rejoicing in France; or in Portugal, upon that day on which Lisbon was laid in ruins by the great earthquake. On the other hand an English General, and an English army, would feel something more than their wonted hope and expectation of victory, if they gave the enemy battle on the anniversaries of Waterloo, or Blenheim, Cressy, Poictiers, or Agincourt. God be thanked neither our fleets, nor armies have ever yet caused a day to be noted with black in the English calendar!

But many a good ship has lost that tide which might have led to fortune, because the captain and the crew thought it unlucky to begin their voyage on a Friday. You were in no danger of being left behind by the packet's sailing on that day, however favourable the wind, if it were possible for the captain to devise any excuse for remaining till the morrow in harbour. Lord Byron partook this superstition; and if any thing of the slightest importance in which he was concerned were commenced on a Friday, he was seriously disconcerted.

Such, however, are the effects of superstitious animosity, that (as the Puritans in the next generation made Christmas-day a fast by an ordinance of Parliament) in James the First's reign Friday was kept as a sort of holyday. The biographer of a Spanish lady, who came to England for the purpose of secretly serving the Roman Catholic cause, says "that among her other griefs she had that of hearing the wheel go round, by which they roasted whole quarters of beef on every Friday, delighting to profane with forbidden food that day on which the catholics, by fasting and other works of penitence, manifested their sense, every week throughout the year, of the sufferings of their Lord and Saviour. In all English houses," he says, " both private and public (to which latter great part of the people went for their meals), all kinds of meat roasted and boiled are seen on Fridays, Good Friday not excepted, as if it were a land of Jews or Turks. The nobles in particular reserve their feasts and entertainment of all kinds of meats and delicacies for Fridays. It is the sport of the great, and their sort of piety, to testify by these sacrileges their hatred to the Roman church."

There is probably some exaggeration in this statement; and if the biographer was conversant with the history of his own country, he must have known that there was a time when his own countrymen made it a point of duty to eat pork on Saturdays, for the sake of despiting the Jews. But the practice cannot have been so common as he represents it; for if it had, Friday would not have retained its inauspicious character to the present time. Yet even this which is in common opinion the most unlucky of all the days, may, from particular circumstances, deserve, it appears, to be marked with a white stone. Upon a trial brought at the Chelmsford Assizes, by a disconsolate widow against a faithless suitor, for breach of promise, a letter of the defendant's was produced, containing this passage: " Mrs. Martha Harris, you say I have used you ill; but I do not think I have at all; for I told you not to count too much, lest something should happen to disappoint. You say the day was mine; but respecting that, I said, ' if before harvest it must be very soon, or it would be in harvest;' and you said ' fix any time soon.' But you said you should like to marry on a Friday, for you thought that a good day; for on a Friday your husband died, and on a Friday I first came to see you, and Friday was market day."

Old opinions, however groundless, are not often so easily overcome. The farmer has let precious days pass by without profiting by favourable weather, because he was warned against them by his almanack, or by tradition; and for the same reason, measures which might have relieved and saved a patient have been fatally procrastinated. There were about thirty days in the Christian year to which such malignant influences were imputed, that the recovery of any person who fell ill upon them was thought to be almost impossible; in any serious disease how greatly must this persuasion have increased the danger!

More than half the days in the year are unlucky in Madagascar: and the Ombiasses, as the sort of bastard Mahomedan jugglers in that great island are called, have made the deluded people believe that any child born on one of those days will, if it be allowed to grow up, prove a parricide, be addicted to every kind of wickedness, and moreover be miserable throughout the whole course of its life. The infant is always exposed in consequence; and unless some humaner parents employ a slave or relation to preserve it, and remove it for ever from their knowledge, it is left for beasts, birds, or reptiles to devour!

The unfortunate days in Christendom, according to the received superstition in different countries, were either a little more or less than thirty,—about a twelfth part of the year; the fortunate were not quite so many, all the rest are left, if the astrologers had so pleased, in their natural uncertainty. And how uncertain all were is acknowledged in the oldest didactics upon this subject, after what were then the most approved rules had been given.

Αἵδε μὲν ἡμέραι εἰσὶν ἐπιχθονίοις μέγ' ὄνειαρ.
Αἵ δ' ἄλλαι μετάδουποι, ἀκήριοι, οὔτι φέρουσαι.
Ἄλλος δ' ἀλλοίην αἰνεῖ, παῦροι δέ τ' ἴσασιν.
Ἄλλοτε μητρυιὴ πέλει ἡμέρη, ἄλλοτε μήτηρ.
Τάων εὐδαίμων τε καὶ ὄλβιος ὃς τάδε πάντα
Εἰδὼς ἐργάζηται ἀναίτιος ἀθανάτοισιν,
*Ὄρνιθας κρίνων, καὶ ὑπερβασίας ἀλεείνων.**

These are the days of which the careful heed
Each human enterprise will favouring speed:
Others there are, which intermediate fall,
Mark'd with no auspice, and unomen'd all:
And these will some, and those will others praise;
But few are vers'd in mysteries of days.
Now as a stepmother the day we find
Severe, and now as is a mother kind.

* Hesiod.

O fortunate the man! O blest is he,
Who skill'd in these, fulfils his ministry!—
He to whose note the auguries are giv'n,
No rite transgress'd, and void of blame to Heaven.*

The fixed days for good and evil were said to have been disclosed by an angel to Job. I know not whether it comes from the Rabbinical mint of fables that Moses determined upon Saturday for the Israelites' Sabbath, because that day is governed by Saturn, and Saturn being a malignant planet, all manner of work that might be undertaken on the Saturday might be expected not to prosper. The Sabbatarians might have found here an astrological argument for keeping their sabbath on the same day as the Jews.

Sunday, however, is popularly supposed in France to be a propitious day for a Romish sabbath,—which is far better than a Sir-Andrew-Agnewish one. *Il est reconnu,*— says a Frenchman, whose testimony on such a point is not invalidated by his madness,— *que les jours de la semaine ne peuvent se ressembler, puisqu'ils coulent sous l'influence de différentes planettes. Le soleil, qui préside au dimanche, est censé nous procurer un beau jour plus riant que les autres jours de la semaine; et voila aussi pourquoi on se reserve ce jour pour se livrer aux plaisirs et amusemens honnêtes.*

The Jews say that the Sun always shines on Wednesdays, because his birthday was on Wednesday, and he keeps it in this manner every week. In Feyjoo's time the Spaniards had a proverbial saying, that no Saturday is ever without sunshine; nor could they be disabused of this notion because in their country it is really a rare thing to have a Saturday, or any other day, in some part or other of which the sun is not seen. But on the Wednesday in Passion week they held that it always rains, because on that day it was that Peter went out and wept bitterly, and they think that it behoves the heavens to weep, after this manner, as if in commemoration of his tears.

The saints indeed have been supposed to affect the weather so much upon their own holydays, that a French Bishop is said to have formed an ingenious project for the benefit of a particular branch of agriculture, by reforming a small part of the Calendar. This prelate was the Bishop of Auxerre, Francis D'Inteville, first of that name. He had observed that for many years the vineyards had suffered severely on certain Saints' days, by frost, hail, cold rains or blighting winds, and he had come to the conclusion that though the said Saints had their festivals during the time when the sun is passing through Taurus, they were nevertheless *Saints gresleurs, geleurs, et gasteurs du bourgeon.*

Now this Bishop loved good wine, *comme fait tout homme de bien;* and he conceived that if these foul-weather Saints, who seemed in this respect to act as if they had enrolled themselves in a Temperance Society, were to have their days changed, and be calendared between Christmas Day and St. Typhaines, they might hail, and freeze, and bluster to their hearts content; and if their old festivals were assigned to new patrons, who were supposed to have no dislike for vineyards, all would go on well. St. George, St. Mark, St. Philip and St. Vitalis were some of the Saints who were to be provided for at Christmas; St. Christopher, St. Dominic, St. Laurence, and St. Magdalene, the most illustrious of those who should have been installed in their places,—for on their days *tant s'en faut qu'on soit en danger de gelée, que lors mestier au monde n'est, qui tant soit de requeste; comme est des faiseurs de friscades, et refraischisseurs de vin.** These changes, however, in the Saints' administration were not effected; and it appears by Rabelais' manner of relating the fact, that the Bishop never got from the optative to the potential mood.

Master Rabelais says that the Bishop called the mother of the Three Kings St. Typhaine;—it is certain that such a Saint was made out of *Le Sainte Epiphanié*, and that the Three Kings of Cologne were filiated upon her. But whether or not this Prelate

* Elton.

* Livre III. c. xxxiii.

were in this respect as ignorant as his flock, he is praised by writers of his own communion for having by his vigilance and zeal kept his diocese, as long as he lived, free from the Lutheran pestilence. And he deserves to be praised by others for having given a fine organ to his cathedral, and a stone pulpit, which was scarcely surpassed in beauty by any in the whole kingdom.

The Japanese, who are a wise people, have fixed upon the five most unfortunate days in the year for their five great festivals; and this they have done purposely, and prudently, in order by this universal mirth to divert and propitiate their Camis, or Deities; and also by their custom on those days of wishing happiness to each other, to avert the mishaps that might otherwise befal them. They too are careful never to begin a journey at an inauspicious time, and therefore in all their road and house books there is a printed table, showing what days of the month are unfortunate for this purpose: they amount to four-and-twenty in the year. The wise and experienced Astrologer, Abino Seimei, who invented the table, was a personage endowed with divine wisdom and the precious gift of prognosticating things to come. It is to be presumed that he derived this from his parentage, which was very remarkable on the mother's side. Take, gentle Reader, for thy contentment, what Lightfoot would have called no lean story.

Prince Abino Jassima was in the Temple of Inari, who, being the God and the Protector of Foxes, ought to have a temple in the Bishopric of Durham, and in Leicestershire, and wherever Foxes are preserved. Foxes' lungs, it seems, were then as much esteemed as a medicine by the Japanese, as Fox-glove may be by European physicians; and a party of Courtiers were fox-hunting at this time, in order to make use of the lungs in a prescription. They were in full cry after a young fox, when the poor creature ran into the temple, and instead of looking for protection to the God Inari, took shelter in Prince Jassima's bosom. The Prince on this occasion behaved very well, and the fox-hunters very ill, as it may be feared most fox-hunters would do in similar circumstances. They insisted upon his turning the fox out; he protested that he would commit no such crime, for a crime it would have been in such a case; they attempted to take the creature by force, and Prince Jassima behaved so bravely that he beat them all, and set the fox at liberty. He had a servant with him, but whether this servant assisted him has not been recorded; neither is it stated that the Fox-God, Inari, took any part in the defence of his own creature and his princely votary; though from what followed it may be presumed that he was far from being an unconcerned spectator. I pass over the historical consequences which make "the hunting of that day" more important in Japanese history, than that of Chevy Chace is in our own. I pass them over because they are not exactly pertinent to this place. Suffice it to say, that King Jassima, as he must now be called, revenged his father's murder upon these very hunters, and succeeded to his throne; and then, after his victory, the fox appeared, no longer in vulpine form, but in the shape of a lady of incomparable beauty, whom he took to wife, and by whom he became the happy father of our Astrologer, Abino Seimei. Gratitude had moved this alopegyne, gynalopex, fox-lady, or lady-fox, to love; she told her love indeed, — but she never told her gratitude: nor did King Jassima know, nor could he possibly suspect, that his lovely bride had been that very fox whose life he had with so much generosity and courage preserved, — that very fox, I say, "another and the same;" — never did he imagine, nor never could he have imagined this, till an extraordinary change took place in his beautiful and beloved wife. Her ears, her nose, her claws and her tail began to grow, and by degrees this wonderful creature became a fox again! My own opinion is, that she must have been a daughter of the great Fox-God Inari himself.

Abino Seimei, her son, proved to be, as might have been expected, a cunning personage, in the old and good meaning of that word. But as he inherited this cunning from his mysterious mother, he derived also an equal share of benevolence from his kind-hearted father, King Jassima: and therefore, after having calculated for the good of mankind the table of unfortunate days, he, for their farther good, composed an *Uta*, or couplet, of mystical words, by pronouncing which the poor traveller who is necessitated to begin a journey upon one of those days, may avert all those evils, which, if he were not preserved by such a spell, must infallibly befal him. He did this for the benefit of persons in humble life, who were compelled at any time to go wherever their lords and masters might send them. I know not whether Lord Byron would have ventured to set out on a Friday, after reciting these words, if he had been made acquainted with their value; but here they are, expressed in our own characters, to gratify the "curious in charms."

Sada Mejesi Tabicatz Fidori Josi Asijwa,
Omojitatz Figo Kitz Nito Sen.

CHAPTER XCII.

CONCERNING PETER HOPKINS AND THE INFLUENCE OF THE MOON AND TIDES UPON THE HUMAN BODY. A CHAPTER WHICH SOME PERSONS MAY DEEM MORE CURIOUS THAN DULL, AND OTHERS MORE DULL THAN CURIOUS.

A man that travelleth to the most desirable home, hath a habit of desire to it all the way; but his present business is his travel; and horse, and company, and inns, and ways, and weariness, &c., may take up more of his sensible thoughts, and of his talk and action, than his home.

BAXTER.

FEW things in this world are useless,—none indeed but what are of man's own invention. It was one of Oberlin's wise maxims that nothing should be destroyed, nothing thrown away, or wasted; he knew that every kind of refuse which will not serve to feed pigs, may be made to feed both man and beast in another way by serving for manure: perhaps he learned this from the Chinese proverb, that a wise man saves even the parings of his nails and the clippings of his beard, for this purpose. "To burn a hair," says Darwin, "or a straw, unnecessarily, diminishes the sum of matter fit for quick nutrition, by decomposing it nearly into its elements: and should therefore give some compunction to a mind of universal sympathy." Let not this cant about universal sympathy nauseate a reader of common sense, and make him regard Darwin's opinion here with the contempt which his affectation deserves. Every thing may be of use to the farmer. And so it is with knowledge; there is none, however vain in itself, and however little it may be worth the pains of acquiring it, which may not at some time or other be turned to account.

Peter Hopkins found that his acquaintance with astrology was sometimes of good service in his professional practice. In his days most of the Almanacks contained Rules Astrological showing under what aspects and positions different modes of remedy were to be administered, and different complexions were to let blood. He had often to deal with persons who believed in their Almanack as implicitly as in their Bible, and who studied this part of it with a more anxious sense of its practical importance to themselves. When these notions were opposed to the course of proceeding which the case required, he could gain his point by talking to them in their own language, and displaying, if it were called for, a knowledge of the art which might have astonished the Almanack-maker himself. If he had reasoned with them upon any other ground, they would have retained their own opinion, even while they submitted to his authority; and would neither have had faith in him, nor in his prescriptions.

Peter Hopkins would never listen to any patient who proposed waiting for a lucky day before he entered upon a prescribed course of medicine. "Go by the moon as much as you please," he would say; "have your hair cut, if you think best, while it wexes, and cut your corns while it wanes; and put off any thing till a lucky day that may as well be done on one day as another. But the right day to be bled is when you want bleeding; the right day for taking physic is when physic is necessary."

He was the better able to take this course, because he himself belonged to the debateable land between credulity and unbelief. Some one has said that the Devil's dubitative is a negative, — *dubius in fide, infidelis est**; and there are cases, as in Othello's, in which, from the infirmity of human nature, it is too often seen that

—— to be once in doubt
Is — once to be resolved.

There is, however, a state of mind, or to speak more accurately, a way of thinking, in which men reverse the Welshman's conclusion in the old comedy, and instead of saying "it may be, but it is very impossible," resolve within themselves that it is very impossible, but it may be. So it was in some degree with Peter Hopkins; his education, his early pursuits, and his turn of mind, disposed him to take part with what was then the common opinion of common men, and counterbalanced, if they did not, perhaps, a little preponderate against the intelligence of the age, and his own deliberate judgment, if he had been called upon seriously to declare it. He saw plainly that astrology had been made a craft by means whereof knaves practised upon fools; but so had his own profession; and it no more followed as a necessary consequence from the one admission that the heavenly bodies exercised no direct influence upon the human frame, than it did from the other that the art of medicine was not beneficial to mankind.

In the high days of astrology, when such an immediate influence was affirmed upon the then undisputed authority of St. Augustin, it was asked how it happened that the professors of this science so frequently deceived others, and were deceived themselves? The answer was that too often, instead of confining themselves within the legitimate limits of the art, they enlarged their phylacteries too much. Farther, that there were many more fixed stars than were known to us, yet these also must have their influence; and moreover that the most learned professors differed upon some of the most important points. Nevertheless, so many causes and effects in the course of nature were so visibly connected, that men, whether astrologers or not, drew from them their own conclusions, and presaged accordingly: *Mirum non est, si his et similibus solerter pensiculatis, non tam astrologi quam philosophi, medici, et longâ experientiâ edocti agricolæ et nautæ, quotidie de futuris multa vera prædicunt, etiam sine astrologiæ regulis de morbis, de annonâ, deque tempestatibus.*

All persons in Peter Hopkins's days believed that change of weather may be looked for at the change of the Moon; and all men, except a few philosophers, believe so still, and all the philosophers in Europe could not persuade an old sailor out of the belief. And that the tides have as much influence over the human body, in certain stages of disease, as the moon has over the tides, is a popular belief in many parts of the world. The Spaniards think that all who die of chronic diseases breathe their last during the ebb.† Among the wonders of the Isle and City of Cadiz, which the historian of that city, Suares de Salazar, enumerates, one is, according to P. Labat, that the sick never die there while the tide is rising or at its height, but always during the ebb: he restricts the notion to the Isle of Leon, but implies that the effect was there believed to take place in diseases of any kind, acute as well as chronic. "Him fever," says the Negro in the West Indies, "shall go when the water come low. Him alway come hot when the tide high."

If the Negroes had ever heard the theory of the tides which Herrera mentions, they would readily believe it, and look upon it as completely explaining the ground of their assertion; for according to that theory the tides are caused by a fever of the sea, which

* Sextus Pythagoras.

† Dame Quickly, in telling of Falstaff's death to Bardolph, says: — "'A parted even just between twelve and one, e'en at turning o' the tide." — *Henry V.* Act II. Scene iii.

rages for six hours, and then intermits for as many more.

But the effect of the tides upon the human constitution in certain states is not a mere vulgar opinion. Major Moor says that near the tropics, especially in situations where the tide of the sea has a great rise and fall, scarcely any person, and certainly no one affected with feverish or nervous symptoms, is exempted from extraordinary sensations at the periods of spring tides. That these are caused by the changes of the moon he will not say, for he had never fully convinced himself, however plausible the theory, that the coincident phenomena of spring tides, and full and change of the moon, were cause and effect; but at the conjunction and opposition, or what amounts to the same, at the spring tides, these sensations are periodically felt. There is an account of one singular case in which the influence was entirely lunar. When Mr. Galt was travelling in the Morea, he fell in with a peasant, evidently in an advanced stage of dropsy, who told him, that his father had died of a similar complaint, but differing from his in this remarkable respect — the father's continued to grow regularly worse, without any intervals of alleviation; but at the change of the moon the son felt comparatively much easier. As the moon advanced to the full, the swelling enlarged; and as she waned, it again lessened. Still, however, though this alteration continued, the disease was gaining ground.

"The moon," Mr. Galt observes, "has, or is believed to have, much more to say in the affairs of those parts, than with us. The climate is more regular; and if the air have tides, like the ocean, of course their effects are more perceptible."

In an early volume of the Philosophical Transactions are some observations made by Mr. Paschal on the motions of diseases, and on the births and deaths of men and other animals, in different parts of the day and night. Having suspected, he says, that the causes of the tides at sea exert their power elsewhere, though the effect may not be so sensibly perceived on the solid as on the fluid parts of the globe, he divided, for trial of this notion, the natural day into four senaries of hours; the first consisting of three hours before the moon's southing, and three after; the second, of the six hours following; and the third and fourth contained the two remaining quarters of the natural day. Observing then the times of birth and death, both in human and other subjects, as many as came within the circle of his knowledge, he found, he says, none that were born or died a natural death in the first and third senaries (which he called first and second tides), but every one either in the second or fourth senaries (which he called the first and second ebbs). He then made observations upon the motions of diseases, other circumstances connected with the human frame, alterations of the weather, and such accounts as he could meet with of earthquakes and other things, and he met with nothing to prevent him from laying down this as a maxim: — that motion, vigour, action, strength, &c., appear most and do best, in the tiding senaries; and that rest, relaxation, decay, dissolution, belong to the ebbing ones.

This theorist must have been strongly possessed with a favourite opinion, before he could imagine that the deep subterranean causes of earthquakes could in any degree be affected by the tides. But that the same influences which occasion the ebb and flow of the ocean have an effect upon certain diseases, is a conclusion to which Dr. Pinckard came in the West Indies, and Dr. Balfour in the East, from what they observed in the course of their own practice, and what they collected from the information of others. "In Bengal," Dr. Balfour says, "there is no room to doubt that the human frame is affected by the influences connected with the relative situations of the sun and moon. In certain states of health and vigour, this influence has not power to show itself by any obvious effects, and in such cases its existence is often not acknowledged. But in certain states of debility and disease it is able to manifest itself by exciting febrile paroxysms. Such paroxysms show themselves more frequently during the period of the spring tides, and as these advance become more violent and obstinate, and on the other hand tend no less invariably to subside and terminate during the recess.

I have no doubt, says this practitioner, that any physician who will carefully attend to the diurnal and nocturnal returns of the tides, and will constantly hold before him the prevailing tendency of fevers to appear at the commencement, and during the period of the spring; and to subside and terminate at the commencement and during the period of the recess, will soon obtain more information respecting the phenomena of fevers, and be able to form more just and certain judgments and prognostics respecting every event, than if we were to study the history of medicine, as it is now written, for a thousand years. There is no revolution or change in the course of fevers that may not be explained by these general principles in a manner consistent with the laws of the human constitution, and of the great system of revolving bodies which unite together in producing them.

Dr. Balfour spared no pains in collecting information to elucidate and confirm his theory during the course of thirty years' practice in India. He communicated upon it with most of the European practitioners in the Company's dominions; and the then Governor General, Lord Teignmouth, considered the subject as so important, that he properly as well as liberally ordered the correspondence and the treatise, in which its results were embodied, to be printed and circulated at the expense of the government. The author drew up his scheme of an astronomical ephemeris, for the purposes of medicine and meteorology, and satisfied himself that he had "discovered the laws of febrile paroxysms, and unfolded a history and theory of fevers entirely new, consistent with itself in every part, and with the other appearances of nature, perfectly conformable to the laws discovered by the immortal Newton, and capable of producing important improvements in medicine and meteorology. He protested against objections to his theory as if it were connected with the wild and groundless delusions of astrology. Yet the letter of his correspondent, Dr. Helenus Scott, of Bombay, shows how naturally and inevitably it would be connected with them in that country. "The influence of the moon on the human body," says that physician, "has been observed in this part of India by every medical practitioner. It is universally acknowledged by the doctors of all colours, of all castes, and of all countries. The people are taught to believe it in their infancy, and as they grow up, they acknowledge it from experience. I suppose that in the northern latitudes this power of the moon is far less sensible than in India. Here we universally think that the state of weakly and diseased bodies is much influenced by its motions. Every full and change increases the number of the patients of every practitioner. That the human body is affected in a remarkable manner by them I am perfectly convinced, and that an attention to the power of the moon is highly necessary to the medical practitioner in India."

This passage tends to confirm, what, indeed, no judicious person can doubt, that the application of astrology to medicine, though it was soon perverted and debased till it became a mere craft, originated in actual observations of the connection between certain bodily affections, and certain times and seasons. Many, if not most of the mischievous systems in physics and divinity have arisen from dim perceptions or erroneous apprehensions of some important truth. And not a few have originated in the common error of drawing bold and hasty inferences from weak premises. Sailors say, what they of all men have most opportunities of observing, that the moon as it rises clears the sky of clouds: *a puesta del sol*, says a Spanish chronicler, *parescio la luna, e comio poco a poco todas las nuves.* The "learned and reverend" Dr. Goad, sometime master of the Merchant Taylors' School, published a work "of vast pains, reading and many years experience," which he called "*Astro-Meteorologia*, or a Demonstration of the Influences of the Stars in the alterations of the Air; proving that there is not an Earthquake, Comet, Parhelia, Halo, Thunder-storm or Tempest, or any other phenomena, but is referable to its particular planetary aspect, as the sub-solar cause thereof."

CHAPTER XCIII.

REMARKS OF AN IMPATIENT READER ANTICIPATED AND ANSWERED.

> Ὦ πολλὰ λέξας ἄρτι κἀνόνητ' ἔπη,
> Οὐ μνημονεύεις οὐκέτ' οὐδέν; SOPHOCLES.

Novel readers are sometimes so impatient to know how the story is to end, that they look at the last chapter, and so — escape, should I say — or forfeit that state of agitating suspense in which it was the author or authoress's endeavour to keep them till they should arrive by a regular perusal at the well-concealed catastrophe. It may be apprehended that persons of this temper, having in their composition much more of Eve's curiosity than of Job's patience, will regard with some displeasure a work like the present, of which the conclusion is not before them: and some, perhaps, may even be so unreasonable as to complain that they go through chapter after chapter without making any progress in the story. "What care the Public," says one of these readers, (for every reader is a self-constituted representative of that great invisible body) — "what do the Public care for Astrology and Almanacks, and the Influence of the Tides upon diseases, and Mademoiselle de Roches's flea, and the Koran, and the Chronology of this fellow's chapters, and Potteric Carr, and the Corporation of Doncaster, and the Theory of Signatures, and the Philosophy of the Alchemists, and the Devil knows what besides! What have these things to do with the subject of the book, and who would ever have looked for them in a Novel?"

"A Novel do you call it, Mr. Reader?"

"Yes, Mr. Author, what else should I call it? It has been reviewed as a Novel and advertised as a Novel."

"I confess that in this very day's newspaper it is advertised in company with four new Novels; the first in the list being 'Warleigh, or the Fatal Oak,' a Legend of Devon, by Mrs. Bray: the second, 'Dacre,' edited by the Countess of Morley; Mr. James's 'Life and Adventures of John Marston Hall,' is the third: fourthly, comes the dear name of 'The Doctor;' and last in the list, 'The Court of Sigismund Augustus, or Poland in the Seventeenth Century.'"

I present my compliments to each and all of the authoresses and authors with whom I find myself thus associated. At the same time I beg leave to apologise for this apparent intrusion into their company, and to assure them that the honour which I have thus received has been thrust upon me. Dr. Stegman had four patients whose disease was that they saw themselves double: "they perceived," says Mr. Turner, "another self, exterior to themselves!" I am not one of Dr. Stegman's patients; but I see myself double in a certain sense, and in that sense have another and distinct self, — the one incog, the other out of cog. Out of cog I should be as willing to meet the novelist of the Polish Court, as any other unknown brother or sister of the quill. Out of cog I should be glad to shake hands with Mr James, converse with him about Charlemagne, and urge him to proceed with his French biography. Out of cog I should have much pleasure in making my bow to Lady Morley or her editor. Out of cog I should like to be introduced to Mrs. Bray in her own lovely land of Devon, and see the sweet innocent face of her humble friend Mary Colling. But without a proper introduction I should never think of presenting myself to any of these persons; and having incog the same sense of propriety as out of cog, I assure them that the manner in which my one self has been associated with them is not the act and deed of my other self, but that of Messrs. Longman, Rees, Orme

Brown, Green and Longman, my very worthy and approved good publishers.

"Why, Mr. Author, you do not mean to say that the book is not printed as a novel, does not appear as one, and is not intended to pass for one. Have you the face to deny it?"

"*Lecteur, mon ami, la demande est bien faite sans doute, et bien apparente; mais la response vous contentera, ou j'ai le sens mal-gallefretu!*"

"*Lecteur, mon ami!* an Incog has no face. But this I say in the face, or in all the faces, of that Public which has more heads than a Hindoo Divinity, that the character and contents of the book were fairly, fully, carefully and considerately denoted, — that is to say, notified or made known, in the title-page. Turn to it, I entreat you, Sir! The first thing which you cannot but notice, is, that it is in motley. Ought you not to have inferred, concerning the author, that in his brain

> — he hath strange places cramm'd
> With observation, the which he vents
> In mangled forms.*

And if you could fail to perceive the conspicuous and capacious

&c,

which in its omnisignificance may promise anything, and yet pledges the writer to nothing; and if you could also overlook the mysterious monograph

your attention was invited to all this by a sentence of Butler's on the opposite page, so apposite that it seems as if he had written it with a second-sight of the application thus to be made of it: 'There is a kind of physiognomy in the titles of books no less than in the faces of men, by which a skilful observer will as well know what to expect from the one as the other.' This was the remark of one whose wisdom can never be obsolete; and whose wit, though much of it has become so, it will always be worth while for an Englishman to study and to understand.

"Mr. D'Israeli has said that 'the false idea which a title conveys is alike prejudicial to the author and the reader, and that titles are generally too prodigal of their promises;' but yet there is an error on the other hand to be avoided, for if they say too little they may fail of attracting notice. I bore in mind what Baillet says upon this subject, to which he has devoted a long chapter: *le titre d'un Livre doit être son abregé, et il en doit renfermer tout l'esprit, autant qu'il est possible. Il doit être le centre de toutes les paroles et de toutes les pensées du Livre; de telle sorte qu'on n'y en puisse pas même trouver une qui n'y dit de la correspondance et du rapport.* From this rule there has been no departure. Everything that is said of Peter Hopkins relates to the Doctor prospectively, because he was the Doctor's master: every thing that may be said of, or from myself, relates to the Doctor retrospectively, or reflectively, because he, though in a different sense, was mine: and everything that is said about anything else relates to him collaterally, being either derivative or tributary, either divergent from the main subject, or convergent to its main end.

"But albeit I claim the privilege of motley, and in right thereof

> — I must have liberty
> Withal, as large a charter as the wind,
> To blow on whom I please;——*

yet I have in no instance abused that charter, nor visited any one too roughly. Nor will I ever do against all the world what John Kinsaider did, in unseemly defiance, — nor against the wind either; though

* Shakespeare.

* Shakespeare.

it has been no maxim of mine, nor ever shall be, to turn with the tide, or go with the crowd, unless they are going my road, and there is no other way that I can take to escape the annoyance of their company."

"And is this any reason, Mr. Author, why you should get on as slowly with the story of your book, as the House of Commons with the business of the nation, in the present reformed Parliament, with Lord Althorpe for its leader?"

"Give me credit, Sir, for a temper as imperturbably good as that which Lord Althorpe presents, like a sevenfold shield of lamb's wool, to cover him against all attacks, and I will not complain of the disparagement implied in your comparison."

"Your confounded good temper, Mr. Author, seems to pride itself upon trying experiments on the patience of your readers. Here I am in the middle of the third volume, and if any one asked me what the book is about, it would be impossible for me to answer the question. I have never been able to guess at the end of one chapter what was likely to be the subject of the next."

"Let me reply to that observation, Sir, by an anecdote. A collector of scarce books was one day showing me his small but curious hoard; 'Have you ever seen a copy of this book?' he asked, with every rare volume that he put into my hands: and when my reply was that I had not, he always rejoined with a look and tone of triumphant delight, 'I should have been exceedingly sorry if you had!'

"Let me tell you another anecdote, not less to the purpose. A thorough-bred fox-hunter found himself so much out of health, a little before the season for his sport began, that he took what was then thought a long journey to consult a physician, and get some advice which he hoped would put him into a condition for taking the field. Upon his return his friends asked him what the Doctor had said, 'Why,' said the Squire, 'he told me that I've got a dyspepsy:—I don't know what that is: but it's some damn'd thing or other I suppose!'—My good Sir, however much at a loss you may be to guess what is coming in the next chapter, you can have no apprehension that it may turn out anything like what he, with too much reason, supposed a dyspepsy to be.

"*Lecteur*, *mon ami*, I have given you the advantage of a motto from Sophocles, and were it as apposite to me, as it seems applicable when coming from you, I might content myself with replying to it in a couplet of the honest old wine-bibbing, Water-poet:—

That man may well be called an idle mome
That mocks the Cock because he wears a comb.

But no one who knows a hawk from a hernshaw, or a sheep's head from a carrot, or the Lord Chancellor Brougham, in his wig and robes, from a Guy Vaux on the fifth of November, can be so mistaken in judgment as to say that I make use of many words in making nothing understood; nor as to think me,

ἄνθρωπον ἀγριοποίον, αὐθαδόστομον,
ἔχοντ' ἀχάλινον, ἀκρατὲς, ἀπύλωτον στόμα,
*ἀπεριλάλητον, κομποφακελοῤῥήμονα.**

"Any subject is inexhaustible if it be fully treated of; that is, if it be treated doctrinally and practically, analytically and synthetically, historically and morally, critically, popularly and eloquently, philosophically, exegetically and æsthetically, logically, neologically, etymologically, archaiologically, Daniologically and Doveologically, which is to say, summing up all in one, Doctorologically.

"Now, my good Reader, whether I handle my subject in any of these ways, or in any other legitimate way, this is certain, that I never handle it as a cow does a musket; and that I have never wandered from it, not even when you have drawn me into a Tattle-de-Moy."

"*Auctor incomparabilis*, what is a Tattle-de-Moy?"

"*Lecteur*, *mon ami*, you shall now know what to expect in the next chapter, for I will tell you there what a Tattle-de-Moy is."

---

* Aristophanes.

CHAPTER XCIV.

THE AUTHOR DISCOVERS CERTAIN MUSICAL CORRESPONDENCIES TO THESE HIS LUCUBRATIONS.

And music mild I learn'd that tells
Tune, time, and measure of the song.
HIGGINS.

A TATTLE-DE-MOY, reader, was "a new-fashioned thing" in the year of our Lord 1676, "much like a Seraband, only it had in it more of conceit and of humour: and it might supply the place of a seraband at the end of a suit of lessons at any time." That simple-hearted, and therefore happy old man, Thomas Mace, invented it himself, because he would be a little modish, he said; and he called it a Tattle-de-Moy, "because it tattles, and seems to speak those very words or syllables. Its humour," said he, "is toyish, jocund, harmless and pleasant; and as if it were one playing with, or tossing, a ball up and down; yet it seems to have a very solemn countenance, and like unto one of a sober and innocent condition, or disposition; not antic, apish, or wild."

If indeed the gift of prophecy were imparted, or imputed to musicians, as it has sometimes been to poets, Thomas Mace might be thought to have unwittingly foreshown certain characteristics of the unique opus which is now before the reader: so nearly has he described them, when instructing his pupils how to give right and proper names to all lessons they might meet with.

"There are, first, Preludes; then, secondly, Fancies and Voluntaries; thirdly, Pavines; fourthly, Allmaines; fifthly, Airs; sixthly, Galliards; seventhly, Corantoes; eighthly, Serabands; ninthly, Tattle-de-Moys; tenthly, Chichonas; eleventhly, Toys or Jiggs; twelfthly, Common Tunes; and, lastly, Grounds, with Divisions upon them.

"The Prelude is commonly a piece of confused, wild, shapeless kind of intricate play (as most use it), in which no perfect form, shape, or uniformity, can be perceived; but a random business, pottering and grooping, up and down, from one stop, or key, to another; and generally so performed, to make trial, whether the instrument be well in tune or not; by which doing, after they have completed their tuning, they will (if they be masters) fall into some kind of voluntary or fancical play more intelligible; which (if he be a master able) is a way whereby he may more fully and plainly show his excellency and ability, than by any other kind of undertaking; and has an unlimited and unbounded liberty, in which he may make use of the forms and shapes of all the rest."

Here the quasi-prophetic lutanist may seem to have described the ante-initial chapters of this opus, and those other pieces which precede the beginning thereof, and resemble

A lively prelude, fashioning the way
In which the voice shall wander.*

For though a censorious reader will pick out such expressions only as may be applied with a malign meaning; yet in what he may consider confused and shapeless, and call pottering and grooping, the competent observer will recognise the hand of a master, trying his instrument and tuning it; and then passing into a voluntary whereby he approves his skill, and foreshows the spirit of his performance.

The Pavines, Master Mace tells us, are lessons of two, three, or four strains, very grave and solemn; full of art and profundity, but seldom used in "these our light days," as in many respects he might well call the days of King Charles the Second. Here he characterises our graver Chapters, which are in strains so deep, so soothing, and so solemn withal, that if such a Pavine had been played in the hall of the palace at Aix, when King Charlemagne asked the Archbishop to dance, the invitation could not have been deemed indecorous.

Allmaines are very airy and lively, and generally in common or plain time. Airs differ from them only in being usually shorter, and of a more rapid and nimble

* KEATS.

performance. — With many of these have the readers of the Doctor been amused.

Galliards, being grave and sober, are performed in a slow and large triple time. Some of the chapters relating to the history of Doncaster come under this description: especially that concerning its Corporation, which may be called a Galliard *par excellence*.

The Corantoes are of a shorter cut, and of a quicker triple time, full of sprightfulness and vigour, lively, brisk, and cheerful: the Serabands of the shortest triple time, and more toyish and light than the Corantoes. There are of both kinds in these volumes, and skilfully are they alternated with the Pavines:

— Now the musician
Hovers with nimble stick o'er squeaking crowd
Tickling the dried guts of a mewing cat * ;

and anon a strain is heard —

Not wanting power to mitigate and swage,
With solemn touches, troubled thoughts, and chase
Anguish and doubt and fear and sorrow and pain
From mortal or immortal minds.†

And there are Chichonas also, which consist of a few conceited notes in a grave kind of humour; these are the Chapters which the Honourable Fastidious Feeblewit condemns as being in bad taste, and which Lord Makemotion Ganderman pronounces poor stuff; but at which Yorickson smiles, Macswift's countenance brightens, and Fitzrabelais laughs outright.

No prophecies can be expected to go upon all fours; and nothing in this opus corresponds to Master Mace's Toys, or Jiggs, which are "light, squibbish things, only fit for fantastical and easy light-headed people;" nor to his common Tunes.

Last in his enumeration is the Ground: this, he says, is "a set number of slow notes, very grave and stately; which, after it is expressed once or twice very plainly, then he that hath good brains and a good hand, undertakes to play several divisions upon it, time after time, till he has shewed his bravery, both of invention and execution." My worthy friend Dr. Dense can need no hint to make him perceive how happily this applies to the ground of the present work, and the manner of treating it. And if Mr. Dulman disputes the application, it can only be because he is determined not to see it. All his family are remarkable for obstinacy.

And ere taking leave for awhile of the good old lutanist, I invite the serious and curious to another Pavine among the stars.

* Marston. † Milton.

CHAPTER XCV.

WHEREIN MENTION IS MADE OF LORD BYRON, RONSARD, RABBI KAPOL AND CO. IT IS SUGGESTED THAT A MODE OF READING THE STARS HAS BEEN APPLIED TO THE RECOVERY OF OBLITERATED ROMAN INSCRIPTIONS; AND IT IS SHOWN THAT A MATHEMATICIAN MAY REASON MATHEMATICALLY, AND YET LIKE A FOOL.

Thus may ye behold
This man is very bold,
And in his learning old
Intendeth for to sit.
I blame him not a whit;
For it would vex his wit,
And clean against his earning
To follow such learning
As now-a-days is taught.

Doctour Double-Ale.

Lord Byron calls the Stars the poetry of heaven, having perhaps in mind Ben Jonson's expression concerning bell-ringing. Ronsard calls them the characters of the sky:

— Alors que Vesper vient embrunir nos yeux,
Attaché dans le ciel je contemple les cieux,
En qui Dieu nous escrit, en notes non obscures,
Les sorts et les destins de toutes creatures.
Car luy, en desdaignant (comme font les humains)
D'avoir encre et papier et plume entre les mains,
Par les astres du ciel, qui sont ses caracteres,
Les choses nous predit et bonnes et contraires.
Mais les hommes, chargez de terres et du trespas,
Meprisent tel escrit, et ne le lisent pas.

The great French poet of his age probably did not know that what he thus said was actually believed by the Cabalists. According to them the ancient Hebrews represented the stars, severally and collectively, by the letters of their alphabet; to read the stars, therefore, was more than a metaphorical expression with them. And an astral alphabet for genethliacal purposes was published near the close of the fifteenth century, at Cracow, by Rabbi Kapol Ben Samuel, in a work entitled "The Profundity of Profundities."

But as this would rest upon an insecure foundation, — for who could be assured that the alphabet had been accurately made out? — it has been argued that the Heavens are repeatedly in the Scriptures called a Book, whence it is to be inferred that they contain legible characters: that the first verse of the first chapter of Genesis ought to be translated, "In the beginning God created the letter, or character of the Heavens;" and that in the nineteenth Psalm we should read "their line," instead of "their sound has gone forth into all lands," this referring to their arrangement in the firmament like letters upon a roll of parchment. Jews, Platonists and Fathers of the Church, are shown to have believed in this celestial writing. And there can be no question but that both the language and the characters must be Hebrew, that being the original speech, and those the original characters, and both divinely communicated to man, not of human invention. But single stars are not to be read as letters, as in the Astral Alphabet. This may be a convenient mode of noting them in astronomical observations; the elements of this celestial science are more recondite in proportion as the science itself is more mysterious. An understanding eye may distinguish that the stars in their groups form Hebrew letters, instead of those imaginary shapes which are called the signs of the Zodiac.

But as the Stars appear to us only as dots of light, much skill and sagacity are required for discovering how they combine into the complex forms of the Hebrew alphabet. The astral scholar reads them as antiquaries have made out inscriptions upon Roman buildings by the marks of the nails, when the letters themselves had been torn away by rapacious hands for the sake of the metal. Indeed it is not unlikely that the Abbé Barthelemi took the hint from the curiously credulous work of his countryman, Gaffarel, who has given examples of this celestial writing from the Rabbis Kapol, Chomer and Abiudan. In these examples the stars are represented by white spots upon the black lines of the Hebrew letter. The Abbé, when he writes upon this subject to Count Caylus, seems not to have known that Peiresc had restored ancient inscriptions by the same means; if, however, he followed the example of Peiresc without choosing to mention his name, that omni-crudite man himself is likely to have seen the books from whence Gaffarel derived his knowledge.

There is yet another difficulty; even the book of Heaven is not stereotyped: its types are continually changing with the motion of the heavenly bodies, and changes of still greater importance are made by the appearance of new stars.

One important rule is to be observed in perusing this great stelliscript. He who desires to learn what good they prefigure, must read them from West to East; but if he would be forewarned of evil, he must read from North to West; in either case beginning with the stars that are most vertical to him. For the first part of this rule, no better reason has been assigned than the conjectural one, that there is a propriety in it, the free and natural motion of the stars being from West to East; but for the latter part a sufficient cause is found in the words of the Prophet Jeremiah: *septentrione pandetur malum:* "Out of the North evil shall break forth."

Dionyse Settle was persuaded that Martin Frobisher, being a Yorkshire-man, had, by his voyage in search of a north-west passage, repelled the rehearsal of those opprobrious words; not only he, but many worthy subjects more, as well as the said Dionyse, who was in the voyage himself, being "Yorkshire too."

But why should evil come from the North? "I conceive," says Gaffarel, "it would stand with sound philosophy to answer, by reason of the darkness and gloominess of the air of those parts, caused by the great distance of the Sun; and also by reason of the Evil Spirits which inhabit dark places." This reason becomes stronger when it is considered that the word which in the Vulgate is rendered *pandetur*, may also be rendered *depingetur*, so that the verse might be translated, "all evils shall be described (or written) from the North;" and if written, then certainly to be read from that direction.

This theory of what Southey has called "the language of the lights of Heaven," is Jewish. Abu Almasar (nominally well known as Albumazar, by which name the knaves called him who knew nothing of him or his history), derived all religions from the Planets. The Chaldean, he said, was produced by the conjunction of Jupiter with Mars; the Egyptian, by Jupiter with the Sun; Judaism, by Jupiter with Saturn; Christianity, by Jupiter with Mercury; Mahommedanism, by Jupiter with Venus. And in the year 1460, when, according to his calculation, the conjunction of Jupiter and Mercury would again occur, he predicted that the Christian religion would receive its death blow, and the religion of Antichrist begin. Pursuing these fancies, others have asserted that the reason why the Jewish nation always has been miserable, and always must be so, is because their religion was formed under the influences of Saturn: —

> Spiteful and cold, an old man melancholy,
> With bent and yellow forehead, he is Saturn.*

A malevolent planet he is, and also an unfortunate one, and it was he that

> With lead-coloured shine lighting it into life,*

threw a tincture of severity and moroseness over the religion of the Jews; he it was that made them obstinate and covetous, and their Sabbath accordingly is his day. In like manner the character of the Turks and their day of rest have been determined by the planet Venus, which is the star of their religion. And as Christianity began under the influence of the Sun, Sunday is the Christian Sabbath; and the visible head of the Christian Church has his seat in Rome, which is a solar city, its foundations having been laid when the Sun was in Leo, his proper House. Farther proof of this influence is, that the Cardinals wear red, which is a solar colour.

Dr. Jenkin, in his Discourses upon the Reasonableness and Certainty of the Christian Religion, takes into his consideration the opinion of those persons who thought that the stars would shine to little purpose unless there were other habitable worlds besides this earth whereon we dwell. One of the uses for which they serve he supposes to be this, that in all ages the wits of many men whose curiosity might otherwise be very ill employed have been busied in considering their end and nature, and calculating their distances and motions: — a whimsical argument, in advancing which he seems to have forgotten the mischievous purposes to which so much of the wit which had taken this direction had been applied.

Yet these fancies of the wildest astrologers are not more absurd than the grave proposition of John Craig, whose "*Theologiæ Christianæ Principia Mathematica*" were published in London at the close of the 17th century. He asserted, and pretended to show by mathematical calculations, that the probability of the truth of the Gospel history was as strong at that time, as it would have been in the days of our Saviour himself, to a person who should have heard it related by twenty-eight disciples; but that, upon the same mathematical grounds, the probability will entirely cease by the year 3150; there would then be no more faith on earth, and, consequently, according to St. Luke, the world would then be at an end, and the Son of Man would come to judge the quick and the dead.

Bayle always ridiculed that sort of evidence which is called mathematical demonstration.

---

* Wallenstein.

CHAPTER XCVI.

A MUSICIAN'S WISH EXCITED BY HERSCHEL'S TELESCOPE. SYMPATHY BETWEEN PETER HOPKINS AND HIS PUPIL. INDIFFERENTISM USEFUL IN ORDINARY POLITICS, BUT DANGEROUS IN RELIGION.

Noi intendiamo parlare alle cose che utili sono alla umana vita, quanto per nostro intendimento si potrà in questa parte comprendere; e sopra quelle particelle che detto avemo di comporre.

BUSONE DA GUBBIO.

WHEN Miller talked of his friend Herschel's good fortune, and of his astronomical discoveries, and of his sister, Miss Caroline Herschel, who, while in his absence she could get possession of his twenty-feet reflector, amused herself with sweeping the sky, and searching for comets in the neighbourhood of the sun, the warm-hearted and musical-minded man used to wish that the science of acoustics had been advanced in the same degree as that of optics, and that his old friend, when he gave up music as a profession, had still retained it as a pursuit; for, had he constructed auditory tubes of proportionate power and magnitude to his great telescope, "who knows," said Miller, "but we might have been enabled to hear the music of the spheres!" Pythagoras used to listen to that music, when he retired into the depths of his own being; and, according to his disciples, to him alone of all mortals has it been audible. But philosophers in modern times have thought that the existence of this music is more than an enthusiast's dream, a poet's fiction, or an impostor's fable. They say it may be inferred as probable from some of Newton's discoveries; and as a consequence of that principle of harmony which in some parts of the system of nature is so clearly shown, and in others so mysteriously indicated.

As for the Doctor, when Miller talked to him of Miss Herschel's performances in sky-sweeping and comet-hunting, it reminded him of the nursery song, and he quoted the lines,

Old woman, old woman, whither so high?
I'm going to sweep cobwebs off the sky,
And I shall be back again by and by:

not meaning, however, any disrespect to the lady, nor knowing any thing of her age.

Herschel would have opened no new field of speculation for Peter Hopkins, if Hopkins had lived till that day; but he would have eradicated the last remains of his lurking belief in astrology, by showing how little those who pretended to read the stars had seen or known of them. The old man would have parted with it easily, though he delighted in obsolete knowledge, and took as much interest in making himself acquainted with the freaks of the human mind, as with the maladies of the human frame. He thought that they belonged to the same study; and the affection which he had so soon contracted for his pupil was in no small degree occasioned by his perceiving in him a kindred disposition. Mr. Danby says, "there is perhaps more of instinct in our feelings than we are aware of, even in our esteem of each other;" it is one of the many wise remarks of a thoughtful man.

This intellectual sympathy contributed much to the happiness of both, and no little to the intellectual progress of the younger party. But Hopkins's peculiar humour had rendered him indifferent upon some points of great moment. It had served as a prophylactic against all political endemics, and this had been a comfortable security for him in times when such disorders were frequent and violent; and when, though far less malignant than those of the present age, they were far more dangerous, in individual cases. The reader may perhaps remember (and if not, he is now reminded of it,) how, when he was first introduced to Peter Hopkins, it was said that any king would have had in him a quiet subject, and any church a contented conformist. He troubled himself with no disputations in religion, and was troubled with no doubts, but believed what he was taught to believe, because he had been taught to believe it; and owing to the same facility of mind, under any change of dynasty, or revolution of government that could have befallen, he would have obeyed the ruling power. Such would always be the politics of the many, if they were let alone; and such would always be their religion. As regards the civil point this is the best condition in which a people can be, both for themselves and their rulers; and if the laws be good and well administered, the form of government is good so far as it is causative of those effects, and so far as it is not causative, it is a trifle for which none but fools would contest. The proper end of all government being the general good, provided that good be attained it is infinitesimally insignificant by what means. That it can be equally attained under any form is not asserted here. The argument from the analogy of nature which might seem to favour such an assertion cannot be maintained. The Bees have their monarchy, and the Ants their republic; but when we are told to go to the Ant and the Bee, and consider their ways, it is not that we should borrow from them formic laws or apiarian policy. Under the worst scheme of government the desired end would be in a great degree attainable, if the people were trained up, as they ought to be, in the knowledge of their Christian duties; and unless they are so trained, it must ever be very imperfectly attained under the best.

Forms of government alone deserving to be so called, of whatever kind, are here intended, not those of savage or barbarous times and countries. Indeed it is only in advanced stages of society that men are left sufficiently to themselves to become reasonably contented; and then they may be expected, like our friend Peter Hopkins, to be better subjects than patriots. It is desirable that they should be so: for good subjects promote the public good at all times, and it is only in evil times that patriots are wanted,—such times as are usually brought on by rash, or profligate and wicked men, who assume the name.

From this political plasticity, in his days and in his station, no harm could arise either to himself or others. But the same temperament in religion, though doubtless it may reach the degree of saving faith, can hardly consist with an active and imaginative mind. It was fortunate, therefore, for the Doctor, that he found a religious friend in Mr. Bacon. While he was at Leyden his position in this respect had not been favourable. Between the Dutch language and the Burgemeester's daughter, St. Peter's Kirk had not been a scene of much devotion for him. Perhaps many Churches in his own Country might have produced no better effect upon him at that time of life; but the loose opinions which Bayle had scattered were then afloat in Holland, and even these were less dangerous to a disposition such as his, than the fierce Calvinistic tenets by which they were opposed. The former might have beguiled him into scepticism, the latter might have driven him into unbelief, if the necessary attention to his professional studies, and an appetite for general knowledge, which found full employment for all leisure hours, had not happily prevented him from entering without a guide upon a field of inquiry, where he would either have been entangled among thorns, or beset with snares and pitfalls.

True indeed it is that nothing but the most injurious and inevitable circumstances could have corrupted his natural piety, for it had been fostered in him by his father's example, and by those domestic lessons which make upon us the deepest and most enduring impressions. But he was not armed, as it behoved him to be, against the errors of the age, neither those which like the pestilence walked in noon-day, nor those which did their work insidiously and in darkness.

Methodism was then in its rampant stage; the founders themselves had not yet sobered down; and their followers, though more decent than the primitive Quakers, and far less offensive in their operations, ran, nevertheless, into extravagancies which made ill-judging magistrates slow in protecting them against the insults and outrages of the rabble. The Dissenters were more engaged in controversy amongst themselves than with the Establishment; their old leaven had at that time no mass whereon to work, but it was carefully preserved. The Nonjurors, of all sects (if they may be called a sect), the most respectable in their origin, were almost extinct. The Roman Catholics were quiet, in fear of the laws,—no toleration being then professed for a Church which proclaimed, and everywhere acted upon, the principle of absolute intolerance; but there were few populous parts of the kingdom in which there was not some secular priest, or some regular, not indeed

Black, white, and grey, with all their trumpery,

for neither the uniform nor the trumpery were allowed,—but Monk, or Friar, or Jesuit, in lay-clothing, employed in secretly administering to the then decreasing numbers of their own communion, and recruiting them whenever they safely could; but more generally venturing no farther than to insinuate doubts, and unsettle the belief, of unwary and unlearned members of the established religion, for this could always be done with impunity. And in this they aided, and were aided by, those who in that age were known by the name, which they had arrogated to themselves, of Free-thinkers.

There was among the higher classes in those days a fashion of infidelity, imported from France; Shaftesbury and "the cankered Bolingbroke" (as Sir Robert Walpole used justly to call that profligate statesman) were beholden for their reputation more to this, than to any solidity of talents, or grace of style. It had made much less way in middle life than in the higher and lower ranks; for men in middle life, being generally trained up when children in the way they should go, were less likely to depart from it than those who were either above or below them in station; indeed they were not exposed to the same dangers. The principles which were veiled, but not disguised, by Lord Chesterfield and Horace Walpole, and exposed in their nakedness by Wilkes and his blasphemous associates at their orgies, were discussed in the Robin Hood Society, by men who were upon the same level with the holders-forth at the Rotunda in our own times, but who differed from them in these respects, that they neither made a trading profession of impiety, nor ventured into the treason-line.

Any man may graduate in the schools of Irreligion and Mispolicy, if he have a glib tongue and a brazen forehead; with these qualities, and a small portion of that talent which is produceable on demand, he may take a wrangler's degree. Such men were often met with in the common walks of society, before they became audacious enough to show themselves upon the public theatre, and aspire to from a party in the state. Peter Hopkins could listen to them just with as much indifference as he did to a Jacobite, a Nonjuror, or one to whom the memory of Oliver and the saints in buff was precious. The Doctor, before he happily became acquainted with Mr. Bacon, held his peace when in the presence of such people, but from a different cause: for though his heart rose against their discourse, and he had an instinctive assurance that it was equally pernicious and false, he had not so stored himself with needful knowledge as to be able to confute the common-places of an infidel propagandist. But it has an ill effect upon others, when a person of sounder judgment and more acquirements than themselves, remains silent in the company of such talkers; for, from whatever motive his silence may proceed, it is likely to be considered, both by the assailants of the truth, and by the listeners, as an admission of his inability to maintain the better cause. Great evil has arisen to individuals, and to the community, from allowing scoffers to go unrebuked in private life; and fallacies and falsehoods to pass uncontradicted and unexposed in those channels through which poison is conveyed to the public mind.

CHAPTER XCVII.

MR. BACON'S PARSONAGE. CHRISTIAN RESIGNATION. TIME AND CHANGE. WILKIE AND THE MONK IN THE ESCURIAL.

The idea of her life shall sweetly creep
Into his study of imagination;
And every lovely organ of her life
Shall come apparell'd in more precious habit,
More moving delicate, and full of life,
Into the eye and prospect of his soul,
Than when she lived indeed.

SHAKESPEARE.

In a Scotch village the Manse is sometimes the only good house, and generally it is the best; almost, indeed, what in old times the Mansion used to be in an English one. In Mr. Bacon's parish, the vicarage, though humble as the benefice itself, was the neatest. The cottage in which he and Margaret passed their childhood had been remarkable for that comfort which is the result and the reward of order and neatness: and when the reunion which blessed them both rendered the remembrance of those years delightful, they returned in this respect to the way in which they had been trained up, practised the economy which they had learned there, and loved to think how entirely their course of life, in all its circumstances, would be after the heart of that person, if she could behold it, whose memory they both with equal affection cherished. After his bereavement it was one of the widower's pensive pleasures to keep everything in the same state as when Margaret was living. Nothing was neglected that she used to do, or that she would have done. The flowers were tended as carefully as if she were still to enjoy their fragrance and their beauty; and the birds who came in winter for their crumbs were fed as duly for her sake, as they had formerly been by her hands.

There was no superstition in this, nor weakness. Immoderate grief, if it does not exhaust itself by indulgence, easily assumes the one character, or the other, or takes a type of insanity. But he had looked for consolation, where, when sincerely sought, it is always to be found; and he had experienced that religion effects in a true believer all that philosophy professes, and more than all that mere philosophy can perform. The wounds which stoicism would cauterise, religion heals.

There is a resignation with which, it may be feared, most of us deceive ourselves. To bear what must be borne, and submit to what cannot be resisted, is no more than what the unregenerate heart is taught by the instinct of animal nature. But to acquiesce in the afflictive dispensations of Providence, — to make one's own will conform in all things to that of our Heavenly Father, — to say to him in the sincerity of faith, when we drink of the bitter cup, "Thy will be done!" — to bless the name of the Lord as much from the heart when He takes away, as when He gives, and with a depth of feeling of which, perhaps, none but the afflicted heart is capable, — this is the resignation which religion teaches, this the sacrifice which it requires.* This sacrifice Leonard had made, and he felt that it was accepted.

Severe, therefore, as his loss had been, and lasting as its effects were, it produced in him nothing like a settled sorrow, nor even that melancholy which sorrow leaves behind. Gibbon has said of himself, that as a mere philosopher he could not agree with the Greeks, in thinking that those who die in their youth are favoured by the Gods:

Ὃν οἱ θεοὶ φιλοῦσιν ἀποθνήσκει νέος.

It was because he was "a mere philosopher," that he failed to perceive a truth which the religious heathen acknowledged, and which is so trivial, and of such practical value, that it may now be seen inscribed upon village tombstones. The Christian knows that "blessed are the dead which die in the Lord; even so saith the Spirit." And the

* This passage was written when Southey was bowing his head under the sorest and saddest of his many troubles. He thus alludes to it in a letter to me, dated October 5. 1834.

"On the next leaf is the passage of which I spoke in my letter from York. It belongs to an early chapter in the third volume; and very remarkable it is that it should have been written just at that time."

heart of the Christian mourner, in its deepest distress, hath the witness of the Spirit to that consolatory assurance.

In this faith Leonard regarded his bereavement. His loss, he knew, had been Margaret's gain. What, if she had been summoned in the flower of her years, and from a state of connubial happiness which there had been nothing to disturb or to alloy? How soon might that flower have been blighted, — how surely must it have faded! how easily might that happiness have been interrupted by some of those evils which flesh is heir to! And as the separation was to take place, how mercifully had it been appointed that he, who was the stronger vessel, should be the survivor! Even for their child this was best, greatly as she needed, and would need, a mother's care. His paternal solicitude would supply that care, as far as it was possible to supply it; but had he been removed, mother and child must have been left to the mercy of Providence, without any earthly protector, or any means of support.

For her to die was gain; in him, therefore, it were sinful as well as selfish to repine, and of such selfishness and sin his heart acquitted him. If a wish could have recalled her to life, no such wish would ever have by him been uttered, nor ever have by him been felt; certain he was that he loved her too well to bring her again into this world of instability and trial. Upon earth there can be no safe happiness.

Ah! male FORTUNÆ *devota est ara* MANENTI!
*Fallit, et hæc nullas accipit ara preces.**

All things here are subject to Time and Mutability:

Quod tibi largâ dedit Hora dextrâ,
Hora furaci rapiet sinistrâ.†

We must be in eternity before we can be secure against change. "The world," says Cowper, "upon which we close our eyes at night, is never the same with that on which we open them in the morning."

It was to the perfect Order he should find in that state upon which he was about to enter, that the judicious Hooker looked forward at his death with placid and profound contentment. Because he had been employed in contending against a spirit of insubordination and schism which soon proved fatal to his country; and because his life had been passed under the perpetual discomfort of domestic discord, the happiness of Heaven seemed, in his estimation, to consist primarily in Order, as, indeed, in all human societies this is the first thing needful. The discipline which Mr. Bacon had undergone was very different in kind: what he delighted to think, was, that the souls of those whom death and redemption have made perfect, are in a world where there is no change, nor parting, where nothing fades, nothing passes away and is no more seen, but the good and the beautiful are permanent.

Miser, chi speme in cosa mortal pone;
Ma, chi non ve la pone? ‡

When Wilkie was in the Escurial, looking at Titian's famous picture of the Last Supper, in the Refectory there, an old Jeronimite said to him, "I have sat daily in sight of that picture for now nearly threescore years; during that time my companions have dropped off, one after another, — all who were my seniors, all who were my contemporaries, and many, or most of those who were younger than myself; more than one generation has passed away, and there the figures in the picture have remained unchanged! I look at them till I sometimes think that they are the realities, and we but shadows!"§

I wish I could record the name of the Monk by whom that natural feeling was so feelingly and strikingly expressed.

"The shows of things are better than themselves,"

says the author of the Tragedy of Nero, whose name also I could wish had been forthcoming; and the classical reader will remember the lines of Sophocles: —

* WALLIUS. † CASIMIR.

‡ PETRARCH.

§ See the very beautiful lines of Wordsworth in the "Yarrow Revisited." The affecting incident is introduced in "Lines on a Portrait."

'Ορῶ γὰρ ἡμᾶς οὐδὲν ὄντας ἄλλο, πλὴν
Εἴδωλ', ὅσοιπερ ζῶμεν, ἢ κούφην σκιάν.*

These are reflections which should make us think

Of that same time when no more change shall be,
But stedfast rest of all things, firmly stayd
Upon the pillars of Eternity,
That is contraire to mutability;
For all that moveth doth in change delight:
But thenceforth all shall rest eternally
With Him that is the God of Sabaoth hight,
O that great Sabaoth God grant me that sabbath's sight.†

CHAPTER XCVIII.

CHRISTIAN CONSOLATION. OPINIONS CONCERNING THE SPIRITS OF THE DEAD.

The voice which I did more esteem
Than music in her sweetest key;
Those eyes which unto me did seem
More comfortable than the day!
Those now by me, as they have been,
Shall never more be heard, or seen;
But what I once enjoyed in them,
Shall seem hereafter as a dream.

All earthly comforts vanish thus;
So little hold of them have we,
That we from them, or they from us,
May in a moment ravished be.
Yet we are neither just nor wise,
If present mercies we despise;
Or mind not how there may be made
A thankful use of what we had.

WITHER.

THERE is a book written in Latin by the Flemish Jesuit Sarasa, upon the Art of rejoicing always in obedience to the Apostle's precept, — '*Ars semper gaudendi, demonstrata ex solâ consideratione Divinæ Providentiæ.*' Leibnitz and Wolf have commended it; and a French Protestant minister abridged it under the better title of *L'Art de se tranquiliser dans tous les evenemens de la vie.* "I remember," says Cowper, "reading, many years ago, a long treatise on the subject of consolation, written in French; the author's name I have forgotten; but I wrote these words in the margin, — 'special consolation!' at least for a Frenchman, who is a creature the most easily comforted of any in the world!" It is not likely that this should have been the book which Leibnitz praised; nor would Cowper have thus condemned one which recommends the mourner to seek for comfort, where alone it is to be found, in resignation to God's will, and in the prospect of the life to come. The remedy is infallible for those, who, like Mr. Bacon, faithfully pursue the course that the only true philosophy prescribes.

At first, indeed, he had felt like the bereaved maiden in Schiller's tragedy, and could almost have prayed like her, for a speedy deliverance, —

Das Herz ist gestorben, die Welt ist leer,
Und weiter giebt sie dem Wunsche nichts mehr.
Du Heilige, rufe dein Kind zurück!
Ich habe genossen das irdische Glück,
Ich habe gelebt und geliebet.

But even at first the sense of parental duty withheld him from such a prayer. The grief, though "fine, full, perfect," was not a grief that

— violenteth in a sense as strong
As that which causeth it,‡

There was this to compress, as it were and perhaps to mitigate it, that it was wholly confined to himself, not multiplied among others, and reflected from them. In great public calamities, when fortunes are wrecked in revolutionary storms, or families thinned or swept off by pestilence, there may be too many who look upon it as

Solamen miseris socios habuisse doloris; §

and this is not so much because

— fellowship in woe doth woe assuage, ‖

and that

— the mind much sufferance doth o'erskip
When grief hath mates and bearing fellowship, ‖

as because the presence of a fellow sufferer at such times calls forth condolence, when that of one who continues in the sunshine of fortune might provoke an envious self comparison, which is the commonest of all evil feelings. But it is not so with those

---

* SOPHOCLES. † SPENCER.

‡ SHAKESPEARE. § INCERTI AUCTORIS.
‖ SHAKESPEARE.

keener griefs which affect us in our domestic relations. The heart-wounds which are inflicted by our fellow-creatures are apt to fester: those which we receive in the dispensations of Almighty wisdom and the course of nature are remedial and sanative. There are some fruits which must be punctured before they can ripen kindly; and there are some hearts which require an analogous process.

He and Margaret had been all in all to each other, and the child was too young to understand her loss, and happily just too old to feel it as an infant would have felt it. In the sort of comfort which he derived from this sense of loneliness, there was nothing that resembled the pride of stoicism; it was a consideration that tempered his feelings and assisted in enabling him to control them, but it concentrated and perpetuated them.

Whether the souls of the departed are cognizant of what passes on earth, is a question which has been variously determined by those who have reasoned concerning the state of the dead. Thomas Burnet was of opinion that they are not, because they "rest from their labours." And South says, "it is clear that God sometimes takes his Saints out of the world for this very cause, that they may not see and know what happens in it. For so says God to King Josiah, 'Behold, I will gather thee to thy fathers, and thou shalt be gathered to thy grave in peace; neither shall thy eyes see all the evil that I will bring upon this place, and the inhabitants thereof.'" This he adduces as a conclusive argument against the invocation of Saints, saying, the "discourse would have been hugely absurd and inconsequent, if so be the saints' separation from the body gave them a fuller and a clearer prospect into all the particular affairs and occurrences that happen here upon earth."

Aristotle came to an opposite conclusion; he thought not only that the works of the deceased follow them, but that the dead are sensible of the earthly consequences of those works, and are affected in the other world by the honour or the reproach which is justly ascribed to their memory in this. So Pindar represents it as one of the enjoyments of the blessed, that they behold and rejoice in the virtues of their posterity:

"Εστι δὲ καί τι θανόντεσσιν μέρος
Καννόμον ἐρδόμενον,
Κατακρύπτει δ' οὐ κόνις
Συγγόνων κεδνὰν χάριν.*

So Sextus, or Sextius, the Pythagorean, taught; *immortales crede te manere in judicio honores et pœnas.* And Bishop Ken deemed it would be an addition to his happiness in Paradise, if he should know that his devotional poems were answering on earth the purpose for which he had piously composed them:

— should the well-meant songs I leave behind
With Jesus' lovers an acceptance find,
'Twill heighten even the joys of Heaven to know
That in my verse the Saints hymn God below.

The *consensus gentium universalis* is with the Philosophers and the Bishop, against South and Burnet: it affords an argument which South would not have disregarded, and to which Burnet has, on another occasion, triumphantly appealed.

All sacrifices to the dead, and all commemorations of them, have arisen from this opinion, and the Romish Church established upon it the most lucrative of all its deceitful practices. Indeed the belief in apparitions could not prevail without it; and that belief, which was all but universal a century ago, is still, and ever will be held by the great majority of mankind. Call it a prejudice if you will; "what is an universal prejudice," says Reginald Heber, "but the voice of human nature?" — And Shakespeare seems to express his own opinion when he writes, "They say miracles are past; and we have our philosophical persons, to make modern and familiar, things supernatural and causeless. Hence it is that we make trifles of terrors, ensconcing ourselves into seeming knowledge, when we should submit ourselves to an unknown fear." †

* Pindar, Ol. viii. 101, &c. See also Pyth. v. 133. &c.
† All's Well that Ends Well, Act ii. Sc. iii.

That the spirits of the departed are permitted to appear only for special purposes is what the most credulous believer in such appearances would probably admit, if he reasoned at all upon the subject. On the other hand, they who are most incredulous on this point would hardly deny that to witness the consequences of our actions may be a natural and just part of our reward or punishment in the intermediate state. We may well believe that they whom faith has sanctified, and who upon their departure join the spirits of the "just made perfect," may at once be removed from all concern with this world of probation, except so far as might add to their own happiness, and be made conducive to the good of others, in the ways of Providence. But by parity of reason, it may be concluded that the sordid and the sensual, they whose affections have been set upon worldly things, and who are of the earth earthy, will be as unable to rise above this earth, as they would be incapable of any pure and spiritual enjoyment. "He that soweth to his flesh, shall of the flesh reap corruption." When life is extinguished, it is too late for them to struggle for deliverance from the body of that death, to which, while the choice was in their power, they wilfully and inseparably bound themselves. The popular belief that places are haunted where money has been concealed (as if where the treasure was, and the heart had been, there would the miserable soul be also), or where some great and undiscovered crime has been committed, shows how consistent this is with our natural sense of likelihood and fitness.

There is a tale in the Nigaristan of Kemal-Pascha-zade, that one of the Sultans of Khorassan saw in a dream, Mahmoud a hundred years after his death, wandering about his palace, — his flesh rotten, his bones carious, but his eyes full, anxious, and restless. A dervise who interpreted the dream, said that the eyes of Mahmoud were thus troubled, because the kingdom, his beautiful spouse, was now in the embrace of another.

This was that great Mahmoud the Gaznevide, who was the first Mohammedan conqueror that entered India, and the first who dropped the title of Malek and assumed that of Sultan in its stead. He it was, who after having broken to pieces with his own hands the gigantic idol of Soumenat, put to death fifty thousand of its worshippers, as a further proof of his holy Mohammedan indignation. In the last days of his life, when a mortal disease was consuming him, and he himself knew that no human means could arrest its course, he ordered all his costliest apparel, and his vessels of silver and gold, and his pearls and precious stones, the inestimable spoils of the East, to be displayed before him, — the latter were so numerous that they were arranged in separate cabinets according to their colour and size. It was in the royal residence which he had built for himself in Gazna, and which he called the Palace of Felicity, that he took from this display, wherewith he had formerly gratified the pride of his eye, a mournful lesson ; and in the then heartfelt conviction that all is vanity, he wept like a child. "What toils," said he, "what dangers, what fatigues of body and mind have I endured for the sake of acquiring these treasures, and what cares in preserving them, and now I am about to die and leave them!" In this same palace he was interred, and there it was that his unhappy ghost, a century afterwards, was believed to wander.

CHAPTER XCIX.

A COUNTRY PARISH. SOME WHOLESOME EXTRACTS, SOME TRUE ANECDOTES, AND SOME USEFUL HINTS, WHICH WILL NOT BE TAKEN BY THOSE WHO NEED THEM MOST.

Non è inconveniente, che delle cose delettabili alcune ne sieno utili, cosi come dell' utili molte ne sono delettabili, et in tutte due alcune si truovano honeste.

LEONE MEDICO (HEBREO).

MR. BACON's parsonage was as humble a dwelling in all respects as the cottage in which his friend Daniel was born. A best kitchen was its best room, and in its furniture an Observantine Friar would have seen nothing that he could have condemned as superfluous. His college and later school books, with a few volumes which had been presented to him by the more grateful of his pupils, composed his scanty library: they were either books of needful reference, or such as upon every fresh perusal might afford new delight. But he had obtained the use of the Church Library at Doncaster, by a payment of twenty shillings, according to the terms of the foundation. Folios from that collection might be kept three months, smaller volumes, one or two, according to their size; and as there were many works in it of solid contents as well as sterling value, he was in no such want of intellectual food, as too many of his brethren are, even at this time. How much good might have been done, and how much evil might probably have been prevented, if Dr. Bray's design for the formation of parochial libraries had been everywhere carried into effect!

The parish contained between five and six hundred souls. There was no one of higher rank among them than entitled him, according to the custom of those days, to be styled gentleman upon his tombstone. They were plain people, who had neither manufactories to corrupt, ale-houses to brutalise, nor newspapers to mislead them. At first coming among them he had won their good-will by his affability and benign conduct, and he had afterwards gained their respect and affection in an equal degree.

There were two services at his church, but only one sermon, which never fell short of fifteen minutes in length, and seldom extended to half-an-hour. It was generally abridged from some good old divine. His own compositions were few, and only upon points on which he wished carefully to examine and digest his own thoughts, or which were peculiarly suited to some or other of his hearers. His whole stock might be deemed scanty in these days; but there was not one in it which would not well bear repetition, and the more observant of his congregation liked that they should be repeated.

Young ministers are earnestly advised long to refrain from preaching their own productions, in an excellent little book addressed by a Father to his Son, preparatory to his receiving holy orders. Its title is a "Monitor for Young Ministers," and every parent who has a son so circumstanced would do well to put it into his hands. "It is not possible," says this judicious writer, "that a young minister can at first be competent to preach his sermons with effect, even if his abilities should qualify him to write well. His very youth and youthful manner, both in his style of writing and in his delivery, will preclude him from being effective. Unquestionably it is very rare indeed for a man of his age to have his mental abilities sufficiently chastened, or his method sufficiently settled, to be equal to the composition of a sermon fit for public use, even if it should receive the advantage of chaste and good delivery. On every account, therefore, it is wise and prudent to be slow and backward in venturing to produce his own efforts, or in thinking that they are fit for the public ear. There is an abundant field of the works of others open to him, from the wisest and the best of men, the weight of whose little fingers, in argument or instruction, will be greater than his own loins, even at his highest maturity. There is clearly no *want* of new compositions, excepting on some new or occasional emergencies: for there is not an open subject in the Christian religion, which has not been discussed by men of the greatest learning and piety, who have left behind them numerous works for our assistance and edification. Many of these are so neglected, that they are become almost new ground for our generation. To these he may freely resort, — till experience and a rational and chastened confidence shall warrant him in believing himself qualified to work upon his own resources."

"He that learns of young men," says Rabbi Jose Bar Jehudah, "is like a man that eats unripe grapes, or that drinks wine out of the wine-press; but he that learneth of the ancient, is like a man that eateth ripe grapes, and drinketh wine that is old." *

It was not in pursuance of any judicious advice like this that Mr. Bacon followed the course here pointed out, but from his own good sense and natural humility. His only ambition was to be useful; if a desire may be called ambitious which originated in the sincere sense of duty. To think of distinguishing himself in any other way, would for him, he well knew, have been worse than an idle dream. The time expended in composing a sermon as a perfunctory official business, would have been worse than wasted for himself, and the time employed in delivering it, no better than wasted upon his congregation. He was especially careful never to weary them, and, therefore, never to preach anything which was not likely to engage their attention, and make at least some present impression. His own sermons effected this, because they were always composed with some immediate view, or under the influence of some deep and strong feeling: and in his adopted ones, the different manner of the different authors produced an awakening effect. Good sense is as often to be found among the illiterate, as among those who have enjoyed the opportunities of education. Many of his hearers who knew but one meaning of the word stile, and had never heard it used in any other, perceived a difference in the manner of Bishops Hall, and Sanderson and Jeremy Taylor, of Barrow, and South and Scott, without troubling themselves about the cause, or being in the slightest degree aware of it.

Mr. Bacon neither undervalued his parishioners, nor overvalued the good which could be wrought among them by direct instruction of this kind. While he used perspicuous language, he knew that they who listened to it would be able to follow the argument; and as he drew always from the wells of English undefiled, he was safe on that point. But that all even of the adults would listen, and that all even of those who did, would do anything more than hear, he was too well acquainted with human nature to expect.

A woman in humble life was asked one day on the way back from church, whether she had understood the sermon; a stranger had preached, and his discourse resembled one of Mr. Bacon's neither in length nor depth. "Wud I hae the persumption?" was her simple and contented answer. The quality of the discourse signified nothing to her; she had done her duty, as well as she could, in hearing it; and she went to her house justified rather than some of those who had attended to it critically; or who had turned to the text in their Bibles when it was given out.

"Well, Master Jackson," said his Minister, walking homeward after service, with an industrious labourer, who was a constant attendant; "well, Master Jackson, Sunday must be a blessed day of rest for you, who work so hard all the week! And you make a good use of the day, for you are always to be seen at Church!" "Ay, Sir," replied Jackson, "it is indeed a blessed day; I works hard enough all the week, and then I comes to Church o' Sundays, and sets me down, and lays my legs up, and thinks o' nothing."

"Let my candle go out in a stink, when I refuse to confess from whom I have lighted it." † The author to whose little book ‡ I am beholden for this true anecdote, after saying "Such was the religion of this worthy man," justly adds, "and such must be the religion of most men of his station. Doubtless, it is a wise dispensation that it is so. For so it has been from the beginning of the world, and there is no visible reason to suppose that it can ever be otherwise."

"In spite," says this judicious writer, "of all the zealous wishes and efforts of the most pious and laborious teachers, the religion of the bulk of the people must and will ever be little more than mere habit, and confidence in others. This must of necessity be the case with all men, who, from defect of

* Lightfoot.

† Fuller. ‡ Few Words on many Subjects.

nature or education, or from other worldly causes, have not the power or the disposition to think ; and it cannot be disputed that the far greater number of mankind are of this class. These facts give peculiar force to those lessons which teach the importance and efficacy of good example from those who are blessed with higher qualifications ; and they strongly demonstrate the necessity that the zeal of those who wish to impress the people with the deep and awful mysteries of religion should be tempered by wisdom and discretion, no less than by patience, forbearance, and a great latitude of indulgence for uncontrollable circumstances. They also call upon us most powerfully to do all we can to provide such teachers, and imbue them with such principles as shall not endanger the good cause by over earnest efforts to effect more than, in the nature of things, can be done ; or disturb the existing good by attempting more than will be borne, or by producing hypocritical pretences of more than can be really felt."

CHAPTER C.

SHOWING HOW THE VICAR DEALT WITH THE JUVENILE PART OF HIS FLOCK ; AND HOW HE WAS OF OPINION THAT THE MORE PLEASANT THE WAY IN WHICH CHILDREN ARE TRAINED UP TO GO CAN BE MADE FOR THEM, THE LESS LIKELY THEY WILL BE TO DEPART FROM IT.

Sweet were the sauce would please each kind of taste,
The life, likewise, were pure that never swerved ;
For spiteful tongues, in cankered stomachs placed,
Deem worst of things which best, percase, deserved.
But what for that ? This medicine may suffice,
To scorn the rest, and seek to please the wise.

SIR WALTER RALEIGH.

THE first thing which Mr. Bacon had done after taking possession of his vicarage, and obtaining such information about his parishioners as the more considerate of them could impart, was to inquire into the state of the children in every household. He knew that to win the mother's good will was the surest way to win that of the family, and to win the children was a good step toward gaining that of the mother. In those days reading and writing were thought as little necessary for the lower class, as the art of spelling for the class above them, or indeed for any except the learned. Their ignorance in this respect was sometimes found to be inconvenient, but by none, perhaps, except here and there by a conscientious and thoughtful clergyman, was it felt to be an evil, — an impediment in the way of that moral and religious instruction, without which men are in danger of becoming as the beasts that perish. Yet the common wish of advancing their children in the world made most parents in this station desire to obtain the advantage of what they called book-learning for any son who was supposed to manifest a disposition likely to profit by it. To make him a scholar was to raise him a step above themselves.

Qui ha les lettres, ha l'adresse
*Au double d'un qui n'en ha point.**

Partly for this reason, and still more that industrious mothers might be relieved from the care of looking after their children, there were few villages in which, as in Mr. Bacon's parish, some poor woman in the decline of life and of fortune did not obtain day-scholars enough to eke out her scanty means of subsistence.

The village Schoolmistress, such as Shenstone describes in his admirable poem, and such as Kirke White drew from the life, is no longer a living character. The new system of education has taken from this class of women the staff of their declining age, as the spinning jennies have silenced the domestic music of the spinning wheel. Both changes have come on unavoidably in the progress of human affairs. It is well when any change brings with it nothing worse than some temporary and incidental evil ; but if the moral machinery can counteract the great and growing evils of the manufacturing system, it will be the greatest moral miracle that has ever been wrought.

Sunday schools†, which make Sunday a

* BAIF.

† See suprà, p. 146.

day of toil to the teachers, and the most irksome day of the week to the children, had not at that time been devised as a palliative for the profligacy of large towns, and the worsened and worsening condition of the poor. Mr. Bacon endeavoured to make the parents perform their religious duty toward their children, either by teaching them what they could themselves teach, or by sending them where their own want of knowledge might be supplied. Whether the children went to school or not, it was his wish that they should be taught their prayers, the Creed, and the Commandments, at home. These he thought were better learned at the mother's knees than from any other teacher; and he knew also how wholesome for the mother it was that the child should receive from her its first spiritual food, the milk of sound doctrine. In a purely agricultural parish, there were at that time no parents in a state of such brutal ignorance as to be unable to teach these, though they might never have been taught to read. When the father or mother could read, he expected that they should also teach their children the catechism; in other cases this was left to his humble co-adjutrix the schoolmistress.

During the summer and part of the autumn, he followed the good old usage of catechising the children, after the second lesson in the evening service. His method was to ask a few questions in succession, and only from those who he knew were able to answer them; and after each answer he entered into a brief exposition suited to their capacity. His manner was so benevolent, and he had made himself so familiar in his visits, which were at once pastoral and friendly, that no child felt alarmed at being singled out; they regarded it as a mark of distinction, and the parents were proud of seeing them thus distinguished. This practice was discontinued in winter; because he knew that to keep a congregation in the cold is not the way either to quicken or cherish devotional feeling. Once a week during Lent he examined all the children, on a week day; the last examination was in Easter week, after which each was sent home happy with a homely cake, the gift of a wealthy parishioner, who by this means contributed not a little to the good effect of the pastor's diligence.

The foundation was thus laid by teaching the rising generation their duty towards God and towards their neighbour, and so far training them in the way that they should go. In the course of a few years every household, from the highest to the lowest,—(the degrees were neither great nor many,)—had learned to look upon him as their friend. There was only one in the parish whose members were upon a parity with him in manners, none in literary culture; but in good will, and in human sympathy, he was upon a level with them all. Never interfering in the concerns of any family, unless his interference was solicited, he was consulted upon all occasions of trouble or importance. Incipient disputes, which would otherwise have afforded grist for the lawyer's mill, were adjusted by his mediation; and anxious parents, when they had cause to apprehend that their children were going wrong, knew no better course than to communicate their fears to him, and request that he would administer some timely admonition. Whenever he was thus called on, or had of himself perceived that reproof or warning was required, it was given in private, or only in presence of the parents, and always with a gentleness which none but an obdurate disposition could resist. His influence over the younger part of his flock was the greater because he was no enemy to any innocent sports, but, on the contrary, was pleased to see them dance round the may-pole, encouraged them to dress their doors with oaken boughs on the day of King Charles's happy restoration, and to wear an oaken garland in the hat, or an oak-apple on its sprig in the button hole; went to see their bonfire on the fifth of November, and entertained the morris-dancers when they called upon him in their Christmas rounds.

Mr. Bacon was in his parish what a moralising old poet wished himself to be, in these pleasing stanzas:—

I would I were an excellent divine,
That had the Bible at my fingers' ends,
That men might hear out of this mouth of mine
How God doth make his enemies his friends;
Rather than with a thundering and long prayer
Be led into presumption, or despair.

This would I be, and would none other be
But a religious servant of my God:
And know there is none other God but He,
And willingly to suffer Mercy's rod,
Joy in his grace and live but in his love,
And seek my bliss but in the world above.

And I would frame a kind of faithful prayer
For all estates within the state of grace;
That careful love might never know despair,
Nor servile fear might faithful love deface;
And this would I both day and night devise
To make my humble spirits exercise.

And I would read the rules of sacred life,
Persuade the troubled soul to patience,
The husband care, and comfort to the wife,
To child and servant due obedience,
Faith to the friend and to the neighbour peace,
That love might live, and quarrels all might cease;

Pray for the health of all that are diseased,
Confession unto all that are convicted,
And patience unto all that are displeased,
And comfort unto all that are afflicted,
And mercy unto all that have offended,
And grace to all, that all may be amended.*

CHAPTER CI.

SOME ACCOUNT OF A RETIRED TOBACCONIST AND HIS FAMILY.

Non fumum ex fulgore, sed ex fumo dare lucem.
HORACE.

IN all Mr. Bacon's views he was fortunate enough to have the hearty concurrence of the wealthiest person in the parish. This was a good man, Allison by name, who having realised a respectable fortune in the metropolis as a tobacconist, and put out his sons in life according to their respective inclinations, had retired from business at the age of threescore, and established himself with an unmarried daughter, and a maiden sister some ten years younger than himself, in his native village, that he might there, when his hour should come, be gathered to his fathers.

* N. B., supposed to be NICHOLAS BRETON.

"The providence of God," says South, "has so ordered the course of things, that there is no action the usefulness of which has made it the matter of duty and of a profession, but a man may bear the continual pursuit of it, without loathing or satiety. The same shop and trade that employs a man in his youth employs him also in his age. Every morning he rises fresh to his hammer and his anvil: custom has naturalised his labour to him; his shop is his element, and he cannot, with any enjoyment of himself, live out of it." The great preacher contrasts this with the wearisomeness of an idle life, and the misery of a continual round of what the world calls pleasure. "But now," says he, "if God has interwoven such a contentment with the works of our ordinary calling, how much superior and more refined must that be that arises from the survey of a pious and well-governed life?"

This passage bears upon Mr. Allison's case, partly in the consolatory fact which it states, and wholly in the application which South has made of it. At the age of fourteen he had been apprenticed to an Uncle in Bishopsgate Street-within; and twenty years after, on that Uncle's death, had succeeded to his old and well-established business. But though he had lived there prosperously and happily six and twenty years longer, he had contracted no such love for it as to overcome the recollections of his childhood. Grateful as the smell of snuff and tobacco had become to him, he still remembered that cowslips and violets were sweeter; and that the breath of a May morning was more exhilarating than the air of his own shop, impregnated as it was with the odour of the best Virginia. So having buried his wife, who was a Londoner, and made over the business to his eldest son, he returned to his native place, with the intention of dying there; but he was in sound health of body and mind, and his green old age seemed to promise,—as far as any thing can promise,—length of days.

Of his two other sons, one had chosen to

be a clergyman, and approved his choice both by his parts and diligence, for he had gone off from Merchant-Taylors' School to St. John's, Oxford, and was then a fellow of that college. The other was a Mate in the Merchants' service, and would soon have the command of a ship in it. The desire of seeing the world led him to this way of life; and that desire had been unintentionally implanted by his father, who, in making himself acquainted with everything relating to the herb out of which his own fortune was raised, had become fond of reading voyages and travels. His conversation induced the lad to read these books, and the books confirmed the inclination which had already been excited; and as the boy was of an adventurous temper, he thought it best to let him follow the pursuit on which his mind was bent.

The change to a Yorkshire village was not too great for Mr. Allison, even after residing nearly half a century in Bishopsgate Street-within. The change in his own household indeed rendered it expedient for him to begin, in this sense, a new life. He had lost his mate; the young birds were full-fledged and had taken flight; and it was time that he should look out a retreat for himself and the single nestling that remained under his wing, now that his son and successor had brought home a wife. The marriage had been altogether with his approbation; but it altered his position in the house, and in a still greater degree his sister's; moreover, the nest would soon be wanted for another brood. Circumstances thus compelled him to put in effect what had been the dream of his youth, and the still remote intention of his middle age.

Miss Allison, like her brother, regarded this removal as a great and serious change, preparatory to the only greater one in this world that now remained for both; but like him she regarded it rather seriously than sadly, or sadly only in the old sober meaning of the word; and there was a soft, sweet, evening sunshine in their prospect, which both partook, because both had retained a deep affection for the scenes of their childhood. To Betsey, her niece, nothing could be more delightful than the expectation of such a removal. She, who was then only entering her teens, had nothing to regret in leaving London; and the place to which she was going was the very spot which, of all others in this wide world, from the time in which she was conscious of forming a wish, she had wished most to see. Her brother, the sailor, was not more taken with the story of Pocahontas and Captain Smith, or Dampier's Voyages, than she was with her aunt's details of the farm and the dairy at Thaxted Grange, the May-games and the Christmas gambols, the days that were gone, and the elders who were departed. To one born and bred in the heart of London, who had scarcely ever seen a flock of sheep, except when they were driven through the streets, to or from Smithfield, no fairy tale could present more for the imagination than a description of green fields and rural life. The charm of truth heightened it, and the stronger charm of natural piety; for the personages of the tale were her near kin, whose names she had learned to love, and whose living memory she revered, but whose countenances she never could behold till she should be welcomed by them in the everlasting mansions of the righteous.

None of the party were disappointed when they had established themselves at the Grange. Mr. Allison found full occupation at first in improving the house, and afterwards in his fields and garden. Mr. Bacon was just such a clergyman as he would have chosen for his parish priest, if it had been in his power to choose, only he would have had him provided with a better benefice. The single thing on which there was a want of agreement between them, was, that the Vicar neither smoked nor took snuff; he was not the worse company on this account, for he had no dislike to the fragrance of a pipe; but his neighbour lost the pleasure which he would have had in supplying him with the best pig-tail, and with Strasburg or Rappee. Miss Allison fell into the habits of her new station the more easily, because they were those which she had witnessed in her early youth; she distilled waters, dried herbs, and prepared conserves,—which were at the service of all who needed them in sickness. Betsey attached herself at first sight to Deborah, who was about five years elder, and soon became to her as a sister. The Aunt rejoiced in finding so suitable a friend and companion for her niece; and as this connexion was a pleasure and an advantage to the Allisons, so was it of the greatest benefit to Deborah.

— What of her ensues
I list not prophecy, but let Time's news
Be known, when 'tis brought forth. Of this allow
If ever you have spent time worse ere now;
If never yet, the Author then doth say
He wishes earnestly you never may.*

INTERCHAPTER XI.

ADVICE TO CERTAIN READERS INTENDED TO ASSIST THEIR DIGESTION OF THESE VOLUMES.

Take this in good part, whosoever thou be,
And wish me no worse than I wish unto thee.

TUSSER.

The wisest of men hath told us that there is a time for everything. I have been considering what time is fittest for studying this elaborate *opus*, so as best to profit by its recondite stores of instruction, as the great chronicler of Garagantua says, *avec espoir certain d'acquerrir moult prudence et preud'hommie à la ditte lecture, la quelle vous relevera de tres-hauts sacrements et mysteres horrifiques.*

The judicious reader must ere this have perceived that this work, to use the happy expression of the Demoiselle de Gournay, is *edifié de telle sort que les mots et la matière sont consubstantiels.* In one sense indeed it is

Meet for all hours and every mood of man;†

but all hours are not equally meet for it. For it is not like Sir Walter Scott's novels, fit for men, women and children, at morning, noon, or night, summer and winter, and every day, among all sorts of people,—Sundays excepted with the religious public. Equally sweet in the mouth it may be to some; but it will not be found equally light of digestion.

Whether it should be taken upon an empty stomach, must depend upon the constitution of the reader. If he is of that happy complexion that he awakes in the morning with his spirits elastic as the air, fresh as the dawn, and joyous as the skylark, let him by all means read a chapter before breakfast. It will be a carminative, a cordial for the day. If, on the contrary, his faculties continue to feel the influence of the leaden sceptre till breakfast has resuscitated them, I advise him not to open the book before the stomach has been propitiated by a morning offering.

Breakfast will be the best time for bachelors, and especially for lawyers. They will find it excellent to prime with.

I do not recommend it at night. Rather, indeed, I caution the reader against indulging in it at that time. Its effect might be injurious, for it would counteract the genial tendency to repose which ought then to be encouraged. Therefore when the hour of sleep approaches, lay this book aside, and read four pages upon political economy,—it matters not in what author, though the Scotch are to be preferred.

Except at night, it may be perused at any time by those who have the *mens sana in corpore sano;* those who fear God, honour the King, love their country and their kind, do their duty to their neighbours, and live in the performance and enjoyment of the domestic charities.

It will be an excellent Saturday book for Rowland Hill; his sermon will be pleasanter for it next day.

The book is good for valetudinarians, and may even be recommended in aid of Abernethy's blue-pill. But I do not advise it with water-gruel nor sago; hardly with chicken-broth, calf's-foot-jelly, or beef-tea. It accords well with a course of tonics. But a convalescent will find it best with his first beef-steak and glass of wine.

---

* SHAKFSPEARE.

† DR. BUTT.

The case is different for those who have either a twist in the head or a morbid affection about the pericardium.

If Grey Bennet will read it, — (from which I dehort him), — he should prepare by taking the following medicine to purge choler: —

℞. *Extract: Colocynth: Comp: gr. x.*
Calomel: gr. v.
Syr: q. s. f. Massa in pilulas iij dividenda. — Sumat pilulas iij horâ somni.

It will do Lord Holland no harm.

Lord John Russell is recommended to use sage tea with it. If this operate as an alterative, it may save him from taking oil of rue hereafter in powerful doses.

For Mr. Brougham a strong decoction of the herb *lunaria* will be needful, — a plant "elegantly so named by the elder botanists, and by all succeeding ones, from *luna*, the moon, on account of the silvery semi-transparent aspect, and broad circular shape of its seed-vessels." *Honesty*, or *satin-flower*, are its trivial names. It is recommended in this case not so much for the cephalic properties which its Linnean appellation might seem to denote, as for its emollient and purifying virtue.

The Lord Chancellor must never read it in his wig. Dr. Parr, never without it.

Mr. Wilberforce may dip into it when he will. At all times it will find him in good humour, and in charity with all men. Nay, if I whisper to him that it will be no sin to allow himself a few pages on a Sunday, and that if the preacher, under whom he has been sitting, should have given his discourse a strong spice of Calvinism, it may then be useful to have recourse to it; — though he should be shocked at the wholesome hint, the worst thing he will say of the incognisable incognito from whom it comes, will be Poo-oo-oo-r cree-ee-eature! shaking his head, and lowering it at the same time, till his forehead almost touches the table, and his voice, gradually quickening in speed and sinking in tone, dies away to a whisper, in a manner which may thus be represented in types;

Pooo-oo-oo-oo-r Creēēature
Poo-oo-oo-oo-r Creēature
Poo-oo-ŏŏ-r Crēature
Pōō-ŏŏ-r Crĕature
Pōōŏŏr Crĕature
Pōŏŏr Crĕature
Pŏŏr Crĕature
Pŏŏr Crĕture
Poor Cretur
Poor Crtur
Poo Crtr
Poo Crt

CHAPTER CII.

MORE CONCERNING THE AFORESAID TOBACCONIST.

> I doubt nothing at all but that you shall like the man every day better than other; for verily I think he lacketh not of those qualities which should become any honest man to have, over and besides the gift of nature wherewith God hath above the common rate endued him.
>
> ARCHBISHOP CRANMER.

MR. ALLISON was as quiet a subject as Peter Hopkins, but he was not like him a political quietist from indifference, for he had a warm sense of loyalty, and a well-rooted attachment to the constitution of his country in church and state. His ancestors had suffered in the Great Rebellion, and much the greater part of their never large estates had been alienated to raise the fines imposed upon them as delinquents. The uncle, whom he succeeded in Bishopsgate Street, had, in his early apprenticeship, assisted at burning the Rump, and in maturer years had joined as heartily in the rejoicings, when the Seven Bishops were released from the Tower: he subscribed to Walker's "Account of the Sufferings of the Clergy," and had heard sermons preached by the famous Dr. Scott, (which were afterwards incorporated in his great work upon the Christian Life,) in the church of St. Peter-le-Poor (oddly so called, seeing that there are few districts within the City of London so rich, insomuch that the last historian of the metropolis believed the parish to have scarcely a poor family in it), — and in All-hallows, Lombard Street, where, during the reign of the Godly, the puritanical vestry passed a resolution that if any persons should come to the church "on the day called Christ's birth-day," they should be compelled to leave it.

In these principles Mr. Allison had grown up; and without any profession of extra-religion, or ever wearing a sanctified face, he had in the evening of his life attained "the end of the commandment, which is charity, proceeding from a pure heart, and a good conscience, and a faith unfeigned." London in his days was a better school for young men in trade than it ever was before, or has been since. The civic power had quietly and imperceptibly put an end to that club-law which once made the apprentices a turbulent and formidable body, at any moment armed as well as ready for a riot; and masters exercised a sort of parental control over the youth entrusted to them, which in later times it may be feared has not been so conscientiously exerted, because it is not likely to be so patiently endured. Trade itself had not then been corrupted by that ruinous spirit of competition, which, more than any other of the evils now pressing upon us, deserves to be called the curse of England in the present age. At all times men have been to be found, who engaged in hazardous speculations, gamester-like, according to their opportunities, or who, mistaking the means for the end, devoted themselves with miserable fidelity to the service of Mammon. But "Live and let live," had not yet become a maxim of obsolete morality. We had our monarchy, our hierarchy, and our aristocracy, — God be praised for the benefits which have been derived from all three, and God in his mercy continue them to us! but we had no plutarchy, no millionaires, no great capitalists to break down the honest and industrious trader with the weight of their overbearing and overwhelming wealth. They who had enriched themselves in the course of regular and honourable commerce withdrew from business, and left the field to others. Feudal tyranny had passed away, and moneyed tyranny had not yet arisen in its stead — a tyranny baser in its origin, not more merciful in its operations, and with less in its appendages to redeem it.

Trade in Mr. Allison's days was a school of thrift and probity, as much as of profit and loss; such his shop had been when he succeeded to it upon his uncle's decease, and such it continued to be when he transmitted it to his son. Old Mr. Strahan the printer (the founder of his typarchical dynasty) said to Dr. Johnson, that "there are few ways in which a man can be more innocently employed than in getting money;" and he added, that "the more one thinks of this the juster it will appear." Johnson agreed with him; and though it was a money-maker's observation, and though the more it is considered now, the more fallacious it will be found, the general system of trade might have justified it at that time. The entrance of an Exciseman never occasioned any alarm or apprehension at No. 113. Bishopsgate-Street-Within, nor any uncomfortable feeling, unless the officer happened to be one, who, by giving unnecessary trouble, and by gratuitous incivility in the exercise of authority, made an equitable law odious in its execution. They never there mixed weeds with their tobacco, nor adulterated it in any worse way; and their snuff was never rendered more pungent by stirring into it a certain proportion of pounded glass. The duties were honestly paid, with a clear perception that the impost fell lightly upon all whom it affected, and affected those only who chose to indulge themselves in a pleasure which was still cheap, and which, without any injurious privation, they might forego. Nay, when our good man expatiated upon the uses of tobacco, which Mr. Bacon demurred at, and the Doctor sometimes playfully disputed, he ventured an opinion that among the final causes for which so excellent an herb had been created, the facilities afforded by it toward raising the revenue in a well-governed country like our own might be one.

There was a strong family likeness between him and his sister, both in countenance and disposition. Elizabeth Allison was a person for whom the best and wisest man might have thanked Providence, if she had been allotted to him for help-mate. But though she had, in Shakespeare's language, "withered on the virgin thorn," hers had not been a life of single blessedness: she had been a blessing first to her parents; then to her brother and her brother's family, where she relieved an amiable, but sickly sister-in-law, from those domestic offices which require activity and forethought; lastly, after the dispersion of his sons, the transfer of the business to the eldest, and the breaking-up of his old establishment, to the widower and his daughter, the only child who cleaved to him, — not like Ruth to Naomi, by a meritorious act of duty, for in her case it was in the ordinary course of things, without either sacrifice or choice; but the effect in endearing her to him was the same.

In advanced stages of society and nowhere more than in England at this time, the tendency of all things is to weaken the relations between parent and child, and frequently to destroy them, reducing human nature in this respect nearer to the level of animal life. Perhaps the greater number of male children who are "born into the world" in our part of it, are *put out* at as early an age, proportionately as the young bird is driven from its nest, or the young beast turned off by its dam as being capable of feeding and protecting itself; and in many instances they are as totally lost to the parent, though not in like manner forgotten. Mr. Allison never saw all his children together after his removal from London. The only time when his three sons met at the Grange was when they came there to attend their father's funeral; nor would they then have been assembled, if the Captain's ship had not happened to have recently arrived in port.

This is a state of things more favourable to the wealth than to the happiness of nations. It was a natural and pious custom in patriarchal times that the dead should be gathered unto their people. "Bury me," said Jacob, when he gave his dying charge to his sons, — "bury me with my fathers, in the cave that is in the field of Machpelah, which is before Mamre in the land of Canaan, which Abraham bought with the field of Ephron the Hittite, for a possession of a burying place. There they buried Abraham and Sarah his wife; there they buried Isaac and Rebecca his wife; and there I buried Leah." Had such a passage occurred in Homer, or in Dante, all critics would have concurred in admiring the truth and beauty of the sentiment. He had buried his beloved Rachel by the way where she died; but although he remembered this at his death, the orders which he gave were that his own remains should be laid in the sepulchre of his fathers. The same feeling prevails among many, or most of those savage tribes who are not utterly degraded. With them the tree is not left to lie where it falls. The body of one who dies on an expedition is interred on the spot, if distance or other circumstances render it inconvenient to transport the corpse; but, however long the journey, it is considered as a sacred duty that the bones should at some time or other be brought home. In Scotland, where the common rites of sepulture are performed with less decency than in any other Christian country, the care with which family burial-grounds in the remoter parts are preserved, may be referred as much to natural feeling as to hereditary pride.

But as indigenous flowers are eradicated by the spade and plough, so this feeling is destroyed in the stirring and bustling intercourse of commercial life. No room is left for it: as little of it at this time remains in wide America as in thickly-peopled England. That to which soldiers and sailors are reconciled by the spirit of their profession and the chances of war and of the seas, the love of adventure and the desire of advancement cause others to regard with the same indifference; and these motives are so prevalent, that the dispersion of families and the consequent disruption of natural ties, if not occasioned by necessity, would now in most instances be the effect of choice. Even those to whom it is an inevitable evil, and who feel it deeply as such, look upon it as something in the appointed course of things, as much as infirmity and age and death.

It is well for us that in early life we never think of the vicissitudes which lie before us; or look to them only with pleasurable anticipations as they approach.

> Youth
> Knows nought of changes: Age hath traced them oft,
> Expects and can interpret them.*

The thought of them, when it comes across us in middle life, brings with it only a transient sadness, like the shadow of a passing cloud. We turn our eyes from them while they are in prospect, but when they are in retrospect many a longing lingering look is cast behind. So long as Mr. Allison was in business he looked to Thaxted Grange as the place where he hoped one day to enjoy the blessings of retirement,—that *otium cum dignitate*, which in a certain sense the prudent citizen is more likely to attain than the successful statesman. It was the pleasure of recollection that gave this hope its zest and its strength. But after the object which during so many years he had held in view had been obtained, his day-dreams, if he had allowed them to take their course, would have recurred more frequently to Bishops-gate-Street than they had ever wandered from thence to the scenes of his boyhood. They recurred thither oftener than he wished, although few men have been more masters of themselves; and then the remembrance of his wife, whom he had lost by a lingering disease in middle age; and of the children, those who had died during their childhood, and those who in reality were almost as much lost to him in the ways of the world, made him alway turn for comfort to the prospect of that better state of existence in which they should once more all be gathered together, and where there would be neither change nor parting. His thoughts often fell into this train, when on summer evenings he was taking a solitary pipe in his arbour, with the church in sight, and the churchyard wherein at no distant time he was to be laid in his last abode. Such musings induced a sense of sober piety,—of thankfulness for former blessings, contentment with the present, and humble yet sure and certain hope for futurity, which might vainly have been sought at prayer-meetings, or evening lectures, where indeed little good can ever be obtained without some deleterious admixture, or alloy of baser feelings.

The happiness which he had found in retirement was of a different kind from what he had contemplated: for the shades of evening were gathering when he reached the place of his long-wished-for rest, and the picture of it which had imprinted itself on his imagination was a morning view. But he had been prepared for this by that slow change of which we are not aware during its progress till we see it reflected in others, and are thus made conscious of it in ourselves; and he found a satisfaction in the station which he occupied there, too worthy in its nature to be called pride, and which had not entered into his anticipations. It is said to have been a saying of George the Third, that the happiest condition in which an Englishman could be placed, was just below that wherein it would have been necessary for him to act as a Justice of the Peace, and above that which would have rendered him liable to parochial duties. This was just Mr. Allison's position: there was nothing which brought him into rivalry or competition with the surrounding Squirarchy, and the yeomen and peasantry respected him for his own character, as well as for his name's-sake. He gave employment to more persons than when he was engaged in trade, and his indirect influence over them was greater; that of his sister was still more. The elders of the village remembered her in her youth, and loved her for what she then had been as well as for what she now was; the young looked up to her as the Lady Bountiful, to whom no one that needed advice or assistance ever applied in vain. She it was who provided those much-

* Isaac Commenus.

approved plum cakes, not the less savoury for being both homely and wholesome, the thought of which induced the children to look on to their Lent examination with hope, and prepare for it with alacrity. Those offices in a parish which are the province of the Clergyman's wife, when he has made choice of one who knows her duty and has both will and ability to discharge it, Miss Allison performed; and she rendered Mr. Bacon the farther, and to him individually the greater, service of imparting to his daughter those instructions which she had no mother to impart. Deborah could not have had a better teacher; but as the present chapter has extended to a sufficient length,

Diremo il resto in quel che vien dipoi,
*Per non venire a noja a me e voi.**

CHAPTER CIII.

A FEW PARTICULARS CONCERNING NO. 113. BISHOPSGATE-STREET-WITHIN; AND OF THE FAMILY AT THAXTED GRANGE.

Opinion is the rate of things,
From hence our peace doth flow;
I have a better fate than kings,
Because I think it so.

KATHARINE PHILIPS.

THE house wherein Mr. Allison realised by fair dealing and frugality the modest fortune which enabled him to repurchase the homestead of his fathers, is still a Tobacconist's, and has continued to be so from "the palmy days" of that trade, when King James vainly endeavoured by the expression of his royal dislike, to discountenance the newly-imported practice of smoking; and Joshua Sylvester thundered from Mount Helicon a Volley of Holy Shot, thinking that thereby "Tobacco" should be "battered, and the Pipes shattered, about their ears that idly idolize so base and barbarous a weed, or at least-wise overlove so loathsome vanity."† For he said,

If there be any Herb in any place
Most opposite to God's good Herb of Grace;
'Tis doubtless this; and this doth plainly prove it,
That for the most, most graceless men do love it.

Yet it was not long before the dead and unsavoury odour of that weed, to which a Parisian was made to say that "sea-coal smoke seemed a very Portugal perfume," prevailed as much in the raiment of the more coarsely-clad part of the community, as the scent of lavender among those who were clothed in fine linen, and fared sumptuously every day: and it had grown so much in fashion, that it was said children "began to play with broken pipes, instead of corals, to make way for their teeth."

Louis XIV. endeavoured just as ineffectually to discourage the use of snuff-taking. His *valets de chambre* were obliged to renounce it when they were appointed to their office; and the Duke of Harcourt was supposed to have died of apoplexy in consequence of having, to please his Majesty, left off at once a habit which he had carried to excess.

I know not through what intermediate hands the business at No. 113. has passed, since the name of Allison was withdrawn from the firm; nor whether Mr. Evans, by whom it is now carried on there, is in any way related by descent with that family. Matters of no greater importance to most men have been made the subject of much antiquarian investigation; and they who busy themselves in such investigations must not be said to be ill-employed, for they find harmless amusement in the pursuit, and sometimes put up a chance truth of which others, soon or late, discover the application. The house has at this time a more antiquated appearance than any other in that part of the street, though it was modernised some forty or fifty years after Mr. Bacon's friend left it. The first floor then projected several feet farther over the street than at present, and the second several feet farther over the first; and the windows, which still extend the whole breadth of the front, were then composed of small casement panes. But in the progress of those improvements which are now carrying on in the city with as much

---

* ORLANDO INNAMORATO.

† Old Burton's was a modified opinion. See Anatomie of Melancholy, part ii. § 2. mem. 2. subs. 2.

spirit as at the western end of the metropolis, and which have almost reached Mr. Evans's door, it cannot be long before the house will be either wholly removed, or so altered as no longer to be recognised.

The present race of Londoners little know what the appearance of the city was a century ago;—their own city, I was about to have said; but it was the city of their great grandfathers, not theirs, from which the elder Allisons retired in the year 1746. At that time the kennels (as in Paris) were in the middle of the street, and there were no foot-paths; spouts projected the rain-water in streams against which umbrellas, if umbrellas had been then in use, could have afforded no defence; and large signs, such as are now only to be seen at country inns, were suspended before every shop *, from posts which impeded the way, or from iron supports strongly fixed into the front of the house. The swinging of one of these broad signs, in a high wind, and the weight of the iron on which it acted, sometimes brought the wall down; and it is recorded that one front-fall of this kind in Fleet Street maimed several persons, and killed "two young ladies, a cobler, and the King's Jeweller."

The sign at No. 113. was an Indian Chief, smoking the calumet. Mr. Allison had found it there; and when it became necessary that a new one should be substituted, he retained the same figure,—though, if he had been to choose, he would have greatly preferred the head of Sir Walter Raleigh, by whom, according to the common belief, he supposed tobacco had been introduced into this country. The Water-Poet imputed it to the Devil himself, and published

A Proclamation,
Or Approbation,
From the King of Execration
To every Nation,
For Tobacco's propagation.

Mr. Allison used to shake his head at such libellous aspersions. Raleigh was a great favourite with him, and held, indeed, in especial respect, though not as the Patron of his old trade, as St. Crispin is of the Gentle Craft, yet as the founder of his fortune. He thought it proper, therefore, that he should possess Sir Walter's History of the World, though he had never found inclination, or summoned up resolution, to undertake its perusal.

Common sense has been defined by Sir Egerton Brydges, "to mean nothing more than an uneducated judgement, arising from a plain and coarse understanding, exercised upon common concerns, and rendered effective rather by experience, than by any regular process of the intellectual powers. If this," he adds, "be the proper meaning of that quality, we cannot wonder that books are little fitted for its cultivation." Except that there was no coarseness in his nature, this would apply to Mr. Allison. He had been bred up with the notion that it behoved him to attend to his business, and that reading formed no part of it. Nevertheless he had acquired some liking for books by looking casually now and then over the leaves of those unfortunate volumes with which the shop was continually supplied for its daily consumption.

——Many a load of criticism,
Elaborate products of the midnight toil
Of Belgian brains,*

went there; and many a tome of old law, old physic, and old divinity; old history as well; books of which many were at all times rubbish; some, which though little better, would now sell for more shillings by the page than they then cost pence by the pound; and others, the real value of which is perhaps as little known now, as it was then. Such of these as in latter years caught his attention, he now and then rescued from the remorseless use to which they had been condemned. They made a curious assortment with his wife's books of devotion or amusement, wherewith she had sometimes beguiled, and sometimes soothed the weary hours of long and frequent illness. Among the former were Scott's "Christian

* The counting of these signs "from Temple Bar to the furthest Conduit in Cheapside," &c., is quoted as a remarkable instance of Fuller's Memory. Life, &c. p. 76. Ed. 1662.

* Akenside.

Life," Bishop Bayly's "Practice of Piety," Bishop Taylor's "Holy Living and Dying," Drelincourt on Death, with De Foe's lying story of Mrs. Veal's ghost as a puff preliminary, and the Night Thoughts. Among the latter were Cassandra, the Guardian and Spectator, Mrs. Rowe's Letters, Richardson's Novels and Pomfret's Poems.

Mrs. Allison had been able to do little for her daughter of that little, which, if her state of health and spirits had permitted, she might have done; this, therefore, as well as the more active duties of the household, devolved upon Elizabeth, who was of a better constitution in mind as well as body. Elizabeth, before she went to reside with her brother, had acquired all the accomplishments which a domestic education in the country could in those days impart. Her book of receipts, culinary and medical, might have vied with the "Queen's Cabinet Unlocked." The spelling indeed was such as ladies used in the reign of Queen Anne, and in the old time before her, when every one spelt as she thought fit; but it was written in a well-proportioned Italian hand, with fine down-strokes and broad upones, equally distinct and beautiful. Her speech was good Yorkshire, that is to say, good provincial English, not the worse for being provincial, and a little softened by five-and-twenty years' residence in London. Some sisters, who in those days kept a boarding-school, of the first repute, in one of the midland counties, used to say, when they spoke of an old pupil, "*her went to school to we.*" Miss Allison's language was not of this kind,—it savoured of rusticity, not of ignorance; and where it was peculiar, as in the metropolis, it gave a raciness to the conversation of an agreeable woman.

She had been well instructed in ornamental work as well as ornamental penmanship. Unlike most fashions, this had continued to be in fashion because it continued to be of use; though no doubt some of the varieties which Taylor, the Water-Poet, enumerates in his praise of the Needle, might have been then as little understood as now:—

Tent-work, Raised-work, Laid-work, Prest-work, Net-work,
Most curious Pearl, or rare Italian Cut-work,
Fine Fern-stitch, Finny-stitch, New-stitch and Chain-stitch,
Brave Bred-stitch, Fisher-stitch, Irish-stitch and Queen-stitch,
The Spanish-stitch, Rosemary-stitch and Maw-stich,
The smarting Whip-stitch, Back-stitch and the Cross-stitch.
All these are good, and these we must allow;
And these are every where in practice now.

There was a book published in the Water Poet's days, with the title of "School House for the Needle;" it consisted of two volumes in oblong quarto, that form being suited to its plates "of sundry sorts of patterns and examples;" and it contained a "Dialogue in Verse between Diligence and Sloth." If Betsey Allison had studied in this "School House," she could not have been a greater proficient with the needle than she became under her Aunt's teaching: nor would she have been more

—— versed in the arts
Of pies, puddings, and tarts,*

if she had gone through a course of practical lessons in one of the Pastry Schools which are common in Scotland, but were tried without success in London, about the middle of the last century. Deborah partook of these instructions at her father's desire. In all that related to the delicacies of a country table, she was glad to be instructed, because it enabled her to assist her friend; but it appeared strange to her that Mr. Bacon should wish her to learn ornamental work, for which she neither had, nor could foresee any use. But if the employment had been less agreeable than she found it in such company, she would never have disputed, nor questioned his will.

For so small a household, a more active or cheerful one could nowhere have been found than at the Grange. Ben Jonson reckoned among the happinesses of Sir Robert Wroth, that of being "with unbought provision blest." This blessing Mr. Allison enjoyed in as great a degree as his position in life permitted; he neither killed his own meat nor grew his own corn; but he had his poultry yard, his garden and his

* T. Warton.

orchard; he baked his own bread, brewed his own beer, and was supplied with milk, cream and butter from his own dairy. It is a fact not unworthy of notice, that the most intelligent farmers in the neighbourhood of London are persons who have taken to farming as a business, because of their strong inclination for rural employments; one of the very best in Middlesex, when the Survey of that County was published by the Board of Agriculture, had been a Tailor. Mr. Allison did not attempt to manage the land which he kept in his own hands; but he had a trusty bailiff, and soon acquired knowledge enough for superintending what was done. When he retired from trade he gave over all desire for gain, which indeed he had never desired for its own sake; he sought now only wholesome occupation, and those comforts which may be said to have a moral zest. They might be called luxuries, if that word could be used in a virtuous sense without something so to qualify it. It is a curious instance of the modification which words undergo in different countries, that luxury has always a sinful acceptation in the southern languages of Europe, and lust an innocent one in the northern; the harmless meaning of the latter word, we have retained in the verb *to list*.

Every one who looks back upon the scenes of his youth has one spot upon which the last light of the evening sunshine rests. The Grange was that spot in Deborah's retrospect.

CHAPTER CIV.

A REMARKABLE EXAMPLE, SHOWING THAT A WISE MAN, WHEN HE RISES IN THE MORNING, LITTLE KNOWS WHAT HE MAY DO BEFORE NIGHT.

> —— Now I love,
> And so as in so short a time I may;
> Yet so as time shall never break that so,
> And therefore so accept of Elinor.
>
> ROBERT GREENE.

ONE summer evening the Doctor on his way back from a visit in that direction, stopped, as on such opportunities he usually did, at Mr. Bacon's wicket, and looked in at the open casement to see if his friends were within. Mr. Bacon was sitting there alone, with a book open on the table before him; and looking round when he heard the horse stop, "Come in Doctor," said he, "if you have a few minutes to spare. You were never more welcome."

The Doctor replied, "I hope nothing ails either Deborah or yourself?" "No," said Mr. Bacon, "God be thanked! but something has occurred which concerns both."

When the Doctor entered the room, he perceived that the wonted serenity of his friend's countenance was overcast by a shade of melancholy thought; "Nothing," said he, "I hope has happened to distress you?" —"Only to disturb us," was the reply. "Most people would probably think that we ought to consider it a piece of good fortune. One who would be thought a good match for her, has proposed to marry Deborah."

"Indeed!" said the Doctor; "and who is he?" feeling, as he asked the question, an unusual warmth in his face.

"Joseph Hebblethwaite, of the Willows. He broke his mind to me this morning, saying that he thought it best to speak with me before he made any advances himself to the young woman: indeed he had had no opportunity of so doing, for he had seen little of her; but he had heard enough of her character to believe that she would make him a good wife; and this, he said, was all he looked for, for he was well to do in the world."

"And what answer did you make to this matter-of-fact way of proceeding?"

"I told him that I commended the very proper course he had taken, and that I was obliged to him for the good opinion of my daughter which he was pleased to entertain: that marriage was an affair in which I should never attempt to direct her inclinations, being confident that she would never give me cause to oppose them; and that I would talk with her upon the proposal, and let him know the result. As soon as I mentioned it to Deborah, she coloured up to her eyes; and with an angry look, of which I did not think those eyes had been capable, she desired me to tell him that he had better lose no time in looking elsewhere, for his thinking of her was of no use. 'Do you know any ill of him?' said I; 'No,' she replied, 'but I never heard any good, and that's ill enough. And I do not like his looks.'"

"Well said, Deborah!" cried the Doctor: clapping his hands so as to produce a sonorous token of satisfaction.

"'Surely, my child,' said I, 'he is not an ill-looking person?' 'Father,' she replied, 'you know he looks as if he had not one idea in his head to keep company with another.'"

"Well said, Deborah!" repeated the Doctor.

"Why Doctor, do you know any ill of him?"

"None. But as Deborah says, I know no good; and if there had been any good to be known, it must have come within my knowledge. I cannot help knowing who the persons are to whom the peasantry in my rounds look with respect and good will, and whom they consider their friends as well as their betters. And in like manner, I know who they are from whom they never expect either courtesy or kindness."

"You are right, my friend; and Deborah is right. Her answer came from a wise heart; and I was not sorry that her determination was so promptly made, and so resolutely pronounced. But I wish, if it had pleased God, the offer had been one which she could have accepted with her own willing consent, and with my full approbation."

"Yet," said the Doctor, "I have often thought how sad a thing it would be for you ever to part with her."

"Far more sad will it be for me to leave her unprotected, as it is but too likely that, in the ordinary course of nature, I one day shall; and as any day in that same ordinary course, I so possibly may! Our best intentions, even when they have been most prudentially formed, fail often in their issue. I meant to train up Deborah in the way she should go, by fitting her for that state of life in which it had pleased God to place her, so that she might have made a good wife for some honest man in the humbler walks of life, and have been happy with him."

"And how was it possible," replied the Doctor, "that you could have succeeded better? Is she not qualified to be a good man's wife in any rank? Her manner would not do discredit to a mansion; her management would make a farm prosperous, or a cottage comfortable; and for her principles, and temper and cheerfulness, they would render any home a happy one."

"You have not spoken too highly in her praise, Doctor. But as she has from her childhood been all in all to me, there is a danger that I may have become too much so to her; and that while her habits have properly been made conformable to our poor means, and her poor prospects, she has been accustomed to a way of thinking, and a kind of conversation, which have given her a distaste for those whose talk is only of sheep and of oxen, and whose thoughts never get beyond the range of their every day employments. In her present circle, I do not think there is one man with whom she might otherwise have had a chance of settling in life, to whom she would not have the same intellectual objections as to Joseph Hebblethwaite: though I am glad that the moral objection was that which first instinctively occurred to her.

"I wish it were otherwise, both for her sake and my own; for hers, because the present separation would have more than enough to compensate it, and would in its consequences mitigate the evil of the final one, whenever that may be; for my own, because I should then have no cause whatever to render the prospect of dissolution otherwise than welcome, but be as willing to die as to sleep. It is not owing to any distrust in Providence, that I am not thus willing now,—God forbid! But if I gave heed to my own feelings, I should think that I am not long for this world; and surely it were wise to remove, if possible, the only cause that makes me fear to think so."

"Are you sensible of any symptoms that

can lead to such an apprehension?" said the Doctor.

"Of nothing that can be called a symptom. I am to all appearance in good health, of sound body and mind; and you know how unlikely my habits are to occasion any disturbance in either. But I have indefinable impressions, — sensations they might almost be called, — which as I cannot but feel them, so I cannot but regard them."

"Can you not describe these sensations?"

"No better than by saying that they hardly amount to sensations, and are indescribable."

"Do not," said the Doctor, "I entreat you, give way to any feelings of this kind. They may lead to consequences, which, without shortening or endangering life, would render it anxious and burthensome, and destroy both your usefulness and your comfort."

"I have this feeling, Doctor; and you shall prescribe for it, if you think it requires either regimen or physic. But at present you will do me more good by assisting me to procure for Deborah such a situation as she must necessarily look for on the event of my death. What I have laid by, even if it should be most advantageously disposed of, would afford her only a bare subsistence; it is a resource in case of sickness, but while in health, it would never be her wish to eat the bread of idleness. You may have opportunities of learning whether any lady within the circle of your practice wants a young person in whom she might confide, either as an attendant upon herself, or to assist in the management of her children, or her household. You may be sure this is not the first time that I have thought upon the subject; but the circumstance which has this day occurred, and the feeling of which I have spoken, have pressed it upon my consideration. And the inquiry may better be made and the step taken while it is a matter of foresight, than when it has become one of necessity."

"Let me feel your pulse!"

"You will detect no other disorder there," said Mr. Bacon, holding out his arm as he spake, "than what has been caused by this conversation, and the declaration of a purpose, which though for some time perpended, I had never till now fully acknowledged to myself."

"You have never then mentioned it to Deborah?"

"In no other way than by sometimes incidentally speaking of the way of life which would be open to her, in case of her being unmarried at my death."

"And you have made up your mind to part with her?"

"Upon a clear conviction that I ought to do so; that it is best for herself and me."

"Well then, you will allow me to converse with her first, upon a different subject. — You will permit me to see whether I can speak more successfully for myself, than you have done for Joseph Hebblethwaite. — Have I your consent?"

Mr. Bacon rose in great emotion, and taking his friend's hand pressed it fervently and tremulously. Presently they heard the wicket open, and Deborah came in.

"I dare say, Deborah," said her father, composing himself, "you have been telling Betsy Allison of the advantageous offer that you have this day refused."

"Yes," replied Deborah; "and what do you think she said? That little as she likes him, rather than that I should be thrown away upon such a man, she could almost make up her mind to marry him herself."

"And I," said the Doctor, "rather than such a man should have you would marry you myself."

"Was not I right in refusing him, Doctor?"

"So right, that you never pleased me so well before; and never can please me better, — unless you will accept of me in his stead."

She gave a little start, and looked at him half incredulously, and half angrily withal; as if what he had said was too light in its manner to be serious, and yet too serious in its import to be spoken in jest. But when he took her by the hand, and said, "Will you, dear Deborah?" with a pressure, and in a tone that left no doubt of his earnest meaning, she cried, "Father, what am I to say? speak for me!"—"Take her, my friend!" said Mr. Bacon; "My blessing be upon you both. And if it be not presumptuous to use the words,—let me say for myself, 'Lord, now lettest thou thy servant depart in peace!'"

CHAPTER CV.

A WORD OF NOBS, AND AN ALLUSION TO CÆSAR. SOME CIRCUMSTANCES RELATING TO THE DOCTOR'S SECOND LOVE, WHEREBY THOSE OF HIS THIRD AND LAST ARE ACCOUNTED FOR.

Un mal que se entra por medio los ojos,
Y va se derecho hasta el corazon;
Alli en ser llegado se torna aficion,
Y da mil pesares, plazeres y enojos:
Causa alegrias, tristezas, antojos;
Haze llorar, y haze reir,
Haze cantar, y haze plañir,
Da pensamientos dos mil a manojos.

QUESTION DE AMOR.

"NOBS," said the Doctor, as he mounted and rode away from Mr. Bacon's garden gate, "when I alighted and fastened thee to that wicket, I thought as little of what was to befal me then, and what I was about to do, as thou knowest of it now."

Man has an inward voice as well as an "inward eye,"* a voice distinct from that of conscience. It is the companion, if not "the bliss of solitude;"* and though he sometimes employs it to deceive himself, it gives him good counsel perhaps quite as often, calls him to account, reproves him for having left unsaid what he ought to have said, or for having said what he ought not to have said, reprehends or approves, admonishes or encourages. On this occasion it was a joyful and gratulatory voice, with which the Doctor spake mentally, first to Nobs and afterwards to himself, as he rode back to Doncaster.

* WORDSWORTH.

By this unuttered address the reader would perceive, if he should haply have forgotten what was intimated in some of the ante-initial chapters, and in the first post-initial one, that the Doctor had a horse, named Nobs; and the question Who was Nobs, would not be necessary, if this were all that was to be said concerning him. There is much to be said; the tongue that could worthily express his merits had need be like the pen of a ready writer; though I will not say of him as Berni or Boiardo has said of

— quel valeroso e bel destriero,

Argalia's horse, Rubicano, that

Un che volesse dir lodando il vero,
Bisogno aria di parlar piu ch' umano.

At present, however, I shall only say this in his praise, he was altogether unlike the horse of whom it was said he had only two faults, that of being hard to catch, and that of being good for nothing when he was caught. For whether in stable or in field, Nobs would come like a dog to his master's call. There was not a better horse for the Doctor's purpose in all England; no, nor in all Christendom; no, nor in all Houyhnhnmdom, if that country had been searched to find one.

Cæsarem vehis, said Cæsar to the Egyptian boatman. But what was that which the Egyptian boat carried, compared to what Nobs bore upon that saddle to which constant use had given its polish bright and brown?

Virtutem solidi pectoris hospitam
Idem portat equus, qui dominum.†

Nobs therefore carried—all that is in these volumes; yea, and as all future generations were, according to Madame Bourignon, actually as well as potentially, contained in Adam,—all editions and translations of them, however numerous.

But on that evening he carried something of more importance; for on the life and weal of his rider there depended from that hour, as far as its dependence was upon any-

† CASIMIR.

thing earthly, the happiness of one of the best men in the world, and of a daughter who was not unworthy of such a father. If the Doctor had been thrown from his horse and killed, an hour or two earlier, the same day, it would have been a dreadful shock both to Deborah and Mr. Bacon; and they would always have regretted the loss of one whose company they enjoyed, whose character they respected, and for whom they entertained a feeling of more than ordinary regard. But had such a casualty occurred now, it would have been the severest affliction that could have befallen them.

Yet till that hour Deborah had never thought of Dove as a husband, nor Dove of Deborah as a wife — that is, neither had ever looked at the possibility of their being one day united to each other in that relation. Deborah liked him, and he liked her; and beyond this sincere liking neither of them for a moment dreamed that the inclination would ever proceed. They had not fallen in love with each other; nor had they run in love, nor walked into it, nor been led into it, nor entrapped into it; nor had they caught it.

How then came they to be in love at last? The question may be answered by an incident which Mr. John Davis relates in his Travels of Four Years and a Half in the United States of America. The traveller was making his way "faint and wearily" on foot to a place called by the strange name of Frying Pan, — for the Americans have given all sorts of names, except fitting ones, to the places which they have settled, or discovered, and their Australian kinsmen seem to be following the same absurd and inconvenient course. It will occasion, hereafter, as much confusion as the sameness of Mahommedan proper names, in all ages and countries, causes in the history of all Mahommedan nations. Mr. Davis had walked till he was tired without seeing any sign of the place at which he expected long before to have arrived. At length he met a lad in the wilderness, and asked him, "how far, my boy, is it to Frying Pan?" The boy replied, "you be in the Pan now."

So it was with the Doctor and with Deborah; — they found themselves in love, as much to their surprise as it was to the traveller when he found himself in the Pan, and much more to their satisfaction. And upon a little after reflection they both perceived how they came to be so.

> There's a chain of causes
> Link'd to effects, — invincible necessity
> That whate'er is, could not but so have been.*

Into such questions, however, I enter not. "*Nolo altum sapere*," they be matters above my capacity: the Cobler's check shall never light on my head, "*Ne sutor ultra crepidam.*"† Opportunity, which makes thieves‡, makes lovers also, and is the greatest of all match-makers. And when opportunity came, the Doctor,

> *Por ubbidir chi sempre ubbidir debbe*
> *La mente*, §

acted promptly. Accustomed as he was to weigh things of moment in the balance, and hold it with as even and as nice a hand, as if he were compounding a prescription on which the life of a patient might depend, he was no shillishallier, nor ever wasted a precious minute in pro-and-conning, when it was necessary at once to decide and act.

> *Chi ha tempo, e tempo aspetta, il tempo perde.*‖

His first love, as the reader will remember, came by inoculation, and was taken at first sight. This third and last, he used to say, came by inoculation also; but it was a more remarkable case, for eleven years elapsed before there was an appearance of his having taken the infection. How it happened that an acquaintance of so many years, and which at its very commencement had led to confidence, and esteem, and familiarity, and friendship, should have led no farther, may easily be explained. Dove, when he first saw Deborah, was in love with another person.

He had attended poor Lucy Bevan from the eighteenth year of her age, when a ten-

* Dryden. † Thomas Lodge.
‡ *Tilfald gjör Tjufen.* Swedish Proverb.
§ Pulci. ‖ Serafino da L'Aquila.

dency to consumption first manifested itself in her, till the twenty-fifth, when she sunk under that slow and insidious malady. She, who for five of those seven years, fancied herself during every interval, or mitigation of the disease, restored to health, or in the way of recovery, had fixed her affections upon him. And he who had gained those affections by his kind and careful attendance upon a case of which he soon saw cause to apprehend the fatal termination, becoming aware of her attachment as he became more and more mournfully convinced that no human skill could save her, found himself unawares engaged in a second passion, as hopeless as his first. That had been wilful; this was equally against his will and his judgment: that had been a folly, this was an affliction. And the only consolation which he found in it was, that the consciousness of loving and of being beloved, which made him miserable, was a happiness to her as long as she retained a hope of life, or was capable of feeling satisfaction in anything relating to this world. Caroline Bowles, whom no authoress or author has ever surpassed in truth, and tenderness, and sanctity of feeling, could relate such a story as it ought to be related, — if stories which in themselves are purely painful ought ever to be told. I will not attempt to tell it: — for I wish not to draw upon the reader's tears, and have none to spare for it myself.

This unhappy attachment, though he never spoke of it, being always but too certain in what it must end, was no secret to Mr. Bacon and his daughter: and when death had dissolved the earthly tie, it seemed to them, as it did to himself, that his affections were wedded to the dead. It was likely that the widower should think so, judging of his friend's heart by his own.

> Sorrow and Time will ever paint too well
> The lost when hopeless, all things loved in vain.*

His feelings upon such a point had been expressed for him by a most prolific and unequal writer, whose poems, more perhaps than those of any other English author, deserve to be carefully winnowed, the grain, which is of the best quality, being now lost amid the heap of chaff.

> Lord keep me faithful to the trust
>   Which my dear spouse reposed in me:
> To her now dead, preserve me just
>   In all that should performed be.
> For tho' our being man and wife
> Extendeth only to this life,
> Yet neither life nor death should end
> The being of a faithful friend.†

The knowledge that the Doctor's heart was thus engaged at the time of their first acquaintance, had given to Deborah's intercourse with him an easy frankness which otherwise might perhaps not have been felt, and could not have been assumed; and the sister-like feeling into which this had grown underwent no change after Lucy Bevan's death. He meantime saw that she was so happy with her father, and supposed her father's happiness so much depended upon her, that to have entertained a thought of separating them (even if the suitableness of such a marriage in other respects had ever entered into his imagination), would have seemed to him like a breach of friendship. Yet, if Mr. Bacon had died before he opened his mind to the Doctor upon occasion of Joseph Hebblethwaite's proposal, it is probable that one of the first means of consolation which would have occurred to him, would have been to offer the desolate daughter a home, together with his hand; so well was he acquainted with her domestic merits, so highly did he esteem her character, and so truly did he admire the gifts with which Nature had endowed her,—

> — her sweet humour
> That was as easy as a calm, and peaceful;
> All her affections, like the dews on roses,
> Fair as the flowers themselves, as sweet and gentle.‡

* Robert Landor.

† Wither.

‡ Beaumont and Fletcher.

INTERCHAPTER XII.

THE AUTHOR REGRETS THAT HE CANNOT MAKE HIMSELF KNOWN TO CERTAIN READERS; STATES THE POSSIBLE REASONS FOR HIS SECRECY; MAKES NO USE IN SO DOING OF THE LICENCE WHICH HE SEEMS TO TAKE OUT IN HIS MOTTO; AND STATING THE PRETENCES WHICH HE ADVANCES FOR HIS WORK, DISCLAIMING THE WHILE ALL MERIT FOR HIMSELF, MODESTLY PRESENTS THEM UNDER A GRECIAN VEIL.

Ενθα γάρ τι δεῖ ψεῦδος λέγεσθαι λεγέσθω.
HERODOTUS.

THERE is more gratitude in the world than the worldly believe, or than the ungrateful are capable of believing. And knowing this, I consequently know how great a sacrifice I make in remaining incognito.

Reputation is a bubble upon the rapid stream of time; popularity, a splash in the great pool of oblivion; fame itself but a full-blown bladder, or at best a balloon. There is no sacrifice in declining them; for in escaping these you escape the impertinences and the intrusions which never fail to follow in their train. But that this book will find some readers after the Author's own heart is certain; they will lose something in not knowing who the individual is with whom they would delight to form a personal, as they have already formed a moral and intellectual friendship;

For in this world, to reckon every thing,
Pleasure to man there is none comparable
As is to read with understanding
In books of wisdom, they ben so delectable
Which sound to virtue, and ben profitable.*

And though my loss is not of this kind, yet it is great also, for in each of these unknown admirers I lose the present advantage of a well-wisher, and the possible, or even probable benefit of a future friend.

Eugenius! Eusebius! Sophron! how gladly would ye become acquainted with my outward man, and commune with me face to face! How gladly would ye, Sophronia! Eusebia! Eugenia!

With how radiant a countenance and how light a step would Euphrosyne advance to greet me! with how benign an aspect would Amanda silently thank me for having held up a mirror in which she has unexpectedly seen herself!

Letitia's eyes would sparkle at the sight of one whose writings had given her new joy. Penserosa would requite me with a gentle look for cheering her solitary hours, and moving her sometimes to a placid smile, sometimes to quiet and pleasurable tears.

And you, Marcellus, from whom your friends, your country, and your kind have everything to hope, how great a pleasure do I forego by rendering it impossible for you to seek me, and commence an acquaintance with the sure presentiment that it would ripen into confidence and friendship!

There is another and more immediate gratification which this resolution compels me to forego, that of gratifying those persons who, if they knew from whom the book proceeded, would peruse it with heightened zest for its author's sake; — old acquaintance who would perceive in some of those secondary meanings which will be understood only by those for whom they were intended, that though we have long been widely separated, and probably are never again to meet in this world, they are not forgotten; and old friends, who would take a livelier interest in the reputation which the work obtains, than it would now be possible for me to feel in it myself.

"And why, Sir," says an obliging and inquisitive reader, "should you deprive your friends and acquaintance of that pleasure, though you are willing to sacrifice it yourself?"

"Why, Sir, — do you ask?"

Ah that is the mystery
Of this wonderful history,
And you wish that you could tell!†

"A question not to be asked," said an odder person than I shall ever pretend to be, "is a question not to be answered."

Nevertheless, gentle reader, in courtesy I

* TREVISA.

† SOUTHEY.

will give sundry answers to your interrogation, and leave you to fix upon which of them you may think likely to be the true one.

The Author may be of opinion that his name, not being heretofore known to the public, could be of no advantage to his book.

Or, on the other hand, if his name were already well known, he might think the book stands in no need of it, and may safely be trusted to its own merits. He may wish to secure for it a fairer trial than it could otherwise obtain, and intend to profit by the unbiassed opinions which will thus reach his ear; thinking complacently with Benedict, that "happy are they that hear their detractions, and can put them to mending." In one of Metastasio's dramatic epithalamiums, Minerva says,

—l'onore, a cui
Venni proposta anch' io
Piu meritar, che conseguir desio ;

and he might say this with the Goddess of Wisdom.

He may be so circumstanced that it would be inconvenient as well as unpleasant for him to offend certain persons,—Sir Andrew Agnewites for example,—whose conscientious but very mischievous notions he nevertheless thinks it his duty to oppose, when he can do so consistently with discretion.

He may have wagers dependent upon the guesses that will be made concerning him.

Peradventure it might injure him in his professional pursuits, were he to be known as an author, and that he had neglected "some sober calling for this idle trade."

He may be a very modest man, who can muster courage enough for publication, and yet dares not encounter any farther publicity.

Unknown, perhaps his reputation
Escapes the tax of defamation,
And wrapt in darkness, laughs unhurt,
While critic blockheads throw their dirt;
But he who madly prints his name,
Invites his foe to take sure aim.*

He may be so shy, that if his book were praised he would shrink from the notoriety into which it would bring him; or so sensitive, that his mortification would be extreme if it were known among his neighbours that he had been made the subject of sarcastic and contemptuous criticism.

Or if he ever possessed this diffidence he may have got completely rid of it in his intercourse with the world, and have acquired that easy habit of simulation without which no one can take his degree as Master of Arts in that great University. To hear the various opinions concerning the book and the various surmises concerning the author, take part in the conversation, mystifying some of his acquaintance and assist others in mystifying themselves, may be more amusing to him than any amusement of which he could partake in his own character. There are some secrets which it is a misery to know, and some which the tongue itches to communicate; but this is one which it is a pleasure to know and to keep. It gives to the possessor, *quasically* speaking, a double existence: the exoteric person mingles, as usual, in society, while the esoteric is like John the Giganticide in his coat of darkness, or that knight who in the days of King Arthur used to walk invisible.

The best or the worst performer at a masquerade may have less delight in the consciousness or conceit of their own talents, than he may take in conversing with an air of perfect unconcern about his own dear book. It may be sport for him to hear it scornfully condemned by a friend, and pleasure to find it thoroughly relished by an enemy.

The secrets of nature
Have not more gift in taciturnity.†

Peradventure he praises it himself with a sincerity for which every reader will give him full credit; or peradventure he condemns it, for the sake of provoking others to applaud it more warmly in defence of their own favourable and pre-expressed opinion. Whether of these courses, thinkest thou, gentle reader, is he most likely to pur-

* LLOYD.

† TROILUS and CRESSIDA.

sue? I will only tell thee that either would to him be equally easy and equally entertaining. "Ye shall know that we may dissemble in earnest as well as in sport, under covert and dark terms, and in learned and apparent speeches, in short sentences, and by long ambage and circumstance of words, and finally, as well when we lie, as when we tell truth."*

In any one of the supposed cases sufficient reason is shown for his keeping, and continuing to keep his own secret.

En nous formant, nature a ses caprices,
Divers penchans en nous elle fait observer.
Les uns, à s'exposer, trouvent mille délices;
Moi, j'en trouve à me conserver.†

And if there be any persons who are not satisfied with this explanation, I say to them, in the words of Jupiter,

—STET PRO RATIONE VOLUNTAS.

Moreover, resting my claim to the gratitude of this generation, and of those which are to come, upon the matter of these volumes, and disclaiming for myself all merit except that of fidelity to the lessons of my philosopher and friend, I shall not fear to appropriate, *mutatis mutandis*, and having thus qualified them, the proud words of Arrian:

Ἀλλ' ἐκεῖνο ἀναγράφω, ὅτι ἐμοὶ πατρίς τε, καὶ γένος, καὶ ἀρχαὶ, οἵδε οἱ λόγοι εἰσί τε — καὶ ἐπὶ τῷ δέ οὐκ ἀπαξιῶ ἐμαυτὸν τῶν πρώτων ἐν τῇ φωνῇ τῇ Ἀγγλίκῇ, εἴπερ οὖν καὶ Δανιὴλ ὁ ἰατρὸς ἐωὸς τῶν ἐν τοῖς φαρμάκοις.

INTERCHAPTER XIII.

A PEEP FROM BEHIND THE CURTAIN.

Ha, ha, ha, now ye will make me to smile,
To see if I can all men beguile.
Ha, my name, my name would ye so fain know?
Yea, I wis, shall ye, and that with all speed.
I have forgot it, therefore I cannot show.
A, a, now I have it! I have it indeed!
My name is Ambidexter, I signify one
That with both hands finely can play.
KING CAMBYSES.

BUT the question has been mooted in the literary and cerulean circles of the metropolis, whether this book be not the joint work of two or more authors. And this duality or plurality of persons in one authorship has been so confidently maintained, that if it were possible to yield upon such a point to any display of evidence and weight of authority, I must have been argued out of my own indivisible individuality.

Fort bien! Je le soutiens par la grande raison
Qu'ainsi l'a fait des Dieux la puissance suprême;
Et qu'il n'est pas en moi de pouvoir dire non,
Et d'etre un autre que moi-même.‡

Sometimes I have been supposed to be the unknown Beaumont of some equally unknown Fletcher,—the moiety of a Siamese duplicate; or the third part of a Geryonite triplicity; the fourth of a quaternion of partners, or a fifth of a Smectymnuan association. Nay, I know not whether they have not cut me down to the dimensions of a tailor, and dwindled me into the ninth part of an author!

Me to be thus served! me, who am an integral, to be thus split into fractions! me, a poor unit of humanity, to be treated like a polypus under the scissors of an experimental naturalist, or unnaturalist.

The reasons assigned in support of this pluri-personal hypothesis are, first, the supposed discrepancy of humour and taste apparent in the different parts of the book. Oh men ignorant of humorology! more ignorant of psychology! and most ignorant of Pantagruelism!

Secondly, the prodigal expenditure of mottoes and quotations, which they think could only have been supported by means of a pic-nic contribution. Oh men whose diligence is little, whose reading less, and whose sagacity least of all!

Yet looking at this fancy of the Public,—a creature entertained with many fancies, beset with many tormenting spirits, and provided with more than the four legs and two voices which were hastily attributed to the son of Sycorax;—a creature which, though it be the fashion of the times to seek for shelter under its gaberdine, is by this

* PUTTENHAM. † MOLIERE.

‡ MOLIERE.

good light, "a very shallow monster," "a most poor credulous monster!" — I say looking at this fancy of the Public in that temper with which it is my wish to regard everything, methinks I should be flattered by it, and pleased (if anything flattering could please me) by having it supposed upon such grounds, that this book, like the *Satyre Menippée*, is the composition of several *bons et gentils esprits du tems,—dans lequel souz paroles et allegations pleines de raillerie, ils boufonnerent, comme en riant le vray se peut dire*; and which *ils firent, selon leurs humeurs, caprices et intelligences, en telle sorte qu'il se peut dire qu'ils n'ont rien oublié de ce qui se peut dire pour servir de perfection à cet ouvrage, qui bien entendu sera grandement estimé par la posterité.**

The same thing occurred in the case of Gulliver's Travels, and in that case Arbuthnot thought reasonably; for, said he, "if this Book were to be decyphered, merely from a view of it, without any hints, or secret history, this would be a very natural conclusion: we should be apt to fancy it the production of two or three persons, who want neither wit nor humour; but who are very full of themselves, and hold the rest of mankind in great contempt; who think sufficient regard is not paid to their merit by those in power, for which reason they rail at them; who have written some pieces with success and applause, and therefore presume that whatever comes from them must be implicitly received by the public. In this last particular they are certainly right; for the superficial people of the Town, who have no judgment of their own, are presently amused by a great name: tell them, by way of a secret, that such a thing is Dr. Swift's, Mr. Pope's, or any other person's of note and genius, and immediately it flies about like wildfire."†

If the Book of the Doctor, instead of continuing to appear, as it originally went forth, *simplex munditiis*, with its own pithy, comprehensive, and well-considered title, were to have a name constructed for it of composite initials, like the joint-stock volume of the five puritanical ministers above referred to, once so well known, but now preserved from utter oblivion by nothing but that name, — *vox et præterea nihil;* — if, I say, the Book of the Doctor were in like manner to be denominated, according to one or other of the various schemes of bibliogony which have been devised for explaining its phenomena, the reader might be expected in good earnest to exclaim,

— Bless us! what a word on
A title page is this! —

For among other varieties, the following present themselves for choice:—

Isdis.
Roso.
Heta.
Harco.
Samro.
Grobe.
Theho.
Heneco.
Thojama.
Johofre.
Reverne.
Hetaroso.
Walaroso.
Rosogrobe.
Venarchly.
Satacoroso.
Samrothomo.
Verevfrawra.
Isdisbendis.
Harcoheneco.
Henecosaheco.
Thehojowicro.
Rosohenecoharco.
Thehojowicrogecro.
Harcohenecosaheco.
Satacoharcojotacohenecosaheco.

And thus, my monster of the Isle, while I have listened and looked on like a spectator at a game of blind-man's-buff, or at a blindfold boat-race, have you, with your errabund guesses, veering to all points of the literary compass, amused the many-hu-

* Cheverny. † Gulliver decyphered.

moured yet single-minded Pantagruelist, the quotationipotent mottocrat, the entire unit, the single and whole *homo*, who subscribes himself,

with all sincerity and good will,
Most delicate Monster,
and with just as much respect as you deserve,
not yours, or any body's humble Servant
(saving always that he is the king's dutiful subject),
and not yours, but his own, to command,
KEWINT-HEKA-WERNER.

CHAPTER CVI.

THE AUTHOR APOSTROPHIZES SOME OF HIS FAIR READERS; LOOKS FARTHER THAN THEY ARE LIKELY TO DO, AND GIVES THEM A JUST THOUGH MELANCHOLY EXHORTATION TO BE CHEERFUL WHILE THEY MAY.

Hark how the birds do sing,
And woods do ring!
All creatures have their joy, and Man hath his:
Yet, if we rightly measure,
Man's joy and pleasure
Rather hereafter, than in present is.
HERBERT.

BERTHA, Arabella, Sarah, Mary, Caroline, Dorothea, Elizabeth, Kate, Susan, — how many answer to these names, each thinking that peradventure she may be the individual especially addressed —

Alcun' è che risponde a chi nol chiama *;

you are looking with impatience for Deborah's wedding-day, and are ready to inveigh against me for not immediately proceeding to that part of my story. Well has Sir William Davenant said,

Slow seems their speed whose thoughts before them run;

but it is true in one sense as applied to you, and in another as applied to myself. To you my progress appears slow, because you are eager to arrive at what, rightly considering it the most important point upon the whole journey of life, you may, perhaps, expect to prove the most interesting in this volume. Your thoughts have sped forward to that point and no farther. Mine travel beyond it, and this, were there no other motive, would retard me now. You are thinking of the bride and bridegroom, and the bridesmaid, and the breakfast at the vicarage, and the wedding dinner at the Grange, and the Doncaster bells which rung that day to the Doctor's ears the happiest peal that ever saluted them, from St. George's tower. My thoughts are of a different complexion; for where now are the joys and the sorrows of that day, and where are all those by whom they were partaken! The elder Allisons have long since been gathered to their fathers. Betsey and her husband (whom at that day she had never seen) are inhabitants of a distant churchyard. Mr. Bacon's mortal part has mouldered in the same grave with Margaret's. The Doctor has been laid beside them; and thither his aged widow Deborah was long ago brought home, earth to earth, ashes to ashes, dust to dust.

"The deaths of some, and the marriages of others," says Cowper, "make a new world of it every thirty years. Within that space of time the majority are displaced, and a new generation has succeeded. Here and there one is permitted to stay longer, that there may not be wanting a few grave Dons like myself to make the observation."

Man is a self-survivor every year
Man like a stream is in perpetual flow.
Death's a destroyer of quotidian prey:
My youth, my noontide his, my yesterday;
The bold invader shares the present hour,
Each moment on the former shuts the grave.
While man is growing, life is in decrease,
And cradles rock us nearer to the tomb.
Our birth is nothing but our death begun,
As tapers waste that instant they take fire.†

Yet infinitely short as the term of human life is when compared with time to come, it is not so in relation to time past. An hundred and forty of our own generations carry us back to the Deluge, and nine more of antediluvian measure to the Creation, — which to us is the beginning of time; for

* PETRARCH.

† YOUNG.

"time itself is but a novelty, a late and upstart thing in respect of the Ancient of Days."* They who remember their grandfather and see their grandchildren, have seen persons belonging to five out of that number; and he who attains the age of threescore has seen two generations pass away. "The created world," says Sir Thomas Browne, "is but a small parenthesis in eternity, and a short interposition for a time, between such a state of duration as was before it, and may be after it." There is no time of life after we become capable of reflection, in which the world to come must not to any considerate mind appear of more importance to us than this; — no time in which we have not a greater stake there. When we reach the threshold of old age all objects of our early affections have gone before us, and in the common course of mortality a great proportion of the later. Not without reason did the wise compilers of our admirable Liturgy place next in order after the form of Matrimony, the services for the Visitation and Communion of the Sick, and for the Burial of the Dead.

I would not impress such considerations too deeply upon the young and happy. Far be it from me to infuse bitters into the cup of hope!

Dum fata sinunt
Vivite læti: properat cursu
Vita citato, volucrique die
Rota præcipitis vertitur anni.
Duræ peragunt pensa sorores,
Nec sua retro fila revolvunt. †

What the Spaniards call *desengaño* (which our dictionaries render "discovery of deceit, the act of undeceiving, or freeing from error," — and for which, if our language has an equivalent word, it is not in my vocabulary,) — that state of mind in which we understand feelingly the vanity of human wishes, and the instability of earthly joys, — that sad wisdom comes to all in time; but if it came too soon, it would unfit us for this world's business and the common intercourse of life. When it comes in due season, it fits us for a higher intercourse and for a happier state of existence.

*Samuel Johnson the elder. † Seneca.

CHAPTER CVII.

THE AUTHOR INTRODUCES HIS READERS TO A RETIRED DUCHESS, AND SUGGESTS A PARALLEL BETWEEN HER GRACE AND THE RETIRED TOBACCONIST.

In midst of plenty only to embrace
Calm patience, is not worthy of your praise;
But he that can look sorrow in the face
And not be daunted, he deserves the bays.
This is prosperity, where'er we find
A heavenly solace in an earthly mind.

Hugh Crompton.

There is a very pleasing passage in a letter of the Duchess of Somerset's, written in the unreserved intimacy of perfect friendship, without the slightest suspicion that it would ever find its way to the press. "'Tis true, my dear Lady Luxborough," she says, "times are changed with us, since no walk was long enough, or exercise painful enough, to hurt us as we childishly imagined; yet after a ball, or a masquerade, have we not come home very well contented to pull off our ornaments and fine clothes, in order to go to rest? Such, methinks, is the reception we naturally give to the warnings of our bodily decays; they seem to undress us by degrees, to prepare us for a rest that will refresh us far more powerfully than any night's sleep could do. We shall then find no weariness from the fatigues which either our bodies or our minds have undergone; but all tears shall be wiped from our eyes, and sorrow and crying and pain shall be no more: we shall then without weariness move in our new vehicles, and transport ourselves from one part of the skies to another, with much more ease and velocity than we could have done in the prime of our strength, upon the fleetest horses, the distance of a mile. This cheerful prospect enables us to see our strength fail, and await the tokens of our approaching dissolution with a kind of awful pleasure. I will ingenuously own to you, dear Madam, that I experience more true happiness in the retired manner of life that I have embraced, than I ever knew from all the splendour or flatteries of the world. There was always a void; they could not satisfy a rational mind: and at the most heedless time of my youth I well remember that I always looked forward with a kind of joy to a decent retreat when the evening of life should make it practicable."

"If one only anticipates far enough, one is sure to find comfort," said a young moraliser, who was then for the first time experiencing some of the real evils of life. A sense of its vanities taught the Duchess that wisdom, before she was visited with affliction. Frances, wife and widow of Algernon seventh Duke of Somerset, was a woman who might perhaps have been happier in a humbler station, but could not have been more uncorrupted by the world. Her husband inherited from his father the honours of the Seymour, from his mother those of the Percy family; but Lord Beauchamp, —

> Born with as much nobility as would,
> Divided, serve to make ten noblemen
> Without a herald; but with so much spirit
> And height of soul, as well might furnish twenty,—*

Lord Beauchamp I say, the son thus endowed, who should have succeeded to these accumulated honours, died on his travels at Bologna of the small-pox, in the flower of his youth. His afflicted mother in reply to a letter of consolation expressed herself thus: "The dear lamented son I have lost was the pride and joy of my heart: but I hope I may be the more easily excused for having looked on him in this light, since he was not so from the outward advantages he possessed, but from the virtues and rectitude of his mind. The prospects which flattered me in regard to him, were not drawn from his distinguished rank, or from the beauty of his person; but from the hopes that his example would have been serviceable to the cause of virtue, and would have shown the younger part of the world that it was possible to be cheerful without being foolish or vicious, and to be religious without severity or melancholy. His whole life was one uninterrupted course of duty and affection to his parents, and when he found the hand of death upon him, his only regret was to think on the agonies which must rend their hearts: for he was perfectly contented to leave the world, as his conscience did not reproach him with any presumptuous sins, and he hoped his errors would be forgiven. Thus he resigned his innocent soul into the hands of his merciful Creator on the evening of his birthday, which completed him nineteen."

In another letter she says, "when I lost my dear, and by me ever-lamented son, every faculty to please (if ever I were possessed of any such) died with him. I have no longer any cheerful thoughts to communicate to my friends; but as the joy and pride of my heart withers in his grave, my mind is continually haunting those mansions of the dead, and is but too inattentive to what passes in a world where I have still duties and attachments which I ought to be, and I hope I may truly say I am, thankful for. But I enjoy all these blessings with trembling and anxiety; for after my dear Beauchamp, what human things can appear permanent? Youth, beauty, virtue, health, were not sufficient to save him from the hand of death, and who then can think themselves secure? These are the melancholy considerations which generally entertain my waking hours; though sometimes I am able to view the bright side of my fate, and ask myself for whom I grieve? only for myself? how narrow an affection does this imply! Could he have lived long as my fondest wish desired, what could I have asked at the end of that term more than the assurance that he should be placed where I humbly hope, and confidently trust, he is, beyond the reach of sorrow, sin, or sickness?"

I have said that this Duchess, the Eusebia of Dr. Watts' Miscellanies, and once more known as the Cleora of her then famous friend Mrs. Rowe's Letters, might perhaps have been happier in a humbler station; but she could not have been more meek and more amiable, nor have possessed in a greater degree the Christian virtue of humility. She was one of the daughters and coheiresses of

* Shirley.

the Honourable Henry Thynne, and was of the bed-chamber to the Princess of Wales, in which office she continued after that Princess became Queen Caroline. It was through her intercession that Savage's life was spared. When the Queen being prejudiced against that wretched man had refused to hear any application in his behalf, "she engaged in it," says Johnson, "with all the tenderness that is excited by pity, and all the zeal that is kindled by generosity; an advocate," he calls her, "of rank too great to be rejected unheard, and of virtue too eminent to be heard without being believed." Her husband's father was commonly called the proud Duke of Somerset,—an odious designation, which could not have been obtained unless it had been richly deserved: but there are some evil examples which incidentally produce a good effect, and Lord Beauchamp, whose affability and amiable disposition endeared him to all by whom he was known, was perhaps more carefully instructed in the principles of Christian humility, and more sensible of their importance and their truth, because there was in his own family so glaring an instance of the folly and hatefulness of this preposterous and ridiculous sin. "It is a most terrible thing for his parents," says Horace Walpole, "Lord Beauchamp's death; if they were out of the question, one could not be sorry for such a mortification to the pride of old Somerset. He has written the most shocking letter imaginable to poor Lord Hartford, telling him that it is a judgment upon him for all his undutifulness, and that he must always look upon himself as the cause of his son's death. Lord Hartford is as good a man as lives, and has always been most unreasonably ill-treated by that old tyrant." The Duke was brute enough to say that his mother had sent him abroad to kill him. It was not his mother's fault that he had not been secured, as far as human precautions avail against the formidable disease of which he died. Three years before that event she said in one of her letters, "Inoculation is at present more in fashion than ever; half my acquaintance are shut up to nurse their children, grandchildren, nephews, or nieces. I could be content notwithstanding the fine weather to stay in town upon the same account, if I were happy enough to see my son desire it; but that is not the case, and at his age it must either be a voluntary act or left undone."

The proud Duke lived to the great age of eighty-six, and his son died little more than twelvemonths after him, leaving an irreproachable name. The Duchess survived her son ten years, and her husband four. Upon the Duke's death the Seymour honours were divided between two distant branches of that great and ancient house; those of the Percys devolved to his only daughter and heiress the Lady Elizabeth, then wife of Sir Hugh Smithson, in whom the Dukedom of Northumberland was afterwards revived. The widow passed the remainder of her days at a seat near Colnbrook, which her husband had purchased from Lord Bathurst, and had named Percy Lodge: Richkings was its former appellation. Pope in one of his letters calls it "Lord Bathurst's *extravagante bergerie*," in allusion to the title of an old mock-romance. "The environs," says the Duchess, "perfectly answer to that title, and come nearer to my idea of a scene in Arcadia than any place I ever saw. The house is old but convenient; and when you are got within the little paddock it stands on, you would believe yourself an hundred miles from London, which I think a great addition to its beauty." Moses Brown wrote a poem upon it, the Duke and Duchess having appointed him their laureate for the nonce; but though written by their command, it was not published till after the death of both, and was then inscribed to her daughter, at that time Countess of Northumberland. If Olney had not a far greater poet to boast of, it might perhaps have boasted of Moses Brown. Shenstone's Ode on Rural Elegance, which is one of his latest productions, related especially to this place. He inscribed it to the Duchess, and communicated it to her in manuscript through their mutual friend Lady Luxborough, sister to Bolingbroke, who possessed much of her brother's talents, but nothing of his cankered nature.

The Duchess was a great admirer of Shenstone's poetry, but though pleased with the poem, and gratified by the compliment, she told him that it had given her some pain, and requested that wherever her name or that of Percy Lodge occurred, he would oblige her by leaving a blank, without suspecting her of an affected or false modesty, for to that accusation she could honestly plead not guilty. The idea he had formed of her character, he had taken, she said, from a partial friend, whose good nature had warped her judgment. The world in general, since they could find no fault in his poem, would blame the choice of the person to whom it was inscribed, and draw mortifying comparisons between the ideal lady, and the real one. "But I," said she, "have a more impartial judge to produce than either my friend or the world,—and that is my own heart, which, though it may flatter me, I am not quite so faulty as the world would represent, at the same time loudly admonishes me that I am still further from the valuable person Lady Luxborough has drawn you in to suppose me. I hope you will accept these reasons as the genuine and most sincere sentiments of my mind, which indeed they are, though accompanied with the most grateful sense of the honour you designed me."

I have said something, and have yet more to say of a retired Tobacconist; and I will here describe the life of a retired Duchess, of the same time and country, drawn from her own letters. Some of Plutarch's parallels are less apposite, and none of them in like manner equally applicable to those of high station and those of low degree.

The duchess had acquired that taste for landscape gardening, the honour of introducing which belongs more to Shenstone than to any other individual, and has been properly awarded to him by D'Israeli, one of the most just and generous of critical authors. Thus she described the place of her retreat, when it came into their possession: "It stands in a little paddock of about a mile and a half round, which is laid out in the manner of a French park, interspersed with woods and lawns. There is a canal in it about twelve hundred yards long, and proportionably broad, which has a stream continually running through it, and is deep enough to carry a pleasure-boat. It is well stocked with carp and tench; and at its upper end there is a green-house, containing a good collection of orange, myrtle, geranium, and oleander trees. This is a very agreeable room, either to drink tea, play at cards, or sit in with a book on a summer's evening. In one of the woods (through all which there are winding paths), there is a cave, which, though little more than a rude heap of stones, is not without charms for me. A spring gushes out at the back of it; which, falling into a basin (whose brim it overflows), passes along a channel in the pavement where it loses itself. The entrance to this recess is overhung with periwinkle, and its top is shaded with beeches, large elms, and birch. There are several covered benches, and little arbours interwoven with lilacs, woodbines, seringas and laurels; and seats under shady trees, disposed all over the park. One great addition to the pleasure of living here, is the gravelly soil, which, after a day of rain (if it holds up only for two or three hours), one may walk over without being wet through one's shoes: and there is one gravel walk that encompasses the whole. We propose to make an improvement, by adding to the present ground a little pasture farm, which is just without the pale, because there is a very pretty brook of clear water which runs through the meadows to supply our canal, and whose course winds in such a manner that it is almost naturally a serpentine river. I am afraid I shall have tired you with the description of what appear to me beauties in our little possession; yet I cannot help adding one convenience that attends it,—this is, the cheap manner in which we keep it, since it only requires a flock of sheep, who graze the lawns fine; and whilst these are feeding, their shepherd cleans away any weeds that spring up in the gravel, and removes dry leaves or broken branches that would litter the walks.

"On the spot where the green-house now stands, there was formerly a chapel, dedicated to St. Leonard, who was certainly esteemed as a tutelar saint of Windsor Forest and its purlieus, for the place we left was originally a hermitage founded in honour of him. We have no relics of the saint; but we have an old covered bench with many remains of the wit of my lord Bathurst's visitors, who inscribed verses upon it. Here is the writing of Addison, Pope, Prior, Congreve, Gay, and what he esteemed no less, of several fine ladies. I cannot say that the verses answered my expectation from such authors; we have, however, all resolved to follow the fashion, and to add some of our own to the collection. That you may not be surprised at our courage for daring to write after such great names, I will transcribe one of the old ones, which I think as good as any of them:

> Who set the trees shall he remember
> That is in haste to fell the timber?
> What then shall of thy woods remain,
> Except the box that threw the main?

There has been only one added as yet by our company, which is tolerably numerous at present. I scarcely know whether it is worth reading or not:

> By Bathurst planted, first these shades arose;
> Prior and Pope have sung beneath these boughs:
> Here Addison his moral theme pursued,
> And social Gay has cheer'd the solitude.

There is one walk that I am extremely partial to, and which is rightly called the Abbey-walk, since it is composed of prodigiously high beech-trees, that form an arch through the whole length, exactly resembling a cloister. At the end is a statue; and about the middle a tolerably large circle, with Windsor chairs round it: and I think, for a person of contemplative disposition, one would scarcely find a more venerable shade in any poetical description."

She had amused herself with improving the grounds of Percy Lodge before her husband's death, as much for his delight as her own.

> Those shady elms, my favourite trees,
> Which near my Percy's window grew,
> (Studious his leisure hours to please)
> I decked last year for smell and shew;
> To each a fragrant woodbine bound,
> And edged with pinks the verdant mound.
>
> Nor yet the areas left ungraced
> Betwixt the borders and each tree;
> But on them damask roses placed,
> Which rising in a just degree,
> Their glowing lustre through the green
> Might add fresh beauties to the scene.

Afterwards when it became her own by the Duke's bequest, and her home was thereby fixed upon the spot of earth which she would have chosen for herself, the satisfaction which she took in adding to it either beauty or convenience was enhanced by the reflection that in adorning it she was at the same time showing her value for the gift, and her gratitude to the lamented giver. "Every thing," said she, "both within and without the house reminds me of my obligations to him; and I cannot turn my eyes upon any object which is not an object of his goodness to me.—And as I think it a duty, while it pleases God to continue us here, not to let ourselves sink into a stupid and unthankful melancholy, I endeavour to find out such entertainments as my retirement, and my dear Lord's unmerited bounty will admit of."

> And oh the transport, most allied to song,
> In some fair villa's peaceful bound,
> To catch soft hints from nature's tongue
> And bid Arcadia bloom around:
> Whether we fringe the sloping hill,
> Or smooth below the verdant mead;
> Whether we break the falling rill,
> Or through meandering mazes lead;
> Or in the horrid bramble's room
> Bid careless groups of roses bloom;
> Or let some sheltered lake serene
> Reflect flowers, woods, and spires, and brighten all the scene.
>
> O sweet disposal of the rural hour!
> O beauties never known to cloy!
> While worth and genius haunt the favour'd bower,
> And every gentle breast partakes the joy.
> While Charity at eve surveys the swain,
> Enabled by these toils to cheer
> A train of helpless infants dear,
> Speed whistling home across the plain;
> Sees vagrant Luxury, her handmaid grown,
> For half her graceless deeds atone,
> And hails the bounteous work, and ranks it with her own.*

* SHENSTONE.

The Duchess was too far advanced in life to find any of that enjoyment in her occupations, which her own poet described in these stanzas, and which he felt himself only by an effort of reflection. But if there was not the excitement of hope, there was the satisfaction of giving useful employment to honest industry. "When one comes," said she, "to the last broken arches of Mirza's bridge, rest from pain must bound our ambition, for pleasure is not to be expected in this world. I have no more notion of laying schemes to be executed six months, than I have six years hence; and this I believe helps to keep my spirits in an even state of cheerfulness, to enjoy the satisfactions that present themselves, without anxious solicitude about their duration. As our journey seems approaching towards the verge of life, is it not more natural to cast our eyes to the prospect beyond it, than by a retrospective view to recall the troublesome trifles that ever made our road difficult or dangerous? Methinks it would be imitating Lot's wife (whose history is not recorded as an example for us to follow) to want to look back upon the miserable scene we are so near escaping from."

In another letter to the same old friend she says, "I have a regular, and I hope a religious, family. My woman, though she has not lived with me quite three years, had before lived twenty-three, betwixt Lord Grantham's and Lady Cowper's: my housekeeper has been a servant as long: the person who takes in my accounts, pays my bills, and overlooks the men within doors, has been in the family thirteen years; and the other, who has lived ten, has the care of the stables, and every thing without. I rise at seven, but do not go down till nine, when the bell rings, and my whole family meet me at chapel. After prayers we go to breakfast; any friend who happens to be there, myself, and my chaplain, have ours in the little library; the others in their respective eating-rooms. About eleven, if the weather permits, we go to walk in the park, or take the air in the coach; but if it be too bad for either, we return to our various occupations. At three we dine, sit perhaps near an hour afterwards, then separate till we meet at eight for prayers; after which we adjourn again to the library, where somebody reads aloud (unless some stranger comes who chooses cards), until half past nine, when we sup, and always part before eleven. This to the fine would sound a melancholy monastic life; and I cannot be supposed to have chosen it from ignorance of the splendour and gaiety of a court, but from a thorough experience that they can give no solid happiness; and I find myself more calmly pleased in my present way of living, and more truly contented, than I ever was in the bloom and pomp of my youth. I am no longer dubious what point to pursue. There is but one proper for the decline of life, and indeed the only one worth the anxiety of a rational creature at any age: but how do the fire of youth, and flattery of the world, blind our eyes, and mislead our fancies, after a thousand imaginary pleasures which are sure to disappoint us in the end!"

The Duchess was a person whose moral constitution had not been injured by the atmosphere of a court. But though she kept aloof from its intrigues, and had acquired even a distaste for its vanities, she retained always an affectionate regard for Queen Caroline's memory. "I should have been glad," she says to Lady Pomfret, "to have shared your reverence, and have indulged my own at Blansfelden, whilst you were overlooking the fields and the shades where our late mistress had passed the first scenes of her life, before the cares of royalty had clouded the natural vivacity of her temper, or the disguise which greatness is often forced to wear had veiled any of her native goodness; and certainly she had a greater stock of both than is often found in any rank. She could never think of her without a sigh," she said. "The most amiable mistress," she calls her, "that ever adorned a court, and so fitted to charm in society, that it was impossible not to grudge her to that life which involved her in cares and encompassed her with such a cloud of different people, that her real lustre could not always reach those who parhaps had the most pleasure in it."

Before the loss of her son (from which the Duchess never entirely recovered), her spirits had been affected by the state of her husband's health. "The many solitary hours I pass in a day," she says, "and the melancholy employment of attending a person in his sufferings, to whom I owe every happiness I enjoy, cannot furnish me with many smiling ideas relating to this world." The country in its wintry appearances accorded with her feelings, "where," said she, "every thing around instructs me that decay is the lot of all created beings; where every tree spreads out its naked arms to testify the solemn truth, which I thank heaven I feel no pain in assenting to. It has long been my fixed opinion, that in the latter part of life, when the duties owing to a family no longer call upon us to act on the public stage of life, it is not only more decent, but infinitely more eligible, to live in an absolute retirement. However this is not the general opinion of the world, and therefore I conclude that it is better it is not so, since Providence undoubtedly orders better for us than we are able to do for ourselves."

During the latter years of her life, however, she enjoyed that absolute retirement which was her heart's desire. But the peaceful mansion in which this wise and amiable woman passed her latter years was, after her decease, inhabited by one of those men who insulted public decency by the open and ostentatious profligacy of their lives. Mrs. Carter writing from the Castle Inn at Marlborough, which had not long before been one of the residences of the Seymour family, says, "this house I consider with great respect and veneration, not without a strong mixture of regret, that what was once the elegant abode of virtue and genius, and honoured by the conversation of the Duchess of Somerset and Mrs. Rowe, should now resound with all the disorderly and riotous clamour of an inn. And yet its fate is more eligible than that of Percy Lodge, as it stands the chance of receiving indifferently good and bad people, and is not destined to be the constant reception of shocking profligate vice."

CHAPTER CVIII.

PERCY LODGE. THAXTED GRANGE. RAPIN THE JESUIT AND SIR THOMAS BROWNE.

> It seems that you take pleasure in these walks,
> Sir.
> *Cleanthes.* Contemplative content I do, my Lord.
> They bring into my mind oft meditations
> So sweetly precious, that in the parting
> I find a shower of grace upon my cheeks,
> They take their leave so feelingly.
>
> MASSINGER.

THE difference was very great between Thaxted Grange and Percy Lodge, though somewhat less than that between Northumberland House and the Tobacconist's at No. 113. Bishopsgate Street. Yet if a landscape painter who could have embodied the spirit of the scene had painted both, the Grange might have made the more attractive picture, though much had been done to embellish the Lodge by consulting picturesque effect, while the Allisons had aimed at little beyond comfort and convenience in their humble precincts.

From a thatched seat in the grounds of the Lodge, open on three sides and constructed like a shepherd's hut, there was a direct view of Windsor Castle, seen under the boughs of some old oaks and beeches. Sweet Williams, narcissuses, rose-campions, and such other flowers as the hares would not eat, had been sown in borders round the foot of every tree. There was a hermitage, absurdly so called, in the wood, with a thatched covering, and sides of straw; and there was a rosary, which though appropriately named, might sound as oddly to the ears of a Roman Catholic. A porter's lodge had been built at the entrance; and after the Duke's death the long drawing-room had been converted into a chapel, in Gothic taste, with three painted windows, which, having been bespoken for Northumberland House, but not suiting the intended alterations in that mansion, were put up here.

The Duchess and her servant had worked cross-stitch chairs for this chapel in fine crimson, the pattern was a Gothic mosaic, and they were in Gothic frames.

Se o mundo nos nao anda a' vontade
Naõ he pera estranhar, pois he hum sonho
Que nunca con ninguem tratou verdade.
Se quando se nos mostra mais risonho,
Mais brande, mais amigo, o desprezemos,
He graõ virtude, e á sua conta o ponho.
Mais se, (o que he mais certo) o desprezamos
Depois que nos engeita e nos despreza,
*Que premio, ou que louvor disso esperamos?**

All here, however, was as it should be: Percy Lodge was the becoming retreat of a lady of high rank, who having in the natural course of time and things outlived all inclination for the pomps and vanities of the world, and all necessity for conforming to them, remembered what was still due to her station; and doing nothing to be seen of men, had retired thither to pass the remainder of her days in privacy and religious peace.

All too was as it should be at Thaxted Grange. Picturesque was a term which had never been heard there; and taste was as little thought of as pretended to; but the right old English word comfort, in its good old English meaning, was nowhere more thoroughly understood. Nor anywhere could more evident indications of it be seen both within and without.

A tradesman retiring from business in these days with a fortune equivalent to what Mr. Allison had made, would begin his improvements upon such a house as the Grange by pulling it down. Mr. Allison contented himself with thoroughly repairing it. He had no dislike to low rooms, and casement windows. The whole furniture of his house cost less than would now be expended by a person of equal circumstances in fitting up a drawing-room. Everything was for use, and nothing for display, unless it were two fowling pieces, which were kept in good order over the fireplace in the best kitchen, and never used but when a kite threatened the poultry, or an owl was observed to frequent the dove-cote in preference to the barn.

* Diogo Bernardes.

But out of doors as much regard was shown to beauty as to utility. Miss Allison and Betsey claimed the little garden in front of the house for themselves. It was in so neglected a state when they took possession, that between children and poultry and stray pigs, not a garden flower was left there to grow wild: and the gravel walk from the gate to the porch was overgrown with weeds and grass, except a path in the middle which had been kept bare by use. On each side of the gate were three yew trees, at equal distances. In the old days of the Grange they had been squared in three lessening stages, the uppermost tapering pyramidally to a point. While the house had been shorn of its honours, the yews remained unshorn; but when it was once more occupied by a wealthy habitant, and a new gate had been set up and the pillars and their stone-balls cleaned from moss and lichen and short ferns, the unfortunate evergreens were again reduced to the formal shape in which Mr. Allison and his sister remembered them in their childhood. This was with them a matter of feeling, which is a better thing than taste. And indeed the yews must either have been trimmed, or cut down, because they intercepted sunshine from the garden and the prospect from the upper windows. The garden would have been better without them, for they were bad neighbours; but they belonged to old times, and it would have seemed a sort of sacrilege to destroy them.

Flower-beds used, like beds in the kitchen garden, to be raised a little above the path, with nothing to divide them from it, till about the beginning of the seventeenth century the fashion of bordering them was introduced either by the Italians or the French. Daisies, periwinkles, feverfew, hyssop, lavender, rosemary, rue, sage, wormwood, camomile, thyme, and box, were used for this purpose: a German horticulturist observes that hyssop was preferred as the most convenient; box, however, gradually obtained the preference. The Jesuit Rapin claims for the French the merit of bringing this plant into use, and embellishes his account of it by one of those school-boy fictions which passed for poetry in his days, and may still pass for it in his country. He describes a feast of the rural gods:

Adfuit et Cybele, Phrygias celebrata per urbes;
Ipsaque cum reliquis Flora invitata deabus
Venit, inornatis, ut erat neglecta, capillis;
Sive fuit fastus, seu fors fiducia formæ.
Non illi pubes ridendi prompta pepercit,
Neglectam risere. Deam Berecynthia mater
Semotam à turba, casum miserata puellæ,
Exornat, certâque comam sub lege reponit,
Et viridi imprimis buxo (nam buxifer omnis
Undique campus erat) velavit tempora nymphæ.
Reddidit is speciem cultus, cœpitque videri
Formosa, et meruit: novus hinc decor additus ori.

Ex illo, ut Floram decuit cultura, per artem
Floribus ille decor posthac quæsitus, et hortis:
Quem tamen Ausonii cultores, quemque Pelasgi
Nescivere, suos nullâ qui lege per hortos
Plantabant flores, nec eos componere norant
Areolis, tonsâque vias describere buxo.
Culta super reliquas Francis topiaria gentes,
Ingenium seu mite soli cœlique benigni
Temperies tantam per sese adjuverit artem;
Sive illam egregiæ solers industria gentis
Extuderit, seris seu venerit usus ab annis.

The fashion which this buxom Flora introduced had at one time the effect of banishing flowers from what should have been the flower garden: the ground was set with box in their stead, disposed in patterns more or less formal, some intricate as a labyrinth and not a little resembling those of Turkey carpets, where Mahommedan laws interdict the likeness of any living thing, and the taste of Turkish weavers excludes any combination of graceful forms. One sense at least was gratified when fragrant herbs were used in these "rare figures of composures," or knots as they were called, hyssop being mixed in them with thyme, as aiders the one to the other, the one being dry, the other moist. Box had the disadvantage of a disagreeable odour; but it was greener in winter and more compact in all seasons. To lay out these knots and tread them required the skill of a master-gardener: much labour was thus expended without producing any beauty. The walks between them were sometimes of different colours, some would be of lighter or darker gravel, red or yellow sand; and when such materials were at hand, pulverised coal and pulverised shells.

Such a garden Mr. Cradock saw at Bordeaux no longer ago than the year 1785; it belonged to Monsieur Rabi, a very rich Jew merchant, and was surrounded by a bank of earth, on which there stood about two hundred blue and white flower-pots; the garden itself was a scroll work cut very narrow, and the interstices filled with sand of different colours to imitate embroidery; it required repairing after every shower, and if the wind rose the eyes were sure to suffer. Yet the French admired this and exclaimed, *superbe! magnifique!*

Neither Miss Allison nor her niece would have taken any pleasure in gardens of this kind, which had nothing of a garden but the name. They both delighted in flowers; the aunt because flowers to her were "redolent of youth," and never failed to awaken tender recollections; Betsey for an opposite reason; having been born and bred in London, a nosegay there had seemed always to bring her a foretaste of those enjoyments for which she was looking forward with eager hope. They had stocked their front garden therefore with the gayest and the sweetest flowers that were cultivated in those days; larkspurs both of the giant and dwarf species, and of all colours; sweet-williams of the richest hues; monk's-hood for its stately growth; Betsey called it the dumbledore's delight, and was not aware that the plant in whose helmet- rather than cowl-shaped flowers that busy and best-natured of all insects appears to revel more than in any other, is the deadly aconite of which she read in poetry: the white lily, and the fleur-de-lis; pæonies, which are still the glory of the English garden; stocks and gillyflowers which make the air sweet as the gales of Arabia; wall-flowers, which for a while are little less fragrant, and not less beautiful; pinks and carnations added their spicy odours; roses red and white peeped at the lower casements, and the jessamine climbed to those of the chambers above. You must nurse your own flowers if you would have them flourish, unless you happen to have a gardener who is as fond of them as yourself. Eve was not busier with her's in

Paradise, her "pleasant task injoined," than Betsey Allison and her aunt, from the time that early spring invited them to their cheerful employment, till late and monitory autumn closed it for the year.

"Solomon in all his glory was not arrayed like one of these;" and Solomon in all his wisdom never taught more wholesome lessons than these silent monitors convey to a thoughtful mind and an "understanding heart." "There are two books," says Sir Thomas Browne, "from whence I collect my divinity; besides that written one of God, another of his servant Nature, that universal and public manuscript that lies expansed unto the eyes of all. Those that never saw him in the one have discovered him in the other. This was the scripture and theology of the heathens: the natural motion of the sun made them more admire him than its supernatural station did the children of Israel; the ordinary effects of nature wrought more admiration in them, than in the other all his miracles. Surely the heathens knew better how to join and read these mystical letters, than we Christians who cast a more careless eye on these common hieroglyphics, and disdain to suck divinity from the flowers of nature."

INTERCHAPTER XIV.

CONCERNING INTERCHAPTERS.

If we present a mingle-mangle, our fault is to be excused, because the whole world is become a hodge-podge.
LYLY.

It occurs to me that some of my readers may perhaps desire to be informed in what consists the difference between a Chapter and an Inter Chapter; for that there is a difference no considerate person would be disposed to deny, though he may not be able to discover it. Gentle readers, — readers after my own heart, you for whom this *opus* was designed long before it was an *opus*, when as Dryden has said concerning one of his own plays, "it was only a confused mass of thoughts, tumbling over one another in the dark; when the fancy was yet in its first work, moving the sleeping images of things towards the light, there to be distinguished, and then either chosen or rejected by the judgment," — good-natured readers, you who are willing to be pleased, and whom therefore it is worth pleasing, — for your sakes,

And for because you shall not think that I
Do use the same without a reason why,*

I will explain the distinction.

It is not like the difference between a Baptist and an Anabaptist, which Sir John Danvers said, is much the same as that between a Whiskey and a Tim-Whiskey, that is to say, no difference at all. Nor is it like that between Dryads and Hamadryads, which Benserade once explained to the satisfaction of a learned lady, by saying, *qu'il avait autant de difference qu'entre les Evêques et les Archevêques.* Nor is it like the distinction taken by him who divided bread into white bread, brown bread, and French rolls.

A panegyrical poet said of the aforesaid Benserade that he possessed three talents, which posterity would hardly be persuaded to believe;

De plaisanter les Grands il ne fit point scrupule,
Sans qu'ils le prissent de travers;
Il fut vieux et galant sans être ridicule,
Et s'enrichit à composer des vers.

He used to say, that he was descended and derived his name from the Abencerrages. Upon a similar presumption of etymological genealogy, it has been said that Aulus Gellius was the progenitor of all the Gells. An Englishman may doubt this, a Welshman would disbelieve, and a Jew might despise it. So might a Mahommedan, because it is a special prerogative of his prophet to be perfectly acquainted with his whole pedigree; the Mussulmen hold that no other human being ever possessed the same knowledge, and that after the resurrection, when all other pedigrees will be utterly destroyed, this alone will be preserved in the archives of Eternity.

* ROBERT GREEN.

Leaving, however, Sir William Gell to genealogise, if he pleases, as elaborately as he has topographised, and to maintain the authenticity and dignity of his Roman descent against all who may impugn it, whether Turk, Jew, or Christian, I proceed with my promised explanation.

The Hebrews call chapters and sections, and other essential or convenient divisions, the bones of a book. The Latins called them *nodi*, knots or links; and every philologist knows that articles, whether grammatical, conventional, or of faith, are so denominated as being the joints of language, covenants, and creeds.

Now, reader, the chapters of this book are the bones wherewith its body is compacted; the knots or links whereby its thread or chain of thoughts is connected; the articulations, without which it would be stiff, lame, and disjointed. Every chapter has a natural dependence upon that which precedes, and in like manner a relation to that which follows it. Each grows out of the other. They follow in direct genealogy; and each could no more have been produced without relation to its predecessor, than Isaac could have begotten Jacob unless Abraham had begotten Isaac.

Sometimes, indeed, it must of necessity happen that a new chapter opens with a new part of the subject, but this is because we are arrived at that part in the natural prosecution of our argument. The disruption causes no discontinuance; it is (to pursue the former illustration) as when the direct line in a family is run out, and the succession is continued by a collateral branch; or as in the mineral world, in which one formation begins where another breaks off.

In my chapters, however, where there is no such natural division of the subject matter, I have ever observed that "one most necessary piece of mastership, which is ever performed by those of good skill in music, when they end a suit of lessons in any one key, and do intend presently to begin another in a differing key." Upon which piece of mastership, the worthy old "Remembrancer of the best practical music, both divine and civil, that has ever been known to have been in the world," thus instructs his readers.

"They do not abruptly and suddenly begin such new lessons, without some neat and handsome interluding-voluntary-like playing; which may by degrees (as it were) steal into that new and intended key.

"Now that you may be able to do it handsomely, and without blemish or incompleteness (for you must know it is a piece of quaintness so to do), you must take notice, that always, when you have made an end of playing upon any one key (if discourse or some other occasion do not cause a cessation of play for some pretty time, so as the remembrance of that former key may, in a manner, be forgotten), it will be very needful that some care be taken that you leave that key handsomely, and come into that other you intend next to play upon without impertinency.

"For such impertinencies will seem to be very like such a thing as this, which I shall name—to wit—

"That when two or more persons have been soberly and very intently discoursing upon some particular solid matter, musing and very ponderously considering thereof, all on the sudden, some one of them shall abruptly (without any pause) begin to talk of a thing quite of another nature, nothing relating to the aforesaid business.

"Now those by-standers (who have judgment), will presently apprehend that, although his matter might be good, yet his manner and his wit might have been better approved of in staying some certain convenient time, in which he might have found out some pretty interluding discourse, and have taken a handsome occasion to have brought in his new matter.

"Just so is it in music, and more particularly in this last-recited matter; as to chop different things of different natures, and of different keys, one upon the neck of another, impertinently.

"For I would have it taken notice of, that music is (at least) as a language, if it will not be allowed a perfect one, because it is not so well understood as it might be. —

"Having thus far prepared you with an apprehension of the needfulness of the thing, I will now show you how it is to be done without abruption and absurdness.

"First, (as abovesaid) it may be that discourse may take off the remembrance of the last key in which you played, or some occasion of a leaving off for some pretty time, by a string breaking or the like; or if not, then (as commonly it happens) there may be a need of examining the tuning of your lute, for the strings will alter a little in the playing of one lesson, although they have been well stretched. But if lately put on, or have been slacked down by any mischance of pegs slipping, then they will need mending, most certainly.

"I say some such occasion may sometimes give you an opportunity of coming handsomely to your new intended key; but if none of these shall happen, then you ought, in a judicious and masterly way, to work from your last key which you played upon, in some voluntary way till you have brought your matter so to pass that your auditors may be captivated with a new attention, yet so insinuatingly, that they may have lost the remembrance of the foregoing key they know not how; nor are they at all concerned for the loss of it, but rather taken with a new content and delight at your so cunning and complete artifice."

With strict propriety then may it be said of these my chapters, as Wordsworth has said of certain sonnets during his tour in Scotland and on the English border, that they

Have moved in order, to each other bound
By a continuous and acknowledged tie
Though unapparent, like those shapes distinct
That yet survive ensculptured on the walls
Of Palace, or of Temple, 'mid the wreck
Of famed Persepolis; each following each,
As might beseem a stately embassy
In set array; these bearing in their hands
Ensign of civil power, weapon of war,
Or gift to be presented at the Throne
Of the Great King; and others as they go
In priestly vest, with holy offerings charged,
Or leading victims dressed for sacrifice.

For an ordinary book then the ordinary division into chapters might very well have sufficed. But this is an extraordinary book. Hath not the Quarterly Review — that Review which among all Reviews is properly accounted *facile Princeps*, — hath not that great critical authority referred to it κατ' ἐξοχὴν as "the extraordinary book called the Doctor"? Yes, reader —

All things within it
Are so digested, fitted and composed
As it shows Wit had married Order.*

And as the exceptions in grammar prove the rule, so the occasional interruptions of order here are proofs of that order, and in reality belong to it.

Lord Bacon (then Sir Francis) said in a letter to the Bishop of Ely upon sending him his writing intitled *Cogitata et Visa*, "I am forced to respect as well my times, as the matter. For with me it is thus, and I think with all men in my case: if I bind myself to an argument, it loadeth my mind; but if I rid my mind of the present cogitation, it is rather a recreation. This hath put me into these miscellanies, which I purpose to suppress if God give me leave to write a just and perfect volume of philosophy."

That I am full of cogitations, like Lord Bacon, the judicious reader must ere this time have perceived, though he may perhaps think me not more worthy on that score to be associated with Bacon, than beans or cabbage, or eggs at best. Like him, however, in this respect I am, however unlike in others; and it is for the reader's recreation as well as mine, and for our mutual benefit, that my mind should be delivered of some of its cogitations as soon as they are ripe for birth.

I know not whence thought comes; who indeed can tell? But this we know, that like the wind it cometh as it listeth. Happily there is no cause for me to say with Sir Philip Sydney,

If I could think how these my thoughts to leave;
Or thinking still, my thoughts might have good end;
If rebel Sense would Reason's law receive,
Or Reason foiled would not in vain contend;
Then might I think what thoughts were best to think,
Then might I wisely swim, or gladly sink.

* B. Jonson.

Nor with Des-Portes,

> *O pensers trop pensez, que rebellez mon ame!*
> *O debile raison! O lacqs! O traits!*

thanks to that kind Providence which has hitherto enabled me, through good and evil fortune, to maintain an even and well-regulated mind. Neither need I say with the pleasant authors of the "Rejected Addresses" in their harmless imitation of a most pernicious author,

> Thinking is but an idle waste of thought,
> And nought is every thing and every thing is nought.

I have never worked in an intellectual tread-mill, which, as it had nothing to act on, was grinding the wind.

"He that thinks *ill*," says Dean Young, (the poet's father,) "*prevents* the Tempter, and does the Devil's business for him; he that thinks *nothing*, *tempts* the Tempter, and offers him possession of an empty room; but he that thinks *religiously*, *defeats* the Tempter, and is proof and secure against all his assaults." I know not whether there be any later example where the word *prevent* is used, as in the Collect, in its Latin sense.

It is a man's own fault if he excogitate vain thoughts, and still more if he enunciate and embody them; but it is not always in his power to prevent their influx. Even the preventive which George Tubervile recommends in his monitory rhymes, is not infallible:

> Eschew the idle life!
> Flee, flee from doing nought!
> For never was there idle brain
> But bred an idle thought.

Into the busiest brain they will sometimes intrude; and the brain that is over-busy breeds them. But the thoughts which are not of our own growth or purchase, and which we receive not from books, society, or visible objects, but from some undiscovered influence, are of all kinds.

> Who has a breast so pure,
> But some uncleanly apprehensions
> Keep leets and law days, and in session sit
> With meditations lawful? *

I dare not affirm that some are suggestions of the enemy; neither dare I deny it; from all such *tela ignea* and *tela venenata*, whatever be their origin, or whencesoever they come, God preserve us! But there are holy inspirations, which philosophy may teach us to expect, and faith to pray for.

My present business is not with these, but it is with those conceptions which float into the solitary mind, and which, if they are unrecorded pass away, like a dream or a rainbow, or the glories of an evening sky. Some of them are no better than motes in the sunbeams, as light, as fleeting, and to all apprehension as worthless. Others may be called seminal thoughts, which, if they light not upon a thorny, or stony, or arid field of intellect, germinate, and bring forth flowers, and peradventure fruit. Now it is in the Interchapters that part of this floating capital is vested; part of these waifs and strays impounded; part of this treasure trove lodged; part of these chance thoughts and fancies preserved: part I say, because

> *J'ay mille autres pensers, et mille et mille et mille,*
> *Qui font qu'incessamment mon esprit se distile.*†

"There are three things," says a Welsh triad, "that ought to be considered before some things should be spoken; the manner, the place, and the time." Touching the manner, I see none whereby they could more conveniently or agreeably be conveyed; and for the place and time these must be allowed to be at my own discretion.

> And howsoever, be it well or ill
> What I have done, it is mine own; I may
> Do whatsoever therewithal I will.‡

(Be it remarked in passing that these lines bear a much greater resemblance to Italian poetry than any of those English sonnets which have been called Petrarcal.) One place being (generally speaking) as suitable as another, it has not been necessary for me to deliberate,

> *Desta antigua preñez de pensamientos*
> *Qual el primero hare, qual el segundo.*§

I have interspersed them where I thought fit, and given them the appellation which

* Othello.

† Des-Portes. ‡ Daniel. § Balbuena.

they bear, to denote that they are no more a necessary and essential part of this *opus*, than the voluntary is of the church service.

> Ἐισὶν δὲ περὶ τοῦ;
> Περὶ Ἀθηνῶν, περὶ Πύλου,
> Περὶ σοῦ, περὶ ἐμοῦ, περὶ ἁπάντων πραγμάτων.*

A Chapter is, as has been explained, both procreated and procreative: an Interchapter is like the hebdomad, which profound philosophers have pronounced to be not only παρθένος, but ἀμήτωρ, a motherless as well as a virgin number.

Here, too, the exception illustrates the rule. There are at the commencement of the third volume four Interchapters in succession, and relating to each other, the first gignitive but not generated; the second and third both generated and gignitive, the fourth generated but not gignitive. They stand to each other in the relation of Adam, Seth, Enoch, Kenan. These are the exceptions. The other chapters are all Melchizedekites.

The gentle Reader will be satisfied with this explanation; the curious will be pleased with it. To the captious one I say in the words of John Bunyan, "Friend, howsoever thou camest by this book, I will assure thee thou wert least in my thoughts when I writ it. I tell thee, I intended the book as little for thee as the goldsmith intended his jewels and rings for the snout of a sow!"

If any be not pleased, let them please themselves with their own displeasure. *Je n'ay pas enterpris de contenter tout le monde: mesme Jupiter n'aggrée à tous.*†

---

* Aristophanes. † Bouchet.

CHAPTER CIX.

INCIDENTAL MENTION OF HAMMOND, SIR EDMUND KING, JOANNA BAILLIE, SIR WILLIAM TEMPLE, AND MR. THOMAS PEREGRINE COURTENAY. PETER COLLINSON AN ACQUAINTANCE OF MR. ALLISON'S. HOLYDAYS AT THAXTED GRANGE.

> And sure there seem of human kind
> Some born to shun the solemn strife;
> Some for amusive tasks design'd
> To soothe the certain ills of life,
> Grace its lone vales with many a budding rose,
> New founts of bliss disclose,
> Call forth refreshing shades and decorate repose.
>
> SHENSTONE.

Dr. Hammond says he had "heard say of a man who, upon his death-bed, being to take his farewell of his son, and considering what course of life to recommend that might secure his innocence, at last enjoined him to spend his time in making verses, and in dressing a garden; the old man thinking no temptation could creep into either of these employments." As to the former part of this counsel, a certain Sir Edmund King was of a different opinion; for meeting with Watts in his youth, he said to him, "Young man, I hear that you make verses! Let me advise you never to do it but when you can't help it." If there were ever a person who could not help it, Joanna Baillie would have said nothing more than what was strictly true, when she observed that "surely writing verses must have some power of intoxication in it, and can turn a sensible man into a fool by some process of mental alchemy."

"Gardening," says Mr. Courtenay, in his Life of Sir William Temple, "is a pursuit peculiarly adapted for reconciling and combining the tastes of the two sexes, and indeed of all ages. It is, therefore, of all amusements the most retentive of domestic affection. It is, perhaps, most warmly pursued by the very young, and by those who are far advanced in life, — before the mind is occupied with worldly business, and after it has become disgusted with it. There is nothing in it to remind of the bustle of political life; and it requires neither a sanguine disposition nor the prospect of a long life, to justify the expectation of a beautiful result from the slight and easy care which it exacts. Is it too much to say that the mind which can with genuine taste occupy itself in gardening, must have preserved some portion of youthful purity; that it must have escaped, during its passage through the active world its deeper contaminations; and that no shame nor remorse can have found a seat in it."

Certainly it is not too much to say this of Sir William Temple; nor would it be too much to say it of his biographer, whether he occupy himself, or not, in gardening as well as in literature, after many laborious years honourably passed in political and official life.

Peter Collinson, whose pious memory ought to be a standing toast at the meetings of the Horticultural Society, used to say that he never knew an instance in which the pursuit of such pleasure as the culture of a garden affords, did not either find men temperate and virtuous, or make them so. And this may be affirmed as an undeniable and not unimportant fact relating to the lower classes of society, that wherever the garden of a cottage, or other humble dwelling, is carefully and neatly kept, neatness and thrift, and domestic comfort, will be found within doors.

When Mr. Allison settled at Thaxted Grange, English gardens were beginning generally to profit by the benevolent and happy endeavours of Peter Collinson to improve them. That singularly good man availed himself of his mercantile connexions, and of the opportunities afforded him by the Royal Society, of which he was one of the most diligent and useful members, to procure seeds and plants from all parts of the world, and these he liberally communicated to his friends. So they found their way first into the gardens of the curious, then of the rich, and lastly, when their beauty recommended them, spread themselves into those of ordinary persons. He divided his time between his counting-house in Gracechurch Street and his country-house and garden, at Mill Hill, near Hendon; it might have grieved him could he have foreseen that his grounds there would pass, after his death, into the hands of a purchaser who, in mere ignorance, rooted out the rarest plants, and cut down trees which were scarcely to be found in perfection anywhere else in the kingdom at that time.

Mr. Collinson was a man of whom it was truly said that, not having any public station, he was the means of procuring national advantages for his country, and possessed an influence in it which wealth cannot purchase, and which will be honoured when titles are forgotten. For thirty years he executed gratuitously the commissions of the Philadelphian Subscription Library, the first which was established in America; he assisted the directors in their choice of books, took the whole care of collecting and shipping them, and transmitted to the directors the earliest accounts of every improvement in agriculture and the arts, and of every philosophical discovery.

Franklin, who was the founder of that library, made his first electrical experiments with an apparatus that had been sent to it as a present by Peter Collinson. He deemed it therefore a proper mark of acknowledgment to inform him of the success with which it had been used, and his first Essays on Electricity were originally communicated in letters to this good man. They were read in the Royal Society, "where they were not thought worth so much notice as to be printed in their transactions;" and his paper in which the sameness of lightning with electricity was first asserted, was laughed at by the connoisseurs. Peter Collinson, however, gave the letters to Cave for the Gentleman's Magazine; Cave forming a better judgment than the Royal Society had done, printed them separately in a pamphlet, for which Dr. Fothergill wrote a preface; the pamphlet by successive additions swelled to a volume in quarto which went through five editions, and, as Franklin observes, "cost Cave nothing for copy money."

What a contrast between this English

Quaker and Monsieur Le Cour (observe, reader, I call him Monsieur, lest you should mistake him for a Dutchman, seeing that he lived at Leyden,) who, having raised a double tuberose from the seed, and propagated it by the roots, till he had as many as he could find room to plant, destroyed the rest as fast as they were produced, that he might boast of being the only person in Europe who possessed it. Another French florist of the same stamp, M. Bachelier was his name, kept in like manner some beautiful species of the anemone to himself, which he had procured from the East Indies, and succeeded in withholding them for ten years from all who wished to possess them likewise. A counsellor of the Parliament, however, one day paid him a visit when they were in seed, and in walking with him round the garden, contrived to let his gown fall upon them; by this means he swept off a good number of the seeds, and his servant, who was apprised of the scheme, dexterously wrapt up the gown and secured them. Any one must have been a sour moralist who should have considered this to be a breach of the eighth commandment.

Mr. Allison was well acquainted with Peter Collinson; he and his sister sometimes visited him at Mill Hill, and upon their removal into Yorkshire they were supplied from thence with choice fruit trees, and fine varieties of the narcissus and polyanthus, which were the good Quaker's favourite tribes. The wall-fruits were under Mr. Allison's especial care; he called himself, indeed, First Lord of the Fruit Department; and if the first lords of certain other departments had taken as much pains to understand their business, and to perform it, the affairs of the state would have been better managed than they were in his days, and than they are in ours. Some part also he took in directing the business of the kitchen-garden; but the flowers were left entirely to Betsey and her aunt.

The old poet who called himself Shepherd Tonie, and whom Sir Egerton, with much likelihood, supposes to have been Anthony Munday, gives in his Woodman's Walk an unfavourable representation of provincial morals, when, after forsaking the court and the city, because he had found nothing but selfishness and deceit in both, he tried the country.

> There did appear no subtle shows,
> But yea and nay went smoothly:
> But Lord ! how country folks can glose
> When they speak most untruly !
> More craft was in a buttoned cap
> And in the old wives' rail,
> Than in my life it was my hap
> To see on down or dale.
> There was no open forgery,
> But underhanded gleaning,
> Which they call country policy,
> But hath a worser meaning.
> Some good bold face bears out the wrong,
> Because he gains thereby;
> The poor man's back is crackt ere long,
> Yet there he lets him lie:
> And no degree among them all
> But had such close intending,
> That I upon my knees did fall
> And prayed for their amending.

If the author of these verses, or any one who entertained the same opinion, had been a guest of Mr. Allison's at Thaxted Grange, and had remained under his roof long enough to see the way of life there, and the condition of the hamlet, he would have gone away with a very different persuasion. It was a remark of Bishop Percy's that you may discern in a country parish whether there is a resident clergyman or not, by the civil or savage manners of the people. The influence of the clergyman, however exemplary he may be, is materially impaired if his benefice is so poor and his means so straitened that his own necessities leave him little or nothing to spare; but when such a parish priest as Mr. Bacon has for his neighbour such a resident landholder as his friend at the Grange, happy are—not the cottagers only, but all who live within their sphere.

There was no alehouse in the hamlet, and as the fashion of preserves had not yet been introduced, there were no poachers, the inhabitants being thus happily exempted from two of the great temptations with which in our days men of that class are continually beset. If a newspaper ever found its way among them, newspapers were at that time harmless; and when a hawker came he had no pestiferous tracts, either seditious or sectarian, for sale, or for gratuitous distribution: a scurvy jest-book was the worst article in his assortment. Mr. Bacon had nothing to counteract his pastoral labours except the pravity of human nature. Of this there must everywhere be but too much; but fortunate indeed is the parish priest who finds himself in like manner stationed where there are no external circumstances to aggravate and excite it.

Wherever more than ordinary pains were bestowed upon a cottager's or farmer's garden, Mr. Allison supplied the housewife with seed of a better kind than she might otherwise have been able to procure, and with grafts from his most serviceable fruit trees. No one who behaved well in his employ was ever left in want of employment; he had always some work going on, the cost of which was allowed for as charity in his accounts: and when he observed in a boy the diligence and the disposition which made it likely that an opportunity of bettering his condition would not be thrown away upon him, he advised, or if need were, enabled the parents to educate him for trade, and at a proper age provided a situation for him in London. If any of their daughters desired to acquire those useful arts which might qualify them for domestic service, they came to assist and learn from Miss Allison when she distilled her waters, made her cowslip, elder, and gooseberry wines, prepared her pickles and preserves, dried her medicinal plants, or constructed the great goose-pye, which in the Christmas week was always dispatched by the York coach to Bishopsgate Street, for the honour of Yorkshire, and the astonishment of the Londoners. They came also when preparations were making for a holiday, for old observances of this kind were maintained as duly there as by the Romans when the Laws of the Twelve Tables were in use, and every man constantly observed his family festivals as thereby enjoined.

Pancakes on Shrove Tuesday are still in general usage; indeed I do not know that it was ever deemed malignant and idolatrous to eat them on that day even under the tyranny of the Puritans. But in Mr. Allison's days Mid-lent Sunday was not allowed to pass without a wholesome and savoury bowl of furmity on the social board: and Easter day brought with it not only those coloured eggs which are the friendly offering of that season throughout the whole north of Europe, but the tansy pudding also, — originally perhaps introduced (and possibly by some compulsory converts from Judaism) as a representative of the bitter herbs with which the Paschal Lamb was to be eaten.

Both Christmas-days were kept at the Grange. There were people in those times who refused to keep what they called Parliament Christmas. But whether the old computation or the new were right, was a point on which neither the master nor mistress of this house pretended to form an opinion. On which day the Glastonbury Thorn blossomed they never thought it necessary to inquire, nor did they go into the byre or the fields to see upon which midnight the oxen were to be found on their knees. They agreed with Mr. Bacon that in other respects it was a matter of indifference, but not so that Christmas should be celebrated on the same day throughout Christendom: and he agreed with them that as the ritual ought to be performed at the time appointed by authority, so the convivial observances might be regulated by the old calendar, or still more fitly, repeated according to the old reckoning, in deference to old feelings and recollections which time had consecrated.

In Bishopsgate Street it had been found convenient to set down the children and their young guests on these occasions at Pope-Joan, or snip-snap-snorum, which was to them a more amusing because a noisier game. But here was room for more legitimate gambols; and when a young party had assembled numerous enough for such pastime, hunt the slipper, hot cockles, or blind-man's buff were the sports of a Christmas evening. These had been days of high enjoyment to Betsey for a few years after their removal into the country; they ceased to be so when she saw that her aunt's hair was passing from the steel to the silver hue, and remembered that her father had reached the term of life, beyond which, in the ordinary course of nature, our strength is but labour and sorrow; — that the one was at an age

> When every day that comes, comes to decay
> A day's work in us *;

the other, —

> Even in the downfall of his mellowed years
> When Nature brought him to the door of Death.*

CHAPTER CX.

A TRANSITIONAL CHAPTER, WHEREIN THE AUTHOR COMPARES HIS BOOK TO AN OMNIBUS AND A SHIP, QUOTES SHAKESPEARE, MARCO ANTONIO DE CAMOS, QUARLES, SPENSER, AND SOMEBODY ELSE, AND INTRODUCES HIS READERS TO SOME OF THE HEATHEN GODS, WITH WHOM PERHAPS THEY WERE NOT ACQUAINTED BEFORE.

> We are not to grudge such interstitial and transitional matter as may promote an easy connection of parts and an elastic separation of them, and keep the reader's mind upon springs as it were.
>
> HENRY TAYLOR'S Statesman.

DEAR impatient readers, — you whom I know and who do not know me, — and you who are equally impatient, but whom I cannot call equally dear, because you are totally strangers to me in my out-of-cog character, — you who would have had me hurry on

> In motion of no less celerity
> Than that of thought *, —

you will not wonder, nor perhaps will you blame me now, that I do not hasten to the wedding-day. The day on which Deborah left her father's house was the saddest that she had ever known till then; nor was there one of the bridal party who did not feel that this was the first of those events, inevitable and mournful all, by which their little circle would be lessened, and his or her manner of life or of existence changed.

There is no checking the course of time. When the shadow on Hezekiah's dial went back, it was in the symbol only that the miracle was wrought: the minutes in every other horologe held their due course. But as Opifex of this opus, I, when it seems good unto me, may take the hour-glass from Time's hand and let it rest at a stand-still, till I think fit to turn it and set the sands again in motion. You who have got into this my omnibus, know that like other omnibuses, its speed is to be regulated, not according to your individual, and perhaps contrariant wishes, but by my discretion.

Moreover, I am not bound to ply with this omnibus only upon a certain line. In that case there would be just cause of complaint, if you were taken out of your road.

> *Mas estorva y desabre en el camino*
> *Una pequeña legua de desvio*
> *Que la jornada larga de contino.*

Whoever has at any time lost his way upon a long journey can bear testimony to the truth of what the Reverend Padre Maestro Fray Marco Antonio de Camos says in those lines. (I will tell you hereafter, reader, (for it is worth telling,) why that namesake of the Triumvir, when he wrote the poem from whence the lines are quoted, had no thoughts of dedicating it, as he afterwards did, to D. Juan Pimentel y de Requesens.) But you are in no danger of being bewildered, or driven out of your way. It is not in a stage coach that you have taken your place with me, to be conveyed to a certain point, and within a certain time, under such an expectation on your part, and such an engagement on mine. We will drop the metaphor of the omnibus, — observing, however, by the bye, which is the same thing in common parlance as by the way, though critically there may seem to be a difference, for by the bye might seem to denote a collateral remark, and by the way a direct one; observing, however, as I said, that as Dexter called his work, or St. Jerome called it for him, *Omnimoda Historia*, so might this opus

---

* SHAKESPEARE.

be not improperly denominated. You have embarked with me, not for a definite voyage, but for an excursion on the water; and not in a steamer, nor in a galley, nor in one of the post-office packets, nor in a man-of-war, nor in a merchant-vessel; but in

A ship that's mann'd
With labouring Thoughts, and steer'd by Reason's hand.
My Will's the seaman's card whereby she sails;
My just Affections are the greater sails,
The top sail is my fancy.*

Sir Guyon was not safer in Phædria's "gondelay bedecked trim" than thou art on "this wide inland sea," in my ship

That knows her port and thither sails by aim;
Ne care, ne fear I how the wind do blow;
Or whether swift I wend, or whether slow,
Both slow and swift alike do serve my turn.†

My turn is served for the present, and yours also. The question who was Mrs. Dove? propounded for future solution in the second Chapter P. I., and for immediate consideration at the conclusion of the 71st Chapter and the beginning of the 72nd, has been sufficiently answered. You have been made acquainted with her birth, parentage, and education; and you may rest assured that if the Doctor had set out upon a tour, like Cœlebs, in search of a wife, he could never have found one who would in all respects have suited him better. What Shakespeare says of the Dauphin and the Lady Blanch might seem to have been said with a second sight of this union:

Such as she is
Is this our Doctor, every way complete;
If not complete, O say, he is not she:
And she again wants nothing, to name want,
If want it be not, that she is not he.
He is the half part of a blessed man,
Left to be finished by such a she;
And she a fair divided excellence
Whose fullness of perfection lies in him.

You would wish me perhaps to describe her person. Sixty years had "written their defeatures in her face" before I became acquainted with her; yet by what those years had left methinks I could conceive what she had been in her youth. Go to your looking-glasses, young ladies, — and you will not be so well able to imagine by what you see there, how you will look when you shall have shaken hands with Threescore.

One of the Elizabethan minor-poets, speaking of an ideal beauty, says,

Into a slumber then I fell,
When fond Imagination
Seemed to see, but could not tell,
Her feature, or her fashion.
But even as babes in dreams do smile,
And sometimes fall a-weeping,
So I awaked, as wise this while,
As when I fell a-sleeping.

Just as unable should I feel myself were I to attempt a description from what Mrs. Dove was when I knew her, of what Deborah Bacon might be supposed to have been, — just as unable as this dreaming rhymer should I be, and you would be no whit the wiser. What the disposition was which gave her face its permanent beauty you may know by what has already been said. But this I can truly say of her and of her husband, that if they had lived in the time of the Romans when Doncaster was called Danum, and had been of what was then the Roman religion, and had been married, as consequently they would have been, with the rites of classical Paganism, it would have been believed both by their neighbours and themselves that their nuptial offerings had been benignly received by the god Domicius and the goddesses Maturna and Gamelia; and no sacrifice to Viriplaca would ever have been thought necessary in that household.

CHAPTER CXI.

CONCERNING MAGAZINES, AND THE FORMER AND PRESENT RACE OF ALPHABET-MEN.

Altri gli han messo nome Santa Croce,
Altri lo chiaman l' A. B. C. guastando
La misura, gl' accenti, et la sua voce.

SANSOVINO.

The reader has now been informed who Mrs. Dove was, and what she was on that day of mingled joy and grief when the bells of

* Quarles: *mutatis mutandis.*

† Spenser.

St. George's welcomed her to Doncaster as a bride. Enough too has been related concerning the Doctor in his single state, to show that he was not unworthy of such a wife. There is, however, more to be told; for any one who may suppose that a physician at Doncaster must have been pretty much the same sort of person in the year 1761 as at present, can have reflected little upon the changes for better and worse which have been going on during the intervening time. The fashions in dress and furniture have not altered more than the style of intellectual upholstery.

Our Doctor flourished in the Golden Age of Magazines, when their pages were filled with voluntary contributions from men who never aimed at dazzling the public, but came each with his scrap of information, or his humble question, or his hard problem, or his attempt in verse.

In those days A was an Antiquary, and wrote articles upon Altars and Abbeys and Architecture. B made a blunder, which C corrected. D demonstrated that E was in error, and that F was wrong in Philology, and neither Philosopher nor Physician, though he affected to be both. G was a Genealogist: H was an Herald, who helped him. I was an inquisitive inquirer, who found reason for suspecting J to be a Jesuit. M was a mathematician. N noted the weather. O observed the stars. P was a poet, who piddled in pastorals, and prayed Mr. Urban to print them. Q came in the corner of the page with his query. R arrogated to himself the right of reprehending every one who differed from him. S sighed and sued in song. T told an old tale, and when he was wrong U used to set him right. V was a virtuoso. W warred against Warburton. X excelled in algebra. Y yearned for immortality in rhyme; and Z in his zeal was always in a puzzle.

Those were happy times when each little star was satisfied with twinkling in his own sphere. No one thought of bouncing about like a cracker, singeing and burning in the mere wantonness of mischief, and then going out with a noise and a stink.

But now

> —— when all this world is woxen daily worse,*

see what a change has taken place through the whole Chriscross Row! As for A, there is Alaric Watts with his Souvenir, and Ackerman with his Forget-me-not, and all the rest of the Annual Albumers. B is a blackguard, and blusters in a popular Magazine. C is a coxcomb who concocts fashionable novels for Colburn; and D is a dunce who admires him. E, being empty and envious, thinks himself eminently qualified for Editor of a Literary Gazette. F figures as a fop in Knight's Quarterly. G is a general reformer, and dealer in Greek scrip. H is Humbug and Hume; and for my I, it may always be found with Mr. Irving and Mrs. Elizabeth Martin. J jeers at the Clergy in Mr. Jeffery's journal. K kicks against the pricks with his friend L, who is Leigh Hunt, the Liberal. M manufactures mischief for the Morning Chronicle. N is nobody knows who, that manufactures jokes for John Bull, and fathers them upon Rogers. O is an obstreperous orator. P was Peter Pindar, and is now Paul Pry. Q is the Quarterly Review, and R S Robert Southey, who writes in it. T tells lies in the Old Times. U is a Unitarian who hopes to be Professor of Theology at the London University. V is Vivian Grey. W is Sir Walter Scott. X the Ex-Sheriff Parkins. Y was the Young Roscius; and Z,—Zounds, who can Z be, but Zachary Macauley?

Oh,—

> —— *se oggidì vivesse in terra*
> *Democrito, (perchè di lagrimare*
> *Io non son vago, e però taccio il nome*
> *D' Eraclito dolente;) or, se vivesse*
> *Fra' mortali Democrito, per certo*
> *Ei si smascellerebbe della risa,*
> *Guardando le sciocchezze de' mortali.*†

---

* Spenser. † Chiabrera.

CHAPTER CXII.

HUNTING IN AN EASY CHAIR. THE DOCTOR'S BOOKS.

That place that does contain
My books, the best companions, is to me
A glorious court, where hourly I converse
With the old sages and philosophers;
And sometimes for variety I confer
With Kings and Emperors, and weigh their counsels,
Calling their victories, if unjustly got,
Unto a strict account, and in my fancy
Deface their ill placed statues.

BEAUMONT and FLETCHER

A CERTAIN Ludovicus Bosch, instead of having his coat of arms, or his cypher engraved to put in his books, had a little print of himself in his library. The room has a venerable collegiate character; there is a crucifix on the table, and a goodly proportion of folios on the shelves. Bosch, in a clerical dress, is seated in an easy chair, cogitabund, with a manuscript open before him, a long pen in his hand, and on his head a wig which, with all proper respect for the dignity and vocation of the wearer, I cannot but honestly denominate a caxon. The caxon quizzifies the figure, and thereby mars the effect of what would otherwise have been a pleasing as well as appropriate design. Underneath in the scrolled framing is this verse,

In tali nunquam lassat venatio sylvâ.

Dr. Charles Balguy, of Peterborough, had for the same purpose a design which, though equally appropriate, was not so well conceived. His escutcheon, with the words

Jucunda oblivia vitæ

above, and his name and place of abode below, is suspended against an architectural pile of books. It was printed in green. I found it in one of our own Doctor's out-of-the-way volumes, a thin foolscap quarto, printed at Turin, 1589, being a treatise *della natura de' cibi et del bere*, by Baldassare Pisanelli, a physician of Bologna.

Dr. Balguy's motto would not have suited our Doctor. For though books were among the comforts and enjoyments of his life from boyhood to old age, they never made him oblivious of its business. Like Ludovicus Bosch, — but remember, I beseech you, Ladies! his wig was not a caxon; and, moreover, that when he gave an early hour to his books, it was before the wig was put on, and that when he had a leisure evening for them, off went the wig, and a velvet or silken cap, according to the season, supplied its place; — like Bosch, I say, when he was seated in his library, — but in no such conventual or collegiate apartment, and with no such assemblage of folios, quartos, and all inferior sizes, substantially bound, in venerable condition, and "in seemly order ranged;" nor with that atmospheric odour of antiquity, and books, which is more grateful to the olfactories of a student than the fumes of any pastille; but in a little room, with a ragged regiment upon his shelves, and an odour of the shop from below, in which rhubarb predominated, though it was sometimes overpowered by valerian, dear to cats, or assafœtida which sprung up, say the Turks, in Paradise, upon the spot where the Devil first set his foot: — like Bosch, I say, once more and without farther parenthesis, —

(περισσοὶ πάντες οἱ 'ν μέσῳ λόγοι,*)

like Bosch, the Doctor never was weary with pursuing the game that might be started in a library. And though there was no forest at hand, there were some small preserves in the neighbourhood, over which he was at liberty to range.

Perhaps the reader's memory may serve him, where mine is just now at fault, and he may do for himself, what some future editor will do for me, that is supply the name of a man of letters who, in his second childhood, devised a new mode of book-hunting: he used to remove one of the books in his library from its proper place, and when he had forgotten, as he soon did, where it had been put, he hunted the shelves till he found it. There will be some who see nothing more in this affecting anecdote than an exemplification of the vanity of human pursuits; but it is not refining too much, if

* EURIPIDES.

we perceive in it a consolatory mark of a cheerful and philosophical mind, retaining its character even when far in decay. For no one who had not acquired a habit of happy philosophy would have extracted amusement from his infirmities, and made the failure of his memory serve to beguile some of those hours which could then no longer be profitably employed.

Circulating libraries, which serve for the most part to promote useless reading, were not known when Daniel Dove set up his rest at Doncaster. It was about that time that a dissenting minister, Samuel Fancourt by name, opened the first in London, of course upon a very contracted scale. Book clubs are of much later institution. There was no bookseller in Doncaster till several years afterwards: sometimes an itinerant dealer in such wares opened a stall there on a market day, as Johnson's father used to do at Birmingham; and one or two of the trade regularly kept the fair. A little of the live stock of the London publishers found its way thither at such times, and more of their dead stock, with a regular supply of certain works popular enough to be printed in a cheap form for this kind of sale. And when, at the breaking up of a household, such books as the deceased or removing owner happened to possess were sold off with the furniture, those which found no better purchaser on the spot usually came into the hands of one of these dealers, and made the tour of the neighbouring markets. It was from such stragglers that the Doctor's ragged regiment had been chiefly raised. Indeed he was so frequent a customer, that the stall-keepers generally offered to his notice any English book which they thought likely to take his fancy, and any one in a foreign language which had not the appearance of a school-book. And when in one book he found such references to another as made him desirous of possessing, or at least consulting it, he employed a person at York to make inquiry for it there.

CHAPTER CXIII.

THOMAS GENT AND ALICE GUY, A TRUE TALE, SHOWING THAT A WOMAN'S CONSTANCY WILL NOT ALWAYS HOLD OUT LONGER THAN TROY TOWN, AND YET THE WOMAN MAY NOT BE THE PARTY WHO IS MOST IN FAULT.

Io dico, non dimando
Quel che tu vuoi udir, perch' io l' ho visto
Ove s' appunta ogni ubi, *e ogni* quando.

DANTE.

THE person whom the Doctor employed in collecting certain books for him, and whom Peter Hopkins had employed in the same way, was that Thomas Gent of whom it was incidentally said in the 47th Chapter that he published the old poem of Flodden Field, from a transcript made by Daniel's kind-hearted schoolmaster, Richard Guy, whose daughter he married. Since that chapter was written an account of Gent's life, written by himself in 1746, when he was in his 53d year, and in his own handwriting, was discovered by Mr. Thorpe, the bookseller, among a collection of books from Ireland, and published by him, with a portrait of the author, copied from a fine mezzotinto engraving by Valentine Green, which is well known to collectors. Gent was a very old man when that portrait was taken; and his fine loose-flowing silver hair gave great effect to a singularly animated and cheerful face. His autobiography is as characteristic as John Dunton's, and like it contains much information relating to the state of the press in his days, and the trade of literature. A few curious notices occur in it of the manners and transactions of those times. But the portion pertinent to the business of these volumes is that which in its consequences led him to become the Doctor's purveyor of old books in the ancient city of York.

Gent, though descended, he says, from the Gents of Staffordshire, was born in Dublin: his parents were good people in humble life, who trained him up in the way he should go, gave him the best education their means could afford, and apprenticed him to a printer, from whom, after three years' service, he ran away, because of the brutal usage which he received. He got on board ship with little more than a shilling in his pocket, and was landed at Parkgate to seek his fortune. But having made good use of the time which he had served with his tyrannical master, he obtained employment in London, and made himself useful to his employers. After having been four years there, he accepted an offer from Mr. White, who, as a reward for printing the Prince of Orange's Declaration when all the printers in London refused to undertake so dangerous a piece of work, was made King's printer for York and five other counties. Mr. White had plenty of business, there being few printers in England, except in London, at that time; "None," says Gent, "I am sure, at Chester, Liverpool, Whitehaven, Preston, Manchester, Kendal, and Leeds. The offer was eighteen pounds a year, with board, washing, and lodging, and a guinea to bear his charges on the road. Twenty shillings of this I offered," he says, "to Crofts the carrier, a very surly young fellow as ever I conversed with, but he would have five or six shillings more; finding him so stiff with me, I resolved to venture on foot. He set out with his horses on Monday, and the next morning, being the 20th of April, 1714, I set forward, and had not, I think, walked three miles, when a gentleman's servant with a horse ready saddled and himself riding another, overtook me, and for a shilling, with a glass or so on the road, allowed me to ride with him as far as Caxton, which was the period of his journey."

Having reached York about twelve o'clock on the Sunday following, and found the way to Mr. White's house, the door was opened by the head-maiden. "She ushered me," says Gent, "into the chamber where Mrs. White lay something ill in bed; but the old gentleman was at his dinner, by the fireside, sitting in a noble arm-chair, with a good large pie before him, and made me partake heartily with him. I had a guinea in my shoe lining, which I pulled out to ease my foot; at which the old gentleman smiled, and pleasantly said, it was more than he had ever seen a journeyman save before. I could not but smile too, because my trunk, with my clothes and eight guineas, was sent, about a month before to Ireland, where I was resolved to go and see my friends had his place not offered to me as it did."

Gent was as happy as he could wish here, and as he earned money bought clothes to serve him till he should rejoin his trunk in Dublin, which at the year's end he determined to do, refusing to renew his engagement till he had visited his parents. "Yet," says he, "what made my departure somewhat uneasy, I scarce then well knew how, was through respect of Mrs. Alice Guy, the young woman who I said first opened the door to me, upper maiden to Mrs. White, who, I was persuaded to believe, had the like mutual fondness for me—she was the daughter of Mr. Richard Guy, schoolmaster at Ingleton, near Lancashire; had very good natural parts, quick understanding, was of a fine complexion, and very amiable in her features. Indeed I was not very forward in love, or desire of matrimony, till I knew the world better, and consequently should be more able to provide such a handsome maintenance as I confess I had ambition enough to desire; but yet my heart could not absolutely slight so lovely a young creature as to pretend I had no esteem for her charms, which had captivated others, and particularly my master's grandson, Mr. Charles Bourne, who was more deserving than any. However I told her (because my irresolution should not anticipate her advancement,) that I should respect her as one of the dearest of friends; and receiving a little dog from her as a companion on the road, I had the honour to be accompanied as far as Bramham Moor by my rival."

He was received by his parents like the Prodigal son, and had engaged himself as journeyman in Dublin, when his old master Powell employed officers to seize him for leaving his apprenticeship. It was in vain that his father and a friendly brother-in-law offered a fair sum for his release, while he concealed himself; more was demanded than would have been proper for them to give; there was no other remedy than to leave Ireland once more, and as about that time he had received a letter from his dearest at York, saying that he was expected there, thither, purely again to enjoy her company, he resolved to direct his course. His friends were much concerned at their parting, "but my unlucky whelp," says he, "that a little before, while taking a glass with Mr. Hume (the printer with whom I had engaged), had torn my new hat in pieces, seemed nowise affected by my taking boat; so I let the rascal stay with my dear parents who were fond of him for my sake, as he was of them for his own; nor was he less pleasant by his tricks to the neighbourhood, who called him Yorkshire, from the country whence I brought him."

There is a chasm in this part of the manuscript: it appears, however, that he remained some months at York, and then went to London, where he was as careful as possible in saving what he had earned, "but yet," says he, "could not perceive a prospect of settlement whereby to maintain a spouse like her as I judged she deserved, and I could not bear the thoughts to bring her from a good settlement, without I could certainly make us both happy in a better." He went on, however, industriously and prosperously, had "the great happiness" in the year 1717 of being made freeman of the company of Stationers, and in the same year commenced citizen of London, his share of the treat that day with other expenses coming to about five pounds. Now that he was beyond his reach, his old tyrant in Dublin was glad to accept of five pounds for his discharge; this money he remitted, and thus became absolutely free both in England and Ireland, for which he gave sincere thanks to the Almighty.

"And now," says he, "I thought myself happy, when the thoughts of my dearest often occurred to my mind: God knows it is but too common, and that with the best and most considerate persons, that something or other gives them disquietude or makes them seek after it." A partnership at Norwich was offered him, and he accepted it; but a few hours afterwards there came a mournful letter from his parents, saying that they were very infirm, and extremely desirous to see him once more before they died. It is to Gent's honour that he immediately gave up his engagement at Norwich, though the stage coach had been ordered to receive him. The person whom he recommended in his stead was Mr. Robert Raikes, who when Gent wrote these memoirs was settled as a master in Gloucester; he became the father of a singularly prosperous family, and one of his sons, his successor in the printing office, is well known as the person who first established Sunday schools.

Yet though Gent acted under an impulse of natural duty on this occasion, he confesses that he was not without some cause for self-reproach: "I wrote," said he, "a lamenting letter to my dear in York, bewailing that I could not find a proper place as yet to settle in, told her that I was leaving the kingdom, and reminded her by what had passed that she could not be ignorant where to direct if she thought proper so to do; that I was far from slighting her, and resigned her to none but the protection of Heaven. But sure never was poor creature afflicted with such melancholy as I was upon my journey, my soul did seem to utter within me, 'wretch that I am, what am I doing, and whither going?' My parents, it's true, as they were constantly most affectionate, so indeed they are, especially in far advanced years, peculiar objects of my care and esteem; but am I not only leaving England, the Paradise of the world, to which as any loyal subject I have now an indubitable right, but am I not also departing, for aught I know for ever, from the dearest creature upon earth? from her that loved me when I knew not well how to respect myself; who was wont to give me sweet counsel in order for my future happiness, equally partook of those deep sorrows which our tender love had occasioned, was willing to undergo all hazards with me in this troublesome life, whose kind letters had so often proved like healing balm to my languishing condition, and whose constancy, had I been as equally faithful and not so timorous of being espoused through too many perplexing doubts, would never have been shaken, and without question would have promoted the greatest happiness for which I was created."

These self-reproaches, which were not undeserved, made him ill on the road. He reached Dublin, however, and though the employment which he got there was not nearly so profitable as what he had had in London, love for his parents made him contented, "and took," he says, "all thoughts of further advantages away, till Mr. Alexander Campbell, a Scotchman in the same printing office with me, getting me in liquor, obtained a promise that I should accompany him to England, where there was a greater likelihood of prosperity. Accordingly he so pressed me, and gave such reasons to my dear parents that it was not worth while to stay there for such small business as we enjoyed, that they consented we should go together: but alas! their melting tears made mine to flow, and bedewed my pillow every night after that I lodged with them. 'What, Tommy,' my mother would sometimes say, 'this English damsel of yours, I suppose, is the chiefest reason why you slight us and your native country!' 'Well,' added she, 'the ways of Providence I know are unsearchable; and whether I live to see you again or no, I shall pray God to be your defender and preserver!'—I thought it not fit to accumulate sorrows to us all, by returning any afflictive answers; but taking an opportunity whilst she was abroad on her business, I embarked with my friend once more for England."

Tommy, however, made the heart of his English damsel sick with hope long deferred. He was provident overmuch; and this he acknowledges even when endeavouring to excuse himself:—"all that I had undergone I must confess," he says, "I thought were but my just deserts for being so long absent from my dear," (it had now been an absence of some years), "and yet I could not well help it. I had a little money it is very true, but no certain home wherein to invite her. I knew she was well fixed; and it pierced me to the very heart to think, if through any miscarriage or misfortune I should alter her condition for the worse instead of the better. Upon this account my letters to her at this time were not so amorously obliging as they ought to have been from a sincere lover; by which she had reason, however she might have been mistaken, to think that I had failed in my part of those tender engagements which had passed between us."

Gent had sometimes the honour of being the Bellman's poet, and used to get heartily treated for the Christmas verses which he composed in that capacity. One lucky day he happened to meet his friend Mr. Evan Ellis, who was the Bellman's printer in ordinary: "Tommy," said his friend, "I am persuaded that some time or other you'll set up a press in the country, where, I believe, you have a pretty northern lass at heart; and as I believe you save money and can spare it, I can help you to a good pennyworth preparatory to your design." Accordingly upon this recommendation he purchased at a cheap price a considerable quantity of old types, which Mr. Mist, the proprietor of a journal well known at that time by his name, had designed for the furnace. To this he added a font almost new, resolving to venture in the world with his dearest, who at first, he says, gave him encouragement. He does not say that she ever discouraged him, and his own resolution appears to have been but half-hearted. His purse being much exhausted by these purchases, he still worked on for further supplies; by and by he bought a new font, and so went on increasing his stock, working for his old first master and for himself also, and occasionally employing servants himself, though the fatigue was exceedingly great and almost more than he could go through. Alas the while for Alice Guy, who was now in the tenth year of her engagement to lukewarm Thomas!

Lukewarm Thomas imagined "things would so fall out that after some little time he should have occasion to invite his dear to London." But let him tell his own story. "One Sunday morning, as my shoes were japanning by a little boy at the end of the lane, there came Mr. John Hoyle, who had been a long time in a messenger's custody on suspicion for reprinting *Vox Populi Vox Dei*, under direction of Mrs. Powell, with whom he wrought as journeyman; 'Mr. Gent,' said he, 'I have been at York to see my parents, and am but just as it were returned to London. I am heartily glad to see you, but sorry to tell you that you have lost your old sweetheart; for I assure you that she is really married to your rival Mr. Bourne!' I was so thunderstruck that I could scarcely return an answer,— all former thoughts crowding into my mind, the consideration of spending my substance on a business I would not have engaged in as a master but for her sake, my own remissness that had occasioned it, and withal that she could not in such a case be much blamed for mending her fortune, — all these threw me under a very deep concern."

He consoled himself as Petrarch had done: and opening his old vein of poetry and bell-metal, gave some vent to his passion by writing a copy of verses to the tune of "Such charms has Phillis!" then much in request, and proper for the flute. He entitled it "The Forsaken Lover's Letter to his former Sweetheart." "When I had done," says he, "as I did not care that Mr. Midwinter (his master) should know of my great disappointment, I gave the copy to Mr. Dodd, who printing the same sold thousands of them, for which he offered me a price; but as it was on my own proper concern, I scorned to accept of anything except a glass of comfort or so." If the Forsaken Lover's Lamentation had been sung about the streets of York, Mrs. Bourne might have listened to it without suspecting that she was the treacherous maid, who for the sake of this world's splendour had betrayed her only sweet jewel, left him to languish alone, and broken his heart,

Proving that none could be falser than she.

Conscience would never have whispered to her that it was lukewarm Thomas who closed his complaint with the desperate determination expressed in the ensuing stanza.

Now to the woods and groves I'll be ranging,
Free from all women I'll vent forth my grief:
While birds are singing and sweet notes exchanging,
This pleasing concert will yield me relief.
Thus like the swan before its departing
Sings forth its elegy in melting strains,
My dying words shall move all the kind powers above
To pity my fate, the most wretched of swains.

He neither went to the woods, nor died; but entered into an engagement with Mr. Dodd's widow to manage her printing business, being the more willing to enter into the service of this gentlewoman since he was disappointed of his first love. The widow was a most agreeable person, daughter to a sea captain, and had been educated at the boarding-school at Hackney: Dodd was her second husband, and she had been left with a child by each. "I thought her," says Gent, "worthy of the best of spouses; for sure there never could be a finer economist or sweeter mother to her dear children, whom she kept exceedingly decent. I have dined with her; but then as in reason I allowed what was fitting for my meals, and her conversation, agreeably to her fine education, almost wounded me with love, and at the same time commanded a becoming reverence. What made her excellent carriage the more endearing was, that I now must never expect to behold my first love at York: though I heard by travellers that not only she, but her husband used to inquire after me. Indeed I was sensible that Mr. Bourne, though a likely young man, was not one of the most healthful persons; but far from imagining otherwise than that he might have outlived me who then was worn to a shadow. But, see the wonderful effects of Divine Providence in all things!

"It was one Sunday morning that Mr. Philip Wood, a quondam partner at Mr. Midwinter's, entering my chambers where I sometimes used to employ him too when slack of business in other places—'Tommy,' said he, 'all these fine materials of yours, must be moved to York!' At which wondering, 'what mean you?' said I. 'Ay,' said he, 'and you must go too, without it's your own fault; for your first sweetheart is now at liberty, and left in good circumstances by her dear spouse, who deceased but of late.' 'I pray heaven,' answered I, 'that his precious soul may be happy: and for aught I know it may be as you say, for, indeed, I think I may not trifle with a widow as I have formerly done with a maid.' I made an excuse to my mistress that I had business in Ireland, but that I hoped to be at my own lodgings in about a month's time; if not, as I had placed everything in order, she might easily by any other person carry on the business. But she said she would not have any beside me in that station I enjoyed, and therefore should expect my return to her again: but respectfully taking leave, I never beheld her after, though I heard she was after very indifferently married. I had taken care that my goods should be privately packed up, and hired a little warehouse and put them in ready to be sent, by sea or land, to where I should order: and I pitched upon Mr. Campbell, my fellow-traveller, as my confidant in this affair, desiring my cousins to assist him; all of whom I took leave of at the Black Swan in Holborn, where I had paid my passage in the stage coach, which brought me to York in four days' time. Here I found my dearest once more, though much altered from what she was about ten years before that I had not seen her. There was no need for new courtship; but decency suspended the ceremony of marriage for some time: till my dearest at length, considering the ill-consequence of delay in her business, as well as the former ties of love that passed innocently between us by word and writing, gave full consent to have the nuptials celebrated,"—and performed accordingly they were, "in the stately cathedral," the very day of Archbishop Blackburne's installation.

CHAPTER CXIV.

THE AUTHOR HINTS AT CERTAIN CIRCUMSTANCES IN THE LIFE OF THOMAS GENT ON WHICH HE DOES NOT THINK IT NECESSARY TO DWELL.

Round white stones will serve, they say,
As well as eggs, to make hens lay.

BUTLER.

If I were given to prolixity, and allowed myself to be led away from the subject before me, I might here be tempted to relate certain particulars concerning Thomas Gent; how under his first London master, Mr. Midwinter, whose house was a ballad-house, "he worked many times from five in the morning till twelve at night, and frequently without food from breakfast till five or six in the evening, through their hurry with hawkers." And how in that same service he wrote, which is to say in modern language *reported*, Dr. Sacheverel's sermon after his suspension, for which his master gave him a crown-piece, and a pair of breeches,—not before they were wanted;—and by which the said master gained nearly thirty pounds in the course of the week. And how he once engaged with Mr. Francis Clifton, who having had a liberal education at Oxford proved a Papist, set up a press, printed a newspaper, and getting in debt moved his goods into the liberty of the Fleet, and there became entered as a prisoner; and how Gent sometimes in extreme weather worked for him under a mean shed adjoining to the prison walls, when snow and rain fell alternately on the cases, yet, he says, the number of wide-mouthed stentorian hawkers, brisk trade, and very often a glass of good ale, revived the drooping spirits of him and his fellow workmen; and he often admired the success of this Mr. Clifton in his station, for whether through pity of mankind, or the immediate hand of Divine Providence to his family, advantageous jobs so often flowed upon him as gave him cause to be merry under his heavy misfortunes.

And how while in this employ a piece of work came in which he composed and helped to work off, but was not permitted to know who was the author. It was a vindication of an honest clergyman who had been committed to the King's Bench upon an action of *scandalum magnatum:* however, says he, "when finished, the papers were packed up, and delivered to my care; and the same night, my master hiring a coach, we were driven to Westminster, where we entered into a large sort of monastic building. Soon were we ushered into a spacious hall, where we sate near a large table covered with an ancient carpet of curious work, and whereon was soon laid a bottle of wine for our entertainment. In a little time we were visited by a grave gentleman in a black lay habit, who entertained us with one pleasant discourse or other. He bid us be secret; for, said he, the imprisoned divine does not know who is his defender; and if he did, I know his temper; in a sort of transport he would reveal it, and so I should be blamed for my good office: and whether his intention was designed to show his gratitude, yet if a man is hurt by a friend, the damage is the same as if done by an enemy: to prevent which is the reason I desire this concealment. 'You need not fear me, Sir,' said my master; 'and I, good Sir,' added I, 'you may be less afraid of; for I protest I do not know where I am, much less your person, nor heard where I should be driven, or if I shall not be driven to Jerusalem before I get home again. Nay, I shall forget I ever did the job by to-morrow, and consequently shall never answer any questions about it, if demanded. Yet, Sir, I shall secretly remember your generosity, and drink to your health with this brimfull glass.' Thereupon this set them both a-laughing, and truly I was got merrily tipsy, so merry that I hardly knew how I was driven homewards. For my part I was ever inclined to secresy and fidelity; and therefore I was nowise inquisitive concerning our hospitable entertainer. — But happening afterwards to behold a state prisoner in a coach, guarded from Westminster to the Tower, God bless me, thought I, it was no less than the Bishop of Rochester, Dr. Atterbury, by whom my master and I had been treated!"

Were I to ramble from my immediate purpose I might relate how Gent saw Mr. John Mathews, a young printer, drawn on a sledge to the place of execution, where he suffered for high treason; and how Mathews's clothes were exceeding neat, the lining of his coat a rich Persian silk, and every other thing as befitted a gentleman; and how he talked of death like a philosopher to some young ladies who came to take their farewell. This poor youth was but in his nineteenth year, and not out of his apprenticeship to his mother and brother. He had been under misfortunes before, and through the favour of the government at that time was discharged, at which time his brother had given public orders to the people in his employ that if ever they found John either doing or speaking anything against the government, they would inform him that he might take a proper method to prevent it. Nevertheless, for ten guineas, he, with the assistance of another apprentice and a journeyman, printed a treasonable paper intitled *Vox Populi Vox Dei*, containing direct incitement to rebellion. I might relate also how this journeyman Lawrence Vezey, who went by the name of *old gentleman* in the printing-office, and who had not the character of an honest man about his printing; and who, moreover, had gone to the criminal's mother and offered to go out of the way if she would give him money, and accordingly had gone to St. Albans, and staid there nine days, but no money coming, he could not stay out of the way longer, but seems rather to have been suspected of putting himself in the way, — I might, I say, relate how this Vezey did not long survive the ill-fated youth; and how at his burial, in an obscure part of Islington churchyard, many of the printers' boys, called devils, made a noise like such, with their ball stocks carried thither for that purpose, and how the minister was much interrupted thereby in the Burial service, and shameful indignities were committed at the grave: and how the printers, who had been at Islington that day, had their names sent off to the Courts of Westminster, where it cost their pockets pretty well before their persons were discharged from trouble. But Gent, who desired to be out of harm's way, had shunned what he called the crew of demons with their incendiaries to a mischief.

I might also relate how he once carried skull caps made of printing balls stuffed with wool to his brother printers, who were to exhibit their faces in that wooden frame called the pillory; in which frame, nevertheless, he seems to think they were properly set; and the mob were of the same opinion, for these skull caps proved but weak helmets against the missiles wherewith they were assailed. Moreover, further to exemplify the perils which in those days environed the men who meddled with printer's types, I might proceed to say how, after a strange dream, poor Gent was in the dead of the night alarmed by a strange thundering noise at the door, and his door broken open, and himself seized in his bed by two king's messengers upon a false information that he had been engaged in printing some lines concerning the imprisoned Bishop of Rochester, which had given offence; and how he was carried to a public-house near St. Sepulchre's Church, whither his two employers Mr. Midwinter and Mr. Clifton were also brought prisoners, and how they were taken to Westminster and there imprisoned in a very fine house in Manchester Court which had nevertheless within the fusty smell of a prison; and how from the high window of his humble back apartment he could behold the Thames, and hear the dashing of the flowing waters against the walls that kept it within due bounds: and how in the next room to him was confined that unhappy young Irish clergyman Mr. Neynoe"—(not Naypoe as the name in these memoirs is erroneously given). "I used," says Gent, "to hear him talk to himself when his raving fits came on; and now and then would he sing psalms with such a melodious voice as produced both admiration and pity from me, who was an object of commiseration myself, in being awhile debarred from friends to see me, or the use of pen, ink, and paper to write to them." And how after five days he was honourably discharged, and took boat from Palace-Yard stairs, in which, he says, "my head seemed to be affected with a strange giddiness; and when I safely arrived at home, some of my kinder neighbours appeared very joyful at my return. And my poor linnet, whose death I very much feared would come to pass, saluted me with her long, pleasant, chirping notes; and, indeed, the poor creature had occasion to be the most joyful, for her necessary stock was almost exhausted, and I was come just in the critical time to yield her a fresh supply." It was some compensation for his fright on this occasion that he printed the Bishop of Rochester's Effigy "with some inoffensive verses that pleased all parties," which sold very well; and that he formed some observations upon the few dying words of Counsellor Layer, in nature of a large speech, which for about three days had such a run of sale that the unruly hawkers were ready to pull his press in pieces for the goods.

Farther I might say of Gent, that in January, 1739, when the Ouse at York was frozen, he set up a press on the ice, and printed names there, to the great satisfaction of young gentlemen, ladies, and others, who were very liberal on the occasion. And how having been unjustly as he thought ejected from a house in Stonegate, which was held under a prebendal lease and which fell to Mr. Laurence Sterne, (to whom, however, it was in vain to apply for redress, it not being in his power to relieve him,) he bought a house in Petergate and built a tower upon it; "by which addition," said he, "my house seems the highest in the city and affords an agreeable prospect round the country: we have a wholesome air whenever we please to ascend, especially the mornings and evenings, with great conveniency for my business when overcrowded in the narrow rooms below; and several gentlemen have occasionally taken a serious pipe there, to talk of affairs in printing, as well as neighbours to satisfy their curiosity in viewing the flowers that grow almost round about upon the walls."

This, and much more than this, might be said of Thomas Gent, and would have been deemed not uninteresting by the collectors of English topography, and typographic curiosities, Gent being well known to them for his "famous history of the City of York, its magnificent Cathedral, St. Mary's Abbey, &c.;" his "History of the Loyal Town of Ripon, Fountains Abbey, Beverley, Wakefield, &c.;" and his "History of the Royal and Beautiful Town of Kingston-upon-Hull." He entered upon a different province when he wrote his Treatise, entitled "Divine Justice and Mercy displayed in the Life of Judas Iscariot." But though it was because of his turn for books and antiquities that the Doctor employed him to hunt the stalls at York, as Browne Willis did to collect for him epitaphs and tradesmen's halfpence, what I had to say of him arises out of his connexion with Richard Guy, and must therefore be confined to his dilatory courtship and late marriage.

CHAPTER CXV.

THE READER IS REMINDED OF PRINCE ABINO JASSIMA AND THE FOX-LADY. GENT NOT LIKE JOB, NOR MRS. GENT LIKE JOB'S WIFE.

A me parrebbe a la storia far torto,
S' io non aggiungo qualche codicillo;
Acciò che ognun chi legge, benedica
L' ultimo effetto de la mia fatica.

PULCI.

I CANNOT think so meanly of my gentle readers as to suppose that any of them can have forgotten the story of the Japanese Prince Abino Jassima, and the gradual but lamentable metamorphosis of his beautiful wife. But perhaps it may not have occurred to them that many a poor man, and without anything miraculous in the case, finds himself in the same predicament, — except that when he discovers his wife to be a vixen he is not so easily rid of her.

Let me not be suspected of insinuating that Alice Gent, formerly Bourne, formerly Guy, proved to be a wife of this description, for which, I know not wherefore, an appellation has been borrowed from the she-fox. Her husband, who found that ten years had wrought a great change in her appearance, complained indeed of other changes. "I found," he says, "her temper much altered from that sweet natural softness and most tender affection that rendered her so amiable to me while I was more juvenile and she a maiden. Not less sincere I must own; but with that presumptive air and conceited opinion (like Mrs. Day in the play of the Committee) which made me imagine an epidemical distemper prevailed among the good women to ruin themselves and families, or, if not prevented by Divine Providence, to prove the sad cause of great contention and of disquietude. However as I knew I was but then a novice in the intricate laws of matrimony, and that nothing but a thorough annihilation can disentangle or break that chain which often produces a strange concatenation for future disorders, I endeavoured to comply with a sort of stoical resolution to some very harsh rules that otherwise would have grated my human understanding. For as by this change I had given a voluntary wound to my wonted liberty, now attacked in the maintenance partly of pretended friends, spunging parasites, and flatterers who imposed on good nature to our great damage; so in this conjugal captivity, as I may term it, I was fully resolved, likewise in a Christian sense, to make my yoke as easy as possible, thereby to give no offence to custom or law of any kind. The tender affection that a good husband naturally has to the wife of his bosom is such, as to make him often pass by the greatest insults that can be offered to human nature; such I mean as the senseless provoking arguments used by one who will not be awakened from delusion till poverty appears, shows the ingratitude of false friends in prosperity, and brings her to sad repentance in adversity: she will then wish she had been foreseeing as her husband, when it is too late; condemn her foolish credulity, and abhor those who have caused her to differ from her truest friend, whose days she has embittered with the most undutiful aggravations, to render everything uncomfortable to him!"

I suspect that Thomas Gent was wrong in thinking thus of his wife; I am sure he was wrong in thus writing of her, and that I should be doing wrong in repeating what he has written, if it were not with the intention of showing that though he represents himself in this passage as another Job, Socrates, or Jerry Sneak, it must not be concluded that his wife resembled the termagant daughter of Sir Jacob Jollup, Xantippe, Rahamat the daughter of Ephraim, her cousin Makher the daughter of Manasseh, or Queen Saba, whichever of these three latter were the wife of Job.

And here let me observe that although I follow the common usage in writing the last venerable name, I prefer the orthography of Junius and Tremellius, who write Hiob, because it better represents the sound of the original Hebrew, and is moreover more euphonous than Job, or Jobab, if those commentators err not who identify that King of Edom with the Man of Uz. Indeed it is always meet and right to follow the established usage, unless there be some valid reason for departing from it; and moreover there is this to be said in favour of retaining the usual form and pronunciation of this well-known name, that if it were disnaturalised and put out of use, an etymology in our language would be lost sight of. For a *job* in the working or operative sense of the word, is evidently something which it requires patience to perform; in the physical and moral sense, as when, for example, in the language of the vulgar, a personal hurt or misfortune is called a bad *job*, it is something which it requires patience to support; and in the political sense it is something which it requires patience in the public to endure: and in all these senses the origin of the word must be traced to Job, who is the proverbial exemplar of this virtue. This derivation has escaped Johnson; nor has that lexicographer noticed the substantives *jobing* and *jobation*, and the verb to *jobe*, all from the same root, and familiar in the mouths of the people.

For these reasons therefore, and especially the etymological one, I prefer the common, though peradventure, and indeed perlikelihood, erroneous manner of writing the name, to Iob, Hiob, Ajob, Ajoub, or Jjob, all which have been proposed. And I do not think it worth while (that is my while or the reader's) to inquire into the derivation of the name, and whether it may with most probability be expounded to mean sorrowful, jubilant, persecuted, beloved, zealous, or wise, in the sense of sage, seer, or magician. Nor whether Job was also called Jasub, Jaschub, Jocab, Jocam, Jobal, Jubab, Hobab, or Uz of that ilk, for this also has been contended. Nor to investigate the position of a territory the name of which has been rendered so famous by its connexion with him, and of which nothing but the name is known. This indeed has occasioned much discussion among biblical chorographers. And not many years have elapsed since, at a late hour of the night, or perhaps an early one of the morning, the watchman in Great Russell Street found it necessary in the discharge of his duty to interpose between two learned and elderly gentlemen, who returning together from a literary compotation, had entered upon this discussion on the way, and forgetting the example of the Man of Uz, quarrelled about the situation of his country. The scene of this dispute,—the only one upon that subject that ever required the interference of the watch in the streets of London at midnight,—was near the Museum Gate, and the Author of the Indian Antiquities was one of the disputants.

Returning, however, to the matter which these last parenthetical paragraphs interrupted, I say that before lukewarm Thomas represented himself as another Job for matrimonial endurance, he ought to have asked himself whether the motives for which he married the widow Bourne, were the same as those for which he wooed the fair maiden Alice Guy; and whether, if Mrs. Gent suspected that as she had been obliged to her first husband for her money, she was obliged to the money for her second, it was not very natural for her to resent any remonstrances on his part, when she entertained or assisted those whom she believed to be her friends, and who peradventure had claims upon her hospitality or her bounty for her late husband's sake.

> A woman's goodness, when she is a wife,
> Lies much upon a man's desert; believe it, Sir.
> If there be fault in her, I'll pawn my life on't
> 'Twas first in him, if she were ever good.*

If there be any reader so inconsiderate as to exclaim, "what have we to do with the temper and character of a low-lived woman who was dead and buried long before we were born, whom nobody ever heard of before, and for whom nobody cares a straw now! What can have induced this most unaccountable of authors to waste his time and thoughts upon such people and such matter!"—Should there, I say, be persons, as in all likelihood there may, so impatient and so unreasonable as to complain in this manner, I might content myself with observing to them in the words of that thoughtful and happy-minded man Mr. Danby of Swinton, that if Common Sense had not a vehicle to carry it abroad, it must always stay at home.

But I am of the school of Job, and will reply with Uzzite patience to these objectors, as soon as I shall have related in a few words the little more that remains to be said of Thomas Gent, printer of York, and Alice his wife. They had only one child, it died an infant of six months, and the father speaks with great feeling of its illness and death. "I buried its pretty corpse," he says, "in the Church of St. Michael le Belfrey, where it was laid on the breast of Mr. Charles Bourne, my predecessor, in the chancel on the south side of the altar." This was in 1726; there he was buried himself more than half a century afterwards, in the 87th year of his age; and Alice, who opened the door to him when he first arrived in York, was no doubt deposited in the same vault with both her husbands.

* Beaumont and Fletcher.

CHAPTER CXVI.

DR. SOUTHEY. JOHN BUNYAN. BARTHOLOMÆUS SCHERÆUS. TERTULLIAN. DOMENICO BERNINO. PETRARCH. JEREMY TAYLOR. HARTLEY COLERIDGE. DIEGO DE SAN PEDRO, AND ADAM LITTLETON.

> Black spirits and white, red spirits and gray;
> Mingle, mingle, mingle, you that mingle may.
> Titty, Tiffin, keep it stiff in!
> Firedrake, Puckey, make it lucky!
> Liard, Robin, you must bob in!
> Round, around, around, about, about!
> All *good* come running in, all *ill* keep out.
>
> Middleton.

Nine years after the convention of Cintra a representation was made to the Laureate in favour of some artillery horses employed in Sir Arthur Wellesley's army. They were cast-off Irish cavalry, and their efficiency had been called in question; indeed it had been affirmed that they were good for nothing; attestations to disprove this were produced, and the Laureate was requested to set this matter right in his History of the Peninsular War.† The good-natured historian has given accordingly a note to the subject, saying that he thought himself bound to notice the representation were it only for the singularity of the case. If Dr. Southey thought it became him for that reason and for truth's sake, to speak a good word of some poor horses who had long ago been worked to death and left to the dogs and wolves by the way-side, much more may I feel myself bound for the sake of Dr. Dove to vindicate the daughter of his old schoolmaster from a splenetic accusation brought against her by her husband. The reader who knows what the Doctor's feelings were

† See vol. i. p. 554. 4to ed.

with regard to Mr. Guy, and what mine are for the Doctor, would I am sure excuse me even if on such an occasion I had travelled out of the record.

Gent, when he penned that peevish page, seems to have thought with Tom Otter, that a wife is a very scurvy clogdogdo! And with John Bunyan that "Women, whenever they would perk it and lord it over their husbands, ought to remember that both by creation and transgression they are made to be in subjection to them." "Such a thing," says the Arch-tinker, "may happen, as that the woman, not the man, may be in the right, (I mean when both are godly), but ordinarily it is otherwise."

Authors of a higher class than the York printer and topographist have complained of their wives. We read in Burton that Bartholomæus Scheræus, Professor of Hebrew at Wittenberg, whom he calls "that famous Poet Laureate," said in the introduction to a work of his upon the Psalms, he should have finished it long before, but amongst many miseries which almost broke his back (his words were *inter alia dura et tristia, quæ misero mihi pene tergum fregerunt,*) he was yoked to a worse than Xantippe. A like lamentation is made more oddly, and with less excuse, by Domenico Bernino, the author of a large history of All Heresies, which he dedicated to Clement XI. Tertullian, he says, being ill advised in his youth, and deceived by that shadow of repose which the conjugal state offers to the travellers in this miserable world, threw himself into the troubled sea of matrimony. And no sooner had he taken a wife, than being made wise by his own misfortunes, he composed his laborious treatise *de molestiis nuptiarum*, concerning the troubles of marriage, finding in this employment the only relief from those continual miseries, to which, he adds, we who now write may bear our present and too faithful testimony,—*delle quali Noi ancora che queste cose scriviamo, siamo per lui testimonio pur troppo vero e presente.*

The Historian of Heresy and the Hebrew Professor might have learned a lesson from Petrarch's Dialogue *de importunâ Uxore*, in that work of his *de Remediis Utriusque Fortunæ.* When Dolor complains of having a bad wife, Ratio reminds him that he might blame his ill-fortune for any other calamity, but this he had brought upon himself and the only remedy was patience.

Est mala crux, conjux mala; crux tamen illa ferenda est
Quâ nemo nisi Mors te relevare potest.

"It is the unhappy chance of many," says Jeremy Taylor, "that finding many inconveniences upon the mountains of single life, they descend into the valleys of marriage to refresh their troubles, and there they enter into fetters, and are bound to sorrow by the cords of a man's or woman's peevishness; and the worst of the evil is, they are to thank their own follies, for they fell into the snare by entering an improper way." To complain of the consequences, which are indeed the proper punishment, is to commit a second folly by proclaiming the first, and the second deserves the ridicule it is sure to meet with. Hartley Coleridge has well said, that there must always be something defective in the moral feelings or very unfortunate in the circumstances of a man who makes the public his confidant!

If Thomas Gent had read Lord Berners' Castle of Love, which might easily, rare as it has now become, have fallen in his way a hundred years ago, he would there have seen fifteen reasons why men do wrong when they speak ill of women, and twenty reasons why they ought to speak well of them. All lovers of our old literature know how greatly we are beholden to John Bouchier, Knight, Lord Berners, who, when Deputy General of the King's Town of Calais and Marches of the same, employed his leisure in translating books out of French into English. But he must have been one of those persons, who, with a great appetite for books, have no discriminating taste, or he would not have translated Arthur of Little Britain, when Gyron le Courtoys and Meliadus were not extant in his own language; nor would he, even at the instance of Lady Elizabeth Carew, if he had known a good book from a bad one, have englished from its French version the Carcel de Amor, which Diego de San Pedro composed at the request of the Alcayde de los Donzelles, D. Diego Hernandez, and of other Knights and Courtiers.

The reader will please to observe that though all worthless books are bad, all bad books are not necessarily worthless. A work, however bad, if written, as the Carcel de Amor was, early in the sixteenth century, and translated into Italian, French, and English, must be worth reading to any person who thinks the history of literature (and what that history includes) a worthy object of pursuit. If I had not been one of those who like Ludovicus Bosch — (my friend in the caxon) — are never weary of hunting in those woods, I could not, gentle reader, have set before you, as I shall incontinently proceed to do, the fifteen above-mentioned and here following reasons, why you will commit a sin if you ever speak in disparagement of womankind.

First then, Leriano, the unhappy hero of Diego de San Pedro's tragic story, says that all things which God has made are necessarily good; women therefore being his creatures, to calumniate them is to blaspheme one of his works.

Secondly, there is no sin more hateful than ingratitude; and it is being ungrateful to the Virgin Mary if we do not honour all women for her sake.

Thirdly, it is an act of cowardice for man who is strong, to offend woman who is weak.

Fourthly, the man who speaks ill of woman brings dishonour upon himself, inasmuch as every man is of woman born.

Fifthly, such evil speaking is, for the last-mentioned reason, a breach of the fifth commandment.

Sixthly, it is an obligation upon every noble man to employ himself virtuously both in word and deed; and he who speaks evil incurs the danger of infamy.

Seventhly, because all knights are bound by their order to show respect and honour to all womankind.

Eighthly, such manner of speech brings the honour of others in question.

Ninthly, and principally, it endangers the soul of the evil speaker.

Tenthly, it occasions enmities and the fatal consequences resulting therefrom.

Eleventhly, husbands by such speeches may be led to suspect their wives, to use them ill, to desert them, and peradventure to make away with them.

Twelfthly, a man thereby obtains the character of being a slanderer.

Thirteenthly, he brings himself in jeopardy with those who may think themselves bound to vindicate a lady's reputation or revenge the wrong which has been done to it.

Fourteenthly, to speak ill of women is a sin because of the beauty which distinguishes their sex, which beauty is so admirable that there is more to praise in one woman than there can be to condemn in all.

Fifteenthly, it is a sin because all the benefactors of mankind have been born of women, and therefore we are obliged to women for all the good that has ever been done in the world.

Such are the fifteen reasons which Diego de San Pedro excogitated to show that it is wrong for men to speak ill of women; and the twenty reasons which he has superinduced to prove that they are bound to speak well of them are equally cogent and not less curious. I have a reason of my own for reserving these till another opportunity. Not, however, to disappoint my fair readers altogether of that due praise which they have so properly expected, I will conclude the present chapter with a few flowers taken from the pulpit of my old acquaintance Adam Littleton. There is no impropriety in calling him so, though he died before my grandfathers and grandmothers were born; and when I meet him in the next world I hope to improve this one-sided acquaintance by introducing myself and thanking him for his Dictionary and his Sermons.

The passage occurs in a sermon preached at the obsequies of the Right Honourable the Lady Jane Cheyne. The text was "Favour is deceitful, and Beauty is vain; but a woman that feareth the Lord, she shall be praised:" in which proposition, says the Preacher, we have, First the subject *Woman*, with her qualification *that fears the Lord:* Secondly the predicate, *she shall be praised*.

"WOMAN, in the primitive design of Nature, God's master-piece, being the last work of creation, and made with a great deal of deliberation and solemnity.

"For to look upon her as a supernumerary creature, and one brought into the world by the bye, besides the Creator's first intention, upon second thoughts,— is to lay a foul imputation upon Divine Wisdom, as if it had been at a stand, and were to seek.

"Wherefore, as we used to argue that all things were made for the use and service of man, because he was made last of all; I do not see, if that argument be good, why the same consequences should not be of like force here too, that Man himself was made for the affectionate care of Woman, who was framed not only *after* him, but *out of* him too, the more to engage his tenderest and dearest respects.

"Certainly this manner of production doth plainly evince the equality of the Woman's merits and rights with Man; she being a noble cyon transplanted from his stock, and by the mystery of marriage implanted into him again, and made one with him.

"She is then equally at least partaker with him of all the *advantages* which appertain to human nature, and alike capable of those *improvements* which by the efforts of reason, and the methods of education and the instincts of the Blessed Spirit, are to be made upon it.—

"Hence it was that all Arts and Sciences, all Virtues and Graces, both divine and moral, are represented in the shape and habit of Women. Nor is there any reason for fancying Angels themselves more of our sex than of the other, since amongst them there is no such distinction, but they may as well be imagined female as male.

"Above all for Piety and Devotion, which is the top-perfection of our nature, and makes it most like angelical; as the capacity of Women is as large, so their inclinations are generally more vigorous, the natural bias and tendency of their spirits lying that way, and their softer temper more kindly receiving the supernatural impression of God's Spirit.

"This is *that*, if any thing, which gives their sex the pre-eminence above us men and gains them just advantages of praise; that whereas those who have only a handsome shape and good features to commend them, are adored and idolised by persons of slight apprehensions and ungoverned passions, pious and virtuous women command the veneration of the most judicious, and are deservedly admired by holy men and Angels."

Thus saith that Adam of whom even Adam Clarke might have been proud as a namesake; and whose portrait the Gentlemen of the name of Adam who meet and dine together at a tavern in London, once a year, ought to have in their club-room.

CHAPTER CXVII.

CONCERNING JOB'S WIFE.

This insertion is somewhat long, and utterly impertinent to the principal matter, and makes a great gap in the tale; nevertheless is no disgrace, but rather a beauty and to very good purpose.

PUTTENHAM.

IT has been a custom in popish countries, when there were no censors of the press civil or ecclesiastical to render it unnecessary, for an author to insert at the beginning of his work a protestation declaring, that if the book contained anything contrary to the established faith, he thereby revoked any such involuntary error of opinion. Something similar has sometimes been done in free countries, and not then as a mere form, nor for prudential considerations, but in the sincerity of an upright intention, and a humble mind.—"Who can tell how oft he offendeth? O cleanse thou me from my secret faults!"

To be sure what I am about to say is upon

a matter of less import, and may seem neither to require nor deserve so grave a prelude. But it is no part of my philosophy to turn away from serious thoughts when they lie before me.

> Φράσω γὰρ δὴ ὅσον μοι
> Ψυχᾷ προσφιλές ἐστιν εἰπειν.*

I had no intention of quoting scripture when I began, but the words came to mind and I gave them utterance, and thou wilt not be displeased, good reader, at seeing them thus introduced.—Good reader, I have said:—if thou art not good, I would gladly persuade thee to become so;—and if thou art good, would fain assist thee in making thyself better. *Si de tout ce que je vous ai dit, un mot peut vous être utile, je n'aurai nul regret à ma peine.*†

Well then benevolent and patient reader, it is here my duty to confess that there is a passage in the last chapter which I am bound to retract. For since that chapter was written I have found cause to apprehend that in vindicating Guy's daughter I have wronged Job's wife, by accrediting a received calumny founded upon a mistranslation. I did not then know, what I have now learned, that a judicious and learned writer, modest enough to conceal his name and designate himself only as a private gentleman, had many years ago, in a Review of the History of Job, stated his reasons for regarding her as a much injured woman.

Every one knows that the wife of Job in our Bible says to her husband, "Dost thou still retain thine integrity? Curse God and die!" Now this writer asserts that the Hebrew verb which our translators render in this place *to curse*, means also *to bless*, *to salute*, *or give the knee*, and that there are but four more places in all the Bible where it can be supposed to have an opposite meaning, and that even in those places it may admit of the better signification. It is not surprising that many verbal difficulties should occur in a book, which, if of later date than the books of Moses, is next to them in antiquity. Such difficulties might be expected whether we have it in its original language, or whether it were written, as many have opined, by Job himself in Syriac, Arabic, or Idumean, and translated into Hebrew; much more if the opinion of Dr. Wall could be admitted, that it was written at first in hieroglyphics, against which the length of the book is a conclusive objection. "I should imagine," says the anonymous defender, "she had so high an opinion of her husband's innocence that she might mean to advise him, seeing notwithstanding his uprightness he was thus amazingly afflicted, to go and kneel or bow down before God, and plead or as it were expostulate with him concerning the reason of these dreadful calamities,—even though he should die. If this sense of her expressions be allowed, it will justify Job's wise rebuke for her inconsiderateness, while, as he still possessed his soul in submissive patience, crying out—'Thou speakest as a rash, thoughtless, or foolish woman: what, shall we receive good at the hands of God, and shall we not receive evil?'—Indeed it should seem that God himself did not behold her as an impious or blasphemous woman, inasmuch as we find she was made a great instrument in Job's future and remarkable prosperity, becoming after their great calamity the mother of seven sons and three most beautiful daughters. I say she was their mother, because we have no intimation that Job had any other wife."

Now upon consulting such authorities as happen to be within my reach, I find that this interpretation is supported by the Vulgate,—*benedic Deo, et morere*; and also by the version of Junius and Tremellius—*adhuc tu retines integritatem tuam, benedicendo Deum atque moriendo.* Piscator too renders the word in its better sense, as I learn from the elder Wesley's elaborate collation of this most ancient book, from which I collect also that the Chaldee version gives the good meaning, the Arabian and Syriac the bad one; and that the words of the Septuagint ἀλλὰ εἰπόν τι ῥῆμα εἰς κύριον καὶ τελεύτα, are interpreted by the Scholiast κατάρασον τὸν θεόν.

* Euripides. † Mad. de Maintenon.

Moreover, a passage of some length which is in no other translation except that of St. Ambrose, is found in three manuscripts of the Septuagint, one* of them being that from which the text of the Oxford edition of 1817 is taken. It is as follows: "But after much time had elapsed, his wife said unto him, how long wilt thou endure thus, saying, 'I will expect yet a little while, awaiting the hope of my salvation?' Behold thy memory hath passed away from the earth, the sons and daughters of my womb, whom I have with pain and sorrow brought forth in vain. Thou thyself sittest among filthy worms, passing the night under the open sky; and I am a wanderer and a servant, from place to place and from house to house, looking for the sun to go down that I may rest from the grief and labour that oppress me. Speak then a word against the Lord, and die!"

If the text were to be considered singly, without reference to anything which may assist in determining its meaning, it would perhaps be impossible now to ascertain among these contrariant interpretations which is the true one. But the generous Englishman who in this country first in our language undertook the vindication of this Matriarch and by whom I have been led to make the present pertinent inquiry, has judiciously (as has been seen) observed in confirmation of his opinion, that the circumstance of her having been made a partaker in her husband's subsequent prosperity is proof that she also had been found righteous under all their trials. This is a valid argument deduced from the book itself.

It would be invalidated were there any truth in what certain Talmudists say, that Job came into the world only to receive his good things in it; that when Satan was permitted to afflict him he began to blaspheme and to revile his Maker, and that therefore the Lord doubled his measure of prosperity in this life, that he might be rejected from the world to come. But when we remember that he is called "a perfect and an upright man, one that feareth God and escheweth evil," we may say with the great Cistercian Rabbinomastix, *Hæc est magna blasphemia et convicium in Iob.* Other Rabbis represent him as a fatalist, put into his mouth the common argument of that false and impious philosophy, and affirm that there is no hope of his salvation: what they say concerning him may safely be rejected. Others of the same school assert that there never was any such person as Job, in the teeth of the Prophet Ezekiel,—and that his whole history is only a parable: if their opinion were right it would be useless to inquire into the character of his wife; *sed isti redarguuntur*, says Bartolocci, *ex nomine ipsius et nomine civitatis ejusdem.* Just as, whatever inconsiderate readers may suppose who take these my reminiscences of the Doctor for a work of fiction, Daniel Dove was Daniel Dove nevertheless, and Doncaster is Doncaster.

There is nothing then among the Jewish traditions, so far as my guides lead me, that can throw any light upon the subject of this inquiry. But there is among the Arabian, where it was more likely to be found; and though the Arabic translation supports the evil meaning of the equivocal text, the tradition on the contrary is in favour of Job's wife. It is indeed a legend, a mere figment, plainly fabulous; but it is founded upon the traditional character of Job's wife in Job's own country. There are two versions of the legend. The one Sale has given as a comment upon the text of the Koran,—"Remember Job when he cried unto his Lord, saying, Verily evil hath afflicted me; but Thou art the most merciful of those who show mercy!"

When Job, says this legend, was in so loathsome a condition that as he lay on a dunghill none could bear to come near him, his wife alone attended him dutifully with great patience, and supported him with what she earned by her labour. One day the Devil appeared to her, reminded her of their former prosperity, and promised to restore all they had lost if she would worship him. He had overcome Eve by a less temptation;

* *I.e.* the Vatican MS.

the Matriarch did not yield like the Mother of Mankind, but neither did she withstand it; she took a middle course, and going to her husband repeated to him the proposal, and asked his consent: whereat he was so indignant that he swore if he recovered to give her an hundred stripes; and then it was that he uttered the ejaculation recorded in the Koran. Immediately the Lord sent Gabriel, who took him by the hand and raised him up; a fountain sprung up at his feet, he drank of it, and the worms fell from his wounds, and he washed in it, and his health and beauty were restored. What his wife had done was not imputed to her for sin, doubtless in consideration of the motive, and the sense of duty and obedience to her lord and master which she had manifested. She also became young and beautiful again; and that Job might keep his oath and neither hurt her nor his own conscience, he was directed to give her one blow with a palm branch having an hundred leaves.

The legend, as related in D'Herbelot, is more favourable to her and exempts her from all blame. According to Khondemir, whom he follows, what Job's wife, here called Rasima, provided for her miserable husband, Satan stole from her, till he deprived her at last of all means of supporting him, and thus rendered him utterly destitute. As soon as the tempter had effected this, he appeared to Rasima in the form of a bald old woman, and offered if she would give him the two locks which hung down upon her neck, to supply her every day with whatever she wanted for her husband. Rasima joyfully accepted the proposal, cut off her locks and gave them to the false old woman. No sooner was Satan possessed of them than he went to Job, told him that his wife had been detected in dishonouring herself and him, and that she had been ignominiously shorn in consequence, in proof of which he produced the locks. Job when he saw that his wife had indeed been shorn of her tresses, believed the story, and not doubting that she had allowed the Devil to prevail over her, swore if ever he recovered his health to punish her severely. Upon this Satan exulting that he had provoked Job to anger, assumed the form of an Angel of Light, and appearing to the people of the land, said he was sent by the Lord to tell them that Job had drawn upon himself the displeasure of the Most High, wherefore he had lost the rank of Prophet which theretofore he had held, and they must not suffer him to remain among them, otherwise the wrath of the Lord would be extended to them also. Job then breathed the prayer which is in the Koran, and the legend proceeds as in the other version, except that nothing is said concerning the manner in which he was discharged of his vow, the vow itself being annulled when Rasima's innocence was made known.

The Koran, where it touches upon this legend, says, it was said to Job, "take a handful of rods in thy hand, and strike thy wife therewith, and break not thine oath." Sale observes upon this that as the text does not express what this handful of rods was to be, some commentators have supposed it to be dry grass, and others rushes, and others (as in the legend) a palm branch. But the elder Wesley takes the words in their direct and rigorous meaning, and says that as the Devil had no small part in the Koran, this passage indubitably bears his stamp, for who but the Devil would instigate any one to beat his wife? This erudite commentator (he deserves to be so called) vindicates the Matriarch in one of his Dissertations, and says that in the speech for which Job reproved her she only advised him to pray for death: in the mouth of a Greek or Roman matron it might have been understood as an exhortation to suicide; — *Hæc ore Græcæ aut Romanæ mulieris prolata ut heroica quædam exhortatio esset suspecta.*

His favourable opinion is entitled to more weight, because it was formed when he made the book of Job his particular study, whereas in an earlier work, the History of the Bible in verse, he had followed the common error, and made Satan as the last and worst of Job's torments play his wife against him, saying that the fiercest shock which the

Patriarch sustained was from the tempest raised by her tongue.

The expositors who comment upon this text of the Koran without reference to the legend, have differed in opinion as to the offence which Job's wife had committed thus to provoke her husband, some asserting that he swore to punish her with stripes because she had stayed too long on an errand, — an opinion by no means consistent with his patience.

Returning to the main argument I conclude, that if upon the meaning of the doubtful word in the Hebrew text authorities are so equipoised as to leave it doubtful, these traditions being of Arabian growth have sufficient weight to turn the scale; even if it were not a maxim that in cases of this kind the most charitable opinion ought to be preferred. And as Dr. Southey has classed this injured Matriarch in a triad with Xantippe and Mrs. Wesley, I cannot but hope that the candid and learned Laureate, who, as I before observed, has condescended to clear the character of some Irish cast-off cavalry horses, will, when he has perused this chapter, render the same justice to Job's wife; and in the next edition of his Life of Wesley, substitute Hooker's in her place.

CHAPTER CXVIII.

POINTS OF SIMILITUDE AND DISSIMILITUDE BETWEEN SIR THOMAS BROWN AND DOCTOR DOVE.

> But in these serious works designed
> To mend the morals of mankind,
> We must for ever be disgraced
> With all the nicer sons of taste,
> If once the shadow to pursue
> We let the substance out of view.
> Our means must uniformly tend
> In due proportion to their end,
> And every passage aptly join
> To bring about the one design.
>
> CHURCHILL.

DR. JOHNSON says that, "perhaps there is no human being, however hid in the crowd from the observation of his fellow mortals, who if he has leisure and disposition to recollect his own thoughts and actions, will not conclude his life in some sort a miracle, and imagine himself distinguished from all the rest of his species by many discriminations of nature or of fortune." This remark he makes in relation to what Sir Thomas Brown asserts of the course of his own life, that it was "a miracle of thirty years, which to relate were not a history, but a piece of poetry, and would sound to common ears like a fable." Now it is not known that any thing extraordinary ever befell him. "The wonders," says Johnson, "probably were transacted in his own mind: self-love, cooperating with an imagination vigorous and fertile as that of Brown, will find or make objects of astonishment in every man's life."

What the Philosopher of Norwich considered as miraculous was probably this, that he had escaped from "Pyrrho's maze," and had never been contaminated in Epicurus' sty; that he had neither striven for place among the "wrangling crew" nor sought to make his way with the sordid herd; that he had not sold himself to the service of Mammon; but in mature years and with deliberate judgment had chosen a calling in which he might continually increase his knowledge and enlarge his views, and entertain a reasonable hope that while he endeavoured to relieve the sufferings of his fellow creatures and discipline his own mind, the labours wherein his life was passed would neither be useless to others nor to himself. He might well consider it a miracle of divine mercy that grace had been given him to fulfil the promise made for him at his baptism, and that he had verily and indeed renounced the pomps and vanities of this wicked world. He might indeed take comfort in his "authentic reflections how far he had performed the great intention of his Maker; — whether he had made good the principles of his nature and what he was made to be; what characteristic and special mark he had left to be observable in his generation; whether he had lived to purpose or in vain; and what he had added, acted, or performed, that might considerably speak him a man."

There were more resemblances between Sir Thomas Brown and the Doctor than Fluellen discovered between Henry of Monmouth and Alexander the Great. Both graduated in the same profession at the same university; and each settled as a practitioner in a provincial town. (Doncaster indeed was an inconsiderable place compared with Norwich; and Brown merely procured his degree at Leyden, which was not in his time, as it was in Daniel Dove's, the best school of physic in Europe.) Both too were Philosophers as well as Physicians, and both were alike speculative in their philosophy and devout. Both were learned men. Sir Thomas Brown might have said of himself with Herbert,

> I know the ways of learning; both the head
> And pipes that feed the press and make it run;
> What reason hath from nature borrowed,
> Or of itself, like a good housewife, spun
> In laws and policy: what the Stars conspire;
> What willing Nature speaks, what forced by fire;
> Both the old discoveries, and the new found seas:
> The stock and surplus, cause and history:
> All these stand open, or I have the keys.

The Doctor could not have said this; he would rather have said,

> I am but one who do the world despise
> And would my thoughts to some perfection raise,
> A wisdom-lover, willing to be wise.*

Yet he was as justly entitled to the appellation of a learned man by his multifarious knowledge, as he was far from pretending to it. There were many things of which he was ignorant, and contented to be ignorant, because the acquirement would not have been worth the cost. Brown would have taken with just confidence a seat at the Banquet of the Philosophers, whereas Dove would have thought himself hardly worthy to gather up the crumbs that fell from their table.

A certain melancholy predominated as much in the constitution of Sir Thomas's mind, as in that of Charles the First, to whom his portrait bears so remarkable a resemblance; and a certain mirth entered as largely into the composition of the Doctor's, as it did into Charles the Second's, to whom in all moral respects no one could be more utterly unlike. The elements have seldom been so happily mixed as they were in the Philosopher of Norwich; he could not have been perfectly homogeneous if a particle of the quintelement had been superadded;—such an ingredient would have marred the harmony of his character: whereas the Philosopher of Doncaster would have been marred without a large portion of it.

It was a greater dissimilarity, and altogether to be regretted, that my Doctor left no "characteristic and special mark to be observable in his generation;" but upon this I shall make some observations hereafter. What led me to compare these persons, incomparable each in his own way, was that my Doctor, though he did not look upon his own history as miraculous, considered that the course of his life had been directed by a singular and special Providence. How else could it have been that being an only son,—an only child, the sole representative in his generation of an immemorial line,—his father, instead of keeping him attached to the soil, as all his forefathers had been, should have parted with him for the sake of his moral and intellectual improvement, not with a view to wealth or worldly advancement, but that he might seek wisdom and ensue it?—that with no other friend than the poor schoolmaster of a provincial townlet, and no better recommendation, he should have been placed with a master by whose care the defects of his earlier education were supplied, and by whose bounty, after he had learned the practical routine of his profession, he was sent to study it as a science in a foreign university, which a little before had been raised by Boerhaave to its highest reputation;—that not only had his daily bread been given him without any of that wearing anxiety which usually attends upon an unsettled and precarious way of life, but in the very house which when sent thither in

* LORD STIRLING.

boyhood he had entered as a stranger, he found himself permanently fixed, as successively the pupil, the assistant, the friend, and finally the successor and heir of his benefactor; — above all, that he had not been led into temptation, and that he had been delivered from evil.

"My life," said an unfortunate poor man who was one of the American Bishop Hobart's occasional correspondents, "has been a chapter of blunders and disappointments." John Wilkes said that "the chapter of accidents is the longest chapter in the book;" and he, who had his good things here, never troubled himself to consider whether the great volume were the Book of Chance, or of Necessity, the Demogorgon of those by whom no other deity is acknowledged. With a wiser and happier feeling Bishop White Kennett when he was asked "where are we?" answered the question thus, — "in a world where nothing can be depended on but a future state; in the way to it, little comfort but prayers and books." White Kennett might have enjoyed more comfort if he had been born in less contentious times, or if he had taken less part in their contentions, or if he had been placed in a less conspicuous station. Yet he had little cause to complain of his lot, and he has left behind him good works and a good name.

There is scarcely any man who in thoughtfully contemplating the course of his own life would not find frequent reason to say,

> *— in fede mia*
> *Ho fatto bene a non fare a mio modo.**

The Doctor, however, was one of the very few who have never been put out of their designed course, and never been disposed to stray from it.

> *Spesso si perde il buono*
> *Cercando il meglio. E a scegliere il sentiero*
> *Chi vuol troppo esser saggio,*
> *Del tempo abusa, e non fa mai viaggio.*†

* Ricciardetto. † Metastasio.

INTERCHAPTER XV.

THE AUTHOR RECOMMENDS A CERTAIN WELL-KNOWN CHARACTER AS A CANDIDATE FOR HONOURS, BOTH ON THE SCORE OF HIS FAMILY AND HIS DESERTS. HE NOTICES ALSO OTHER PERSONS WHO HAVE SIMILAR CLAIMS.

> *Thoricht, auf Bessrung der Thoren zu harren!*
> *Kinder der klugheit, o habet die Narren*
> *Eben zum Narren auch, wie sich's gehort.* Goethe.

In these days when honours have been so profusely distributed by the most liberal of Administrations and the most popular of Kings, I cannot but think that Tom Fool ought to be knighted. And I assure the reader that this is not said on the score of personal feeling, because I have the honour to be one of his relations, but purely with regard to his own claims, and the fitness of things, as well as to the character of the Government.

It is disparaging him, and derogatory to his family, which in undisputed and indisputable antiquity exceeds any other in these kingdoms, — it is disparaging him, I say, to speak of him as we do of Tom Duncombe, and Tom Cribb, and Tom Campbell; or of Tom Hood and Tom Moore, and Tom Sheridan; and before them of Tom Browne and Tom D'Urfey, and Tom Killigrew. Can it be supposed if he were properly presented to his Majesty (Lord Nugent would introduce him), and knelt to kiss the royal hand, that our most gracious and good-natured King would for a moment hesitate to give him the accollade, and say to him "Rise Sir Thomas!"

I do not ask for the Guelphic Order: simple Knighthood would in this case be more appropriate.

It is perfectly certain that Sir Thomas More, if he were alive, would not object to have him for a brother knight and namesake. It is equally certain that Sir Thomas Lethbridge could not, and ought not.

Dryden was led into a great error by his animosity against Hunt and Shadwell when he surmised that "dullness and clumsines were fated to the name of Tom." "There are," says Serjeant Kite, "several sorts of Toms; Tom o' Lincoln, Tom Tit, Tom Tell-truth, Tom o' Bedlam and Tom Fool!" With neither of these is dulness or clumsiness associated. And in the Primitive World, according to the erudite philologist who with so much industry and acumen collected the fragments of its language, the word itself signified just or perfect. Therefore the first Decan of the constellation Virgo was called Tom, and from thence Court de Gebelin derives Themis: and thus it becomes evident that Themistocles belongs to the Toms. Let no Thomas then or Sir Thomas, who has made shipwreck of his fortune or his reputation or of both, consider himself as having been destined to such disgrace by his godfathers and godmothers when they gave him that name. The name is a good name. Any one who has ever known Sir Thomas Acland may like it and love it for his sake: and no wise man will think the worse of it for Tom Fool's.

No! the name Thomas is a good name, however it has been disparaged by some of those persons who are known by it at this time. Though Bovius chose to drop it and assume the name Zephiriel in its stead in honour of his tutelary Angel, the change was not for the better, being indeed only a manifestation of his own unsound state of mind. And though in the reign of King James the First, Mr. William Shepherd of Towcester christened his son by it for a reason savouring of disrespect, it is not the worse for the whimsical consideration that induced him to fix upon it. The boy was born on the never-to-be-forgotten fifth of November 1605, about the very hour when the Gunpowder Treason was to have been consummated; and the father chose to have him called Thomas, because he said this child, if he lived to grow up, would *hardly believe* that ever such wickedness could be attempted by the sons of men.

It is recorded that a parrot which was seized by a kite and carried into the air, escaped by exclaiming *Sancte Thoma adjuva me!* for upon that powerful appeal the kite relaxed his hold, and let loose the intended victim. This may be believed, though it is among the miracles of Thomas à Becket, to whom and not to the great schoolman of Aquino, nor the Apostle of the East, the invocation was addressed. Has any other human name ever wrought so remarkable a deliverance?

Has any other name made a greater noise in the world. Let Lincoln tell, and Oxford; for although, *omnis clocha clochabilis in clocherio clochando, clochans clochativo, clochare facit clochabiliter clochantes*, yet among them all, Master Janotus de Bragmardo would have assigned pre-eminence to the mighty Toms.

The name then is sufficiently vindicated, even if any vindication were needed, when the paramount merits of my claimant are considered.

Merry Andrew likewise should be presented to receive the same honour, for sundry good reasons, and especially for this, that there is already a Sir Sorry Andrew.

I should also recommend Tom Noddy, were it not for this consideration, that the honour would probably soon be merged in an official designation, and therefore lost upon him; for when a certain eminent statesman shall be called from the Lower House, as needs he must ere long, unless the party who keep moving and push him forward as their leader, should before that time relieve him of his hereditary rights, dignities, and privileges, no person can possibly be found so worthy to succeed him in office and tread in his steps, as Tom Noddy.

Nor is Jack Pudding to be forgotten, who is cousin-german to that merry man Andrew! He moreover deserves it by virtue of his Puddingship; the Puddings are of an ancient and good family: the Blacks in particular boast of their blood.

Take, reader, this epigram of that cheerful and kind-hearted schoolmaster Samuel Bishop of Merchant Taylors, written in his vocation upon the theme *Aliusque et Idem*—

Five countries from five favorite dishes name
The popular stage buffoon's professional name.

Half fish himself, the Dutchman never erring
From native instinct, styles him *Pickle Herring*.
The German whose strong palate *haut-gouts* fit,
Calls him *Hans Werst*, that is *John-Sausage-Wit*.
The Frenchman ever prone to *badinage*
Thinks of his soup, and shrugs, *Eh! voila Jean Potage!*
Full of ideas his sweet food supplies,
The Italian, *Ecco Macaroni!* cries.
While English Taste, whose board with dumplin smokes,
Inspired by what it loves, applauds *Jack Pudding*'s jokes.
A charming bill of fare, you'll say, to suit
One dish, and that one dish a Fool, to boot!

"A learned man will have it," says Fuller, "that Serapis is nothing more than Apis with the addition of the Hebrew *Sar*, a Prince, whence perchance our English Sir." Odd, that the whole beast should have obtained this title in Egypt, and a part of it in England. For we all know that Loin of Beef has been knighted, and who is not pleased to meet with him at dinner? and John Barleycorn has been knighted, and who is not willing to pledge him in all companies in a glass?

But wherefore should I adduce precedents, as if in this age any regard were paid to them in the distribution of honours, or there could be any need of them in a case which may so well stand upon its own merits.

CHAPTER CXIX.

THE DOCTOR IN HIS CURE. IRRELIGION THE REPROACH OF HIS PROFESSION.

Virtue, and that part of philosophy
Will I apply, that treats of happiness
By virtue especially to be achieved.
TAMING OF THE SHREW.

A PRACTITIONER of medicine possesses in what may be called his cure, that knowledge of all who are under his care, which the parochial priest used to possess in former times, and will it is to be hoped regain whenever the most beneficial of all alterations shall be effected in the Church Establishment, and no Clergyman shall have a duty imposed upon him which it is impossible to fulfil,—impossible it is, if his parishioners are numbered by thousands instead of hundreds. In such cases one of two consequences must inevitably ensue. Either he will confine himself to the formalities of his office, and because he cannot by any exertions do what ought to be done, rest contented with performing the perfunctory routine; or he will exert himself to the utmost till his health, and perhaps his heart also, is broken in a service which is too often found as thankless as it is hopeless.

Our Doctor was, among the poorer families in his cure, very much what Herbert's Country Parson is imagined to be in his parish. There was little pauperism there at that time; indeed none that existed in a degree reproachful to humanity; or in that obtrusive and clamorous form which at present in so many parts of this misgoverned country insults, and outrages, and endangers society. The labourers were not so ill paid as to be justly discontented with their lot; and he was not in a manufacturing district. His profession led him among all classes; and his temper as well as his education qualified him to sympathise with all, and accommodate himself to each as far as such accommodation was becoming. Yet he was everywhere the same man; he spoke the King's English in one circle, and the King's Yorkshire in another; but this was the only difference in his conversation with high and low. Before the professors of his art indeed, in the exercise of their calling, the distinctions of society disappear, and poor human nature is stripped to its humanities. Rank, and power, and riches,—these—

—cannot take a passion away, Sir,
Nor cut a fit but one poor hour shorter.*

The most successful stock-jobber or manufacturer that ever counted his wealth by hundreds of thousands—

—must endure as much as the poorest beggar
That cannot change his money,—this is equality
In our impartial essences!*

Death is not a more inexorable leveller than his precursors age, and infirmity, and sickness, and pain.

Hope, and fear, and grief, and joy act with the same equitable disregard of conventional

* BEAUMONT and FLETCHER.

distinctions. And though there is reason for disbelieving that the beetle which we tread upon feels as much as a human being suffers in being crushed, it is yet undoubtedly true that except in those cases where individuals have so thoroughly corrupted their feelings as to have thereby destroyed the instinctive sense of right and wrong, making evil their good, what may be termed the primitive affections exist in as much strength among the rudest as among the most refined. They may be paralysed by pauperism, they may be rotted by the licentiousness of luxury; but there is no grade of society in which they do not exhibit themselves in the highest degree. Tragic poets have been attracted by the sufferings of the great, and have laid the scene of their fables in the higher circles of life; yet tragedy represents no examples more touching or more dreadful, for our admiration or abhorrence, to thrill us with sympathy or with indignation, than are continually occurring in all classes of society.

They who call themselves men of the world and pride themselves accordingly upon their knowledge, are of all men those who know least of human nature. It was well said by a French biographer, though not well applied to the subject* of his biography, that *il avait pu, dans la solitude, se former à l'amour du vrai et du juste, et même à la connoissance de l'homme, si souvent et si mal à propos confondue avec celle des hommes; c'est-à-dire, avec la petite experience des intrigues mouvantes d'un petit nombre d'individus plus ou moins accrédités et des habitudes étroites de leurs petites coteries. La connoissance des hommes est à celle de l'homme ce qu'est l'intrigue sociale à l'art social.*

Of those passions which are or deserve to be the subject of legal and judicial tragedy, the lawyers necessarily see most, and for this reason perhaps they think worse of human nature than any other class of men, except the Roman Catholic Clergy. Physicians, on the contrary, though they see humanity in its most humiliating state, see it also in the exercise of its holiest and most painful duties. No other persons witness such deep emotions and such exertions of self-control. They know what virtues are developed by the evils which flesh is heir to, what self-devotion, what patience, what fortitude, what piety, what religious resignation.

Wherefore is it then that physicians have lain under the reproach of irreligion, who of all men best know how fearfully and wonderfully we are made, and who, it might be thought, would be rendered by the scenes at which they are continually called upon to assist, of all men the most religious? Sir Thomas Brown acknowledges that this was the general scandal of his profession, and his commentator Sir Kenelm Digby observes upon the passage, that "Physicians do commonly hear ill in this behalf," and that "it is a common speech (but," he parenthesises, "only amongst the unlearned sort) *ubi tres medici duo athei.*" Rabelais defines a Physician to be *animal incombustible propter religionem.*

"As some mathematicians," says an old Preacher, "deal so much in Jacob's staff that they forget Jacob's ladder, so some Physicians (God decrease the number!) are so deep naturalists that they are very shallow Christians. With us, Grace waits at the heels of Nature, and they dive so deep into the secrets of philosophy that they never look up to the mysteries of Divinity."

Old Adam Littleton, who looked at every thing in its best light, took a different view of the effect of medical studies, in his sermon upon St. Luke's day. "His character of Physician," said he, "certainly gave him no mean advantage, not only in the exercise of his ministry by an acceptable address and easy admission which men of that profession everywhere find among persons of any civility; but even to his understanding of Christian truths and to the apprehending the mysteries of faith.

"For having, as that study directed him, gone orderly over all the links of that chain by which natural causes are mutually tied to one another, till he found God the supreme

* The Abbe Sieyes.

cause and first mover at the top; having traced the footsteps of Divine Goodness through all the most minute productions of his handmaid Nature, and yet finding human reason puzzled and at a loss in giving an account of his almighty power and infinite wisdom in the least and meanest of his works; with what pious humility must he needs entertain supernatural truths, when upon trial he had found every the plainest thing in common nature itself was mystery, and saw he had as much reason for his believing these proposals of faith, as he had for trusting the operations of sense, or the collections of reason itself.

"I know there is an unworthy reproach cast upon this excellent study that it inclines men to atheism. 'Tis true the ignorance and corruption of men that profess any of the three honourable faculties bring scandal upon the faculty itself. Again, sciolists and half-witted men are those that discredit any science they meddle with. But he that pretends to the noble skill of physic, and dares to deny that which doth continually *incurrere in sensus*, that which in all his researches and experiments he must meet with at every turn, I dare to say he is no Physician; or at least that he doth at once give his profession and his conscience too the lye."

CHAPTER CXX.

EFFECT OF MEDICAL STUDIES ON DIFFERENT DISPOSITIONS. JEW PHYSICIANS. ESTIMATION AND ODIUM IN WHICH THEY WERE HELD.

Confiesso la digression; mas es facil al que no quisiere leerla, passar al capitulo siguiente, y esta advertencia sirva de disculpa.

LUIS MUNOZ.

IF the elder Daniel had thought that the moral feelings and religious principles of his son were likely to be endangered by the study of medicine, he would never have been induced to place him with a medical practitioner. But it seemed to him, good man, that the more we study the works of the Creator, the more we must perceive and feel his wisdom, and his power, and his goodness. It was so in his own case, and, like Adam Littleton and all simple-hearted men, he judged of others by himself.

Nevertheless that the practice of Physic, and still more of surgery, should have an effect like that of war upon the persons engaged in it, is what those who are well acquainted with human nature might expect, and would be at no loss to account for. It is apparent that in all these professions coarse minds must be rendered coarser, and hard hearts still farther indurated; and that there is a large majority of such minds and hearts in every profession, trade and calling, few who have had any experience of the ways of the world can doubt. We need not look farther for the immediate cause. Add to a depraved mind and an unfeeling disposition either a subtle intellect or a daring one, and you have all the preparations for atheism that the Enemy could desire.

But other causes may be found in the history of the medical profession, which was an art, in the worst sense of the word, before it became a science, and long after it pretended to be a science, was little better than a craft. Among savages the sorcerer is always the physician; and to this day superstitious remedies are in common use among the ignorant in all countries. But wherever the practice is connected with superstition as free scope is presented to wickedness as to imagination; and there have been times in which it became obnoxious to much obloquy, which on this score was well deserved.

Nothing exposed the Jews to more odium in ages when they were held most odious, than the reputation which they possessed as physicians. There is a remarkable instance of the esteem in which they were held for their supposed superiority in this art as late as the middle of the sixteenth century. Francis I. after a long illness in which he found no benefit from his own physicians, dispatched a courier into Spain, requesting Charles V. to send him the most skilful

Jewish practitioner in his dominions. This afforded matter for merriment to the Spaniards; the Emperor, however, gave orders to make inquiry for one, and when he could hear of none who would trust himself in that character, he sent a New-Christian physician, with whom he supposed Francis would be equally satisfied. But when this person arrived in France, the King by way of familiar discourse sportively asked him if he were not yet tired of expecting the Messiah? Such a question produced from the new Convert a declaration that he was a Christian, upon which the King dismissed him immediately without consulting him, and sent forthwith to Constantinople for a Jew. The one who came found it necessary to prescribe nothing more for his royal patient than Asses' milk.

This reputation in which their physicians were held was owing in great measure to the same cause which gave them their superiority in trade. The general celebrity which they had obtained in the dark ages, and which is attested by Eastern tales as well as by European history, implies that they had stores of knowledge which were not accessible to other people. And indeed as they communicated with all parts of the known world, and with parts of it which were unknown to the Christian nations, they had means of obtaining the drugs of the East, and the knowledge of what remedies were in use there, which was not of less importance in an art, founded, as far as it was of any avail, wholly upon experience. That knowledge they reserved to themselves, perhaps as much with a view to national as to professional interests.

Nicolas Antonio sent to Bertolacci a manuscript entitled *Otzar Haanijm*, that is, "The Treasure of the Poor," written by a certain Master Julian in the Portuguese language, but in rabbinical characters. It was a collection of simple receipts for all diseases, and appears to have been written thus that it might be serviceable to those only who were acquainted with Hebrew. There was good policy in this. A king's physician in those days was hardly a less important person than a king's confessor; with many princes indeed he would be the more influential of the two, as being the most useful, and frequently the best informed; and in those times of fearful insecurity, it might fall within his power, like Mordecai, to avert some great calamity from his nation.

Among the articles which fantastic superstition, or theories not less fantastic, had introduced into the *materia medica*, there were some which seemed more appropriate to the purposes of magic than of medicine, and some of an atrocious kind. Human fat was used as an unguent,—that of infants as a cosmetic. Romances mention baths of children's blood; and there were times and countries in which such a remedy was as likely to be prescribed, as imagined in fiction. It was believed that deadly poisons might be extracted from the human body;—and they who were wicked enough to administer the product, would not be scrupulous concerning the means whereby it was procured. One means indeed was by tormenting the living subject. To such practices no doubt Harrison alludes when, speaking, in Elizabeth's reign, of those who graduated in the professions or law or physic, he says, "one thing only I mislike in them, and that is their usual going into Italy, from whence very few without special grace do return good men, whatever they pretend of conference or practice; chiefly the physicians, who under pretence of seeking of foreign simples, do oftentimes learn the framing of such compositions as were better unknown than practised, as I have often heard alleged." The suspicion of such practices attached more to the Jewish than to any other physicians, because of the hatred with which they were supposed to regard all Christians, a feeling which the populace in every country, and very frequently the Rulers also, did everything to deserve. The general scandal of atheism lay against the profession; but to be a Jew was in common opinion to be worse than an atheist, and calumnies were raised against the Jew Physicians on the specific ground of their religion, which, absurd and monstrous as they were, popular credulity was ready to receive. One imputation was that they made it a point of conscience to kill one patient in five, as a sacrifice of atonement for the good which they had done to the other four. Another was that the blood of a Christian infant was always administered to a Jewess in child-bed, and was esteemed so necessary an ingredient in their superstitious ceremonies or their medical practice at such times, that they exported it in a dried and pulverised form to Mahommedan countries, where it could not be obtained fresh.

They are some pages in Jackson's Treatise upon the Eternal Truth of Scripture and Christian Belief, which occurring in a work of such excellent worth, and coming from so profound and admirable a writer, must be perused by every considerate reader with as much sorrow as surprise. They show to what a degree the most judicious and charitable mind may be deluded when seeking eagerly for proofs of a favourite position or important doctrine, even though the position and the doctrine should be certainly just. Forgetful of the excuse which he has himself suggested for the unbelief of the Jews since the destruction of Jerusalem, saying, with equal truth and felicity of expression, that "their stubborness is but a strong hope malignified, or, as we say, grown wild and out of kind," he gives credit * to the old atrocious tales of their crucifying Christian children, and finds in them an argument for confirming our faith at which the most iron-hearted supralapsarian might shudder. For one who passes much of his time with books, and with whom the dead are as it were living and conversing, it is almost as painful to meet in an author whom he reveres and loves, with anything which shocks his understanding and disturbs his moral sense, as it is to perceive the faults of a dear friend. When we discover aberrations of this kind in such men, it should teach us caution for ourselves as well as tolerance for others; and thus we may derive some benefit even from the errors of the wise and good.

That the primitive Christian should have regarded the Jews with hostile feelings as their first persecutors, was but natural, and that that feeling should have been aggravated by a just and religious horror for the crime which has drawn upon this unhappy nation its abiding punishment. But it is indeed strange that during so many centuries this enmity should have continued to exist, and that no sense of compassion should have mitigated it. For the Jews to have inherited the curse of their fathers was in the apprehension of ordinary minds to inherit their guilt; and the cruelties which man inflicted upon them were interpreted as proofs of the continued wrath of Heaven, so that the very injuries and sufferings which in any other case would have excited commiseration, served in this to close the heart against it. Being looked upon as God's outlaws, they were everywhere placed as it were under the ban of humanity. And while these heart-hardening prepossessions subsisted against them in full force, the very advantages of which they were in possession rendered them more especial objects of envy, suspicion, and popular hatred. In times when literature had gone to decay throughout all Christendom, the Jews had not partaken of the general degradation. They had Moses and the Prophets, whose everlasting lamps were kept trimmed amongst them, and burning clearly through the dark when the light of the Gospel had grown dim in the socket, and Monkery and Popery had well nigh extinguished it. They possessed a knowledge of distant countries which was confined to themselves; for being dispersed everywhere, they travelled everywhere with the advantage of a language which was spoken by the Children of Israel wherever they were found, and nowhere by any other people. As merchants therefore and as statesmen they had opportunities peculiar to themselves. In both capacities those Princes who had any sense of policy found them eminently useful. But wealth made them envied, and the way in which they increased

* *E.g.* vol. i. p. 148. &c. Ed. Folio.

it by lending money made them odious in ages when to take any interest was accounted usury.* That odium was aggravated whenever they were employed in raising taxes; and as they could not escape odium, they seem sometimes to have braved it in despite or in despair, and to have practised extortion if not in defiance of public opinion, at least as a species of retaliation for the exactions which they themselves endured, and the frauds which unprincipled debtors were always endeavouring to practise upon them.

But as has already been observed, nothing exposed them to greater obloquy than the general opinion which was entertained of their skill in medicine, and of the flagitious practices with which it was accompanied. The conduct of the Romish Church tended to strengthen that obloquy, even when it did not directly accredit the calumnies which exasperated it. Several Councils denounced excommunication against any persons who should place themselves under the care of a Jewish Physician, for it was pernicious and scandalous they said, that Christians, who ought to despise and hold in horror the enemies of their holy religion, should have recourse to them for remedies in sickness. They affirmed that medicines administered by such impious hands became hurtful instead of helpful; and, moreover, that the familiarity thus produced between a Jewish practitioner and a Christian family gave occasion to great evil and to many crimes. The decree of the Lateran Council by which physicians were enjoined, under heavy penalties, to require that their patients should confess and communicate before they administered any medicines to them, seems to have been designed as much against Jewish practitioners as heretical patients. The Jews on their part were not more charitable, when they could express their feelings with safety. It appears in their own books that a physician was forbidden by the Rabbis to attend upon either a Christian or Gentile, unless he dared not refuse; under compulsion it was lawful, but he was required to demand payment for his services, and never to attend any such patients gratuitously.

* See the remarkable words of Jewel on 1 Thess. iv. 6. pp. 78—86. Ed. Folio. 1611. Archbishop Abbot's Lectures on Jonah, p. 90. Ed. 1613. 4to.

CHAPTER CXXI.

WHEREIN IT APPEARS THAT SANCHO'S PHYSICIAN AT BARATARIA ACTED ACCORDING TO PRECEDENTS AND PRESCRIBED LAWS.

Lettor, tu vedi ben com' io innalzo
La mia materia, e però con piu arte
Non ti maravigliar s' i' la rincalzo. DANTE.

BUT the practice both of medicine and of surgery, whatever might be the religion of the practitioner, was obnoxious to suspicions for which the manners of antiquity, of the dark ages, and of every corrupted society, gave but too much cause. It was a power that could be exercised for evil as well as for good.

One of the most detestable acts recorded in ancient history is that of the Syrian usurper Tryphon, who, when he thought it expedient to make away with young Antiochus, the heir to the kingdom, delivered him into a surgeon's hands to be cut for the stone, that he might in that manner be put to death. It is a disgraceful fact that the most ancient operation known to have been used in surgery, is that abominable one which to the reproach of the civil and ecclesiastical authorities is still practised in Italy.

Physicians were not supposed to be more scrupulous than surgeons. The most famous and learned Doctor Christopher Wirtzung, whose General Practice of Physic was translated from German into English at the latter end of Queen Elizabeth's reign, by his countryman Jacob Mosan, Doctor in the same faculty, has this remarkable section in his work:

"Ancient Physicians were wont to have an old proverb, and to say that Venom is so proud that it dwelleth commonly in gold and silver; whereby they meant that great personages that eat and drink out of gold and silver, are in greater danger to be poisoned than the common people that do eat and drink out of earthen dishes." Christopher Wirtzung might have quoted Juvenal here:

> *Nulla aconita bibuntur*
> *Fictilibus. Tunc illa time, cum pocula sumes*
> *Gemmata, et lato Setinum ardebit in auro.*

"Wherefore," proceeds the German Doctor, "must such high personages that are afraid to be poisoned, diligently take heed of the meat and drink that they eat, and that are dressed of divers things. Also they must not take too much of all sweet, salt and sour drinks; and they must not eat too eagerly, nor too hastily; and they must at all times have great regard of the first taste of their meat and drink. But the most surest way is, that before the mealtide he take somewhat that may resist venom, as figs, rue, or nuts, each by himself, or tempered together. The citrons, rape-seed, nepe, or any of those that are described before, the weight of a drachm taken with wine, now one and then another, is very much commended. Sometimes also two figs with a little salt, then again mithridate or treacle, and such like more may be used before the mealtide."

"It is a matter of much difficulty," says Ambrose Paré, "to avoid poisons, because such as at this time temper them are so thoroughly prepared for deceit and mischief that they will deceive even the most wary and quick-sighted; for they so qualify the ingrate taste and smell by the admixture of sweet and well-smelling things that they cannot easily be perceived even by the skilful. Therefore such as fear poisoning ought to take heed of meats cooked with much art, very sweet, salt, sour, or notably endued with any other taste. And when they are opprest with hunger or thirst, they must not eat nor drink too greedily, but have a diligent regard to the taste of such things as they eat or drink. Besides, before meat let them take such things as may weaken the strength of the poisons, such as is the fat broth of good nourishing flesh-meats. In the morning let them arm themselves with treacle or mithridate, and conserve of roses, or the leaves of rue, a walnut and dry figs: besides let him presently drink a little draught of muscadine, or some other good wine."

How frequent the crime of poisoning had become in the dark ages appears by the old laws of almost every European people, in some of which indeed its frequency, *Proh dolor!* is alleged as a reason for enacting statutes against it. And whilst in the empire the capital sentence might be compounded for, like other cases of homicide, by a stated compensation to the representatives of the deceased, no such redemption was allowed among the Wisi-Goths, but the poisoner, whether freeman or slave, was to suffer the most ignominious death. In the lower ranks of life men were thought to be in most danger of being thus made away with by their wives, in the higher by their Physicians and their cooks.

There are two curious sections upon this subject in the Laws of Alphonso the Wise, the one entitled *Quáles deben ser los fisicos del Rey, et qué es lo que deben facer;*— What the Physicians of a King ought to be, and what it is they ought to do:—the other, *Quáles deben ser los oficiales del Rey que le han de servir en su comer et en su beber:* What the officers of a King ought to be who minister to him at his eating and at his drinking.

"Physic," says the royal author, "according as the wise antients have shown, is as much as to say the knowledge of understanding things according to nature, what they are in themselves, and what effect each produces upon other things; and therefore they who understand this well, can do much good, and remove many evils; especially by preserving life and keeping men in health, averting from them the infirmities whereby they suffer great misery, or are brought to death. And they who do this are called Physicians, who not only must endeavour to deliver men from their maladies, but also to preserve their health in such manner that they may not become sick; wherefore it is necessary that those whom the King has with him should be right good. And as Aristotle said to Alexander, four things are required in them; — First that they should be knowing in their art; secondly, that they should be well approved in it; thirdly, that they should be skilled in the cases which may occur; fourthly, that they should be right loyal and true. For if they are not knowing in their art, they will not know how to distinguish diseases; and if they are not well approved in it, they will not be able to give such certain advice, which is a thing from whence great hurt arises; and if they are not skilful, they will not be able to act in cases of great danger when such may happen; and if they are not loyal, they can commit greater treasons than other men, because they can commit them covertly. And when the King shall have Physicians in whom these four aforesaid things are found, and who use them well, he ought to do them much honour and much good; and if peradventure they should act otherwise knowingly, they commit known treason, and deserve such punishment as men who treacherously kill others that have confided in them.

"Regiment also in eating and drinking is a thing without which the body cannot be maintained, and therefore the officers who have to minister to the King or others have no less place than those of whom we have spoken above, as to the preservation of his life and his health. For albeit the Physicians should do all their endeavours to preserve him, they will not be able to do it if he who prepares his food for him should not choose to take the same care; we say the same also of those who serve him with bread, and wine, and fruit, and all other things of which he has to eat, or drink. And according as Aristotle said to Alexander, in these officers seven things are required; — First, that they be of good lineage, for if they be, they will always take heed of doing things which would be ill for them; secondly, that they be loyal, for if they be not so, great danger might come to the King from them; thirdly, that they be skilful, so that they may know how to do those things well which appertain to their offices: fourthly, that they be of good understanding, so that they may know how to comprehend the good which the King may do them, and that they be not puffed up, nor become insolent because of their good fortune; fifthly, that they be not over covetous, for great covetousness is the root of all evil; sixthly, that they be not envious in evil envy, lest if they should be, they might haply be moved thereby to commit some wrong; seventhly, that they be not much given to anger, for it is a thing which makes a man beside himself, and this is unseemly in those who hold such offices. And also besides all those things which we have specified, it behoveth them greatly that they be debonair and clean, so that what they have to prepare for the King, whether to eat or drink, may be well prepared; and that they serve it to him cleanlily, for if it be clean he will be pleased with it, and if it be well prepared he will savour it the better, and it will do him the more good. And when the King shall have such men as these in these offices, he ought to love them, and to do them good and honour; and if peradventure he should find that any one offends in not doing his office loyally, so that hurt might come thereof to the person of the King, he ought to punish him both in his body and in his goods, as a man who doth one of the greatest treasons that can be."

The fear in which the Princes of more barbarous states lived in those ages is nowhere so fully declared as in the Palace-laws compiled by that King of Majorca who was slain at the battle of Cressy, from which laws those of his kinsman Pedro the Ceremonious of Arragon, who drove him from his kingdom, were chiefly taken. His butler, his under butler, his major domo, and his cooks were to swear fealty and homage, *quia tam propter nefandissimam infidelitatem aliquorum ministrorum, quam ipsorum negligentiam, quæ est totius boni inimica, quâ ministrante omittuntur præcavenda, audivimus pluries tam Regibus quàm aliis Principibus maxima pericula evenisse, quod est plus quam summè abhorrendum.* No stranger might approach the place where any food for the King's table was prepared or kept; and all the cooks, purveyors and sub-purveyors, and the major domo, and the chamberlain were to taste of every dish which was served up to him. The noble who ministered to him when he washed at table was to taste the water, and the barber who washed his head was to do the like; for great as the King was, being mindful that he was still but a man, he acknowledged it necessary that he should have a barber, *pro humanis necessitatibus, quibus natura hominum quantâcunque fretum potentiâ nullum fecit expertem, etiam nos Barbitonsorum officio indigemus.* His tailor was to work in a place where no suspicious people could have access; and whatever linen was used for his bed, or board, or more especially for his apparel, was to be washed in a secret place, and by none but known persons. The Chief Physician was to taste all the medicines that he administered. Every morning he was to inspect the royal urinal, and if he perceived any thing amiss prescribe accordingly. He was to attend at table, caution the King against eating of anything that might prove hurtful, and if, notwithstanding all precautions, poisons should be administered, he was to have his remedies at hand.

By the Chinese laws, if either the superintending or dispensing officer, or the cook, introduces into the Emperor's kitchen any unusual drug, or article of food, he is to be punished with an hundred blows, and compelled to swallow the same.

CHAPTER CXXII.

A CHAPTER WHEREIN STUDENTS IN SURGERY MAY FIND SOME FACTS WHICH [illegible] TO THEM IN THE HISTORY OF THEIR OWN PROFESSION.

> If I have more to spin,
> The wheel shall go. HERBERT.

ANOTHER reproach to which the medical profession was exposed arose from the preparatory studies which it required. The natural but unreflecting sentiment of horror with which anatomy is everywhere regarded by the populace, was unfortunately sanctioned by the highest authorities of the Roman Church. Absolutely necessary for the general good as that branch of science indisputably is, it was reprobated by some of the Fathers in the strongest and most unqualified terms; they called it butchering the bodies of the dead; and all persons who should disinter a corpse for this purpose were excommunicated by a decree of Boniface the VIIIth, wherein the science itself was pronounced abominable both in the eyes of God and man. In addition to this cause of obloquy, there was a notion that cruel experiments, such as are now made upon animals and too often unnecessarily, and therefore wickedly repeated, were sometimes performed upon living men.* The Egyptian Physician who is believed first to have taught that the nerves are the organs of sensation, is said to have made the discovery by dissecting criminals alive. The fact is not merely stated by Celsus, but justified by him. Deducing its justification as a consequence from the not-to-be-disputed assertion *cum in interioribus partibus et dolores, et morborum varia genera nascantur, neminem his adhibere posse remedia, quæ ipse ignoret: — necessarium ergo esse*, he proceeds to say, *incidere corpora mortuorum, eorumque viscera atque intestina scrutari.* LONGEQUE OPTIME FECISSE *Herophilum et Erasistratum, qui nocentes homines à regibus ex carcere acceptos,* VIVOS INCIDERINT; *considerarintque,* ETIAM SPIRITU MANENTE, *ea quæ natura antea clausisset, eorumque posituram, colorem, figuram, magnitudinem, ordinem, duritiem, mollitiem, lævorem, contactum; processus deinde singulorum et recessus; et sive quid inseritur alteri, sive quid partem alterius in se recipit.* As late as the sixteenth century surgeons were wont to beg (as it was called) condemned malefactors, whom they professed to put to death in their own way, by opium before they opened them. It might well be suspected that these disciples of Celsus were

* The curious reader should refer to *Nicolai Klimii Iter Subterraneum*, c. ix. p. 139. Ed. 1766.

not more scrupulous than their master; and they who thus took upon themselves the business of an executioner, had no reason to complain if they shared in the reproach attached to his infamous office.

A French author * of the sixteenth century says that the Physicians at Montpelier, which was then a great school of medicine, had every year two criminals, the one living, the other dead, delivered to them for dissection. He relates that on one occasion they tried what effect the mere expectation of death would produce upon a subject in perfect health, and in order to this experiment they told the gentleman (for such was his rank) who was placed at their discretion, that, as the easiest mode of taking away his life they would employ the means which Seneca had chosen for himself, and would therefore open his veins in warm water. Accordingly they covered his face, pinched his feet without lancing them, and set them in a foot-bath, and then spoke to each other as if they saw that the blood were flowing freely, and life departing with it. The man remained motionless, and when after a while they uncovered his face they found him dead.

It would be weakness or folly to deny that dangerous experiments for the promotion of medical or surgical practice may, without breach of any moral law, or any compunctious feeling, be tried upon criminals whose lives are justly forfeited. The Laureate has somewhere in his farraginous notes *de omnibus rebus et quibusdam aliis*, produced a story of certain Polish physicians who obtained permission to put on the head of a criminal as soon as it had been cut off, and an assurance of his pardon if they should succeed in reuniting it. There is nothing to be objected to such an experiment, except its utter unreasonableness.

When it was necessary that what was at that time a most difficult and dangerous surgical operation should be performed upon Louis XIV., inquiry was made for men afflicted with the same disease; they were conveyed to the house of the minister Louvois, and there in the presence of the King's physician Fagon, Felix the chief surgeon operated upon them. Most of these patients died; they were interred by night, but, notwithstanding all precautions, it was observed that dead bodies were secretly carried from that house, and rumours got abroad that a conspiracy had been discovered, that suspected persons had been brought before the minister, and had either died under the question or been made away with by poison under his roof. The motive for this secresy was that the King might be saved from that anxiety which the knowledge of what was going on must have excited in him. In consequence of these experiments, Felix invented new instruments which he tried at the Hotel des Invalides, and when he had succeeded with them the result was communicated to the King, who submitted to the operation with characteristic fortitude. The surgeon performed it firmly and successfully; but the agitation which he had long struggled against and suppressed, produced then a general tremour from which he never recovered. The next day, in bleeding one of his own friends he maimed him for life.

This was a case in which the most conscientious practitioner would have felt no misgiving; there was no intentional sacrifice of life, or infliction of unnecessary suffering. So too when inoculation for the smallpox was introduced into this country; some condemned criminals gladly consented to be inoculated instead of hanged, and saved their lives by the exchange.

It is within the memory of some old members of the profession, that a man was sentenced to death at the Old Bailey, who had a wen upon his throat weighing between thirty and forty pounds. To hang him was impossible without circumstances of such revolting cruelty as would, even at that time, have provoked a general outcry of indignation. The case found its way from the lawyers to the surgeons; the latter obtained his pardon, and took off the tumour. John Hunter was the operator; the man,

* Bouchet.

his offence not having been of a very heinous kind, though the indiscriminating laws made it at that time capital, was taken into his service, and used to show his own wen in his master's museum; it was the largest from which any person had ever been relieved. The fate of the poor Chinese who underwent a similar operation in London with a different result, is fresh in remembrance and will long be remembered. The operation was made a public exhibition for medical students, instead of being performed with all circumstances that could tend to soothe the patient; and to the consequent heat of a crowded room, and partly perhaps to the excitement which such an assemblage occasioned in the object of their curiosity, the fatal termination was, with too much probability, imputed. We may be sure that no such hazardous operation will ever again be performed in this country in the same public manner.

The remarks which were called forth on that occasion are proofs of the great improvement in general feeling upon such points, that has taken place in modern times. In the reign of Louis XI. a franc-archer of Meudon was condemned to be hanged for robbery and sacrilege; he appealed to the Court of Parliament, but that Court confirmed the sentence, and remanded him to the Provost of Paris for execution. The appeal, however, seems to have brought the man into notice, and as he happened to afford a surgical case as well as a criminal one, the surgeons and physicians of the French capital petitioned the King for leave to operate upon him. They represented that many persons were afflicted with the stone and other internal disorders; that the case of this criminal resembled that of the Sieur de Bouchage, who was then lying dangerously ill; it was much to be desired for his sake that the inside of a living man should be inspected, and no better subject could have occurred than this franc-archer who was under sentence of death. This application was made at the instance of Germaine Colot, a practitioner who had learned his art under one of the Norsini, a Milanese family of itinerant surgeons*, celebrated during several generations for their skill in lithotomy. Whether the criminal had his option of being hanged, or opened alive, is not stated; but Monstrelet, by whom the fact is recorded, says that permission was granted, that the surgeons and physicians opened him, inspected his bowels, replaced them, and then sewed him up; that the utmost care was taken of him by the King's orders, that in the course of fifteen days he was perfectly cured, and that he was not only pardoned but had a sum of money given him. To such means were the members of this profession driven, because anatomy was virtually if not formally prohibited.

A much worse example occurred when the French King Henry II. was mortally wounded in tilting with Montgomery. It is stated by most historians, that a splinter from Montgomery's spear entered the King's visor and pierced his eye; but Vincent Carloix, who probably was present, and if not, had certainly the best means of information, shows that this is altogether an erroneous statement. He says that when the Scot had broken his spear upon the King, instead of immediately throwing away the truncheon, as he ought to have done, he rode on holding it couched; the consequence of this inadvertence was, that it struck the King's visor, forced it up, and ran into his eye. His words are these, *ayans tous deux fort valeureusement couru et rompu d'une grande dexterité et adresse leurs lances, ce mal-habile Lorges ne jecta pas, selon l'ordinaire coustume, le trousse qui demoura en la main la lance rompue; mais le porta tousjours baissé, et en courant, rencontra la teste du Roy, du quel il donna droit dedans la visiere qui le coup haulsa, et luy creva un œil.*

The accuracy of this account happens to be of some importance, because the course which the King's surgeons pursued in consequence illustrates the state of surgery at that time, and of manners and laws also;

* The "Whitworth Doctors," as they were called, were all of one family, in our own country. Their roughness and their skill were about on a par.

for with the hope of ascertaining in what direction the broken truncheon had entered the brain, and how they might best proceed to extract the splinters, they cut off the heads of four criminals, and drove broken truncheons into them, as nearly as they could judge at the same inclination, and then opened the heads. But after these lessons, five or six of the most expert surgeons in France were as much at a loss as before.

It was well that there were criminals ready upon the occasion, otherwise perhaps, in the then temper of the French Court, the first Huguenots who came to hand might have been made to serve the turn. And it was well for the subjects that it was not thought advisable to practise upon them alive; for no scruples would have been entertained upon the score of humanity. When Philip Von Huten, whom the Spanish writers call Felipe de Utre, made his expedition from Venezuela in search of the Omeguas, an Indian wounded him with a spear, under the right arm, through the ribs. One Diego de Montes, who was neither surgeon nor physician, undertook to treat the wound, because there was no person in the party better qualified to attempt it. A life was to be sacrificed for his instruction, and accordingly a friendly Cacique placed the oldest Indian in the village at his disposal. This poor creature was dressed in Von Huten's coat of mail (*sayo o escaulpil*) and set on horseback; Montes then ran a spear into him through the hole in this armour, after which he opened him, and found that the integuments of the heart had not been touched, this being what he wished to ascertain. The Indian died; but Von Huten's wound was opened and cleansed in full reliance upon the knowledge thus obtained, and he recovered.

CHAPTER CXXIII.

SOME ALLUSION TO, AND SOME USE OF THE FIGURE OF SPEECH CALLED PARENTHESIS.

J'ecrirai ici mes pensées sans ordre, et non pas peut-être dans une confusion sans dessein; c'est le veritable ordre, et qui marquera toujours mon objet par le desordre même. PASCAL.

GENTLE reader, — and if gentle, good reader, — and if good, patient reader: for if not gentle, then not good; and if not good, then not gentle; and neither good nor gentle, if not patient; — dear reader, who art happily for thyself all three, it is, I know, not less with thy good will than with my own, that I proceed with this part of my subject. *Quelle matière que je traite avec vous, c'est toujours un plaisir pour moi.** You will say to me, "amuse yourself (and me) in your own way; ride your own round-about, so you do but come to the right point at last." † To that point you are well assured that all my round-abouts tend; and my care must be to eschew the error of that author, engineer, statesman, or adventurer of any kind,

> Which of a weak and niggardly projection,
> Doth like a miser spoil his coat with scanting
> A little cloth.‡

Lady Hester Stanhope had an English Physician with her in Syria, who, if he be living, can bear testimony that her Ladyship did not commit this fault, when she superintended the cutting out of his scarlet galligaskins. Neither will I commit it.

You indeed, dear reader, would express no displeasure if, instead of proceeding in the straight line of my purpose, I should sometimes find it expedient to retrograde; or, borrowing a word of barbarous Latin coined in the musician's mint, *cancrizare*, which may be rendered to crab-grade. For as Roger North says, when, at the commencement of his incomparable account of his brother the Lord Keeper's life, he confesses that it would be hard to lead a thread

---

* MADAME DE MAINTENON. † CUMBERLAND.
‡ SHAKESPEARE.

in good order of time through it — "there are many and various incidents to be remembered, which will interfere, and make it necessary to step back sometimes, and then again forwards ; — and in this manner I hope to evacuate my mind of every matter and thing I know and can remember materially concerning him. And if some things are set down which many may think too trivial, let it be considered that the smallest incidents are often as useful to be known, though not so diverting, as the greater, and profit must always share with entertainment."

I am not, however, side-ling toward my object crab-like ; still less am I starting back from it, like a lobster, whose spring upon any alarm is stern-foremost : nor am I going I know not where, like the three Princes Zoile, Bariandel and Lyriamandre, when, having taken leave of Olivier King of England, to go in search of Rosicler, they took ship at London *sans dessein d'aller plustôt en un lieu qu'en un autre.* Nor like the more famous Prince Don Florisel and Don Falanges, when having gone on board a small vessel, *y mandada por ellos en lo alto de la mar meter, hazen con los marineros que no hagan otro camino mas de aquel que la nao movido por la fuerza de los ayres, quisiesse hazer, queriendo yr a buscar con la aventura lo que a ella hallar se permitia segun la poca certinidad que para la demanda podian llevar.*

I should say falsely were I to say with Petrarch,

> *Vommene in guiza d'orbo senza luce,*
> *Che non sa ove si vada, e pur si parte.*

But I may say with the Doctor's namesake Daniel de Bosola in Webster's tragedy,* "I look no higher than I can reach : they are the gods that must ride on winged horses. A lawyer's mule, of a slow pace, will both suit my disposition and business ; for mark me, when a man's mind rides faster than his horse can gallop, they quickly both tire." — Moreover

> ——— This I hold
> A secret worth its weight in gold
> To those who write as I write now,
> Not to mind where they go, or how,
> Thro' ditch, thro' bog, o'er hedge and stile,
> Make it but worth the reader's while,
> And keep a passage fair and plain
> Always to bring him back again.†

"You may run from major to minor," says Mrs. Bray in one of her letters to Dr. Southey, "and through a thousand changes, so long as you fall into the subject at last, and bring back the ear to the right key at the close."

Where we are at this present reading, the attentive reader cannot but know ; and if the careless one has lost himself, it is his fault, not mine. We are in the parenthesis between the Doctor's courtship and his marriage. Life has been called a parenthesis between our birth and death‡ ; the history of the human race is but a parenthesis between two cataclasms of the globe which it inhabits ; time itself only a parenthesis in eternity. The interval here, as might be expected after so summary a wooing, was not long ; no settlements being required, and little preparation. But it is not equally necessary for me to fix the chapter, as it was for them to fix the day.

Montaigne tells us that he liked better to forge his mind than to furnish it. I have a great liking for old Michel, Seigneur de Montaigne, which the well-read reader may have perceived ;—who indeed has ever made his acquaintance without liking him ? I have moreover some sympathies with him ; but upon this point we differ. It is more agreeable to me to furnish than to forge,—intellectually speaking, to lay in than to lay out ; — to eat than to digest. There is however (following the last similitude) an intermediate process enjoyed by the flocks and herds, but denied to Aldermen ; that process affords so apt a metaphor for an operation of the mind, that the word denoting it has passed into common parlance in its metaphorical acceptation, and its original meaning is not always known to those who use it.

* Duchess of Malfi.

† Churchill.

‡ See suprà, p. 250.

It is a pleasure to see the quiet full contentment which is manifested both in the posture and look of animals when they are chewing the cud. The nearest approach which humanity makes toward a similar state of feeling, seems to be in smoking, when the smoker has any intellectual cud on which to chew. But ruminating is no wholesome habit for man, who, if he be good for anything, is born as surely to action as to trouble; it is akin to the habit of indulging in day-dreams, which is to be eschewed by every one who tenders his or her own welfare.

There is, however, a time for everything. And though neither the Doctor nor Deborah had thought of each other in the relation of husband and wife, before the proposal was made, and the silent assent given, they could not choose but ruminate upon the future as well as the past, during the parenthesis that ensued. And though both parties deliberately approved of what had been suddenly determined, the parenthesis was an uneasy time for both.

The commentators tell us that readers have found some difficulty in understanding what was Shakespeare's meaning when he made Macbeth say

> If it were done when 'tis done, then 'twere well
> It were done quickly.

Johnson says he never found them agreeing upon it. Most persons, however, are agreed in thinking, that when anything disagreeable must be done, the sooner it is done the better. Who but a child ever holds a dose of physic in his hand, — rhubarb to wit, — or Epsom salts, — delaying as long as possible to take the nauseous draught? Who ever, when he is ready for the plunge, stands lingering upon the side of the river, or the brink of the cold bath? — Who that has entered a shower-bath and closed the door, ever hesitates for a moment to pull the string? It was upon a false notion of humanity that the House of Commons proceeded, when it prolonged the interval between the sentence of a murderer and the execution. The merciful course in all cases would be, that execution should follow upon the sentence with the least possible delay.

"Heaven help the man," says a good-natured and comely reader who has a ring on the fourth finger of her left hand, — "Heaven help the man! Does he compare marriage to hanging, to a dose of physic, and to a plunge over head and ears in cold water?" No, madam, not he: he makes no such unseemly comparisons. He only means to say that when any great change is about to take place in our circumstances and way of life, — anything that is looked on to with anxiety and restlessness, anything that occasions a yeasty sensation about the pericardium, — every one who is in that state wishes that the stage of fermentation were past, — that the transition were over.

I have said that little preparation was needed for a marriage which gave little employment to the upholsterers, less to the dress-makers, and none to the lawyers. Yet there was something to be done. Some part of the furniture was to be furbished, some to be renewed, and some to be added. The house required papering and painting, and would not be comfortably habitable while the smell of the paint overpowered or mingled with the odour of the shop. Here then was a cause of unavoidable delay; and time which is necessarily employed, may be said to be well employed, though it may not be upon the business which we have most at heart. If there be an impatient reader, that is to say an unreasonable one, who complains that, instead of passing rapidly over this interval or parenthesis (as aforesaid), I proceed in such a manner with the relation, that many of my chapters are as parenthetical as the Euterpe of Herodotus, which whole book, as the present Bishop Butler used to say, is one long parenthesis, and the longest that ever was written; — if, I say, there be so censorious a reader, I shall neither contradict him, nor defend myself, nor yet plead guilty to the fault of which he accuses me. But I will tell him what passed on a certain occasion, between Doctor, afterwards Archbishop, Sharp, when he was

Rector of St. Giles's, and the Lord Chancellor Jefferies.

In the year 1686, Dr. Sharp preached a sermon wherein he drew some conclusions against the Church of Rome, to show the vanity of her pretensions in engrossing the name of Catholic to herself. The sermon was complained of to James II., and the Lord Chancellor Jefferies was directed to send for the preacher, and acquaint him with the King's displeasure. Dr. Sharp accordingly waited upon his Lordship with the notes of his sermon, and read it over to him. "Whether," says his son, "the Doctor did this for his own justification, and to satisfy his Lordship that he had been misrepresented, or whether my Lord ordered him to bring his sermon and repeat it before him, is not certain; but the latter seems most probable: because Dr. Sharp afterwards understood that his Lordship's design in sending for him and discoursing with him, was, that he might tell the King that he had reprimanded the Doctor, and that he was sorry for having given occasion of offence to his Majesty, hoping by this means to release Dr. Sharp from any further trouble. However it was, his Lordship took upon him, while the Doctor was reading over his sermon, to chide him for several passages which the Doctor thought gave no occasion for chiding; and he desired his Lordship when he objected to these less obnoxious passages, to be patient, for there was a great deal worse yet to come."

The sermon nevertheless was a good sermon, as temperate as it was properly timed, and the circumstance was as important in English history, as the anecdote is pertinent in this place. For that sermon gave rise to the Ecclesiastical Commission, which, in its consequences, produced, within two years, the Revolution.

CHAPTER CXXIV.

THE AUTHOR MORALISES UPON THE VANITY OF FAME; AND WISHES THAT HE HAD BOSWELLISED WHILE IT WAS IN HIS POWER TO HAVE DONE SO.

Mucho tengo que llorar,
Mucho tengo que reir. GONGORA.

It is a melancholy consideration that Fame is as unjust as Fortune. To Fortune, indeed, injustice ought not to be imputed; for Fortune is blind, and disposes of her favours at random. But Fame, with all her eyes and ears and tongues, overlooks more than she perceives, and sees things often in a wrong light, and hears and reports as many falsehoods as truths.

We need not regret that the warriors who lived before Agamemnon should be forgotten, for the world would have been no worse if many of those who lived after him had been forgotten in like manner. But the wise also perish, and leave no memorial. What do we know of "Ethan the Ezrahite, and Heman and Chalcol, and Darda, the sons of Mahol," whom it was accounted an honour for Solomon to have excelled in wisdom? Where is now the knowledge for which Gwalchmai ab Gwyar, and Llechau ab Arthur, and Rhiwallawn Wallt Banadlen were leashed in a Triad as the three Physiologists or Philosophers of the Isle of Britain; because "there was nothing of which they did not know its material essence, and its properties, whether of kind, or of part, or of quality, or of compound, or of coincidence, or of tendency, or of nature, or of essence, whatever it might be?" Where is their knowledge? where their renown? They are now "merely *nuda nomina*, naked names!" "For there is no remembrance of the wise, more than of the fool for ever; seeing that which now is, in the days to come shall all be forgotten!"

—— If our virtues
Did not go forth of us, 'twere all alike
As if we had them not.*

* SHAKESPEARE.

The Seven Wise Men have left almost as little as the Sybils.

"What satisfaction," says Sir John Hawkins, "does the mind receive from the recital of the names of those who are said to have increased the chords of the primitive lyre from four to seven, Chorebus, Hyagius, and Terpander? Or when we are told that Olympus invented the enarmonic genus, as also the Harmatian mood? Or that Eumolpus and Melampus were excellent musicians, and Pronomus, Antigenides and Lamia celebrated players on the flute? In all these instances, where there are no circumstances that constitute a character, and familiarise to us the person spoken of, we naturally inquire who he is, and for want of farther information become indifferent as to what is recorded of him." The same most learned and judicious historian of his favourite art, laments that most of the many excellent musicians who flourished in the ages preceding our own are all but utterly forgotten. "Of Tye," he says, "of Redford, Shephard, Douland, Weelkes, Welbye, Est, Bateson, Hilton and Brewer, we know little more than their names. These men composed volumes which are now dispersed and irretrievably lost; yet did their compositions suggest those ideas of the power and efficacy of music, and those descriptions of its manifold charms, that occur in the verses of our best poets."

Is there one of my Readers in a thousand who knows that Philistes was a Greco-Phœnician, or Phœnico-Grecian Queen of Malta and Gozo, before the Carthaginians obtained the dominion of those islands, in which their language continues living, though corrupted, to this day?—Are there ten men in Cornwall who know that Medacritus was the name of the first man who carried tin from that part of the world?

What but his name is now known of Romanianus, who in St. Augustin's opinion was the greatest genius that ever lived; and how little is his very name known now! What is now remembered "of the men of renown before the Flood?" Sir Walter Raleigh hath a chapter concerning them, wherein he says, "of the war, peace, government and policy of these strong and mighty men, so able both in body and wit, there is no memory remaining; whose stories if they had been preserved, and what else was then performed in that newness of the world, there could nothing of more delight have been left to posterity. For the exceeding long lives of men, (who to their strength of body and natural wits had the experience added of eight hundred and nine hundred years,) how much of necessity must the same add of wisdom and understanding?* Likely it is that their works excelled all whatsoever can be told of after-times; especially in respect of this old age of the world, when we no sooner begin to know than we begin to die: according to Hippocrates, *Vita brevis, ars longa, tempus præceps;* which is, Life is short, art is long, and time is headlong. And that those people of the first age performed many things worthy of admiration, it may be gathered out of these words of Moses, *These were mighty men, which in old time were men of renown.*" What is known of them now? Their very names have perished!

Who now can explain the difference between the Agenorian, the Eratoclean, the Epigonian, and the Damonian sects of musicians, or knows anything more than the names of their respective founders, except that one of them was Socrates's music-master?

What Roman of the age of Horace would have believed that a contemporaneous Consul's name should only live to posterity, as a record of the date of some one of the Poet's odes?

Who now remembers that memorable Mr. Clinch, "whose single voice, as he had learned to manage it, could admirably represent a number of persons at sport and in hunting, and the very dogs and other animals,"—himself a whole pack and a whole

* The passage will be found in Book i. c. v. § vii. of the History of the World. The reading in the Oxford Edition is "undertakings," but Southey, it is likely, preferred to write as in the text, and had authority for it. He had no opinion of this edition, and once told me that letters were not used which might have been, as an Appendix to the Life.

field in full cry: "but none better than a quire of choristers chanting an Anthem"—himself a whole quire.

"How subdued,"—says Mr. David Laing, who has rescued from oblivion so much that is worthy of being held in remembrance,—"how subdued is the interest that attaches to a mere name, as for instance, to that of Dunbar's contemporaries, Stobo, Quintyne, or St. John the Ross, whose works have perished!"

Who was that famous singer nick-named Bonny Boots, who, because of his excellent voice, or as Sir John Hawkins says, "for some other reason, had permission to call Queen Elizabeth his Lady:" and of whom it is said in the canzonet,

> Our Bonny Boots could toot it,
> Yea and foot it,
> Say, lusty lads, who now shall Bonny-Boot it?

Sir John thinks it might "possibly be one Mr. Hale." But what is Fame when it ends in a poor possibility that Bonny Boots who called the Queen his Lady, and that Queen, not Bergami's popular Queen, but Queen Elizabeth, the nation's glorious Queen Elizabeth, the people's good Queen Bess,—what, I repeat, is Fame, when it ends in a mere conjecture that the Bonny Boots who was permitted to call such a Queen his Lady, might be "one Hale or Hales in whose voice she took some pleasure." Well might Southey say

> Fame's loudest blast upon the ear of Time
> Leaves but a dying echo!

And what would posterity have heard of my Dove, my Daniel, my Doctor,—my Doctor Daniel Dove,—had it not been for these my patient and humble labours;—patient, but all too slow; humble, if compared with what the subject deserves, and yet ambitious, in contemplation of that desert, that inadequate as they are, they will however make the subject known; so that my Dove, my Daniel, my Doctor, shall be everybody's Dove, everybody's Daniel, every-body's Doctor,—yea the World's Doctor, the World's Doctor Daniel Dove!

> O his desert speaks loud; and I should wrong it,
> To lock it in the wards of covert bosom,
> When it deserves with characters of brass
> A forted residence, 'gainst the tooth of time
> And razure of oblivion.*

Alas that there should have been in that generation but one Boswell. Why did Nature break his mould? Why did she not make two? for I would not have had Johnson deprived of what may almost be called his better part;—but why were there not two Boswells, as there are two Dromios in the Comedy of Errors, and two Mr. Bulwers at this day, and three Hunchbacks in the Arabian Tale. Why was there not a duplicate Boswell, a fac-simile of the Laird of Auchinleck, an undistinguishable twin-brother, to have lived at Doncaster, and have followed my Doctor, like his dog, or his shadow, or St. Anthony's pig, and have gathered up the fragments of his wit and his wisdom, so that nothing should have been lost? Sinner that I am, that I should have had so little forethought in the golden days of youth and opportunity! As Brantôme says when speaking of Montluc, *J'etois fort souvent avec luy, et m'aymoit fort, et prenoit grand plaisir quand je le mettois en propos et on train et luy faisois quelques demandes,—car je ne suis jamais esté si jeune, que je n'aye tousjours esté fort curieux d'apprendre; et luy, me voyant en cette volonté, il me respondoit de bon cœur, et en beaux termes; car il avoit une fort belle eloquence.* Truly therefore may I say of thee, O my friend and Master!

> *—— S' alcun bel frutto*
> *Nasce di me, da voi vien prima il seme.*
> *Io per me son quasi un terreno asciutto*
> *Colto da voi, e 'l pregio è vostro in tutto.*†

Sinner that I was! not to have treasured up all his words when I enjoyed and delighted in his presence; improvident wretch! that I did not faithfully record them every night before I went to bed, while they were yet fresh in memory! How many things would I fain recall, which are now irrecoverably lost! How much is there, that if it were possible to call back the days that are past, I would eagerly ask and learn! But the hand of Time is on me. *Non solebat*

---

* Measure for Measure. † Petrarch.

*mihi tam velox tempus videri; nunc incredibilis cursus apparet: sive quia admoveri lineas sentio, sive quia attendere cœpi et computare damnum meum.** I linger over these precious pages while I write, pausing and pondering in the hope that more recollections may be awakened from their long sleep; that one may jog and stir up another. By thus rummaging in the stores of memory many things which had long been buried there have been brought to light;—but O reader! how little is this all to what it might have been! It is but as a poor armful of gleanings compared to a waggon well piled with full sheaves, carrying the harvest home.

Here too I may apply with the alteration of only one word what that good man Gotthilf Franck says in his Preface to the History of the Danish Mission in India, as translated into Latin from Niecamp's German Work. *Quamquam vero huic æquo desiderio gratificandi animum tanto promptiorem gessimus, quanto plus ad illustrationem nominis dilecti ex tali compendio redundaturum esse perspeximus, multa tamen impedimenta in dies subnata sunt, quo minus res in effectum dari potuerit. Siquidem ad ejusmodi epitomen accurate conscribendum et res præcipuas breviter complectendas non solum multum temporis, patientiæ et laboris, sed singularis etiam epitomatoris* ἱκανότης *et dexteritas requiritur.*

The Doctor himself was careless of Fame. As he did nothing to be seen of men, so he took no thought for anything through which he might be remembered by them. It was enough for him if his jests, and whims, and fancies, and speculations, whether sportive or serious, pleased himself, brought a smile to his wife's lips and a dimple to her cheek, or a good-humoured frown, which was hardly less agreeable, to her brow;—it was enough for him if they amused or astonished those to whom they were addressed. Something he had for every one within the sphere of his little rounds; a quip for this person and a crank for that; "nods and becks and wreathed smiles" for those who were in the May-day of youth, or the hey-day of hilarity and welfare; a moral saying in its place and a grave word in season; wise counsel kindly given for those who needed it, and kind words for all,—with which kind actions always kept pace, instead of limping slowly and ungraciously behind. But of the world beyond that circle, he thought as little as that world thought of him; nor had he the slightest wish for its applause. The passion which has been called "the last infirmity of noble minds" had no place in his;—for he was a man *in quo*, as Erasmus says of his Tutor Hegius, *unum illud vel Momus ipse calumniari fortasse potuisset, quod famæ plus æquo negligens, nullam posteritatis haberet rationem.*

* Seneca.

CHAPTER CXXV.

FAME IN THE BOROUGH ROAD. THE AUTHOR DANIELISES.

Duc, Fama,—
Duc me insolenti tramite; devius
Tentabo inaccessos profanis
Invidiæ pedibus recessus.

VINCENT BOURNE.

Guess, Reader, where I once saw a full-sized figure of Fame, erect, tip-toe, in the act of springing to take flight and soar aloft, her neck extended, her head raised, the trumpet at her lips, and her cheeks inflated, as if about to send forth a blast which the whole city of London was to hear? Perhaps thou mayest have seen this very figure thyself, and surely if thou hast, thou wilt not have forgotten it. It was in the Borough Road, placed above a shop-board which announced that Mr. Somebody fitted up Water-Closets upon a new and improved principle.

But it would be well for mankind if Fame were never employed in trumpeting anything worse. There is a certain stage of depravity, in which men derive an unnatural satisfaction from the notoriety of their wickedness, and seek for celebrity *ob magnitudinem infamiæ, cujus apud prodigos novis-*

*sima voluptas est.** —*Ils veulent faire parler d'eux*, says Bayle, *et leur vanité ne seroit pas satisfaite s'il n'y avoit quelque chose de superlatif et d'eminent dans leur mauvaise reputation. Le plus haut degré de l'infamie est le but de leurs souhaits, et il y a des choses qu'ils ne feroient pas si elles n'etoient extraordinairement odieuses.*

Plutarch has preserved the name of Chærephanes, who was notorious among the ancients for having painted such subjects as Julio Romano has the everlasting infamy of having designed for the flagitious Aretine. He has also transmitted to posterity the name of Parmeno, famous for grunting like a pig, and of Theodorus, not less famous for the more difficult accomplishment of mimicking the sound of a creaking cart-wheel. Who would wish to have his name preserved for his beggarliness, like Pauson the painter, and Codrus the poet? Or for his rascality and wickedness like Phrynondas? Or like Callianax the physician for callous brutality? Our Doctor used to instance these examples when he talked of "the bubble reputation," which is sometimes to be had so cheaply, and yet for which so dear a price has often been paid in vain. It amused him to think by what odd or pitiful accidents that bubble might be raised. "Whether the regular practitioner may sneer at Mr. Ching," says the Historian of Cornwall, "I know not; but the Patent Worm-Lozenges have gained our Launceston Apothecary a large fortune, and secured to him perpetual fame."

Would not John Dory's name have died with him, and so been long ago dead as a door-nail, if a grotesque likeness for him had not been discovered in the Fish, which being called after him has immortalised him and his ugliness? But if John Dory could have anticipated this sort of immortality when he saw his own face in the glass, he might very well have "blushed to find it fame." There would have been no other memorial of Richard Jaquett at this day, than the letters of his name in an old dead and obsolete hand, now well nigh rendered illegible by time, if he had not in the reign of Edward VI. been Lord of the Manor of Tyburn with its appurtenances, wherein the gallows was included, wherefore, from the said Jaquett it is presumed by antiquaries that the hangman hath been ever since corruptly called Jack Ketch. A certain William Dowsing, who during the Great Rebellion was one of the Parliamentary Visitors for demolishing superstitious pictures and ornaments of Churches, is supposed by a learned critic to have given rise to an expression in common use among school-boys and blackguards. For this worshipful Commissioner broke so many "mighty great Angels" in glass, knocked so many Apostles and Cherubims to pieces, demolished so many pictures and stone-crosses, and boasted with such puritanical rancour of what he had done, that it is conjectured the threat of giving any one *a dowsing* preserves his rascally name. So too while Bracton and Fleta rest on the shelves of some public Library, Nokes and Stiles are living names in the Courts of Law: and for John Doe and Richard Roe, were there ever two litigious fellows so universally known as these eternal antagonists?

Johnson tells a story of a man who was standing in an inn kitchen with his back to the fire, and thus accosted a traveller who stood next to him, "Do you know, Sir, who I am?" "No, Sir," replied the traveller—"I have not that advantage." "Sir," said the man, "I am the great Twalmley who invented the new Flood-gate Iron."—Who but for Johnson would have heard of the great Twalmley now? Reader, I will answer the question which thou hast already asked, and tell thee that his invention consisted in applying a sliding door, like a flood-gate, to an ironing-box, flat-irons having till then been used, or box-irons with a door and bolt.

Who was Tom Long the Carrier? when did he flourish? what road did he travel? did he drive carts, or waggons, or was it in the age of pack-horses? Who was Jack Robinson? not the once well-known Jack

* Tacitus.

Robinson of the Treasury, (for his celebrity is now like a tale that is told,) but the one whose name is in every body's mouth, because it is so easily and so soon said. Who was Magg? and what was his diversion? was it brutal, or merely boorish? the boisterous exuberance of rude and unruly mirth or the gratification of a tyrannical temper and a cruel disposition? Who was Crop the Conjuror, famous in trivial speech, as Merlin in romantic lore, or Doctor Faustus in the school of German extravagance? What is remembered now of Bully Dawson? all I have read of him is, that he lived three weeks on the credit of a brass shilling because nobody would take it of him. "There goes a story of Queen Elizabeth," says Ray, "that being presented with a Collection of English Proverbs, and told by the Author that it contained them all, 'Nay,' replied she, 'Bate me an ace, quoth Bolton!' which proverb being instantly looked for, happened to be wanting in his collection." "Who this Bolton was," Ray says, "I know not, neither is it worth inquiring." Nevertheless I ask who was Bolton? and when Echo answers "*who?*" say in my heart *Vanitas Vanitatum, omnia Vanitas.* And having said this, conscience smites me with the recollection of what Pascal has said, *Ceux qui écrivent contre la gloire, veulent avoir la gloire d'avoir bien écrit; et ceux qui le lisent, voulent avoir la gloire de l'avoir lu; et moi qui écris ceci, j'ai peut-être cette envie, et peut-être que ceux qui le liront, l'auront aussi.*

Who was old Ross of Pottern, who lived till all the world was weary of him? All the world has forgotten him now. Who was Jack Raker, once so well known that he was named proverbially as a scapegrace by Skelton, and in the Ralph Roister Doister of Nicholas Udall, — that Udall, who on poor Tom Tusser's account, ought always to be called the bloody schoolmaster? Who was William Dickins, whose wooden dishes were sold so badly, that when any one lost by the sale of his wares, the said Dickins and his dishes were brought up in scornful comparison? Out-roaring Dick was a strolling singer of such repute that he got twenty shillings a day by singing at Braintree Fair: but who was that Desperate Dick that was such a terrible cutter at a chine of beef, and devoured more meat at ordinaries in discoursing of his frays and deep acting of his flashing and hewing, than would serve half a dozen brewers' draymen? It is at this day doubtful whether it was Jack Drum or Tom Drum, whose mode of entertainment no one wishes to receive; — for it was to haul a man in by the head and thrust him out by the neck and shoulders. Who was that other Dick who wore so queer a hat-band that it has ever since served as a standing comparison for all queer things? By what name besides Richard was he known? Where did he live and when? His birth, parentage, education, life, character and behaviour, who can tell? "Nothing," said the Doctor, "is remembered of him now, except that he was familiarly called Dick, and that his queer hat-band went nine times round and would not tie."

O vain World's glory, and unstedfast state
Of all that lives on face of sinful earth!*

Who was Betty Martin, and wherefore should she so often be mentioned in connexion with my precious eye or your's? Who was Ludlam, whose dog was so lazy that he leant his head against a wall to bark? And who was Old Cole whose dog was so proud that he took the wall of a dung-cart and got squeezed to death by the wheel? Was he the same person of whom the song says,

Old King Cole
Was a merry old soul,
And a merry old soul was he?

And was his dog proud because his master was called King? Here are questions to be proposed in the Examination papers of some Australian Cambridge, two thousand years hence, when the people of that part of the world shall be as reasonably inquisitive concerning our affairs, as we are now concerning those of the Greeks. But the Burneys, the Parrs and the Porsons, the Elmsleys, Monks and Blomfields of that

* Spenser.

age, will puzzle over them in vain, for we cannot answer them now. *

"Who was the Vicar of Bray? I have had a long chase after him," said Mr. Brome to Mr. Rawlins, in 1735. "Simon Aleyn, or Allen, was his name; he was Vicar of Bray about 1540, and died in 1588; so he held the living near fifty years. You now partake of the sport that has cost me some pains to take. And if the pursuit after such game seems mean, one Mr. Vernon followed a butterfly nine miles before he could catch him." Reader, do not refuse your belief of this fact, when I can state to you on my own recollection that the late Dr. Shaw, the celebrated Naturalist, a librarian of the British Museum and known by the name of the learned Shavius, from the facility and abundance of his Latin compositions, pointed out to my notice there many years ago two volumes written by a Dutchman upon the wings of a butterfly. "The dissertation is rather voluminous, Sir, perhaps you will think," said the Doctor, with somewhat of that apologetic air, which modest science is wont occasionally to assume in her communications with ignorance, "but it is immensely important."† Good-natured, excellent enthusiast! fully didst thou appreciate the Book, the Dutchman, and above all the Butterfly.

"I have known a great man," says Taylor the Water-Poet, "very expert on the Jews'-harp; a rich heir excellent at Noddy; a Justice of the Peace skilful at Quoytes; a Merchant's Wife a quick gamester at Irish, especially when she came to bearing of men, that she would seldom miss entering." Injurious John Taylor! thus to defraud thy friends of their fame, and leave in irremediable oblivion the proper name of that expert Jews'-Harper, that person excellent at Noddy, that great Quoytes-man, and that Mistress who played so masterly a game at Irish!—But I thank thee for this, good John the Water-Poet; thou hast told us that Monsieur La Ferr, a Frenchman, was the first inventor of the admirable game of Double-hand, Hot Cockles, &c., and that Gregory Dawson, an Englishman, devised the unmatchable mystery of Blind-man's-buff. But who can tell me what the game of Carps was, the *Ludus Carparum*, which Hearne says was used in Oxford much, and being joined with cards, and reckoned as a kind of *alea*, is prohibited in some statutes? When Thomas Hearne, who learned whatever Time forgot, was uncertain what game or play it really was, and could only conjecture that perhaps it might be a sort of Back-gammon, what antiquary can hope to ascertain it?

"Elizabeth Canning, Mary Squires the Gipsey, and Miss Blandy," says one who remembered their days of celebrity, "were such universal topics in 1752, that you would have supposed it the business of mankind to talk only of them; yet now, in 1790, ask a young man of twenty-five or thirty a question relative to these extraordinary personages, and he will be puzzled to answer."

Who now knows the steps of that dance, or has heard the name of its author, of which in our fathers' days it was said in verse, that

— Isaac's rigadoon shall live as long
As Rafael's painting, or as Virgil's song.

Nay, who reads the poem wherein those lines are found, though the author predicted for them in self-applauding pleasantry, that

Whilst birds in air, or fish in streams we find,
Or damsels fresh with aged partners join'd,
As long as nymphs shall with attentive ear
A fiddle rather than a sermon hear,
So long the brightest eyes shall oft peruse
These useful lines of my instructive muse.

Even of the most useful of those lines, the "uses are gone by." Ladies before they leave the ball-room are now no longer fortified against the sudden change of temperature by a cup of generous white wine mulled with ginger; nor is it necessary now to caution them at such times against a

* On Elmsley's putting forth his edition of the Œdipus Coloneus, some one asked him how it came about that he left so much unexplained? "How should it be otherwise," said he, "when we are unable to explain our own Shakespeare?"

† This anecdote was inserted by the late Grosvenor Bedford, Southey's old and tried friend.

draught of cold small beer, because, as the Poet in his own experience assured them,

> Destruction lurks within the poisonous dose,
> A fatal fever, or a pimpled nose.*

CHAPTER CXXVI.

MR. BAXTER'S OFFICES. MILLER'S CHARACTER OF MASON; WITH A FEW REMARKS IN VINDICATION OF GRAY'S FRIEND AND THE DOCTOR'S ACQUAINTANCE.

> —— *Te sonare quis mihi*
> *Genique vim dabit tui?*
> *Stylo quis æquor hocce arare charteum,*
> *En arva per papyrina*
> *Satu loquace seminare literas?*
>
> JANUS DOUSA.

THAT dwelling house which the reader may find represented in Miller's History of Doncaster, as it was in his time, and in the Doctor's, and in mine,—that house in which the paper-hangers and painters were employed during the parenthesis, or to use a more historical term, the Interim of this part of our history,—that house which when, after an interval of many years, I saw it last, had the name R. Dennison on the door, is now, the Sheffield Mercury tells me, occupied as Mr. Baxter's Offices. I mean no disrespect to Mr. R. Dennison. I mean no disrespect to Mr. Baxter. I know nothing of these gentlemen, except that in 1830 the one had his dwelling there, and in 1836 the other his offices. But for the house itself, which can now be ascertained only by its site, totally altered as it is in structure and appearance, without and within,—when I think of it I cannot but exclaim, in what Wordsworth would call "that inward voice" with which we speak to ourselves in solitude, "If thou be'est it," with reference to that alteration,—and with reference to its change of tenants and present appropriation, I cannot but carry on the verse, and say—"but oh how fallen, how changed!"

In that house Peter Hopkins had entertained his old friend Guy; and the elder Daniel once, upon an often pressed and special invitation, had taken the longest journey he ever performed in his life, to pass a week there. For many years Mr. Allison and Mr. Bacon made it their house of call whenever they went to Doncaster. In that house Miller introduced Herschel to Dr. Dove; and Mason, when he was Mr. Copley's guest, never failed to call there, and inquire of the Doctor what books he had added to his stores,—for to have an opportunity of conversing with him was one of the pleasures which Mason looked for in his visits at Netherhall.

Miller disliked Mason: described him as sullen, reserved, capricious and unamiable; and this which he declared to be "the real character of this celebrated poet," he inserted, he said, "as a lesson to mankind, to show them what little judgment can be formed of the heart of an author, either by the sublimity of his conceptions, the beauty of his descriptions, or the purity of his sentiments."

Often as Miller was in company with Mason, there are conclusive proofs that the knowledge which he attained of Mason's character was as superficial as the poet's knowledge of music, for which, as has heretofore been intimated, the Organist regarded him with some contempt.

He says that the reason which Mason assigned for making an offer to the lady whom he married, was, that he had been a whole evening in her company with others, and observed, that during all that time she never spoke a single word. Mason is very likely to have said this; but the person who could suppose that he said it in strict and serious sincerity, meaning that it should be believed to the letter, must have been quite incapable of appreciating the character of the speaker.

Mason whom Gray described, a little before this offer, as repining at his four-and-twenty weeks' residence at York, and longing for the flesh-pots and coffee-houses of Cambridge, was notwithstanding in his friend and fellow-poet's phrase, a long while *mariturient*, "and praying to heaven to give him a good and gentle governess." "No man,"

---

* SOAME JENYNS.

says Gray, "wants such a thing more in all senses; but his greatest wants do not make him move a foot faster, nor has he, properly speaking, anything one can call a passion about him, except a little malice and revenge." Elsewhere he speaks of Mason's "insatiable repining mouth." Yet there was no malice in these expressions. Gray loved him, taking him for all in all, and to have been the friend of Gray will always be considered as evidence of no ordinary worth; for it is not on intellect alone that the friendship of so good and wise a man as Gray could be founded.

When Gray first became acquainted with Mason he wrote concerning him thus. "He has much fancy, little judgment, and a good deal of modesty. I take him for a good and well-meaning creature; but then he is really in simplicity a child, and loves everybody he meets with: he reads little or nothing, writes abundance, and that with a design to make his fortune by it." In another letter "Mason grows apace in my good graces; he is very ingenious, with great good-nature and simplicity; a little vain, but in so harmless and so comical a way that it does not offend one at all; a little ambitious, but withal so ignorant in the world and its ways, that this does not hurt him in one's opinion. So sincere and so undisguised, that no mind with a spark of generosity would ever think of hurting him, he lies so open to injury; but so indolent that if he cannot overcome this habit, all his good qualities will signify nothing at all."

This surely is the character of an amiable and very likeable man. Mason said when he printed it, "my friends, I am sure, will be much amused at this; my enemies (if they please) may sneer at it, and say (which they will very truly) that twenty-five years have made a very considerable abatement in my general philanthropy. Men of the world will not blame me for writing from so prudent a motive, as that of making my fortune by it; and yet the truth, I believe, at the time was, that I was perfectly well satisfied if my publications furnished me with a few guineas to see a Play, or an Opera."

During the short time that his wife lived after his marriage, Miller observed that he appeared more animated and agreeable in his conversation, that is to say, he was cheerful because he was happy. After her death (and who has ever perused her epitaph without emotion?) he relapsed into a discontented habit of mind, as might be expected from one who had remained unmarried too long, and who, although he might be said in the worldly sense of the word to have been a fortunate man, was never, except during the short duration of his marriage, a happy one. He had no near relations, none to whom he was in any degree attached; and in Gray he lost the most intimate of his friends, probably the only one towards whom he ever felt anything approaching to a warmth of friendship. This produced a most uncomfortable effect upon him in the decline of life; for knowing that he was looked upon as one who had wealth to leave for which there were no near or natural claimants, he suspected that any marks of attention which were shown him, whether from kindness or from respect, proceeded from selfish views. That in many cases such suspicions may be well-founded, any one who knows what the world is will readily believe; and if they made him capricious, and rendered him liable to be accused of injustice and want of feeling, the effect is not so extraordinary as it is pitiable. It is one of the evils attendant upon the possession of riches where there is no certain heir; it is part of the punishment which those persons bring upon themselves who accumulate unnecessary wealth, without any just or definite object.*

But Mason is chargeable with no such sin. When a young man he made a resolution that if he came into possession of an estate which was entailed upon him, he would accept of no additional preferment; and he adhered to that resolution, though many offers were made to him which might have induced

* How applicable is this to the history of the late Dr. Bell! Pity 'tis he did not apply his riches, as he told Southey he would, to the increase of poor livings. What came from the church might well have been returned.

a worldly man to depart from it. The first thing he did after the inheritance fell to him was to resign his King's Chaplainship: "a priest in that situation," he said, "could not help looking forward to a bishoprick, a species of ambition incompatible with the simplicity and purity of the Christian character, for, the moment a man aspires to the purple, that moment virtue goes out of him." Mr. Greville, who, after a visit to Mason, related this in a letter to his friend Polwhele, was informed that his income was about £1500 a-year, and that of this one-third was appropriated to patronage and charity.

He had made another resolution, which was not kept, because it was not reasonable. When the Earl of Holdernesse offered him the Rectory of Aston, he was not in orders, and he called upon Warburton to ask his advice. "I found him," says Warburton, "yet unresolved whether he should take the Living. I said, was the question about a mere secular employment, I should blame him without reserve if he refused the offer. But as I regarded going into orders in another light, I frankly owned to him he ought not to go, unless he had a *call:* by which I meant, I told him, nothing fanatical or superstitious; but an inclination, and, on that, a resolution, to dedicate all his studies to the service of religion, and totally to abandon his poetry. This sacrifice, I said, I thought was required at any time, but more indispensably so in this, when we are fighting with infidelity *pro aris et focis*. This was what I said; and I will do him the justice to say, that he entirely agreed with me in thinking that decency, reputation, and religion, all required this sacrifice of him; and, that if he went into orders, he intended to give it." "How much shall I honour him," says Warburton in another letter, "if he performs his promise to me of putting away those idle baggages after his sacred espousals!" This unwise promise explains Mason's long silence as a poet, and may partly account for his uncomfortable state of mind as long as he considered himself bound by it.

There were other circumstances about him which were unfavourable to happiness; he seems never to have been of a cheerful, because never of a hopeful temper, otherwise Gray would not have spoken of his "insatiable repining mouth,"—the lively expression of one who clearly perceived his constitutional faults, and yet loved him as he deserved to be loved, in spite of them. The degree of malice also, which Gray noticed as the strongest passion in his nature, is to be reckoned among those circumstances. By far the most popular of his compositions were those well-known satires which he never owned, and which professional critics, with their usual lack of acumen, pronounced not to be his because of their sarcastic humour and the strength of their language. He had a great deal of that sarcastic humour, and this it was which Gray called malice; in truth it partakes of maliciousness, and a man is the worse for indulging it, if he ever allows himself to give it a personal direction, except in cases where strong provocation may warrant and strict justice require it. That these satires were written by Mason will appear upon the most indisputable proof whenever his letters shall be published; and it is earnestly hoped those letters may not be allowed to perish, for in them and in them only will the character of the writer appear in its natural lights and shades.

Mason would not (especially after their signal success) have refrained from acknowledging these satires, which are the most vigorous of his compositions, unless he had been conscious that the turn of mind they indicated was not that which ought to be found in a member of his profession. And it can only have been the same feeling which induced the Editor to withhold them from the only collective edition of his works. That edition was delayed till fourteen years after his death, and then appeared without any memoir of the author, or any the slightest prefatory mark of respect: it seems, therefore, that he had left none by whom his memory was cherished. But though this may have been in some degree his fault, it was probably in a far greater degree his misfortune.

Mason had obtained preferment for his literary deserts, and in such just measure as to satisfy himself, and those also who would wish that ecclesiastical preferment were always so properly bestowed. But he was not satisfied with his literary fame. Others passed him upon the stream of popularity with all their sails set, full speed before the wind, while he lay quietly upon his oars in a pleasant creek; and he did not sufficiently bear in mind that he was safe at his ease, when some of those who so triumphantly left him behind were upset and went to the bottom. He had done enough to secure for himself a respectable place among the poets of his country, and a distinguished one among those of his age. But more through indolence than from any deficiency or decay of power, he had fallen short of the promise of his youth, and of his own early aspirations. Discontent, especially when mingled with self-reproach, is an uneasy feeling, and like many others he appears to have sought relief by projecting it, and transferring as much of it as he could upon the world. He became an acrimonious whig, and took an active part in the factious measures by which Yorkshire was agitated about the close of the American war. Gray, if he had been then living, might perhaps have been able to have rendered him more temperate and more reasonable in his political views; certainly he would have prevailed upon him not to write, or having written not to publish or preserve, the last book of his English Garden, which is in every respect miserably bad; bad in taste as recommending sham castles and modern ruins; bad in morals, as endeavouring to serve a political cause and excite indignation against the measures of Government by a fictitious story, (which if it had been true could have had no bearing whatever upon the justice or injustice of the American war;) and bad in poetry, because the story is in itself absurd. Not the least absurd part of this puerile tale is the sudden death of the heroine, at the unexpected sight of her betrothed husband, whom she was neither glad nor sorry to see; and the description of the *facies Hippocratica* is applied to this person, thus dying in health, youth, and beauty! Dr. Dove used to instance this as a remarkable example of knowledge ignorantly misapplied.

Yet though the Doctor did not rank him higher as a physiologist than Miller did as a musician, or than Sir Joshua must have done as a painter, he found more pleasure than the organist could do in his conversation; partly because there was an air of patronage in Mason's intercourse with Miller at first, and afterwards an air of estrangement, (a sufficient reason); and partly because Mason was more capable of enjoying the richness of the Doctor's mind, and such of its eccentricities as were allowed to appear in company where he was not wholly without reserve, than he was of appreciating the simplicity of Miller's. That vein of humour which he indulged in his correspondence opened when he was conversing with one, like the Doctor, upon whom nothing was lost; at such times the heavy saturnine character of Mason's countenance, which might almost be called morose, seemed to be cast off; and pleasantry and good-nature animated its intellectual strength. But according to Polwhele's friend, there was a "sedate benignity in his countenance, which taught me," says Mr. Greville, "instantaneously to rely on him as a man the leading traits of whose disposition were feeling and reflection. This immediate impression of his character I found afterwards to be strictly just. I never yet met with a human being whose head and heart appear to act and react so reciprocally, so concordantly upon each other as his.—In his style of conversation, you can trace nothing of the *vis vivida* of the poet. Here his inventive powers apparently lie dormant. Those flashes of genius, those intellectual emanations which we are taught to believe great men cannot help darting forward in order to lighten up the gloom of colloquial communication, he seems to consider as affected; he therefore rejects them whenever they occur, and appears to pride himself on the preference which he gives to simplicity and perspicuity. Conversation, (if you will excuse a pedantic allusion,) with him resembles the style of painting mentioned in the earlier part of the Athenian History, which consisted in representing the artist's ideas in a simple unaffected point of view, through the medium of one colour only; whereas his writings are like the pictures of Polygnotus. They glow with all the warmth of an invigorated imagination, an animated diction, and a rich luxuriant phraseology.

"His manners, too, are equally as chaste and unaffected as his conversation. The stream that winds its easy way through woods and verdant meads, is not less artificial or more insinuating than he is in doing the honours of the table, or promoting the graces of the drawing-room. That peculiar happiness which some few I have met with possess, of reconciling you implicitly to their superiority, he enjoys in an eminent degree, by the amiability of his sentiments, the benignity of his attention, and particularly by an indescribable way with him, of making you appear to advantage, even when he convinces you of the erroneousness of your opinions, or the inconclusiveness of your reasoning.

"In regard to his morals, I believe from what I have collected, that few can look back upon a period of sixty years' existence, spent so uniformly pure and correct. In the course of our chit-chat, he informed me, in an unostentatious unaffected manner, that he never was intoxicated but once."

There was another point of resemblance, besides their vein of humour, between Mason and the Doctor, in their latter days; they were nearly of the same age, and time had brought with it to both the same sober, contemplative, deep feeling of the realities of religion.

The French Revolution cured Mason of his whiggery, and he had the manliness to sing his palinode. The fearful prevalence of a false and impious philosophy made him more and more sensible of the inestimable importance of his faith. On his three last birth-days he composed three sonnets, which for their sentiment and their beauty ought to be inserted in every volume of select poems for popular use. And he left for posthumous publication a poem called RELIGIO CLERICI; as a whole it is very inferior to that spirited satire of Smedley's which bears the same title, and which is the best satire of its age; but its concluding paragraph will leave the reader with a just and very favourable impression of the poet and the man.

FATHER, REDEEMER, COMFORTER DIVINE!
This humble offering to thy equal shrine
Here thy unworthy servant grateful pays,
Of undivided thanks, united praise,
For all those mercies which at birth began,
And ceaseless flow'd thro' life's long-lengthened span,
Propt my frail frame thro' all the varied scene,
With health enough for many a day serene;
Enough of science clearly to discern
How few important truths the wisest learn;
Enough of arts ingenuous to employ
The vacant hours, when graver studies cloy;
Enough of wealth to serve each honest end,
The poor to succour, or assist a friend;
Enough of faith in Scripture to descry,
That the sure hope of immortality,
Which only can the fear of death remove,
Flows from the fountain of REDEEMING LOVE.

One who visited York a few years after the death of the Poet, says, "the Verger who showed us the Minster upon my inquiring of him concerning Mason, began an encomium upon him in an humble way indeed, but more honourable than all the factitious praises of learned ostentation; his countenance brightened up when I asked him the question; his very looks told me that Mason's charities did not evaporate in effusions of sensibility; I learned that he was humble, mild, and generous; the father of his family; the delight of all that came within the sphere of his notice. Then he was so good in his parish. My soul contemplates, with fond exultation, the picture of a man, endowed with genius, wit and every talent to please the great, but *suâ se virtute involventem*, resigning himself with complacency to the humble duties of a country pastor, — turning select Psalms into Verse to be sung in his Church; simplifying and arranging, and directing to the purposes of devotion his church music; and performing his duties as a minister with meekness, perseverance, and brotherly love."

Enough has now been adduced to vindicate Mason's character from Miller's aspersion. They who desire to see his merits as a poet appreciated with great ability and equal justice should peruse his life in Hartley Coleridge's Boreal Biography,—what a boisterous title for a book in which there is not one blustering sentence, and so many sweet strains of feeling and of thought!

CHAPTER CXXVII.

THE DOCTOR'S THEORY OF PROGRESSIVE EXISTENCE.

Quam multæ pecudes humano in corpore vivunt!
PALINGENIUS.

LIKE Mason, Dr. Dove looked to the future in that sure and certain hope without which the present would be intolerable to a thinking mind and feeling heart. But in his speculations he looked to the past also.

Watson Bishop of Llandaff amused himself with asking from whom his mind descended? where it existed before he was born? and who he should have been if he had not been Richard Watson? "The Bishop was a philosopher," says Dr. Jarrold, "and ought not to have asked such idle questions."

My Doctor would not have agreed with Dr. Jarrold in this opinion. Who the Bishop might have been if he had not been the discontented hero of his own autobiography, he could not indeed have pretended to divine; but what he was before he was Richard Watson, where his mind had existed before he was born, and from whom, or rather from what, it had been transmitted, were questions which, according to his notions, might admit of a probable solution.

It will not surprise the judicious reader to be told that the Doctor was a professed physiognomist, though Lavater had not in those days made it fashionable to talk of physiognomy as a science. Baptista Porta led him to consider the subject; and the coarse wood-cuts of a bungling Italian elucidated the system as effectually as has since been done by Mr. Holloway's graver. But Dr. Dove carried it farther than the Swiss enthusiast after, or the Neapolitan physician before him. Conceiving in a deeper sense than Lebrun, *que chacun avait sa bête dans la figure*, he insisted that the strong animal likenesses which are often so distinctly to be traced in men, and the correspondent propensities wherewith they are frequently accompanied, are evidence of our having pre-existed in an inferior state of being. And he deduced from it a theory, or notion as he modestly called it, which he would have firmly believed to be a part of the patriarchal faith, if he had known how much it resembled the doctrine of the Druids.

His notion was that the Archeus, or living principle, acquires that perfect wisdom with which it acts, by passing through a long progression in the lower world, before it becomes capable of being united to a rational and immortal soul in the human body. He even persuaded himself that he could discover in particular individuals indications of the line by which their Archeus had travelled through the vegetable and animal kingdoms.

There was a little pragmatical exciseman, with a hungry face, sharp nose, red eyes, and thin, coarse, straggling hair of a yellow cast, (what was formerly called Judas-colour,) whom he pronounced to have been a ferret in his last stage. "Depend upon it," he said, "no rat will come under the roof where he resides!" And he was particularly careful when they met in the open air always to take the wind of him.

One lawyer, a man of ability and fair character, but ready to avail himself of every advantage which his profession afforded, he traced from a bramble into a wasp, thence into a butcher bird, and lastly into a fox, the vulpine character being manifestly retained in his countenance. There was another, who, from sweeping his master's office and blacking his shoes, had risen to be the most noted pettifogger in those parts. This fellow was his peculiar abhorrence; his living principle, he affirmed, could never have existed in any other form than that of a nuisance; and accordingly he made out his genealogy thus:—a stinker (which is the trivial name of the *phallus impudicus*,) a London bug, an ear-wig, a pole-cat,—and, still worsening as he went on, a knavish attorney.

He convicted an old Major in the West York Militia of having been a turkey cock; and all who knew the Major were satisfied of the likeness, whatever they might be of the theory.

One of the neighbouring justices was a large, square-built, heavy person, with a huge head, a wide mouth, little eyes, and a slender proportion of intellect. Him he set down for a hippopotamus.

A brother magistrate of the Major's had been a goose, beyond all dispute. There was even proof of the fact; for it was perfectly well remembered that he had been born web-fingered.

All those persons who habitually sit up till night is far spent, and as regularly pass the best hours of the morning in bed, he supposed to have been bats, night-birds, night-prowling beasts, and insects whose portion of active life has been assigned to them during the hours of darkness. One indication of this was, that candle-light could not have such attractions for them unless they had been moths.

The dog was frequently detected in all its varieties, from the lap-dog, who had passed into the whipper-snapper *petit-maître*, and the turn-spit, who was now the bandy-legged baker's boy,—to the Squire's eldest son, who had been a lurcher,—the Butcher, who had been a bull-dog, and so continued still in the same line of life;—Lord A——'s domestic chaplain, harmless, good-natured, sleek, obsequious, and as fond of ease, indulgence and the fire-side, as when he had been a parlour spaniel; Sir William B——'s huntsman, who exercised now the whip which he had felt when last upon four legs, and who was still an ugly hound, though staunch; and the Doctor's own man, Barnaby, whom, for steadiness, fidelity, and courage, he pronounced to have been a true old English mastiff, and one of the best of his kind.

Chloris had been a lily. You saw it in the sickly delicacy of her complexion. Moreover she toiled not, neither did she spin.

A young lady, in whose family he was perfectly familiar, had the singular habit of sitting always upon one or other foot, which as she sat down she conveyed so dexterously into the seat of her chair, that no one who was not previously acquainted with her ways, could possibly perceive the movement. Upon her mother's observing one day that this was a most unaccountable peculiarity, the Doctor replied, "No, madam! I can account for it to my own entire satisfaction. Your daughter was a bird of some gentle and beautiful species, in her last stage of existence; in that state she used always to draw up one leg when at rest. The habits that we acquire in our pre-existent state, continue with us through many stages of our progress; your daughter will be an Angel in her next promotion, and then, if Angels close their eyes in slumber, she will sleep with her head under her wing."

The landlady of the White Lion had been a cabbage, a blue-bottle fly, a tame duck, and a bacon-pig.

Who could doubt that Vauban had been an earthworm, a mole, and a rabbit? that Euclid acquired the practical knowledge of geometry when he was a spider; and that the first builder of a pyramid imitated unconsciously the proportionately far greater edifices which he had been employed in raising when he was one of a nation of white ants?

Mrs. Dove had been a cowslip, a humble bee, and, lastly, a cushat.

He himself had been a Dove and a Serpent—for "Dan was a Serpent by the way;" and moreover, he flattered himself that he had the wisdom of the one, and the simplicity of the other. Of his other stages he was not so certain,—except that he had probably once been an inhabitant of the waters, in the shape of some queer fish.

CHAPTER CXXVIII.

ELUCIDATIONS OF THE COLUMBIAN THEORY.

Thou almost makest me waver in my faith,
To hold opinion with Pythagoras,
That souls of animals infuse themselves
Into the trunks of men.

MERCHANT OF VENICE.

MANY facts in illustration or exemplification of the Doctor's theory concerning progressive existence must have occurred to every one within the circle of his own observations. One of the scientific persons who abridged the Philosophical Transactions says, he "was acquainted with a medical practitioner of considerable eminence who could not refrain from eating toasted cheese, though he was subject to an alarming pulmonary complaint which was uniformly aggravated by it, and which terminated fatally at an age by no means advanced." This practitioner, the Doctor would have said, had been either a mouse or a rat, and in that pre-existent form had nibbled at such a bait,—perhaps once too often. This would account for the propensity, even if he were not a Welshman to boot.

The same author says "there is now living a physician of my acquaintance who at an autumnal dessert never ceases eating all the filberts he can lay his hands upon, although he very candidly acknowledges that they are extremely indigestible and hurtful things." Upon the Doctor's theory, who can doubt that he had been a squirrel?

"I remember," says a certain Mr. George Garden, in a letter written from Aberdeen in 1676, "when Mrs. Scougall and I were with you last summer, we had occasion to speak of a man in this country very remarkable for something peculiar in his temper, that inclines him to imitate unawares all the gestures and motions of those with whom he converses. We then had never seen him ourselves. Since our return we were together at Strathbogie where he dwells, and notwithstanding all we had heard of him before, were somewhat surprised with the oddness of this dotterel quality. This person named Donald Munro, being a little old and very plain man, of a thin slender body, has been subject to this infirmity, as he told us, from his very infancy. He is very loath to have it observed, and therefore casts down his eyes when he walks in the streets, and turns them aside when he is in company. We had made several trials before he perceived our design, and afterwards had much ado to make him stay. We caressed him as much as we could, and had then the opportunity to observe that he imitated not only the scratching of the head, but also the wringing of the hands, wiping of the nose, stretching forth of the arms, &c., and we needed not strain compliments to persuade him to be covered, for he still put off and on as he saw us do, and all this with so much exactness, and yet with such a natural and unaffected air, that we could not so much as suspect that he did it on design. When we held both his hands and caused another to make such motions, he pressed to get free; but when we would have known more particularly how he found himself affected, he could only give us this simple answer, that it vexed his heart and his brain."

The writer of this letter had hit upon the solution of the idiosyncracy which he describes, but had not perceived it. The man had been a dotterel.

"Have we not heard," said the Doctor, "of persons who have ruminated? Do we not read well-authenticated cases of some whose skins were tuberculated? Is it not recorded of Dioscorides, not the botanist, but the Alexandrian physician of Cleopatra's time, that he was called Phacas because his body was covered with warts? And where was this so likely to have happened as in Egypt? He had been a crocodile. The cases are more frequent of people who in the scaliness of their skins have borne testimony of their piscine origin.

Was not Margaret Griffith, wife of David Owen of Llan Gaduain in Montgomeryshire shown in London, because a crooked horn four inches long grew out of the middle of her forehead? "A miraculous and monstrous, but yet most true and certain account" of her, with her rude portrait affixed, was imprinted at London by Thomas Owen, in the year of the Spanish Armada, and sold by Edward White, at the little north door of St. Paul's Church, at the Sign of the Gun. And in the British Museum there is not only the picture of another horned woman, Davies by name, who was born at Shotwick in Cheshire, but one of the horns also which she shed.

There was a Mistress Bomby, (not the Mother Bombie of the old play, but a person of our own times,) who having been a schoolmistress till the age of fifty, married at that age, and on the day of her marriage became deranged. She never recovered her reason, but she lived to be fourscore; and in the latter year of her life a crooked horn sprouted from the side of her forehead, and grew to the length of nearly six inches. Another made its appearance, but its growth was stopped. It is to be regretted that the person who recorded this did not say whether the second horn made its appearance on the other side of the forehead, so as to correspond with the former and form a pair.

Blumenbach had three human horns in his collection, all the growth of one woman. She had broken her head by a fall, and the first of them grew from the wound; it continued growing for thirty years, till it was about ten inches long, then it dropped off; a second grew from its place, this was short, thick, and nearly straight, and she shed it in less time; the third was growing when she died, and the Professor had it cut from the corpse. The first was completely twisted like a ram's horn, was round and rough, of a brownish colour, and full half an inch in diameter at the roots. All three appeared to be hollow, and were blunt, and rounded at the termination. It has been said that all the cases of this kind which have been observed have been in women; the remark, whether it were made by Blumenbach, or by the intelligent traveller who describes this part of his collection, would, if it were true, be unimportant, because of the paucity of cases that have been recorded: but there is a case of a male subject, and it is remarkable for the circumstances attending it.

Marshal Laverdin in the year 1599 was hunting in the province of Maine, when his attendants came in sight of a peasant who, instead of waiting to pay his obeisance to their master, fled from them. They pursued and overtook him; and as he did not uncover to salute the Marshal, they plucked off his cap, and discovered that he had a horn growing on his head. François Trouillu was this poor man's name, and he was then aged thirty-four years: the horn began to sprout when he was about seven years old; it was shaped almost like that of a ram, only the flutings were straight instead of spiral, and the end bowed inwards toward the cranium. The fore part of his head was bald, and his beard red and tufted, such as painters bestow upon Satyrs. He had retired to the woods hoping to escape exposure there, and there he wrought in the coal-pits. Marshal Laverdin took possession of him as he would of a wild beast, and sent him as a present to Henry IV.; and that King, with even more inhumanity than the Marshal, bestowed him upon somebody who carried him about as a show. Mezeray, who relates this without any comment upon the abominable tyranny of the Marshal and the King, concludes the story by saying, "the poor man took it so much to heart to be thus led about like a bear and exposed to the laughter and mockery of his fellow creatures, that he very soon died."

Blumenbach says "it has been ascertained by chemical analysis that such horns have a greater affinity in their composition with the horns of the rhinoceros than of any other animal." It may be so; but the short and straight horns were stunted in their growth; their natural tendency was to twist like a sheep's horn; — and the habit of cornification is more likely to have been formed nearer home than in the interior of Africa.

The first rope-dancer, or as Johnson would have called him "funambulist," the Doctor said, had been a monkey; the first fellow who threw a somerset, a tumbler pigeon.

The Oneirocrites, or Oneirologists, as they who pretended to lay down rules for the interpretation of dreams called themselves, say that if any one dreams he has the head of a horse on his shoulders instead of his own, it betokens poverty and servitude. The Doctor was of opinion that it presaged nothing, but that it bore a retrospective interpretation, being the confused reminiscence of a prior state.

Amateur thieves, — for there are persons who commit petty larcenies with no other motive than the pleasure of stealing, — he supposed to have been tame magpies or jackdaws. And in the vulgar appellation which is sometimes bestowed upon an odious woman, he thought that though there was not more meant than meets the ear, there was more truth conveyed than was intended.

A dramatist of Charles the First's reign, says,

> 'Tis thought the hairy child that's shown about
> Came by the mother's thinking on the picture
> Of Saint John Baptist, in his camel's coat.

But for this and other recorded cases of the same kind the Doctor accounted more satisfactorily to himself by his own theory. For though imagination, he said, might explain these perfectly well, (which he fully admitted,) yet it could not explain the horned, nor the tubercular, nor the ruminating cases; nor the case of John Ferguisson, of the parish of Killmelfoord in Argyleshire, who lived eighteen years without taking any other sustenance than water, and must therefore either have been a leech, tortoise, or some other creature capable of being so supported. Nor could anything so well as his hypothesis explain the cases in which various parts of the human body had been covered with incrustations, which were shed and reproduced in continual succession, a habit retained from some crustaceous stage of existence, and probably acquired in the form of a crab or lobster. Still more remarkable was the case of a German, communicated by Dr. Steyerthall to the Royal Society: this poor man cast his leg by an effort of nature, not by an immediate act of volition, as he would have done in his crab or lobster state, for the power had not been retained with the habit, but after long and severe suffering; the limb, however, at last separated of itself, and the wound healed.

Neither, he said, could imagination explain the marvellous and yet well-attested story of the Danish woman who lay in, like Leda, of two eggs. The neighbours who were called in at the delivery, most improperly broke one and found that it contained a yolk and white, to all appearance as in that of a hen, which it also resembled in size. The other, instead of endeavouring to hatch it, they sent to Olaus Wormius, and it is still to be seen at Copenhagen.

How, he would ask, was the case of Samuel Chilton, near Bath, to be explained, who used to sleep for weeks and months at a time; but as an old habit of hibernation, acting at irregular times, because it was no longer under the direction of a sane instinct. And how that of the idiot at Ostend, who died at last in consequence of his appetite for iron, no fewer than eight-and-twenty pieces to the amount of nearly three pounds in weight, having been found in his stomach after death. Who but must acknowledge that he had retained this habit from an ostrich?

This poor creature was really ferrivorous. The Doctor, though he sometimes pressed into his service a case to which some exceptions might have been taken, would not have classed as a quondam ostrich the sailor who used to swallow knives for a feat of desperate bravery, and died miserably, as might be expected. Nor would he have formed any such conclusion concerning the person of whom Adam Clarke has preserved the following remarkable story, in the words of Dr. Fox, who kept a lunatic asylum near Bristol.

"In my visits among my patients, one morning, I went into a room where two, who were acquaintances of each other, were accustomed to live: immediately I entered, I noticed an unusual degree of dejection about one of them, and a feverish kind of excitement in the other. I inquired what was the matter? 'Matter!' said the excited one, 'matter enough! he has done for himself!'—'Why? what has he done?'—'Oh he has only swallowed the poker!' During this short conversation the other looked increasingly mournful; and on my inquiring what was the matter with him, he replied, 'He has told you true enough; I have swallowed the poker, and do not know what I shall do with it!' 'I will tell you how it happened,' said the first. 'My friend and I were sitting by the fire talking on different things, when I offered to lay him a wager that he could not eat any of the poker: he said he could and would; took it up, twisted the end of it backward and forward between the bars of the grate, and at last broke off some inches of it, and instantly swallowed it; and he has looked melancholy ever since.' I did not believe," said Dr. Fox, "a word of this tale; and I suppose the narrator guessed as much, for he added, 'O, you can see that it is true, for there is the rest of the poker.' I went to the grate and examined the poker, which, being an old one, had been much burned; and where the action of the fire had been fiercest and had worn away the iron, a piece of between two and three inches had been wrenched off, and was missing. Still I could hardly credit that the human stomach could receive such a dose and remain 'feeling,' as the professed swallower of it said, 'nothing particular.' However the constant affirming of the first, united to the assent and rueful looks of the second, induced me to use the patient as though the account were true: I administered very strong medicines, and watched their effects constantly. The man ate, and drank, and slept as usual, and appeared to suffer nothing but from the effect of the medicines. At last, to my astonishment, the piece of the poker came away, and the man was as well as ever. The iron had undergone a regular process of digestion, and the surface of it was deeply honey-combed by the action of the juices. This was a most singular case, and proves how the God of Nature has endowed our system with powers of sustaining and redressing the effects of our own follies."

The tales of lycanthropy which are found in such different ages and remote countries strongly supported the Doctor's theory. Virgil, and Ovid in his story of Lycaon, had only adapted a popular superstition to their purposes. And like its relator he regarded as a mere fable the legend which Pliny has preserved from the lost works of Evanthes, a Greek author not to be despised. Evanthes had found it written among the Arcadians that a man from the family of a certain Antæus * in that country was chosen by lot, and taken to a certain lake; there he stript, hung his garments upon an oak, swam across and going into the wilderness, became a wolf, and herded with wolves for nine years; and if during that time he abstained from doing any hurt to men, he returned to the lake, recrossed it, resumed his human form, with the only change of being the worse, not for the wear indeed, but for the lapse of those nine years; and moreover found his clothes where he had left them. Upon which Pliny observes, *Mirum est quo procedat Græca credulitas! Nullum tam impudens mendacium est quod teste careat.*

A worse manner of effecting the same metamorphosis Pliny relates from the Olympionics of Agriopas; that at a human sacrifice offered by the Arcadians to Jupiter Lycæus, one Demænetus Parrhasius tasted the entrails, and was transformed into a wolf; at the expiration of ten years he resumed his original form, and obtained the prize of pugilism at the Olympic games.

But the Doctor differed from Pliny's opinion that all which is related concerning lycanthropy must be rejected or all believed; —*Homines in lupos verti rursumque restitui sibi, falsum esse confidenter existimare debemus; aut credere omnia, quæ fabulosa tot seculis comperimus.* The belief, however, he admits, was so firmly fixed in the common people that their word for turncoat was derived from it;—*Unde tamen ista vulgo infixa sit fama in tantum, ut in maledictis*

* The original is *ex gente Antæi cujusdam.* Cf. Lib. viii. c. xxiii. In the original edition Antæus is written *author* by mistake, which is the occasion of this note, and must have puzzled many a reader.

versipelles habeat, indicabitur. These fables, the Doctor argued, could not invalidate the testimony of ancient physicians, that there was an actual and well-known species of madness, in which men howled like wolves, and wandered by night about in lonely places or among the tombs. It was most severe at the commencement of spring; and was sometimes epidemic in certain countries. Pieter Forest, whose character for accuracy and sagacity stands high among medical writers, affirms that he, in the sixteenth century, had seen the disease, and that it was as it had been described by the ancients. He must have been a credulous person who believed Constantinople had been so infested by these wolf-men, that the Grand Seignior and his guards had been obliged to go out against them; killing a hundred and fifty, and putting the rest of the pack to flight. This was a traveller's tale; and the stories related in books of demonology and witchcraft, concerning wretches who had been tried and executed for having, in the shape of wolves, killed and eaten children, and who had confessed their guilt, might be explained, like other confessions of witchcraft, by the effects of fear and tortures; yet there were cases upon which the Doctor thought no doubt could be entertained.

One case upon which the Doctor insisted was that of an Italian peasant near Pavia, who in the year 1541 was seized with this madness, and fancying himself to be a wolf, attacked several persons in the fields and killed some of them. He was taken at last, but not without great difficulty; and when in the hands of his captors he declared that he was a wolf, however much they might doubt the avowal, and that the only difference between him and other wolves was, that they had their fur on the outside of the skin, but his was between the skin and the flesh. The madman asserted this so positively that some of the party, *trop inhumains et loups par effect*, as Simon Goulart says with a humanity above the standard of his age, determined to see, and made several slashes in his arms and legs. Repenting of their cruelty, when they had convinced themselves by this experiment that the poor wretch was really insane, they put him under the care of a surgeon; and he died in the course of a few days under his hands. "Now," said the Doctor, "if this were a solitary case, it would evidently be a case of madness; but as lycanthropy is recognised by physicians of different times and countries, as a specific and well-known affection of the human mind, can it be so satisfactorily explained in any other manner, as by the theory of progressive existence,—by the resurrection of a habit belonging to the preceding stage of the individual's progress?"

The superstition was not disbelieved by Bishop Hall. In the account of what he observed in the Netherlands, he says of Spa, "the wide deserts on which it borders are haunted with three kinds of ill cattle, free-booters, wolves, and witches, though these two last are often one."

When Spenser tells us it was said of the Irish, as of the Scythians, how they were once a year turned into wolves, "though Master Camden in a better sense doth suppose it was the disease called Lycanthropia,"—he adds these remarkable words, "yet some of the Irish do use to make the wolf their gossip." Now it must be observed that gossip is not here used in its secondary meaning of a talking, tattling, or tippling companion, but in its original import, though wickedly detorted here: "Our Christian ancestors," says Verstegan, "understanding a spiritual affinity to grow between the parents and such as undertook for the child at baptism, called each other by the name of God-sib, which is as much as to say as that they were *sib* together, that is, of kin together, through God." The Limerick schoolmaster whose words are transcribed by Camden, says, "they receive wolves as gossips, calling them *Chari-Christ*, praying for them, and wishing them happy; upon which account they are not afraid of them." There was great store of wolves in Ireland at that time; and the Doctor asked whether so strange a custom could be satisfactorily explained in any way but by a blind consciousness of physical affinity,—by supposing that those who chose wolves to be godfathers and godmothers for their children, had in the preceding stage of their own existence been wolves themselves?

How triumphantly would be have appealed to a story which Captain Beaver relates in his African Memoranda. "In the evening," says that most enterprising, resolute, able, and right-minded man, "two or three of the grumetas came to me and said that Francisco, one of their party, was not a good man: that he wanted to eat one of them, John Basse, who had been this day taken very ill. As I could not comprehend what they meant by saying that one of them wanted to eat another, I sent for Johnson to explain. He said that the man accused of eating the other was a witch, and that he was the cause of John Basse's illness, by sucking his blood with his infernal witchcraft; and that these people had come to request that I would let them tie him to a tree and flog him, after they had finished their work. I told them that there was no such thing as a witch; that it was impossible for this man to suck the blood of another, by any art which he could possibly possess; that he could not be the cause of another man's illness by such means; and that with respect to flogging, no one punished on the island but myself. Johnson, who is as bigoted in this instance as any of them, says that he is well known to be a witch: that he has killed many people with his infernal art, and that this is the cause of his leaving his own country, where, if he should ever be caught, he would be sold as a slave; and that he with difficulty had prevented the other grumetas from throwing him overboard on their passage from Bissao hither. Johnson moreover told me that there was another witch among the grumetas, who had the power of changing himself into an alligator, and that he also had killed many people by his witchcraft, and was consequently obliged to run from his country. They therefore most earnestly entreated me to let them punish them, country fashion, and they promised not to kill either of them. Astonished at the assurance that neither of them should be killed if they were permitted to punish them, I told Johnson that if such a thing should occur, I would immediately hang all those concerned in it, and then endeavoured to reason them out of their foolish notions respecting these two poor men. Johnson replied, that it was the custom of the country for white men never to interfere in these cases, and that at Bissao the governor never took notice of their thus punishing one another according to their own country fashion, and that they expected the same indulgence here; for that if these people were in their own country, they would either be killed or sold, as witchcraft was never forgiven, and its professors never suffered to remain in their own country, when once found out. I had now all the grumetas round me, among whom were the accused themselves, and endeavoured again to convince them of the innocence of these people, by pointing out the impossibility of their hurting others by any magic or spell, or of transforming themselves into any other shape. When many of them said this man had often avowed his turning himself into an alligator to devour people: 'How say you, Corasmo,' said I, 'did you ever say so to any of these people?' 'Yes,' was his reply. 'What do you mean? do you mean to say that you ever transformed yourself into any other shape than that which you now bear?' 'Yes,' was the answer. 'Now, Corasmo, you know that white man knows everything; you cannot deceive me; therefore avow to those people, that you never changed yourself into an alligator, and that these are all lies.' 'No,' was his reply,—who can believe it? 'I can change myself into an alligator, and *have often* done it." This was such an incorrigible witch that I immediately gave him up to the grumetas to punish him, but desired them to be merciful. —It is scarcely credible that a man can so work upon his own weak imagination as to believe, which I doubt not this man did, its own fanciful creations to be realities.—After the grumetas had left me last night I regretted having delivered up to them the two poor miserable wretches accused of witchcraft. From ten till twelve at night their cries were most piteous and loud, and though distant a full half mile, were distinctly heard. This morning they cannot move."

There was a Mr. William Wright, of Saham Tony in Norfolk, who used to cast his skin every year, sometimes once, sometimes twice; it was an uneasy and distressing effort of nature, preceded by itching, red spots, and swellings; the fingers became stiff, hard, and painful at the ends, and about the nails the pain was exquisite. The whole process of changing was completed in from ten to twelve days, but it was about six months before the nails were perfectly renewed. From the hands the skin came off whole like a glove: and a print representing one of these gloves is given with the account of the case in the Gentleman's Magazine.

When this was related to the Doctor it perplexed him. The habit was evidently that of a snake; and it did not agree with his theory to suppose that the Archeus would pass, as it were *per saltum*, from so low a stage of existence to the human form. But upon reading the account himself he was completely satisfied as soon as he found that the subject was an Attorney.

He did not know, because it was not known till Mr. Wilkin published his excellent edition of Sir Thomas Browne's Works, that that Philosopher sent to his son Dr. Edward Browne, "the skin of the palm of a woman's hand, cast off at the end of a fever, or in the declination thereof. I called it," he says, "*exuvium palmæ muliebris*, the Latin word being *exuvia* in the plural, but I named it *exuvium*, or *exuvia* in the singular number. It is neat, and worthy to be shown when you speak of the skin. Snakes, and lizards, and divers insects cast their skins, and they are very neat ones: men also in some diseases, by pieces, but I have not met with any so neat as this: a palmister might read a lecture of it. The whole soles of the feet came off, and I have one." If the Doctor had heard of this case, and had not suspected the woman of having once belonged to a generation of vipers, or some *snekki-famili* as the words are rendered in the Talkee-talkee version, he would have derived her from an eel, and expressed a charitable hope that she might not still be a slippery subject.

CHAPTER CXXIX.

WHEREIN THE AUTHOR SPEAKS OF A TRAGEDY FOR THE LADIES, AND INTRODUCES ONE OF WILLIAM DOVE'S STORIES FOR CHILDREN.

Y donde sobre todo de su dueño
El gran tesoro y el caudal se infiere,
Es que al grande, al mediano, y al pequeño,
Todo se da de balde á quien lo quiere.

BALBUENA.

HERE might be the place for inquiring how far the Doctor's opinions or fancies upon this mysterious subject were original. His *notion* he used to call it; but a person to whom the reader will be introduced ere long, and who regarded him with the highest admiration and the profoundest respect, always spoke of it as the Columbian Theory of Progressive Existence. Original indeed in the Doctor it was not; he said that he had learned it from his poor Uncle William; but that William Dove originated it himself there can be little doubt. From books it was impossible that he should have derived it, because he could not read; and nothing can be more unlikely than that he should have met with it as a traditional opinion. The Doctor believed that this poor Uncle, of whom he never spoke without some expression of compassionate kindness, had deduced it intuitively as an inference from his instinctive skill in physiognomy.

When subjects like these are treated of, it should be done discreetly. There should be, in the words of Bishop Andrewes, "Οἰκονομία, a dispensation, not a dissipation; a laying forth, not διασκορπισμὸς, a casting away; a wary sowing, not a heedless scattering; and a sowing χειρὶ, οὐ θυλάκῳ, by handfulls, not by basket-fulls, as the heathen-man well said." Bearing this in mind I have given a Chapterfull, not a

Volumefull, and that Chapter is for physiologists and philosophers; but this Opus is not intended for them alone; they constitute but a part only of that "fit audience" and not "few," which it will find.

One Andrew Henderson, a Scotchman, who kept a bookseller's shop, or stand, in Westminster Hall, at a time when lawyers' tongues and witnesses' souls were not the only commodities exposed for sale there, published a tragedy called "Arsinoe, or The Incestuous Marriage." The story was Egyptian; but the drama deserves to be called Hendersonian, after its incomparable author; for he assured the reader, in a prefatory advertisement, that there were to be found in it "the most convincing arguments against incest and self-murder, interspersed with an inestimable treasure of ancient and modern learning, and the substance of the principles of the illustrious Sir Isaac Newton, adapted to the meanest capacity, and very entertaining to the Ladies, containing a nice description of the passions and behaviour of the Fair Sex."

The Biographer, or Historian, or Anecdotist, or rather the reminiscent relator of circumstances concerning the birth, parentage and education, life, character and behaviour, of Dr. Daniel Dove, prefers not so wide a claim upon the gratitude of his readers as Andrew Henderson has advanced. Yet, like the author of "Arsinoe," he trusts that his work is "adapted to the meanest capacity;" that the lamb may wade in it, though the elephant may swim, and also that it will be found "very entertaining to the Ladies." Indeed, he flatters himself that it will be found profitable for old and young, for men and for women, the married and the single, the idle and the studious, the merry and the sad; that it may sometimes inspire the thoughtless with thought, and sometimes beguile the careful of their cares. One thing alone might hitherto seem wanting to render it a catholic, which is to say, an universal book, and that is, that as there are Chapters in it for the closet, for the library, for the breakfast room, for the boudoir, (which is in modern habitations what the oriel was in ancient ones,) for the drawing-room, and for the kitchen, if you please, — (for whatever you may think, good reader, I am of opinion, that books which at once amuse and instruct may be as useful to servant men and maids, as to their masters and mistresses) — so should there be one at least for the nursery. With such a chapter, therefore, will I brighten the countenance of many a dear child, and gladden the heart of many a happy father, and tender mother, and nepotious uncle or aunt, and fond brother or sister;

Ηδεῖαν φάτιν
Φέροιμεν αὐτοῖς.*

For their sakes I will relate one of William Dove's stories, with which he used to delight young Daniel, and with which the Doctor in his turn used to delight his young favourites; and which never fails of effect with that fit audience for which it is designed, if it be told with dramatic spirit, in the manner that our way of printing it may sufficiently indicate, without the aid of musical notation. *Experto crede.* Prick up your ears then,

My good little women and men †;

and ye who are neither so little, nor so good, *favete linguis*, for here follows the Story of the Three Bears.

THE STORY OF THE THREE BEARS.

A tale which may content the minds
Of learned men and grave philosophers.
GASCOYNE.

Once upon a time there were Three Bears, who lived together in a house of their own, in a wood. One of them was a Little, Small, Wee Bear; and one was a Middle-sized Bear, and the other was a Great, Huge Bear. They had each a pot for their porridge, a little pot for the Little, Small, Wee Bear; and a middle-sized pot for the Middle Bear, and a great pot for the Great, Huge

* Sophocles. † Southey.

Bear. And they had each a chair to sit in; a little chair for the Little, Small, Wee Bear; and a middle-sized chair for the Middle Bear; and a great chair for the Great, Huge Bear. And they had each a bed to sleep in; a little bed for the Little, Small, Wee Bear; and a middle-sized bed for the Middle Bear; and a great bed for the Great, Huge Bear.

One day, after they had made the porridge for their breakfast, and poured it into their porridge-pots, they walked out into the wood while the porridge was cooling, that they might not burn their mouths, by beginning too soon to eat it. And while they were walking, a little old Woman came to the house. She could not have been a good, honest old Woman; for first she looked in at the window, and then she peeped in at the keyhole; and seeing nobody in the house, she lifted the latch. The door was not fastened, because the Bears were good Bears, who did nobody any harm, and never suspected that any body would harm them. So the little old Woman opened the door, and went in; and well pleased she was when she saw the porridge on the table. If she had been a good little old Woman, she would have waited till the Bears came home, and then, perhaps, they would have asked her to breakfast; for they were good Bears, — a little rough or so, as the manner of Bears is, but for all that very good-natured and hospitable. But she was an impudent, bad old Woman, and set about helping herself.

So first she tasted the porridge of the Great, Huge Bear, and that was too hot for her; and she said a bad word about that. And then she tasted the porridge of the Middle Bear, and that was too cold for her; and she said a bad word about that too. And then she went to the porridge of the Little, Small, Wee Bear, and tasted that; and that was neither too hot, nor too cold, but just right; and she liked it so well, that she ate it all up: but the naughty old Woman said a bad word about the little porridge-pot, because it did not hold enough for her.

Then the little old Woman sate down in the chair of the Great, Huge Bear, and that was too hard for her. And then she sate down in the chair of the Middle Bear, and that was too soft for her. And then she sate down in the chair of the Little, Small, Wee Bear, and that was neither too hard, nor too soft, but just right. So she seated herself in it, and there she sate till the bottom of the chair came out, and down came her's, plump upon the ground. And the naughty old Woman said a wicked word about that too.

Then the little old Woman went up stairs into the bed-chamber in which the three Bears slept. And first she lay down upon the bed of the Great, Huge Bear; but that was too high at the head for her. And next she lay down upon the bed of the Middle Bear; and that was too high at the foot for her. And then she lay down upon the bed of the Little, Small, Wee Bear; and that was neither too high at the head, nor at the foot, but just right. So she covered herself up comfortably, and lay there till she fell fast asleep.

By this time the Three Bears thought their porridge would be cool enough; so they came home to breakfast. Now the little old Woman had left the spoon of the Great, Huge Bear, standing in his porridge.

"Somebody has been at my porridge!"

said the Great, Huge Bear, in his great, rough, gruff voice. And when the Middle Bear looked at his, he saw that the spoon was standing in it too. They were wooden spoons; if they had been silver ones, the naughty old Woman would have put them in her pocket.

"Somebody has been at my porridge!"

said the Middle Bear, in his middle voice.

Then the Little, Small, Wee Bear looked

at his, and there was the spoon in the porridge-pot, but the porridge was all gone.

"Somebody has been at my porridge, and has eaten it all up!"

said the Little, Small, Wee Bear, in his little, small, wee voice.

Upon this the Three Bears, seeing that some one had entered their house, and eaten up the Little, Small, Wee Bear's breakfast, began to look about them. Now the little old Woman had not put the hard cushion straight when she rose from the chair of the Great, Huge Bear.

"Somebody has been sitting in my chair!"

said the Great, Huge Bear, in his great, rough, gruff voice.

And the little old Woman had squatted down the soft cushion of the Middle Bear.

"Somebody has been sitting in my chair!"

said the Middle Bear, in his middle voice.

And you know what the little old Woman had done to the third chair.

"Somebody has been sitting in my chair, and has sate the bottom of it out!"

said the Little, Small, Wee Bear, in his little, small, wee voice.

Then the Three Bears thought it necessary that they should make farther search; so they went up stairs into their bed-chamber. Now the little old Woman had pulled the pillow of the Great, Huge Bear, out of its place.

"Somebody has been lying in my bed!"

said the Great, Huge Bear, in his great, rough, gruff voice.

And the little old Woman had pulled the bolster of the Middle Bear out of its place.

"Somebody has been lying in my bed!"

said the Middle Bear, in his middle voice.

And when the Little, Small, Wee Bear came to look at his bed, there was the bolster in its place; and the pillow in its place upon the bolster; and upon the pillow was the little old Woman's ugly, dirty head,—which was not in its place, for she had no business there.

"Somebody has been lying in my bed,—and here she is!"

said the Little, Small, Wee Bear, in his little, small, wee voice.

The little old Woman had heard in her sleep the great, rough, gruff voice of the Great, Huge Bear; but she was so fast asleep that it was no more to her than the roaring of wind, or the rumbling of thunder. And she had heard the middle voice of the Middle Bear, but it was only as if she had heard some one speaking in a dream. But when she heard the little, small, wee voice of the Little, Small, Wee Bear, it was so sharp, and so shrill, that it awakened her at once. Up she started; and when she saw the Three Bears on one side of the bed, she tumbled herself out at the other, and ran to the window. Now the window was open, because the Bears, like good, tidy Bears, as they were, always opened their bed-chamber window when they got up in the morning. Out the little old Woman jumped; and whether she broke her neck in the fall; or ran into the wood and was lost there; or found her way out of the wood, and was taken up by the constable and sent to the House of Correction for a vagrant as she was, I cannot tell. But the Three Bears never saw anything more of her.*

---

* The lamented Southey was very much pleased with the Story of the Three Bears as versified by G. N., and published specially for the amusement of "little people," lest in the volumes of "The Doctor, &c.," it should "escape their sight."

CHAPTER CXXX.

CHILDREN AND KITTENS. APHORISMS ASCRIBED TO THE LAUREATE, DOCTOR SOUTHEY. MORE COLUMBIAN PHILOSOPHY.

Oh ! if in after life we could but gather
The very refuse of our youthful hours !

CHARLES LLOYD.

O DEAR little children, you who are in the happiest season of human life, how will you delight in the Story of the Three Bears, when Mamma reads it to you out of this nice book, or Papa, or some fond Uncle, kind Aunt, or doting Sister; Papa and Uncle will do the Great, Huge Bear, best; but Sister, and Aunt, and Mamma, will excel them in the Little, Small, Wee Bear, with his little, small, wee voice. And O Papa and Uncle, if you are like such a Father and such an Uncle as are at this moment in my mind's eye, how will you delight in it, both for the sake of that small, but "fit audience," and because you will perceive how justly it may be said to be

— a well-writ story,
Where each word stands so well placed that it passes
Inquisitive detraction to correct.*

It is said to be a saying of Dr. Southey's, that "a house is never perfectly furnished for enjoyment, unless there is a child in it rising three years old, and a kitten rising six weeks."

Observe, reader; this is repeated upon *On-dit's* authority, which is never to be taken for more than it is worth. I do not affirm that Dr. Southey has said this, but he is likely enough to have said it; for I know that he sometimes dates his letters from Cat's Eden. And if he did say so, I agree with him, and so did the Doctor; he *specialiter* as regards the child, I *specialiter* as regards the kitten.

Kitten is in the animal world what the rosebud is in the garden; the one the most beautiful of all young creatures, the other the loveliest of all opening flowers. The rose loses only something in delicacy by its development, — enough to make it a serious emblem to a pensive mind; but if a cat could remember kittenhood, as we remember our youth, it were enough to break a cat's heart, even if it had nine times nine heart strings.

Do not the flowers spring fresh and gay,
Pleasant and sweet, in the month of May;
And when their time cometh they fade away.†

It is another saying of the Laureate's, according to *On-dit*, that, "live as long as you may, the first twenty years are the longest half of your life." They appear so while they are passing; they seem to have been so when we look back upon them; and they take up more room in our memory than all the years that succeed them.

But in how strong a light has this been placed by the American teacher Jacob Abbott, whose writings have obtained so wide a circulation in England. "Life," he says, "if you understand by it the season of preparation for eternity, is more than half gone; — life so far as it presents opportunities and facilities for penitence and pardon, — so far as it bears on the formation of character, and is to be considered as a period of probation, — is unquestionably more than half gone, to those who are between fifteen and twenty. In a vast number of cases it is more than half gone, even *in duration:* and if we consider the thousand influences which crowd around the years of childhood and youth, winning us to religion, and making a surrender of ourselves to Jehovah easy and pleasant, — and, on the other hand, look forward beyond the years of maturity, and see these influences losing all their power, and the heart becoming harder and harder under the deadening effects of continuance in sin, — we shall not doubt a moment that the years of immaturity make a far more important part of our time of probation than all those that follow."

That pious man, who, while he lived, was the Honourable Charles How, and might properly now be called the honoured, says

* DAVENPORT.

† LUSTY JUVENTUS.

that "twenty years might be deducted for education, from the three-score and ten which are the allotted sum of human life; this portion," he observes, "is a time of discipline and restraint, and young people are never easy till they are got over it."

There is, indeed, during those years, much of restraint, of wearisomeness, of hope, and of impatience; all which feelings lengthen the apparent duration of time. Suffering, I have not included here; but with a large portion of the human race, in all Christian countries, (to our shame be it spoken!) it makes a large item in the account: there is no other stage of life in which so much gratuitous suffering is endured, — so much that might have been spared,—so much that is a mere wanton, wicked addition to the sum of human misery, — arising solely and directly from want of feeling in others, their obduracy, their caprice, their stupidity, their malignity, their cupidity, and their cruelty.

Algunos sabios han dicho que para lo que el hombre tiene aprender es muy corta la vida; mas yo añado que es muy larga para los que hemos de padecer. "Some wise men," writes Capmany, "have said that life is very short for what man has to learn,—but I (he says) must add, that it is very long for what we have to suffer." Too surely this is but too true; and yet a more consolatory view may be taken of human existence. The shortest life is long enough for those who are more sinned against than sinning; whose good instincts have not been corrupted, and whose evil propensities have either not been called into action, or have been successfully resisted and overcome.

The Philosopher of Doncaster found, in his theory of progressive existence, an easy solution for some of those questions on which it is more presumptuous than edifying to speculate, yet whereon that restless curiosity which man derives from the leaven of the forbidden fruit makes it difficult for a busy mind to refrain from speculating. The horrid opinion which certain Fathers entertained concerning the souls of unbaptized infants, he never characterised by any lighter epithet than *damnable*, for he used to say, "it would be wicked to use a weaker expression:" and the more charitable notion of the Limbo he regarded as a cold fancy, neither consonant to the heart of man, nor consistent with the wisdom and goodness of the Creator. He thought that when the ascent of being has been from good to better through all its stages, in moral qualities as well as in physical development, the immortal spirit might reach its human stage in such a state that it required nothing more than the vehicle of humanity, and might be spared its probation. As Enoch had been translated without passing through death, so he thought such happy spirits might be admitted into a higher sphere of existence without passing through the trials of sin and the discipline of sorrow.

CHAPTER CXXXI.

THE DOCTOR ABSTAINS FROM SPECULATING ON PERILOUS SUBJECTS. A STORY OF ST. ANSELM.

This field is so spacious, that it were easy for a man to lose himself in it; and if I should spend all my pilgrimage in this walk, my time would sooner end than my way.

BISHOP HALL.

THE Doctor, though he played with many of his theories as if they were rather mushrooms of the fancy than fruits of the understanding, never expressed himself sportively upon this. He thought that it rested upon something more solid than the inductions of a speculative imagination, because there is a feeling in human nature which answers to it, acknowledges, and confirms it. Often and often, in the course of his painful practice, he had seen bereaved parents seek for consolation in the same conclusion, to which faith and instinctive reason led them, though no such hypothesis as his had prepared them for it. They believed it simply and sincerely; and it is a belief, according to his philosophy, which nature has implanted in the heart for consolation, under one of the griefs that affect it most.

He had not the same confidence in another

view of the same branch of his hypothesis, relating to the early death of less hopeful subjects. Their term, he supposed, might be cut short in mercy, if the predisposing qualities which they had contracted on their ascent were such as would have rendered their tendency toward evil fatally predominant. But this, as he clearly saw, led to the brink of a bottomless question; and when he was asked after what manner he could explain why so many in whom this tendency predominates are, to their own destruction, permitted to live out their term, he confessed himself at fault. It was among the things, he said, which are inexplicable by our limited powers of mind. When we attain a higher sphere of existence, all things will be made clear. Meantime, believing in the infinite goodness of God, it is enough for us to confide in His infinite mercy, and in that confidence to rest.

When St. Anselm, at the age of seventy-six, lay down in his last illness, and one of the Priests who stood around his bed said to him, it being then Palm Sunday, "Lord Father, it appears to us, that, leaving this world, you are about to keep the Passover in the Palace of your Lord!" the ambitious old theologue made answer,—*et quidem, si voluntas ejus in hoc est, voluntati ejus non contradico. Verum si mallet me adhuc inter vos saltem tamdiu manere, donec quæstionem quam de animæ origine mente revolvo, absolvere possem, gratiosus acciperem, eo quod nescio, utrum aliquis eam, me defuncto, sit absoluturus.*—"If indeed this be his will, I gainsay it not. But if He should chuse rather that I should yet remain among you at least long enough to settle the question which I am revolving in my mind concerning the origin of the Soul, I should take it gratefully; because I do not know whether any one will be able to determine it, after I am dead." He added, *Ego quippe, si comedere possem, spero convalescere; nam nihil doloris in aliqua parte sentio, nisi quod lassescente stomacho, ob cibum quem capere nequit, totus deficio.**—"If I could but eat, I might hope to recover, for I feel no pain in any part, except that as my stomach sinks for lack of food, which it is unable to take, I am failing all over."

* Eadmer.

The Saint must have been in a most satisfactory state of self-sufficiency when he thus reckoned upon his own ability for disposing of a question which he thought it doubtful whether any one who came after him would be able to solve. All other appetite had forsaken him; but that for unprofitable speculation and impossible knowledge clung to him to the last; so strong a relish had he retained of the forbidden fruit:

Letting down buckets into empty wells,
And growing old in drawing nothing up! †

So had the Saint lived beyond the allotted term of three-score years and ten, and his hand was still upon the windlass when the hand of death was upon him. One of our old Dramatists ‡ represented a seven years' apprenticeship to such a craft as sufficient for bringing a man to a just estimate of it:

I was a scholar; seven useful springs
Did I deflower in quotations
Of cross'd opinions 'bout the soul of man;
The more I learnt, the more I learnt to doubt.
Delight, my spaniel, slept, whilst I baused § leaves,
Toss'd o'er the dunces, pored on the old print
Of titled words; and still my spaniel slept.
Whilst I wasted lamp-oil, baited my flesh,
Shrunk up my veins: and still my spaniel slept.
And still I held converse with Zabarell,
Aquinas, Scotus, and the musty saw
Of antick Donate; still my spaniel slept.
Still on went I; first, *an sit anima?*
Then an it were mortal? O hold, hold; at that
They're at brain-buffets, fell by the ears amain
Pell-mell together: still my spaniel slept.
Then whether 'twere corporeal, local, fixt,
Ex traduce, but whether't had free will
Or no, hot Philosophers
Stood banding factions, all so strongly propt,
I staggered, knew not which was firmer part,
But thought, quoted, read, observed and pryed,
Stufft noting-books; and still my spaniel slept.
At length he waked and yawn'd; and by yon sky,
For aught I know he knew as much as I.

In a more serious mood than that of this scholar, and in a humbler and holier state of mind than belonged to the Saint, our philosopher used to say, "little indeed does

† Cowper. ‡ Marston.
§ *Baisser*, Fr., and in vulgar English "Buss," which is the same as *Bause*.

it concern us, in this our mortal stage, to inquire whence the spirit hath come,—but of what infinite concern is the consideration whither is it going!"

CHAPTER CXXXII.

DOCTOR CADOGAN. A REMARKABLE CASE OF HEREDITARY LONGEVITY. REMARKS ON THE ORDINARY TERM OF HUMAN LIFE.

> Live well, and then how soon so e'er thou die,
> Thou art of age to claim eternity. RANDOLPH.

DR. CADOGAN used to say that the life of man is properly ninety years instead of three-score and ten; thirty to go up, thirty to stand still, and thirty to go down.

Who told him so? said Dr. Dove; and who made him better informed upon that point than the Psalmist?

Any one who far exceeded the ordinary term, beyond which "our strength is but labour and sorrow," was supposed by our philosopher, to have contracted an obstinate habit of longevity in some previous stage of existence. Centenaries he thought must have been ravens and tortoises; and Henry Jenkins, like Old Parr, could have been nothing in his preceding state, but a toad in a block of stone or in the heart of a tree.

Cardinal D'Armagnac, when on a visitation in the Cevennes, noticed a fine old man sitting upon the threshold of his own door and weeping; and as, like the Poet, he had

> —— not often seen
> A healthy man, a man full-grown,
> Weep in the public roads, alone,

he went up to him, and asked wherefore he was weeping? The old man replied he wept because his father had just beaten him. The Cardinal, who was amazed to hear that so old a man had a father still living, was curious enough to inquire what he had beaten him for: "because," said the old man, "I passed by my grandfather without paying my respects to him." The Cardinal then entered the house that he might see this extraordinary family, and there indeed he saw both father and grandfather, the former still a hale though a *very* aged man; the latter unable to move because of his extreme age, but regarded by all about him with the greatest reverence.

That the habit in this instance, as in most others of the kind, should have been hereditary, was what the Doctor would have expected: good constitutions and ill habits of body are both so;—two things which seldom co-exist, but this obstinate longevity, as he called it, was proof both of the one and the other. A remarkable instance of hereditary longevity is noticed in the Statistical Account of Arklow. A woman who died at the age of an hundred and ten, speaking of her children, said that her youngest boy was eighty; and that old boy was living several years afterwards, when the account was drawn up. The habit, however, he thought, was likely in such cases to correct itself and become weaker in every generation. An ill habit he deemed it, because no circumstances can render extreme old age desirable: it cannot be so in a good man, for his own sake; nor in a bad one for the sake of everybody connected with him. On all accounts the appointed term is best, and the wise and pious Mr. How has given us one cogent reason why it is so.

"The viciousness of mankind," that excellent person says, "occasioned the flood; and very probably God thought fit to drown the world for these two reasons; first to punish the then living offenders; and next to prevent men's plunging into those prodigious depths of impiety, for all future ages. For if in the short term of life, which is now allotted to mankind, men are capable of being puffed up to such an insolent degree of pride and folly, as to forget God and their own mortality, his power and their own weakness; if a prosperity bounded by three-score and ten years, (and what mortal's prosperity, since the deluge, ever lasted so long?) can swell the mind of so frail a creature to such a prodigious size of vanity, what boundaries could be set to his arrogance, if his life and prosperity, like that of the Patriarchs, were likely to continue eight or nine hundred years together? If under the existing circumstances of life, men's passions can rise so high; if the present short and uncertain enjoyments of the world are able to occasion such an extravagant pride, such unmeasurable ambition, such sordid avarice, such barbarous rapine and injustice, such malice and envy, and so many other detestable things, which compose the numerous train of vice, — how then would the passions have flamed, and to what a monstrous stature would every vice have grown, if those enjoyments which provoked and increased them were of eight or nine hundred years' duration? If eternal happiness and eternal punishment are able to make no stronger impressions upon men's minds, so near at hand, it may well be imagined that at so great a distance, they would have made no impression at all; that eternal happiness would have been entirely divested of its allurements, and eternal misery of its terrors; and the Great Creator would have been deprived of that obedience and adoration, which are so justly due to him from his creatures. Thus, the inundation of vice has in some measure, by the goodness of God, been prevented by an inundation of water. That which was the punishment of one generation may be said to have been the preservation of all those which have succeeded. For if life had not been thus clipped, one Tiberius, one Caligula, one Nero, one Louis XIV. had been sufficient to have destroyed the whole race of mankind; each of whose lives had they been ten times as long, and the mischiefs they occasioned multiplied by that number, it might easily be computed how great a plague one such long-lived monster would have been to the world."

Reflect, reader, upon this extract. The reasoning is neither fantastic, nor far-fetched; but it will probably be as new to you as it was to me, when I met with it in Mr. How's Devout Meditations. The republication of that book is one of those good works for which this country is beholden to the late excellent Bishop Jebb. Mr. Hetherington in his very original and able treatise upon the Fullness of Time, has seen this subject in the same point of view. He says "Even our three-score and ten years, broken and uncertain as that little span is, can delude us into the folly of putting death and its dread reckoning far from us, as if we were never to die, and might therefore neglect any preparation for the after judgment. But if we were to see before us the prospect of a life of one thousand years, we should doubtless regard death as a bugbear indeed, and throw off all the salutary restraint which the fear of it now exercises. Suppose our tendencies to every kind of sinful indulgence as strong as at present, with the prospect of such lengthened enjoyment and immunity from danger, and we may easily imagine with what hundred-fold eagerness we should plunge into all kinds of enormity, and revel in the wildest licentiousness. But this is the very consummation to which the race of Adam had reached, when 'God looked on the earth, and behold it was corrupt and filled with violence;' and God determined to destroy the earth with its inhabitants."

A remark of Brantome's may be quoted as the curious confirmation of a pious man's opinion by a thoroughly corrupt one. It occurs in his Discourse upon the Emperor Charles the Fifth. *Il faut certes confesser*, he says, *comme j'ouy dire une fois à un vieux Capitaine Espagnol, que si ce grand Empereur eust été immortel, ou seulement de cent ans bien sain et dispos, il auroit esté par guerre le vray Fleau du Monde, tant il estoit frappé d'ambition, si jamais Empereur le fut.*

CHAPTER CXXXIII.

MORE THOUGHTS CONCERNING LIFE, DEATH, AND IMMORTALITY.

Clericus es? legito hæc. Laicus? legito ista libenter,
Crede mihi, invenies hic quod uterque voles.
D. Du-Tr. Med.

If we look to the better part of the human race as well as the worse, with regard to them also the ordinary term of human life will be found the best that could have been appointed both for themselves and for the purposes of society, the wisdom and the goodness of the ways of Providence becoming evident in this, as in all other things upon which our limited faculties are capable of forming a comprehensive judgment.

The term is long enough for all we have to learn. Madame de Sevigné said sportively, that she should be a very wise person if she could but live about two hundred years: *je tâche tous les jours à profiter de mes reflexions; et si je pouvois vivre seulement deux cents ans, il me semble que je serois une personne bien admirable.* This the Doctor thought might hold good in the case of Madame de Sevigné herself, and of all other persons who regarded the acquirement of information as an amusement, or at most an accomplishment; "One small head might carry all they knew," though their lives should be prolonged to the length of antediluvian old age. But in his opinion it would be otherwise with those who devoted themselves to the pursuit of knowledge, for the purpose of storing their own minds, and enabling themselves to instruct their fellow creatures. For although the mind would retain its faculties unimpaired for a length of time in proportion to the greater length of life, it by no means follows that its capacity would be enlarged. Horace Walpole lived forty years after he had said "my mould has taken all its impressions, and can receive no more. I must grow old upon the stock I have." It is indeed highly probable that the most industrious students for some time before they reach the confines of senility forget as much as they learn. A short life is long enough for making us wise to salvation, if we will but give our hearts to the wisdom which is from above: and this is the one thing needful.

There are some, however, who in their eulogistic and extravagant lamentations seem to have thought no lease long enough for the objects of their admiration. A certain John Fellows published an elegy on the death of the Reverend John Gill, D.D. This learned Doctor in Dissent died at a good old age; nevertheless the passionate mourner in rhyme considered his death as a special mark of the Almighty's displeasure, and exclaimed,

> How are the mighty fallen! Lord when will
> Thine anger cease? The great, the learned Gill
> Now pale and breathless lies!

Upon which a reviewer not improperly remarked that without dwelling upon the *presumption* of the writer, he could not but notice the *folly* of thus lamenting, as though it were an untimely stroke, the natural departure of a venerable old man of near eighty. "Was this," said he, "sufficient cause for raising such an outcry in Zion, and calling on her sons and daughters to weep and wail as if the Day of Judgment were come."

Nothing, however, in former times excited so great a sensation in the small world of Noncons as the death of one of their Divines. Their favourite poet Dr. Watts wished when the Reverend Mr. Gouge died that he could make the stones hear and the rocks weep,

> And teach the Seas and teach the Skies
> Wailings and sobs and sympathies.
> Heaven was impatient of our crimes,
> And sent his minister of death
> To scourge the bold rebellion of the times,
> And to demand our prophet's breath.
> He came commissioned for the fates
> Of awful Mead and charming Bates:
> There he essay'd the vengeance first,
> Then took a dismal aim, and brought GREAT GOUGE to dust.
> GREAT GOUGE to dust! how doleful is the sound!
> How vast the stroke is! and how wide the wound!—
> Sion grows weak and England poor;
> Nature herself with all her store
> Can furnish such a pomp for death no more.

This was pretty well for a threnodial flight. But Dr. Watts went farther. When Mr. How should die, (and How was then seventy years of age,) he thought it would be time that the world should be at an end,—and prayed that it might be so.

> Eternal God! command his stay!
> Stretch the dear months of his delay;—
> O we could wish his age were one immortal day!
> But when the flaming chariot's come
> And shining guards to attend thy Prophet home,
> Amidst a thousand weeping eyes,
> Send an Elisha down, a soul of equal size;
> *Or burn this worthless globe, and take us to the skies!*

What would the Dissenters have said if a clerical poet had written in such a strain upon the decease of a Bishop or Archbishop?

We pray in the Litany to be delivered from sudden death. Any death is to be deprecated which should find us unprepared: but as a temporal calamity with more reason might we pray to be spared from the misery of an infirm old age. It was once my fortune to see a frightful instance of extreme longevity,—a woman who was nearly in her hundredth year. Her sight was greatly decayed, though not lost; it was very difficult to make her hear, and not easy then to make her understand what was said, though when her torpid intellect was awakened she was, legally, of sane mind. She was unable to walk, or to assist herself in any way. Her neck hung in such wrinkles that it might almost be likened to a turkey's; and the skin of her face and of her arms was cleft like the bark of an oak, as rough, and almost of as dark a colour. In this condition, without any apparent suffering, she passed her time in a state between sleeping and waking, fortunate that she could thus beguile the wearisomeness of such an existence.

Instances of this kind are much rarer in Europe than in tropical climates. Negresses in the West Indies sometimes attain an age which is seldom ascertained because it is far beyond living memory. They outlive all voluntary power, and their descendants of the third or fourth generation carry them out of their cabins into the open air, and lay them, like logs, as the season may require, in the sunshine, or in the shade. Methinks if Mecænas had seen such an object, he would have composed a palinode to those verses in which he has perpetuated his most pitiable love for life. A woman in New Hampshire, North America, had reached the miserable age of 102, when one day as some people were visiting her, the bell tolled for a funeral; she burst into tears and said, "Oh when will the bell toll for me! It seems as if it never would toll for me! I am afraid that I shall never die!" This reminds me that I have either read, or heard, an affecting story of a poor old woman in England,—very old, and very poor,—who retained her senses long after the body had become a weary burden; she too when she heard the bell toll for a funeral used to weep, and say she was afraid God had forgotten her! Poor creature, ignorantly as she spake, she had not forgotten Him; and such impatience will not be accounted to her for a sin.

These are extreme cases, as rare as they are mournful. Life indeed is long enough for what we have to suffer, as well as what we have to learn; but it was wisely said by an old Scottish Minister (I wish I knew his name, for this saying ought to have immortalised it,) "Time is short; and if your cross is heavy you have not far to carry it."

> *Chi ha travaglio, in pace il porti:*
> *Dolce è Dio, se il mondo è amaro.*
> *Sappia l'uom, che al Cielo è caro;*
> *Abbia fede, è aura conforti.**

Were the term shorter it would not suffice for the development of those moral qualities which belong peculiarly to the latter stage of life; nor could the wholesome influence which age exercises over the young in every country where manners are not so thoroughly corrupted as to threaten the dissolution of society, be in any other manner supplied.

Il me semble que le mal physique attendrit autant que le mal moral endurcit le cœur, said Lord Chesterfield, when he was growing old, and suffering under the infirmities of a broken constitution. Affliction in its lightest form, with the aid of time, had brought his heart into this wholesome state.

> *O figliuol' d'Adam, grida Natura,*
> *Onde i tormenti? Io vi farà tranquilli,*
> *Se voi non rebellate alla mia legge.*†

There is indeed a tranquillity which Nature brings with it as duly toward the close of life, as it induces sleep at the close of day. We may resist the salutary influence in both cases, and too often it is resisted, at the cost of health in the one, and at a still dearer

* Maggi. † Chiabrera.

cost in the other: but if we do this, we do it wilfully, the resistance is our own act and deed, — it is our own error, our own fault, our sin, and we must abide the consequences.

The greatest happiness to which we can attain in this world is the peace of God. Ask those who have attained the height of their ambition, whether in the pursuit of wealth, or power, or fame, if it be not so? Ask them in their sane mind and serious hours, and they will confess that all else is vanity.

Fond man, that looks on earth for happiness,
And here long seeks what here is never found! *

This His own peace, which is his last and crowning gift, our Heavenly Father reserves for us in declining life, when we have earned our discharge from its business and its cares; and He prepares us for it by the course of nature which he has appointed.

O all the good we hope, and all we see,
That Thee we know and love, comes from Thy love and
Thee.*

Hear, reader, the eloquent language of Adam Littleton when speaking of one who has received this gift: — it occurs in a funeral sermon, and the preacher's heart went with his words. After describing the state of a justified Christian, he rises into the following strain: "And now what has this happy person to do in this world any longer, having his debts paid and his sins pardoned, his God reconciled, his conscience quieted and assured, his accusers silenced, his enemies vanquished, the law satisfied, and himself justified, and his Saviour glorified, and a crown of Immortality, and a robe of righteousness prepared for him? What has he to do here more, than to get him up to the top of Pisgah and take a view of his heavenly Canaan; to stand upon the Confines of Eternity, and in the contemplation of those joys and glories, despise and slight the vanities and troubles of this sinful and miserable world; and to breathe after his better life, and be preparing himself for his change; when he shall be called off to weigh anchor, and hoist sail for another world, where he is to make discoveries of unutterable felicities, and inconceivable pleasures?

"Oh what a happy and blest condition is it to live, or to die in the midst of such gracious deliverances and glorious assurances; with this fastening consideration to boot, that 'neither life nor death, nor things present, nor things to come, nor any creature is able to separate him from the love of God, which is in Jesus Christ his Lord!'"

* Phineas Fletcher.

CHAPTER CXXXIV.

A TRANSITION, AN ANECDOTE, AN APOSTROPHE, AND A PUN, PUNNET, OR PUNDIGRION.

Est brevitate opus, ut currat sententia, neu se
Impediat verbis lassas onerantibus aures;
Et sermone opus est, modo tristi, sæpe jocoso. Horace.

The Reader is now so far acquainted with the Doctor and his bride elect, — (for we are still in the Interim,) — he knows so much of the birth, parentage, and education of both, so much of their respective characters, his way of thinking and her way of life, that we may pass to another of those questions propounded in the second post-initial chapter.

The minister of a very heterodox congregation in a certain large city, accosted one of his friends one day in the street with these words, which were so characteristic and remarkable that it was impossible not to remember and repeat them, — "I am considering whether I shall marry or keep a horse." — He was an eccentric person, as this anecdote may show; and his inspirited sermons (I must not call them inspired) were thought in their style of eloquence and sublimity to resemble Klopstock's Odes.

No such dubitation could ever have entered the Doctor's head. Happy man, he had already one of the best horses in the world: — (Forgive me, O Shade of Nobs in thine Elysian pastures, that I have so long delayed thy eulogy!) — and in Deborah he was about to have one of the best of wives.

If he had hesitated between a horse and a wife, he would have deserved to meet with a Grey Mare.

CHAPTER CXXXV.

REGINALD HEBER. A MISTAKE OBVIATED, WHICH MIGHT OTHERWISE EASILY BE MADE.

Perhaps some Gull, as witty as a Goose,
Says with a coy skew look, "it's pretty, pretty!
But yet that so much wit he should dispose
For so small purpose, faith," saith he, "'tis pity!"
DAVIES OF HEREFORD.

Who was Nobs?

Nobs, I may venture to affirm, is not mentioned by Reginald Heber. I have never had an opportunity of ascertaining the fact by a careful examination of his volumes, but the inquiries which it has been in my power to make have led to this conclusion. Judicious readers will, I hope, acknowledge, that in consequence of the scrupulous care with which I guard against even the appearance of speaking positively upon subjects whereon there may be any reasonable doubt, I am, comparatively with most authors, superlatively correct.

Now as Reginald Heber must have seen Nobs, and having seen could not but have remarked him, and having remarked must also have perceived how remarkable he was for all the outward and visible signs of a good horse, this omission is to be lamented. A culpable omission it must not be called, because it was not required that he should mention him; but it could not have been considered as *hors d'œuvre* to have noticed his surpassing merits, merits which Reginald Heber could have appreciated, and which no one perhaps could have described so well; for of Nobs it may veritably be said that he was a horse

—— tanto buono e bello
Che chi volesse dir le lodi sue,
Bisognarebbe haver un gran cervello,
*Bisognarebbe un capo come un bue.**

* VARCHI.

Perhaps some captious reader may suppose that he has here detected a notable error in my chronology. Nobs, he may say, was made dog's-meat before Reginald Heber was born, or at least before he had exchanged his petticoats for the garb-masculine, denominated galligaskins in philippic verse.

Pardon me, reader; the mistake is on your part; and you have committed two in this your supposition. Mistakes indeed, like misfortunes, seldom come single.

First, it is a mistake, and what, if it were not altogether inconsiderate, would be a calumnious one, — to suppose that Nobs ever was made dog's-meat. The Doctor had far too much regard for his good horse, to let his remains be treated with such indignity. He had too much sense of obligation and humanity to part with an old dumb servant when his strength began to fail, and consign him to the hard usage which is the common lot of these poor creatures, in this, in this respect, hard-hearted and wicked nation. Nobs, when his labour was past, had for the remainder of his days the run of the fields at Thaxted Grange. And when, in due course of nature, he died of old age, instead of being sent to the tanners and the dogs, he became, like "brave Percy" food for — worms. — A grave was dug, wherein he was decently deposited, with his shoes on, and Barnaby and his master planted a horse-chesnut on the spot. Matthew Montagu and Montagu Matthew ought to have visited it in joint pilgrimage.

Hadst thou been a bay horse, Nobs, it would have been a bay-tree instead. But though the tree which was thy monument was deciduous, and has perhaps been doomed to fall by some irreverent or ignorant hand, thy honours are perennial.

Secondly, the captious reader is mistaken in supposing me to have spoken of Bishop Heber, — that Heber, who if he had been a Romish Bishop would already have been Saint Reginald by the courtesy of Rome, as in due time he must have been by right of canonisation. Sir Edward Lloyd would smile at such a mistake. So would a Yorkshire or a Shropshire Genealogist. I am not enough of one to know in what degree the two Reginalds were related; but that they were of the same family is apparent, and the elder, who is of the equestrian order of Authors and ought to have taken the name of Philip, was contemporary with the Doctor. He published yearly lists of horse matches run from 1753 to 1758,—I know not how much longer. If such registers as his had been preserved of the Olympic Games, precious would they be to historians and commentators, examining Masters, and aspirant Under-Graduates.

CHAPTER CXXXVI.

THE PEDIGREE AND BIRTH OF NOBS, GIVEN IN REPLY TO THE FIRST QUERY IN THE SECOND CHAPTER P. I.

Theo. Look to my Horse, I pray you, well.
Diego. He shall, Sir.
Inc. Oh! how beneath his rank and call was that now!
Your Horse shall be entreated as becomes
A Horse of fashion, and his inches.

BEAUMONT AND FLETCHER.

WHO was Nobs?

A troop of British cavalry which had served on the continent was disbanded in the City of York, and the horses were sold. Their commander Sir Robert Clayton was a wealthy man, and happening to be a noble-minded man also, he could not bear to think that his old fellow campaigners, who had borne brave men to battle, should be ridden to death as butchers' hacks, or worked in dung-carts till they became dog's meat. So he purchased a piece of ground upon Knavesmire heath, and turned out the old horses to have their run there for life. There may be persons living who remember to have heard of this honourable act, and the curious circumstance which has preserved it from being forgotten. For once these horses were grazing promiscuously while a summer storm gathered, and when the first lightnings flashed from the cloud, and the distant thunder began to roll; but presently, as if they supposed these fires and sounds to be the signal of approaching battle, they were seen to get together and form in line, almost in as perfect order as if they had had their old masters upon their backs.

One of these old soldiers was what the Spaniards with the gravity peculiar to their language call a *Caballo Padre;* or what some of our own writers, with a decorum not less becoming, appellate an Entire horse; — or what a French interpreter accompanying an Englishman to obtain a passport wherein the horse as well as the rider was to be described, denominated *un cheval de pierre* to the astonishment of the clerks in the office, whose difficulty was not at all removed by the subsequent definition of the English applicant, which the said interpreter faithfully rendered thus, *un cheval de pierre est un cheval qui couvre les officiers municipaux*. He had found his way in a Cossack regiment from the Steppes of Tartary to the plains of Prussia; had run loose from a field of battle in which his master was killed, and passing from hand to hand had finally been sold by a Jew into the service of his Majesty King George II. In the course of this eventful life he had lost his Sclavonic name, and when he entered the British regiment was naturalised by that of Moses in honour of his late possessor.

It so happened that a filly by name Miss Jenny had been turned out to recover from a sprain in a field sufficiently near Knavesmire heath for a Houyhnhnm voice to be within hearing of Houyhnhnm ears. In this field did Miss Jenny one day beguile the solitude by exclaiming "heigh-ho for a husband!" an exclamation which exists in the Equine as well as in the English language. It is also found in the Feline tongue, but Grimalkin has set it to very unpleasant music. Moses heard the strain and listened to the voice of love. The breezes did for him what many a lover has in vain requested them to do in sonnet, and in elegy, and in song; — they wafted back his sympathetic wishes, and the wooing was carried on at a quarter of a mile distance: after which the Innamorato made no more of hedge and ditch than Jupiter was wont to do of a brazen Tower. Goonhilly in Cornwall was indebted for its once famous breed of horses to a Barb, which was turned loose (like Moses) by one of the Erisey family, — the Erisey estate joining the down.

A few days afterwards, Miss Jenny, having perfectly recovered of her sprain, was purchased by Dr. Dove. The alteration which took place in her shape was so little that it excited no suspicion in any person: — a circumstance which will not appear extraordinary to those who remember that the great Mr. Taplin himself having once booked his expectations of a colt, kept the mare eleven lunar months and a fortnight by the Almanack, and then parted with her, after taking the opinion of almost every farmer and breeder in the country, upon an universal decision that she had no foal in her; — ten days afterwards the mare showed cause why the decision of the judges should be reversed. Those persons, I say, who know the supereminent accuracy of Mr. Taplin, and that in matters of this kind everything passed under his own eye, (for he tells you that it was a trust which he never delegated to another), will not be so much surprised as the Doctor was at what happened on the present occasion. The Doctor and Nicholas were returning from Adwick-in-the-Street where they had been performing an operation. It was on the eleventh of June; the day had been unusually hot; they were overtaken by a thunderstorm, and took shelter in a barn. The Doctor had no sooner alighted than Miss Jenny appeared greatly distressed; and to the utter astonishment both of Dr. Dove and Nicholas, who could scarcely believe their own eyes, there was — almost as soon as they could take off the saddle — what I once saw called in the letter of a waiting gentlewoman — *dishion* to the family. To express the same event in loftier language,

Ἦλθεν δ' ὑπὸ σπλάγχνων ὑπ' ὠ-
δῖνος τ' ἐρατᾶς ΝΟΨ
Ἐς φάος αὐτίκα.*

* In the original Ἴαμος takes the place of Nobs. Cf. Olymp. vi. 72.

It is for the gratification of the learned Thebans who will peruse this history that I quote Pindar here.

INTERCHAPTER XVI.

THE AUTHOR RELATES SOME ANECDOTES, REFERS TO AN OPINION EXPRESSED BY A CRITIC ON THE PRESENT OPUS, AND DESCANTS THEREON.

Every man can say B to a battledore, and write in praise of virtue and the seven liberal sciences; thrash corn out of full sheaves, and fetch water out of the Thames. But out of dry stubble to make an after-harvest, and a plentiful crop without sowing, and wring juice out of a flint, that is Pierce a God's name, and the right trick of a workman. NASH.

THERE is an anecdote related of the Speaker in one of Queen Elizabeth's Parliaments, who when the Queen, during a session in which small progress had been made in the public business, asked him what the House had got through, made answer, "May it please your Majesty, eight weeks." In like manner, if it be asked what I have got through in the prosecution of this my Opus, I reply, "May it please your Readership, four volumes."

This brings to my recollection another anecdote, which, though not matter of history like the former, is matter of fact, and occurred in the good town of Truro. A lady in that town hired a servant, who at the time of hiring thought herself bound to let the lady know that she had once "had a misfortune." When she had been some time in service, she spoke of something to her Mistress, inadvertently, as having happened just after the birth of her first child. "Your first!" said the Lady; "why how many have you had then?" — "Oh, Ma'am," said she, "I've had four." "Four!" exclaimed the Mistress; "why you told me you had had but one. However I hope you mean to have no more." "Ma'am," replied the woman, "that must be as it may please God."

"We are," says Lord Camelford, "as it pleases God, — and sometimes as it displeases him."

The reflection is for every one; but the anecdote is recommended to the special notice of a Critic on the Athenæum establishment, who in delivering his opinion upon the third volume of this Opus, pronounced it to be "clear to him," that the Author had "expended" on the two former "a large portion of his intellectual resources, no less than of his lengthy common-place book."

The aforesaid Critic has also pronounced that the Opus entitled The Doctor might have been and ought to have been a Novel. *Might* have been is one consideration, *ought* to have been is another, and whether it would have been better that it *should* have been, is a third; but without discussing either of these propositions, because as Calderon says,

> *Sobre impossibles y falsas*
> *proposiciones, no hai*
> *argumento;*

without, I say, inquiring into what might, would, could, or should have been, neither of which imports of the preterperfect tense, optative, potential or subjunctive, are suitable to the present case, the Author of this Opus replies to the aforesaid Critic's assertion that the Opus might have been a Novel, —That, Sir, *must* have been as it pleased ME.

When Corporal Trim in one of his many attempts to begin the immortal story of the King of Bohemia and his Seven Castles, called that King unfortunate, and Uncle Toby compassionately asked "was he unfortunate then?" the Corporal replied, the King of Bohemia, an' please your honour was *unfortunate*, as thus, — that taking great pleasure and delight in navigation and all sort of sea affairs, and there happening throughout the whole Kingdom of Bohemia to be no sea-port town whatever, — "How the Deuce should there, Trim? cried my Uncle Toby; for Bohemia being totally inland, it could have happened no otherwise." — "It might, said Trim, if it had pleased God." — "I believe not, replied my Uncle Toby, after some pause — for being inland, as I said, and having Silesia and Moravia to the East; Lusatia and Upper Saxony to the North; Franconia to the West, and Bavaria to the South, Bohemia could not have been propelled to the sea, without ceasing to be Bohemia, — nor could the sea, on the other hand, have come up to Bohemia, without overflowing a great part of Germany, and destroying millions of unfortunate inhabitants who could make no defence against it, which would bespeak, added my Uncle Toby, mildly, such a want of compassion in Him who is the Father of it, — that, I think, Trim — the thing could have happened no way."

Were I to say of a Homo on any establishment whatsoever, political, commercial or literary, public or private, legal or ecclesiastical, orthodox or heterodox, military or naval, — I include them all that no individual in any may fancy the observation was intended for himself and so take it in snuff — (a phrase of which I would explain* the origin if I could), — and moreover that no one may apply to himself the illustration which is about to be made, I use the most generic term that could be applied, — Were I to say of any Homo (and how many are there of whom it might be said!) that he might have been whelped or foaled, instead of having been born, no judicious reader would understand me as predicating this to be possible, but as denoting an opinion that such an animal might as well have been a quadruped as what he is; and that for any use which he makes of his intellect, it might have been better for society if he had gone on four legs and carried panniers.

"There stands the Honourable Baronet, hesitating between two bundles of opinions" — said a certain noble Lord of a certain County Member in the course of an animated debate in the House of Commons on a subject now long since forgotten. I will not say of any Homo on any establishment that his fault is that of hesitating too long or hazarding too little; but I will say of any such hypothetical Homo as might better

* The explanation is probably to be drawn from the idea expressed in the words of Horace: *Naso* suspendis adunco. *Nasibus* uti Formido. Cf. 1 Sat. vi. 5.; 1 Epist. xix. 45. Doëring quotes the German phrase "*über einen die Nase rümpfen*. For examples see Nare's Gloss. in v.

have been foaled, that I wish his panniers had supplied him with better bundles to choose of.

"How," says Warburton, "happened it in the definitions of Man, that *reason* is always made essential to him? Nobody ever thought of making *goodness* so. And yet it is certain that there are as few reasonable men as there are good. To tell you my mind, I think Man might as properly be defined, *an animal to whom a sword is essential*, as one to *whom reason is essential*. For there are as few that *can*, and yet fewer that *dare*, use the one as the other."—And yet, he might have added, too many that misuse both.

The aforesaid Critic on the Athenæum establishment spoke with as little consideration as Trim, when he said that the Opus might have been a novel, implying the while—if it had so pleased the Author; and I make answer advisedly like my Uncle Toby in saying that it could not have pleased me.

> The moving accident is not my trade;
> To freeze the blood I have no ready arts.*

Wherefore should I write a novel? There is no lack of novels nor of novel-writers in these days, good, bad, and indifferent. Is there not Mr. James, who since the demise of Sir Walter, is by common consent justly deemed King of the historical Novelists? And is there not Mrs. Bray, who is as properly the Queen? Would the Earl of Mulgrave be less worthily employed in writing fashionable tales upon his own views of morality, than he is in governing Ireland as he governs it? Is there any season in which some sprigs of nobility and fashion do not bring forth hothouse flowers of this kind? And if some of them are rank or sickly, there are others (tell us, Anne Grey! are there not?) that are of delicate penciling, rich colours, and sweet scent. What are the Annuals but schools for Novelists, male and female? and if any lady in high life has conceived a fashionable tale, and when the critical time arrives wishes for a temporary concealment, is not Lady Charlotte Bury kindly ready to officiate as *Sage Femme?*

The Critic was not so wide of the mark in saying that this Opus ought to have been a novel—to have pleased him, being understood.

> Oh, like a book of sport thou'lt read me o'er;
> But there's more in me than thou understandest.†

And indeed, as Chapman says in his Commentary on the Iliad, "where a man is understood there is ever a proportion between the writer's wit and the writees,—that I may speak with authority, according to my old lesson in philosophy, *intellectus in ipsa intelligibilia transit*."

Le role d'un auteur est un role assez vain, says Diderot, *c'est celui d'un homme qui se croit en etat de donner des leçons au public. Et le role du critique? Il est plus vain encore; c'est celui d'un homme qui se croit en etat de donner des leçons à celui qui se croit en etat d'en donner au public. L'auteur dit, Messieurs, écoutez-moi, car je suis votre maitre. Et le critique, C'est moi, Messieurs, qu'il faut écouter, car je suis le maitre de vos maitres.*

The Athenæum Critic plays the Master with me,—and tops his part. "It is clear," he says, "from every page of this book that the Author does not, in vulgar parlance, think Small Beer of himself." Right, my Master? certainly I do not. I do not think that the contents of this book would be truly compared to small beer, which is either weak and frisky, or weak and flat; that they would turn sour upon a sound, that is to say, an orthodox stomach, or generate flatulence except in an empty one. I am more inclined, as my Master insinuates, to think Strong Beer of myself, Cwrw, Burton, Audit Ale, Old October,—what in his parlance used to be called Stingo; or Porter, such as Thrale's Entire, and old Whitbread's, in days when the ingredients came from the malster and the hop merchant, not from the Brewer's druggist. Or Cider, whether of Herefordshire, Somersetshire, or Devonshire growth, no matter; Stire, Cokaghee, or Fox-

* Wordsworth.

† Troilus and Cressida.

whelp, a beverage as much better than Champagne, as it is honester, wholesomer, and cheaper. Or Perry, the Teignton-Squash. These are right old English liquors, and I like them all. Nay, I am willing if my Master pleases, to think Metheglin of myself also, though it be a Welsh liquor, for there is Welsh blood in my veins, and Metheglin has helped to make it, and it is not the worse for the ingredient. Moreover with especial reference to the present Opus, there is this reason why I should think Metheglin of myself,—that Metheglin is made of honey, and honey is collected from all the flowers of the fields and gardens: and how should I have been able to render this tribute to the Philosopher of Doncaster, my true Master, if I had not been busy as a bee in the fields and gardens of literature, yea in the woods and wilds also? And in the orchards,—for have I not been plying early and late amongst

—— the orchard trees
Last left and earliest found by birds and bees? *

Of Bees, however, let me be likened to a Dumbledore, which Dr. Southey says is the most goodnatured of God's Insects; because great must be the provocation that can excite me to use my sting.

My Master's mention of Small Beer, in vulgar parlance Swipes, reminds me of Old Tom of Oxford's Affectionate Condolence with the Ultras, some years ago, whereby it appears that he thought Small Beer at that time of some very great Patriots and Queenites.

I see your noble rage too closely pent;
I hear you Whigs and Radicals ferment,
Like close-cork'd bottles filled with fizzing barm.

Now, Gentlemen, whose stopper is the strongest?
Whose eloquence will bottle-in the longest?
Who'll first explode, I wonder, or who last?
As weak small Beer is sure to fly the first,
Lo! poor Grey Bennet hath already burst,
And daub'd with froth the Speaker as he past.

Who next? Is't Lambton, weak and pert and brisk,
And spitting in one's face, like Ginger-frisk?
Lord John, keep in *thy* cork, for Heaven's sake do!
The strength and spirit of Champagne is thine,
Powers that will mellow down to generous wine;
Thy premature explosion I should rue.

* Ebenezer Elliott.

The Oxford Satirist thought Champagne of Lord John in the reign of Queen Caroline. I think Champagne of him still, which the Satirist assuredly does not, but we differ in opinion upon this point only because we differ concerning the merits of the wine so called. I request him to accept the assurance of my high consideration and good will; I shake hands with him mentally and cordially, and entreat him to write more songs, such as gladden the hearts of true Englishmen.

Dr. Clarke says in a note to his Travels, that Champagne is an artificial compound: that "the common champagne wine drunk in this country is made with green grapes and sugar; and that the imitation of it, with green gooseberries and sugar, is full as salutary, and frequently as palatable." A Frenchman who translated these Travels remarks upon this passage thus, *C'est sans doute par un sentiment de patriotisme, et pour degoûter ses compatriotes du vin de Champagne, que le Docteur Clarke se permet de hasarder de pareilles assertions. Croit-il que le vin de Champagne se fasse avec du sucre et des raisins verts, ou des groseilles, et qu'un semblable mélange puisse passer, même en Angleterre, pour un analogue des vins d'Ai et d'Epernai?* Dr. Clarke, as it became him to do, inserted this remark in his next edition, and said in reply to it, "It so happens that the author's information does not at all depend upon any conjectures he may have formed; it is the result of inquiries which he made upon the spot, and of positive information relative to the chemical constituents '*des vins d'Ai et d'Epernai*,' from Messrs. Moett and Company, the principal persons concerned in their fabrication. It was in the town of Epernai, whither the author repaired for information upon this subject, that in answer to some written questions proposed to Mons. Moett, the following statement was given by that gentleman touching the admission of sugar into the composition of their wine:

Peut-être regarderoit-on en Champagne comme un indiscretion, la réponse a cette question, puisque la révélation de ce qu'on appelle

LE SECRET DU PROPRIÉTAIRE *pourroit nuire a la reputation des vins de Champagne: mais les hommes instruits et éclairés doivent connoître les faits et les causes, parcequ'ils savent apprecier et en tirer les justes consequences.*

Il est tres vrai que dans les années froides ou pluvieuses, le raisin n'ayant pas acquis assez de maturité, ou ayant été privé de la chaleur du soleil, les vins n'ont plus cette liqueur douce et aimable qui les characterise: dans ce cas quelques propriétaires y ont supplée par l'introduction dans leur vins d'une liqueur tres eclaire, dont la base est nécessairement du sucre; sa fabrication est un secrêt; cette liqueur meslée en très petites quantités aux vins verts, corrige le vice de l'année, et leur donne absolument la même douceur que celle que procure le soleil dans les années chaudes. Il s'est élevé en Champagne même des frequentes querelles entre des connoisseurs qui pretendoient pouvoir distinguer au goût la liqueur artificielle de celle qui est naturelle; mais c'est une chimère. Le sucre produit dans le raisin, comme dans toute espèce de fruit par le travail de la nature, est toujours du sucre, comme celui que l'art pourroit y introduire, lorsque l'intemperance des saisons les en a privé. Nous nous sommes plûs très souvent à mettre en defaut l'expérience de ces prétendus connoisseurs; et il est si rare de les voir rencontrer juste, que l'on peut croire que c'est le hazard plus que leur goût qui les a guidé.

Having thus upon the best authority shown that Champagne in unfavourable years is doctored in the country, and leaving the reader to judge how large a portion of what is consumed in England is made from the produce of our own gardens, I repeat that I think Champagne of Lord John Russell, — not such as my friend of Oxford intended in his verses, — but Gooseberry Champagne, by no means brisk, and with a very disagreeable taste of the Cork.

If the Oxford Satirist and I should peradventure differ concerning Champagne, we are not likely to differ now concerning Lord John Russell. I am very well assured that we agree in thinking of his Lord Johnship as he is thought of in South Devonshire. Nor shall we differ in our notions of some of Lord John's Colleagues, and their left-handed friends. If he were to work out another poem in the same vein of satire, some of the Whole-hoggery in the House of Commons he would designate by Deady, or Wet and Heavy, some by weak tea, others by Blue-Ruin, Old Tom which rises above Blue-Ruin to the tune of threepence a glass — and yet more fiery than Old Tom, as being a fit beverage for another Old one who shall be nameless, — Gin and Brimstone.

There is a liquor peculiar to Cornwall, with which the fishermen regale, and which because of its colour they call Mahogany, being a mixture of two parts gin and one part treacle, well beaten together. Mahogany then may be the representative *liqueur* of Mr. Charles Buller, the representative of a Cornish borough; and for Sir John Campbell there is Athol porridge, which Boswell says is the counterpart of Mahogany, but which Johnson thought must be a better liquor, because being a similar mixture of whiskey and honey, both its component parts are better: *qui non odit* the one, *amet* the other.

Mr. Sheil would put the Satirist in mind of Whiskey "unexcised by Kings," and consequently above proof. Mr. Roebuck of Bitters, Mr. Joseph Hume of Ditch Water, Mr. Lytton Bulwer of Pop, Mr. Ward of *Pulque*, Mr. O'Connell of *Aqua Tofana*, and Lord Palmerston of *Parfait Amour*.

Observe, good Reader, it was to bottled Small Beer that the Oxford Satirist likened Grey Bennet, not to Brown Stout, which is a generous liquor having body and strength.

Hops and Turkeys, Carp and Beer,
Came into England all in one year,

and that year was in the reign of Henry VIII. The Turkeys could not have come before the discovery of America, nor the Beer before the introduction of the Hops Bottled Beer we owe to the joint agency of Alexander Nowell, Bishop Bonner, and Mr. Francis Bowyer, afterwards Sheriff of London.

Alexander Nowell, Dean of St. Paul's,

A famous preacher in the halcyon days
Of Queen Elizabeth of endless praise,

was at the beginning of Queen Mary's cruel reign Master of Westminster School. Izaak Walton would have pronounced him a very honest man from his picture at Brazen Nose College (to which he was a great Benefactor), inasmuch as he is there represented "with his lines, hooks, and other tackling, lying in a round on one hand, and his angles of several sorts on the other." But, says Fuller, whilst Nowell was catching of Fishes, Bonner was catching of Nowell, and understanding who he was, designed him to the shambles, whither he had certainly been sent, had not Mr. Francis Bowyer, then a London merchant, conveyed him upon the seas. Nowell was fishing upon the Banks of the Thames when he received the first intimation of his danger, which was so pressing that he dared not go back to his own house to make any preparation for his flight. Like an honest angler he had taken with him provision for the day; and when in the first year of England's deliverance he returned to his own country and his own haunts, he remembered that on the day of his flight he had left a bottle of beer in a safe place on the bank; there he looked for it, and "found it no bottle, but a gun, such the sound at the opening thereof; and this," says Fuller, "is believed (casualty is mother of more inventions than industry), the original of Bottled Ale in England."

Whatever my Master may think of me, whether he may class me with Grey Bennet's weak and frothy, or Dean Nowell's wholesome and strong, be the quality of the liquor what it may, he certainly mistook the capacity of the vessel, even if he allowed it to be a Magnum Bonum or Scotch Pint. Greatly was he mistaken when he supposed that a large portion of my intellectual resources was expended, and of my commonplace Book also.—The former come from a living spring,—and the latter is like the urn under a River God's arm. I might hint also at that Tun which the Pfalzgraf Johannes Kasimir built at Heidelberg in the year 1591,

Dessgleichen zu derselben zeit
War keines in der Christenheit:

but alas! it is now a more melancholy object than the Palace to which it appertained,—for the ruins of that Palace are so beautiful, that the first emotion with which you behold them is that of unmingled pleasure:—and the tun is empty! My Master, however, who imagines that my vat runs low, and is likely to be drawn dry, may look at one of the London Brewers' great casks.

CHAPTER CXXXVII.

DIFFERENCE OF OPINION BETWEEN THE DOCTOR AND NICHOLAS CONCERNING THE HIPPOGONY OR ORIGIN OF THE FOAL DROPPED IN THE PRECEDING CHAPTER.

—— his birth day, the eleventh of June
When the Apostle Barnaby the bright
Unto our year doth give the longest light.
BEN JONSON.

"IT's as fine a foal as ever was dropped," said Nicholas;—"but I should as soon thought of dropping one myself!"

"If thou hadst, Nicholas," replied the Doctor, "'twould have been a foal with longer ears, and a cross upon the shoulders. But I am heartily glad that it has happened to the Mare rather than to thee; for in the first place thou wouldst hardly have got so well through it, as, with all my experience, I should have been at a loss how to have rendered thee any assistance; and secondly, Nicholas, I should have been equally at a loss how to account for the circumstance, which certainly never could have been accounted for in so satisfactory a manner. The birth of this extraordinary foal supports a fact which the wise ancients have attested, and the moderns in their presumptuous ignorance have been pleased to disbelieve: it also agrees with a notion which I have long been disposed to entertain. But had it been thy case instead of the Mare's it would have been to no purpose except to contradict all facts and confound all notions."

"As for that matter," answered Nicholas,

all my notions are struck in a heap. You bought that Mare on the 29th of July, by this token that it was my birth-day, and I said she would prove a lucky one. One, — two, — three, — four, — five, — six, — seven,—eight,—nine,—ten,—" he continued, counting upon his fingers, — " ten Kalendar months, and to-day the eleventh of June; — in all that time I'll be sworn she has never been nearer a horse than to pass him on the road. It must have been the Devil's doing, and I wish he never did worse. However, Master, I hope you'll sell him, for, in spite of his looks, I should never like to trust my precious limbs upon the back of such a misbegotten beast."

"*Un*begotten, Nicholas," replied the Doctor; "*un*begotten, — or rather begotten by the winds, — for so with every appearance of probability we may fairly suppose him to have been."

"The Winds!" said Nicholas. — He lifted up the lids of his little eyes as far as he could strain them, and breathed out a whistle of a half minute long, beginning in C alt and running down two whole octaves!

"It was common in Spain," pursued Dr. Dove, "and consequently may have happened in our less genial climate, but this is the first instance that has ever been clearly observed. I well remember," he continued, "that last July was peculiarly fine. The wind never varied more than from South South East to South West; the little rain which fell descended in gentle, balmy, showers, and the atmosphere never could have been more full of the fecundating principle."

That our friend really attached any credit to this fanciful opinion of the Ancients is what I will not affirm, nor perhaps would he himself have affirmed it. But Henry More, the Platonist, Milton's friend, undoubtedly believed it. After quoting the well-known passage upon this subject in the Georgics, and a verse to the same effect from the Punics, he adds, that you may not suspect it "to be only the levity and credulity of Poets to report such things, I can inform you that St. Austin, and Solinus the historian, write the same of a race of horses in Cappadocia. Nay, which is more to the purpose, Columella and Varro, men expert in rural affairs, assert this matter for a most certain and known truth." Pliny also affirms it as an undoubted fact: the foals of the Wind, he says, were exceedingly swift, but short-lived, never outliving three years. And the Lampongs of Sumatra, according to Marsden, believe at this time that the Island Engano is inhabited entirely by females, whose progeny are all children of the Wind.

CHAPTER CXXXVIII.

DOUBTFUL PEDIGREE OF ECLIPSE. SHAKESPEARE (N. B. NOT WILLIAM) AND OLD MARSK. A PECULIARITY OF THE ENGLISH LAW.

> *Lady Percy.* But hear you, my Lord!
> *Hotspur.* What say'st thou, my lady?
> *Lady Percy.* What is it carries you away?
> *Hotspur.* Why my Horse, my love, my Horse.
>
> SHAKESPEARE.

AFTER having made arrangements with the owner of the barn for the accommodation of the Mare in-the-straw, the Doctor and Nicholas pursued their way to Doncaster on foot, the latter every now and then breaking out into exclamations of the "Lord bless me!" and sometimes with a laugh of astonishment annexing the Lord's name to a verb of opposite signification governing a neuter pronoun. Then he would cry, "Who would have thought it? Who'll believe it?" and so with interjections benedictory or maledictory, applied indiscriminately to himself and Miss Jenny and the foal, he gave vent to his wonder, frequently, however, repeating his doubts how the come-by-chance, as he called it, would turn out.

A doubt to the same purport had come across the Doctor; for it so happened that one of his theories bore very much in support of Nicholas's unfavourable prepossession. Eclipse was at that time in his glory; and Eclipse was in the case of those children who are said by our Law to be more than ordinarily legitimate, tho' * he was not, like one of these double legitimates, enabled at years of discretion to choose for himself between the two possible fathers. Whether Eclipse was got by Shakespeare or by Old Marsk was a point of which the Duke of Cumberland and his Stud Groom at one time confessed themselves ignorant; and though at length, as it was necessary that Eclipse should have a pedigree, they filiated him upon Old Marsk, Dr. Dove had amused himself with contending that the real cause of the superiority of that wonderful horse to all other horses was, that in reality he was the Son of both, and being thus doubly begotten had derived a double portion of vigour. It is not necessary to explain by what process of reasoning he had arrived at this conclusion; but it followed as a necessary inference that if a horse with two Sires inherited a double stock of strength, a horse who had no Sire at all must, *pari ratione*, be in a like proportion deficient. And here the Doctor must have rested had he not luckily called to mind that Canto of the Faery Queen in which

> The birth of fayre Belphœbe and
> Of Amorett is told:

how

> — wondrously they were begot and bred
> Through influence of the Heavens fruitfull ray.
>
> Miraculous may seem to him that reades
> So strange ensample of conception;
> But reason teacheth that the fruitfull seedes
> Of all things living, through impression
> Of the sunbeames in moyst complexion
> Doe life conceive, and quick'ned are by kynd;
> So after Nilus' inundation
> Infinite shapes of creatures men doe fynd
> Informed in the mud on which the Sunne hath shynd.
>
> Great Father he of Generation
> Is rightly called, th' Authour of life and light;
> And his faire sister for creation
> Ministreth matter fit, which tempred right
> With heate and humour breedes the living wight.

So delighted was he with this recollection, and with the beautiful picture of Belphœbe which it recalled, that he would instantly have named the foal Belphœbe,—if it had happened to be a filly. For a moment it occurred to him to call him Belphœbus; but then again he thought that Belphœbus was too like Belphegor, and he would not give any occasion for a mistake, which might lead to a suspicion that he favoured Nicholas's notion of the Devil's concern in the business.

But the naming of this horse was not so lightly to be decided. Would it have been fitting under all the circumstances of the case to have given him any such appellation as Buzzard, Trumpeter, Ploughboy, Master Jackey, Master Robert, Jerry Sneak, Trimmer, Swindler, Deceiver, Diddler, Boxer, Bruiser, Buffer, Prize-fighter, Swordsman, Snap,—would it have been fitting, I say, to have given to a Colt who was dropped almost as unexpectedly as if he had dropped from the clouds,—would it, I repeat, have been fitting to have given him any one of these names, all known in their day upon the Turf, or of the numberless others commonly and with equal impropriety bestowed upon horses.

* It will be observed by critical readers that tho', thro', altho', are thus written in the latter portions of "The Doctor, &c.," after Swift; not in the earlier ones, or very rarely.

CHAPTER CXXXIX.

FACTS AND OBSERVATIONS RELATING TO ONOMATOLOGY.

> Moreover there are many more things in the World than there are names for them; according to the saying of the Philosopher; *Nomina sunt finita, res autem infinitæ; ideo unum nomen plura significat*: which saying is by a certain, or rather uncertain, author approved: *Multis speciebus non sunt nomina; idcirco necessarium est nomina fingere, si nullum ante erit nomen impositum.*
>
> GWILLIM.

NAMES, Reader, are serious things; and certain philosophers, as well as Mr. Shandy, have been, to use the French-English of the day, deeply penetrated with this truth

The name of the Emperor of Japan is never known to his subjects during his life. And the people of ancient Rome never knew the true and proper name of their own City, which is indeed among the things that have utterly perished. It was concealed as the most awful of all mysteries, lest if it were known to the enemies of the City, they might by force of charms and incantations deprive it of the aid of its tutelary Gods.— As for that mystery which has occasioned among Hebrew Critics the Sect of the Adonists, I only hint thereat.—

Names, Reader, are serious things, so serious that no man since Adam has been able, except by special inspiration, to invent one which should be perfectly significant.

Adan, antes que el bien le fuera oposito,
Fue tan grande filosofo y dialectico,
Que a todo quanto Dios le dio en deposito,
(Aunque pecando fue despues frenetico,)
De nombres adorno tan a proposito
Como quien tuvo espiritu profetico;
Porque naturaleza en modo tacito
Las causas descubrio a su beneplacito.

Esta virtud tan alta fue perdiendose
De los que del vinieron derivandose,
Tanto que todos van desvaneciendose.
En aplicar los nombres, y engañandose,
Sino es por algun Angel descubriendose,
*O por inspiracion manifestandose.**

Names, Reader, I repeat, are serious things: and much ingenuity has been exerted in inventing appropriate ones, not only for man and beast, but for inanimate things. Godfathers and Godmothers, Navigators, Shipbuilders, Florists, Botanists, Chemists, Jockeys, Feeders, Stage Coach Proprietors, Quacks, Perfumers, Novelists and Dramatists, have all displayed their taste in the selection of Names.

More whimsically consorted names will seldom be found than among the Lodges of the Manchester Unity of the Independent Order of Odd Fellows — You find there Apollo and St. Peter; the Rose of Sharon, and the Rose of Cheetham; Earl Fitzwilliam, Farmer's Glory, and Poor Man's Protection; Philanthropic and Lord Byron, Lord John Russell and Good Intent; Queen Caroline (Bergami's Queen not George the Second's) and Queen Adelaide.

Reader, be pleased to walk into the Garden with me. You see that bush,—what would you call the fruit which it bears?— The Gooseberry.—But its more particular name?— Its botanical name is *ribes* — or *grossularia*, which you will, Mr. Author.— Still, Reader, we are in generals. For you and I, and our wives and children, and all plain eaters of gooseberry-pie and gooseberry-fool, the simple name gooseberry might suffice. Not so for the scientific in gooseberries, the gooseberryologists. They could distinguish whether it were the King or the Duke of York; the Yellow Seedling or the Prince of Orange; Lord Hood or Sir Sidney Smith; Atlas or Hercules; the Green Goose, or the Green Bob, or the Green Chisel; the Colossus or the Duke of Bedford; Apollo or Tickle Toby; the Royal Oak or the Royal Sovereign; the Hero or the Jolly Smoaker; the Game Keeper or the Sceptre; the Golden Gourd, or the Golden Lion, or the Gold-finder; Worthington's Conqueror or Somach's Victory; Robinson's Stump or Davenport's Lady; Blakeley's Chisel or Read's Satisfaction; Bell's Farmer or the Creeping Ceres; the White Muslin, the White Rose, the White Bear, the White Noble, or the White Smith; the Huntsman, the Gunner, the Thrasher, the Viper, the Independent, the Glory of Eccles, or the Glory of England; Smith's Grim-Mask, Blomerly's John Bull, Hamlet's Beauty of England, Goodier's Nelson's Victory, Parkinson's Scarlet Virgin, Milling's Crown Bob, Kitt's Bank of England, Yeat's Wild-Man of the Wood, Davenport's Jolly Hatter, or Leigh's Fiddler.—For all these are Gooseberries: and yet this is none of them: it is the Old Ironmonger.

Lancashire is the County in which the Gooseberry has been most cultivated; there is a Gooseberry book annually printed at Manchester; and the Manchester Newspapers recording the death of a person, and saying that he bore a severe illness with Christian fortitude and resignation, add that he was much esteemed among the Class of Gooseberry Growers. — A harmless class they must needs be deemed, but even in growing Gooseberries emulation may be carried too far.—

The Royal Sovereign, which in 1794 was grown by George Cook of Ashton, near Preston, which weighed seventeen pennyweights, eighteen grains, was thought a Royal Gooseberry at that day. But the

* Cayrasco de Figueroa.

growth of Gooseberries keeps pace with the March of Intellect. In 1830 the largest Yellow Gooseberry on record was shown at Stockport; it weighed thirty-two pennyweights, thirteen grains, and was named the Teazer. The largest Red one was the Roaring Lion, of thirty-one pennyweights, thirteen grains, shown at Nantwich; and the largest White was the Ostrich, shown at Ormskirk; falling far short of the others, and yet weighing twenty-four pennyweights, twenty grains. They have been grown as large as Pigeon's eggs. But the fruit is not improved by the forced culture which increases its size. The Gooseberry growers, who show for the prizes which are annually offered, thin the fruit so as to leave but two or three berries on a branch; even then prizes are not gained by fair dealing: they contrive to support a small cup under each of these, so that the fruit shall for some weeks rest in water that covers about a fourth part, and this they call suckling the gooseberry.

Your Orchard, Sir! you are perhaps content with Codlins and Pippins, Non-pareils, and Russets, with a few nameless varieties. But Mr. Forsyth will tell you of the Beauty of Kent, of the Belle Grisdeline, the Boomrey, the Hampshire Nonsuch, the Dalmahoy, the Golden Mundi, the Queening, the Oak Peg, the Nine Square, the Paradise Pippin, the Violet Apple, the Corpendu, the Trevoider, the Ramborn, the Spanish Onion, the Royal George, the Pigeonette, the Norfolk Paradise, the Long-laster, the Kentish Fill-baskets, the Maiden's Blush, the Lady's Finger, the Scarlet Admirable, the Hall-Door, the Green Dragon, the Fox's Whelp, the Fair Maid of Wishford, Coble-dick-longerkin — an apple in the North of Devon and Cornwall, which Mr. Polwhele supposes to have been introduced into the parish of Stratton by one Longerkin who was called Cobble-dick, because his name was Richard and he was a Cobler by trade. John Apple,

— whose withered rind, intrench'd
With many a furrow, aptly represents
Decrepid age *, —

the King of the Pippins (of him hereafter in the Chapter of Kings) and the Seek-no-farther, — after which, no farther will we seek.

Of Pears, the *Bon Chrêtien*, called by English Gardeners the Bum-Gritton, the *Teton de Venus*, and the *Cuisse Madame*, three names which equally mark the country from whence they came. The last Bishop of Alais before the French Revolution visiting a Rector once who was very rich and very avaricious, gave him some gentle admonitory hint of the character he had heard of him. "*Mais, Monseigneur*," said the Man, "*il faut garder une Poire pour la soif.*" "*Vous avez bièn raison*," replied the Bishop: "*prenez garde seulement qu'elle soit du bon Chrêtien.*" The first Lord Camelford, in one of whose letters this pun is preserved, thought it perfect. But to proceed with the nomenclature of Pears, there are the Supreme, the Bag-pipe of Anjou, the Huff Cap, the Grey Good Wife, the Goodman's Pear, the Queen's Pear, the Prince's Pear, the Marquis's Pear, the Dean's Pear, the Knave's Pear, the Pope's Pear, the Chaw Good, the Vicar, the Bishop's Thumb, the Lady's Lemon, the Lord Martin, the St. Austin, La Pastorelle and Monsieur John, the Great Onion, the Great Mouthwater, the King of Summer, the Angelic Pear, — and many others which I would rather eat than enumerate. At present the Louis Philippe holds pre-eminence.

The *Propria quæ Potatibus* will be found not less rich, — though here we perceive a lower key of invention, as adapted to a lower rank of fruit, and affording a proof of Nature's Aristocracy; — here we have Red Champions, White Champions, Late Champions and English Champions, Early Manlys, Rough Reds, Smooth Yellows, Silver Skins, Pink Eyes, Golden Tags, Golden Gullens, Common Wise, Quaker Wise, Budworth's Dusters, Poor Man's Profit, Lady Queens, Drunken Landlords, Britons, Crones, Apples, Magpies, Lords, Invincibles, the Painted Lady and the Painted Lord, the Golden Dun, the Old Red Rough, and the Ox Noble:

Cum multis aliis quæ nunc perscribere longum est.

* Philips.

For Roses, methinks Venus, and the Fair Maid, and Flora, and Favourite, and Diana may well keep company with our old favourite the Maiden Blush. There may be, too, though it were to be wished there were not, a Miss Bold, among these beautiful flowers. Nor would I object to Purple nor to Ruby, because they are significant, if nothing more. But for Duchess, with double blush, methinks the characteristic and the name go ill together. The Great Mogul is as bad as the Vagrant; the Parson worse than either; and for Mount Etna and Mount Vesuvius, it excites an explosion of anger to hear of them.

Among the trees in Barbadoes, we read of Anchovy the Apple, the Bread and Cheese, or Sucking Bottle, the Belly Ache, and the Fat Pork Tree!

From the fields and gardens to the Dairy. In the Vaccine nomenclature we pass over the numerals and the letters of the Alphabet. Would you have more endearing appellations than Curly, Curl-pate, Pretty, Browny, Cot Lass, Lovely Lass, — (a name peradventure imposed by that person famous in the proverb, as the old Woman who kissed her Cow,) — more promising than Bee, Earnest, Early, Standfast, Fill-bouk, Fill-pan, — more romantic than Rose, Rosely, Rosebud, Roseberry, Rosamond, Rosella, Rosalina, Furba, Firbrella, Firbrina, — more rural than Rurorea.

Then for Bulls, — was there not the Bull Shakespeare, by Shakespeare off young Nell, who was sold in the year 1793 for £400 with a condition that the seller should have the privilege every year of introducing two Cows to the said Shakespeare. And was there not the Bull Comet who was sold for 1000 guineas. I say nothing of Alderman Bull, nor of John Bull, nor of the remarkable Irish Breed.

For horses I content myself with remembering the never-to-be-forgotten Pot-o-o-o-o-o-o-o-os, sometimes written Pot8os. Whose was the proudest feeling of exultation, his who devised this numerico-literal piece of wit, — or that of Archimedes when he exclaimed Ἕυρηκα? And while touching the Arithmographic mode of writing, let us not forget the Frenchman, who by the union of a pun and a hieroglyph described his Sovereign's style thus — Louis with ten-oysters in a row after the name.

As for the scientific names of Plants, — if Apollo had not lost all power he would have elongated the ears of Tournefort and Linnæus, and all their followers, as deservedly as he did those of Midas.

Of the Knights or Horsemen, Greeks and Trojans, Rustics and Townsmen among — Butterflies, — and the Gods, Goddesses, Muses and Graces, Heroes, Worthies and Unworthies, who feed in their grub state upon lettuces and cabbages, sleep through their aurelian term of existence, and finally obtain a name in the naturalist's nomenclature, and perhaps a local habitation in his Cabinet with a pin through their bodies, I say nothing, farther than to state why one tribe of them is denominated Trojans. Be it known then in the words of a distinguished Entomologist, that "this tribe has been dedicated by Entomologists to the memory of the more distinguished worthies of the Trojan race, and above others to preserve the memory of those heroes whose exploits in the defence of that rich and potent station of the ancient world, the town of Troy, have been commemorated in the Iliad by the immortal Homer." Lest Homer therefore and all the works derived from him should perish from remembrance the Entomologists have very considerately devised this means for preserving the memory of Hector.

Hath not Daniel Girton, of the County of Bucks, in his Complete Pigeon-Fancier, wherein he points out to the Gentlemen of the Fancy, the foul marks and the real perfections of every valuable species of Fancy Birds and Toys which in his time were bred in England, France and Holland; — hath not Daniel Girton, I say, (tho' Boswell thought that a sentence so formed as to require an *I say* to keep it together, resembled a pair of ill-mended breeches, and candidly acknowledged the resemblance in his own, — the sentence I mean, which he was then penning, not the breeches which he wore;)

— hath not Daniel Girton, I say, particularly enumerated in his Title-Page among the varieties of such Fancy Birds, Powters, Carriers, Horsemen, Dragoons, Croppers, Powting Horsemen, Uplopers, Fantails, Chinese Pigeons, Lace-Pigeons, Tumblers, Runts, Spots, Laughers, Trumpeters, Jacobines, Capuchines, Nuns, Shakers, Helmets, Ruffs, Finnikins, Turners, Barbs, Mahomets, Turbits, Owls, and Smiters, concluding the imperfect enumeration with an &c.

The Foul Fiends also have odd names. Witness the list which John Gee collected after the veracious Romish Priests of his time: Lusty Dick, Killico, Hob, Corner-Cap, Puffe, Purre, Frateretto, Fliberdigibbet, Haberdicut, Cocabelto, Maho, (this Maho, who was a gentleman as Shakespeare * tells us, maintained his ground against a Priest for seven hours,) Kellicocam, Wilkin, Smolkin, Lusty Jolly Jenkin, (this must have been a Welsh Devil and of a noble race,) Porto Richo, (peradventure a Creole Devil,) Pudding of Thame — (fie on such pudding!) — Pour Dieu (Pour Diable!), Bonjour, Motubizanto, Nur, Bernon, Delicate.

The familiar of that "damnable and malicious witch Elizabeth Southerns, alias Dimdikes, was called Tibb: she dwelt in the forest of Pendle, a vast place fit for her profession, and she was a general Agent for the Devil in all those parts."

There was one Mr. Duke, a busy fanatic, in Devonshire in Charles II.'s days, whom old Sir Edward Seymour used to call Spirit Po, that said Po being a *petit diable*, a small devil that was *presto* at every Conjuror's nod. He (the said Mr. Duke) "was a common runner up and down on factious errands; and there could not be a meeting in the country for business or mirth, but Spirit Po was there."

Actæus Megalesius, Ormenus, Lycus, Nicon and Mimon are five of the Chief Telchinnes or Alastores, who take the waters of Styx in their hands and sprinkle them over the earth, thereby causing all kinds of diseases and calamities.

* Lear, Act iii. sc. iv.

It is known upon testimony which has received the sanction of the Holy Office, that Lucifer has three Lord Lieutenants, whose names are Aquias, Brum, and Acatu: whether the second assumed his name in prospective compliment to the Queen's Attorney-General, or whether the name itself has some appropriate and amiable signification in the infernal tongue must be left to conjecture. These Lord Lieutenants were sent with a whole army of Devils to make war against a person of the feminine gender called in her own language Anna de Santiago, but in the language of Hell, Catarruxa, which, according to the interpretation given by the Devils themselves, means the Strong Woman. The General was named Catacis, and the names of the subordinate Commanders have been faithfully recorded by a Franciscan Chronicler of unquestioned veracity, for the use of Exorcists, experience having shown that it is of signal use in their profession to know the names of the enemies with whom they are contending, the Devils perhaps having learned from the Lawyers, (who are able to teach the Devil,) to take advantage of a misnomer. This indeed is so probable that it cannot be superfluous to point out to Exorcists a received error, which must often have frustrated their laudable endeavours, if the same literal accuracy be required in their processes as in those of the Law. They no doubt have always addressed the Prince of the Devils by the name of Beelzebub, but his real name is Beelzebul; and so St. Jerome found it in all his Manuscripts, but not understanding what was then the common, and true reading, he altered Βεελζεβοὺλ into Βεελζεβοὺβ, — by which he made the word significant to himself, but enabled Beelzebul to quash all actions of ejectment preferred against him in this false name. The value of this information will be appreciated in Roman Catholic Countries. Gentlemen of the long robe will think it beautiful; and I have this additional motive for communicating it, to wit, that it may be a warning to all verbal Critics. I now return to my nomenclature.

If a catalogue of plants or animals in a newly-discovered country be justly esteemed curious, how much more curious must a genuine muster-roll of Devils be esteemed, all being Devils of rank and consequence in the Satanic service. It is to Anna de Santiago herself that we are originally beholden for it, when at her Confessor's desire,

Θεοὺς δ' ὀνομήνεν ἅπαντας
Τοὺς ὑποταρταρίους *

"The reader (as Fuller says) will not be offended with their hard names here following, seeing his eye may run them over in perusing them, though his tongue never touch them in pronouncing them." And when he thinks how many private and non-commissioned officers go to make up a legion, he may easily believe that Owen Glendower might have held Hotspur

——— at least nine hours
In reckoning up the several Devil's names
That were his lackeys.—

Barca, Maquias, Acatam, Ge, Arri, Macaquias, Ju, Mocatam, Arra, Vi, Macutu, Laca, Machehe, Abriim, Maracatu, Majacatam, Barra, Matu, the Great Dog, (this was a dumb devil), Arracatorra, Mayca, Oy, Aleu, Malacatan, Mantu, Arraba, Emay, Alacamita, Olu, Ayvatu, Arremabur, Aycotan, Lacahabarratu, Oguerracatam, Jamacatia, Mayacatu, Ayciay, Ballà, Luachi, Mayay, Buzache, Berrà, Berram, Maldequita, Bemaqui, Moricastatu, Anciaquias, Zamata, Bu, Zamcapatujas, Bellacatuaxia, Go, Bajaque, and Baa, — which seems but a sheepish name for a Devil.

Can there be yet a roll of names more portentous in appearance, more formidable in sound, more dangerous in utterance? Look, reader, at the ensuing array, and judge for thyself; *look* I say, and mentally peruse it, but attempt not to enunciate the words, lest thou shouldst loosen thy teeth or fracture them in the operation.

Angheteduff, otherwise Anghutuduffe, otherwise Ballyhaise, Kealdragh, Caveneboy, Aghugrenoase, otherwise Aghagremous, Killataven, Kilnaverley, Kelvoryvybegg, Tonnegh, Briehill, Drommody, Amraghduffe, Drumhermshanbeeg, Dranhill, Cormaghscargin, Corlybeeg, Cornashogagh, Dromhome, Trimmigan, Knocklyeagh, Carrigmore, Clemtegrit, Lesdamenhuffe, Correamyhy, Aghnielanagher, otherwise Agnigamagh, Prittage, Aghaiasgim, Tobogamagh, Dromaragh, otherwise Dromavragh, Cnockamyhee, Lesnagvan, Kellarne, Gargaran, Cormodyduffe, Curraghchinrin, Annageocry, Brocklagh, Aghmaihi, Drungvin, otherwise Dungen, Dungenbegg, Dungemore, Sheina, Dremcarplin, Shaghtany, Knocksegart, Keillagh, Tinlaghcoole, Tinlagheryagh, Lyssybrogan, Lyssgallagh, Langarriah, Sheanmullagh, Celgvane, Drombomore, Lissgarre, Toncantany, Knockadawe, Dromboobegg, Drumpgampurne, Listiarta, Omrefada, Corranyore, Corrotober, Clere, Biagbire, Lurgriagh, Tartine, Drumburne, Aghanamaghan, Lusmakeragh, Nucaine, Cornamuck, Crosse, Coyleagh, Cnocknatratin, Toanmore, Ragasky, Longamonihity, Atteantity, Knockfodda, Tonaghmore, Drumgrestin, Owley, Dronan, Vushinagh, Carricknascan, Lyssanhany, otherwise Lysseyshanan, Knockaduyne, Dromkurin, Lissmakearke, Dromgowhan, Raghege, Dromacharand, Moneyneriogh, Drinsurly, Dromillan, Agunylyly, Gnockantry, Ellyn, Keileranny, otherwise Kulrany, Koraneagh, and Duigary.

"Mercy on us," says the Reader, "what are these!"—Have patience, Reader, we have not done yet, there are still—Magheryhillagh, Drung, Clefern, Castleterra, Killana, Moybolgace, Kilfort, Templefort, Killaghadon, Laragh, Cloncaughy, Annaghgiliffe, Towninmore, Rathany, Drumgoone, Tyrelatrada, Lurganboy, Ballyclanphilip, Killinkery, Ballintampel, Kilbride, Crosserlough, Drumlawnaught, Killanaburgh, Kilsherdan, otherwise Killersherding, Dremakellen, Aughaurain, Drumgress and Shanaraghan.

"For mercy's sake," exclaims the Reader, "enough—enough! what are they?" The latter, dear Reader, are all Poles and Termons. And the whole of them were set up for sale by public cant in Dublin, pursuant to a Decree of his Majesty's High Court of Chancery in Ireland, dated the 18th of May, 1816.

* Homer.

CHAPTER CXL.

HOW THERE AROSE A DISPUTE BETWEEN BARNABY AND NICHOLAS CONCERNING THE NAMING OF THIS COLT, AND OF THE EXTRAORDINARY CIRCUMSTANCES THAT ENSUED.

Quoiqu'il en soit, je ne tairai point cette histoire ; je l'abandonne à la credulité, ou à l'incredulité des Lecteurs, ils prendront à cet égard quel parti il leur plaira. Je dirai seulement, s'ils ne la veulent pas croire, que je les defie de me prouver qu'elle soit absolument impossible ; ils ne le prouveront jamais. GOMGAM.

WHILE the Doctor was deliberating by what significant name to call the foal of which he had in so surprising a manner found himself possessed, a warm dispute upon the same subject had arisen between Barnaby and Nicholas : for though a woman does not consider herself complimented when she is called a horse-godmother, each was ambitious of being horse-godfather on this occasion, and giving his own name to the colt, which had already become a pet with both.

Upon discovering each other's wish they first quietly argued the point. Nicholas maintained that it was not possible any person, except his master, could have so good a right to name the colt as himself, who had actually been present when he was dropped. Barnaby admitted the force of the argument, but observed that there was a still stronger reason for naming him as he proposed, because he had been foaled on the eleventh of June, which is St. Barnabas's day.

" Nicholas," quoth his antagonist, " it ought to be, for I was there at the very nick of time."—" Barnaby," retorted the other, " it ought to be ; for in a barn it happened."

" Old Nick was the father of him !" said Nicholas.—" The more reason," replied Barnaby, " for giving him a Saint's name."

" He shall be nicked to suit his name," said Nicholas ; — " and that's a good reason !"—" It's a wicked reason," cried Barnaby, " he shall never be nicked. I love him as well as if he was a bairn of my own : and that's another reason why he should be called Barnaby. He shall be neither nicked nor Nicholased."

Upon this Nicholas grew warm, and asserted that his name was as good as the other's, and that he was ready to prove himself the better man. The other, who had been made angry at the thought of nicking his pet, was easily put upon his mettle, and they agreed to settle the dispute by the *ultima ratio regum.* But this appeal to the immortal Gods was not definitive, for John Atkinson the Miller's son came up and parted them ; and laughing at them for a couple of fools when he heard the cause of their quarrel, he proposed that they should determine it by running a race to the gate at the other end of the field.

Having made them shake hands, and promise to abide by the issue, he went before them to the goal, and got on the other side to give the signal and act as umpire.

" One!—Two!—Three and away!"—They were off like race-horses. They jostled midway. It was neck and neck. And each laid his hand at the same moment on the gate.

John Atkinson then bethought him that it would be a more sensible way of deciding the dispute, if they were to drink for it, and see who could swallow most ale at the Black Bull, where the current barrel was much to his taste. At the Black Bull, therefore, they met in the evening. John chalked pint for pint; but for the sake of good fellowship he drank pint for pint also; the Landlord (honest Matthew Sykes) entered into the spirit of the contest, and when his wife refused to draw any more beer, went for it himself as long as he had a leg to stand on, or a hand to carry the jug, and longer than any one of the party could keep the score.

The next day they agreed to settle it by a sober game at Beggar-my-Neighbour. It was a singular game. The cards were dealt with such equality that after the first round had shown the respective hands, the ablest calculator would have been doubtful on which side to have betted. Captures were made and re-made,—the game had all and more than all its usual ups and downs, and it ended in tyeing the two last cards. Never in any contest had Jupiter held the scales with a more even hand.

"The Devil is in the business to be sure," said Nicholas, "let us toss up for it!"—"Done," said Barnaby; and Nicholas placing a halfpenny on his thumb nail sent it whizzing into the air.

"Tails!" quoth Barnaby.—"'Tis heads," cried Nicholas, "hurrah!"

Barnaby stamped with his right foot for vexation—lifted his right arm to his head, drew in his breath with one of those sounds which grammarians would class among interjections, if they could express them by letters, and swore that if it had been an honest halfpenny, it would never have served him so! He picked it up,—and it proved to be a *Brummejam* of the coarsest and clumsiest kind, with a head on each side. They now agreed that the Devil certainly must be in it, and determined to lay the whole case before the Doctor.

The Doctor was delighted with their story. The circumstances which they related were curious enough to make the naming of this horse as remarkable as his birth. He was pleased also that his own difficulties and indecision upon this important subject should thus as it were be removed by Fate or Fortune; and taking the first thought which now occurred, and rubbing his forehead as he was wont to do, when any happy conception struck him, (Jupiter often did so when Minerva was in his brain), he said, "we must compromise the matter, and make a compound name in which both shall have an equal share. Nicholas Ottley, and Barnaby Sutton; N. O.—B. S.—Nobs shall be his name."

Perhaps the Doctor remembered Smectymnuus at that time, and the notorious Cabal, and the fanciful etymology that because news comes from all parts, and the letters N. E. W. S. stand for North, East, West, and South—the word was thence compounded. Perhaps, also, he called to mind that Rabbi Moses Ben Maimon, the famous Maimonides, was called Rambam from the initials of his titles and his names; and that the great Gustavus Adolphus when he travelled incognito assumed the name of M. Gars, being the four initials of his name and title. He certainly did not remember that in the Dialogue of Solomon and Saturnus the name of Adam is said to have been in like manner derived from the four Angels Archox, Dux, Arocholem, and Minsymbrie. He did not remember this—because he never knew it; this very curious Anglo-Saxon poem existing hitherto only in manuscript, and no other portions or account of it having been printed than those brief ones for which we are indebted to Mr. Conybeare, a man upon whose like we of his generation shall not look again.

CHAPTER CXLI.

A SINGULAR ANECDOTE AND NOT MORE SAD THAN TRUE.

Oh penny Pipers, and most painful penners
Of bountiful new Ballads, what a subject,
What a sweet subject for your silver sounds!

BEAUMONT and FLETCHER.

THE chance of the Birmingham halfpenny was a rare one. I will not so far wrong the gentle Reader as to suppose that he will doubt the accuracy of anything which is recorded in this true history; and I seriously assure him that such a halfpenny I have myself seen in those days when the most barefaced counterfeits were in full circulation,—a halfpenny which had a head on either side, and consequently was like the fox in the fable, or a certain noble Marquis, and now more noble Duke when embassador at Petersburg,—not as being doublefaced, but as having lost its tail.

A rare chance it was, and yet rarer ones have happened.—I remember one concerning a more serious appeal to fortune with the same instrument. An Organist not without some celebrity in his day, (Jeremiah Clark was his name,) being hopelessly in love with a very beautiful lady, far above his station in life, determined upon suicide, and walked into the fields to accomplish his purpose. Coming to a retired spot where there was a convenient pond, surrounded with equally convenient trees, he hesitated which to prefer, whether to choose a dry death, or a watery one; — perhaps he had never heard of the old riddle concerning Ælia Lælia Crispis, which no Œdipus has yet solved. But that he might not continue like the Ass between two bundles of hay in the sophism, or Mahomet's coffin in the fable, he tossed a halfpenny in the air to decide whether he should hang or drown himself, — and the halfpenny stuck edgeways in the dirt.

The most determined infidel would at such a moment have felt that this was more than accident. Clark, as may well be supposed, went home again; but the salutary impression did not remain upon his poor disordered mind, and he shot himself soon afterwards.

CHAPTER CXLII.

A DEFECT IN HOYLE SUPPLIED. GOOD ADVICE GIVEN, AND PLAIN TRUTH TOLD. A TRIBUTE OF RESPECT TO THE MEMORY OF F. NEWBERY, THE CHILDREN'S BOOKSELLER AND FRIEND.

Neither is it a thing impossible or greatly hard, even by such kind of proofs so to manifest and clear that point, that no man living shall be able to deny it, without denying some apparent principle such as all men acknowledge to be true. HOOKER.

THERE are many things in these kingdoms which are greatly under-valued: strong beer for example in the cider countries, and cider in the countries of good strong beer; bottled twopenny in South Britain; sprats and herrings by the rich, — (it may be questioned whether his Majesty ever tasted them, though food for the immortal Gods,) — and fish of every kind by the labouring classes; — some things because they are common, and others because they are not.

But I cannot call to mind anything which is estimated so much below its deserts as the game of Beggar-my-Neighbour. It is generally thought fit only for the youngest children, or for the very lowest and most ignorant persons into whose hands a pack of cards can descend; whereas there is no game whatever in which such perpetual opportunities of calculation are afforded to the scientific gamester; not indeed for playing his cards, but for betting upon them. Zerah Colburn, George Bidder and Professor Airy would find their faculties upon the stretch, were they to attempt to keep pace with its chances.

It is, however, necessary that the Reader should not mistake the spurious for the genuine game, for there are various ways of playing it, and as in all cases only one which is the orthodox way. You take up trick by trick. The trump, as at other games, takes every other suit. If suit is not followed the leader wins the trick; but if it is, the highest card is the winner. These rules being observed (I give them because they will not be found in Hoyle) the game is regular and affords combinations worthy to have exercised the power of that calculating machine of flesh and blood, called Jedediah Buxton.

Try it, Reader, if you have the slightest propensity for gambling. — But first pledge your sacred word of honour to the person whose good opinion you are most desirous of retaining, that you will never at any game, nor in any adventure, risk a sum which would involve you in any serious difficulties, or occasion you any reasonable regret if it should be lost. Make that resolution, and keep it; — and you and your family will have cause to bless the day in which you read the History of Dr. Dove.

Observe, it is your word of honour that I have requested, and not your oath. Either with you might and ought to be equally binding, as *in foro conscientiæ*, so everywhere else. But perhaps you are, or may hereafter be a Member of Parliament, (a propensity whether slight or not for gambling which has been presupposed, renders this the more likely;) and since what is called the Catholic Relief Bill was passed, the obligation of an oath has been done away by the custom of Parliament, honourable

Members being allowed to swear with whatever degree of mental reservation they and their Father Confessors may find convenient.

A Frenchman some fifteen years ago published a Treatise upon the game of Thirty-One; and which is not always done by Authors, in French or English, thought it necessary to make himself well acquainted with the subject upon which he was writing. In order, therefore, to ascertain the chances, he made one million five hundred and sixty thousand throws, which he computed as equivalent to four years' uninterrupted play. If this indefatigable Frenchman be living, I exhort him to study Beggar-my-Neighbour with equal diligence.

There are some games which have survived the Revolutions of Empires, like the Pyramids; but there are more which have been as short-lived as modern Constitutions. There may be some old persons who still remember how Ombre was played, and Tontine and Lottery; but is there any one who has ever heard of Quintill, Piquemdrill, Papillon, L'Ambigu, Ma Commère, La Mariée, La Mouche, Man d'Auvergne, L'Emprunt, Le Poque, Romestecq, Sizette, Guinguette, Le Sixte, La Belle, Gillet, Cul Bas, Brusquembrille, the Game of Hoc, the Reverse, the Beast, the Cuckoo and the Comet? — is there any one, I say, who has ever heard of these Games, unless he happens to know as I do, that rules for playing them were translated from the French of the Abbé Bellecour, and published for the benefit of the English people some seventy years ago by Mr. F. Newbery, a publisher never to be named without honour by those who have read in their childhood the delectable histories of Goody Two-Shoes, and Giles Gingerbread.

CHAPTER CXLIII.

A FEEBLE ATTEMPT TO DESCRIBE THE PHYSICAL AND MORAL QUALITIES OF NOBS.

Quant à moi, je desirerois fort scavoir bien dire, ou que j'eusse eu une bonne plume, et bien taillée à commandement, pour l'exalter et louër comme il le mérite. Toutesfois, telle quelle est, je m'en vais l'employer au hazard.

BRANTOME.

SUCH, O Reader, were the circumstances concerning Nobs, before his birth, at his birth, and upon his naming. Strange indeed would it have been, if anything which regarded so admirable a horse had been after the manner of other horses.

Fate never could a horse provide
So fit for such a man to ride;
Nor find a man with strictest care
So fit for such a horse to bear.*

To describe him as he was would require all the knowledge, and all the eloquence of the immortal Taplin. Were I to attempt it in verse, with what peculiar propriety might I adopt the invocation of the Polish Poet.

— Ducite Gratiæ
E valle Permessi vagantem
Pegason; alipedemque sacris
Frenate sertis. — Ut micat auribus!
Vocemque longé vatis amabili
Agnoscit hinnitu! Ut Dearum
Frena ferox, hilarique bullam
Collo poposcit.† —

Might I not have applied the latter part of these verses as aptly, as they might truly have been applied to Nobs, when Barnaby was about to saddle him on a fine spring morning at the Doctor's bidding? But what have I to do with the Graces, or the Muses and their winged steed? My business is with plain truth and sober prose.

— Io non so dov' io debba comminciare,
Dal capo, da gli orecchi, o dalla coda.
Egli è per tutto tanto singulare,
Ch' io per me vò lodarlo, intero, intero;
Poi pigli ognun qual membro più gli pare.‡

Stubbs would have found it difficult to paint him, Reginald Heber himself to describe him as he was. I must begin by saying what he was not.

---

* CHURCHILL. † CASIMIR. ‡ BUSINI.

And grant me now,
Good reader, thou!
Of terms to use
Such choice to chuse,
As may delight
The country wight,
  And knowledge bring:
For such do praise
The country phrase,
The country acts,
The country facts,
The country toys,
Before the joys
  Of any thing.*

He was not jogged under the jaw, nor shoulder-splat, neck-cricked, pricked in the sole or loose in the hoof, horse-hipped, hide-bound, broken-winded, straight or heavy shouldered, lame in whirl-bone, run-away, restiff, vicious, neck-reversed or cock-thrappled, ewe-necked or deer-necked, high on the leg, broken-knee'd, splent, oslett, false-quartered, ring-boned, sand-cracked, groggy, hollow-backed, bream-backed, long-backed or broken-backed, light-carcased, ragged hipped, droop-Dutchman'd, Dutch buttock'd, hip shot-stifled, hough-boney or sickle-hammed. He had neither his head ill set on, nor dull and hanging ears, nor wolves' teeth, nor bladders in the mouth, nor gigs, nor capped-hocks, nor round legs, nor grease, nor the chine-gall, the navel-gall, the spur-gall, the light-gall, or the shackle-gall; nor the worms, nor the scratches, nor the colt-evil, nor the pole-evil, nor the quitter bones, nor the curbs, nor the Anticoré, nor the pompardy, nor the rotten-frush, nor the crown-scab, nor the cloyd, nor the web, nor the pin, nor the pearl, nor the howks, nor the haws, nor the vines, nor the paps, nor the pose: nor the bladders, nor the surbate, nor the bloody riffs, nor sinews down, nor mallenders, nor fallenders, nor sand cracks, nor hurts in the joints, nor toes turned out, nor toes turned in, nor soft feet, nor hard feet, nor thrushes, nor corns. Nor did he beat upon the hand, nor did he carry low, nor did he carry in the wind. Neither was he a crib-biter, nor a high-goer, nor a daisy cutter, nor a cut-behind, nor a hammer and pinchers, nor a wrong-end-first, nor a short stepper, nor a roarer, nor an interferer. For although it hath been said that "a man cannot light of any horse young or old, but he is furnished with one, two, or more of these excellent gifts," Nobs had none of them: he was an immaculate horse; —such as Adam's would have been, if Adam had kept what could not then have been called a saddle-horse, in Eden.

He was not, like the horse upon which Petruchio came to his wedding, "possessed with the glanders and like to mose in the chine; troubled with the lampass, infected with the fashions, full of wind-galls, sped with spavins, raied with the yellows, past cure of the fives, stark spoiled with the staggers, begnawn with the bots, swayed in the back and shoulder-shotten."† But he was in every respect the reverse.

A horse he was worthy to be praised like that of the Sieur Vuyart.

Un courtaut brave, un courtaut glorieux,
Qui ait en l'air ruade furieuse,
Glorieux trot, la bride glorieuse.‡

A horse who like that famous charger might have said in his Epitaph

J'allay curieux
En chocs furieux,
  Sans craindre estrapade;
Mal rabotez lieux
Passez a cloz yeux,
  Sans faire chopade.
La viste virade,
Pompante pennade,
  Le saut soubzlevant,
La roide ruade,
Prompte petarrade
  Je mis en avant.
Escumeur bavant
Au manger sçavant,
  Au penser très-doux;
Relevé devant,
Jusqu'au bout servant
  J'ay esté sur tous.

Like that Arabian which Almanzar sent to Antea's father, the Soldan,

Egli avea tutte le fattezze pronte
Di buon caval, come udirete appresso.§

Like those horses, described by Mr. Milman in his version of the episode of Nala from the Mahábhárata, he was

* Tusser.

† Taming of the Shrew. ‡ Clement Marot.
§ Pulci.

—— fit and powerful for the road;
Blending mighty strength with fleetness, — high in courage and in blood:
Free from all the well-known vices, — broad of nostril, large of jaw,
With the ten good marks distinguished,—born in Sindhu, fleet as wind.

Like these horses he was, — except that he was born in Yorkshire; — and being of Tartarian blood it may be that he was one of the same race with them.

He was not like the horses of Achilles;

Ἐξ ἀφθίτων γὰρ ἄφθιτοι πεφυκότες
Τὸν Πηλέως φέρουσι θούριον γόνον.
Δίδωσι δ' αὐτοὺς πωλοδαμνήσας ἄναξ
Πηλεῖ Ποσειδῶν, ὡς λέγουσι, πόντιος.*

Like them therefore Nobs could not be, because he was a mortal horse; and moreover because he was not amphibious, as they must have been. If there be any of their breed remaining, it must be the immortal River, or more properly Water-Horse of Loch Lochy, who has sometimes, say the Highlanders, been seen feeding on the banks: sometimes entices mares from the pasture, sometimes overturns boats in his anger and agitates the whole lake with his motion.

He was of a good tall stature; his head lean and comely; his forehead out-swelling; his eyes clear, large, prominent and sparkling, with no part of the white visible; his ears short, small, thin, narrow and pricking; his eye-lids thin; his eye-pits well-filled; his under-jaw thick but not fleshy; his nose arched; his nostrils deep, open, and extended; his mouth well split and delicate; his lips thin; his neck deep, long, rising straight from the withers, then curving like a swan's; his withers sharp and elevated; his breast broad; his ribs bending; his chine broad and straight; his flank short and full; his crupper round and plump; his haunches muscular: his thighs large and swelling; his hocks round before, tendonous behind, and broad on the sides, the shank thin before, and on the sides broad; his tendons strong, prominent, and well detached; his pasterns short; his fetlocks well-tufted, the coronet somewhat raised; his hoofs black, solid, and shining; his instep high, his quarters round; the heel broad; the frog thin and small; the sole thin and concave.

Here I have to remark that the tufted fetlocks Nobs derived from his dam Miss Jenny. They belong not to the thorough-bred race; — witness the hunting song,

Your high bred nags,
Your hairy legs,
We'll see which first come in, Sir.

He had two properties of a man, to wit, a proud heart, and a hardy stomach.

He had the three parts of a woman, the three parts of a lion, the three parts of a bullock, the three parts of a sheep, the three parts of a mule, the three parts of a deer, the three parts of a wolf, the three parts of a fox, the three parts of a serpent, and the three parts of a cat, which are required in a perfect horse.

For colour he was neither black-bay, brown-bay, dapple-bay, black-grey, iron-grey, sad-grey, branded-grey, sandy-grey, dapple-grey, silver-grey, dun, mouse-dun, flea-backed, flea-bitten, rount, blossom, roan, pye-bald, rubican, sorrel, cow-coloured sorrel, bright sorrel, burnt sorrel, starling-colour, tyger-colour, wolf-colour, deer-colour, cream-colour, white, grey or black. Neither was he green, like the horse which the Emperor Severus took from the Parthians, and reserved for his share of the spoil, with a Unicorn's horn and a white Parrot; *et qu'il estima plus pour la rareté et couleur naïve et belle que pour la valeur, comme certes il avoit raison: car, nul butin, tant precieux fut-il, ne l'eust pu esgaler, et sur tout ce cheval, verd de nature.* —Such a horse Rommel saw in the Duke of Parma's stables; because of its green colour it was called Speranza, and the Duke prized it above all his other horses for the extreme rarity of the colour, as being a jewel among horses, — yea a very emerald.

Nor was he peach-coloured roan, like that horse which Maximilian de Bethune, afterwards the famous Duc de Sully, bought at a horse-market for forty crowns, and which was so poor a beast in appearance *qu'il ne sembloit propre qu'a porter la malle*, and yet

* Euripides.

turned out to be so excellent a horse that Maximilian sold him to the Vidasme of Chartres for six hundred crowns. Sully was an expert horse-dealer. He bought of Monsieur de la Roche-Guyon one of the finest Spanish horses that ever was seen, and gave six hundred crowns for him. Monsieur de Nemours not being able to pay the money, *une tapisserie des forces de Hercule* was received either in pledge or payment, which tapestry adorned the great hall at Sully, when the veteran soldier and statesman had the satisfaction of listening to the *Memoires de ce que Nous quatre*, say the writers, *qui avons esté employex en diverses affaires de France sous Monseigneur le Duc de Sully, avons peu sçavoir de sa vie, mœurs, dicts, faicts, gestes et fortunes; et de ce que luy-mesme nous peut avoir appris de ceux de nostre valeureux Alcide le Roy Henry le Grand, depuis le mois de May* 1572 (*qu'il fut mis à son service,*) *jusques au mois de May* 1610, *qu'il laissa la terre pour aller au Ciel.*

No! his colour was chesnut; and it is a saying founded on experience that a chesnut horse is always a good one, and will do more work than any horse of the same size of any other colour. The horse which Wellington rode at the Battle of Waterloo for fifteen hours without dismounting, was a small chesnut horse.*

This was the "thorough-bred red chesnut charger" mentioned by Sir George Head, when he relates an anecdote of the Duke of Wellington and Sir Thomas Picton, who, contrary to the Duke's intentions, seemed at that moment likely to bring on an engagement, not long after the battle of Orthez. Having learned where Sir Thomas was, the Duke set spurs to his horse; the horse "tossed up its head with a snort and impetuously sprang forward at full speed, and in a few minutes, *ventre à terre*, transported its gallant rider, his white cloak streaming in the breeze, to the identical copse distant about half a mile from whence the firing of the skirmishers proceeded. As horse and rider furiously careered towards the spot, I fancied," says Sir George, "I perceived by the motion of the animal's tail, a type, through the medium of the spur, of the quickened energies of the noble Commander, on the moment when for the first time he caught view of Picton."

This famous horse, named Copenhagen because he was foaled about the time of the expedition against that City, died on the 12th of February, 1836, at Strathfieldsaye of old age; there, where he had passed the last ten years of his life in perfect freedom, he was buried, and by the Duke's orders a salute was fired over his grave. The Duchess used to wear a bracelet made of his hair. Would that I had some of thine in a broche, O Nobs!

Copenhagen has been wrongly described in a newspaper as slightly made. A jockey hearing this said of a horse would say, "*ay a thready thing*;" but Copenhagen was a large horse in a small compass, as compact a thorough-bred horse as ever run a race,—which he had done before he was bought and sold to the Duke in Spain. "He was as sweet gentle a creature," says a right good old friend of mine, "as I ever patted, and he came of a gentle race, by the mother's side; she was Meteora, daughter of Meteor, and the best trait in her master's character, Westminster's Marquis, was that his eyes dropped tears when they told him she had won a race, but being over weighted had been much flogged."

He was worthy, like the horses of the Greek Patriarch Theophylact, to have been fed with pistachios, dates, dried grapes, and figs steeped in the finest wines, — that is to say, if he would have preferred this diet to good oats, clean hay, and sometimes, in case of extraordinary exertion, an allowance of bread soaked in ale. Wine the Doctor did not find it necessary to give him, even in his old age; although he was aware of the

* William Nicol, the printer of the original volumes, and the friend of Southey and Bedford, added this paragraph: — The following extract is from Gleig's Story of the Battle of Waterloo: "The gallant animal which had carried his master safely through the fatigues and dangers of the day, as if proud of the part which he had played in the great game, threw up his heels just as the Duke turned from him, and it was by a mere hair's breadth that the life was preserved which, in a battle of ten hours' duration, had been left unscathed." c. xxxi. p. 254.

benefit which the horse of Messire Philippe De Comines derived from it after the battle of Montl'hery: *J'avoye*, says that sagacious soldier, *un cheval extremement las et vieil; Il beut un seau plein de vin; par aucun cas d'aventure il y mit le museau; Je le laissay achever; Jamais ne l'avoye trouvé si bon ne si frais.*

He was not such a horse as that famous one of Julius Cæsar's, which had feet almost like human feet, the hoofs being cleft after the manner of toes. Leo X. had one which in like manner had what Sir Charles Bell calls digital extremities; and Geoffrey St. Hilaire, he tells us, had seen one with three toes on the fore-foot and four on the hind-foot; and such a horse was not long since exhibited in London and at Newmarket, — No! Nobs was not such a horse as this; — if he had been so mis-shapen he would have been a monster. The mare which the Tetrarch of Numidia sent to Grandgousier, and upon which Gargantua rode to Paris, had feet of this description; but that mare was *la plus enorme et la plus grande que fut oncques veüe, et la plus monstreuse.*

He was a perfect horse;—worthy to belong to the perfect doctor, — worthy of being immortalised in this perfect history. And it is not possible to praise him too much,

— οὕνεκ' ἄριστος
Ιππῶν, ὅσσοι ἔασιν ὑπ' ἠῶ τ' ἠέλιόν τε· *

not possible I repeat, *porque*, as D. Juan Perez de Montalvan says, *parece que la Naturaleza le avia hecho, no con la prisa que suele, sino con tanto espacio y perfeccion, que, como quando un pintor acaba con felicidad un lienzo, suele poner á su lado su nombre, assi pudo la Naturaleza escrivir el suyo, como por termino de su ciencia:* which is, being translated, "Nature seemed to have made him, not with her wonted haste, but with such deliberation and perfection, that as a painter when he finishes a picture successfully uses to mark it with his name, so might Nature upon this work have written hers, as being the utmost of her skill!" As Shakespeare would have expressed it —

Nature might stand up
And say to all the world, this was a Horse.

In the words of an old romance, to describe him *ainsi qu'il apartient seroit difficile jusques à l'impossibilité*, beyond which no difficulty can go.

He was as excellent a horse, the Doctor used to say, as that which was first chosen to be backed by Cain, and which the divine Du Bartas, as rendered by the not less divine Sylvester, thus describes,

With round, high, hollow, smooth, brown, jetty hoof;
With pasterns short, upright, but yet in mean;
Dry sinewy shanks; strong fleshless knees and lean;
With hart-like legs; broad breast, and large behind,
With body large, smooth flanks, and double chined;
A crested neck, bowed like a half bent bow,
Whereon a long, thin, curled mane doth flow;
A firm full tail, touching the lowly ground,
With dock between two fair fat buttocks drown'd;
A pricked ear, that rests as little space
As his light foot; a lean, bare, bony face,
Thin joule, and head but of a middle size;
Full, lively-flaming, quickly-rolling eyes;
Great foaming mouth, hot fuming nostril wide;
Of chesnut hair, his forehead starrified;
Three milky feet, a feather in his breast,
Whom seven-years-old at the next grass he guest.

In many respects he was like that horse which the elder of the three Fracassins won in battle in the Taprobanique Islands, in the wars between the two dreadful Giant Kings Gargamitre and Tartabas. *Ce furieux destrier estoit d'une taille fort belle, à jambe de cerf, la poictrine ouverte, la croupe large, grand corps, flancs unis, double eschine, le col vouté comme un arc mi-tendu, sur lequel flottoit un long poil crespu; la queue longue, ferme et espesse; l'oreille poinctue et sans repos, aussi bien que le pied, d'une corne lissee, retirant sur le noir, haute, ronde, et creuse, le front sec, et n'ayant rien que l'os; les yeux gros prompts et relevez; la bouche grande, escumeuse; le nareau ronflant et ouvert; poil chastain, de l'age de sept ans. Bref qui eut voulu voir le modelle d'un beau, bon et genereux cheval en estoit un.*

Like this he was, except that he was never *Nobs furieux*, being as gentle and as docile at seven years old, as at seventeen when it was my good fortune to know and my privilege sometimes to ride him.

He was not such a horse as that for which Muley, the General of the King of Fez, and

* Homer.

the *Principe Constante* D. Fernando fought, when they found him without an owner upon a field covered with slain; a horse

tan monstruo, que siendo hijo
del Viento, adopcion pretende
del Fuego; y entre los dos
lo desdize y lo desmiente
el color, pues siendo blanco
dize el Agua, parto es este
de mi esfera, sola yo
pude quaxarle de nieve.

Both leaped upon him at once, and fought upon his back, and Calderon's Don Fernando thus describes the battle,—

En la silla y en las ancas
puestos los dos juntamente,
mares de sangre rompimos;
por cuyas ondas crueles
este baxel animado,
hecho proa de la frente,
rompiendo el globo de nacar.
desde el codon al copete,
parecio entre espuma y sangre,
ya que baxel quise hazerle,
de quatro espuelas herido,
que quatro vientos le mueven.

He did not either in his marks or trappings resemble Rabicano, as Chiabrera describes him, when Rinaldo having lost Bayardo, won this famous horse from the Giant to whose keeping Galafron had committed him after Argalia's death.

Era sì negro l'animal guerriero,
Qual pece d'Ida; e solamente en fronte
E sulla coda biancheggiava il pelo,
E del piè manco, e deretano l'unghia;
Ma con fren d'oro, e con dorati arcioni.
Sdegna tremando ogni reposo, e vibra
Le tese orecchie, e per levarsi avvampa,
E col ferrato piè non è mai stanco
Battere il prato, e tutte l'aure sfida
Al sonar de magnanimi nitriti.

Galafron had employed

Tutto l'Inferno a far veloce in corso
Qual negro corridor.

Notwithstanding which Rabicano appears to have been a good horse, and to have had no vice in him; and yet his equine virtues were not equal to those of Nobs, nor would he have suited the Doctor so well.

Lastly, he was not such a Horse as that goodly one "of Cneiüs Seiüs which had all the perfections that could be named for stature, feature, colour, strength, limbs, comeliness, belonging to a horse; but withal, this misery ever went along with him, that whosoever became owner of him was sure to die an unhappy death." Nor did the possession of that fatal horse draw on the destruction of his owner alone, but the ruin of his whole family and fortune. So it proved in the case of his four successive Masters, Cneiüs Seiüs, Cornelius Dolabella, Caius Cassius, and Mark Antony, whom, if I were to call by his proper name Marcus Antonius, half my readers would not recognise. This horse was foaled in the territory of Argos*, and his pedigree was derived from the anthropophagous stud of the tyrant Diomedes. He was of surpassing size, *haud credibili pulchritudine vigore et colore exuberantissimo*,—being purple with a tawney mane. No! Nobs was not such a horse as this.

Though neither in colour nor in marks, yet in many other respects the description may be applied to him which Merlinus Cocaius has given in his first Macaronea of the horse on which Guido appeared at that tournament where he won the heart of the Princess Baldovina.

Huic mantellus erat nigrior carbone galantus,
Parvaque testa, breves agilesque movebat orecchias;
Frontis et in medio faciebat stella decorem.
Frena biassabat, naresque tenebat apertas.
Pectore mostazzo tangit, se reddit in unum
Groppettum, solusque viam galopando misurat,
Goffiat, et curtos agitant sua colla capillos.
Balzanus tribus est pedibus, cum pectore largo,
Ac inter gambas tenet arcto corpore caudam;
Spaventat, volgitque oculos hinc inde fogatos;
Semper et ad solam currit remanetque sbriatam,
Innaspatque pedes naso boffante priores.

That he should have been a good horse is not surprising, seeing that though of foreign extraction on the one side, he was of English birth, whereby, and by his dam, he partook the character of English horses. Now as it has been discreetly said, "Our English horses have a mediocrity of all necessary good properties in them, as neither so slight as the Barbe; nor so slovenly as the Flemish; nor so fiery as the Hungarian; nor so aery as the Spanish Gennets, (especially if, as reported, they be conceived of the wind;) nor so earthly as those in the Low Countries, and generally all the German Horse.

* Cf. Aul. Gell. Noct. Att. lib. iii. c. ix., where the other proverb of *Aurum Tolosanum*, so often referred to in our old writers, is explained likewise.

For stature and strength they are of a middle size, and are both seemly and serviceable in a good proportion. And whilst the seller praiseth them too much, the buyer too little, the indifferent stander-by will give them this due commendation." *

A reasonably good horse therefore he might have been expected to prove as being English, and better than ordinary English horses as being Yorkshire. For saith the same judicious author, "Yorkshire doth breed the best race of English horses, whose keeping commonly in steep and stony ground bringeth them to firmness of footing and hardness of hoof; whereas a stud of horses bred in foggy, fenny ground, and soft, rotten morasses, — (delicacy marrs both man and beast,) — have often a fen in their feet, being soft, and soon subject to be foundered. Well may Philip be so common a name amongst the gentry of this country, who are generally so delighted in horsemanship."

Very good therefore there might have been fair ground for hoping that Nobs would prove; but that he should have proved so good, so absolutely perfect in his kind and for his uses, was beyond all hope — all expectation.

"I have done with this subject, the same author continues, when I have mentioned the monition of David, 'an Horse is but a vain thing to save a man,' though it is no vain thing to slay a man, by many casualties: such need we have, whether waking or sleeping, whether walking or riding, to put ourselves by prayer into Divine Protection."

Such a reflection is in character with the benevolent and pious writer; and conveys indeed a solemn truth which ought always to be borne in mind. Its force will not be weakened though I should remark that the hero of a horse which I have endeavoured to describe may in a certain sense be said to afford an exception to David's saying: for there were many cases in which, according to all appearance, the patient could not have been saved unless the Doctor had by means of his horse Nobs arrived in time.

* Fuller.

His moral qualities indeed were in as great perfection as his physical ones; but — *il faut faire desormais une fin au discours de ce grand cheval; car, tant plus que j'entrerois dans le labyrinthe de ses vertus, tant plus je m'y perdrois.* With how much more fitness may I say this of Nobs, than Brantome said it of Francis I.!

When in the fifteenth century the noble Valencian Knight, Mossen Manuel Diez accompanied Alonso to the conquest of the kingdom of Naples, he there had occasion to remark of how great importance it was that the knights should be provided with good horses in time of war, that they might thereby be the better able to increase the honour and extend the dominions of their king; and that in time of their old age and the season of repose they should have for their recreation good mules. He resolved therefore to compose a book upon the nature and qualities of these animals, and the way of breeding them, and preserving them sound, and in good condition and strong. And although he was well versed in these things himself, nevertheless he obtained the king's orders for calling together all the best *Albeytares*, that is to say in old speech, farriers, horse-doctors, or horse-leeches, and in modern language Veterinary surgeons; all which could assemble were convened, and after due consultation with them, he composed that *Libre de Menescalià*, the original of which in the Valencian dialect was among the MSS. that Pope Alexander VII. collected, and which began *In nome sia de la Sancta Trinitat, que es Pare, è Fill, e Sant Spirit, tot hum Deu;* and which he as *Majordom* of the *molt alt e poderos Princep, e victorios Signior Don Alfonso, Re de Ragona, &c.* set forth to show to *als jovents Cavellers, gran part de la practica è de la conexenza del Cavalls, e de lurs malaties, è gran part de les cures di aquells.* If Nobs had lived in those days, worthy would he have been to have been in all particulars described in that work, to have had an equestrian order instituted in his honour, and have been made a *Rico Cavallo*, the first who obtained that rank.

CHAPTER CXLIV.

HISTORY AND ROMANCE RANSACKED FOR RESEMBLANCES AND NON-RESEMBLANCES TO THE HORSE OF DOCTOR DANIEL DOVE.

Renowned beast! (forgive poetic flight!)
Not less than man, deserves poetic right.
THE BRUCIAD.

WHEN I read of heroic horses in heroic books, I cannot choose but remember Nobs, and compare him with them, not in particular qualities, but in the sum total of their good points, each in his way. They may resemble each other as little as Rabelais and Rousseau, Shakespeare and Sir Isaac Newton, Paganini and the Duke of Wellington, yet be alike in this, that each had no superior in his own line of excellence.

Thus when I read of the courser which Prince Meridiano presented to Alphebus, the Knight of the Sun, after the Prince had been defeated by him in the presence of his Sister Lindabridis, I think of Nobs, though Cornelin was marvellously unlike the Doctor's perfect roadster. For Cornelin was so named because he had a horn growing from the middle of his forehead; and he had four joints at the lower part of his legs, which extraordinary formation, (I leave anatomists to explain how,) made him swifter than all other horses, insomuch that his speed was likened to the wind. It was thought that his Sire was an Unicorn, though his dam was certainly a mare: and there was this reason for supposing such to be the case, that Meridiano was son to the emperor of Great Tartary, in which country the hybrid race between Unicorn and Mare was not uncommon in those days.

When the good Knight of the Sun engaged in single combat with the Giant Bradaman, this noble horse stood him in good stead: for Bradaman rode an elephant, and as they ran at each other, Cornelin thrust his natural spike into the elephant's poitrel, and killed him on the spot.

Cornelin did special service on another occasion, when some Knights belonging to a Giant King of the Sards, who had established one of those atrocious customs which it was the duty of all Errant Knights to suppress, met with the Good Knight of the Sun; and one of them said he would allow him to turn back and go away in peace, provided he gave him his arms and his horse, "if the horse be thine own," said he, "inasmuch as he liketh me hugely." The Good Knight made answer with a smile "my arms I shall not give, because I am not used to travel without them; and as for my horse, none but myself can mount him." The discourteous Knight made answer with an oath that he would see whether he could defend the horse; and with that he attempted to seize the bridle. No sooner had he approached within Cornelin's reach, than that noble steed opened his mouth, caught him by the shoulder, lifted him up, dropped him, and then trampled on him *si rudement que son ame s'envola à celuy à qui elle estoit pour ses malefices*. Upon this another of these insolent companions drew his sword, and was about to strike at Cornelin's legs, but Cornelin reared, and with both his fore-feet struck him on the helmet with such force, that no armourer could repair the outer head-piece, and no surgeon the inner one.

It was once disputed in France whether a horse could properly be said to have a mouth; a wager concerning it was laid, and referred to no less a person than a Judge, because, says a Frenchman, "our French Judges are held in such esteem that they are appealed to upon the most trifling occasions." The one party maintained *qu'il falloit dire la gueule à toutes bestes, et qu'il n'y avoit que l'homme qui eust bouche;* but the Judge decided, *qu'à cause de l'excellence du cheval, il falloit dire la bouche*. The Giant King's Knights must have been of the Judge's opinion when they saw Cornelin make but a mouthful of their companion.

When our English Judges are holden in such esteem as to be referred to on such occasions, they do not always entertain the appeal. Mr. Brougham when at the Bar — that Mr. Brougham (if posterity inquires whom I mean) who was afterwards made Lord Chancellor and of whom Sir Edward

Sugden justly observed, that if he had but a smattering of law he would know something of everything — Mr. Brougham, I say, opened before Lord Chief Justice Tenterden an action for the amount of a wager laid upon the event of a dog-fight, which through some unwillingness of dogs or men had not been brought to an issue: "We, My Lord," said the advocate, "were minded that the dogs should fight" — "Then I," replied the Judge, "am minded to hear no more of it;" and he called another cause.

No wager would ever have been left undecided through any unwillingness to fight on the part of Cornelin or of his Master the Knight of the Sun.

When that good Knight of the Sun seeking death in his despair landed upon the Desolate Island, there to encounter a monster called Faunus el Endemoniado, that is to say, the Bedevilled Faun, he resolved in recompense for all the service that Cornelin had done him to let him go free for life: so taking off his bridle and saddle and all his equipments, he took leave of him in these sorrowful words: — "O my good Horse, full grievously do I regret to leave thee! Would it were but in a place where thou mightest be looked to and tended according to thy deserts! For if Alexander of Macedon did such honour to his dead horse that he caused a sepulchre to be erected for him and a city to be called after his name, with much more reason might I show honour to thee while thou art living, who art so much better than he. Augustus had his dead horse buried that he might not be devoured by carrion birds. Didius Julianus consecrated a marble statue of his in the Temple of Venus. Lucius Verus had the likeness of his while living cast in gold. But I who have done nothing for thee, though thou surpassest them all in goodness, what can I do now but give thee liberty that thou mayest enjoy it like other creatures? Go then, my good Horse, the last companion from whom I part in this world!" Saying this, he made as if he would have struck him to send him off. But here was a great marvel in this good horse: for albeit he was now free and with nothing to encumber him, he not only would not go away, but instead thereof approached his master, his whole body trembling, and the more the Knight threatened the more he trembled and the nearer he drew. The Knight of the Sun knew not what he should do, for on the one hand he understood in what danger this good horse would be if he should be perceived by the Faun; and on the other threaten him as he would he could not drive him away. At length he concluded to leave him at liberty, thinking that peradventure he would take flight as soon as he should see the Faun. He was not mistaken; Cornelin would have stood by his Master in the dreadful combat in which he was about to engage, and would peradventure have lost his life in endeavouring to aid him; but the Bedevilled Faun had been so named because he had a hive of Devils in his inside; fire came from his mouth and nostrils as he rushed against the Knight, and swarms of armed Devils were breathed out with the flames; no wonder therefore that even Cornelin took fright and galloped away.

But when Alphebus had slain the Bedevilled Faun, and lived alone upon the Desolate Island, like a hermit, waiting and wishing for death, eating wild fruits and drinking of a spring which welled near some trees, under which he had made for himself a sort of bower, Cornelin used often to visit him in his solitude. It was some consolation to the unhappy Knight to see the good horse that he loved so well: but then again it redoubled his grief as he called to mind the exploits he had performed when mounted upon that famous courser. The displeasure of his beautiful and not less valiant than beautiful mistress the Princess Claridiana had caused his wretchedness, and driven him to this state of despair; and when Claridiana being not less wretched herself, came to the Desolate Island in quest of him, the first thing that she found was the huge and broken limb of a tree with which he had killed the Faun, and the next was Cornelin's saddle and bridle and trappings, which she knew by the gold and silk embroidery, tarnished as it was, and by the precious stones. Presently she saw the good horse Cornelin himself, who had now become well nigh wild, and came toward her bounding and neighing, and rejoicing at the sight of her horse, for it was long since he had seen a creature of his own kind. But he started off when she would have laid hold of him, for he could not brook that any but his own master should come near him now. Howbeit she followed his track, and was thus guided to the spot where her own good Knight was wasting his miserable life.

Nobs was as precious a horse to the Doctor as Vegliantino was to Rinaldo,—that noble courser whom the Harpies killed, and whom Rinaldo, after killing the whole host of Harpies, buried sorowfully, kneeling down and kissing his grave. He intended to go in mourning and afoot for his sake all the rest of his life, and wrote for him this epitaph upon a stone, in harpy's blood and with the point of his sword.

Quì giace Vegliantin, caval de Spagna,
Orrido in guerra, e tutto grazie in pace ;
Servi Rinaldo in Francia ed in Lamagna,
Ed ebbe ingegno e spirto si vivace
Che averebbe coi piè fatto una ragna ;
Accorto, destro, nobile ed audace,
Morì qual forte, e con fronte superba ;
*O tu, che passi, gettagli un pò d'erba.**

He was as sagacious a horse and as gentle as Frontalatte, who in the heroic age of horses was

Sopra ogni altro caval savio ed umano.†

When the good Magician Atlante against his will sent his pupil Ruggiero forth, and provided him with arms and horse, he gave him this courser which Sacripante had lost, saying to him

— certamente so che potrai dire
Che 'l principe Rinaldo e 'l conte Orlando
Non ha miglior caval.†
Avendo altro signore, ebbe altro nome ;

His new master called him Frontino

Il mondo non avea più bel destriero,
* * * * * *
Or sopra avendo il giovane Ruggiero,
Piu vaga cosa non si vide mai.
Chi guardasse il cavallo e' l cavaliero
Starebbe a dar giudicio in dubbio assai,
Se fusser vivi, o fatti col pennello,
Tanto era l' un e l' altro egregio e bello.†

Nobs was not like that horse now living at Brussels, who is fond of raw flesh, and getting one day out of his stable found his way to a butcher's shop and devoured two breasts of mutton, mutton it seems being his favourite meat. If his pedigree could be traced we might expect to find that he was descended from the anthropophagous stud of that abominable Thracian King whom Hercules so properly threw to his own horses for food.

Nor was he like that other horse of the same execrable extraction, whom in an evil day Rinaldo, having won him in battle, sent as a present by the damsel Hipalca to Ruggiero,—that Clarion

A quien el cielo con rigor maldixo,
Y una beldad le diò tan codiciada ;

that fatal horse who, as soon as Ruggiero mounted him, carried his heroic master into the ambush prepared for him, in which he was treacherously slain. The tragedy not ending there, for one of the traitors took this horse for his reward, and his proper reward he had with him.

Púsole el traidor pernas, corrió el fuerte
Desenfrenado potro hasta arrojallo,
En medio de la plaza de Marsella,
A ojos de Bradamante, y su doncella.
Alli en presencia suyo hecho pedazos
Al Magancés dexó el caballo fiero :
Viendole Hipalca muerto entre los brazos,
Y no en su silla qual penso a Rugero,
Notorios vió los cavilosos lazos
Del fementido bando de Pontiero.
Alteróse la bella Bradamante
Y el sobresalto le abortó un infante.

Y al quinto dia con la nueva cierta
De la muerte infeliz del paladino,
La antes dudosa amante quedó muerta,
Y cumplido el temor del adivino.
Y por tantas desgracias descubierta
La traicion de Maganza, un rio sanguino
Labró Morgana, y de la gente impia
Cien falsos Condes degolló en un dia.‡

Eso quieren decir las desgracias del Caballo Clarion, says the author of this poem El Doctor Don Bernardo de Balbuena, in the allegory which he annexes to the Carto, *que la fuerza de las estrellas predomina en los brutos, y en la parte sensitiva, y no en el albedrio humano y voluntad racional.*

Neither did Nobs resemble in his taste

* Ricciardetto. † Orlando Inamorato. ‡ Balbuena.

that remarkable horse which Dr. Tyson frequently saw in London at the beginning of the last century. This horse would eat oysters with great delight, scrunching them shells and all between his teeth. Accident developed in him this peculiar liking; for being fastened one day at a tavern-door where there happened to be a tub standing with oysters in it, the water first attracted him, and then the fresh odour of fish induced him to try his teeth upon what promised to be more savoury than oats and not much harder than horse-beans. From that time he devoured them with evident satisfaction whenever they were offered him; and he might have become as formidable a visitor to the oyster-shops, if oyster-shops there then had been, as the great and never-to-be-forgotten Dando himself.

He was not like the Colt which Boyle describes, who had a double eye, that is to say two eyes in one socket, in the middle of his forehead, a Cyclops of a horse.

Nor was he like the coal-black steed on which the Trappist rode, fighting against the *Liberales* as heartily as that good Christian the Bishop Don Hieronimo fought with the Cid Campeador against the Moors, elevating the Crucifix in one hand, and with his sword in the other smiting them for the love of Charity. That horse never needed food or sleep: he never stumbled at whatever speed his master found it needful to ride down the most precipitous descent; his eyes emitted light to show the Trappist his way in the darkness; the tramp of his hoofs was heard twenty miles around, and whatsoever man in the enemy's camp first heard the dreadful sound knew that his fate was fixed, and he must inevitably die in the ensuing fight. Nobs resembled this portentous horse as little as the Doctor resembled the terrible Trappist. Even the great black horse which used to carry old George, as William Dove called the St. George of Quakerdom, far exceeded him in speed. The Doctor was never seen upon his back in the course of the same hour at two places sixty miles apart from each other. There was nothing supernatural in Nobs. His hippogony, even if it had been as the Doctor was willing to have it supposed he thought probable, would upon his theory have been in the course of nature, though not in her usual course.

Olaus Magnus assigns sundry reasons why the Scandinavian horses were hardier, and in higher esteem than those of any other part of the World. They would bear to be shod without kicking or restraint. They would never allow other horses to eat their provender. They saw their way better in the dark. They regarded neither frost nor snow. They aided the rider in battle both with teeth and hoofs. Either in ascending or descending steep and precipitous places they were sure-footed. At the end of a day's journey a roll in the sand or the snow took off their fatigue and increased their appetite. They seldom ailed anything, and what ailments they had were easily cured. Moreover they were remarkable for one thing,

Ch' à dire è brutto, ed à tacerlo è bello — *

and which, instead of translating or quoting the Dane's Latin, I must intimate —— by saying that it was never necessary to whistle to them.

Nobs had none of the qualities which characterised the Scandinavian horses, and in which their excellencies consisted, as peculiarly fitting them for their own country. But he was equally endowed with all those which were required in his station. There was not a surer-footed beast in the West Riding; and if he did not see his way in the dark by the light of his own eyes like the black horse of the Trappist, and that upon which the Old Woman of Berkeley rode double behind One more formidable than the Trappist himself, when she was taken out of her coffin of stone and carried bodily away, — he saw it as well as any mortal horse could see, and knew it as well as John Gough the blind botanist of Kendal, or John Metcalf the blind guide of Knaresborough.

But of all his good qualities that for which the Doctor prized him most was the kind-

* Rucellai.

ness of his disposition, not meaning by those words what Gentlemen-feeders and professors of agriculture mean. "It is the Grazier's own fault," says one of those professors, "if ever he attempts to fatten an unkind beast," — kindness of disposition in a beast importing in their language, that it fattens soon. What it meant in the Doctor's, the following authentic anecdote may show.

The Doctor had left Nobs one day standing near the door of a farm-house with his bridle thrown over a gate-post; one of the farmer's children, a little boy just old enough to run into danger, amused himself by pulling the horse's tail with one hand and striking him with a little switch across the legs with the other. The mother caught sight of this and ran in alarm to snatch the urchin away; but before she could do this, Nobs lifted up one foot, placed it against the boy's stomach, and gently pushed him down. The ground was wet, so that the mark of his hoof showed where he had placed it, and it was evident that what he had done was done carefully not to injure the child, for a blow upon that part must have been fatal. This was what the Doctor called kindness of disposition in a horse. Let others argue if they please *que le cheval avoit quelque raison, et qu'il ratiocinoit entre toutes les autres bestes, à cause du temperament de son cerveau* *; here, as he justly said, was sufficient proof of consideration, and good nature.

He was not like the heroic horse which Amadis won in the Isle Perilous, when in his old age he was driven thither by a tempest, though the adventure has been pretermitted in his great history. After the death of that old, old, very old and most famous of all Knights, this horse was enchanted by the Magician Alchiso. Many generations passed away before he was overcome and disenchanted by Rinaldo; and he then became so famous by his well-known name Bajardo, that for the sole purpose of winning this horse and the sword Durlindana, which was as famous among swords as Bajardo among horses, Gradasso came from India to invade France with an army of an hundred and fifty thousand knights. If Nobs had been like him, think what a confusion and consternation his appearance would have produced at Doncaster races!

Ecco appare il cavallo, e i calci tira,
E fa saltando in ciel ben mille rote;
Delle narici il foco accolto spira,
Muove l' orecchie, e l' empie membra scuote;
A sassi, a sterpi, a piante ei non rimira,
Ma fracassando il tutto, urta e percote;
Col nitrito i nemici a fiera guerra
Sfida, e cò piè fa rimbombar la tierra.†

Among the Romans he might have been in danger of being selected for a victim to Mars, on the Ides of December. The Massagetæ would have sacrificed him to the Sun, to whom horses seem to have been offered wherever he was worshipped.‡ He might have escaped in those countries where white horses were preferred on such occasions; — a preference for which a commentator upon Horace accounts by the unlucky conjecture that it was because they were swifter than any others. §

No better horse was ever produced from that celebrated breed which Dionysius the Tyrant imported into Sicily from the Veneti. No better could have been found among all the progeny of the fifty thousand Mares belonging to the Great King, upon the Great Plain which the Greeks called Hippobotus because the Median herb which was the best pasture for horses abounded there. Whether the Nisæan horses, which were used by kings, were brought from thence or from Armenia, ancient Authors have not determined.

There was a tomb not far from the gates at Athens, ascending from the Piræus, on which a soldier was represented standing beside a Horse. All that was known of this monument in the age of Adrian was that it

* Bouchet.

† Tasso.

‡ "Ne detur celeri victima tarda Deo." Ovid, *Fast.* Cf. 2 Kings, xxiii. 11.

§ Is there any mistake here? The allusion is to *Sat.* vii. 8. "Equis præcurreret albis?" Horace had in view Iliad, x. 436. Virgil has, with reference to Pilumnus' horses, "Qui candore nives anteirent, cursibus auras." *Æn.* xii. 84.

was the work of Praxiteles; the name of the person whose memory it was intended to preserve had perished. If Nobs and his Master had flourished at the same time with Praxiteles, that great sculptor would have thought himself worthily employed in preserving likenesses for posterity of the one and the other. He was worthy to have been modelled by Phidias or Lysippus. I will not wish that Chantrey had been what he now is, the greatest of living sculptors, fourscore years ago: but I may wish that Nobs and the Doctor had lived at the time when Chantrey could have made a bust of the one and a model of the other, or an equestrian statue to the joint honour of both.

Poppæa would have had such a horse shod with shoes of gold. Caligula would have made him Consul. William Rufus would have created him by a new and appropriate title Lord Horse of London Town.

When the French had a settlement in the Island of Madagascar, their Commander, who took the title of Viceroy, assembled a force of 3000 natives against one of the most powerful native Chiefs, and sent with them 140 French under the Sieur de Chamargou. This officer had just then imported from India the first horse which had ever been seen in Madagascar, and though oxmanship was practised by this people, as by some of the tribes on the adjacent coast of Africa, those oxriders were astonished at the horse; *ils luy rendoient même des respects si profonds, que tous ceux qui envoyoient quelque deputation vers le General de cette armée, ne manquoient point de faire des presens et des complimens a Monsieur le Cheval.* If Nobs had been that Horse, he would have deserved all the compliments that could have been paid him.

He would have deserved too, as far as Horse could have deserved, the more extraordinary honours which fell to the lot of a coal-black steed, belonging to a kinsman of Cortes by name Palacios Rubios. In that expedition which Cortes made against his old friend and comrade Christoval de Olid, who in defiance of him had usurped a government for himself, the Spaniards, after suffering such privations and hardships of every kind as none but Spaniards could with the same patience have endured, came to some Indian settlements called the Mazotecas, being the name of a species of deer in the form of one of which the Demon whom the natives worshipped had once, they said, appeared to them, and enjoined them never to kill or molest in any way an animal of that kind. They had become so tame in consequence, that they manifested no fear at the appearance of the Spaniards, nor took flight till they were attacked. The day was exceedingly hot, and as the hungry hunters followed the chase with great ardour, Rubios's horse was overheated, and as the phrase was, melted his grease. Cortes therefore charged the Indians of the Province of Itza to take care of him while he proceeded on his way to the Coast of Honduras, saying that as soon as he fell in with the Spaniards of whom he was in quest, he would send for him; horses were of great value at that time, and this was a very good one. The Itzaex were equally in fear of Cortes and the Horse; they did not indeed suppose horse and rider to be one animal, but they believed both to be reasonable creatures, and concluded that what was acceptable to the one would be so to the other. So they offered him fowls to eat, presented nosegays to him of their most beautiful and fragrant flowers, and treated him as they would have treated a sick Chief, till, to their utter dismay, he was starved to death. What was to be done when Cortes should send for him? The Cacique, with the advice of his principal men, gave orders that an Image of the Horse should be set up in the temple of his town, and that it should be worshipped there by the name of Tziminchac, as the God of Thunder and Lightning, which it seemed to them were used as weapons by the Spanish Horsemen. The honour thus paid to the Horse would they thought obtain credit for the account which they must give to the Spaniards, and prove that they had not wilfully caused his death.

The Itzaex, however, heard nothing of the Spaniards, nor the Spaniards of Rubios's black horse, till nearly an hundred years afterwards two Franciscans of the province of Yucatan went as Missionaries among these Indians, being well versed in the Maya tongue, which is spoken in that country; their names were Bartolomé de Fuensalida and Juan de Orbita. The chief settlement was upon an Island in the Lake of Itza; there they landed, not with the good will either of the Cacique or the people, and entering the place of worship, upon one of their great Cus or Pyramids they beheld the Horse-Idol, which was then more venerated than all the other Deities. Indignant at the sight, Father Orbita took a great stone and broke to pieces the clay statue, in defiance of the cries and threats with which he was assailed. "Kill him who has killed our God," they exclaimed; "kill him! kill him!" The Spaniards say the serene triumph and the unwonted beauty which beamed in Orbita's countenance at that moment made it evident that he was acting under a divine impulse. His companion Fuensalida, acting in the same spirit, held up the Crucifix, and addressed so passionate and powerful an appeal to the Itzaex in their own language upon the folly and wickedness of their Idolatry and the benefits of the Gospel which he preached, that they listened to him with astonishment, and admiration, and awe, and followed the Friars respectfully from the place of worship, and allowed them to depart in safety.

These Franciscan Missionaries, zealous and intrepid as they were, did but half their work. Many years afterwards when D. Martin de Ursua defeated the Itzaex in an action on the Lake, and took the Petén or Great Island, he found, in what appears to have been the same Adoratory, a decayed shin bone, suspended from the roof by three strings of different coloured cotton, a little bag beneath containing smaller pieces of bone in the same state of decay; under both there were three censers of the Indian fashion with storax and other perfumes burning, and a supply of storax near wrapt in dry leaves of maize, and over the larger bone an Indian coronet. These, he was told upon inquiry, were the bones of the Horse which the Great Captain had committed to the care of their Cacique long ago.

If it had been the fate of Nobs thus to be idolified, and the Itzaex had been acquainted with his character, they would have compounded a name for him, not from Thunder and Lightning, but from all the good qualities which can exist in horse-nature, and for which words could be found in the Maya tongue.

CHAPTER CXLV.

WILLIAM OSMER. INNATE QUALITIES. MARCH OF ANIMAL INTELLECT. FARTHER REVEALMENT OF THE COLUMBIAN PHILOSOPHY.

> There is a word, and it is a great word in this Book*, ἐπὶ τὸ αὐτὸ, — *In id ipsum*, that is, to look to the thing itself, the very point, the principal matter of all; to have our eye on that, and not off it, upon *alia omnia*, any thing but it. — To go to the point, drive all to that, as also to go to the matter real, without declining from it this way or that, to the right hand or to the left. BP. ANDREWES.

A CERTAIN William Osmer once wrote a dissertation upon the Horse, wherein he affirmeth, it is demonstrated by matters of fact, as well as from the principles of philosophy, that innate qualities do not exist, and that the excellence of this animal is altogether mechanical and not in the blood. In affirming this of the Horse, the said William Osmer hath gone far toward demonstrating himself an Ass; for he might as well have averred that the blood hath nothing to do with the qualities of a black pudding. When Hurdis said

> — Give me the steed
> Whose noble efforts bore the prize away,
> I care not for his grandsire or his dam,

it was well said, but not wisely.

The opinion, which is as old as anything known concerning this animal, that the good qualities of a horse are likely to bear some resemblance to those of its sire or dam, Mr. Osmer endeavoured to invalidate by arguing

---

* The New Testament which the Preacher had before him. — *R. S.*

that his strength and swiftness depend upon the exactness of his make, and that where this was defective, these qualities would be deficient also, — a foolish argument, for the proposition rests upon just the same ground as that against which he was reasoning. But what better reasoning could be looked for from a man who affirmed that if horses were not shod they might travel upon the turnpike road without injury to their feet, because, in his own language, "when time was young, when the earth was in a state of nature, and turnpike roads as yet were not, the Divine Artist had taken care to give their feet such defence as it pleased him."

If the Doctor had known that Nobs was of Tartarian extraction, this fact would sufficiently have accounted for the excellences of that incomparable roadster. He explained them quite as satisfactorily to himself by the fancy which he amused himself with supporting on this occasion, that this marvellous horse was a son of the Wind. And hence he inferred that Nobs possessed the innate qualities of his kind in greater perfection than any other horse, as approaching near to the original perfection in which the species was created. For although animals are each in their kind less degenerate than man, whom so many circumstances have tended to injure in his physical nature, still, he argued, all which like the horse have been made subservient to the uses of man, were in some degree deteriorated by that subjection. Innate qualities, however, he admitted were more apparent in the brute creation than in the human creature, because even in those which suffer most by domestication, the course of nature is not so violently overruled.

I except the Duck, he would say. That bird, which Nature hath made free of earth, air and water, loses by servitude the use of one element, the enjoyment of two, and the freedom of all three.

Look at the Pig also, said the Doctor. In his wild state no animal is cleaner, happier, or better able to make himself respected. Look at him when tamed, — I will not say in a brawn-case, for I am not speaking now of those cruelties which the Devil and Man between them have devised, — but look at him prowling at large about the purlieus of his sty. What a loathsome poor despised creature hath man made him!

*Animal propter convivia natum.**

Every cur thinks itself privileged to take him by the ear; whereas if he were once more free in the woods, the stoutest mastiff or wolf-dog would not dare look him in the face.

Yet he was fond of maintaining that the lower creation are capable of intellectual improvement. In Holland, indeed, he had seen the school for dogs, where poodles go through a regular course of education, and where by this time perhaps the Lancasterian inventions have been introduced. But this was not what the Doctor contemplated. Making bears and elephants dance, teaching dogs to enact ballets, and horses to exhibit tricks at a fair, he considered as the freaks of man's capricious cruelty, and instances of that abuse of power which he so frequently exercises over his inferior creatures, and for which he must one day render an account, together with all those whose countenance of such spectacles affords the temptation to exhibit them.†

In truth, the power which animals as well as men possess, of conforming themselves to new situations and forming new habits adapted to new circumstances, is proof of a capability of improvement. The wild dogs in the plains of La Plata burrow, because there is no security for them above ground against stronger beasts of prey. In the same country owls make their nests in the ground, because there are neither trees nor buildings to afford them concealment. A clergyman in Iceland by sowing angelica upon a Lake-island some miles from the sea, not only attracted gulls and wild ducks to breed there, but brought about an alliance between those birds, who are not upon neighbourly

* Juvenal.

† Cf. Jonah, iv. 11.; Prov. xii. 10., with Ps. xxxvi. 6.

terms elsewhere. Both perceived that the new plants afforded better shelter from wind and rain, than anything which they had seen before; there was room enough for both; and the neighbourhood produced so much good will, that the gulls protected the weaker birds not only against the ravens who are common enemies, but against another species of gull also which attacks the duck's nest.

A change more remarkable than either of these is that which the common hearth-cricket has undergone in its very constitution as well as in all its ways of life, since men built houses and inhabited cold climates.

The field-cricket in North America, which buries itself during the winter ten inches deep, and there lies torpid, began about an hundred years ago to avail itself of the work of man and take up its abode in the chimnies. This insect even likes man for a bed-fellow, not with any such felonious intentions as are put in execution by smaller and viler vermin, but for the sake of warmth. The Swedish traveller, Kalm, says that when he and his companions were forced to sleep in uninhabited places, the crickets got into the folds of their garments, so that they were obliged to make some tarriance every morning, and search carefully before they could get rid of them.

Two species of Swallows have domesticated themselves with man. We have only* that which builds under the eaves in England, but in North America they have both the house swallow and the chimney swallow; the chimnies not being made use of in summer, they take possession, and keep it sometimes in spite of the smoke, if the fire is not very great. Each feather in this bird's tail ends in a stiff point, like the end of an awl; they apply the tail to the side of the wall, and it assists in keeping them up, while they hold on with their feet. "They make a great thundering noise all day long by flying up and down in the chimnies;" now as the Indians had not so much as a hearth made of masonry, it is an obvious question, says Kalm, where did these swallows build before the Europeans came, and erected houses with chimnies? Probably, it is supposed, in hollow trees, but certainly where they could; and it is thus shown that they took the first opportunity of improving their own condition.

But the Doctor dwelt with most pleasure on the intellectual capabilities of Dogs. There had been Dogs, he said, who, from the mere desire of following their master's example, had regularly frequented either the Church or the Meeting House; others who attended the Host whenever they heard the bell which announced that it was carried abroad; one who so modulated his voice as to accompany instrumental music through all the notes of a song; and Leibnitz had actually succeeded in teaching one to speak. A dog may be made an epicure as well as his master. He acquires notions of rank and respectability; understands that the aristocracy are his friends, regards the beggar as his rival for bones, and knows that whoever approaches in darkness is to be suspected for his intentions. A dog's physiognomical discernment never deceives him; and this the Doctor was fond of observing, because wherever he was known the dogs came to return the greeting they expected. He has a sense of right and wrong as far as he has been taught; a sense of honour and of duty, from which his master might sometimes take a lesson; and not unfrequently a depth and heroism of affection, which the Doctor verily believed would have its reward in a better world. John Wesley held the same opinion, which has been maintained also by his enemy, Augustus Toplady, and by his biographer, the laureated LL. D. or the El-el-deed Laureate. The Materialist, Dr. Dove would argue, must allow, upon his own principles, that a dog has as much soul as himself; and the Immaterialist, if he would be consistent, must perceive that the

* This looks like a mistake; we have the chimney swallow also, the *Hirundo rustica*. It is the Martin, or the *Hirundo urbica*, that builds under the eaves. Besides these we have the *Hirundo riparia*, or Sand-Martin, and the *Hirundo Apus*, or Swift. I say it looks like a mistake, — but what follows makes it doubtful.

life, and affections, and actions of an animal are as little to be explained as the mysteries of his own nature by mere materiality. The all-doubting, and therefore always half-believing Bayle has said that *les actions des bêtes sont peut-être un des plus profonds abîmes sur quoi notre raison se puisse exercer.*

But here the Doctor acknowledged himself to be in doubt. That another state of existence there must be for every creature wherein there is the breath of life he was verily persuaded.* To that conclusion the whole tenor of his philosophy led him, and what he entertained as a philosophical opinion, acquired from a religious feeling something like the strength of faith. For if the whole of a brute animal's existence ended in this world, then it would follow that there are creatures born into it, for whom it had been better never to have been, than to endure the privations, pains, and wrongs and cruelties, inflicted upon them by human wickedness; and he would not, could not, dared not believe that any, even the meanest of God's creatures, has been created to undergo more of evil than of good — (where no power of choice was given) — much less to suffer unmingled evil, during its allotted term of existence. Yet this must be, if there were no state for animals after death.

A French speculator upon such things (I think it was P. Bougeant) felt this so strongly as to propose the strange hypothesis that fallen Angels underwent their punishment in the bodies of brutes, wherein they were incarnate and incarcerate as sentient, suffering and conscious spirits. The Doctor's theory of progressive life was liable to no such objections. It reconciled all seeming evil in the lower creation to the great system of benevolence. But still there remained a difficulty. Men being what they are, there were cases in which it seemed that the animal soul would be degraded instead of advanced by entering into the human form. For example, the Doctor considered the beast to be very often a much worthier animal than the butcher; the horse than the horse-jockey or the rider; the cock than the cock-fighter; the young whale than the man who harpoons the reasonable and dutiful creature when it suffers itself to be struck rather than forsake its wounded mother.

In all these cases indeed, a migration into some better variety of the civilised biped might be presumed, Archeus bringing good predispositions and an aptitude for improvement. But when he looked at a good dog — (in the best acceptation of the epithet), — a dog who has been humanised by human society, — who obeys and loves his master, pines during his illness, and dies upon his grave (the fact has frequently occurred), the Doctor declared his belief, and with a voice and look which told that he was speaking from his heart, that such a creature was ripe for a better world than this, and that in passing through the condition of humanity it might lose more than it could gain.

The price of a dog might not, among the Jews, be brought into the House of the Lord, "for any vow," for it was an abomination to the Lord. This inhibition occurs in the same part of the Levitical law which enjoins the Israelites not to deliver up to his master the servant who had escaped from him: and it is in the spirit of that injunction, and of those other parts of the Law which are so beautifully and feelingly humane, that their very tenderness may be received in proof of their divine origin. It looks upon the dog as standing to his master in far other relation than his horse or his ox or his ass,— as a creature connected with him by the moral ties of companionship, and fidelity, and friendship.

---

* But see Eccles. c. iii. v. 21.

CHAPTER CXLVI.

DANIEL DOVE VERSUS SENECA AND BEN JONSON. ORLANDO AND HIS HORSE AT RONCESVALLES. MR. BURCHELL. THE PRINCE OF ORANGE. THE LORD KEEPER GUILDFORD. REV. MR. HAWTAYN. DR. THOMAS JACKSON. THE ELDER SCALIGER. EVELYN. AN ANONYMOUS AMERICAN. WALTER LANDOR, AND CAROLINE BOWLES.

— Contented with an humble theme
I pour my stream of panegyric down
The vale of Nature, where it creeps and winds
Among her lovely works with a secure
And unambitious course, reflecting clear,
If not the virtues, yet the worth of brutes.

COWPER.

THE Doctor liked not Seneca when that philosopher deduced as a consequence from his definition of a benefit, that no gratitude can be due to beasts or senseless things: *nam, qui beneficium mihi daturus est*, he says, *debet non tantum prodesse, sed velle. Ideo nec mutis animalibus quidquam debetur; et quam multos è periculo velocitas equi rapuit! Nec arboribus; et quam multos æstu laborantes ramorum opacitas texit!* that is,—"for he who is about to render me a good service, not only ought to render it, but to intend it. Nothing, therefore, can be owed to dumb animals, and yet how many have the speed of a horse saved from danger! Nor to trees, and yet how many when suffering under the summer sun, have the thick boughs shaded!" To the same tenor Ben Jonson speaks. "Nothing is a courtesy," he says, "unless it be meant us, and that friendly and lovingly. We owe no thanks to rivers that they carry our boats; or winds that they be favouring, and fill our sails; or meats that they be nourishing; for these are what they are necessarily. Horses carry us, trees shade us, but they know it not."

What! our friend would say, do I owe thee nothing, Nobs, for the many times that thou hast carried me carefully and safely, through bad ways, in stormy weather, and in dark nights? Do I owe thee nothing for thy painful services, thy unhesitating obedience, thy patient fidelity? Do I owe thee nothing for so often breaking thy rest, when thou couldest not know for what urgent cause mine had been broken, nor wherefore I was compelled by duty to put thee to thy speed? Nobs, Nobs, if I did not acknowledge a debt of gratitude to thee, and discharge it as far as kind usage can tend to prolong thy days in comfort, I should deserve to be dropped as a colt in my next stage of existence, to be broken in by a rough rider, and broken down at last by hard usage in a hackney coach.

There is not a more touching passage in Italian poetry than that in which Pulci relates the death of Orlando's famous horse (his Nobs) in the fatal battle of Roncesvalles:

Vegliantin come Orlando in terra scese,
A piè del suo signor caduto è morto,
E inginocchiossi e licenzia gli chiese,
Quasi dicesse, io t' ho condotto a porto.
Orlando presto le braccia distese
A l' acqua, e cerca di dargli conforto,
Ma poi che pure il caval non si sente,
Si condolca molto pietosamente.

O Vegliantin, tu m' hai servito tanto:
O Vegliantin, dov' è la tua prodezza?
O Vegliantin, nessun si dia piu vanto;
O Vegliantin, venuta è l' ora sezza:
O Vegliantin, tu m' hai cresciuto il pianto;
O Vegliantin, tu non vuoi piu cavezza;
O Vegliantin, s' io ti feci mai torto,
Perdonami, ti priego, cosi morto.

Dice Turpin, che mi par maraviglia,
Che come Orlando perdonami disse,
Quel caval parve ch' aprisse le ciglia,
*E col capo e co gesti acconsentisse.**

A traveller in South Africa, Mr. Burchell, who was not less adventurous and persevering than considerate and benevolent, says that "nothing but the safety of the whole party, or the urgency of peculiar and inevitable circumstances, could ever, during his whole journey, induce him to forget the consideration due to his cattle, always regarded as faithful friends whose assistance was indispensable. There may be in the world," he says, "men who possess a nature so hard, as to think these sentiments misapplied; but I leave them to find, if they can, in the coldness of their own hearts, a satisfaction equal to that which I have enjoyed in paying a grateful attention to

* MORGANTE MAGGIORE.

animals by whose services I have been so much benefited."

The Prince of Orange would once have been surprised and taken in his tent by the Spaniards if his dog had not been more vigilant than his guards. Julian Romero planned and led this night attack upon the Prince's camp; the camisado was given so suddenly, as well as with such resolution, "that the place of arms took no alarm, until their fellows," says Sir Roger Williams, "were running in with the enemy in their tail; whereupon this dog, hearing a great noise, fell to scratching and crying, and withal leaped on the Prince's face, awaking him, being asleep, before any of his men." Two of his secretaries were killed hard by the tent, and "albeit the Prince lay in his arms, with a lacquey always holding one of his horses ready bridled, yet at the going out of his tent, with much ado he recovered his horse before the enemy arrived. One of his squires was slain taking horse presently after him, and divers of his servants which could not recover theirs, were forced to escape amongst the guards of foot. Ever after until the Prince's dying day, he kept one of that dog's race, — so did many of his friends and followers. The most or all of these dogs were white little hounds, with crooked noses, called camuses."

The Lord Keeper Guildford "bred all his horses, which came to the husbandry first colts, and from thence, as they were fit, were taken into his equipage; and as by age or accident they grew unfit for that service, they were returned to the place from whence they came, and there expired." This is one of the best traits which Roger North has related of his brother.

"A person," says Mr. Hawtayn, who was a good kind-hearted clergyman of the Church of England, "that can be insensible to the fidelity and love which dumb animals often express, must be lower in nature than they."

Grata e Natura in noi; fin dalla cuna
Gratitudine è impressa in uman core;
Ma d'un instinto tal questo è lo stile,
*Che lo seconda più, chi è piu gentile.**

* Carlo Maria Maggi.

The gentlest natures indeed are the best, and the best will be at the same time the most grateful and the most tender. "Even to behold a flourishing tree, first bereft of bark," says Dr. Jackson, "then of all the naked branches, yet standing, lastly the green trunk cut down and cast full of sap into the fire, would be an unpleasant spectacle to such as delighted in setting, pruning, or nourishing plants."

The elder Scaliger, as Evelyn tells us, never could convince Erasmus but that trees feel the first stroke of the axe; and Evelyn himself seems to have thought there was more probability in that opinion than he liked to allow. "The fall of a very aged oak," he says, "giving a crack like thunder, has been often heard at many miles' distance; nor do I at any time hear the groans without some emotion and pity, constrained, as I too often am, to fell them with much reluctancy." Mr. Downes, in his Letters from the Continent, says, "There is at this time a forest near Bolsena so highly venerated for its antiquity, that none of the trees are ever cut." †

One who, we are told, has since been honourably distinguished for metaphysical speculation, says, in a juvenile letter to the late American Bishop Hobart, "I sometimes converse a considerable time with a tree that in my infancy invited me to play under its cool and refreshing shade; and the old dwelling in which I have spent the greater part of my life, though at present unoccupied and falling into ruin, raises within me such a musing train of ideas, that I know not whether it be pleasing or painful. Now whether it arise from an intimate association of ideas, or from some qualities in the insensible objects themselves to create an affection, I shall not pretend to determine; but certain it is that the love we bear for objects incapable of making a return, seems always more disinterested, and frequently affords us more lasting happiness than even that which we feel toward rational creatures."

† "Stat vetus, et multos *incædua* silva per annos," &c. Ovid.

But never by any author, ancient or modern, in verse or prose, has the feeling which ascribes sentience as well as life to the vegetable world, been more deliciously described than by Walter Landor, when, speaking of sweet scents, he says,

They bring me tales of youth, and tones of love ;
And 'tis and ever was my wish and way
To let all flowers live freely and all die,
Whene'er their Genius bids their souls depart,
Among their kindred in their native place.
I never pluck the rose ; the violet's head
Hath shaken with my breath upon its bank
And not reproach'd me ; the ever sacred cup
Of the pure lily hath between my hands
Felt safe, unsoil'd, nor lost one grain of gold.

These verses are indeed worthy of their author, when he is most worthy of himself. And yet Caroline Bowles's sweet lines will lose nothing by being read after them.

THE DEATH OF THE FLOWERS.

How happily, how happily the flowers die away !
Oh ! could we but return to earth as easily as they ;
Just live a life of sunshine, of innocence and bloom,
Then drop without decrepitude or pain into the tomb.

The gay and glorious creatures ! " they neither toil nor spin,"
Yet lo ! what goodly raiment they're all apparelled in ;
No tears are on their beauty, but dewy gems more bright
Than ever brow of Eastern Queen endiademed with light.

The young rejoicing creatures ! their pleasures never pall,
Nor lose in sweet contentment, because so free to all ;
The dew, the shower, the sunshine ; the balmy blessed air,
Spend nothing of their freshness, though all may freely share.

The happy careless creatures ! of time they take no heed ;
Nor weary of his creeping, nor tremble at his speed ;
Nor sigh with sick impatience, and wish the light away ;
Nor when 'tis gone, cry dolefully, " Would God that it were day."

And when their lives are over, they drop away to rest,
Unconscious of the penal doom, on holy Nature's breast ;
No pain have they in dying, no shrinking from decay.
Oh ! could we but return to earth as easily as they !

CHAPTER CXLVII.

OLD TREES. SHIPS. FIGURATIVE LANGUAGE. LIFE AND PASSIONS ASCRIBED TO INANIMATE OBJECTS. FETISH WORSHIP. A LORD CHANCELLOR AND HIS GOOSE.

Ce que j'en ay escrit, c'est pour une curiosité, qui plaira possible à aucuns : et non possible aux autres.

BRANTOME.

" CONSIDER," says Plutarch, in that precious volume of Philemon Holland's translating, which was one of the elder Daniel's treasures, and which the Doctor valued accordingly as a relic, " consider whether our forefathers have not permitted excessive ceremonies and observations in these cases, even for an exercise and studious meditation of thankfulness ; as namely, when they reverenced so highly the Oaks bearing acorns as they did. Certes the Athenians had one Fig-tree which they honoured by the name of the holy and sacred Fig-Tree ; and they expressly forbade to cut down the Mulberry-tree. For these ceremonies, I assure you, do not make men inclined to superstition as some think, but frame and train us to gratitude and sociable humanity one toward another, whenas we are thus reverently affected to such things as these that have no soul nor sense." But Plutarch knew that there were certain Trees to which something more than sense or soul was attributed by his countrymen.

There was a tradition at Corinth which gave a different account of the death of Pentheus from that in the Metamorphoses, where it is said that he was beholding the rites of the Bacchanals, from an open eminence surrounded by the woods, when his mother espied him, and in her madness led on the frantic women by whom he was torn to pieces. But the tradition at Corinth was that he climbed a tree for the purpose of seeing their mysteries, and was discovered amid its branches ; and that the Pythian Oracle afterwards enjoined the Corinthians to find out this Tree, and pay divine honours to it, as to a God. The special motive here was to impress the people with an awful respect for the Mysteries, none being felt for any part of the popular religion.

Old Trees, without the aid of an Oracle to consecrate them, seem to have been some of the most natural objects of that contemplative and melancholy regard which easily passes into superstitious veneration. No longer ago than during the peace of Amiens a Frenchman * describing the woods on the banks of the Senegal, says, *On éprouve*

* GOLBERRY.

un doux ravissement en contemplant ces nobles productions d'une nature tranquille, libre et presque vierge; car là elle est encore respectée, et la vieillesse des beaux arbres y est pour ainsi dire l'objet d'un culte. Mon ame reconnoissante des émotions qu'elle ressentait, remerciait le Créateur d'avoir fait naître ces magnifiques végétables sur un sol où elles avaient pu croitre indépendantes et paisibles, et conserver ces formes originales et naïves que l'art sait alterer, mais qu'il ne saura jamais imiter.—

Quelques-uns des sites qu'on rencontre etalent les attraits et les grâces d'une nature virginale; dans d'autres, on admire ce que l'âge, de sa plus grande force, peut avoir de plus imposant et de plus auguste; et d'antiques forêts, dont les arbres ont une grosseur et une élévation qui attestent leur grand âge, excitent une admiration mêlée de respect; et ces prodigieux végêtaux encore verts, encore beaux, après une vie de tant de siecles, semblent vouloir nous apprendre, que dans ces contrées solitaires et fertiles, la nature vit toujours, et ne vieillit jamais.

There are Tribes among the various races in the Philippines who are persuaded that the souls of their ancestors use old trees as their habitations, and therefore it is deemed a sacrilege to cut one down. The Lezgis used to erect pillars under the boughs of decayed Oaks to support them as long as possible; *Murlooz* is the name which they give to such spurs, or stay-pillars.

The Rector of Manafon, Mr. Walter Davies, in his View of the Agriculture and Domestic Economy of North Wales, says, "Strangers have oftentimes listened with attention to Gentlemen of the County of Montgomery inquiring anxiously into the conduct and fate of the Windsor Castle, the Impregnable, the Brunswick, and other men of war, in some particular naval engagements; and were led to imagine that they had some near and dear relations holding important commissions on board; but upon further inquiry, found the ground of this curiosity to be no other than that such ships had been partly built of timber that had grown upon their estates; as if the inanimate material contained some magic virtue." The good Rector might have perceived in what he censures one indication of that attachment to our native soil, on which much of the security of states depends, much of the happiness of individuals, and not a little of their moral and intellectual character.

But indeed the same cause which renders personification a common figure not only with poets and orators, but in all empassioned and even in ordinary speech, leads men frequently both to speak and act as if they ascribed life and consciousness to inanimate things.

When the Cid Campeador recovered from the Infantes of Carrion his two swords Colada and Tizona, "his whole frame," says the Chronicler, "rejoiced, and he smiled from his heart. And he laid them upon his lap and said, "Ah my swords, Colada and Tizona, truly may I say of you that you are the best swords in Spain; and I won you, for I did not get you either by buying or by barter. I gave ye in keeping to the Infantes of Carrion that they might do honour to my daughters with ye. But ye were not for them! They kept ye hungry, and did not feed ye with flesh as ye were wont to be fed. Well is it for you that ye have escaped that thraldom and are come again to my hands."

The same strong figure occurs in the Macaronea,

Gaude, Baldus ait, mi brande! cibaberis; ecce
Carnis et sanguis tibi præsententur abunde.

The Greek Captain who purchases a vessel which he is to command himself takes possession of it by a ceremony which is called espousing the ship; on this occasion he suspends in it a laurel crown as a symbol of the marriage, and a bag of garlic as a preservative against tempests.—In the year 1793, the ship Darius belonging to a Hindoo, or more probably, as may be inferred from the name, a Parsee owner, was run ashore off Malacca by its Commander Captain Laughton, to save it from falling into the hands of a French Privateer. The Captain and his Officers, when they had thus disappointed the enemy, succeeded afterwards, by great exertion and great skill, in getting the vessel off, and brought it safely home to Bombay; where the grateful owner, thinking the Ship itself was entitled to some signal mark of acknowledgment, treated it with a complete ablution, which was performed not with water, but with sugar and milk. —

Our own sailors sometimes ascribe consciousness and sympathy to their ship. It is a common expression with them that "she behaves well;" and they persuade themselves that an English Man of War, by reason of its own good will, sails faster in pursuit of a Frenchman than at any other time. Poor old Captain Atkins was firmly possessed with this belief. On such occasions he would talk to his ship, as an Arabian to his horse, urge and intreat her to exert herself and put forth all her speed, and promise to reward her with a new coat of paint as soon as they should get into harbour. —"Who," says Fuller, "can without pity or pleasure behold that trusty vessel which carried Sir Francis Drake about the World?" — So naturally are men led to impute something like vitality to so great a work of human formation, that persons connected with the shipping trade talk of the average *life* of a ship, which in the present state of our naval affairs is stated to be twenty-two years. —

At one of the Philosophers' Yearly-Meetings it was said that every Engine-man had more or less pride in his engine, just as a sailor had in his ship. We heard then of the *duty* of an engine, and of how much *virtue* resides in a given quantity of coals. This is the language of the Mines, so easily does a figurative expression pass into common speech. The *duty* of an engine has been taken at raising 50 millions of cubic-feet of water one foot in an hour; some say 100 millions, some 120; but the highest duty which the reporter had ascertained was 90 millions, the lowest 70. And the *virtue* in a bushel of coals is sufficient to raise 125 millions of cubic-feet of water one foot, being from 800 to 1070 at the cost of one farthing. No one will think this hard duty for the Engine, but all must allow it to be cheap virtue in the coals.

This, however, is merely an example of the change which words undergo in the currency of speech as their original stamp is gradually effaced: what was metaphorical becomes trivial; and this is one of the causes by which our language has been corrupted, more perhaps than any other, recourse being had both in prose and verse to forced and fantastic expressions as substitutes for the freshness and strength that have been lost. Strong feelings and strong fancy are liable to a more serious perversion.

M. de Custine, writing from Mont Anvert, in the rhapsodical part of his travels, exclaims, *Qu'on ne me parle plus de nature morte; on sent ici que la Divinité est partout, et que les pierres sont pénétrées comme nous-mêmes d'une puissance créatricé! Quand on me dit que les rochers sont insensibles, je crois entendre un enfant soutenir que l'aiguille d'une montre ne marche pas, parce qu'il ne la voit pas se mouvoir.*

It is easy to perceive that feelings of this kind may imperceptibly have led to the worship of any remarkable natural objects, such as Trees, Forests, Mountains, Springs, and Rivers, as kindred feelings have led to the adoration of Images and of Relics. Court de Gebelin has even endeavoured to show that Fetish worship was not without some reasonable cause in its origin. The author of a treatise *Du Culte des Dieux Fétiches, ou Parallèle de l'ancienne Religion de l'Egypte avec la Religion actuelle de la Nigritie*, had asserted that this absurd superstition originated in fear. But Court de Gebelin asks, "why not from gratitude and admiration as well? Are not these passions as capable of making Gods as Fear? Is not experience itself in accord with us here? Do not all savage nations admit of Two Principles, the one Good, who ought not to be feared, the other Evil, to whom sacrifices must be offered in order to avert the mischief in which he delights? If fear makes them address their homage to the one, it has no part in the feeling which produces it toward the other. Which then of these sentiments has led to Fetish worship? Not fear, considered as the sentiment which moves us to do nothing that might displease a Being whom we regard as our superior, and as the source of our happiness; for Fétishes cannot be regarded in this light. Will it then be fear considered as the sentiment of our own weakness, filling us with terror, and forcing us to seek the protection of a Being more powerful than ourselves and capable of protecting us? But how could any such fear have led to the worship of Fetishes? How could a Savage, seized with terror, ever have believed that an onion, a stone, a flower, water, a tree, a mouse, a cat, &c. could be his protector and secure him against all that he apprehended? I know that fear does not reason, but it is not to be understood in this sense; we frequently fear something without knowing why; but when we address ourselves to a Protector we always know why; it is in the persuasion that he can defend us, a persuasion which has always a foundation, — a basis. But in Fetish worship where is the motive? What is there to afford confidence against alarm? Who has said that the Fetish is superior to man? — It is impossible to conceive any one so blockish, so stupid, so terrified as to imagine that inanimate things like these are infinitely above him, much more powerful than himself, in a state to understand his wants, his evils, his fears, his sufferings, and to deliver him from all in acknowledgment of the offering which he makes to them.

"Moreover, the Fetish is not used till it has been consecrated by the Priest: this proves an opinion in the savage, that the Fetish of itself cannot protect him; but that he may be made by other influence to do so, and that influence is exercised by the Priest in the act of consecration." Court de Gebelin argues therefore that this superstition arose from the primary belief in a Supreme Being on whom we are altogether dependent, who was to be honoured by certain ceremonies directed by the Priest, and who was to be propitiated by revering these things whereby it had pleased him to benefit mankind; and by consecrating some of them as pledges of future benefits to be received from him, and of his presence among his Creatures who serve him and implore his protection. But in process of time it was forgotten that this was only a symbolic allegory of the Divine Presence, and ignorant nations who could no longer give a reason for their belief, continued the practice from imitation and habit.

This is ascribing too much to system, too little to superstition and priestcraft. The name Fetish, though used by the Negroes themselves, is known to be a corrupt application of the Portuguese word for Witchcraft, *feitiço;* the vernacular name is *Bossum* or *Bossifoe.* Upon the Gold Coast every nation has its own, every village, every family, and every individual. A great hill, a rock any way remarkable for its size or shape, or a large Tree, is generally the national Fetish. The king's is usually the largest tree in his country. They who choose or change one take the first thing they happen to see, however worthless. A stick, a stone, the bone of a beast, bird or fish, unless the worshipper takes a fancy for something of better appearance, and chooses a horn or the tooth of some large animal. The ceremony of consecration he performs himself, assembling his family, washing the new object of his devotion, and sprinkling them with the water. He has thus a household or personal God in which he has as much faith as the Papist in his relics, and with as much reason. Barbot says that some of the Europeans on that coast not only encouraged their slaves in this superstition, but believed in it, and practised it themselves.

Thus low has man sunk in his fall. The debasement began with the worship of the Heavenly Bodies. When he had once departed from that of his Creator, his religious instinct became more and more corrupted, till at length no object was too vile for his adoration; as in a certain state of disease the appetite turns from wholesome food, and longs for what would at other times be loathsome.

The Negro Fetishes are just such objects as, according to the French Jesuits, the Devil used to present to the Canadian Indians, to bring them good luck in fishing, hunting, gaming, and such traffic as they carried on. This may probably mean that they dreamt of such things; for in dreams many superstitions have originated, and great use has been made of them in Priestcraft.

The same kind of superstition has appeared in different ages and in different parts of the World, among the most civilised nations and the rudest savages *, and among the educated as well as the ignorant. The belief in Omens prevails among us still, and will long continue to prevail, notwithstanding national schools, cheap literature and Societies for promoting knowledge.

A late Lord Chancellor used to travel with a Goose in his carriage, and consult it on all occasions; whether according to the rules of Roman augury I know not, nor whether he decided causes by it; but the causes might have been as well decided if he did. The Goose was his Fetish. It was not Lord Brougham,—Lord Brougham was his own Goose while he held the Seals; but it was the only Lord Chancellor in our times who resembled him in extraordinary genius, and as extraordinary an unfitness for his office. One of the most distinguished men of the age, who has left a reputation which will be as lasting as it is great, was, when a boy, in constant fear of a very able but unmerciful schoolmaster; and in the state of mind which that constant fear produced he fixed upon a great Spider for his Fetish, and used every day to pray to it that he might not be flogged.

* Omens from birds are taken in the island of Borneo with as much faith as they were amongst the Greeks or Romans. The Rajah Brooke says, "the Singè Dyacks, like the others, attend to the warning of birds of various sorts, some birds being in more repute than others," &c. &c. — *The Expedition to Borneo of H. M. S. Dido*, vol. i. p. 232.

CHAPTER EXTRAORDINARY.

PROCEEDINGS AT A BOOK CLUB. THE AUTHOR ACCUSED OF "LESE DELICATESSE," OR WHAT IS CALLED AT COURT "TUM-TI-TEE." HE UTTERS A MYSTERIOUS EXCLAMATION, AND INDIGNANTLY VINDICATES HIMSELF.

Rem profecto mirabilem, longeque stupendam, rebusque veris veriorem describo. HIERONYMUS RADIOLENSIS.

A CIRCUMSTANCE has come to my knowledge so remarkable in itself and affecting me so deeply, that on both accounts I feel it necessary to publish a Chapter Extraordinary on the occasion.

There is a certain Book-Club, or Society, (no matter where) in which the Volumes of this Opus have been regularly ordered as they appeared, and regularly perused, to the edification of many Readers, the admiration of more, and the amusement of all. But I am credibly informed that an alarm was excited in that select literary Circle by a Chapter in the fourth volume †, and that the said volume was not allowed to circulate by the Managing Directors or Committee, of the said Book Club, till the said Chapter had been exscinded, that is to say, cut out.

Aballiboozo!

When a poor wretch fell into the hands of that hellish Tribunal which called itself the Holy Office, the Inquisitors always began by requiring him to tell them what he was accused of; and they persisted in this course of examination time after time, till by promises and threats, long suspense, and solitary confinement, with the occasional aid of the rack, they had extorted from him matter of accusation against himself and as many of his friends, relations and acquaintances, as they could induce, or compel, or entrap him to name. Even under such a judicial process I should never have been able to discover what Chapter in this Opus could have been thought to require an operation, which, having the fear of the expurgatorial scissars before my eyes, I must not venture to men-

† See *suprà*, p. 339., of this edition.

tion here, by its appropriate name, though it is a Dictionary word, and the use of it is in this sense strictly technical. My ignorance, however, has been enlightened, and I have been made acquainted with what in the simplicity of my heart I never could have surmised.

The Chapter condemned to that operation, the chapter which has been not bisked, but semiramised, is the Hundred and thirty-sixth Chapter, concerning the Pedigree and Birth of Nobs; but whether the passage which called forth this severe sentence from the Censors were that in which Moses and Miss Jenny, the Sire and Dam of Nobs, are described as meeting in a field near Knavesmire Heath, like *Dido dux et Trojanus;* or whether it were the part where the consequences of that meeting are related as coming unexpectedly to light, in a barn between Doncaster and Adwick-in-the-Street, my informant was not certain.

From another quarter I have been assured, that the main count in the indictment was upon the story of *Le Cheval de Pierre, et les Officiers Municipaux.* This I am told it was which alarmed the Literary Sensitives. The sound of the footsteps of the Marble Statue in Don Juan upon the boards of the stage never produced a more awful sense of astonishment in that part of the audience who were fixed all eyes and ears upon its entrance, than this *Cheval de Pierre* produced among the Board of Expurgators. After this I ought not to be surprised if the Publishers were to be served with a notice that the Lord Mayors of London and York, and the simple Mayors of every corporate town in England, reformed or unreformed, having a Magistrate so called, whether gentle or simple, had instituted proceedings against them for *Scandalum Magnatum.* This, however, I have the satisfaction of knowing, that Miss Graveairs smiled in good humour when she heard the Chapter read; the only serious look put on was at the quotation from Pindar, as if suspecting there might be something in the Greek which was not perfectly consistent with English notions of propriety. Nothing, however, could be more innocent than that Greek. And, even after what has passed, she would agree with me that this Chapter, which made the Elders blush, is one which Susanna would have read as innocently as it was written.

Nevertheless I say, *O tempora! O mores!* uttering the words exultantly, not in exprobration. I congratulate the age and the British Public. I congratulate my Countrymen, my Country-women, and my Country-children. I congratulate Young England upon the March of Modesty! How delightful that it should thus keep pace with the March of Intellect! *Redeunt Saturnia regna.* In these days Liberality and Morality appear hand-in-hand upon the stage like the Two Kings of Brentford; and Piety and Profit have kissed each other at religious Meetings.

We have already a Family Shakespeare; and it cannot be supposed that the hint will always be disregarded which Mr. Matthew Gregory Lewis introduced so properly some forty years ago into his then celebrated novel called the Monk, for a Family Bible, upon the new plan of removing all passages that could be thought objectionable on the score of indelicacy. We may look to see Mr. Thomas Moore's Poems adapted to the use of Families; and Mr. Murray cannot do less than provide the Public with a Family Byron.

It may, therefore, be matter of grave consideration for me whether, under all circumstances, it would not be highly expedient to prepare a semiramised edition of this Opus, under the Title of the Family Doctor. It may be matter for consultation with my Publishers, to whose opinion, as founded on experience and a knowledge of the public taste, an author will generally find it prudent to defer. Neither by them or me would it be regarded as an objection that the title might mislead many persons, who, supposing that the "Family Doctor" and the "Family Physician" meant the same kind of Book, would order the Opus, under a mistaken notion that it was a new and consequently improved work, similar to Dr. Buchan's, formerly well known as a stock-book. This would be no objection I say, but, on the contrary, an advantage to all parties. For a book which directs people how to physic themselves ought to be entitled Every Man his own Poisoner, because it cannot possibly teach them how to discriminate between the resemblant symptoms of different diseases. Twice fortunate, therefore, would that person have reason to think him or herself, who, under such a misapprehension of its title, should purchase the Family Doctor!

Ludicrous mistakes of this kind have sometimes happened. Mr. Haslewood's elaborate and expensive edition of the Mirror for Magistrates was ordered by a gentleman in the Commission of the Peace, not a hundred miles from the Metropolis; he paid for it the full price, and his unfortunate Worship was fain to take what little he could get for it from his Bookseller under such circumstances, rather than endure the mortification of seeing it in his book-case.* A lady who had a true taste as well as a great liking for poetry, ordered an Essay on Burns for the Reading Society of which she was a member. She opened the book expecting to derive much pleasure from a critical disquisition on the genius of one of her favourite Poets; and behold it proved to be an Essay on Burns and Scalds by a Surgeon!

But in this case it would prove an Agreeable Surprise instead of a disappointment; and if the intention had been to mislead, and thereby entrap the purchaser, the end might be pleaded, according to the convenient morality of the age, as justifying the means. Lucky indeed were the patient who sending for Morison's Pills should be supplied with Tom D'Urfey's in their stead; happy man would be his dole who when he had made up his mind in dismal resolution to a dreadful course of drastics, should find that gelastics had been substituted, not of the Sardonian kind, but composed of the most innocent and salutiferous ingredients, gently and genially alterative, mild in their operation, and safe and sure in their effects.

On that score, therefore, there could be no objection to the publication of a Family Doctor. But believing as I believe, or rather, knowing as I know, that the Book is free from any such offence,

> *— mal cupiera alli*
> *tal aspid en tales flores;* †

maintaining that it is in this point immaculate, which I will maintain as confidently because as justly, and as publicly were it needful, (only that my bever must be closed) as Mr. Dymock at the approaching Coronation will maintain Queen Victoria's right to the Crown of these Kingdoms (God save the Queen!),—it is impossible that I should consent to a measure which must seem like acknowledging the justice of a charge at once ridiculous and wrongful.

> — I must not disesteem
> My rightful cause for being accused, nor must
> Forsake myself, tho I were left of all.
> Fear cannot make my innocence unjust
> Unto itself, to give my Truth the fall.‡

The most axiomatic of English Poets has said

> Do not forsake yourself; for they that do,
> Offend and teach the world to leave them too.

Of the Book itself, — (the Opus) — I can say truly, as South said of the Sermon which he preached in 1662 before the Lord Mayor and Aldermen of the city of London, "the subject is inoffensive, harmless, and innocent as the state of innocence itself;" and of the particular chapter, that it is "suitable to the immediate design, and to the genius of the book." And in saying this I call to mind the words of Nicolas Perez, el Setabiense; —*el amor propio es nuestro enemigo mas perjudicial; es dificil acabar con el, por lo mismo un sabio le compara à la camisa, que es el ultimo de los vestidos que nos quitamos.*

Bear witness *incorrupta Fides, nudaque Veritas!* that I seek not to cover myself with what the Spaniard calls Self-Love's last Shirt; for I am no more guilty of *Lese Modestie* than of *Lese Majesté.* If there were a Court of Delicacy as there has been a

* Whoever purchased Southey's copy will find this anecdote in his own handwriting, on the fly leaf. I transcribed it from thence into my own copy many years ago.

† Lope de Vega. ‡ Daniel.

Court of Honour, a Court Modest as there is a Court Martial, I would demand a trial, and in my turn arraign my arraigners,

Porque en este limpio trigo
*Siembren zizaña y estrago.**

It is said in the very interesting and affecting Memoir of Mr. Smedley's Life that he had projected with Mr. Murray "a castigated edition of the Faery Queen." He was surprised, says the biographer, "to find how many passages there were in this the most favourite poem of his youth, which a father's acuter vision and more sensitive delicacy discovered to be unfit for the eyes of his daughters." It appears, too, that he had actually performed the task; but that "Mr. Murray altered his opinion as to the expediency of the publication, and he found to his annoyance that his time had been employed to no purpose."

Poor Smedley speaks thus of the project in one of his letters. "I am making the Faery Queen a poem which may be admitted into *family* reading, by certain omissions, by modernising the spelling and by appending, where necessary, brief glossarial foot-notes. I read Spenser so very early and made him so much a part of the furniture of my mind, that until I had my attention drawn to him afresh I had utterly forgotten how much he required the pruning-knife, how utterly impossible it is that he should be read aloud: and I cannot but think that when fitted for general perusal, he will become more attractive by a new coat and waistcoat. If we were to print Shakespeare, and Beaumont and Fletcher, or even Milton, *literatim* from the first editions, the spelling would deter many readers. Strange to say, when Southey was asked some time ago whether he would undertake the task, he said, 'No, I shall print every word of him!' And he has done so in a single volume. Can he have daughters? Or any who, like my Mary, delight in such portions as they are permitted to open?"

Did Southey say so? — Why then, well said Southey! And it is very like him; for he is not given to speak, as his friends the Portuguese say, *enfarinhadamente* — which is, being interpreted, mealy-mouthedly. Indeed his moral and intellectual constitution must be much feebler than I suppose it to be, if his daughters are not "permitted to open" any book in his library. He must have been as much astonished to hear that the Faery Queen was unfit for their perusal as he could have been when he saw it gravely asserted by an American Professor, Critic and Doctor of Divinity, that his Life of Wesley was composed in imitation of the Iliad!

Scott felt like Southey upon this subject, and declared that he would never deal with Dryden as Saturn dealt with his father Uranus. Upon such publications as the Family Shakespeare he says, — "I do not say but that it may be very proper to select correct passages for the use of Boarding-Schools and Colleges, being sensible no improper ideas can be suggested in these seminaries unless they are introduced or smuggled under the beards and ruffs of our old dramatists. But in making an edition of a Man of Genius's Works for libraries and collections, (and such I conceive a complete edition of Dryden to be), I must give my author as I find him, and will not tear out the page even to get rid of the blot, little as I like it. Are not the pages of Swift, and even of Pope, larded with indecency and often of the most disgusting kind, and do we not see them upon all shelves, and dressing-tables and in all boudoirs? Is not Prior the most indecent of tale-tellers, not even excepting La Fontaine? and how often do we see his works in female hands. In fact, it is not passages of ludicrous indelicacy that corrupt the manners of a people; it is the sonnets which a prurient genius like Master Little sings *virginibus puerisque*, — it is the sentimental slang, half lewd, half methodistic, that debauches the understanding, inflames the sleeping passions, and prepares the reader to give way as soon as a tempter appears."

How could Mr. Smedley have allowed himself to be persuaded that a poem like the Faery Queen which he had made from early

* Lope de Vega.

youth "a part of the furniture of his own mind," should be more injurious to others than it had proved to himself? It is one of the books which Wesley in the plan which he drew up for those young Methodists who designed to go through a course of academical learning, recommended to students of the second year. Mr. Todd has noticed this in support of his own just estimate of this admirable poet. "If," says he, "our conceptions of Spenser's mind may be taken from his poetry, I shall not hesitate to pronounce him entitled to our warmest approbation and regard for his gentle disposition, for his friendly and grateful conduct, for his humility, for his exquisite tenderness, and above all for his piety and morality. To these amiable points a fastidious reader may perhaps object some petty inadvertencies; yet can he never be so ungrateful as to deny the efficacy which Spenser's general character gives to his writings, — as to deny that Truth and Virtue are graceful and attractive, when the road to them is pointed out by such a guide. Let it always be remembered that this excellent Poet inculcates those impressive lessons, by attending to which the gay and the thoughtless may be timely induced to treat with scorn and indignation the allurements of intemperance and illicit pleasure."

When Izaak Walton published "Thealma and Clearchus," a pastoral history written long since in smooth and easy verse by John Chalkhill, Esq., he described him in the Title page as "An Acquaintant and Friend of Edmund Spenser." He says of him "that he was in his time a man generally known and as well beloved, for he was humble and obliging in his behaviour, a gentleman, a scholar, very innocent and prudent, and indeed his whole life was useful, quiet, and virtuous." Yet to have been the friend of Edmund Spenser was considered by the biographer of Hooker and Donne and Bishop Sanderson and George Herbert, as an honourable designation for this good man, a testimonial of his worth to posterity, long after both Chalkhill and Spenser had been called to their reward.

It was well that Mr. Murray gave up the project of a Family Faery Queen. Mr. Smedley when employed upon such a task ought to have felt that he was drawing upon himself something like Ham's malediction.

With regard to another part of these projected emendations there is a fatal objection. There is no good reason why the capricious spelling of the early editions should be scrupulously and pedantically observed in Shakespeare, Milton, or any author of their respective times; — no reason why words which retain the same acceptation, and are still pronounced in the same manner, should not now be spelt according to the received orthography. Spenser is the only author for whom an exception must be made from this obvious rule. Malone was wrong when he asserted that the language of the Faery Queen was that of the age in which Spenser lived; and Ben Jonson was not right when, saying that Spenser writ no language, he assigned as the cause for this, his "affecting the Ancients." The diction, or rather dialect, which Spenser constructed, was neither like that of his predecessors, nor of his contemporaries. Camoens also wrote a language of his own, and thereby did for the Portuguese tongue the same service which was rendered to ours by the translators of the Bible. But the Portuguese Poet, who more than any other of his countrymen refined a language which was then in the process of refining, attempted to introduce nothing but what entirely accorded with its character, and with the spirit of that improvement which was gradually taking place: whereas both the innovations and renovations which Spenser introduced were against the grain. Yet such is the magic of his verse, that the Faery Queen if modernised, even though the structure of its stanza — (the best which has ever been constructed) — were preserved, would lose as much as Homer loses in the best translation.

Mr. Wordsworth has modernised one of Chaucer's Poems with "no farther deviation from the original than was necessary for the fluent reading and instant understanding of the author, supplying the place of whatever he removed as obsolete with as little incongruity as possible." This he has done very skilfully. But the same skill could not be exercised upon the Faery Queen with the same success. The peculiarities of language there are systematic; to modernise the spelling, as Mr. Smedley proposed, would in very many cases interfere with the rhyme, and thus dislocate the stanza. The task, therefore, would have been extremely difficult; it would have been useless, because no one who is capable of enjoying that delightful Poem ever found any difficulty in understanding its dialect, and it would have been mischievous, because it would have destroyed the character of the Poem. And this in the expectation of rendering Spenser more attractive by a new coat and waistcoat! Spenser of whom it has been truly said that more poets have sprung from him than from all other English writers; Spenser by whom Cowley tells us he was made a Poet; of whom Milton acknowledged to Dryden that he was his original; and in whom Pope says "there is something that pleases one as strongly in one's old age as it did in one's youth. I read the Faery Queen," he proceeds, "when I was about twelve, with a vast deal of delight, and I think it gave me as much when I read it over about a year or two ago."

No, a new suit of clothes would not render Spenser more attractive, not even if to a coat and waistcoat of Stultz's fabric, white satin pantaloons were added, such as the handsomest and best dressed of modern patriots, novelists and poets was known by on the public walk of a fashionable watering-place.

Save us from the Ultradelicates and the Extrasuperfines! for if these are to prevail—

What can it avail
To drive forth a snail
Or to make a sail
Of a herring's tail?
To rhyme or to rail,
To write or to indite
Either for delight
Or else for despite?
Or books to compile
Of divers manner of style,
Vice to revile,
And sin to exile,
To teach or to preach
As reason will reach?

So said Skelton three centuries ago, and for myself I say once more what Skelton would have been well pleased to have heard said by any one.

Aballiboozo!

Dear Author, says one of those Readers who deserve to be pleased, and whom, therefore, there is a pleasure in pleasing, dear Author! may I not ask wherefore you have twice in this Chapter Extraordinary given us part of your long mysterious word, and only part, instead of setting it before us at full length?

Dear Reader! you may; and you may also ask unblamed whether a part of the word is not as good, that is to say, as significant, as the whole? You shall have a full and satisfactory answer in the next Chapter.

CHAPTER CXLVIII.

WHEREIN A SUBSTITUTE FOR OATHS, AND OTHER PASSIONATE INTERJECTIONS IS EXEMPLIFIED.

What have we to do with the times? We cannot cure 'em:
Let them go on: when they are swoln with surfeits
They'll burst and stink: Then all the world shall smell 'em.

BEAUMONT AND FLETCHER.

ONCE more, Reader, I commence with

Aballiboozobanganorribo;

Do not suppose that I am about to let thee into the mysteries of that great decasyllabon! *Questo è bene uno de' piu profondi segreti ch' abbia tutto il mondo, e quasi nessuno il sa; e sia certo che ad altri nol direi giammai.** No, Reader! not if I were before the High Court of Parliament, and the House of Commons should exert all its inquisitorial and tyrannical powers to extort it from me, would I let the secret pass that ἕρκος ὀδόντων within which my little trowel of speech has learned not to be an unruly member. I would behave as magnanimously as Sir Abraham Bradley King did upon a not-

* BIBBIENA.

altogether dissimilar occasion. Sir Abraham might have said of his secret as Henry More says of the Epicurean Philosophy, "Truly it is a very venerable secret; and not to be uttered or communicated but by some old Silenus lying in his obscure grot or cave; nor that neither but upon due circumstances, and in a right humour, when one may find him with his veins swelled out with wine, and his garland fallen off from his head through his heedless drowsiness. Then if some young Chromis and Mnasylus, especially assisted by a fair and forward Ægle, that by way of a love-frolic will leave the tracts of their fingers in the blood of mulberries on the temples and forehead of this aged Satyr, while he sleeps dog-sleep, and will not seem to see for fear he forfeit the pleasure of his feeling, — then I say, if these young lads importune him enough, — he will utter it in a higher strain than ever."

But by no such means can the knowledge of my profounder mystery be attained. I will tell thee, however, good Reader, that the word itself, apart from all considerations of its mystical meaning, serves me for the same purpose to which the old tune of Lilliburlero was applied by our dear Uncle Toby, — *our* dear Uncle I say, for is he not *your* Uncle Toby, gentle Reader? yours as well as mine, if you are worthy to hold him in such relationship; and so by that relationship, you and I are Cousins.

The Doctor had learned something from his Uncle William, which he used to the same effect, though not in the same way. William Dove in that capacious memory of his, into which everything that he heard was stored, and out of which nothing was lost, had among the fragments of old songs and ballads which he had picked up, sundry burdens or choruses, as unmeaning as those which O'Keefe used to introduce in some of the songs of his farces, always with good farcical effect. Uncle Toby's favourite was one of them;

> Lilli burlero bullen a-la;
> Lero lero, lilli burlero, lero lero, bullen a-la;
> Lero lero, lilli burlero, lero lero, bullen a-la.

Without knowing that it was designed as an insult to the French, he used to say and sing in corrupted form,

> Suum, mun, hey no nonny,
> Dolphin, my boy, my boy,
> Sessa, let him trot by.

Another was that from the ballad in honour of the Earl of Essex, called Queen Elizabeth's Champion, which Johnson quoted in the Isle of Sky; and Johnson is not the only omnivorous reader in whose memory it has stuck;

> Raderer too, tandaro tee
> Radarer, tandorer, tan do ree.

And he had treasured up the elder fragment,

> Martin Swart and his men.
> Sodledum, sodledum,
> Martin Swart and his men,
> Sodledum bell,
> With hey troly loly lo, whip here Jack,
> Alumbeck, sodledum, syllerum ben,
> Martin Swart and his merry men.

He had also this relic of the same age, relating as it seems to some now forgotten hero of the strolling minstrels,

> Rory-bull Joyse,
> Rumble down, tumble down, hey, go now now.

Here is another, for he uttered these things "as he had eaten ballads."

> A story strange I will you tell,
> But not so strange as true,
> Of a woman that danced upon the rope,
> And so did her husband too:
> With a dildo, dildo, dildo,
> With a dildo, dildo, dee.

And he had one of Irish growth, which he sometimes tacked on to this last for the rhyme's sake

> Callino, callino,
> Callino, castore me,
> Era ëe, Era ëe
> Loo loo, loo loo lee.

All these were favourites with little Daniel; and so especially for his name's sake, was

> My juggy, my puggy, my honey, my coney,
> My deary, my love, my dove.

There was another with which and the Dovean use thereof, it is proper that the reader should now be made acquainted, for it would otherwise require explanation, when he meets with it hereafter. This was the one which, when William Dove trotted little Daniel upon his knee, he used to sing more frequently than any other, because the child, then in the most winning stage of childhood, liked it best of all, and it went to the tune of "God save great George our King," as happily as if that noble tune had been composed for it. The words were,

Fa la la lerridan,
Dan dan dan derridan,
Dan dan dan derridan,
Derridan dee.

To what old ditty they formed the burden I know not, nor whether it may be (as I suspect) a different reading of "Down, down, down derry down," which the most learned of living Welshmen supposes to be a Druidical fragment: but the frequent repetition of his own abbreviated name seldom failed to excite in the child one of those hearty and happy laughs which are never enjoyed after that blessed age has past. Most of us have frequently laughed till our sides ached, and many not unfrequently it may be feared laugh till their hearts ache. But the pure, fresh, unalloyed innocent laughter of children, in those moods when they

— seem like birds, created to be glad,* —

that laughter belongs to them and to them only. We see it and understand it in them; but nothing can excite more than a faint resemblance of it in ourselves.

The Doctor made use of this burden when anything was told him which excited his wonder, or his incredulity; and the degree in which either was called forth might be accurately determined by his manner of using it. He expressed mirthful surprise, or contemptuous disbelief by the first line, and the tune proceeded in proportion as the surprise was greater, or the matter of more moment. But when anything greatly astonished him, he went through the whole, and gave it in a base voice when his meaning was to be most emphatic.

In imitation, no doubt, of my venerable friend in this his practice, though perhaps at first half unconscious of the imitation, I have been accustomed to use the great decasyllabon, with which this present Chapter commences, and with which it is to end. In my use of it, however, I observe this caution,— that I do not suffer myself to be carried away by an undue partiality, so as to employ it in disregard of ejaculatory propriety or to the exclusion of exclamations which the occasion may render more fitting. Thus if I were to meet with Hercules, *Mehercule* would doubtless be the interjection which I should prefer; and when I saw the Siamese Twins, I could not but exclaim, *O Gemini!*†

Further, good Reader, if thou wouldest profit by these benevolent disclosures of Danielism and Dovery, take notice I say, and not only take notice, but take good notice, — N.B. — there was this difference between the Doctor's use of his burden, and mine of the decasyllabon, that the one was sung, and the other said, and that they are not "appointed to be said or sung," but that the one being designed for singing must be sung, and the other not having been adapted to music must be said. And if any great Composer should attempt to set the Decasyllabon, let him bear in mind that it should be set in the hypodorian key, the proslambanomenos of which mode is, in the judgement of the Antients, the most grave sound that the human voice can utter, and that the hearing can distinctly form a judgement of.

Some such device may be recommended to those who have contracted the evil habit of using oaths as interjectional safety-valves or convenient expletives of speech. The manner may be exemplified in reference to certain recent events of public notoriety.

We see which way the stream of time doth run,
And are enforced from our most quiet sphere
By the rough torrent of occasion.‡

Upon hearing one morning that in the Debate of the preceding night Mr. Brougham had said no change of administration could possibly affect him, I only exclaimed *A*! A short-hand writer would have mistaken it for the common interjection, and have written it accordingly Ah! But it was the first syllable of my inscrutable word, and signified mere notation without wonder or belief.

* Gondibert.

† This last paragraph was inserted by Mr. H. Tayler.

‡ Shakespeare.

When in the course of the same day there came authentic intelligence that Mr. Brougham was to be the Lord Chancellor of the New Administration, so little surprise was excited by the news, that I only added another syllable and exclaimed *Abal!*

Reading in the morning papers that Sir James Graham was to be first Lord of the Admiralty, and Lord Althorp to lead the House of Commons, the exclamation proceeded one step farther, and became *Aballi!*

This was uttered in a tone that implied disbelief; for verily I gave Cabinet Makers credit for a grain of sense more than they possessed, (a *grain* mark you, because they had nothing to do with *scruples;*) I supposed there was a mistake as to the persons, — that Sir James Graham, whose chief knowledge was supposed to lie in finance, and his best qualification in his tongue, was to be Chancellor of the Exchequer, and that Lord Althorp, who had no other claim to consideration whatever than as being Earl Spencer's eldest son, (except that as Hodge said of Diccon the Bedlam, he is "even as good a fellow as ever kissed a cow,") was intended for the Admiralty, where Spencer is a popular name. But when it proved that there was no mistake in the Newspapers, and that each of these ministers had been deliberately appointed to the office for which the other was fit, then I said *Aballiboo!*

The accession of Mr. Charles Grant and his brother to such an Administration brought me to *Aballiboozo!* with a shake of the head and in a mournful tone; for I could not but think how such a falling off would astonish the Soul of Canning, if in the intermediate state there be any knowledge of the events which are passing on earth.

When the Ministry blundered into their Budget, I exclaimed *Aballiboozobang!* with a strong emphasis upon the final syllable, and when they backed out of it, I came to *Aballiboozobanga!*

The Reform Bill upon a first glance at its contents called forth *Aballiboozobanganor*— I would have hurried on two steps farther, to the end of the decasyllabon, if I had not prudently checked myself and stopped there, — foreseeing that new cause for astonishment must now arise daily.

When Sir Robert Peel did not upon the first reading kick out this mass of crudities, and throw out the Cabinet after it, neck and shoulders, hip and thigh, I said in bitterness *Aballiboozobanganorri!*

And when that Cabinet waxing insolent because they had raised the mob to back them, declared that they would have the Bill, the whole Bill, and nothing but the Bill, then I expressed my contempt, amazement, and indignation, by uttering in its omnisignificant totality the great word

ABALLIBOOZOBANGANORRIBO.

CHAPTER CXLIX.

A PARLOUS QUESTION ARISING OUT OF THE FOREGOING CHAPTER. MR. IRVING AND THE UNKNOWN TONGUES. TAYLOR THE WATER POET. POSSIBLE SCHEME OF INTERPRETATION PROPOSED. OPINIONS CONCERNING THE GIFT OF TONGUES AS EXHIBITED IN MADMEN.

> Speak what terrible language you will, though you understand it not yourselves, no matter! Chough's language, gabble enough and good enough.
>
> SHAKESPEARE.

BUT here, gentle reader, occurs what Bishop Latimer would call a parlous question, if he had lived in these portentous times. There is no apparent meaning in Lilli burlero bullen a-la, nor in Raderer too, tandaro tee, nor in Dan dan dan derridan, any more than there is in Farra diddle dyno, — Hayley gayly gamborayly, higgledy piggledy, galloping draggle-tail dreary dun, and other burthens of a similar kind, which are to be found in the dramas of poor old blind O'Keeffe, and in Tom D'Urfey's songs. There is I say no apparent meaning in them; but we must not too confidently apply the legal maxim in this case, and conclude that *de non apparente et non existente eadem est ratio;* for although these choruses are not in any known tongue, they may by possibility be in an unknown one: and if Mr. Irving has not a cast in his intellect as well as in his eye, there is a mystery in an unknown tongue; and they who speak it, and consequently they who write it, may be inspired for the nonce — though they may be as little conscious of their inspiration as they are of their meaning. There may be an unknown inspiration as well as an unknown tongue. If so what mighty revelations may lie unrevealed in the gibberish of Taylor the Water Poet! Now if Mr. Irving would but read one of the wine-drinking Water Poet's effusions of this kind, in his chapel, on a day appointed for that purpose, some of his inspired speakers male or female might peradventure be moved to expound it in their kindred language; and as two negatives make an affirmative, it might be found that two unintelligibles make a meaning, and the whole affair would thus become intelligible to every one.

Two specimens therefore of the Taylorian tongues I shall here set before the public, in the hope that this important experiment may be tried with them. They were both intended as epitaphs for Thomas Coriat the famous Odcombian traveller; the first was supposed by the inspired Water Poet to be in the Bermuda tongue.

Hough gruntough wough Thomough Coriatough, Adcough robunquogh
Warawogh bogh Comitogh sogh wogh termonatogrogh,
Callimogh gogh whobogh Ragamogh demagorgogh palemogh,
Lomerogh nogh Tottertogh illemortogh eagh Allaquemquogh
Toracominogh Jagogh Jamerogh mogh Carnogh pelepsogh,
Animogh trogh deradrogh maramogh hogh Flondrogh calepsogh.

This, Taylor says, must be pronounced with the accent of the grunting of a hog. He gives no directions for pronouncing the second specimen, which is in the Utopian tongue.

Nortumblum callimumquash omystoliton quashte burashte
Scribuke woshtay solusbay perambulatushte;
Grekay sous Turkay Paphay zums Jerusalushte.
Neptus esht Ealors Interrimoy diz dolorushte,
Confabuloy Odcumbay Prozeugmolliton tymorumynoy,
Omulus oratushte paralescus tolliton umbroy.

The Water Poet gave notice as Professor of these tongues that he was willing to instruct any gentlemen or others who might be desirous of learning them.

But with regard to a gift of tongues, either known or unknown, there are more things than are dreamed of in the Irvingite philosophy or in the Lerry-cum-twang school. It was a received opinion in the seventeenth century that maniacs, and other persons afflicted with morbid melancholy, spoke in strange languages, and foretold things that were to come, by virtue, — that is to say, — in consequence of their mental malady. But some philosophers who in the march of intellect were in advance of their age, denied the fact, and accounted for the persuasion by supposing that such patients, when in a state of great agitation, uttered unmeaning words or sounds which ignorant people took to be Greek, Latin or Hebrew, merely because they could not understand them. Two questions therefore arose; whether the received opinion were true? and if it were true, how was the fact to be accounted for?

The first of these questions was easily disposed of by Sennertus, one of the most eminent Professors and practitioners of the medical science in that age. Facts he said, which were attested by trustworthy authors, were not to be disputed. Many were the impudent falsehoods which this great, and in other respects wise man, received implicitly as facts conformably to the maxim which he thus laid down; and many were the perilous consequences which he deduced in good faith, and on fair reasoning from such premises. Upon this occasion he instanced the case of a countryman, who at certain periods of the moon used to compose Latin verses, though he knew not a word of Latin at any other time. And of a man who spoke languages which he had never learned, and became unable to speak any one of them as soon as he was restored to health by the effect of some powerful worm-medicines. And of a sailor's son, who being wounded in the head and becoming delirious in consequence, made perfect syllogisms in German, but as soon as his wound was healed, lost all the logic which had been beaten into his head in so extraordinary a way.

Antonius Guainerius, who vouched for one of these cases as having witnessed the fact and all its circumstances, accounted for it by a brave hypothesis. The soul, he said, before its infusion into the body, possesses a knowledge of all things, and that knowledge is, in a certain manner, obliterated, or offuscated by its union with the body; but it is restored either by the ordinary means of instruction or by the influence of the star which presided at the time of its union. The body and the bodily senses resist this influence, but when these are as it were bound, or suspended, *quod fiat in melancholia*, the stars can then impart their influences to the soul without obstruction, and the soul may thus be endowed with the power of effecting what the stars themselves effect, and thus an illiterate person may become learned, and may also predict events that are to come. Sennertus is far from assenting to this theory. He says, *Magna petita sunt quæ præsupponit et sibi concedi postulat Guainerius.*

A theory quite as extraordinary was advanced by Juan Huarte in his *Examen de Ingenios*, a book which obtained at one time far more reputation than it deserved. Take the passage, curious Reader, from the English version, entitled, "The Examination of Men's Wits," in which by discovering the variety of natures is shewed for what profession each one is apt, and how far he shall profit therein. Translated out of the Spanish tongue by M. Camillo Camilli. Englished out of his Italian by R. C.*, Esquire, 1594. "The frantic person's speaking of Latin, without that he ever learned the same in his health-time, shews the consonance which the Latin tongue holds with the reasonable soul; and (as we will prove hereafter) there is to be found a particular wit applicable to the invention of languages, and Latin words; and the phrases of speech in that tongue are so fitting with the ear, that the reasonable soul, possessing the necessary temperature for the invention of some delicate language, suddenly encounters with this. And that two devisers of languages may shape the like words, (having the like wit and hability) it is very manifest; pre-supposing, that when God created Adam, and set all things before him, to the end he might bestow on each its several name whereby it should be called, he had likewise at that instant molded another man with the same perfection and supernatural grace; now I demand if God had placed the same things before this other man, that he might also set them names whereby they should be called, of what manner those names should have been? For mine own part I make no doubt but he would have given these things those very names which Adam did: and the reason is very apparent, for both carried one selfsame eye to the nature of each thing, which of itself was no more but one. After this manner might the frantic person light upon the Latin tongue; and speak the same without ever having learned it in his health; for the natural temperature of his brain conceiving alteration through the infirmity, it might for a space become like his who first invented the Latin tongue, and feign the like words, but yet not with that concert and continued fineness, for this would give token that the Devil moved that tongue, as the Church teacheth her Exorcists."

This theory found as little favour with Sennertus as that of Guainerius, because he says, Huarte assumes more than can be granted; and moreover because he supposes that the Latin language has a peculiar consonance with the rational soul, and that there are certain natures which are peculiarly constituted for inventing languages. And therefore if by disease that temperament be excited in the brain which is necessary for the invention of any most elegant language the patient would fall into the Latin tongue; and Latin words would occur to him, without any deliberation, or act of will on his part. This opinion Sennertus argued cannot be maintained as probable, being indeed disproved by the very cases upon which the question had been raised, for Greek and Hebrew had been spoken by some of the patients, as well as Latin. The facts

* *i. e.* Richard Carew. See Life of Camden prefixed to the Britannia, note p. xv.

he admits as not to be doubted, because they are related by veracious authors; and his way of accounting for them is by the agency of evil spirits, who take advantage of bodily diseases and act upon them, especially such as arise from melancholy; for that humour or passion has such attractions for evil spirits that it has been called *Balneum Diaboli*, the Devil's Bath. When therefore a patient speaks in tongues which he has never learned, *eo ipso Dæmon se manifeste prodit.*

This opinion, than which one of greater weight could not have been produced in the seventeenth century, is recommended to the serious consideration of the Irvingites

The Doctor would have sung Fa-la-la-lerridan to all this reasoning, and I say Aballiboo!

CHAPTER CL.

THE WEDDING PEAL AT ST. GEORGE'S, AND THE BRIDE'S APPEARANCE AT CHURCH.

See how I have strayed! and you'll not wonder when you reflect on the whence and the whither.

ALEXANDER KNOX.

WELL dear Reader, I have answered your question concerning the great Decasyllabon. I have answered it fairly and explicitly, not like those Jesuitical casuists

That palter with us in a double sense,
That keep the word of promise to our ear
And break it to our hope.

You have received an answer as full and satisfactory as you could expect or desire, and yet the more than cabalistic mysteries of the word are still concealed with Eleusinian secresy. Enough of this. For the present also we will drop the subject which was broken off by the extraordinary circumstances that called forth our Chapter Extraordinary,

— τὸ δὲ καὶ τετελεσμένον ἔσται *

for awhile, however, it will be convenient to leave it unfinished, and putting an end to the parenthesis in the most important part of the Doctor's life, tell thee that the Interim is past, that in the month of April, 1761, he brought home his bride, and the bells of St. George rang that peal, — that memorable peal which was anticipatively mentioned in the 32d chapter. Many such peals have they rung since on similar occasions, but they have rung their last from St. George's Tower, for in 1836 it was thought necessary to remove them, lest they should bring that fine old fabric down.

Webster libelled the most exhilarating and the most affecting of all measured sounds when he said,

— those flattering bells have all
One sound at weddings and at funerals.

Es cierta experiencia que la musica crece la pena donde la halla, y acrecieuta el plazer en el corazon contento; this is more true of bell ringing than of any other music; but so far are church bells from having one sound on all occasions, that they carry a different import on the same to different ears and different minds. The bells of St. George's told a different tale to Daniel Dove, and to Deborah, on their wedding day. To her, they said, as in articulate words, varying, but melancholy alike in import as in cadence,

Deborah Bacon hath changed her name;
Deborah Bacon hath left her home;
Deborah Bacon is now no more.

Yet she had made what in every one's opinion was considered a good match, and indeed was far better than what is commonly called good; it promised in all human likelihood to be a happy one, and such it proved. In the beautiful words of Mrs. Hutchinson, neither she nor her husband, "ever had occasion to number their marriage among their infelicities."

Many eyes were turned on the Doctor's bride, when she made her appearance at St.

* HOMER.

George's Church. The novelty of the place made her less regardful of this than she might otherwise have been. Hollis Pigot, who held the vicarage of Doncaster thirty years, and was then in the last year of his incumbency and his life, performed the service that day. I know not among what description of preachers he was to be classed; whether with those who obtain attention, and command respect, and win confidence, and strengthen belief, and inspire hope, or with the far more numerous race of Spintexts and of Martexts. But if he had preached that morning with the tongue of an angel, the bride would have had no ears for him. Her thoughts were neither upon those who on their way from church would talk over her instead of the sermon, nor of the service, nor of her husband, nor of herself in her new character, but of her father, — and with a feeling which might almost be called funereal, that she had passed from under his pastoral as well as his paternal care.

CHAPTER CLI.

SOMETHING SERIOUS.

If thou hast read all this Book, and art never the better, yet catch this flower before thou go out of the garden, and peradventure the scent thereof will bring thee back to smell the rest. HENRY SMITH.

DEBORAH found no one in Doncaster to supply the place of Betty Allison in the daily intercourse of familiar and perfect friendship. That indeed was impossible; no aftermath has the fragrance and the sweetness of the first crop. But why do I call her Deborah? She had never been known by that name to her new neighbours; and to her very Father she was now spoken of as Mrs. Dove. Even the Allisons called her so in courteous and customary usage, but not without a melancholy reflection that when Deborah Bacon became Mrs. Dove, she was in a great measure lost to them.

— Friendship, although it cease not
In marriage, is yet at less command
Than when a single freedom can dispose it.*

* FORD.

Doncaster has less of the *Rus in Urbe* now than it had in those days, and than Bath had when those words were placed over the door of a Lodging House, on the North Parade. And the house to which the Doctor brought home his bride had less of it than when Peter Hopkins set up the gilt pestle and mortar there as the cognizance of his vocation. It had no longer that air of quiet respectability which belongs to such a dwelling in the best street of a small country town. The Mansion House by which it was dwarfed and inconvenienced in many ways occasioned a stir and bustle about it, unlike the cheerful business of a market day. The back windows, however, still looked to the fields, and there was still a garden. But neither fields nor garden could prevail over the odour of the shop, in which, like

Hot, cold, moist and dry, four champions fierce,

in Milton's Chaos, rhubarb and peppermint, and valerian, and assafetida, " strove for mastery," and to battle brought their atoms. Happy was the day when peppermint predominated; though it always reminded Mrs. Dove of Thaxted Grange, and the delight with which she used to assist Miss Allison in her distillations. There is an Arabian proverb which says, " The remembrance of youth is a sigh." Southey has taken it for the text of one of those juvenile poems in which he dwells with thoughtful forefeeling upon the condition of declining life.

Miss Allison had been to her, not indeed as a mother, but as what a step-mother is, who is led by natural benevolence and a religious sense of duty, to perform as far as possible a mother's part to her husband's children. There are more such step-mothers than the world is willing to believe, and they have their reward here as well as hereafter. It was impossible that any new friend could fill up her place in Mrs. Dove's affections,— impossible that she could ever feel for another woman the respect, and reverence, and gratitude, which blended with her love for this excellent person. Though she was born within four miles of Doncaster, and had lived till her marriage in the humble vicarage in which she was born, she had never passed four-and-twenty hours in that town before she went to reside there; nor had she the slightest acquaintance with any of its inhabitants, except the few shopkeepers with whom her little dealings had lain, and the occasional visitants whom she had met at the Grange.

An Irish officer in the army, happening to be passenger in an armed vessel during the last war, used frequently to wish that they might fall in with an enemy's ship, because he said, he had been in many land battles, and there was nothing in the world which he desired more than to see what sort of a thing a sea fight was. He had his wish, and when after a smart action, in which he bore his part bravely, an enemy of superior force had been beaten off, he declared with the customary emphasis of an Hibernian adjuration, that a sea-fight was a mighty *sairious* sort of thing.

The Doctor and Deborah, as soon as they were betrothed, had come to just the same conclusion upon a very different subject. Till the day of their engagement, nay till the hour of proposal on his part, and the very instant of acceptance on hers, each had looked upon marriage, when the thought of it occurred, as a distant possibility, more or less desirable, according to the circumstances which introduced the thought, and the mood in which it was entertained. And when it was spoken of sportively, as might happen, in relation to either the one or the other, it was lightly treated as a subject in which they had no concern. But from the time of their engagement, it seemed to both the most serious event of their lives.

In the Dutch village of Broek, concerning which, singular as the habits of the inhabitants are, travellers have related more peculiarities than ever prevailed there, one remarkable custom shows with how serious a mind some of the Hollanders regard marriage. The great house door is never opened but when the Master of the House brings home his Bride from the altar, and when Husband and Wife are borne out to the grave. Dr. Dove had seen that village of great Baby-houses, but though much attached to Holland, and to the Dutch as a people, and disposed to think that we might learn many useful lessons from our prudent and thrifty neighbours, he thought this to be as preposterous, if not as shocking a custom, as it would be to have the bell toll at a marriage, and to wear a winding sheet for a wedding garment.

We look with wonder at the transformations that take place in insects, and yet their physical metamorphoses are not greater than the changes which we ourselves undergo morally and intellectually, both in our relations to others and in our individual nature. *Chaque individu, considéré separément, differe encore de lui même par l'effet du tems; il devient un autre, en quelque maniere, aux diverses epoques de sa vie. L'enfant, l'homme fait, le vieillard, sont comme autant d'etrangers unis dans une seule personne par le lien mysterieux du souvenir.** Of all changes in life, marriage is certainly the greatest, and though less change in every respect can very rarely be produced by it in any persons than in the Doctor and his wife, it was very great to both. On his part it was altogether an increase of happiness; or rather from having been contented in his station he became happy in it, so happy as to be experimentally convinced that there can be no "single blessedness" for man. There were some drawbacks on her part, — in the removal from a quiet vicarage to a busy street; in the obstacle which four miles opposed to that daily and intimate intercourse with her friends at the Grange which had been the chief delight of her maiden life; and above all in the separation from her father, for even at a distance which may appear so inconsiderable, such it was; but there was the consolatory reflection that those dear friends and that dear father concurred in approving her marriage, and in rejoicing in it for her sake; and the experience of every day and every year made her more and more thankful for her lot. In the full liturgic sense of the word, he worshipped her, that is, he

* Necker.

loved, and cherished, and respected, and honoured her; and she would have obeyed him cheerfully as well as dutifully, if obedience could have been shown where there was ever but one will.

CHAPTER CLII.

ODD OPINIONS CONCERNING BIOGRAPHY AND EDUCATION. THE AUTHOR MAKES A SECOND HIATUS AS UNWILLINGLY AS HE MADE THE FIRST, AND FOR THE SAME COGENT REASON.

Ya sabes — pero es forzoso
Repetirlo, aunque lo sepas. CALDERON.

UNWILLINGLY, as the Reader may remember, though he cannot possibly know with how much unwillingness, I passed over fourteen years of Daniel Dove's youth, being the whole term of his adolescence, and a fifth part of that appointed sum, beyond which the prolongation of human life is but labour and sorrow. Mr. Coleridge has said that "the history of a man for the nine months preceding his birth would probably be far more interesting, and contain events of greater moment than all the threescore and ten years that follow it." * Mr. Coleridge was a philosopher, in many points, of the first order, and it has been truly said by one of the ancients that there is nothing so absurd but that some philosopher has advanced it. Mr. Coleridge, however, was not always in earnest when he said startling things; and they who suppose that the opinions of such a man are to be collected from what he says playfully in the freedom of social intercourse to amuse himself, and perhaps to astonish others, may as well expect to hold an eel by the tail.

There were certain French legislators in the days of Liberty and Equality, who held that education ought to begin before birth, and therefore they proposed to enact laws for the benefit of the homunculus during that portion of its existence to which Mr. Coleridge is said to have attached such metaphysical, or, in his own language, such psychological importance. But even these Ultra-philosophers would not have maintained that a biographer ought to begin before the birth of his subject. All antecedent matter belongs to genealogical writers; astrologers themselves are content to commence their calculations from the hour and minute of the nativity. The fourteen years over which I formerly passed for the reasons stated in the 25th Chapter of this Opus, would have supplied more materials than any equal portion of his life, if the Doctor had been his own historian; for in those years his removal from home took place, his establishment at Doncaster, and his course of studies at Leyden, the most momentous events in his uneventful history, except the great one of marriage, — which either makes or mars the happiness of both parties.

From the time of that "crowning event" I must pass over another but longer interval, and represent the Doctor in his married state, such as he was when it was my fortune in early life to be blessed with his paternal friendship, for such it might be called. Age like his, and Youth might well live together, for there was no crabbedness in his age. Youth, therefore, was made the better and the happier by such society. It was full of pleasure instead of care; not like winter, but like a fine summer evening, or a mild autumn, or like the light of a harvest moon,

> Which sheds o'er all the sleeping scene
> A soft nocturnal day.†

---

* Most probably Mr. Coleridge said this with reference to Sir Thomas Browne, who maintained that every man, at his birth, was nine months old.

† JAMES MONTGOMERY.

CHAPTER CLIII.

MATRIMONY AND RAZORS. LIGHT SAYINGS LEADING TO GRAVE THOUGHTS. USES OF SHAVING.

> I wonder whence that tear came, when I smiled
> In the production on't! Sorrow's a thief
> That can, when joy looks on, steal forth a grief.
>
> MASSINGER.

Oh pitiable condition of human kind! One colour is born to slavery abroad, and one sex to shavery at home! — A woman, to secure her comfort and well-being in this country, stands in need of one thing only, which is a good husband; but a man hath to provide himself with two things, a good wife, and a good razor, and it is more difficult to find the latter than the former. The Doctor made these remarks one day, when his chin was smarting after an uncomfortable operation; and Mrs. Dove retorted by saying that women had still the less favourable lot, for scarce as good razors might be, good husbands were still scarcer.

"Ay," said the Doctor, "Deborah is right, and it is even so; for the goodness of wife, husband, and razor depends upon their temper, and, taking in all circumstances and causes natural and adventitious, we might reasonably conclude that steel would more often be tempered precisely to the just degree, than that the elements of which humanity is composed should be all nicely proportioned and amalgamated happily. Rarely indeed could Nature stand up, and pointing out a sample of its workmanship in this line say to all the world this is a Man! meaning thereby what man, rational, civilised, well educated, redeemed, immortal man, may and ought to be. Where this could be said in one instance, in a thousand or ten thousand others she might say this is what Man has by his own devices made himself, a sinful and miserable creature, weak or wicked, selfish, sensual, earthly-minded, busy in producing temporal evil for others, — and everlasting evil for himself!"

But as it was his delight to find good, or to look for it, in everything, and especially when he could discover the good which may be educed from evil, he used to say that more good than evil resulted from shaving, preposterous as he knew the practice to be, irrational as he admitted it was, and troublesome as to his cost he felt it. The inconvenience and the discomfort of the operation no doubt were great, — very great, especially in frosty weather, and during March winds, and when the beard is a strong beard. He did not extenuate the greatness of this evil, which was moreover of daily recurrence. Nay, he said, it was so great, that had it been necessary for physical reasons, that is to say, were it a law of nature, instead of a practice enjoined by the custom of the country, it would undoubtedly have been mentioned in the third chapter of the book of Genesis, as the peculiar penalty inflicted upon the sons of Adam, because of his separate share in the primal offence. The daughters of Eve, as is well known, suffer expressly for their mother's sin; and the final though not apparent cause why the practice of shaving, which is apparently so contrary to reason, should universally prevail in all civilised christian countries, the Doctor surmised might be, that by this means the sexes were placed in this respect upon an equality, each having its own penalty to bear, and those penalties being — perhaps — on the whole equal; or if man had the heavier for his portion, it was no more than he deserved, for having yielded to the weaker vessel. These indeed are things which can neither be weighed nor measured; but it must be considered that shaving comes every day to all men of what may be called the clean classes, and to the poorest labourer or handicraft once a week; and that if the daily shavings of one year, or even the weekly ones, could be put into one shave, the operation would be fatal, — it would be more than flesh and blood could bear.

In the case of man this penalty brought with it no after compensation, and here the female had the advantage. Some good nevertheless resulted from it, both to the community and to the individual shaver, unless he missed it by his own fault.

To the community because it gives employment to Barbers, a lively and loquacious race, who are everywhere the great receivers and distributors of all news, private or public in their neighbourhood.

To the individual, whether he were, like the Doctor himself, and as Zebedee is familiarly said to have been, an autokureus, which is being interpreted a self-shaver, or shaver of himself; or merely a shavee, as the labouring classes almost always are, the operation in either case brings the patient into a frame of mind favourable to his moral improvement. He must be quiet and composed when under the operator's hands, and not less so if under his own. In whatever temper or state of feeling he may take his seat in the barber's chair, or his stand at the looking-glass, he must at once become calm. There must be no haste, no impatience, no irritability; so surely as he gives way to either, he will smart for it. And however prone to wander his thoughts may be, at other and perhaps more serious times, he must be as attentive to what he is about in the act of shaving, as if he were working a problem in mathematics.

As a lion's heart and a lady's hand are among the requisites for a surgeon, so are they for the Zebedeean shaver. He must have a steady hand, and a mind steadied for the occasion; a hand confident in its skill, and a mind assured that the hand is competent to the service upon which it is ordered. Fear brings with it its immediate punishment as surely as in a field of battle; if he but think of cutting himself, cut himself he will.

I hope I shall not do so to-morrow; but if what I have just written should come into my mind, and doubt come over me in consequence, too surely then I shall! Let me forget myself, therefore, as quickly as I can, and fall again into the train of the Doctor's thoughts.

Did not the Duc de Brissac perform the operation himself for a moral and dignified sentiment, instead of letting himself be shaved by his valet-de-chambre? Often was he heard to say unto himself in grave soliloquy, while holding the razor open, and adjusting the blade to the proper angle, in readiness for the first stroke, "Timoleon de Cossé, God hath made thee a Gentleman, and the King hath made thee a Duke. It is nevertheless right and fit that thou shouldst have something to do; therefore thou shalt shave thyself!" — In this spirit of humility did that great Peer "mundify his muzzel."

*De sçavoir les raisons pourquoy son pere luy donna ce nom de Timoleon, encore que ce ne fut nom Chretien, mais payen, il ne se peut dire; toutesfois, à l'imitation des Italiens et des Grecs, qui ont emprunté la plus part des noms payens, et n'en sont corrigez pour cela, et n'en font aucun scruple,— il avoit cette opinion, que son pere luy avoit donné ce nom par humeur, et venant à lire la vie de Timoleon elle luy pleut, et pour ce en imposa le nom à son fils, présageant qu'un jour il luy seroit semblable. Et certes pour si peu qu'il a vesçu, il luy a ressemblé quelque peu; mais, s'il eust vesçu il ne l'eust ressemblé quelque peu en sa retraite si longue, et en son temporisement si tardif qu'il fit, et si longue abstinence de guerre; ainsi que luy-mesme le disoit souvent, qu'il ne demeureroit pour tous les biens du monde retiré si longuement que fit ce Timoleon.** This is a parenthesis: I return to our philosopher's discourse.

And what lectures, I have heard the Doctor say, does the looking-glass, at such times, read to those men who look in it at such times only! The glass is no flatterer, the person in no disposition to flatter himself, the plight in which he presents himself assuredly no flattering one. It would be superfluous to have Γνῶθι Σεαυτὸν inscribed upon the frame of the mirror; he cannot fail to know himself, who contemplates his own face there, long and steadily, every day. Nor can he as he waxes old need a death's head for a memento in his closet or his chamber; for day by day he traces the defeatures which the hand of Time is making, — that hand which never suspends its work.

> Thus his good melancholy oft began
> On the catastrophe and heel of pastime.†

* Brantome. † Shakespeare.

"When I was a round-faced, red-faced, smooth-faced boy," said he to me one day, following the vein upon which he had thus fallen, "I used to smile if people said they thought me like my father, or my mother, or my uncle. I now discern the resemblance to each and all of them myself, as age brings out the primary and natural character of the countenance, and wears away all that accidental circumstances had superinduced upon it. The recognitions, — the glimpses which at such times I get of the departed, carry my thoughts into the past; — and bitter, — bitter indeed would those thoughts be, if my anticipations — (wishes I might almost call them, were it lawful as wishes to indulge in them) — did not also lead me into the future, when I shall be gathered to my fathers in spirit, though these mortal *exuviæ* should not be laid to moulder with them under the same turf." *

There were very few to whom he talked thus. If he had not entirely loved me, he would never have spoken to me in this strain.

CHAPTER CLIV.

A POET'S CALCULATION CONCERNING THE TIME EMPLOYED IN SHAVING, AND THE USE THAT MIGHT BE MADE OF IT. THE LAKE POETS LAKE SHAVERS ALSO. A PROTEST AGAINST LAKE SHAVING.

Intellect and industry are never incompatible. There is more wisdom, and will be more benefit, in combining them than scholars like to believe, or than the common world imagine. Life has time enough for both, and its happiness will be increased by the union.

SHARON TURNER.

THE poet Campbell is said to have calculated that a man who shaves himself every day, and lives to the age of threescore and ten, expends during his life as much time in the act of shaving, as would have sufficed for learning seven languages.

The poet Southey is said to carry shaving to its *ne plus ultra* of independency, for he shaves *sans* looking-glass, *sans* shaving-brush, *sans* soap, or substitute for soap, *sans* hot-water, *sans* cold-water, *sans* everything except a razor. And yet among all the characters which he bears in the world, no one has ever given him credit for being a cunning shaver!

(Be it here observed in a parenthesis that I suppose the word *shaver* in this so common expression to have been corrupted from shaveling; the old contemptuous word for a Priest.)

But upon reflection, I am not certain whether it is of the poet Southey that this is said, or of the poet Wordsworth. I may easily have confounded one with the other in my recollections, just as what was said of Romulus might had been repeated of Remus while they were both living and flourishing together; or as a mistake in memory might have been made between the two Kings of Brentford when they both quitted the stage, each smelling to his nosegay, which it was who made his exit P. S. and which O. P.

Indeed we should never repeat what is said of public characters (a denomination under which all are to be included who figure in public life, from the high, mighty and most illustrious Duke of Wellington at this time, down to little Waddington) without qualifying it as common report, or as newspaper, or magazine authority. It is very possible that the Lake poets may, both of them, shave after the manner of other men. The most attached friends of Mr. Rogers can hardly believe that he has actually said all the good things which are ascribed to him in a certain weekly journal; and Mr. Campbell may not have made the remark which I have repeated, concerning the time employed in mowing the chin, and the use to which the minutes that are so spent might be applied. Indeed so far am I from wishing to impute to this gentleman

* The passage following is from a letter of Southey's, published by Sir Egerton Brydges in his Autobiography: "Did you ever remark how remarkably old age brings out family likenesses,—which, having been kept, as it were, in abeyance while the passions and the business of the world engrossed the parties, come forth again in age (as in infancy), the features settling into their primary characters — before dissolution? I have seen some affecting instances of this, — a brother and sister, than whom no two persons in middle life could have been more unlike in countenance or in character, becoming like as twins at last. . I now see my father's lineaments in the looking-glass, where they never used to appear."—Vol. ii. p. 270.

upon common report, anything which might not be to his credit, or which he might not like to have the credit of, that it is with the greatest difficulty I can persuade myself to believe in the authenticity of his letter to Mr. Moore upon the subject of Lord and Lady Byron, though he has published it himself, and in his own name.

Some one else may have made the calculation concerning shaving and languages, some other poet, or proser, or one who never attempted either prose or rhyme. Was he not the first person who proposed the establishment of the London University, and if this calculation were his, is it possible that he should not have proposed a plan for it founded thereon, which might have entitled the new institution to assume the title of the Polyglot College?

Be this as it may, I will not try the *sans*-every-thing way of shaving, let who will have invented it: never will I try it, unless thereto by dire necessity enforced! I will neither shave dry, nor be dry-shaved, while any of those things are to be obtained which either mitigate or abbreviate the operation. I will have a brush, I will have Naples soap, or some substitute for it, which may enable me always to keep a dry and clean apparatus. I will have hot-water for the sake of the razor, and I will have a looking-glass for the sake of my chin and my upper lip. No, never will I try Lake shaving, unless thereto by dire necessity enforced.

Nor would I be enforced to it by any necessity less dire than that with which King Arthur was threatened by a messager from Kynge Ryons of North-walys; and Kynge he was of all Ireland and of many Iles. And this was his message, gretynge wel Kynge Arthur in this manere wyse, sayenge, "that Kynge Ryons had discomfyte and overcome eleaven Kynges, and everyche of hem did hym homage, and that was this; they gaf hym their beardys clene flayne off, as moche as ther was; wherfor the messager came for King Arthurs beard. For King Ryons had purfyled * a mantel with Kynges berdes, and there lacked one place of the mantel, wherfor he sent for his berd, or els he wold entre in to his landes, and brenne and slee, and never leve tyl he have thi hede and thi berd." If the King of the Lakes should require me to do him homage by shaving without soap, I should answer with as much spirit as was shown in the answer which King Arthur returned to the Messenger from King Ryons. "Wel, sayd Arthur, thow hast said thy message, the whiche is the most vylanous and lewdest message that ever man herd sente unto a Kynge. Also thow mayst see, my berd is ful yong yet to make a purfyl of hit. But telle thow thy Kynge this; I owe hym none homage, ne none of mine elders; but or it be longe to, he shall do me homage on bothe his kneys, or els he shall lese his hede by the feithe of my body, for this is the most shamefullest message that ever I herd speke of. I have aspyed, thy King met never yet with worshipful man; but telle hym, I wyll have his hede without he doo me homage: Then the messager departed."

* *i. e. Ornamented.* See Halliwell's Dictionary of Archaic and Provincial Words, v. PURFLE.

CHAPTER CLV.

THE POET'S CALCULATION TESTED AND PROVED.

Fiddle-faddle, don't tell of this and that, and every thing in the world, but give me mathematical demonstration.
CONGREVE.

BUT I will *test* (as an American would say, —though let it be observed in passing that I do not *advocate* the use of Americanisms,) — I will *test* Mr. Campbell's assertion. And as the Lord President of the New Monthly Magazine has not favoured the world with the calculations upon which his assertion, if his it be, is founded, I will investigate it, step by step, with which intent I have this morning, Saturday, May the fifteenth, 1830, minuted myself during the act of shaving.

The time employed was, within a second or two more or less, nine minutes.

I neither hurried the operation, nor lingered about it. Everything was done in my ordinary orderly way, steadily, and without waste of time.

Now as to my beard, it is not such a beard as that of Domenico d'Ancona, which was *delle barbe la corona*, that is to say the crown of beards, or rather, in English idiom, the king.

> *Una barba la più singulare*
> *Che mai fosse discritta in verso o'n prosa,*
> A beard the most unparallell'd
> That ever was yet described in prose or rhyme,

and of which Berni says that the Barber ought to have felt less reluctance in cutting the said Domenico's throat, than in cutting off so incomparable a beard. Neither do I think that mine ever by possibility could vie with that of Futteh Ali Shah, King of Persia at this day: nay, I doubt whether Macassar Oil, Bear's grease, Elephant's marrow, or the approved recipe of sour milk with which the Persians cultivate their beards, could ever bring mine to the far inferior growth of his son's, Prince Abbas Mirza. Indeed no Mussulmen would ever look upon it, as they did upon Mungo Park's, with envious eyes, and think that it was too good a beard for a Christian. But for a Christian, and moreover an Englishman, it is a sufficient beard; and for the individual a desirable one: *nihil me pœnitet hujus barbæ;* desirable I say, inasmuch as it is in thickness and rate of growth rather below the average standard of beards. Nine minutes, therefore, will be about the average time required for shaving, by a Zebedeean, — one who shaves himself. A professional operator makes quicker work; but he cannot be always exactly to the time, and at the year's end as much may have been lost in waiting for the barber, as is gained by his celerity of hand.

Assuming, then, the moderate average of nine minutes, nine minutes per day amount to an hour and three minutes per week; an hour and three minutes per week are fifty-four hours thirty-six minutes per year. We will suppose that our shaver begins to operate every day when he has completed his twentieth year; many, if not most men, begin earlier; they will do so if they are ambitious of obtaining whiskers; they must do so if their beards are black, or carroty, or of strong growth. There are, then, fifty years of daily shaving to be computed; and in that time he will have consumed two thousand, seven hundred and thirty hours in the act of shaving himself. I have stated the numbers throughout in words, to guard against the mistakes which always creep into the after editions of any book, when figures are introduced.

Now let us see whether a man could in that time acquire a competent knowledge of seven languages.

I do not, of course, mean such a knowledge as Professor Porson and Dr. Elmsley had attained of Greek, or as is possessed by Bishop Blomfield and Bishop Monk, — but a passable knowledge of living languages, such as would enable a man to read them with facility and pleasure, if not critically, and to travel without needing either an interpreter — or the use of French in the countries where they are spoken.

Dividing, therefore, two thousand seven hundred and thirty, being the number of hours which might be appropriated to learning languages, — by seven, — the number of languages to be learnt, we have three hundred and ninety hours for each language; three hundred and ninety lessons of an hour long, — wherein it is evident that any person of common capacity might with common diligence learn to read, speak, and write — sufficiently well for all ordinary purposes, any European language. The assertion, therefore, though it might seem extravagant at first, is true as far as it goes, and is only inaccurate because it is far short of the truth.

For take notice that I did not strop the razor this morning, but only passed it, after the operation, ten or twelve times over the palm of the hand, according to my every-day practice. One minute more at least would have been required for stropping. There are many men whose beards render it necessary for them to apply to the strop every day, and for a longer time, — and who are obliged to try first one razor and then another. But let us allow only a minute for this — one minute a day amounts to six hours five minutes in the year; and in fifty years to three hundred and four hours ten minutes, — time enough for an eighth language.

Observe, also, that some languages are so easy, and others so nearly related to each other, that very much less than half the number of hours allowed in this computation would suffice for learning them. It is strictly true that in the time specified a man of good capacity might add seven more languages to the seven for which that computation was formed; and that a person who has any remarkable aptitude for such studies might in that time acquire every language in which there are books to be procured.

Hé bien, me suis-je enfin rendu croyable? Est-on content? *

See, Reader, what the value of time is, when put out at simple interest. But there is no simple interest in knowledge. Whatever funds you have in that Bank go on increasing by interest upon interest, — till the Bank fails.

CHAPTER CLVI.

AN ANECDOTE OF WESLEY, AND AN ARGUMENT ARISING OUT OF IT, TO SHOW THAT THE TIME EMPLOYED IN SHAVING IS NOT SO MUCH LOST TIME; AND YET THAT THE POET'S CALCULATION REMAINS OF PRACTICAL USE.

Questo medesimo anchora con una altra gagliardissima ragione vi confermo. LODOVICO DOMINICHI.

THERE was a poor fellow among John Wesley's followers, who suffered no razor to approach his chin, and thought it impossible that any one could be saved who did: shaving was in his opinion a sin for which there could be no redemption. If it had been convenient for their interests to put him out of the way, his next of kin would have had no difficulty in obtaining a *lettre de cachet* against him from a mad-doctor, and he might have been imprisoned for life, for this harmless madness. This person came one day to Mr. Wesley, after sermon, and said to him in a manner which manifested great concern, "Sir, you can have no place in Heaven without a beard! therefore, I entreat you, let your's grow immediately!"

Had he put the matter to Wesley as a case of conscience, and asked that great economist of time how he could allow himself every day of his life to bestow nine precious minutes upon a needless operation, the Patriarch of the Methodists might have been struck by the appeal, but he would soon have perceived that it could not be supported by any just reasoning.

For in the first place, in a life of such incessant activity as his, the time which Wesley employed in shaving himself, was so much time for reflection. However busy he might be, as he always was, — however hurried he might be on that particular day, here was a portion of time, small indeed, but still a distinct and apprehensible portion, in which he could call his thoughts to council. Like our excellent friend, he was a person who knew this, and he profited by it, as well knowing what such minutes of reflection are worth. For although thought cometh, like the wind, when it listeth, yet it listeth to come at regular appointed times, when the mind is in a state of preparation for it, and the mind will be brought into that state, unconsciously, by habit. We may be as ready for meditation at a certain hour, as we are for dinner, or for sleep; and there will be just as little need for an effort of volition on our part.

Secondly, Mr. Wesley would have considered that if beards were to be worn, some care and consequently some time must be bestowed upon them. The beard must be trimmed occasionally, if you would not have it as ragged as an old Jew Clothes-man's: it must also be kept clean, if you would not have it inhabited like the Emperor Julian's; and if you desired to have it like Aaron's you would oil it. Therefore it is probable that a Zebedeean, who is cleanly in his habits would not save any time by letting his beard grow.

But it is certain that the practice of shaving must save time for fashionable men,

* PIRON.

though it must be admitted that these are persons whose time is not worth saving, who are not likely to make any better use of it, and who are always glad when any plea can be invented for throwing away a portion of what hangs so heavily upon their hands.

> Alas, Sir, what is a Gentleman's time !
> ———— there are some brains
> Can never lose their time, whate'er they do.*

For in former times as much pains were bestowed on dressing the beard, as in latter ones upon dressing the hair. Sometimes it was braided with threads of gold. It was dyed to all colours, according to the mode, and cut to all shapes, as you may here learn from John Taylor's *Superbiæ Flagellum.*

> Now a few lines to paper I will put,
> Of men's beards strange and variable cut :
> In which there's some do take as vain a pride,
> As almost in all other things beside.
> Some are reap'd most substantial like a brush,
> Which make a natural wit known by the bush :
> (And in my time of some men I have heard,
> Whose wisdom hath been only wealth and beard,)
> Many of these the proverb well doth fit,
> Which says Bush natural, more hair than wit.
> Some seem as they were starched stiff and fine,
> Like to the bristles of some angry swine :
> And some (to set their Love's desire on edge)
> Are cut and pruned like to a quickset hedge.
> Some like a spade, some like a fork, some square,
> Some round, some mowed like stubble, some stark bare,
> Some sharp stiletto fashion, dagger like,
> That may with whispering a man's eyes out pike :
> Some with the hammer cut or Roman T,
> Their beards extravagant reformed must be,
> Some with the quadrate, some triangle fashion,
> Some circular, some oval in translation,
> Some perpendicular in longitude,
> Some like a thicket for their crassitude,
> That heights, depths, breadths, triform, square, oval, round,
> And rules geometrical in beards are found ;
> Beside the upper lips strange variation,
> Corrected from mutation to mutation ;
> As't were from tithing unto tithing sent,
> *Pride* gives to *Pride* continual punishment.
> Some (*spite their teeth*) like thatched eaves downward grows,
> And some grow upwards in despite their nose.
> Some their mustachios of such length do keep,
> That very well they may a manger sweep ?
> Which in Beer, Ale, or Wine, they drinking plunge,
> And suck the liquor up as't were a sponge ;
> But 'tis a Sloven's beastly *Pride* I think
> To wash his beard where other men must drink.
> And some (because they will not rob the cup)
> Their upper chaps like pot hooks are turned up,
> The Barbers thus (like Tailors) still must be,
> Acquainted with each cut's variety.†

In comparison with such fashions, clean shaving is clear gain of time. And to what follies and what extravagances would the whiskerandoed macaronies of Bond Street and St. James's proceed, if the beard once more were, instead of the neckcloth, to "make the man!" — They who have put on the whole armour of Dandeyism, having their loins girt with — stays, and having put on the breast-plate of — buckram, and having their feet shod — by Hoby!

I myself, if I wore a beard, should cherish it, as the Cid Campeador did his, for my pleasure. I should regale it on a summer's day with rose water; and, without making it an Idol, I should sometimes offer incense to it, with a pastille, or with lavender and sugar. My children when they were young enough for such blandishments would have delighted to stroke, and comb, and curl it, and my grand-children in their turn would have succeeded to the same course of mutual endearment.

Methinks then I have shown that although the Campbellian, or Pseudo-Campbellian assertion concerning the languages which might be acquired in the same length of time that is consumed in shaving, is no otherwise incorrect than as being short of the truth, it is not a legitimate consequence from that proposition that the time employed in shaving is lost time, because the care and culture of a beard would in all cases require as much, and in many would exact much more. But the practical utility of the proposition, and of the demonstration with which it has here been accompanied, is not a whit diminished by this admission. For, what man is there, who, let his business, private or public, be as much as it will, cannot appropriate nine minutes a-day to any object that he likes?

---

* May.

† Taylor *the Water Poet.*

CHAPTER CLVII.

WHICH THE READER WILL FIND LIKE A ROASTED MAGGOT, SHORT AND SWEET.

Malum quod minimum est, id minimum est malum.
PLAUTUS.

BUT here one of those persons who acting upon the proverbial precept which bids us look before we leap, look so long that they never leap at all, offers a demurrer.

It may be perfectly true, he observes, that a language may be learned in three hundred and ninety lessons of an hour each. But in your proposition the hour is broken into several small parts; we will throw in an additional minute, and say six such portions. What I pray you can a lesson of ten minutes be worth?

To this I reply that short lessons are best, and are specifically enjoined in the new System of Education. Dr. Bell says in his Manual of Instructions for conducting Schools, "in the beginning never prescribe a lesson or task, which the Scholar can require more than ten minutes, or a quarter of an hour, to learn."

On this authority, and on the authority of experience also, I recommend short lessons. For the same reasons, or for reasons nearly or remotely related to them, I like short stages, short accounts, short speeches, and short sermons; I do not like short measure or short commons; and, like Mr. Shandy, I dislike short noses. I know nothing about the relative merit of short-horned cattle. I doubt concerning the propriety of short meals. I disapprove of short parliaments and short petticoats; I prefer puffpaste to short pie-crust; and I cut this chapter short for the sake of those readers who may like short chapters.

CHAPTER CLVIII.

DR. DOVE'S PRECEPTORIAL PRESCRIPTION TO BE TAKEN BY THOSE WHO NEED IT.

Some strange devise, I know, each youthful wight
Would here expect, or lofty brave assay:
But I'll the simple truth in simple wise convey.
HENRY MORE.

NOW comes the question of a youth after my own heart, so quick in his conclusions that his leap seems rather to keep pace with his look than to follow it. He will begin to-morrow, and only asks my advice upon the method of proceeding.

Take the Grammar of any modern language, and read the dialogues in it, till you are acquainted with the common connecting words, and know the principal parts of speech by sight. Then look at the declensions and the verbs — you will already have learned something of their inflections, and may now commit them to memory, or write them down. Read those lessons, which you ought to read daily — in a bible of this language, having the English bible open beside it. Your daily task will soon be either to learn the vocabulary, or to write exercises, or simply to read, according to the use which you mean to make of your new acquirement. You must learn *memoriter*, and exercise yourself in writing if you wish to educate your ear and your tongue for foreign service; but all that is necessary for your own instruction and delight at home may be acquired by the eye alone.

Qui mihi Discipulus es — cupis atque doceri,

try this method for ten minutes a-day, perseveringly, and you will soon be surprised at your own progress.

Quod tibi deest, à te ipso mutuare, —

it is Cato's advice.

Ten minutes you can bestow upon a modern language, however closely you may be engaged in pursuits of immediate necessity; even tho' you should be in a public office from which Joseph Hume, or some of his worthy compeers, has moved for voluminous returns. (Never work at extra hours upon such returns, unless extra pay is allowed for the additional labour and confinement to the desk, as in justice it ought to be. But if you are required to do so by the superiors, who ought to protect you from such injustice, send petition after petition to Parliament, praying that when the abolition or mitigation of slavery shall be taken into consideration, your case may be considered also.)

Any man who will, may command ten minutes. *Exercet philosophia regnum suum*, says Seneca; *dat tempus, non accipit. Non est res subcisiva, ordinaria est, domina est; adest, et jubet.* Ten minutes the Under Graduate who reads this may bestow upon German, even though he should be in training for the University races. Ten minutes he can bestow upon German, which I recommend because it is a master-key for many doors both of language and of knowledge. His mind will be refreshed even by this brief change of scene and atmosphere. In a few weeks (I repeat) he will wonder at his own progress: and in a few years, if he is good for anything — if the seed has not been sown upon a stony place, nor among thorns, — he will bless me his unknown benefactor, for showing him by what small savings of time a man may become rich in mind. "And so I end my counsel, beseeching thee to begin to follow it." *

But not unto me be the praise! O Doctor, O my guide, philosopher and friend!

> Like to the bee thou everywhere didst roam
> Spending thy spirits in laborious care,
> And nightly brought'st thy gathered honey home,
> As a true workman in so great affair;
> First of thine own deserving take the fame,
> Next of thy friend's; his due he gives to thee,
> That love of learning may renown thy name,
> And leave it richly to posterity.†

I have but given freely what freely I have received. This knowledge I owe, — and what indeed is there in my intellectual progress which I do not owe to my ever-beloved friend and teacher, my moral physician?

> — his plausive words
> He scattered not in ears, but grafted them
> To grow there and to bear.‡

To his alteratives and tonics I am chiefly (under Providence) indebted for that sanity of mind which I enjoy, and that strength, — whatever may be its measure, — which I possess. It was his method, — his *way*, he called it; in these days when we dignify everything, it might be called the Dovean system or the Columbian, which he would have preferred.

CHAPTER CLIX.

THE AUTHOR COMPARES HIMSELF AND THE DOCTOR TO CARDINAL WOLSEY AND KING HENRY VIII., AND SUGGESTS SUNDRY SIMILES FOR THE STYLE OF HIS BOOK.

> I doubt not but some will liken me to the Lover in a modern Comedy, who was combing his peruke and setting his cravat before his mistress; and being asked by her when he intended to begin his court? replied, he had been doing it all this while. DRYDEN.

It cannot be necessary for me to remind the benevolent reader, that at those times when a half or a quarter-witted critic might censure me for proceeding egotistically, I am nevertheless carrying on the primary intention with which this work was undertaken, as directly as if the Doctor were the immediate and sole theme of every chapter; —

> *Non enim excursus hic — sed opus ipsum est.*§

For whatever does not absolutely relate to him is derived directly or indirectly from him; it is directly derivative when I am treating upon subjects which it has been my good fortune to hear him discuss; and indirectly when I am led to consider the topics that incidentally arise, according to the way of thinking in which he trained me to go.

As Wolsey inscribed upon one of his magnificent buildings the words *Ego et Rex Meus*, so might I place upon the portal of this Edifice *Ego et Doctor Meus*, for I am as much his creature as Wolsey was the creature of bluff King Harry, — as confessedly

* EUPHUES, A. M. † RESTITUTA.

‡ SHAKESPEARE. § PLINY.

so, and as gratefully. Without the King's favour Wolsey could not have founded Christ Church; without the Doctor's friendship I could not have edified this monument to his memory. Without the King's favour Wolsey would never have obtained the Cardinal's hat; and had it not been for the favour, and friendship, and example of the Doctor, never should I have been entitled to wear that cap, my reasons for not wearing which have heretofore been stated,—that cap which to one who knows how to wear it becomingly, is worth more than a coronet or a mitre; and confers upon the wearer a more lasting distinction.

His happy mind, like the not less happy and not more active intellect of Humboldt King of Travellers, was excursive in its habits. To such discursive — or excursiveness I also was prone, and he who observed in me this propensity encouraged it, tempering, however, that encouragement with his wonted discretion. Let your imagination, he said, fly like the lady-bird,

North, south, and east, and west,

but take care that it always comes home to rest.

Perhaps it may be said therefore of his unknown friend and biographer as Passovier said of Michel de Montaigne, *il estoit personnage hardy, qui se croyoit, et comme tel se laissoit aisement emporter à la beauté de son esprit; tellement que par ses ecrits il prenoit plaisir de desplaire plaisamment.*

Perhaps also some one who for his own happiness is conversant with the literature of that affluent age, may apply to the said unknown what Balzac said of the same great Michael, Michael the second, (Michael Angelo was Michael the first,) *Montaigne sçait bien ce qui il dit; mais, sans violer le respect qui luy est deu, je pense aussi, qu'il ne sçait pas toujours ce qu'il va dire.*

Dear Reader you may not only say this of the unknown, *sans violer le respect qui luy est deu*, but you will pay him what he will consider both a great and a just compliment, in saying so.

For I have truly endeavoured to observe the precepts of my revered Mentor, and to follow his example, which I venture to hope the judicious reader will think I have done with some success. He may have likened me for the manner in which I have conducted this great argument to a gentle falcon, which, however high it may soar to command a wider region with its glance, and however far it may fly in pursuit of its quarry, returns always to the falconer's hand.

Learned and discreet reader, if you should not always discern the track of associations over which I have passed as fleetly as Camilla over the standing corn; — if the story which I am relating to thee should seem in its course sometimes to double like a hare in her flight, or in her sport, — sometimes to bound forward like a jerboa, or kangaroo, and with such a bound that like Milton's Satan it overleaps all bounds; or even to skip like a flea, so as to be here, there and everywhere, taking any direction rather than that which will bring it within your catch; — learned and discreet reader, if any of these similitudes should have occurred to you, think of Pindar, read Landor's Gebir, and remember what Mr. Coleridge has said for himself formerly, and prophetically for me, *intelligenda non intellectum adfero.* Would you have me plod forward like a tortoise in my narration, foot after foot in minute steps, dragging his slow tail along? Or with such deliberate preparation for progressive motion that like a snail the slime of my way should be discernible?

A bye-stander at chess who is ignorant of the game presently understands the straight and lateral movement of the rooks, the diagonal one of the bishops, and the power which the Queen possesses of using both. But the knight perplexes him, till he discovers that the knight's leap, eccentric as at first it seems, is nevertheless strictly regulated.

We speak of erratic motions among the heavenly bodies; but it is because the course they hold is far beyond our finite comprehension.

Therefore I entreat thee, dear reader, thou who hast the eye of a hawk or of a sea gull, and the intellectual speed of a greyhound, do not content thyself with glancing over this book as an Italian Poet says

Precipitevolissimevolmente.

But I need not exhort thee thus, who art quick to apprehend and quick to feel, and sure to like at first sight whatever upon better acquaintance deserves to be loved.

CHAPTER CLX.

MENTION OF ONE FOR WHOM THE GERMANS WOULD COIN A DESIGNATION WHICH MIGHT BE TRANSLATED A ONCE-READER. MANY MINDS IN THE SAME MAN. A POET'S UNREASONABLE REQUEST. THE AUTHOR OFFERS GOOD ADVICE TO HIS READERS, AND ENFORCES IT BY AN EPISCOPAL OPINION.

> Judge not before
> Thou know mine intent:
> But read me throughout,
> And then say thy fill;
> As thou in opinion
> Art minded and bent,
> Whether it be
> Either good or ill. E. P.

I HAVE heard of a man who made it a law for himself never to read any book again which had greatly pleased him on a first perusal; lest a second reading should in some degree disturb the pleasurable impression which he wished to retain of it. This person must have read only for his amusement, otherwise he would have known that a book is worth little if it deserves to be perused but once: and moreover that as the same landscape appears differently at different seasons of the year, at morning and at evening, in bright weather and in cloudy, by moonlight and at noon-day, so does the same book produce a very different effect upon the same reader at different times and under different circumstances.

I have elsewhere said that the man of one book is proverbially formidable; but the man of one reading, though he should read through an ample library would never become so.

The studious man who at forty re-peruses books which he has read in his youth or early manhood, vivid as his recollections of them may be, finds them new, because he brings another mind to the perusal. Worthless ones with which he may formerly have been delighted appear flat and unprofitable to his maturer judgment; and on the other hand sterling merit which he was before unable to appreciate, he can now understand and value, having in his acquired knowledge and habits of reflection the means of assaying it.

Sometimes a Poet, when he publishes what in America would be called a lengthy poem, with lengthy annotations, advises the reader in his preface, not to read the notes in their places, as they occur, lest they should interrupt his clear perception and enjoyment of the piece, but to read the poem by itself at first; and then, for his more full contentment, to begin again, and peruse the notes in their order, whereby he will be introduced to the more minute and recondite merits of the work.

If the poets who calculate upon many such readers are not wise in their generation, they are happy in it.

What I request of my dear readers is far more reasonable, and yet perhaps not much more likely to be granted; I request them, that in justice to themselves,—for that they may not lose any part of the pleasure which I have designed for them; and in justice to me, — that I may not be defrauded of any portion of that grateful applause, which after a due perusal they will undoubtedly bestow upon the benevolent unknown;— and in justice to the ever-honoured subject of these volumes,—lest a hasty and erroneous judgment of his character should be formed, when it is only partially considered; — I request that they would not dip into these volumes before they read them, nor while they are reading them, but that they would be pleased to go through the book regularly, in the order of the chapters, and that when they recommend the book to their friends, (as they will do with the friendly intention of contributing to their entertainment and instruction,) they would particularly advise them to begin at the beginning, or more accurately speaking at the seventh chapter before the beginning, and so peruse it consecutively.

So doing, reader, thou wilt perceive the method and the order of the work, developing before thee as thou readest; thou wilt then comprehend and admire the connection of the parts, and their dependence upon each other, and the coherence and beauty of the whole. Whereas were you only to dip into it here and there, you would from such a cursory and insufficient inspection come perhaps to the same conclusion, "wherein nothing was concluded" as the man did concerning Bailey's Dictionary, who upon returning the book to a neighbour from whom he had borrowed it, said that he was much obliged to him for the loan, and that he had read it through, from beginning to end, and had often been much entertained by it, and was sure that the Author must have been a very knowing person; — but — added he — to confess the truth, I have never been able clearly to make out what the book is about.

Now as opposite causes will sometimes produce a like effect, thou mightest, by reading this book partially, come to the same inconclusive conclusion concerning it, that our friend did by reading straight forward through Bailey's Dictionary; though considering what there is in that Dictionary, his time might have been worse employed. — I very well remember when I was some ten years old, learning from an abridgment of it as much about Abracadabra as I know now. I exhort thee therefore to begin *ab ovo*, with the ante-initial chapters, and to read the whole regularly; and this advice I give, bearing in mind what Bishop Hacket says in his life of the Lord Keeper, Archbishop Williams, when he inserts a speech of that Chancellor-Prelate's, at full length:

"This he delivered, thus much: and I took counsel with myself not to abbreviate it. For it is so compact and pithy that he that likes a little, must like it all. Plutarch gives a rule for sanity to him that eats a tortoise, ἢ ὅλην, ἢ μὴ ὅλως, "eat it up all, or not a whit." The reason assigned for this rule would look better in Plutarch's Greek than in the Episcopal English; being paraphrased it imports that a small portion of such food is apt to produce intestinal pains; but that a hearty meal has the wholesome effect of those pills which by a delicate and beautiful euphuism of Dr. Kitchener's are called Peristaltic Persuaders. "So," proceeds the Bishop, "the speech of a great orator is instructive when it is entire: pinch it into an epitome, you mangle the meaning and avile the eloquence."

CHAPTER CLXI.

WESLEY AND THE DOCTOR OF THE SAME OPINION UPON THE SUBJECT OF THESE CHAPTERS. A STUPENDOUS EXAMPLE OF CYCLOPÆDIAN STOLIDITY.

> A good razor never hurts, or scratches. Neither would good wit, were men as tractable as their chins. But instead of parting with our intellectual bristles quietly, we set them up, and wriggle. Who can wonder then if we are cut to the bone? GUESSES AT TRUTH.

BOTH Mr. Wesley and Dr. Dove, who, much as they differed concerning Methodism, agreed remarkably well in their general method of thinking, would have maintained the morality and propriety of shaving, against all objections founded upon the quantity of time expended in that practice. If the one had preached or the other descanted on the 27th verse of the 19th Chapter of Leviticus, each would have shown that no general application could be made of the prohibition therein contained. But what would they have said to the following physical argument which is gravely advanced in Dr. Abraham Rees's New Cyclopædia?

"The practice of cutting the hair of the head and the beard is attended with a prodigious increase of the secretion of the matter of hair. It is ascertained that a man of fifty years of age will have cut from his head above thirteen feet, or twice his own length of hair; and of his beard, in the last twenty-five years of the same period — above eight feet. The hair likewise, besides this enormous length, will be thicker than if it had been left uncut, and must lose most of its juices by evaporation, from having its tube and the ends of its fibres always exposed. — The custom of shaving the beard, and cutting the hair of the head, has, we believe, been justly deprecated by some physiologists. The latter has been supposed, and with much apparent reason, to weaken the understanding, by diverting the blood from the brain to the surface of the head. The connection which exists between the beard and the organs of generation, and likewise between the muscular strength of the individual, would seem to render it improper to interfere with its natural mode of growth. Bichat attributes the superior strength of the ancients to their custom of wearing their beards; and those men who do not shave at present are distinguished for vigour and hardihood."

Thus far we have had to deal only with a grave folly, and I shall follow the writer no farther.

What would John Wesley and Daniel Dove have said to the speculations and assertions in this curious passage? They were both men of reading, both speculative men and both professors, each in his way, of the art of medicine. They would have asked what proof could be produced that men who let their beards grow are stronger than those who shave, or that the ancients were superior in bodily strength to the men of the present day? Thus they would have treated his assumed facts; and for his philosophy, they would have inferred, that if cutting the hair weakened the understanding, and the story of Samson were a physical allegory, the person who wrote and reasoned thus must have been sheared at least twice a week from his childhood.

If on the other hand they had been assured that the writer had worn his hair long, then they would have affirmed that, as in the case of the Agonist, it was "robustious to no purpose."

When the Russian soldiers were first compelled to part with their beards that they might look like other European troops, they complained that the cold struck into their jaws and gave them the tooth-ache. The sudden deprivation of a warm covering might have occasioned this and other local affections. But they are not said to have complained that they had lost their wits.

They are said indeed in the days of Peter the Great to have made a ready use of them in relation to this very subject. Other arguments had been used in vain for persuading them to part with that comfortable covering which nature had provided for their cheeks and chins, when one of their Priests represented to them that their good Czar had given orders for them to be shaved only from the most religious motives and a special consideration of what concerned them most nearly. They were about to march against the Turks. The Turks as they well knew wore beards, and it was of the utmost importance that they should distinguish themselves from the misbelievers by this visible mark, for otherwise their protector St. Nicholas in whom they trusted would not know his own people. This was so cogent a reason that the whole army assented to it, and a general shaving took place. But when the campaign against the Turks was over and the same troops were ordered to march against the Swedes, the soldiers called for the Priest, and told him they must now let their beards grow again; — for the Swedes shaved, and they must take care St. Nicholas might know his friends from his foes.

CHAPTER CLXII.

AMOUNT OF EVERY INDIVIDUAL'S PERSONAL SINS ACCORDING TO THE ESTIMATE OF MR. TOPLADY. THE DOCTOR'S OPINION THEREON. A BILL FOR CERTAIN CHURCH REPAIRS. A ROMISH LEGEND WHICH IS LIKELY TO BE TRUE, AND PART OF A JESUIT'S SERMON.

Mankind, tho' satirists with jobations weary us,
  Has only two weak parts if fairly reckon'd;
The first of which, is trifling with things serious;
  And seriousness in trifles is the second.
Remove these little rubs, whoe'er knows how,
And fools will be as scarce, — as wise men now.
BISHOP.

It is not often that a sportive or fanciful calculation like that of Mr. Campbell can be usefully applied, or in the dialect of the Evangelical Magazine, improved.

I remember well the look, and the voice and the manner with which my ever-to-be-honoured friend pointed out to me a memorable passage of this kind in the works of the Reverend Augustus Toplady, of whom he used to say that he was a strong-headed, wrong-headed man; and that in such men you always found the stronger the head, the wronger the opinions; and the more wrongly their opinions were taken up, the more strongly they were persisted in.

Toplady after some whimsical calculations concerning the national debt, proceeds to a "spiritual improvement" of the subject. He asserts that because "we never come up to that holiness which God requires, we commit a sin every second of our existence," and in this view of the matter, he says, our dreadful account stands as follows. At ten years old each of us is chargeable with 315,036,000 sins; and summing up the account at every intermediate stage of ten years, he makes the man of fourscore debtor for 2,510,288,000.

In Toplady's creed there were no venial sins, any more than in Sir George Mackenzie's, who used this impious argument for the immortality of the soul, that it must needs be immortal because the smallest sin, "the least peccadillo against the Almighty who is Infinite cannot be proportionably punished in the swift glass of man's short life."

And this man, said the Doctor, laying his finger upon Toplady's book, thinks himself a Christian, and reads the Bible and believes it! He prints and vouches for the authenticity of a painter's bill at Cirencester delivered in to the Churchwarden of an adjacent parish in these words:—Mr. Charles Ferebee, Churchwarden of Siddington, to Joseph Cook, Debtor: To mending the Commandments, altering the Belief, and making a new Lord's Prayer, £1 1*s*.

The Painter made no such alteration in the Christian creed, as he himself did, when he added to it, that the Almighty has predestined the infinitely greater number of his creatures to eternal misery!

"God," says good old Adam Littleton, "made no man purposely to damn him. Death was one of man's own inventions, and will be the reward of his evil actions."

The Roman Catholics have a legend from which we may see what proportion of the human race they suppose to be redeemed from perdition; it relates that on the day of St. Bernard's death there died threescore thousand persons, of whom only four souls were saved, the Saint's being one;—the salvage therefore is one in fifteen thousand!

But one legend may be set against another, and Felix Faber the Monk of Ulm gives us one of better import, when he relates the story of a lovely child who in her twelfth year was stricken with the plague, during the great pestilence, which, in the middle of the fourteenth century, swept off a greater portion of the human race than is ever known to have perished in any similar visitation. As the disease increased upon her, she became more beautiful and more cheerful, looking continually upward and rejoicing; for she said she saw that Heaven was open, and innumerable lights flowing upward thither, as in a stream,—which were the souls of the elect, ascending as they were released. When they who stood beside her bed were silent and seemed as if they gave no credit to her words, she told them that what she saw was no delusion, and added in token of its sure truth, that her own death would take place that night, and her father die on the third day following: she then pointed to seven persons, foretelling to each the day of their decease, and named some others who were not present, who would, in like manner, be cut off by the plague, saying at what time each of them would expire; and in every instance, according to the legend, the prediction was punctually fulfilled. This is a tale which may in all its parts be true; for such predictions at such a time, when whole cities were almost depopulated by the pestilence, were likely not only to be verified, but in a great degree to bring about their own verification; and the state of her mind would lead to her interpretation of those ocular spectra which were probably effects of the disease, without supposing it to be a happy delirium, heightening her expectation of that bliss which faith had assured to her, and into which her innocent spirit was about to enter.

Had the story been fabricated it would not have been of so humane a character. The Roman Catholics, as is well known, believe that all who are not of what they please to call the Holy, Roman, Catholic and Apostolic Church, are doomed to everlasting perdition; this doctrine is part of the creed which their laity profess, and to which their clergy swear. If any member of that Church reject an opinion so uncharitable in itself, and in its consequences so infinitely mischievous, he may be a Roman Catholic by his connections, by courtesy, by policy, or by fear; but he is not so in reality, for he refuses to believe in the infallibility of his Church, which has on no point declared itself more peremptorily than upon this. All other Christians of every persuasion, all Jews, all Mahometans, and all Heathens are goats; only the Romanists are the Sheep of God's pasture, — and the Inquisitors, we may suppose, his Lambs! Of this their own flock they hold that one half are lost sheep: though a liberal opinion, it is esteemed the most probable one upon that subject, and the best founded, because it is written that one shall be taken and one left, and that of the ten virgins who went with their lamps to meet the bridegroom, five were wise, and five foolish.

An eloquent Jesuit preaching before the Court in his own country stated this opinion, and made an application from it to his hearers with characteristic integrity and force. "According to this doctrine," said he, "which is held by many Saints, (and is not the most straitened, but a large and favourable one,) if I were this day preaching before another auditory, I should say that half of those who heard me belonged to the right hand, and half unto the left. Truly a most wonderful and tremendous consideration, that of Christians and Catholics, enlightened with the faith, bred up with the milk of the Church, and assisted by so many sacraments and aids, half only should be saved! That of ten men who believe in Christ, and for whom Christ died, five should perish! That of an hundred fifty should be condemned! That of a thousand five hundred go to burn eternally in Hell! who is there that does not tremble at the thought? But if we look at the little Christianity and the little fear of God with which men live, we ought rather to give thanks to the Divine Mercy, than to be astonished at this justice.

"This is what I should say if I were preaching before a different audience. But because to-day is a day of undeceiving," — (it was the first Sunday in Advent,) — "and the present Auditory is what it is, let not those who hear me think or persuade themselves, that this is a general rule for all, even although they may be or call themselves Catholics. As in this life there is a wide difference between the great and powerful and those who are not so, so will it be in the Day of Judgement. They are on the right hand to-day, but as the world will then have had so great a turn, it is much to be feared that many of them will then be on the left. Of others half are to be saved, and of the great and powerful, how many? Will there be a third part saved? Will there be a tenth? I shall only say (and would not venture to say it, unless it were the expressed oracle and infallible sentence of supreme Truth,) I shall only say that they will be very few, and those by great wonder. Let the great and mighty listen, not to any other than the Lord himself in the Book of Wisdom. *Prœbite aurem vos qui continetis multitudinem, quoniam data est a Domino potestas vobis.* 'Give ear ye that rule the people, for power is given you of the Lord.' Ye princes, ye ministers who have the people under your command, ye to whom the Lord hath given this power to rule and govern the commonwealth, *prœbite aurem*, give ear to me! And what have they to hear from God who give ear so ill to men? A proclamation of the Day of Judgement far more portentous and terrible than that which has to summon the dead! *Judicium durissimum his qui præsunt fiet; exiguo enim conceditur misericordia; potentes autem potenter tormenta patientur:* A sharp judgement shall be to them that be in high places. For mercy will pardon the mean; but mighty men shall be mightily tormented. The Judgement with which God will judge those who rule and govern is to be a sharp Judgement, because mercy will be granted to the mean; but the mighty shall be mightily tormented, *potentes potenter tormenta patientur.* See here in what that power is to end which is so greatly desired, which is so panted after, which is so highly esteemed, which is so much envied! The mighty fear no other power now, because the power is in their own hands, but when the sharp Judgement comes they will then see whose Power is greater than theirs; *potentes potenter patientur.*"

This was a discourse which might have made Felix tremble.

CHAPTER CLXIII.

AN OPINION OF EL VENERABLE PADRE MAESTRO FRAY LUIS DE GRANADA, AND A PASSAGE QUOTED FROM HIS WORKS, BECAUSE OF THE PECULIAR BENEFIT TO WHICH PERSONS OF A CERTAIN DENOMINATION WILL FIND THEMSELVES ENTITLED UPON READING OR HEARING IT READ.

Chacun tourne en réalités,
Autant qu'il peut, ses propres songes;
L'homme est de glace aux vérités,
Il est de feu pour les mensonges.

LA FONTAINE.

THE translated extract in the preceding Chapter from the most eloquent of the Portuguese preachers, *el mismissimo Vieyra, en su mesma mesmedad,* as he is called in Fray Gerundio, brings to my mind the most eloquent and the most popular of the Spanish divines, P. M. Luis de Granada. He held an opinion wherein, (as will appear hereafter,) the Philosopher of Doncaster did not agree with him, that everything under the sky was created for man directly or indirectly, either for his own use, or for the use of those creatures which minister to it; for, says the Spaniard, if he does not eat mosquitoes he eats the birds that eat them; if he does not eat the grass of the field, the cattle graze there that are necessary for his use.

I have a very particular reason for giving the famous and Venerable Dominican's opinion in his own words.

Todo quanto ay debaxo del Cielo, ó es para el hombre, ó para cosas de que se ha de servir el hombre; porque si el no come el mosquito que buela por el ayre, come lo el pajaro de que el se mantiene; y si el no pace la yerva del campo, pacela el ganado, de que el tiene necessidad.

My reason for transcribing this sentence in its original language, is that by so doing I might confer a great act of kindness upon every Roman Catholic who reads the present Chapter. For be it known unto every such reader, that by perusing it, he becomes entitled to an indulgence of an hundred days, granted by D. Pasqual Aragon, Cardinal by the Title of Santa Balbina, and Archbishop of Toledo; and moreover to eighteen several indulgences of forty days each, granted by eighteen most illustrious and most reverend Lords Archbishops and Bishops; such indulgences having been proclaimed, *para los que leyeren, ó oyeren leer qualquier capitulo, parrafo, ó periodo de lo que escrivio el dicho V. P. M. Fray Luis de Granada.*

It might be a question for the casuists whether a good papist reading the paragraph here presented to him, and not assenting to the opinion expressed therein, would be entitled to this discount of eight hundred and twenty days from his time due in Purgatory. But if he accords with the Venerable Dominican, he can no more doubt his own right to participate in the Episcopal and Archiepiscopal grants, than he can call in question the validity of the grants themselves.

CHAPTER CLXIV.

AN INQUIRY, IN THE POULTRY-YARD, INTO THE TRUTH OF AN OPINION EXPRESSED BY ARISTOTLE.

This is some liquor poured out of his bottle ;
A deadly draught for those of Aristotle.
J. C. sometime of M. H. Oxon.

ARISTOTLE was of opinion that those animals which have been tamed, or are capable of being so, are of a better nature, or higher grade, than wild ones, and that it is advantageous for them that they should be brought into subjection by man, because under his protection they are safe.

Τὰ μὲν γὰρ ἥμερα τῶν ἀγρίων βελτίω τὴν φύσιν, τούτοις δὲ πᾶσι βέλτιον ἄρχεσθαι ὑπ' ἀνθρώπου, τυγχάνει γὰρ σωτηρίας οὕτως.

Our Philosopher was not better disposed to agree with Aristotle upon this point, than with the more commonly received notion of Father Luis de Granada. He thought that unless men were more humane in the days of Alexander the Great than they are now, and than they have been in all times of which we have any knowledge, the Stagyrite must have stated what ought to be, rather than what is.

So our Philosopher thought; and so I, faithfully retaining the lessons of my beloved Master, am prepared to prove. I will go no farther than to the Poultry Yard, and borrowing the names of the Dramatis Personæ from a nursery story, one of his Uncle William's, which has been told with the greatest possible success to all my children in succession, as it was to me, and their Uncles and Aunts before them, I will question the Poultry upon the subject, and faithfully report their evidence.

Voi ch' avete gl' intelletti sani
Mirate la dottrina che s'asconde
*Sotto queste coperte alte e profonde.**

"Chick-pick, Chick-pick, which is best for you; to be a wild Chick-pick, or to live, as you are living, under the protection, and care, and regular government of Man?"

Chick-pick answers and says, "Nature provides for my support quite as abundantly and as surely as you can do, and more wisely; you do not make my life happier or more secure while it lasts, and you shorten it; I have nothing to thank you for."

"Hen-pen, Hen-pen, which is best for you; to be a wild Hen-pen, or to live as you are living, under the protection, and care, and regular government of Man?"

Hen-pen answers and says: "Had I been bred up as my mother if she had been a wild Hen-pen would have bred me, I should have had the free use of my wings. I have nothing to thank you for! You take my eggs. Sometimes you make me hatch in their stead a little unnatural brood who run into the water, in spite of all my fears and of all that I can do to prevent them. You afford me protection when you can from foumarts and foxes; and you assist me in protecting my chicken from the kite, and the hawk, but this is that you may keep them for your own eating; you fatten them in coops, and then comes the Cook!"

"Cock-lock which is best for you; to be a wild Cock-lock, or to live as you are living, under the protection, and care, and regular government of Man?"

Cock-lock answers and says, "Is there a man impudent enough to ask me the question! You squail† at us on Shrove Tuesday; you feed us with Cock-bread, and arm us with steel spurs, that we may mangle and kill each other for your sport; you build cock-pits; you make us fight Welsh mains, and give subscription cups to the winner. And what would that Cock-lock say, who was a Cock-lock till you made him a Capon-lapon!"

"Duck-luck, Duck-luck, which is best for you, to be a wild Duck-luck, or to live as you are living under the protection, and care, and regular government of Man?"

Duck-luck answers and says, "I was created to be one of the most privileged of God's creatures, born to the free enjoyment

* ORLANDO INNAMORATO.

† SQUAIL: "To throw a stick, as at a cock." Grose's Provincial Glossary.

of three elements. My wings were to bear me whither I would thro' the sky, as change of season required change of climate for my well being; the waters were to afford me pastime and food, the earth repose and shelter. No bird more joyous, more active, more clean or more delighting in cleanliness than I should be, if the society of man had not corrupted my instincts. Under your regular government my wings are rendered useless to me; I waddle about the miserable precincts to which I am confined, and dabble in the dirt and grope for garbage in your gutters. And see there are green peas in the garden!"

"Turkey-lurkey, Turkey-lurkey, which is best for you; to be a wild Turkey-lurkey, or to live as you are living, under the protection and care, and regular government of Man?"

Turkey-lurkey answers and says, "You cram us as if to show that there may be as much cruelty exercised in giving food as in withholding it. Look at the Norwich coaches for a week before Christmas! Can we think of them, think you? without wishing ourselves in the woods like our blessed ancestors, where chine, sausages and oyster-sauce are abominations which never have been heard of!" Sir Turkey-lurkey then shook and ruffled and reddened the collops of his neck, and gobbled out his curses upon man.

"Goosey-loosey, Goosey-loosey, which is best for you; to be a wild Goosey-loosey, or to live as you are living, under the protection, and care, and regular government of Man?"

Goosey-loosey answers and says, "It is not for any kindness to us that you turn us into your stubbles. You pluck us that you may lie the softer upon our feathers. You pull our quills that you may make pens of them. O St. Michael, what havoc is committed amongst us under the sanction of your arch-angelic name! And O Satan! what punishment wilt thou exact from those inhuman wretches who keep us in a state of continual suffering in order to induce a disease by which our livers may be enlarged for the gratification of wicked epicures! We might curse man for all that we know of his protection, and care, and regular government; *but*,"—

"But!" said Goosey-loosey, and lifting up her wings significantly she repeated a third time that word "But!" and with a toss of the head and a twist of the snaky neck which at once indicated indignation and triumph, turned away with all the dignity that Goose-nature could express.

I understood the meaning of that But.

It was not one of those dreaded, ominous, restrictive, qualifying, nullifying or negativing Buts of which Daniel, the tenderest of all tender poets, says,

Ah! now comes that bitter word of *But*,
Which makes all nothing that was said before!
That smoothes and wounds, that strokes and dashes more
Than flat denial, or a plain disgrace.

It was not one of those heart-withering, joy-killing, and hope-annihilating Buts. It was a minatory But, full of meaning as ever Brewer's Butt was full of beer.

However, I will not broach that But in this Chapter.

CHAPTER CLXV.

A QUESTION ASKED AND RIGHTLY ANSWERED, WITH NOTICES OF A GREAT IMPORTATION ANNOUNCED IN THE LEITH COMMERCIAL LIST.

"But tell me yet what followed on that But."
DANIEL.

Great, Reader, are the mysteries of Grammarians! Dr. Johnson considered But as only a Conjunction, whereas, says Mr. Todd, it is in a fact a Conjunction, Preposition, Adverb and Interjection, as Dr. Adam Smith long since ingeniously proved. With Horne Tooke it is a verb to boot, being according to him the imperative of the Saxon beon-uτan, *to be out;* but in this Mr. Todd supposes him to be out himself. And Noah Webster says it is also a Participle and a Noun. Pity that some one has not proved it to be a Pronoun; for then it would have belonged to all the eight parts of speech.

Great are the mysteries of Grammarians!

O Reader, had you in your mind
Such stores as subtlety can bring,
O gentle Reader, you would find
A mystery in every thing.

For once, dear Reader, I who pride myself upon lucid order of arrangement, and perspicuity of language, instead of making, which I have heretofore done, and shall hereafter do, the train of my associations as visible as the tract of a hare in the dewy grass or in the snow, will let it be as little apparent as that of a bird in the air, or a serpent on a rock; or as Walter Landor in his poems, or his brother Robert's, whose poetry has the true Landorean obscurity, as well as the Landorean strength of diction and the Landorean truth and beauty of feeling and of thought: perhaps there is no other instance of so strongly marked an intellectual family likeness.

Thus having premised, I propound the following question: Of all the Birds in the air, and all the beasts in the field, and all the fishes in the sea, and all the creatures of inferior kind, who pass their lives wholly, or in part, according to their different stages of existence, in air, earth or water, what creature has produced directly or indirectly the most effect upon mankind? — *That*, which you, Reader, will deserve to be called, if you do not, after a minute's reflection, answer the question rightly.

The Goose!

Now, Reader, you have hit the *But*.

Among the imports in the Leith Commercial List, for June 1830, is an entry of 1,820,000 goose quills, brought by the Anne from Riga, for Messrs. Alexander Duncan and Son of Edinburgh.

One million, eight hundred and twenty thousand goose quills! The number will present itself more adequately to thy imagination when it is thus expressed in words.

O Reader, consider in thy capacious mind the good and the evil in which that million, eight hundred and twenty thousand quills will be concerned!

Take notice that the whole quantity is of foreign growth — that they are all imported quills, and so far from being all that were imported, that they were brought by one ship, and for only one house. Geese enough are not bred in Great Britain for supplying pens to schools, counters, public offices, private families, authors, and last not least in their consumption of this article, young ladies, — though they call in the crow-quills to their aid. Think of the Lawyers, Reader! and thou wilt then acknowledge that even if we were not living at this time under a government of Newspapers, the Goose is amply revenged upon mankind.

And now you understand Goosey-loosey's But.

CHAPTER CLXVI.

A WISH CONCERNING WHALES, WITH SOME REMARKS UPON THEIR PLACE IN PHYSICAL AND MORAL CLASSIFICATION. DOCTOR ABRAHAM REES. CAPTAIN SCORESBY. THE WHALE FISHERY.

Your Whale he will swallow a hogshead for a pill;
But the maker of the mouse-trap is he that hath skill.

Ben Jonson.

When gas-lights came into general use, I entertained a hope that Whales would no longer be slaughtered for the sake of their oil. The foolishness of such a hope may be excused for its humanity.

I will excuse you Reader, if in most cases you distrust that word humanity. But you are not to be excused if you suspect me of its counterfeit, that mock humanity which is one characteristic of this dishonourable and dishonest age. I say you are not to be excused, if being so far acquainted as by this time you must be with the philosophy of the Doctor, you suspect me his faithful and dutiful disciple of this pitiful affectation.

How the thought concerning Whales came just now into my mind will be seen when its application shall in due course be made apparent. Where I am is always well known to myself, though every Reader may not always discover my whereabout. And before the thought can be applied I must show upon what our Philosopher's opinions concerning Whales, or fancies if you think proper so to call them, were founded; mine — upon this and most other matters, having been as I gratefully acknowledge, derived from him.

Linnæus in his classification, as is well known, arranges Whales with Quadrupeds, an arrangement at which Uncle Toby, if he had been told of it, would have whistled Lilli-bullero, and the Doctor if he had not been a man of science himself, would have sung

Fa la la lerridan
Dan dan dan derridan
Dan dan dan derridan
Derridan dee.

But Uncle Toby never could have been told of it, because he good man died before Linnæus dreamt of forming a system; and Doctor Dove was a man of science, so that Lilli-bullero was never whistled upon this occasion, nor Dan dan dan derridan sung.

Whistle the one, Reader, or sing the other, which you will, or if you will, do both; when you hear that in Dr. Rees's Cyclopædia it is said, "the Whale has no other claim to a place among fishes, than from its fish-like appearance and its living in the water." The Whale has its place among them, whatever the Cyclopædists may think of its claim, and will never have it any where else; and so very like a fish it is, — so strongly in the odour of fishiness, which is a good odour if it be not too strong, — that if the Greenlanders had been converted by the Jesuits instead of the Moravians, the strictest disciplinarian of that order would without doubt have allowed his converts to eat Whale upon fish days.

But whether Whale be fish or flesh, or if makers of system should be pleased to make it fowl, (for as it is like a Quadruped except that it has no feet, and cannot live upon land, so it may be like a bird, except that it has neither legs, wings, nor feathers, and cannot live in the air,) wherever naturalists may arrange it, its local habitation is among fishes, and fish in common language it always will be called. This whole question matters not to our present purpose. Our Philosopher had regard to its place in the scale of existence, a scale which he graduated not according to size, (tho' that also must sometimes be taken into the account,) nor by intellect, which is yet of greater consideration, but according to those affections or moral feelings, which, little acquainted as we are with the nature of the lower creatures, are in many instances too evident to be called in question.

Now in this respect no other creature in the water ranks so high as the Whale.

The affection of the parent for its young is both in itself and its consequences purely good, however those men seek to degrade it who ascribe all feelings, and all virtuous emotions, whether in man or beast, to selfishness, being themselves conscious that they have no worthier motive for any of their own actions.* Martin Luther says that the Hebrew word which we translate by *curse*, carries not with it in the original language so strong a meaning as is given to it in his mother tongue, — consequently in ours. The Hebrew imprecation, he says, imports no more than "ill betide thee!" intending by *ill* temporal misfortune, or punishment, the proper reward of ill deeds; not what is implied by cursing in its dreadful acceptation. A curse, then, in the Hebrew sense, be upon those who maintain this sensual, and sensualising opinion; an opinion of which it is the sure effect to make bad men worse, and the folly and falsehood of which birds and beasts might teach them, were it not that — because their hearts are gross, seeing they see not, and hearing they hear not, neither do they understand.

The Philosopher of Doncaster affirmed that virtue as well as reason might be clearly perceived in the inferior creation, and that their parental affection was proof of it. The longer the continuance of this affection in any species the higher he was disposed to place that species in the scale of animated life. This continuance bears no relation to their size in birds, and little in quadrupeds; but in the whale it seems to be somewhat more proportionate, the young depending upon

* "They who affirm all natural acts declare
Self-love to be the ruler of the mind,
Judge from their own mean hearts, and foully
wrong mankind."
A Tale of Paraguay, canto ii. 13.

the mother more than twelve months certainly, how much longer has not been ascertained. And so strong is the maternal affection that it is a common practice among whalers to harpoon the cub as a means of taking the mother; for this creature, altho' harmless and timid at all other times, totally disregards danger when its young is to be defended, gives every possible indication of extreme agony for its young's sake, and suffers itself to be killed without attempting to escape. The mighty Ceticide Captain Scoresby describes a most affecting instance of this. "There is something," he observes, "extremely painful in the destruction of a whale, when thus evincing a degree of affectionate regard for its offspring, that would do honour to the superior intelligence of human nature; yet," he adds, "the object of the adventure, the value of the prize, the joy of the capture, cannot be sacrificed to feelings of compassion." That conclusion, if it were pursued to its legitimate consequences, would lead farther than Captain Scoresby would follow it!

The whale fishery has indeed been an object of almost portentous importance according to the statements made by this well-informed and very able writer. That on the coast of Greenland proved, he says, in a short time the most lucrative and the most important branch of national commerce that had ever been offered to the industry of man. The net profits which the Dutch derived from the Greenland fishery during an hundred and seven years are stated at more than 20 millions sterling.

The class of Captains and seamen, employed in the southern whale-fishery, says a person engaged in that business himself, are quite different from any other. Lads taken from the streets without shoes and stockings, become many of them masters of ships and men of very large property. "There was an instance, a short time ago, of one dying worth £60,000; and I can point out twenty instances of persons worth 7 or 8, or £10,000 who have risen, without any patronage whatever, by their own exertions. It does not require any patronage to get on in the fishery." Such is the statement of one who was examined before a Committee of the House of Commons in 1833, upon the state of Manufactures, Commerce and Shipping.

In a pamphlet written about the middle of the last century to recommend the prosecution of this trade, is was stated that the whale-fishery is of the nature of a lottery, where tho' the adventurers are certain losers on the whole, some are very great gainers; and this, it was argued, instead of being a discouragement, was in fact the most powerful motive by which men were induced to engage in it.

If indeed the pleasure of gambling be in proportion to the stake, as those miserable and despicable persons who are addicted to that vice seem to think it is; and if the pleasure which men take in field sports be in proportion to the excitement which the pursuit calls forth, whaling must be in both respects the most stimulating of all maritime adventures. One day's sport in which Captain Scoresby took three whales, produced a return of £2,100, and several years before he retired from this calling he had been personally concerned in the capture of three hundred and twenty-two. And his father in twenty-eight voyages, in which he commanded a ship, brought home 498 whales, producing 4246 tons of oil, the value of which, with that of the whale-bone, exceeded £150,000, "all fished for under his own direction out of the sea."

The whale fishery is even of more importance as a nursery for seamen, for of all naval services it is the most severe; and this thorough seaman describes the excitement and the enjoyment of a whaler's life as being in proportion to the danger. "The difficulties and intricacies of the situation, when the vessel is to be forced through masses of drift ice, afford exercise," he says, "for the highest possible exertion of nautical skill, and are capable of yielding to the person who has the management of a ship a degree of enjoyment, which it would be difficult for navigators accustomed to mere common-place operations duly to appreciate.

The ordinary management of a ship, under a strong gale, and with great velocity, exhibits evolutions of considerable elegance; but these cannot be compared with the navigation in the intricacies of floating ice, where the evolutions are frequent, and perpetually varying; where manœuvres are to be accomplished, that extend to the very limits of possibility; and where a degree of hazard attaches to some of the operations, which would render a mistake of the helm, — or a miscalculation of the powers of a ship, irremediate and destructive." — How wonderful a creature is man, that the sense of power should thus seem to constitute his highest animal enjoyment!

In proportion to the excitement of such a life, Captain Scoresby describes its religious tendency upon a well disposed mind, and this certainly has been exemplified in his own person. "Perhaps there is no situation in life," he says, "in which an habitual reliance upon Providence, and a well founded dependance on the Divine protection and support, is of such sensible value as it is found to be by those employed in seafaring occupations, and especially in the fishery for whales. These are exposed to a great variety of dangers, many of which they must voluntarily face; and the success of their exertions depends on a variety of causes, over many of which they have no controul. The anxiety arising from both these causes is greatly repressed, and often altogether subdued, when, convinced of the infallibility and universality of Providence by the internal power of religion, we are enabled to commit all our ways unto God, and to look for his blessing as essential to our safety, and as necessary for our success."

John Newton of Olney has in his narrative of his own remarkable life, a passage that entirely accords with these remarks of Captain Scoresby, and which is in like manner the result of experience. "A seafaring life," he says, "is necessarily excluded from the benefit of public ordinances, and christian communion. — In other respects, I know not any calling that seems more favourable, or affords greater advantages to an awakened mind, for promoting the life of God in the soul, especially to a person who has the command of a ship, and thereby has it in his power to restrain gross irregularities in others, and to dispose of his own time. — To be at sea in these circumstances, withdrawn out of the reach of innumerable temptations, with opportunity and a turn of mind disposed to observe the wonders of God, in the great deep, with the two noblest objects of sight, the expanded heavens and the expanded ocean, continually in view; and where evident interpositions of Divine Providence in answer to prayer occur almost every day; these are helps to quicken and confirm the life of faith, which in a good measure supply to a religious sailor the want of those advantages which can be only enjoyed upon the shore. And indeed though my knowledge of spiritual things (as knowledge is usually estimated) was at this time very small, yet I sometimes look back with regret upon those scenes. I never knew sweeter or more frequent hours of divine communion than in my two last voyages to Guinea, when I was either almost secluded from society on ship-board, or when on shore among the natives."

What follows is so beautiful (except the extravagant condemnation of a passionate tenderness which he, of all men, should have been the last to condemn) that the passage, though it has set us ashore, must be continued a little farther. "I have wandered," he proceeds, "thro' the woods, reflecting on the singular goodness of the Lord to me in a place where, perhaps, there was not a person who knew him, for some thousand miles round me. Many a time upon these occasions I have restored the beautiful lines of Tibullus * to the right owner; lines full of blasphemy and madness, when addressed to a creature, but full of comfort and propriety in the mouth of a believer.

Sic ego desertis possum bene vivere sylvis,
Quà nulla humano sit via trita pede.
Tu mihi curarum requies, in nocte vel atra
Lumen, et in solis tu mihi turba locis.

* Mr. Newton, by an easy slip of the memory, has ascribed the lines to Propertius. R. S.

CHAPTER CLXVII.

A MOTTO WHICH IS WELL CHOSEN BECAUSE NOT BEING APPLICABLE IT SEEMS TO BE SO. THE AUTHOR NOT ERRANT HERE OR ELSEWHERE. PHILOSOPHY AND OTHER-OSOPHIES.

Much from my theme and friend have I digressed,
But poor as I am, poor in stuff for thought,
And poor in thought to make of it the best,
Blame me not, Gentles, if I soon am caught
By this or that, when as my theme suggest
Aught of collateral aid which may be wrought
Into its service: Blame me not, I say:
The idly musing often miss their way.

CHARLES LLOYD.

THE pleasing pensive stanza, which thou, gentle Reader, hast just perused, is prefixed to this Chapter because it would be so felicitous a motto, if only it were applicable; and for that very reason it is felicitous, its non-applicability furnishing a means of happy application.

*Il y a du bonheur et de l'esprit à employer les paroles d'un poëte à une chose à quoy le poëte ne pense jamais, et à les employer si à propos qu'elles semblent avoir esté faites exprés pour le sujet auquel elles sont appliquées.**

"Good Sir, you understand not;"—yet I am not saying with the Pedagogue at the Ordinary,

— Let's keep them
In desperate hope of understanding us;
Riddles and clouds are very lights of speech.
I'll veil my careless anxious thoughts as 'twere
In a perspicuous cloud, that so I may
Whisper in a loud voice, and even be silent
When I do utter words.† —

Here, as everywhere, my intention is to be perfectly intelligible; I have not digressed either from my theme or friend; I am neither poor in stuff for thought, nor in thought for working; nor, (if I may be permitted so to say) in skill for manipulating it. I have not been idly musing, nor have I missed my road, but have kept the track faithfully, and not departed from the way in which I was trained up. All that I have been saying belongs to, and is derived from the philosophy of my friend: yes, gentle Reader, all that is set before thee in these well stored volumes. *Una est enim philosophia, quascumque in oras disputationis regionesve delata est. Nam sive de cœli naturâ loquitur, sive de terræ, sive de divinâ vi, sive de humanâ, sive ex inferiore loco, sive ex æquo, sive ex superiore, sive ut impellat homines, sive ut doceat, sive ut deterreat, sive ut concitet, sive ut incendat, sive ut reflectat, sive ut leniat, sive ad paucos, sive ad multos, sive inter alienos, sive cum suis, sive secum, rivis est deducta philosophia, non fontibus.*

We speak of the philosophy of the Porch, and of the Grove, and of the Sty when we would express ourselves disdainfully of the Epicureans. But we cannot, in like manner, give to the philosophy which pervades these volumes, a local habitation and a name, because the philosophy of Doncaster would popularly be understood to mean the philosophy of the Duke of Grafton, the Marquis of Exeter, and Mr. Gully, tho' that indeed belongs not to Philosophy but to one of its dialects, varieties, or corrupted forms, which are many; for example, there is Fallosophy practised professionally by Advocates, and exhibited in great perfection by Quacks and Political Economists; Failosophy, the science of those who make bankruptcy a profitable adventure; Fellowsophy, which has its habitat in common rooms at Cambridge and Oxford; Feelosophy common to Lawyers and Physicians; Fillyosophy well understood on the turf, and nowhere better than in Doncaster; and finally the Foolosophy of Jeremy Bentham, and of all those who have said in their hearts—what it saddens a compassionate heart to think that even the Fool should say!

* P. BOUHOURS.

† CARTWRIGHT.

CHAPTER CLXVIII.

NE-PLUS-ULTRA-WHALE-FISHING. AN OPINION OF CAPTAIN SCORESBY'S. THE DOCTOR DENIES THAT ALL CREATURES WERE MADE FOR THE USE OF MAN. THE CONTRARY DEMONSTRATED IN PRACTICE BY BELLARMINE.

Sequar quo vocas, omnibus enim rebus omnibusque sermonibus, aliquid salutare miscendum est. SENECA.

THE hardiest of Captain Scoresby's sailors would never, methinks, have ventured upon a manner of catching the whale used by the Indians in Florida, which Sir Richard Hawkins says is worthy to be considered, inasmuch as the barbarous people have found out so great a secret, by the industry and diligence of one man, to kill so great and huge a monster. Let not the reader think meanly of an able and judicious, as well as brave, adventurous, and unfortunate man, because he believed what he thus relates:

"The Indian discovering a whale, procureth two round billets of wood, sharpened both at one end, and so binding them together with a cord, casteth himself with them into the sea, and swimmeth towards the whale. If he come to him the whale escapeth not; for he placeth himself upon his neck; and altho' the whale goeth to the bottom, he must of force rise presently to breathe, for which nature hath given him two great holes in the top of his head by which every time that he breatheth, he spouteth out a great quantity of water; the Indian forsaketh not his hold, but riseth with him, and thrusteth in a log into one of his spouters, and with the other knocketh it in so fast, that by no means the whale can get it out: that fastened, at another opportunity, he thrusteth in the second log into the other spouter, and with all the force he can, keepeth it in. The whale not being able to breathe swimmeth presently ashore, and the Indian a cock-horse upon him!" Hawkins says that many Spaniards had discoursed to him upon this subject, who had been eye-witnesses of it!

"Most other animals when attacked," says Captain Scoresby, "instinctively pursue a conduct which is generally the best calculated to secure their escape; but not so the whale. Were it to remain on the surface after being harpooned, to press steadily forward in one direction, and to exert the wonderful strength that it possesses; or were it to await the attacks of its enemies, and repel them by well-timed flourishes of its tremendous tail, it would often victoriously dispute the field with man, whose strength and bulk scarcely exceed a nine-hundredth part of its own. But, like the rest of the lower animals, it was designed by Him who 'created great whales,' and every living creature that moveth to be subject to man; and therefore when attacked by him, it perishes by its simplicity."

Captain Scoresby now holds a commission in the spiritual service as a fisher of men, — a commission which I verily believe has been most properly applied for and worthily bestowed. Whether this extraordinary change in life has produced any change in his opinion upon this subject I know not; or whether he still thinks that whales were made subject to man, in order that man might slaughter them for the sake of their blubber and their whalebone.

Nevertheless it was a foolish wish of mine that gas-lights might supersede the use of train-oil; foolish because a little foresight might have made me apprehend that oil-gas might supersede coal-gas; and a little reflection would have shown that tho' collieries are much more necessary than the Greenland fishery can be pretended to be, far greater evil is connected with them, and that this evil is without any incidental good. For the Greenland fishery unquestionably makes the best seamen; and a good seaman, good in the moral and religious, as well as in the nautical sense of the word, is one of the highest characters that this world's rough discipline can produce. "Ay," says an old Lieutenant, living frugally upon his poor half-pay, "ay that he is, by ——."

But it was not otherwise a foolish wish; for that the whale was made for the use of man in any such way as the whalers take for granted, I am very far from believing.

All creatures animate and inanimate, are constituent parts of one great system; and so far dependent upon each other, and in a certain sense each made for all. The whale is a link in the chain, and the largest that has yet been found, for no one has yet caught a Kraken.

Cicero makes Crassus the orator commend the ancient philosophy which taught that all things were thus connected: — *Mihi quidem veteres illi, majus quiddam animo complexi, multo plus etiam vidisse videntur, quam quan-*

tum nostrorum ingeniorum acies intueri potest; qui omnia hæc, quæ supra et subter, unum esse, et unâ vi atque unâ consensione naturæ constricta esse dixerunt. Nullum est enim genus rerum quod aut avulsum a cæteris per seipsum constare, aut, quo cætera si careant, vim suam atque æternitatem conservare possint. He expresses a doubt indeed that *hæc major esse ratio videtur, quam ut hominum possit sensu, aut cogitatione, comprehendi:* and with the proper reserve of such a doubt, our Philosopher gave a qualified assent to the opinion, restricting it, however, religiously to the inferior and visible creation: but as to the notion that all things were made for the use of man, in the sense that vulgar men believe, this he considered to be as presumptuous and as absurd as the converse of the proposition which Pope puts into the mouth of the pampered Goose. "The monstrous faith of many made for one," might seem reasonable and religious when compared with such a supposition.

"Made for thy use," the Doctor would say, "tyrant that thou art, and weak as thou art tyrannical! Will the unicorn be willing to serve thee, or abide by thy crib? Canst thou bind him with his band in the furrow; or will he harrow the vallies after thee? Canst thou draw out leviathan with an hook, will he make a covenant with thee, wilt thou take him for a servant! Wilt thou bind him for thy maidens? Shall thy companions make a banquet of him? Shall they part him among the merchants? Made for thy use,—when so many may seem to have been made for thy punishment and humiliation!"

There is a use indeed in these, but few men are so ready to acknowledge and act upon it as Bellarmine was, who being far more indulgent to musquitos and other small deer than to heretics, allowed them free right of pasture upon his corporal domains. He thought they were created to afford exercise for our patience, and moreover that it is unjust for us to interrupt them in their enjoyment here, when we consider that they have no other paradise to expect. Yet when the Cardinal Controversialist gave breakfast, dinner, or supper of this kind, he was far from partaking any sympathetic pleasure in the happiness which he imparted; for it is related of him that at one time he was so terribly bitten *à bestiolis quibusdam nequam ac damnificis,* (it is not necessary to inquire of what species,) as earnestly to pray that if there were any torments in Hell itself so dreadful as what he was then enduring, the Lord would be pleased not to send him there, for he should not be able to bear it.

What could the Cardinal then have thought of those Convents that were said to have an apartment or dungeon into which the Friars every day during the warm season, brushed or shook the fleas from their habits thro' an aperture above, (being the only entrance,) and where, whenever a frail brother was convicted of breaking the most fragile of his vows, he was let down naked and with his hands tied! This earthly Purgatory was called *la Pulciara,* that is, the Fleaery, and there the culprit was left till it was deemed that he had suffered punishment enough in this life for his offence.

Io tengo omai per infallibil cosa,
Che sian per nostro mal nati gl' insetti
Per renderci la vita aspra e nojosa.
Certo in quei primi giorni benedetti
Ne gli orti del piacer non abitaro
Questi sozzi e molesti animaletti;
Ne' con gli altri animali a paro a paro
Per saper come avessero a chianarsi
Al cospetto d' Adam si presentaro:

* * *

Nacquero dunque sol per nostro male
Queste malnate bestie, e fur prodotte
In pena de la colpa originale.

* * *

E come l' uomo a sospirar ridutto
Per l' interno sconcerto de gli affetti
Pravi, germoglia miserabil frutto;
Cosè la terra fra suoi varj effetti
Pel reo fermento, onde bollir si sente,
Da se produce i velenosi insetti.
Infin, da la materia putrescente,
Nascon l' abbominevoli bestiuole,
Ed è questa per me cosa evidente.
So che nol voglion le moderne scuole;
Ma ciò che monta? In simile argomento
*E' lecito a ciascun dir ciò che vuole.**

* Cordara.

CHAPTER CLXIX.

LINKS AND AFFINITIES. A MAP OF THE AUTHOR'S INTELLECTUAL COURSE IN THE FIVE PRECEDING CHAPTERS.

Ὦ φίλε Φαῖδρε, ποῖ δὴ καὶ πόθεν; PLATO.

AND now it may be agreeable to the reader to be presented here with a sort of synopsis, or itinerary, whereby as in a chart he may trace what he perhaps has erroneously considered the erratic course of association in the five antecedent Chapters.

First, then, Aristotle held that domesticated animals were benefited by their connection with man.

Secondly, the Biographer and Disciple of Dr. Dove thought that Aristotle was not altogether right when he held that domesticated animals were benefited by their connection with man.

Thirdly, Chick-Pick, and Hen-Pen, and Cock-Lock, and Duck-Luck, and Turkey-Lurkey, and Goosey-Loosey, being consulted, confirmed the opinion of the Biographer and Disciple of Dr. Dove, that Aristotle was not altogether right when he held that domesticated animals were benefited by their connection with man.

Fourthly, it was seen that Goosey-Loosey ended her speech abruptly and significantly with the word *But:* When Chick-Pick and Hen-Pen, and Cock-Lock, and Duck-Luck, and Turkey-Lurkey, and Goosey-Loosey, being consulted, confirmed the opinion of the Biographer and Disciple of Dr. Dove, that Aristotle was not altogether right when he held that domesticated animals were benefited by their connection with man.

Fifthly, it was observed that Grammarians have maintained many and mysterious opinions concerning the nature of the word *But*, with which Goosey-Loosey ended her speech abruptly and significantly, after Chick-Pick, and Hen-Pen, and Cock-Lock, and Duck-Luck, and Turkey-Lurkey, and Goosey-Loosey, being consulted, had confirmed the opinion of the Biographer and Disciple of Dr. Dove, that Aristotle was not altogether right when he held that domesticated animals were benefited by their connection with man.

Sixthly, a question was propounded, after it had been observed that Grammarians have maintained many and mysterious opinions concerning the nature of the word *But*, with which Goosey-Loosey ended her speech abruptly and significantly, after Chick-Pick, and Hen-Pen, and Cock-Lock, and Duck-Luck, and Turkey-Lurkey, and Goosey-Loosey, being consulted, had confirmed the opinion of the Biographer and Disciple of Dr. Dove, that Aristotle was not altogether right when he held that domesticated animals were benefited by their connection with man.

Seventhly, the Reader answered the question which the writer propounded, after it had been observed that Grammarians have maintained many and mysterious opinions concerning the nature of the word *But*, with which Goosey-Loosey ended her speech abruptly and significantly, after Chick-Pick, and Hen-Pen, and Cock-Lock, and Duck-Luck, and Turkey-Lurkey, and Goosey-Loosey, being consulted, had confirmed the opinion of the Biographer and Disciple of Dr. Dove, that Aristotle was not altogether right when he held that domesticated animals were benefited by their connection with man.

Eighthly, it appeared that the Reader had hit the *But*, when he answered the question which the writer propounded, after it had been observed that Grammarians have maintained many and mysterious opinions concerning the nature of the word *But*, with which Goosey-Loosey ended her speech abruptly and significantly, after Chick-Pick, and Hen-Pen, and Cock-Lock, and Duck-Luck, and Turkey-Lurkey, and Goosey-Loosey, being consulted, had confirmed the opinion of the Biographer and Disciple of Dr. Dove, that Aristotle was not altogether right when he held that domesticated animals were benefited by their connection with man.

Ninthly, there was an entry of one million, eight hundred and twenty thousand Goose Quills, entered in that place, because the Reader had hit the *But*, when he answered the question which the writer propounded, after it had been observed that Grammarians have maintained many and mysterious opinions concerning the nature of the word *But*, with which Goosey-Loosey ended her speech abruptly and significantly, after Chick-Pick, and Hen-Pen, and Cock-Lock, and Duck-Luck, and Turkey-Lurkey, and Goosey-Loosey, being consulted, had confirmed the opinion of the Biographer and Disciple of Dr. Dove, that Aristotle was not altogether right when he held that domesticated animals were benefited by their connection with man.

Tenthly, the Reader was called upon to consider the good and evil connected with those one million, eight hundred and twenty thousand goose quills, the entry of which was entered in that place, because the Reader had hit the *But*, when he answered the question which the writer propounded, after it had been observed that Grammarians have maintained many and mysterious opinions concerning the nature of the word *But*, with which Goosey-Loosey ended her speech abruptly and significantly, after Chick-Pick, and Hen-Pen, and Cock-Lock, and Duck-Luck, and Turkey-Lurkey, and Goosey-Loosey, being consulted, had confirmed the opinion of the Biographer and Disciple of Dr. Dove, that Aristotle was not altogether right when he held that domesticated animals were benefited by their connection with man.

Eleventhly, a wish concerning Whales was expressed, which was associated, it has not yet appeared how, with the feeling in which the Reader is called upon to consider the good and the evil connected with those one million, eight hundred and twenty thousand goose quills, the entry of which was entered in that place, because the Reader had hit the *But*, when he answered the question which the writer propounded, after it had been observed that Grammarians have maintained many and mysterious opinions concerning the nature of the word *But*, with which Goosey-Loosey ended her speech abruptly and significantly, after Chick-Pick, and Hen-Pen, and Cock-Lock, and Duck-Luck, and Turkey-Lurkey, and Goosey-Loosey, being consulted, had confirmed the opinion of the Biographer and Disciple of Dr. Dove, that Aristotle was not altogether right when he held that domesticated animals were benefited by their connection with man.

Twelfthly, Captain Scoresby was introduced in consequence of a wish concerning Whales having been expressed, which was associated, it has not yet appeared how, with the feeling in which the Reader was called upon to consider the good and the evil connected with those one million, eight hundred and twenty thousand goose quills, the entry of which was entered in that place, because the Reader had hit the *But*, when he answered the question which the writer propounded, after it had been observed that Grammarians have maintained many and mysterious opinions concerning the nature of the word *But*, with which Goosey-Loosey ended her speech abruptly and significantly, after Chick-Pick, and Hen-Pen, and Cock-Lock, and Duck-Luck, and Turkey-Lurkey, and Goosey-Loosey, being consulted, had confirmed the opinion of the Biographer and Disciple of Dr. Dove, that Aristotle was not altogether right when he maintained that domesticated animals were benefited by their connection with man.

Thirteenthly, some curious facts concerning the Greenland fishery were stated on the authority of Captain Scoresby, who was introduced in consequence of a wish concerning Whales having been expressed, which was associated, it has not yet appeared how, with the feeling to which the Reader was called upon to consider the good and the evil connected with those one million, eight hundred and twenty thousand goose quills, the entry of which was entered in that place, because the Reader had hit the *But*, when he answered the question which the writer propounded, after it had been observed that Grammarians have maintained many and mysterious opinions concerning the nature of the word *But*, with which Goosey-Loosey ended her speech abruptly and significantly, after Chick-Pick, and Hen-Pen, and Cock-Lock, and Duck-Luck, and Turkey-Lurkey, and Goosey-Loosey, being consulted, confirmed the opinion of the Biographer and Disciple of Dr. Dove, that Aristotle was not altogether right when he held that domesticated animals were benefited by their connection with man.

Fourteenthly, a beautiful stanza was quoted from a poem by Mr. Charles Lloyd, which, becoming applicable as a motto because it seemed inapplicable, was applied, after some curious facts concerning the Greenland fishery had been stated on the authority of Captain Scoresby, who was introduced in consequence of a wish concerning Whales having been expressed, which was associated, it has not yet appeared how, with the feeling in which the Reader was called upon to consider the good and the evil connected with those one million, eight hundred and twenty thousand goose quills, the entry of which was entered in that place, because the Reader had hit the *But*, when he answered the question which the writer propounded, after it had been observed that Grammarians have maintained many and mysterious opinions concerning the nature of the word *But*, with which Goosey-Loosey ended her speech abruptly and significantly, after Chick-Pick, and Hen-Pen, and Cock-Lock, and Duck-Luck, and Turkey-Lurkey, and Goosey-Loosey, being consulted, confirmed the opinion of the Biographer and Disciple of Dr. Dove, that Aristotle was not altogether right when he held that domesticated animals were benefited by their connection with man.

Fifteenthly, that the writer in all which went before had adhered, and was at present adhering to the philosophy of Dr. Dove, was shown in relation to a beautiful stanza that had been quoted from a poem by Mr. Charles Lloyd, which, becoming applicable as a motto because it seemed to be inapplicable, was applied, after some curious facts concerning the Greenland fishery had been stated on the authority of Captain Scoresby, who was introduced in consequence of a wish concerning Whales having been expressed, which was associated, it has not yet appeared how, with the feeling in which the Reader was called upon to consider the good and the evil connected with those one million, eight hundred and twenty thousand goose quills, the entry of which was entered in that place, because the Reader had hit the *But*, when he answered the question which the writer propounded, after it had been observed that Grammarians have maintained many and mysterious opinions concerning the nature of the word *But*, with which Goosey-Loosey ended her speech abruptly and significantly, after Chick-Pick, and Hen-Pen, and Cock-Lock, and Duck-Luck, and Turkey-Lurkey, and Goosey-Loosey, being consulted, confirmed the opinion of the Biographer and Disciple of Dr. Dove, that Aristotle was not altogether right when he held that domesticated animals were benefited by their connection with man.

Sixteenthly, an assertion of Captain Scoresby's that Whales were created for man was brought forward, when it had been shown that the writer in all which went before had adhered, and was at present adhering to the philosophy of Dr. Dove, in relation to a beautiful stanza that had been quoted from a poem by Mr. Charles Lloyd, which, becoming applicable as a motto because it seemed to be inapplicable, was applied, after some curious facts concerning the Greenland fishery had been stated on the authority of Captain Scoresby, who was introduced in consequence of a wish concerning Whales having been expressed, which was associated, it has not yet appeared how, with the feeling in which the reader was called upon to consider the good and the evil connected with those one million, eight hundred and twenty thousand goose quills, the entry of which was entered in that place, because the Reader had hit the *But*, when he answered the question which the writer propounded, after it had been observed that Grammarians have maintained many and mysterious opinions concerning the nature of the word *But*, with which Goosey-Loosey ended her speech abruptly and significantly, after Chick-Pick, and Hen-Pen, and Cock-Lock, and Duck-Luck, and Turkey-Lurkey, and Goosey-Loosey, being consulted, confirmed the opinion of the Biographer and Disciple of Dr. Dove, that Aristotle was not altogether right when he held that domesticated animals were benefited by their connection with man.

Seventeenthly and lastly, the Biographer and Disciple of Dr. Dove opposed the assertion of Captain Scoresby that Whales were created for man, which assertion was brought forward when it had been shown, that the writer in all which went before had adhered, and was at present adhering to the philosophy of Dr. Dove, in relation to a beautiful stanza that had been quoted from a poem of Mr. Charles Lloyd, which, becoming applicable as a motto because it seemed to be inapplicable, was applied, after some curious facts concerning the Greenland fishery had been stated on the authority of Captain Scoresby, who was introduced in consequence of a wish concerning Whales having been expressed, which was associated, it has not yet appeared how, with the feeling in which the Reader was called upon to consider the good and the evil connected with those one million, eight hundred and twenty thousand goose quills, the entry of which was entered in that place, because the Reader had hit the But, when he answered the question which the writer propounded, after it had been observed that Grammarians have maintained many and mysterious opinions concerning the nature of the word *But*, with which Goosey-Loosey ended her speech abruptly and significantly, after Chick-Pick, and Hen-Pen, and Cock-Lock, and Duck-Luck, and Turkey-Lurkey, and Goosey-Loosey, being consulted, confirmed the opinion of the Biographer and Disciple of Dr. Dove, that Aristotle was not altogether right when he held that domesticated animals were benefited by their connection with man.

You see, Reader, where we are, and whence we came, and I have thus retraced for you the seventeen stages of association by which we have proceeded from the one point to the other, because you will have much more satisfaction in seeing the substance of the aforesaid five chapters thus clearly and coherently recapitulated, than if it had been in the common form, simply and compendiously capitulated at the head of each. For in this point I agree with that good, patient, kind-hearted, industrious, ingenious, odd, whimsical and yet withal *dullus homo*, James Elphinstone, Radical Reformer of English Orthography. He says, and you shall have the passage in Elphinstonography, as he printed it, "I own myself an ennemy to hwatevver seems quaint in dhe verry contents ov a chapter; and dho dhe starts ov surprize be intollerabell, wons plezzure iz no les balked by anticipation. Hoo indeed prezents a bil ov fare, widh an entertainment? Hwen dhe entertainment iz over, dhe bil may doubtles com in, to refresh dhe memmory, edher widh plan or particulers, dhat hav regaled dhe various pallates ov dhe company."

CHAPTER CLXX.

THE AUTHOR REPEATS A REMARK OF HIS DAUGHTER UPON THE PRECEDING CHAPTER; COMPLIMENTS THE LORD BROUGHAM AND VAUX UPON HIS LUNGS AND LARYNX; PHILOSOPHISES AND QUOTES, AND QUOTES AND PHILOSOPHISES AGAIN AND AGAIN.

Fato, Fortuna, Predestinazione,
Sorte, Caso, Ventura, son di quelle
Cose che dan gran noja a le persone,
E vi si dicon su di gran novelle.
Ma in fine Iddio d' ogni cose é padrone:
E chi é savio domina a le stelle;
Chi non é savio paziente e forte,
Lamentisi di se, non de la sorte. ORL. INN.

"PAPPA, it's a breathless chapter!" says one whose eyes when they are turned toward me I never meet without pleasure, unless sorrow has suffused them, or illness dimmed their light.

Nobody then can give so much effect to it in reading aloud as the Lord Chancellor Brougham and Vaux, he having made a speech of nine hours long upon the state of the law, and thereby proved himself to be the most long-winded of living men. And fit it is that he should be so; for there are very few men to whom, whether he be right or wrong, it can be so well worth while to listen.

Yet give me space a while for to respire,
And I myself shall fairly well out-wind.*

* HENRY MORE.

For I have read no idle or unprofitable lesson in this renumeration. Were we thus to retrace the course of our own lives, there are few of us who would not find that that course had been influenced, and its most important events brought about, by incidents which might seem as casually or capriciously connected as the seventeen links of this mental chain. Investigate anything backward through seventeen generations of motives, or moving causes, whether in private or in public life: see from what slight and insignificant circumstances friendships have originated, and have been dissolved; by what accidents the choice of a profession, or of a wife, have been determined, and on how inconsiderable a point the good or ill fortune of a life has depended; — deaths, marriages, wealth or poverty, opinions more important than all other things, as in their consequence affecting our happiness not only here but hereafter; victories and defeats, war and peace, change of ministries and of dynasties, revolutions, the overthrow of thrones, the degradation, and the ruin, and the destruction, and the disappearance of nations! Trace any of these backward link by link, and long before we are lost in the series of causes, we shall be lost in thought, and in wonder; so much will there be to humble the pride of man, to abate his presumption, and to call for and confirm his faith.

On dit que quand les Chinois, qui n'ont pas l'usage des horologes, commencerent à voir ces rouës, ces balanciers, ces volans, ces contrepoids, et tout l'attirail de ces grandes machines, considerant les pieces à part et comme desmembrées, ils n'en firent pas grand estat, pource qu'ils ne sçavoient à quel usage devoient servir toutes ces pieces: mais comme elles furent montées, et qu'ils oüyrent les heures sur le tymbre, ils furent si surpris d'estonnement, qu'ils s'assembloient à trouppes pour voir le mouvement de l'aiguille, et pour entendre les heures; et appellerent ces machines en leur langue, LE FER QUI PARLE. *Je dis que qui considera les parties de la Providence Divine comme desmembrées et à piece, tant de ressorts, tant d'accordans divers, tant d'evenemens qui nous semblent casuels, ne se pourra jamais imaginer la beauté de cette machine, la sagesse de cette Providence, la conduitte de ce grand corps; à cause qu'on fait tort à un ouvrage fait à la Mosaïque de le voir à lambeaux; il le faut voir monté et rangé par le menu pour marquer sa beauté. Mais quand on entend l'heure qui sonne sur le tymbre, on commence à cognoistre qu'il y avoit au dedans une belle et agreable police qui paroist au dehors par la sonnerie. Ainsi en est il à peu pres de la vie d'un homme.**

May not that which frequently has been, instruct us as to what will be! is a question which Hobbes proposes, and which he answers in the negative. "No;" he replies to it, "for no one knows what may be, except He who knows all things, because all things contribute to everything." —

Nonne
Id quod sæpe fuit, nos docet id quod erit;
Non; scit enim quod erit, nisi qui sciat omnia, nemo;
Omni contribuunt omnia namque rei.

The philosopher of Doncaster was far from agreeing with the philosopher of Malmesbury upon this as upon many other points. *De minimis non curat lex*, was a maxim with him in philosophy as well as in law. There were many things he thought, which ended in as little as they began, fatherless and childless actions, having neither cause nor consequence, bubbles upon the stream of events, which rise, burst, and are no more:—

A moment seen, then gone for ever.†

What John Newton said is nevertheless true; the way of man is not in himself! nor can he conceive what belongs to a single step. "When I go to St. Mary Woolnoth," he proceeds, "it seems the same whether I turn down Lothbury or go through the Old Jewry; but the going through one street and not another may produce an effect of lasting consequence." He had proof enough of this in the providential course of his own eventful life; and who is there that cannot

* GARASSE. — This passage is remarkable. Paley evidently borrowed the illustration from Burnet's Theoria Sacra; — whether Burnet borrowed it from Garasse is not so clear: he was about forty years Burnet's senior.

† BURNS.

call to mind some striking instances in his own?

"There is a time coming," said this good man, "when our warfare shall be accomplished, our views enlarged, and our light increased; then with what transports of adoration and love shall we look back upon the way by which the Lord led us! We shall then see and acknowledge that mercy and goodness directed every step; we shall see that what our ignorance once called adversities and evils, were in reality blessings which we could not have done well without; that nothing befell us without a cause, that no trouble came upon us sooner, or pressed us more heavily, or continued longer, than our case required: in a word, that our many afflictions were each in their place, among the means employed by divine grace and wisdom, to bring us to the possession of that exceeding and eternal weight of glory which the Lord has prepared for his people. And even in this imperfect state, though we are seldom able to judge aright of our present circumstances, yet if we look upon the years of our past life, and compare the dispensations we have been brought through, with the frame of our minds under each successive period; if we consider how wonderfully one thing has been connected with another; so that what we now number amongst our greatest advantages, perhaps took their first rise from incidents which we thought hardly worth our notice; and that we have sometimes escaped the greatest dangers that threatened us, not by any wisdom or foresight of our own, but by that intervention of circumstances, which we neither desired nor thought of; — I say, when we compare and consider these things by the light afforded us in the Holy Scriptures, we may collect indisputable proof from the narrow circle of our own concerns, that the wise and good providence of God watches over his people from the earliest moment of their life, over-rules and guards them through all their wanderings in a state of ignorance, and leads them in a way they know not, till at length his providence and grace concur in those events and impressions which bring them to the knowledge of Him and themselves."

"All things are brought upon us by Nature and Fate," says the unknown speculator who foisted his theology upon the world under the false name of Hermes Trismegistus: "and there is no place deserted by Providence. But Providence is the reason, perfect in itself, of super-celestial Deity. From it are the two known Powers, Necessity and Fate. Fate is the Minister of Providence and of Necessity; and the Stars are the ministers of Fate. And no one can fly from Fate, nor protect himself against its mighty force; for the Stars are the arms of Fate, and according to it all things are affected in Nature and in Men." Take the passage in the Latin of Franciscus Patricius, who produced these mystic treatises from the Ranzovian Library.

Omnia vero fiunt Naturâ et Fato. Et non est locus desertus a Providentiâ. Providentia vero est per se perfecta ratio supercœlestis Dei. Duæ autem sunt ab eâ notæ potentiæ. Necessitas et Fatum. Fatum autem ministrum est Providentiæ et Necessitatis. Fati vero ministræ sunt stellæ. Neque enim Fatum fugere quis potest, neque se custodire ab ipsius vi magnâ. Arma namque Fati sunt Stellæ, secùndum ipsum namque cuncta efficiuntur Naturæ et hominibus.

Thus, says P. Garasse, there are six or seven steps down to man; Providence, Necessity, Fate, the Stars, Nature, and then Man at the lowest step of the ladder. For Providence, being *ratio absoluta cœlestis Dei*, is *comme hors de pair:* and has under her a servant, who is called Necessity, and Necessity has under her, her valet Fate, and Fate has the Stars for its weapons, and the Stars have Nature for their arsenal, and Nature has them for her subjects: The one serves the other, *en sorte que le premier qui manque à son devoir, desbauche tout l'attirail; mais à condition, qu'il est hors de la puissance des hommes d'eviter les armes du Destin qui sont les Estoiles. Or je confesse que tout ce discours m'est si obscur et enigmatique que j'entendrois mieux les resveries d'un phrenetique, ou les pensées obscures de Lycophron; je m'asseure que Trismegiste ne s'entendoit non plus lors qu'il faisoit ce discours, que nous l'entendons maintenant.*"

The Jesuit is right. Necessity, Fate and Nature are mere abstractions. The Stars keep their courses and regard not us. Between Man and his Maker nothing is interposed; nothing can be interposed between the Omnipresent Almighty and the creatures of His hand. Receive this truth into thy soul whoever thou be'est that readest, and it will work in thee a death unto sin and a new birth unto righteousness! And ye who tremble at the awful thought, remember that, though there be nothing *between* us and our Judge, we have a Mediator and Advocate *with* Him, who is the propitiation for our sins, and who is "able to save them to the uttermost that come to God through Him."

CHAPTER CLXXI.

CONTAINING PART OF A SERMON, WHICH THE READER WILL FIND WORTH MORE THAN MOST WHOLE ONES THAT IT MAY BE HIS FORTUNE TO HEAR.

Je fais une grande provision de bon sens en prenant ce que les autres en ont. MADAME DE MAINTENON.

READER! I set some learning before you in the last chapter, and "however some may cry out that all endeavours at learning in a book like this, especially where it steps beyond their little, (or let me not wrong them) no brain at all, is superfluous, I am contented," with great Ben, "that these fastidious stomachs should leave my full tables, and enjoy at home their clean empty trenchers."

In pursuance of the same theme I shall set before you here some divine philosophy in the words of Dr. Scott, the author of the Christian Life. "The goods and evils that befall us here," says that wise and excellent preacher, who being dead yet speaketh, and will continue to speak while there be any virtue and while there be any praise,—"the goods and evils, which befall us here, are not so truly to be estimated by themselves as by their effects and consequents. For the Divine Providence which runs through all things, hath disposed and connected them into such a series and order, that there is no single event or accident (but what is purely miraculous) but depends upon the whole system, and hath innumerable causes antecedent to it, and innumerable consequents attending it; and what the consequents will be, whether good or bad, singly and apart by itself, yet in conjunction with all those consequents that will most certainly attend it, the best event, for aught we know, may prove most mischievous, and the worst most beneficial to us. So that for us boldly to pronounce concerning the good or evil of events, before we see the train of consequents that follow them, is very rash and inconsiderate. As, for instance, you see a good man oppressed with sorrows and afflictions, and a bad man crowned with pleasures and prosperities; and considering these things apart by themselves, you conclude that the one fares very ill, and the other very well: but did you at the same time see the consequents of the one's adversity and the other's prosperity, it's probable you would conclude the quite contrary, *viz.* that the good man's adversity was a blessing, and the bad man's prosperity a curse. For I dare boldly affirm that good men generally reap more substantial benefit from their afflictions, than bad men do from their prosperities. The one smarts indeed at present, but what follows? perhaps his mind is cured by it of some disease that is ten times worse to him than his outward affliction; of avarice and impatience, of envy or discontent, of pride or vanity of spirit; his riches are lessened, but his virtues are improved by it; his body is impaired, but his mind is grown sound and hale by it, and what he hath lost in health, or wealth, or pleasure, or honour, he hath gained with vast advantage in wisdom and goodness, in tranquillity of mind and self-enjoyment, and methinks no man who believes he hath a soul should grudge to suffer any tolerable affliction for bettering of his mind, his will, and his conscience.

"On the other hand the bad man triumphs and rejoices at present; but what follows? His prosperity either shrivels him into miserableness, or melts him into luxury; the former of which impoverishes, and the latter diseases him: for if the former be the effect of his prosperity, it increases his needs, because before he needed only what he had not, but now he needs both what he hath not, and what he hath, his covetous desires treating him as the falconer doth his hawk, luring him off from what he hath seized to fly at new game, and never permitting him to prey upon his own quarry: and if the latter be the effect of his prosperity, that is if it melts him into luxury, it thereby wastes his health to be sure, and commonly his estate too, and so whereas it found him poor and well, it leaves him poor and diseased, and only took him up from the plough, and sets him down at the hospital. In general, while he is possessed of it, it only bloats and swells him, makes him proud and insolent, griping and oppressive; pampers and enrages his lust, stretches out his desires into insatiable bulimy, sticks his mind full of cares, and his conscience of guiles, and by all those woeful effects it inflames his reckoning with God, and treasures up wrath for him against the day of wrath; so that comparing the consequences of the good man's adversity, with those of the bad man's prosperity, it is evident that the former fares well even in his worst condition, and the latter ill in his best. 'It is well for me,' saith David, 'that I was afflicted, for before I was afflicted I went astray, but now I have kept thy commandments.' But, on the contrary, when the wicked spring as the grass, saith the same author, and when all the workers of iniquity do flourish, then it is that they shall be destroyed for ever! If then in the consequents of things, good men are blessed in their afflictions and bad men plagued in their prosperities, as it is apparent they generally are, these unequal distributions are so far from being an argument against Providence, that they are a glorious instance of it. For wherein could the divine Providence better express its justice and wisdom together, than by benefiting the good, and punishing the bad by such cross and unprobable methods?"

INTERCHAPTER XVII.

A POPULAR LAY NOTICED, WITH SUNDRY REMARKS PERTINENT THERETO, SUGGESTED THEREBY, OR DEDUCED THEREFROM.

Look, he's winding up the watch of his wit: by and by it will strike. TEMPEST.

THERE was a female personage of whom I will venture to say that every one of my English readers, (Quakers perhaps excepted) has heard tell; and a great many of my Scotch, Welsh, Irish, and Transatlantic ones also—I venture to say this because her remarkable story has been transmitted to us in a Lay, a species of composition the full value of which has never been understood till the present age. Niebuhr and his learned followers assure us that the whole early history of Rome is founded upon no other authority than that of Lays, which have long since perished. And very possibly there may be German professors of Divinity who in like manner trace the Jewish history before Samuel to the Lays of Samson, Jephthah, Gideon, and other heroes of the Kritarchy, of Joshua, and of Moses, and so of the Patriarchs upwards.

To be sure it might startle us somewhat if these Lays were called by the old-fashioned name of Ballads, or old songs; and had either of those appellations been used we might hesitate a little before we gave implicit credit to so great a discovery.

Returning, however, to the personage of the Lay to which I have alluded, and which has been handed down from mother and nurse to child by immemorial tradition, and not stopping to inquire whether the tale itself is an historical matter of fact, or what is now called a mythos, and whether the personage is a mythological personage, the

Lay of the Little Woman when reduced to history, or prose narration, says that she went to market to sell her eggs; — in historifying the fact from this metrical document, I must take care to avoid any such collocation of words as might lead me into the worst of all possible styles, that of poetical prose. Numerous prose indeed not only carries with it a charm to the ear but affords such facility to the utterance, that the difference between reading aloud from a book so composed, or from one which has been written without any feeling of numerousness on the writer's part, is as great and perceptible as the difference between travelling upon an old road, or a macadamised one. Twenty pages of the one will exhaust the reader more than threescore of the other, just as there was more fatigue in a journey of fifty miles, fifty years ago, than there is in thrice the distance now. The fact is certain, and may no doubt be physically explained. But numerous prose and poetical prose are things as different as gracefulness and affectation.

All who remember the story will recollect that the Little Woman fell asleep by the wayside; and probably they will agree with me in supposing, that this must have happened on her return from market, after she had sold her eggs, and was tired with the business and excitement of the day. A different conclusion would perhaps be drawn from the Lay itself, were it not that in historical Lays many connecting circumstances are passed over because they were so well known at the time the Lay was composed that it was deemed unnecessary to touch upon them; moreover it should be observed that in Lays which have been orally transmitted for many generations before they were committed to writing, the less important parts are liable to be dropped. Of this there is evidently an example in the present case. Most countrywomen who keep the market go on horseback, and it is not mentioned in the Lay that the Little Woman went on foot; yet that she did so is certain; for nothing could be more likely than that being tired with walking she should sit down to rest herself by the way-side, and nothing more unlikely than that if she had been on horseback, she should have alighted for that purpose.

And here it is proper in this glose, commentary or exposition, to obviate an injurious suspicion which might arise concerning the character of the Little Woman, namely, that she must have been in liquor. Had it been a Lay of present times, this, it must be admitted, would have been very probable, the British Parliament having thought fit to pass an Act, by virtue, or by vice of which, in addition to the public-houses previously established, which were so numerous that they have long been a curse to the country, — in addition I say to these, 39,654 beer shops, as appears by a Parliamentary paper, were licensed in the year 1835. This Utilitarian law ought to have been entitled an Act for the increase of Drunkenness, and the promotion of sedition, brutality, wretchedness, and pauperism. But the Little Woman lived when there were not more public houses than were required for the convenience of travellers; perhaps before there were any, when strangers were entertained in monasteries, or went to the parsonage, as was the custom within the present century in some parts of Switzerland. In Iceland they are lodged in the Church at this time; but this seems never to have been the case in England.

It was a hot day, probably at the latter end of summer, or perhaps in autumn; this must be inferred from the circumstances of the story; and if the Little Woman called at a gossip's house, and was offered some refreshment, it is very possible that being thirsty she may have drank a peg lower in the cup than she generally allowed herself to do; and that being somewhat exhausted, the ale, beer, cyder, or metheglin may have had more effect upon her than it would have had at another time, and that consequently she may have felt drowsy as soon as she sate down. This may be admitted without impeaching her reputation on the score of temperance; and beyond this it is certain, as will presently be made appear, that her head could not have been affected.

Sleep, however,

— weigh'd her eye-lids down
And steep'd her senses in forgetfulness.

It will sometimes press heavily on the lids, even when the mind is wakeful, and feverishly, or miserably employed; but it will seldom steep the senses unless it be of that sound kind which denotes a healthy body and a heart at ease. They who sleep soundly must be free from care. In the south of Europe men of the lower classes lie down in the sun or shade according to the season, and fall asleep like dogs at any time. The less they are raised above animal life, the sounder the sleep is, and the more it seems to be an act of volition with them; when they close their eyes there is nothing within to keep them waking.

Well, our Little Woman was sleeping on a bank beside the way, when a Pedlar happened to come by. Not such a Pedlar as the one in Mr. Wordsworth's Excursion, who was what Randolph's Pedlar describes himself to be, "a noble, generous, understanding, royal, magnificent, religious, heroical, and thrice illustrious Pedlar;" if Randolph had been a Highlander this description might have been adduced as a proof of the prophetic faculty, — a second sight of that glorious poem, the well established fame of which and the effect which it has produced and is producing upon the present generation both of authors and readers must be so peculiarly gratifying to Lord Jeffrey. No; he was such a Pedlar as Autolycus, and if the Little Woman lived in the days of King Leontes, it may possibly have been Autolycus himself; for he had "a quick eye and a nimble hand," and was one who "Held honesty for a fool and Trust, his brother, for a very simple gentleman." The distance between Bohemia and England makes no difficulty in this supposition. Gypsies used to be called Bohemians; and moreover, as Uncle Toby would have told Trim, Bohemia might have been a maritime country in those days; and when he found it convenient to return thither, the readiest way was to get on board ship.

It is said, however, in the Lay, that the Pedlar's name was Stout. It may have been so; and yet I am disposed to think that this is a corrupt passage, and that stout in this place is more probably an epithet, than a name. The verse may probably have run thus,

There came by a Pedlar, a losell stout,

a stout thief being formerly as common a designation as a sturdy beggar. This rogue seeing her asleep by the way-side, cut her petticoats all round about up to the knee; whence it appears not only how soundly she must have been sleeping, and how expert he was in this branch of his trade, but also that her pockets were in her petticoats and not a separate article of her dress.

At the marriage of Sir Philip Herbert with the Lady Susan Vere, which was performed at the Court of Whitehall, in the year 1604, with all the honour that could be done to a great favourite, many great ladies were made shorter by the skirts, like the Little Woman; and Sir Dudley Carleton says "they were well enough served that they could keep cut* no better." If the reader asks what is keeping cut? he asks a question I cannot answer.

I have already observed that the weather was warm, and the proof is twofold, first in the Little Woman's sitting down by the way, which in cold weather she would not have done; and, secondly, because when she awoke and discovered the condition in which this cut-purse had left her, she began to quiver and quake, for these words are plainly intended to denote at the same time a sense of chilliness, and an emotion of fear. She quivered perhaps for cold, having been deprived of so great a part of her lower garments; but she quaked for fear, considering as well the danger she had been in, as the injury which she had actually sustained. The confusion of mind produced by these mingled emotions was so remarkable that Mr. Coleridge might have thought it not unworthy of his psychological and transcendental investigations; and Mr. Words-

* *Quære?* To be in the fashion — to be as others are?

worth might make it the subject of a modern Lay to be classed either among his poems of the Fancy, or of the Imagination as might to him seem fit. For the Lay says that the Little Woman, instead of doubting for a while whether she were asleep or awake, that is to say whether she were in a dream because of the strange, and indecorous, and uncomfortable, and unaccountable condition in which she found herself, doubted her own identity, and asked herself whether she were herself, or not? So little was she able to answer so subtle a question satisfactorily that she determined upon referring it to the decision of a little dog which she had left at home, and whose fidelity and instinctive sagacity could not, she thought, be deceived. "If it be I," said she, "as I hope it be, he will wag his little tail for joy at my return; if it be not I, he will bark at me for a stranger." Homeward, therefore, the Little Woman went, and confused as she was, she found her way there instinctively like Dr. Southey's Ladurlad, and almost in as forlorn a state. Before she arrived, night had closed, and it became dark. She had reckoned rightly upon her dog's fidelity, but counted too much upon his sagacious instinct. He did not recognise his mistress at that unusual hour, and in a curtailed dress wherein he had never seen her before, and instead of wagging his tail, and fawning, and whining, to bid her welcome as she had hoped, he began to bark angrily, with faithful but unfortunate vigilance, mistaking her for a stranger who could have no good reason for coming about the premises at that time of night. And the Lay concludes with the Little Woman's miserable conclusion that as the dog disowned her, she was not the dog's Mistress, not the person who dwelt in that house, and whom she had supposed herself to be, in fact not herself, but somebody else, she did not know who.

INTERCHAPTER XVIII.

APPLICATION OF THE LAY. CALEB D'ANVERS. IRISH LAW. ICON BASILIKE. JUNIUS. THOMAS À KEMPIS. FELIX HEMMERLIN. A NEEDLE LARGER THAN GAMMER GURTON'S AND A MUCH COARSER THREAD. THOMAS WARTON AND BISHOP STILL. THE JOHN WEBSTERS, THE ALEXANDER CUNINGHAMS, THE CURINAS AND THE STEPHENS.

Lo que soy, razona poco
Porque de sombra a mi va nada, o poco.
FUENTE DESEADA.

THE sagacious reader will already have applied the Lay of the Little Woman to the case of Dr. Dove's disciple and memorialist, and mentally apostrophising him may have said,

— *de te*
Fabula narratur.

Even so, dear Reader, the Little Woman was a type of me, and yet but an imperfect one, for my case is far more complicated than hers. The simple doubt which distressed her, (and a most distressing one it must be admitted that it was,) was whether she were herself or not; but the compound question which has been mooted concerning me is whether I am myself or somebody else, and whether somebody else is himself or me.

When various conjectures were formed and assertions hazarded concerning the Author or Editor of the Craftsman, some representing Caleb D'Anvers as an imaginary person, a mere fictitious character made use of to screen the performances of men in the dark, that formidable opponent of Sir Robert Walpole's administration said, "I hope it will not be expected that I should stand still and see myself reasoned out of my existence."

Every one knows that it is possible to be reasoned out of our rights and despoiled in consequence of our property in a court of law; but every one may not know that it is possible to be reasoned out of our existence there: I do not mean condemned to death, and executed accordingly upon the testimony of false witnesses, as those who suffered for the Popish plot were; or upon circumstantial evidence, honestly produced, and disproved when it was too late; but that an individual may be judicially declared to be not in existence, when actually present in the Court to give the Lawyers and the Law the lie.

On the 2d of March, 1784, the Irish Attorney General was heard before the Irish House of Lords in the case of Hume and Loftus. In the course of his argument he contended that judgments were of the most sacred nature, and that to reverse one was in effect to overturn the law and the constitution; the record was binding, and a bar to all other evidence being produced to the Court. "He instanced a case wherein a judgment had been given on the presumed death of a man's wife, who, as afterwards appeared, was not dead, but was produced in person to the Court, and was properly identified, and it was prayed to the Court to reverse the judgment given on supposition of her death which had been pronounced by the same Court, as in the pleading stated. Nevertheless the Court, with the Woman before their eyes, pronounced her dead, and confirmed the judgment, saying, that the verdict was not that which was binding, but the judgment, in consequence of the verdict having become a record, could not be reversed."

This woman, upon hearing such a decision concerning herself pronounced, might well have called in question not her identity, but the evidence of her senses, and have supposed that she was dreaming, or out of her wits, rather than that justice could be so outraged, and common sense so grossly insulted in a Court of Law.

Happily my case is in no worse court than a Court of Criticism, a Court in which I can neither be compelled to plead nor to appear.

Dr. Wordsworth rendered good service to English History when he asked who wrote Εἰκὼν Βασιλικὴ, for it is a question of great historical importance, and he has shown, by a careful investigation of all the evidence which it has been possible to collect, that it is the work of Charles himself, confirming thus that internal evidence which is of the most conclusive kind.

Who was Junius is a question which is not likely ever to be determined by discussion after so many fruitless attempts; but whenever the secret shall by any chance be discovered, considerable light will be thrown upon the political intrigues of the earlier part of a most important reign.

But who or what I am can be of no importance to any but myself.

More than one hundred and fifty treatises are said to have been published upon the question whether Thomas à Kempis was the Author of the well-known book *de Imitatione Christi*. That question affects the Augustinians; for if it were proved that this native of Kemp near Cologne, Thomas Hammerlein by name, were the transcriber only and not the writer of that famous treatise, they would lose the brightest ornament of their order. This Hammerlein has never been confounded with his namesake Felix, once a Doctor and *Precentor Clarissimus*, under whose portrait in the title page of one of his volumes where he stands Hammer in hand, there are these verses.

Felicis si te juvat indulsisse libellis
Malleoli, presens dilige lector opus.
Illius ingenium variis scabronibus actum
Perspicis, et stimulos sustinuisse graves.
Casibus adversis, aurum velut igne, probatus
Hostibus usque suis Malleus acer erat.
Hinc sibi conveniens sortitus nomen, ut esset
Hemmerlin dictus, nomine, reque, statu.
At Felix tandem, vitioque illæsus ab omni
Carceris e tenebris sydera clara subit.

This Hemmerlin in his Dialogue between a Nobleman and a Rustic, makes the Rustic crave license for his rude manner of speech saying, *Si ruralis consuetudine moris ineptissime loquar per te non corripiar, quia non sermonis colorum quoque nitorem, sed sensus sententiarumque requiro rigorem. Nam legitur quod Demon sedebat et braccam cum reste suebat; et dixit, si non est pulchra, tamen est consucio firma.* The needle must have been considerably larger than Gammer Gurton's, which is never-the-less and ever will be the most famous of all needles.

Well was it for Hodge when Diccon the Bedlam gave him the good openhanded blow which produced the catastrophe of that Right Pithy, Pleasant, and Merry Comedy entitled Gammer Gurton's Needle, — Well was it I say for Hodge that the Needle in the episcopal comedy was not of such calibre as that wherewith the Auld Gude Man, as the Scotch, according to Sir Walter, respectfully call the Old Wicked One, in their caution never to give any unnecessary offence, — Well, again I say, was it for Hodge that his Gammer's Neele, her dear Neele, her fair long straight Neele that was her only treasure, was of no such calibre as the Needle which that Old One used, when mending his breeks with a rope he observed that though it was not a neat piece of sewing it was strong, — for if it had been such a Needle, Diccon's manual joke must have proved fatal. Our Bishops write no such comedies now; yet we have more than one who could translate it into Aristophanic Greek.

Wherefore did Thomas Warton (never to be named without respect and gratitude by all lovers of English literature) say that when the Sermons of Hugh Latimer were in vogue at Court, the University might be justified in applauding Gammer Gurton's Needle? How could he who so justly appreciated the Comedy, disparage those sermons? He has spoken of the play as the first in our language in which a comic story is handled with some disposition of plot and some discrimination. "The writer," he says, "has a degree of jocularity which sometimes rises above buffoonery, but is often disgraced by lowness of incident. Yet in a more polished age he would have chosen, nor would he perhaps have disgraced, a better subject. It has been thought surprising that a learned audience could have endured some of these indelicate scenes. But the established festivities of scholars were gross; nor was learning in that age always accompanied by gentleness of manners." Nor is it always now, nor has it ever been, O Thomas Warton! — if it had, you would not when you wore a great wig, — had taken the degree of B.D., — been Professor of Poetry in the University of Oxford, — and wast moreover Poet Laureate, — most worthy of that office of all who have held it since Great Ben, — you would not in your mellow old age, when your brother was Master of Winchester School, have delighted as you did in hunting rats with the Winchester Boys.

O Thomas Warton! you had and could not but have a hearty liking for all that is properly comic in the pithy old episcopal comedy! but that you should even seem to disparage Latimer's Sermons is to me more than most strange. For Latimer would have gained for himself a great and enduring name in the pulpit, if he had not been called upon to bear the highest and holiest of all titles. The pithy comedy no doubt was written long before its author was consecrated Bishop of Bath and Wells, and we may be sure that Bishop Still never reckoned it among his sins. If its language were rendered every where intelligible and its dirtiness cleaned away, for there is nothing worse to be removed, Gammer Gurton's Needle might succeed in these days as a farce.

Fuller says he had read in the Register of Trinity College, Cambridge, this commendation of Bishop Still that he was ἀγαθὸς κουροτρόφος *nec Collegio gravis aut onerosus.* Still was Master of that College, as he had been before of St. John's.

"What style," says Sir John Harrington, "shall I use to set forth this Still, whom (well nigh thirty years since) my reverend tutor in Cambridge styled by this name, 'Divine Still,' who, when myself came to him to sue for my grace to be bachelor, first examined me strictly, and after answered me kindly, that 'the grace he granted me was not of grace but of merit;' who was often content to grace my young exercises with his venerable presence; who, from that time to this, hath given me some helps, more hopes, all encouragements, in my best studies; to whom I never came, but I grew more religious; from whom I never went, but I parted better instructed: Of him, therefore, my acquaintance, my friend, my instructor, and last my diocesan; if I speak much it were not to be marvelled; if I speak frankly, it is not to be blamed; and though I speak partially, it were to be pardoned. Yet to keep within my proportion, custom and promise, in all these, I must say this much of him; his breeding was from his childhood in good literature, and partly in music *, which was counted in those days a preparative to Divinity; neither could any be admitted to *primam tonsuram*, except he could first *bene le, bene con, bene can* (as they call it), which is to read well, to construe well, and to sing well; in which last he hath good judgment, and I have heard good music of voices in his house.

"In his full time, more full of learning, he became Bachelor of Divinity, and after Doctor; and so famous for a Preacher, and especially a disputer, that the learned'st were even afraid to dispute with him; and he finding his own strength would not stick to warn them in their arguments to take heed to their answers, like a perfect fencer that will tell beforehand in which button he will give the venew, or like a cunning chess-player that will appoint beforehand with which pawn, and in what place, he will give the mate.

"One trifling accident happened to his Lordship at Bath, that I have thought since of more consequence, and I tell him that I never knew him *non plus* in argument, but there. There was a craft's-man in Bath, a recusant puritan, who, condemning our Church, our Bishops, our sacraments, our prayers, was condemned himself to die at the assizes, but, at my request, Judge Anderson reprieved him, and he was suffered to remain at Bath upon bail. The Bishop conferred with him, in hope to convert him, and first, My Lord alleged for the authority of the church, St. Augustine! The Shoemaker answered, 'Austin was but a man.' He (Still) produced, for the antiquity of Bishops, the Fathers of the Council at Nice. He answered, 'They were also but men, and might err.' 'Why then,' said the Bishop, 'thou art but a man, and must, and dost err.' 'No, Sir,' saith he, 'the Spirit bears witness to my spirit; I am the child of God.' 'Alas!' said the Bishop, 'thy blind spirit will lead thee to the gallows.' 'If I die,' saith he, 'in the Lord's cause, I shall be a martyr.' The Bishop turning to me, stirred as much to pity as impatience;—'This man,' said he, 'is not a sheep strayed from the fold, for such may be brought in again on the shepherd's shoulders, but this is like a wild buck broke out of a park, whose pale is thrown down, that flies the farther off, the more he is hunted.' Yet this man, that stopped his ears like the adder to the charms of the Bishop, was after persuaded by a lay-man, and grew conformable. But to draw to an end; in one question this Bishop, whom I count an oracle for learning, would never yet give me satisfaction, and that was, when I asked him his opinion of witches. He saith 'he knows other men's opinions, both old and new writers, but could never so digest them, to make them an opinion of his own.' All I can get is 'this, that the Devil is the old Serpent our enemy, that we pray to be delivered from daily; as willing to have us think he can do too much as to have us persuaded he doth nothing.'"

In the account of Webster and his Writings, prefixed to his Works by their able editor Mr. Dyce, that editor finds it necessary to bestow much pains in showing that John Webster the Dramatist and Player, was not John Webster the Puritan and Chaplain in the Army; but, on the other hand, Mr. Payne Collier, who is a great authority in our stage literature, contends that he was one and the same person, and that when in the Prefatory Address to his Saint's Guide, he speaks of the "damnable condition" from which the Lord in his wonderful mercy had brought him, he could hardly mean anything but his condition as a player. It remained then to be argued, whether either of these persons were the John Webster, Practitioner in Physic and Chirurgery, who wrote or com-

* The Greek sense of μουσικὸς is well known. Cf Arist. Pol. lib. viii. c. iii. As Cicero says, "Summam eruditionem Græci sitam censebant in nervorum vocumque cantibus," &c. Cic. Tuscul. i. c. ii.

piled a work entitled Metalographia, a volume of Sermons entitled The Judgment set and the Books opened, and a tract called *Academiarum Examen*, or the Examination of Academies, wherein is discussed and examined the Matter, Method, and Customs of Academic and Scholastic Learning, and the insufficiency thereof discovered and laid open: as also some expedients proposed for the reforming of schools and the perfecting and promoting of all kind of science. A powerful Tract Mr. Dyce calls it; and it must have been thought of some importance in its day, for it provoked an answer from Seth Ward, afterwards Bishop of Salisbury, and Wilkins, afterwards the well known Bishop of Chester, (from whom Peter Wilkins may perhaps have been named,) wrote in it an Epistle to the Author. One of these Websters wrote a remarkable book against the then prevalent belief in witchcraft, though he was himself a believer in astrology and held that there are great and hidden virtues in metals and precious stones, as they are by Nature produced, by mystical Chemistry prepared and exalted, or commixed and insculped in their due and fit constellation. Which of the John Websters was this? If it has not been satisfactorily ascertained, whether there were one, two, three or four John Websters after so much careful investigation by the most eminent bibliologists, though it is not supposed that on the part of any John Webster there was any design to conceal himself and mystify the public, by whom can the question be answered concerning the authorship of this Opus, except by me the Opifex, and those few persons trusted and worthy of the trust, who are, like me, secret as the grave?

There is a history (and of no ordinary value) of Great Britain from the Revolution to the Accession of George I. written in Latin by Alexander Cunningham, translated from the Author's Manuscript by Dr. William Thompson, and published in two quarto volumes by Dr. Hollingbery in 1787. That the Author was Minister for George I. to the Venetian Republic is certain; but whether he were the Alexander Cunningham that lived at the same time, whose editions of Virgil and Horace are well known, and whose reputation as a critic stood high among the continental scholars of the last century, is altogether doubtful. If they were two persons, each was born in Scotland and educated in Holland, each a friend and favourite of Carstares, King William's confidential secretary for Scotch affairs, each a remarkably good Chess Player, each an accomplished Latinist, and each concerned in the education of John Duke of Argyle. Upon weaker evidence, says Dr. Thompson, than that which seems to prove the identity of the two Cunninghams, decisions have been given that have affected fortunes, fame, life, posterity and all that is dear to mankind; and yet, notwithstanding these accumulated coincidences, he comes at length to the conclusion, that there are circumstances which seem incompatible with their identity, and that probably they were different persons.

But what signifies it now to any one whether certain books published in the seventeenth century were written by one and the same John Webster, or by four persons of that name? What signifies it whether Alexander Cunningham the historian was one and indivisible, like the French Republic, or that there were two Alexander Cunninghams, resembling each other as much as the two Sosias of the ancient drama, or the two Dromios and their twin masters in the Comedy of Errors? What signifies it to any creature upon earth? It may indeed afford matter for inquiry in a Biographical Dictionary, or in the Gentleman's Magazine, and by possibility of the remotest kind, for a law-suit. And can we wonder that an identity of names has sometimes occasioned a singular confusion of persons, and that Biographers and Bibliographers should sometimes be thus at fault, when we find that the same thing has deceived the most unerring of all Messengers, —Death himself.

Thus it was. There was a certain man, Curina by name, who lived in a village not far from Hippo in the days of St. Augustine. This man sickened and died; but because there seemed to be some faint and intermitting appearances of life, his friends delayed burying him for some days. Those appearances at length ceased; it could no longer be doubted that he was indeed dead; when behold he opened his eyes, and desired that a messenger might immediately be sent to his neighbour and namesake Curina the blacksmith, and inquire how he was. The answer was that he had just expired. The resuscitated Curina then related that he himself had verily and indeed died, and that his soul had been carried before the Judge of the Dead, who had vehemently reproved the Ministering Spirits that brought him thither, seeing it was not for him but for Curina the Blacksmith that they had been sent. This was not only a joyful surprise for the reprieved or replevied Curina, but a most happy adventure in other respects. He had not only an opportunity of seeing Paradise in his excursion, but a friendly hint was given him there, that as soon as his health was restored he should repair to Hippo and there receive baptism from St. Augustine's hands.

When the wrong soul happens thus to be summoned out of the body, Pope St. Gregory the Great assures us that there is no mistake; and who shall question what the Infallible Pope and Saint affirms? "Peter," saith he, in one of his Dialogues, "when this happeneth, it is not, if it be well considered, any error, but an admonition. For God of his great and bountiful mercy so disposeth, that some after their death do straightways return again to life, in order that having seen the torments of Hell, which before when they heard of they would not believe, they may at least tremble at them after they have with their own eyes beheld them. For a certain Sclavonian who was a Monk, and lived with me here in this city, in my Monastery, used to tell me, that at such time as he dwelt in the wilderness, he knew one Peter, a Monk born in Spain, who lived with him in the vast desert called Evasa, which Peter (as he said) told him how before he came to dwell in that place, he by a certain sickness died, and was straightway restored to life again, affirming that he had seen the torments and innumerable places of Hell, and divers who were mighty men in this world hanging in those flames; and that as himself was carried to be thrown also into the same fire, suddenly an Angel in a beautiful attire appeared, who would not suffer him to be cast into those torments, but spake unto him in this manner: 'Go thy way back again, and hereafter carefully look unto thyself how thou leadest thy life!' after which words his body by little and little became warm, and himself waking out of the sleep of everlasting death, reported all such things as had happened about him; after which time he bound himself to such fasting and watching, that though he had said nothing, yet his life and conversation did speak what torments he had seen and was afraid of; and so God's merciful providence wrought in his temporal death that he died not everlastingly.

"But because man's heart is passing obdurate and hard, hereof it cometh that though others have the like vision and see the same pains, yet do they not always keep the like profit. For the honourable man Stephen, whom you knew very well, told me of himself, that at such time as he was upon business, resident in the City of Constantinople, he fell sick and died; and when they sought for a surgeon to bowel him and to embalm his body and could not get any, he lay unburied all the night following; in which space his soul was carried to the dungeon of Hell, where he saw many things which before when he heard of, he had little believed. But when he was brought before the Judge that sat there, the Judge would not admit him to his presence, saying, 'I commanded not this man to be brought, but Stephen the Smith!' upon which words he was straightway restored to life, and Stephen the Smith, that dwelt hard by, at that very hour departed this life, whose death did show that the words which he had heard were most true. But though the foresaid Stephen escaped death in this manner at that time, yet three years since, in that mortality which lamentably wasted this city, (and in which, as you know, men with their corporal eyes did behold arrows that came from Heaven, which did strike divers,) the same man ended his days. At which time a certain soldier being also brought to the point of death, his soul was in such sort carried out of his body that he lay void of all sense and feeling, but coming quickly again to himself, he told them that were present what strange things he had seen. For he said, (as many report who knew it very well,) that he saw a Bridge, under which a black and smoaky river did run that had a filthy and intolerable smell; but upon the further side thereof there were pleasant green meadows full of sweet flowers; in which also there were divers companies of men apparelled in white; and such a delicate savour there was that the fragrant odour thereof did give wonderful content to all them that dwelt and walked in that place. Divers particular mansions also there were, all shining with brightness and light, and especially one magnifical and sumptuous house, which was a-building, the bricks whereof seemed to be of Gold; but whose it was that he knew not.

"There were also upon the bank of the foresaid river certain houses, but some of them the stinking vapour which rose from the river did touch, and some other it touched not at all. Now those that desired to pass over the foresaid Bridge were subject to this manner of trial; if any that was wicked attempted to go over, down he fell into that dark and stinking river; but those that were just and not hindered by sin, securely and easily passed over to those pleasant and delicate places. There he said also that he saw Peter, who was Steward of the Pope's family, and died some four years since, thrust into a most filthy place, where he was bound and kept down with a great weight of iron; and inquiring why he was so used, he received this answer, which all we that knew his life can affirm to be most true; for it was told him that he suffered that pain, because when himself was upon any occasion to punish others, that he did it more upon cruelty than to show his obedience; of which his merciless disposition none that knew him can be ignorant. There also he said that he saw a Priest whom he knew, who coming to the foresaid Bridge passed over with as great security as he had lived in this world sincerely.

"Likewise upon the same Bridge he said that he did see this Stephen whom before we spake of, who, being about to go over, his foot slipped, and half his body hanging beside the Bridge, he was of certain terrible men that rose out of the river drawn by the legs downward, and by certain other white and beautiful persons he was by the arms pulled upward, and while they strove thus, the wicked spirits to draw him downward and the good to lift him upward, he that beheld all this strange sight returned to life, not knowing in conclusion what became of him. By which miraculous vision we learn this thing concerning the life of Stephen, to wit, that in him the sins of the flesh did strive with his works of alms. For in that he was by the legs drawn downward, and by the arms plucked upward, apparent it is, that both he loved to give alms, and yet did not perfectly resist the sins of the flesh which did pull him downward; but in that secret examination of the Supreme Judge, which of them had the victory, that neither we know nor he that saw it. Yet more certain it is that the same Stephen after that he had seen the places of Hell, as before was said, and returned again to his body, did never perfectly amend his former wicked life, seeing many years after he departed this world leaving us in doubt whether he were saved or damned"

Hereupon Peter the Deacon said to Pope St. Gregory the Great, "What, I beseech you, was meant by the building of that house in those places of delight, with bricks of gold? For it seemeth very ridiculous that in the next life we should have need of any such kind of metal." Pope Gregory the Great answered and said, "What man of sense can think so? But by that which was shown there, (whosoever he was for whom that house was built,) we learn plainly what virtuous works he did in this world; for he that by plenty of alms doth merit the reward of eternal light, certain it is that he doth build his house with gold. For the same soldier who had this vision said also, (which I forgot to tell you before,) that old men and young, girls and boys, did carry those bricks of gold for the building of that house, by which we learn that those to whom we show compassion in this world do labour for us in the next. There dwelt hard by us a religious man called Deusdedit, who was a shoemaker, concerning whom another saw by revelation that he had in the next world a house a-building, but the workmen thereof laboured only upon the Saturday; who afterward inquiring more diligently how he lived, found that whatsoever he got by his labour all the week, and was not spent upon necessary provision of meat and apparel, all that upon the Saturday he bestowed upon the poor in alms, at St. Peter's Church; and therefore see what reason there was that his building went forward upon the Saturday."

It was a very reasonable question that Peter the Deacon asked of Gregory the Great, when he desired to know how it came to pass that certain persons who were summoned into the other world, were told when they got there that they were not the persons who had been sent for. And it was not ill answered by the Pope that if properly considered, this when it happeneth is not an error, but an admonition. Yet that there was a mistake in the two cases of Curina and Stephen and their respective namesakes and blacksmiths cannot be disputed, — a mistake on the part of the Ministering Spirits. This may be accounted for by supposing that inferior Spirits were employed in both cases, those for whom they were sent not being of a condition to be treated with extraordinary respect on such an occasion. Comets were never kindled to announce the death of common men, and the lowest Spirits might be deputed to take charge of the Blacksmiths. But Azrael himself makes no mistakes.

Five things the Mahommedans say are known to no created Beings, only to the Creator; the time of the Day of Judgment; the time of rain; whether an unborn child shall be male or female; what shall happen to-morrow, and when any person is to die. These the Arabians call the five keys of secret knowledge, according to a tradition of their Prophet, to whom questions of this kind were propounded by Al Hareth Ebnn Amru. But it may be inferred from a tradition which Al Beidâwi has preserved that one of these keys is committed to the Angel of Death, when he is sent out in person to execute the irrevocable decree.

The Arabians tell us that Solomon was exercising his horses one day when the hour for evening prayer was announced. Immediately he alighted, and would not allow either his own horse or any other in the field to be taken to the stables, but gave orders that they should be turned loose, being from thenceforth dedicated to the Almighty's service, which the Arabians we are told call *Rebath fi sebil Allah*. To reward the king for this instance of his piety, Allah gave him a mild and pleasant, but strong wind, to be at his orders from that time forth and carry him whithersoever he would.

Once on a time Azrael passed by Solomon in a visible form, and in passing looked earnestly at a certain person who was sitting with the king. That person not liking the earnestness and the expression of his look, asked Solomon who it was, and Solomon replied it was the Angel of Death. He looks as if he wanted me, said the affrighted man; I beseech you, therefore, order the Wind to carry me instantly to India! Solomon spake the word, and no sooner was it spoken, than the Wind took him up and set him down where he desired to be. The Angel then said to Solomon, I looked so earnestly at that Man out of wonder, because that being commanded to take his soul in India, I found him here with thee in Palestine.

But, my good Reader, you and I must make no tarriance now with Solomon Ben Daoud, wisest of men and mightiest of Magicians, nor with St. Gregory the Great, Pope and Punster, and his friend Peter the Deacon, though you and I might delight in the Pope's veracious stories as much as good

Peter himself. We must wind up the volume * with one Interchapter more.

Saggio e' il consigliator che sol ricorre
A quell' ultimo fin, che in cor si fisse,
Quel sol rimira, e tutto l'altro abborre,
Come al suo proprio danno consentisse;
E' chi farà in tal guisa, raro fia
Che d' incontrare il ver perda la via. †

INTERCHAPTER XIX.

THE AUTHOR DIFFERS IN OPINION FROM SIR EGERTON BRYDGES, AND THE EMPEROR JULIAN. SPEAKS CHARITABLY OF THAT EMPEROR, VINDICATES PROTEUS FROM HIS CENSURE, AND TALKS OF POSTHUMOUS TRAVELS AND EXTRA MUNDANE EXCURSIONS, AND THE PUBLIC LIBRARY IN LIMBOLAND.

Petulant. If he says black's black, — if I have a humour to say it is blue — let that pass. All's one for that. If I have a humour to prove it, it must be granted.
Witwould. Not positively must, — But it may, it may.
Petulant Yes, it positively must,— upon proof positive.
Witwould. Ay, upon proof positive it must; but upon proof presumptive it only may. That's a logical distinction now.
CONGREVE.

"IN the *ignotum pro magnifico*," says Umbra, "resides a humble individual's best chance of being noticed or attended to at all." Yet many are the attempts which have been made, and are making, in America too as well as in Great Britain, by Critics, Critickins and Criticasters, (for there are of all degrees,) to take from me the *Ignotum*, and force upon me the *Magnificum* in its stead, to prove that I am not the humble, and happily unknown disciple, friend, and, however unworthy, memorialist of Dr. Dove, a nameless individual as regards the public, holding the tenour of my noiseless way contentedly towards that oblivion which sooner or later must be the portion of us all; but that I am what is called a public character, a performer upon the great stage, whom every one is privileged to hiss or to applaud; myself a Doctor, LL.D. according to the old form, according to the present usage D.C.L. — a Doctor upon whom that trilateral dignity was conferred in full theatre, amid thundering peals of applauding hands, and who heard himself addressed that day in Phillimorean voice and fluent latinity by all eulogistic epithets ending in *issimus* or *errimus*. I an *issimus!* — I an *errimus!*—No other *issimus* than that *Ipsissimus ego* which by these critics I am denied to be.

These critics will have it that I am among living authors what the ever memorable Countess of Henneberg was among women; that I have more tails to my name than the greatest Bashaw bears among his standards, or the largest cuttle fish to his headless body or bodyless head; that I have executed works more durable than brass, and loftier than the Pyramids, and that I have touched the stars with my sublime forehead, — what could have saved my poor head from being moonstruck if I had.

Believe them not, O Reader! I never executed works in any material more durable than brass, I never built any thing like a pyramid, *Absurdo de tamaña grandeza no se ha escrito en letras de molde.* And as for the alleged proofs, which, depriving me of my individuality and divesting me even of entity, would consubstantiate me with the most prolific of living writers, *no son mas que ayre ó menos que ayre, una sombra ó menos que sombra, pues son nada, y nada es lo que nunca ha tenido ser verdadero.* ‡ "It is in vain," as Mr. Carlyle says when apostrophising Mirabeau the father upon his persevering endeavours to make his son resemble him in all points of character, and be as it were his second self, "it is in vain. He will not be Thou, but must and will be himself, another than Thou." In like manner, It is in vain, say I: I am not, and will not and cannot be any body but myself; nor is it of any consequence to any human being who or what I am, though perhaps those persons may think otherwise who say that "they delight more in the shadow of something than to converse with a nothing in substance." §

Lord Shaftesbury has said that "of all the artificial relations formed between mankind,

* *Note.* This refers to the former Editions in seven volumes.
† L' AVARCHIDE.
‡ NICOLAS PERES.
§ HURLOTHRUMBO.

the most capricious and variable is that of Author and Reader." He may be right in this; but when he says 'tis evident that an Author's art and labour are for his Reader's sake alone, I cannot assent to the position. For though I have a great and proper regard for my readers, and entertain all due respect for them, it is not for their sake alone that my art and labour have been thus employed, — not for their benefit alone, still less for their amusement, that this Opus has been edified. Of the parties concerned in it, the Readers, sooth to say, are not those who have been either first or second in my consideration. The first and paramount object was to preserve the Doctor's memory; the second to gratify myself by so doing; for what higher gratification can there be than in the performance of a debt of gratitude, one of those debts truly to be called immense, which

— A grateful mind
By owing owes not, but still pays, at once
Indebted and discharged.*

That there are some readers who would think themselves beholden, though in far less degree, to me, as I am to the revered subject of these memorials, was an after consideration.

Sir Egerton Brydges says he never took up a book which he could read without wishing to know the character and history of the author. "But what is it," he says, "to tell the facts that he was born, married or lived single and died? What is common to all can convey no information. We desire to know an author's feelings, his temper, his disposition, his modes of thinking, his habits; nay even his person, his voice, and his mode of expressing himself, the society in which he has lived, and the images and lessons which attended upon his cradle." Most of this, Sir Egerton, you can never know otherwise than by guess work. Yet methinks my feelings, my temper, my disposition, and my modes of thinking are indicated here, as far as a book can indicate them. You have yourself said; "if it could be proved that what one writes, is no index to what he thinks and feels, then it would be of little value and no interest;" but you are confident that such delusive writers always betray themselves; "Sincerity," you say, "has always a breath and spirit of its own." Yes, Sir Egerton, and if there is not that spirit in these volumes, there is no vitality in them; if they have not that breath of life, they must be still-born.

Yet I cannot agree with you in the opinion that those who make a false display of fine feelings, whether in prose or verse, always betray themselves. The cant of sentimentalism passes as current with the Reading Public, as cant of a different description with those who call themselves the Religious Public. Among the latter, the proudest and the most uncharitable people in this nation are to be found; and in proof that the most intensely selfish of the human race may be sentimentalists, and super-sentimentalists, it is sufficient to name Rousseau.

Perhaps some benevolent and sagacious Reader may say to me as Randolph said to his friend Owen Feltham,—

Thy book I read, and read it with delight,
Resolving so to live as thou dost write;
And yet I guess thy life thy book produces
And but expresses thy peculiar uses.

But the Reader who should apply to me and my Opus the French lines,

A l'auteur on connoît l'ouvrage,
A l'ouvrage on connoît l'auteur,

though he may be equally benevolent, would not be equally sagacious. It is not for mere caprice that I remain *Ignotus* and *Innominabilis;* not a Great Unknown, an *Ignotolemagne*, but simply an Unknown, Ἄγνωστος, *l'Inconnu*, *Sconciuto*, the *Encubierto*, the *Desconocido*—

This precious secret let me hide.
I'll tell you every thing beside.†

Critics, we know, affect always to have strange intelligence; but though they should say to me

You may
As soon tie up the sunbeams in a net
As keep yourself unknown ‡,

* Milton.

† Cotton.

‡ Shirley.

I shall still continue in darkness inscrutable. Nor am I to be moved from this determination by the opinion which the Emperor Julian expressed concerning Proteus, when he censured him for changing himself into divers forms, lest men should compel him to manifest his knowledge. For, said Julian, "if Proteus were indeed wise, and knew, as Homer says, many things, I praise him indeed for his knowledge, but I do not commend his disposition; seeing that he performed the part, not of a philanthropist, but rather of an impostor, in concealing himself lest he should be useful to mankind."

This was forming a severer opinion of the Ancient of the Deep, the old Prophet of the Sea, than I would pronounce upon Julian himself, though the name of Apostate clings to him. Unhappy as he was in the most important of all concerns, he was at least a true believer in a false religion, and therefore a better man than some of those kings who have borne the title of Most Christian or Most Catholic. I wish he had kept his beard clean! But our follies and weaknesses, when they are nothing worse, die with us, and are not like unrepented sins to be raised up in judgment. The beard of the imperial Philosopher is not populous now. And in my posthumous travels, if in some extramundane excursion I should meet him in that Limbo which is not a place of punishment, but where odd persons as well as odd things are to be found, and in the Public Library of that Limbo we should find a certain Opus conspicuously placed and in high repute, translated, not into the Limbo tongue alone, but into all languages, and the Imperial Philosopher should censure the still incognoscible Author for still continuing in incognoscibility for the same reason that he blamed the Ancient of the Deep, I should remind him of the Eleusinian Mysteries, whisper the Great Decasyllabon in his ear, and ask him whether there are not some secrets which it is neither lawful nor fitting to disclose.

THE DOCTOR,

&c.

PART THE SECOND.

Posthumous.

"There is a physiognomy in the Titles of Books no less than in the faces of men, by which a skilful observer will as well know what to expect from the one as the other." — *Butler's Remains.*

Preface

TO THE SECOND PART.

INVENIAS ETIAM DISJECTI MEMBRA POETÆ.

In the distribution of the lamented Southey's literary property, the History of the Brazils, his much treasured MS. History of Portugal, The Doctor, &c. and the MS. materials for its completion, fell to the share of Edith May Warter, his eldest child, and, as he used to call her, his right hand, — to whom he addressed the Dedication of the Tale of Paraguay, and to whom he commenced a little Poem of which the lines following are almost the last, if not the very last, he ever wrote in verse.

O daughter dear, who bear'st no longer now
Thy Father's name, and for the chalky flats
Of Sussex hast exchanged thy native land
Of lakes and mountains, — neither change of place,
Condition, and all circumstantial things,
Nor new relations, and access of cares
Unfelt before, have alienated thee
Nor wean'd thy heart from this beloved spot,
Thy birth place, and so long thy happy home!

The present portion of "The Doctor, &c." is drawn up from the MS. materials alluded to, as nearly as possible in the order the Author had intended, and the seventh and concluding volume is in the press and will shortly be published.*

The whole of the MS. sheets, previous to being sent to the press, were cautiously examined by his no less amiable and excellent, than highly gifted Widow, who, at the time, was staying with us on a visit at West-Tarring. Had the lamented Southey continued the work, it was his intention, in this volume, to have advanced a step in the story, — and the Interchapters, no doubt, would have been enlarged, according to custom. His habit was, as he said, "to lay the timbers of them, and to jot down, from time to time, remarks serious or jocose, as they occurred to him." Full readily would this holy and humble man of heart have acceded to the truth conveyed in these lines from Martin Tupper's Proverbial Philosophy, — and none the less for their dactylic cadence.

There is a grave-faced folly, and verily a laughter loving wisdom;
And what, if surface judges account it vain frivolity?
There is indeed an evil in excess, and a field may lie fallow too long;
Yet merriment is often as a froth, that mantleth on the strong mind:
And note thou this for a verity, — the subtlest thinker when alone,
From ease of thoughts unbent, will laugh the loudest with his fellows:
And well is the loveliness of wisdom mirrored in a cheerful countenance,
Justly the deepest pools are proved by dimpling eddies;
For that, a true philosophy commandeth an innocent life,
And the unguilty spirit is lighter than a linnet's heart;
Yea, there is no cosmetic like a holy conscience;
The eye is bright with trust, the cheek bloomed over with affection,
The brow unwrinkled with a care, and the lip triumphant in its gladness.†

The only liberty taken with the original MS. is the omission of, now and then a name, or even a paragraph, which might have given pain to the living. Such passages were thrown off playfully, and were, as Mrs. Southey can testify, erased by the author continually. It was no custom of Southey to cast "fire-brands, arrows, and death," and to say, "Am I not in sport?"‡

It only remains to add that the Editor has carefully verified all references, — that he is responsible for the headings of the chapters (some few excepted,) — for the Mottoes to Chapters CLXXX. and CLXXXI., — and for the casual foot notes.

John Wood Warter.

Vicarage House,
West-Tarring, Nov. 25th, 1846.

* This refers to the Edition in Seven Volumes, 8vo.

† Of Ridicule, 1st Series. On my acquainting Mrs. Southey with my intention of quoting these lines, she wrote me word back: — "That very passage I had noted, as singularly applicable to him *we* knew so well, — whom the world, the children of this generation, — knew so little!"

‡ Prov. xxvi. 18, 19.

The ancient sage who did so long maintain
That bodies die, but souls return again,
With all the births and deaths he had in store,
Went out Pythagoras and came no more.
And modern Asgill, whose capricious thought
Is yet with stores of wilder notions fraught,
Too soon convinced, shall yield that fleeting breath,
Which play'd so idly with the darts of death.

PRIOR.

I swell with my imaginations,
Like a tall ship, bound out for the Fortunate Islands ;
Top and top-gallant ! my flags, and my figaries,
Upon me, with a lusty gale of wind
Able to rend my sails. I shall o'errun
And sink thy little bark of understanding
In my career.

SHIRLEY.

Tu as icy dequoy faire un grand repas : la sotise, l'egarement, le desordre, la negligence, la paresse, et milles autres defauts cacher à mon aveuglement, ou à mon ignorance, sont seruis en piramide et à plats renforcez. Gobe, gobe, mon cher Lecteur à ton aise ! qu'il ne te reste ny faim ny appetit, puis que tu peus satisfaire l'un et l'autre, et que tu as tout, Abastanza, comme disent les Italiens ; c'est à dire presque à gogo.

LA PRECIEUSE.

Let the looks and noses of judges hover thick, so they bring the brains ; or if they do not, I care not. When I suffered it to go abroad, I departed with my right ; and now, so secure an interpreter I am of my chance, that neither praise nor dispraise shall affect me.

BEN JONSON.

Deep-reaching wits, here is no deep stream for you to angle in. Moralizers, you that wrest a never-meant meaning out of every thing, applying all things to the present time, keep your attention for the common stage ; for here are no quips in characters for you to read ! Vain glozers, gather what you will ! Spite, spell backward what thou canst !

NASH, *Summer's Last Will.*

MSS. MOTTOES FOR THE DOCTOR, &c.

THE DOCTOR,

&c.

PART THE SECOND.

CHAPTER CLXXII.

DESCARTES' NOTION CONCERNING THE PROLONGATION OF LIFE. A SICILIAN PROPOSAL FOR BREEDING UP CHILDREN TO BE IMMORTAL. ASGILL'S ARGUMENT AGAINST THE NECESSITY OF DYING.

O harmless Death! whom still the valiant brave,
The wise expect, the sorrowful invite;
And all the good embrace, who know the Grave
A short dark passage to eternal light.

SIR WILLIAM DAVENANT.

SIR KENELM DIGBY went to Holland for the purpose of conversing with Descartes, who was then living in retirement at Egmont. Speculative knowledge, Digby said to him, was, no doubt, a refined and agreeable pursuit, but it was too uncertain and too useless to be made a man's occupation, life being so short that one has scarcely time to acquire well the knowledge of necessary things. It would be far more worthy of a person like Descartes, he observed, who so well understood the construction of the human frame, if he would apply himself to discover means of prolonging its duration, rather than attach himself to the mere speculation of philosophy. Descartes made answer that this was a subject on which he had already meditated; that as for rendering man immortal, it was what he would not venture to promise, but that he was very sure he could prolong his life to the standard of the Patriarchs.

Saint-Evremond, to whom Digby repeated this, says that this opinion of Descartes was well known both to his friends in Holland and in France. The Abbé Picot, his disciple and his martyr, was so fully persuaded of it, that it was long before he would believe his master was dead, and when at length unwillingly convinced of what it was no longer possible to deny or doubt, he exclaimed, *que c'en étoit fait et que la fin du Genre humain alloit venir!*

A certain Sicilian physician who commented upon Galen, was more cautious if not more modest than Descartes. He affirmed that it was certainly possible to render men immortal, but then they must be bred up from the earliest infancy with that view; and he undertook so to train and render them,—if they were fit subjects.—Poor children! if it had indeed been possible thus to divest them of their reversionary interest in Heaven.

A much better way of abolishing death was that which Asgill imagined, when he persuaded himself from Scripture that it is in our power to go to Heaven without any such unpleasant middle passage. Asgill's is the worst case of intolerance that has occurred in this country since persecution has ceased to affect life or member.

This remarkable man was born about the middle of the seventeenth century, and bred to the Law in Lincoln's Inn, under Mr. Eyre, a very eminent lawyer of those days. In 1698 he published a treatise with this title—"Several assertions proved, in order to create another species of money than Gold and Silver," and also an "Essay on a Registry for Titles of Lands." Both subjects seem to denote that on these points he was considerably advanced beyond his age. But the whole strength of his mind was devoted to his profession, in which he had so completely trammelled and drilled his intellectual powers, that he at length acquired a habit of looking at all subjects in a legal point of view. He could find flaws in an hereditary title to the crown. But it was not to seek flaws that he studied the Bible; he studied it to see whether he could not claim under the Old and New Testament something more than was considered to be his share. The result of this examination was, that in the year 1700 he published "An Argument proving that according to the Covenant of Eternal Life revealed in the Scriptures Man may be translated from hence into that Eternal Life without passing through death, although the Human Nature of Christ himself could not be thus translated till he had passed through death."

That the old motto (says he), worn upon tomb-stones, "Death is the Gate of Life," is a lie, by which men decoy one another into death, taking it to be a thoroughfare into Eternal Life, whereas it is just so far out of the way. For die when we will, and be buried where we will, and lie in the grave as long as we will, we must all return from thence, and stand again upon the Earth before we can ascend into the Heavens. *Hinc itur ad astra.* He admitted that "this custom of the world to die hath gained such a prevalency over our minds by prepossessing us of the necessity of death, that it stands ready to swallow his argument whole without digesting it." But the dominion of death, he said, is supported by our fear of it, by which it hath bullied the world to this day. Yet "the custom of the World to die is no argument one way or other;" however, because he knew that custom itself is admitted as an evidence of title, upon presumption that such custom had once a reasonable commencement, and that this reason doth continue, it was incumbent upon him to answer this Custom by showing the time and reason of its commencement, and that the reason was determined.

"First then," says he, "I do admit the custom or possession of Death over the world to be as followeth: that Death did reign from Adam to Moses by an uninterrupted possession over all men, women and children, created or born, except one breach made upon it in that time by Enoch; and hath reigned from Moses unto this day by the like uninterrupted possession, except one other breach made upon it in this time by Elijah. And this is as strong a possession as can be alledged against me.

"The religion of the World now is that Man is born to die. But from the beginning it was not so, for Man was made to live. God made not Death till Man brought it upon himself by his delinquency. Adam stood as fair for Life as Death, and fairer too, because he was in the actual possession of Life, — as Tenant thereof at the Will of God, and had an opportunity to have made that title perpetual by the Tree of Life, which stood before him with the Tree of Knowledge of Good and Evil. And here 'tis observable how the same act of man is made the condition both of his life and death: 'put forth thy hand and pull and eat and die,' or 'put forth thy hand and pull and eat and live for ever.' 'Tis not to be conceived that there was any physical virtues in either of these Trees whereby to cause life or death; but God having sanctified them by those two different names, he was obliged to make good his own characters of them, by commanding the whole Creation to act in such a manner as that Man should feel the effects of this word, according to which of the Trees he first put forth his hand. And it is yet more strange, that man having life and death set before him at the same time and place, and both to be had upon the same condition, that he should single out his own death, and leave the Tree of Life untouched. And what is further strange, even after his election of death he had an interval of time before his expulsion out of Paradise, to have retrieved his fate by putting forth his hand to the Tree of Life; and yet he omitted this too!

"But by all this it is manifest that as the form or person of man in his first creation was capable of eternal life without dying, so the fall of man, which happened to him after his creation, hath not disabled his person from that capacity of eternal life. And, therefore, durst Man even then have broken through the Cherubim and flaming sword, or could he now any way come at the Tree of Life, he must yet live for ever, notwithstanding his sin committed in Paradise and his expulsion out of it. But this Tree of Life now seems lost to Man; and so he remains under the curse of that other Tree, 'in the day that thou eatest thereof thou shalt die.' Which sentence of the Law is the cause of the death of Man, and was the commencement of the Custom of Death in the World, and by the force of this Law Death has kept the possession (before admitted) to this day.

"By his act of delinquency and the sentence upon it, Adam stood attainted and became a dead man in law, though he was not executed till about nine hundred years afterwards." Lawyer as Asgill was, and legally as he conducts his whole extraordinary argument, he yet offers a moral extenuation of Adam's offence. Eve after her eating and Adam before his eating, were, he says, in two different states, she in the state of Death, and he in the state of Life; and thereby his was much the harder case. For she by her very creation was so much a part of himself that he could not be happy while she was miserable. The loss of her happiness so much affected him by sympathy that all his other enjoyments could do him no good; and, therefore, since he thought it impossible for her to return into the same state with him, he chose, rather than be parted from her, to hazard himself in the same state with her. Asgill then resumes his legal view of the case: the offence, he says, was at last joint and several; the sentence fell upon Mankind as descendants from these our common ancestors, and so upon Christ himself. And this is the reason why in the genealogy of our Saviour as set down by two Evangelists his legal descent by Joseph is only counted upon, "because all legal descents are accounted from the father." As he was born of a Virgin to preserve his nature from the defilement of humanity, so was he of a Virgin espoused to derive upon himself the curse of the Law by a legal father: for which purpose it was necessary that the birth of Christ should, in the terms of the Evangelists, be on this wise and no otherwise. And hence the Genealogy of Christ is a fundamental part of Eternal Life.

The reader will soon perceive that technically as Asgill treated his strange argument, he was sincerely and even religiously convinced of its importance and its truth. "Having shewn," he proceeds, "how this Law fell upon Christ, it is next incumbent on me to shew that it is taken away by his death, and consequently that the long possession of Death over the World can be no longer a title against Life. But when I say this Law is taken away, I don't mean that the words of it are taken away; for they remain with us to this day, and being matter of Record must remain for ever; but that it is satisfied by other matter of Record, by which the force of it is gone. Law satisfied is no Law, as a debt satisfied is no debt. Now the specific demand of the Law was Death; and of a man; and a man made under the Law. Christ qualified himself to be so: and as such suffered under it, thus undergoing the literal sentence. This he might have done and not have given the Law satisfaction, for millions of men before him had undergone it, and yet the Law was nevertheless dissatisfied with them and others, but He declared *It is finished* before he gave up the ghost. By the dignity of his person he gave that satisfaction which it was impossible for mankind to give."

For the Law, he argues, was not such a civil contract that the breach of it could be satisfied; it was a Law of Honour, the breach whereof required personal satisfaction for the greatest affront and the highest act of ingratitude to God, inasmuch as the slighter the thing demanded is, the greater is the affront in refusing it. "Man by his very creation entered into the labours of the Creator and became Lord of the Universe which was adapted to his enjoyments. God left him in possession of it upon his parole of honour, only that he would acknowledge it to be held of Him, and as the token of this tenure that he would only forbear from eating of one tree, withal telling him that if he did eat of it, his life should go for it. If man had had more than his life to give, God would have had it of him. This was rather a resentment of the affront, than any satisfaction for it; and therefore to signify the height of this resentment, God raises man from the dead to demand further satisfaction from him. Death is a commitment to the prison of the Grave till the Judgment of the Great Day; and then the grand Habeas Corpus will issue to the Earth and to the Sea, to give up their dead: to remove the Bodies, with the cause of their commitment.

"Yet was this a resentment without malice; for as God maintained his resentment under all his love, so He maintained his love under all his resentment. For his love being a love of kindness flowing from his own nature, could not be diminished by any act of man; and yet his honour being concerned to maintain the truth of his word, he could not falsify that to gratify his own affection. And thus he bore the passion of his own love, till he had found out a salvo for his honour by that Son of Man who gave him satisfaction at once by the dignity of his person. Personal satisfactions by the Laws of Honour are esteemed sufficient or not, according to the equality or inequality between the persons who give or take the affront. Therefore God to vindicate his honour was obliged to find out a person for this purpose equal to Himself: the invention of which is called the manifold wisdom of God, the invention itself being the highest expression of the deepest love, and the execution of it, in the death of Christ, the deepest resentment of the highest affront.

"Now inasmuch as the person of our Saviour was superior to the human nature, so much the satisfaction by his death surmounted the offence. He died under the Law, but he did not arise under it, having taken it away by his death. The life regained by him in his resurrection was by Conquest, by which, according to all the Laws of Conquest, the Law of Death is taken away. For by the Laws of Conquest the Laws of the conquered are *ipso facto* taken away, and all records and writings that remain of them are of no more force than waste paper. Hence the title of Christ to Eternal Life is become absolute, — by absolute,"— says this theologo-jurist, — "I mean discharged from all tenure or condition, and consequently from all forfeiture. And as his title to life is thus become absolute by Conquest, so the direction of it is become eternal by being annexed to the Person of the Godhead: thus Christ ever since his resurrection did, and doth, stand seized of an absolute and indefeazable Estate of Eternal Life, without any tenure or condition or other matter or thing to change or determine it for ever." "I had reason," says Asgill, "thus to assert the title of Christ at large; because this is the title by and under which I am going to affirm my argument, and to claim Eternal Life for myself and all the world.

"And first I put it upon the Profession of Divinity to deny one word of the fact as I have repeated it. Next I challenge the Science of the Law to shew such another Title as this is. And then I defy the Logicians to deny my Argument: of which this is the abstract: That the Law delivered to Adam before the Fall is the original cause of Death in the World: That this Law is taken away by the Death of Christ: That therefore the legal power of death is gone. And I am so far from thinking this Covenant of Eternal Life to be an allusion to the forms of Title amongst men, that I rather adore it as the precedent for them all; believing with that great Apostle that the things on Earth are but the patterns of things in the Heavens where the Originals are kept." This he says because he has before made it appear that in the Covenant of Eternal Life all things requisite to constitute a legal instrument are found, to wit, the date, the parties, the contents, and consideration, the sealing, and execution, the witnesses, and the Ceremony required of Man, whereby to execute it on his part and take the advantage of it.

By the sacrifice which our Lord offered of himself, this technical but sincere and serious enthusiast argues, more than an atonement was made. "And that this superabundancy might not run to waste, God declared that Man should have Eternal Life absolute as Christ himself had it; and hence Eternal Life is called the Gift of God through our Lord and Saviour Jesus Christ, over and above our redemption. Why then," he asks, "doth Death remain in the World? Why because Man knows not the Way of Life — 'the way of Life they have not known.' Because our faith is not yet come to us — 'when the Son of Man comes shall he find faith upon the earth?' Because Man is a beast of burden that knows not his own strength in the virtue of the Death and the power of the Resurrection of Christ. Unbelief goes not by reason or dint of argument, but is a sort of melancholy madness, by which if we once fancy ourselves bound, it hath the same effect upon us as if we really were so. Death is like Satan, who appears to none but those who are afraid of him: Resist the Devil and he will flee from you. Because Death had once dominion over us, we think it hath, and must have it still. And this I find within myself, that though I can't deny one word I have said in fact or argument, yet I can't maintain my belief of it without making it more familiar to my understanding, by turning it up and down in my thoughts and ruminating upon some proceedings already made upon it in the World.

"The Motto of the Religion of the World is *Mors Janua Vitæ;* if we mean by this the Death of Christ, we are in the right; but if we mean our own Death, then we are in the wrong. Far be it from me to say that Man may not attain to Eternal Life, though he should die; for the Text runs double. '*I am the Resurrection and the Life; he that liveth and believeth on me, shall never die; and though he were dead he shall live.*' This very Text shews that there is a nearer way of entering into Eternal Life than by the way of Death and Resurrection. Whatever circumstances a man is under at the time of his death, God is bound to make good this Text to him, according to which part of it he builds his faith upon; if he be dead there's a necessity for a resurrection; but if he be alive there's no occasion for Death or Resurrection either. This text doth not maintain two religions, but two articles of faith in the same religion, and the article of faith for a present life without dying is the higher of the two.

"No man can comprehend the heights and depths of the Gospel at his first entrance into it; and in point of order, 'the last enemy to be destroyed is Death.' The first essay of Faith is against Hell, that though we die we may not be damned; and the full assurance of this is more than most men attain to before Death overtakes them, which makes Death a terror to men. But they who attain it can sing a requiem 'Lord, now lettest thou thy Servant depart in peace!' and if God takes them at their word, they lie down in the faith of the Resurrection of the Just. But whenever he pleases to continue them, after that attainment, much longer above ground, that time seems to them an interval of perfect leisure, till at last espying Death itself, they fall upon it as an enemy that must be conquered, one time or other, through faith in Christ. This is the reason why it seems intended that a respite of time should be allotted to believers after the first Resurrection and before the dissolution of the World, for perfecting that faith which they began before their death but could not attain to in the first reach of life: for Death being but a discontinuance of Life, wherever men leave off at their death, they must begin at their resurrection. Nor shall they ascend after their resurrection, till they have attained to this faith of translation, and by that very faith they shall be then convinced that they need not have died.

"When Elijah courted death under the juniper tree in the wilderness, and 'said — now, Lord, take away my life, for I am not better than my fathers,' that request shews that he was not educated in this faith of translation, but attained it afterwards by study. Paul tells 'we shall not all die but we shall

all be changed;' yet though he delivered this to be his faith in general, he did not attain to such a particular knowledge of the way and manner of it as to prevent his own death: he tells us he had not yet attained the Resurrection of the dead, but was pressing after it. He had but a late conversion, and was detained in the study of another part of divinity, the confirming the New Testament by the Old and making them answer one another,—a point previous to the faith of translation, and which must be learned before it—in order to it. But this his pressing (though he did not attain) hath much encouraged me," says Asgill, "to make this enquiry, being well assured that he would not have thus pursued it, had he not apprehended more in it than the vulgar opinion.

"We don't think ourselves fit to deal with one another in human affairs till our age of one and twenty. But to deal with our offended Maker, to counterplot the malice of fallen Angels, and to rescue ourselves from eternal ruin, we are generally as well qualified before we can speak plain, as all our life-time after. Children can say over their religion at four or five years old, and their parents that taught them can do no more at four or five and fifty. The common Creed of the Christian religion may be learned in an hour: and one day's philosophy will teach a man to die. But to know the virtue of the Death and Power of the Resurrection of Christ, is a science calculated for the study of Men and Angels for ever.

"But if man may be thus changed without death, and that it is of no use to him in order to Eternal Life; what then is Death? Or, whereunto serveth it? What is it? Why 'tis a misfortune fallen upon man from the beginning, and from which he has not yet dared to attempt his recovery: and it serves as a spectre to fright us into a little better life (perhaps) than we should lead without it. Though God hath formed this Covenant of Eternal Life, Men have made an agreement with Death and Hell, by way of composition to submit to Death, in hope of escaping Hell by that obedience; and under this allegiance we think ourselves bound never to rebel against it! The study of Philosophy is to teach men to die, from the observations of Nature; the profession of Divinity is to enforce the doctrine from Revelation: and the science of the Law is to settle our civil affairs pursuant to these resolutions. The old men are making their last Wills and Testaments; and the young are expecting the execution of them by the death of the testators; and thus

Mortis ad exemplum totus componitur orbis.

I was under this Law of Death once; and while I lay under it, I felt the terror of it, till I had delivered myself from it by those thoughts which must convince them that have them. And in this thing only, I wish, for their sakes, that all men were as I am. The reason why I believe that this doctrine is true, is, because God hath said it: yet I could not thus assert it by argument, if I did not conceive it with more self-conviction than I have from any maxims or positions in human science. The Covenant of Eternal Life is a Law of itself and a science of itself, which can never be known by the study of any other science. It is a science out of Man's way, being a pure invention of God. Man knows no more how to save himself than he did to create himself; but to raise his ambition for learning this, God graduates him upon his degree of knowledge in it, and gives him badges of honour as belonging to that degree, upon the attainment whereof a man gains the title of a Child of the Resurrection: to which title belongs this badge of honour, to die no more but make our exit by translation, as Christ, who was the first of this Order, did before us. And this world being the academy to educate Man for Heaven, none shall ever enter there till they have taken this degree here.

"Let the Dead bury the Dead! and the Dead lie with the Dead! And the rest of the Living go lie with them! I'll follow him that was dead, and is alive, and living for ever. And though I am now single, yet I believe that this belief will be general before the general change, of which Paul speaks, shall come; and that then, and not before, shall be the Resurrection of the Just, which is called the first Resurrection; and after that the Dead so arisen, with the Living, then alive, shall have learned this faith, which shall qualify them to be caught up together in the air, then shall be the General Resurrection, after which Time shall be no more.

"The beginning of this faith, like all other parts of the Kingdom of Heaven, will be like a grain of mustard seed, spreading itself by degrees till it overshadow the whole earth. And since 'the things concerning Him must have an end,' in order to this they must have a beginning. But whoever leads the van will make the world start, and must expect for himself to walk up and down, like Cain, with a mark on his forehead, and run the gauntlet for an Ishmaelite, having every man's hand against him because his hand is against every man; than which nothing is more averse to my temper. This makes me think of publishing with as much regret as he that ran away from his errand when sent to Nineveh: but being just going to cross the water —" (he was going to Ireland, —) "I dared not leave this behind me undone, lest a Tempest send me back again to do it. And to shelter myself a little, (though I knew my speech would betray me,) I left the Title page anonymous. Nor do I think that any thing would now extort my name from me but the dread of the sentence, 'he that is ashamed of me and of my words, of him will I be ashamed before my Father and his Angels:' for fear of which I dare not but subscribe my argument, though with a trembling hand; having felt two powers within me all the while I have been about it, one bids me write, and the other bobs my elbow. But since I have wrote this, as Pilate did his inscription, without consulting any one, I'll be absolute as he was; 'what I have written, I have written.'

"Having pursued that command, 'Seek first the Kingdom of God,' I yet expect the performance of that promise, to receive in this life an hundred fold, and in the world to come life everlasting.' I have a great deal of business yet in this world, without doing of which Heaven itself would be uneasy to me: but when that is done I know no business I have with the dead, and therefore do depend that I shall not go hence by 'returning to the dust,' which is the sentence of that law from which I claim a discharge: but that I shall make my exit by way of translation, which I claim as a dignity belonging to that Degree in the Science of Eternal Life of which I profess myself a graduate. And if after this I die like other men, I declare myself to die of no religion. Let no one be concerned for me as a desperade: I am not going to renounce the other part of our religion, but to add another article of faith to it, without which I cannot understand the rest. And if it be possible to believe too much in God, I desire to be guilty of that sin.

"Behold ye despisers and wonder! Wonder to see Paradise lost, with the Tree of Life in the midst of it! Wonder and curse at Adam for an original fool, who in the length of one day never so much as thought to put forth his hand, for him and us, and pull and eat and live for ever! Wonder at and damn ourselves for fools of the last impression, that in the space of seventeen hundred years never so much as thought to put forth our hands, every one for himself, and seal and execute the Covenant of Eternal Life.

"To be even with the World at once, he that wonders at my faith, I wonder at his unbelief. The Blood of Christ hath an incident quality which cleaneth from sin; and he that understands this never makes any use of his own personal virtues as an argument for his own salvation, lest God should overbalance against him with his sins; nor doth God ever object a man's sins to him in the day of his faith; therefore till I am more sinful than He was holy, my sins are no objection against my faith. And because in Him is all my hope, I care not (almost) what I am myself.

"It is observed in the mathematics that the practice doth not always answer the theory; and that therefore there is no dependence upon the mere notions of it as they lie in the brain, without putting them together in the form of a tool or instrument, to see how all things fit. This made me distrust my own thoughts till I had put them together, to see how they would look in the form of an argument. But in doing this, I thank God I have found every joint and article to come into its own place, and fall in with and suit one another to a hair's breadth, beyond my expectation: or else I could not have had the confidence to produce this as an engine in Divinity to convey man from Earth to Heaven. I am not making myself wings to fly to Heaven with, but only making myself ready for that conveyance which shall be sent me. And if I should lose myself in this untrodden path of Life, I can still find out the beaten Road of Death blindfold. If therefore, after this, 'I go the way of my fathers,' I freely waive that haughty epitaph, *Magnis tamen excidit ausis*, and instead knock under table that Satan hath beguiled me to play the fool with myself, in which however he hath shewed his master-piece; for I defy the whole clan of Hell to produce another lye so like to truth as this is. But if I act my motto, and go the way of an Eagle in the air, then have I played a trump upon Death, and shewn myself a match for the Devil.

"And while I am thus fighting with Death and Hell, it looks a little like foul play for Flesh and Blood to interpose themselves against me. But if any one hath spite enough to give me a polt, thinking to falsify my faith by taking away my life, I only desire them first to qualify themselves for my executioners, by taking this short test in their own consciences: whoever thinks that any thing herein contained is not fair dealing with God and Man, let him — or her — burn this book, and cast a stone at him that wrote it."

CHAPTER CLXXIII.

MORE CONCERNING ASGILL. HIS DEFENCE IN THE HOUSE OF COMMONS, HIS EXPULSION, FARTHER SPECULATIONS AND DEATH.

Let not that ugly Skeleton appear!
Sure Destiny mistakes; this Death's not mine!
DRYDEN.

The substance of Asgill's argument has been given in his own words, but by thus abstracting and condensing it his peculiar manner is lost. This, though it consisted more perhaps in appearance than in reality, is characteristic of the author, and may be well exemplified in the concluding passage of one of his political pamphlets:

"But I shall raise more choler by this way of writing,
For writing and reading are in themselves commendable things,
But 'tis the way of writing at which offence is taken,
And this is the misfortune of an Author,
That unless some are angry with him, none are pleased.
Which puts him under this dilemma,
That he must either ruin himself or his Printer.

But to prevent either, as far as I can, I would rather turn Trimmer and compound too. And to end all quarrels with my readers (if they please to accept the proposal,

And to shew withal that I am no dogmatical Author,)

I now say to them all, in print, what I once did to one of them, by word of mouth. Whoever meets with any thing in what I publish, which they don't like,

Let 'em strike it out.
But to take off part of the Odium from me,
They say others write like me,
In short paragraphs:
(An easy part of a mimick,)
But with all my heart!
I don't care who writes like me,
So I don't write like them."

Many a book has originated in the misfortunes of its Author. Want, imprisonment, and disablement by bodily infirmity from active occupation, have produced almost as many works in prose or rhyme, as leisure, voluntary exertion, and strong desire. Asgill's harmless heresy began in an involuntary confinement to which he was reduced in consequence of an unsuccessful speculation. He had engaged in this adventure (by which better word our forefathers designated what the Americans call a *spec*,) with the hope of increasing his fortune, instead of which he incurred so great a loss, that he found it necessary to keep his chamber in the Temple for some years. There he fell to examining that "Book of Law and Gospel," both which we call the Bible; and examining it as he would have perused an old deed, with the hope of discovering in it some clause upon which to ground a claim at law, this thought, he says, first came into his head; but it was a great while coming out. He was afraid of his own thoughts, lest they were his own only, and as such a delusion. And when he had tried them with pen, ink and paper, and they seemed to him plainer and plainer every time he went over them, and he had formed them into an Argument, "to see how they would bear upon the proof," even then he had no intention of making them public.

"But writing an ill hand," says he, "I resolved to see how it would look in print. On this I gave the Printer my Copy, with money for his own labour, to print off some few for myself, and keep the press secret. But I remember before he got half way through, he told me his men fancied I was a little crazed, in which I also fancied he spoke one word for them and two for himself. However I bid him go on; and at last it had so raised his fancy, that he desired my leave to print off one edition at the risque of his own charge, saying he thought some of the Anabaptists would believe it first. I being just then going for Ireland, admitted him, with this injunction, he should not publish them 'till I was got clear out of Middlesex; which I believe he might observe; though by what I heard afterwards, they were all about town by that time I got to St. Albans: and the book was in Ireland almost as soon as I was, (for a man's works will follow him,) with a noise after me that I was gone away mad."

Asgill was told in Ireland that the cry which followed him would prevent his practice; it had a contrary effect, for "people went into Court to see him as a Monster and heard him talk like a man." In the course of two years he gained enough by his profession to purchase Lord Kenmure's forfeited estate, and to procure a seat in the Irish House of Commons. The purchase made him enemies; as he was on the way to Dublin he met the news that his book had been burnt by Order of the House. He proceeded however, took the oaths and his seat, and the Book having been condemned and executed without hearing the author in its defence, nothing more was necessary than to prove him the Author and expel him forthwith, and this was done in the course of four days. After this he returned to England and obtained a seat for Bramber, apparently for the mere sake of securing himself against his creditors. This borough he represented for two years; but in the first Parliament after the Union some of the Scotch Members are said to have looked upon it as a disgrace to the House of Commons, that a man who enjoyed his liberty only under privilege should sit there, and instead of attempting to remedy a scandal by straightforward means, they took the easier course of moving for a Committee to examine his book. Their report was that it was profane and blasphemous, highly reflecting upon the Christian Religion. He was allowed, however, to make his defence, which he thus began.

"Mr. Speaker, this day calls me to something I am both unapt and averse to—Preaching. For though, as you see, I have vented some of my thoughts in religion, yet I appeal to my conversation, whether I use to make that the subject of my discourse. However that I may not let this accusation go against me by a *Nihil dicit*, I stand up to make my defence. I have heard it from without doors that I intended to withdraw myself from this day's test and be gone; which would have given them that said it an opportunity to boast that they had once spoken truth. But *quo me fata trahunt*, I'll give no man occasion to write *fugam fecit* upon my grave-stone."

He then gave the history of his book and of his expulsion in Ireland, and thanked the

House for admitting him to a defence before they proceeded to judgment. "I find," said he, "the Report of the Committee is not levelled at the argument itself which I have advanced, nor yet against the treatise I have published to prove it, but against some expressions in that proof, and which I intend to give particular answers to. But there is something else laid to my charge as my design in publishing that argument, of higher concern to me than any expressions in the treatise, or any censure that can fall on me for it; as if I had wrote it with a malicious intention to expose the Scriptures as false, because they seemed to contain what I asserted; and that therefore if that assertion did not hold true, the Scripture must be false. Now whether this was my intention or no, there is but one Witness in Heaven or Earth can prove, and that is He that made me, and in whose presence I now stand, and Who is able to strike me dead in my place; and to Him I now appeal for the truth of what I protest against: that I never did write or publish that argument with any intention to expose the Scriptures; but on the contrary, (though I was aware that I might be liable to that censure, which I knew not how to avoid,) I did both write and publish it, under a firm belief of the truth of the Scriptures: and with a belief (under that) that what I have asserted in that argument is within that truth. And if it be not, then I am mistaken in my argument, and the Scripture remains true. Let God be true and every man a lyar. And having made this protestation, I am not much concerned whether I am believed in it or not; I had rather tell a truth than be believed in a lie at any time."

He then justified the particular passage which had been selected for condemnation, resting his defence upon this ground, that he had used familiar expressions with the intent of being sooner read and more readily understood. There was indeed but a single word which savoured of irreverence, and certainly no irreverence was intended in its use; no one who fairly perused his argument but must have perceived that the levity of his manner in no degree detracted from the seriousness of his belief. "Yet," said he, "if by any of those expressions I have really given offence to any well-meaning Christian, I am sorry for it, though I had no ill intention in it: but if any man be captious to take exceptions for exception sake, I am not concerned. I esteem my own case plain and short. I was expelled one House for having too much land; and I am going to be expelled another for having too little money. But if I may yet ask one question more; pray what is this blasphemous crime I here stand charged with? A belief of what we all profess, or at least what no one can deny. If the death of the body be included in the Fall, why is not the life of the body included in the Resurrection? And what if I have a firmer belief of this than some others have? Am I therefore a blasphemer? Or would they that believe less take it well of me to call them so? Our Saviour in his day took notice of some of little faith and some of great faith, without stigmatizing either of them with blasphemy for it. But I do not know how 'tis, we are fallen into such a sort of uniformity that we would fain have Religion into a Tyrant's bed, torturing one another into our own size of it only. But it grows late, and I ask but one saying more to take leave of my friends with. I do believe that had I turned this Defence into a Recantation, I had prevented my Expulsion: but I have reserved my last words as my ultimate reason against that Recantation. He that durst write that book, dares not deny it!"

"And what then?" said this eccentric writer, when five years afterwards he published his Defence. "Why then they called for candles; and I went away by the light of 'em: and after the previous question and other usual ceremonies, (as I suppose) I was expelled the House. And from thence I retired to a Chamber I once had in the Temple; and from thence I afterwards surrendered myself in discharge of my bail, and have since continued under confinement. And under that confinement God hath been pleased to take away 'the Desire of mine

Eyes with a stroke,' which hath, however, drowned all my other troubles at once; for the less are merged in the greater;

Qui venit hic fluctus, fluctus supereminet omnes.

And since I have mentioned her, I'll relate this of her. She having been educated a Protestant of the Church of England, by a Lady her Grandmother, her immediate parents and other relations being Roman Catholics, an honest Gentleman of the Romish persuasion, who knew her family, presented her, while she was my fellow-prisoner, with a large folio volume, being the history of the Saints canonised in that Church, for her reading; with intention, as I found, to incline her that way. With which, delighting in reading, she entertained herself 'till she had gone through it; and some time after that she told me that she had before some thoughts towards that religion, but that the reading that history had confirmed her against it.

"And yet she would never read the book I was expelled for 'till after my last expulsion; but then reading it through, told me she was reconciled to the reasons of it, though she could not say she believed it. However she said something of her own thoughts with it, that hath given me the satisfaction that she is 'dead in Christ,' and thereby sure of her part in the first Resurrection: the Dead in Christ shall arise first. And this *pars decessa mei* leaving me half dead while she remains in the grave, hath since drawn me, in diving after her, into a nearer view and more familiar though more unusual thoughts of that first Resurrection than ever I had before. From whence I now find that nothing less than this *fluctus decumanus* would have cast me upon, or qualified me for, this theme, if yet I am so qualified. And from hence I am advancing that common Article in our Creed, the Resurrection of the Dead, into a professed study; from the result of which study I have already advanced an assertion, which (should I vent alone) perhaps would find no better quarter in the world than what I have advanced already. And yet, though I say it that perhaps should not, it hath one quality we are all fond of,—it is News; and another we all should be fond of, it is good News: or, at least, good to them that are so, 'for to the froward all things are froward.'

"Having made this Discovery, or rather collected it from the Word of Life; I am advancing it into a Treatise whereby to prove it in special form, not by arguments of wit or sophistry, but from the evidence and demonstration of the truth as it is in Jesus: which should I accomplish I would not be prevented from publishing that edition to gain more than I lost by my former; nor for more than Balak ever intended to give, or than Balaam could expect to receive, for cursing the people of Israel, if God had not spoilt that bargain. I find it as old as the New Testament, 'if by any means I may attain the Resurrection of the Dead.' And though Paul did not then so attain, (not as if I had already attained), yet he died in his calling, and will stand so much nearer that mark at his Resurrection. But if Paul, with that effusion of the Spirit upon him in common with the other Apostles, and that superabundant revelation given him above them all, by that rapture unto things unutterable, did not so attain in that his day; whence should I, a mere Lay, (and that none of the best neither,) without any function upon me, expect to perfect what he left so undone?—In pursuit of this study I have found, (what I had not before observed,) that there are some means since left us towards this attainment, which Paul had not in his day; for there now remain extant unto the world, bound up with that now one entire record of the Bible, two famous Records of the Resurrection that never came to Paul's hands; and for want whereof, perhaps, he might not then so attain. But having now this intelligence of them, and fearing that in the day of Account I may have a special surcharge made upon me for these additional Talents and further Revelations; and bearing in mind the dreadful fate of that cautious insuring servant who took so much care to redeliver what he had received *in statu quo* as he had it, that it might not be said to be the worse for his keeping, I have rather adventured to defile those Sacred Records with my own study and thoughts upon them, than to think of returning them wrapt up in a napkin clean and untouched.

"Whether ever I shall accomplish to my own satisfaction what I am now so engaged in, I do not yet know; but 'till I do, I'll please myself to be laughed at by this cautious insuring world, as tainted with a frenzy of dealing in Reversions of Contingencies. However in the mean time I would not be thought to be spending this interval of my days by myself in beating the air, under a dry expectancy only of a thing so seemingly remote as the Resurrection of the Dead: like Courtiers-Extraordinary fretting out their soles with attendances in ante-rooms for things or places no more intended to be given them than perhaps they are fit to have them. For though I should fall short of the attainment I am attempting, the attempt itself hath translated my Prison into a Paradise; treating me with food and enamouring me with pleasures that man knows not of: from whence, I hope, I may without vanity say,

Deus nobis hæc otia fecit."

What the farther reversion might be to which Asgill fancied he had discovered a title in the Gospels, is not known. Perhaps he failed in satisfying himself when he attempted to arrange his notions in logical and legal form, and possibly that failure may have weakened his persuasion of the former heresy: for though he lived twenty years after the publication of his Defence and the announcement of this second discovery in the Scriptures, the promised argument never appeared. His subsequent writings consist of a few pamphlets in favour of the Hanoverian succession. They were too inconsiderable to contribute much towards eking out his means of support, for which he was probably chiefly indebted to his professional knowledge. The remainder of his life was passed within the Rules of the King's Bench Prison, where he died in 1738 at a very advanced age, retaining his vivacity and his remarkable powers of conversation to the last. If it be true that he nearly attained the age of an hundred, (as one statement represents,) and with these happy faculties unimpaired, he may have been tempted to imagine that he was giving the best and only convincing proof of his own argument. Death undeceived him, and Time has done him justice at last. For though it stands recorded that he was expelled the House of Commons as being the Author of a Book in which are contained many profane and blasphemous expressions, highly reflecting upon the Christian Religion! nothing can be more certain than that this censure was undeserved, and that his expulsion upon that ground was as indefensible as it would have been becoming, if, in pursuance of the real motives by which the House was actuated, an Act had been passed disqualifying from that time forward any person in a state of insolvency from taking or retaining a seat there.

In the year 1760 I find him mentioned as "the celebrated gentleman commonly called "translated Asgill." His name is now seen only in catalogues, and his history known only to the curious:—*Mais, c'est assez parlé de luy, et encore trop, ce diront aucuns, qui pourront m'en blasmer, et dire que j'estois bien de loisir quand j'escrivis cecy; mais ils seront bien plus de loisir de la lire, pour me reprendre.**

CHAPTER CLXXIV.

THE DOCTOR INDULGES IN THE WAY OF FANTASTIC AND TYPICAL SPECULATION ON HIS OWN NAME, AND ON THE POWERS OF THE LETTER D., WHETHER AS REGARDS DEGREES AND DISTINCTIONS, GODS AND DEMIGODS, PRINCES AND KINGS, PHILOSOPHERS, GENERALS, OR TRAVELLERS.

My mouth's no dictionary; it only serves as the needful interpreter of my heart. — QUARLES.

THERE were few things in the way of fantastic and typical speculation which de-

* BRANTOME.

lighted the Doctor so much as the contemplation of his own name:

DANIEL DOVE.

D. D. it was upon his linen and his seal. D. D., he used to say, designated the highest degree in the highest of the sciences, and he was D. D. not by the forms of a University, but by Nature or Destiny.

Besides, he maintained, that the letter D was the richest, the most powerful, the most fortunate letter in the alphabet, and contained in its form and origin more mysteries than any other.

It was a potential letter under which all powerful things were arranged; Dictators, Despots, Dynasties, Diplomas, Doctors, Dominations; Deeds and Donations and Decrees; Dioptrics and Dynamics; Dialectics and Demonstrations.

Diaphragm, Diathesis, Diet, Digestion, Disorder, Disease, Diagnosis; Diabrosis, Diaphragmatis, Diaphthora, Desudation, Defluxions, Dejection, Delirium, Delivery, Dyspepsy, Dysmenorrhœa, Dysorœxia, Dyspnœa, Dysuria, Dentition, Dropsy, Diabetes, Diarrhœa, Dysentery; then passing almost in unconscious but beautiful order from diseases to remedies and their consequences, he proceeded with Dispensation, Diluents, Discutients, Deobstruents, Demulcents, Detergents, Desiccatives, Depurantia, Diaphoretics, Dietetics, Diachylon, Diacodium, Diagrydium, Deligations, Decoctions, Doses, Draughts, Drops, Dressings, Drastics, Dissolution, Dissection. What indeed he would say, should we do in our profession without the Ds?

Or what would the Divines do without it —Danger, Despair, Dea h, Devil, Doomsday, Damnation; look to the brighter side, there is the Doxology, and you ascend to Διὸς, and Deus and Deity.

What would become of the farmer without Dung, or of the Musician without the Diapason? Think also of Duets in music and Doublets at Backgammon. And the soldier's toast in the old Play, "the two Ds Drink and your Duty." *

* SHIRLEY, Honoria and Mammon.

Look at the moral evils which are ranged under its banners, Dissentions, Discord, Duels, Dissimulation, Deceit, Dissipation, Demands, Debts, Damages, Divorce, Distress, Drunkenness, Dram-drinking, Distraction, Destruction.

When the Poet would describe things mournful and calamitous, whither doth he go for epithets of alliterative significance? where but to the letter D? there he hath Dim, Dusky, Drear, Dark, Damp, Dank, Dismal, Doleful, Dolorous, Disastrous, Dreadful, Desperate, Deplorable.

Would we sum up the virtues and praise of a perfect Woman, how should we do it but by saying that she was devout in religion, decorous in conduct, domestic in habits, dextrous in business, dutiful as a wife, diligent as a mother, discreet as a mistress, in manner debonnaire, in mind delicate, in person delicious, in disposition docile, in all things delightful. Then he would smile at Mrs. Dove and say, I love my love with a D. and her name is Deborah.

For degrees and distinctions, omitting those which have before been incidentally enumerated, are there not Dauphin and Dey, Dux, Duke, Doge. Dominus, with its derivatives Don, the Dom of the French and Portugueze, and the Dan of our own early language; Dame, Damsel, and Damoisel in the untranslated masculine. Deacons and Deans, those of the Christian Church, and of Madagascar, whose title the French write Dian, and we should write Deen not to confound them with the dignitaries of our Establishment. Druids and Dervises, Dryads, Demigods, and Divinities.

Regard the Mappa Mundi. You have Denmark and Dalecarlia, Dalmatia and the fertile Delta, Damascus, Delos, Delphi and Dodona, the Isles of Domingo and Dominica, Dublin and Durham and Dorchester and Dumfries, the shires of Devon, Dorset and Derby and the adjoining Bishoprick. Dantzic and Drontheim, the Dutchy of Deux Ponts; Delhi the seat of the Great Mogul, and that great city yet unspoiled, which

Geryon's sons
Call El Dorado, —

the Lakes Dembea and Derwentwater, the rivers Dwina, Danube and Delawar, Duero or Douro call it which you will, the Doubs and all the Dons, and our own wizard Dee, —which may be said to belong wholly to this letter, the vowels being rather for appearance than use.

Think also, he would say of the worthies, heroes and sages in D. David, and his namesake of Wales. Diogenes, Dædalus, Diomede, and Queen Dido, Decebalus the Dacian King, Deucalion, Datames the Carian whom Nepos hath immortalised, and Marshal Daun who so often kept the King of Prussia in check, and sometimes defeated him. Nay if I speak of men eminent for the rank which they held, or for their exploits in war, might I not name the Kings of Persia who bore the name of Darius, Demaratus of Sparta, whom the author of Leonidas hath well pourtrayed as retaining in exile a reverential feeling toward the country which had wronged him: and Deodatus, a name assumed by, or given to Louis the 14th, the greatest actor of greatness that ever existed. Dion who lives for ever in the page of Plutarch; the Demetrii, the Roman Decii, Diocletian, and Devereux Earl of Essex, he by whom Cadiz was taken, and whose execution occasioned the death of the repentant Elizabeth by whom it was decreed. If of those who have triumphed upon the ocean shall we not find Dragat the far-famed corsair, and our own more famous and more dreadful Drake. Dandolo the Doge who at the age of * triumphed over the perfidious Greeks, and was first chosen by the victorious Latins to be the Emperor of Constantinople: Doria of whom the Genoese still boast. Davis who has left his name so near the Arctic Pole. Dampier of all travellers the most observant and most faithful.† Diaz who first attained that Stormy Cape, to which from his time the happier name of Good Hope hath been given; and Van Diemen the Dutchman. If we look to the learned, are there not Duns Scotus and Descartes? Madame Dacier and her husband. Damo the not-degenerate daughter of Pythagoras, and though a woman renowned for secrecy and silence; Dante and Davila, Dugdale and Dupin; Demosthenes, Doctor Dee, (he also like the wizard stream all our own,) and Bishop Duppa to whom the Εἰκὼν Βασιλικὴ, whether truly or not, hath been ascribed: Sir Kenelm Digby, by whom it hath been proved that Dogs make syllogisms; and Daniel Defoe. Here the Doctor always pronounced the christian name with peculiar emphasis, and here I think it necessary to stop, that the Reader may take breath.

* The blank is in the original MS. Quære, *ninety-five?*

† "One of the most faithful, as well as exact and excellent of all voyage writers." *Vindiciæ Eccl. Angl.* p. 115. Unhappily Southey's wish to continue this work was not responded to. The continuation would have proved invaluable now; for who, so well as he, knew the wiles of the Romish Church, and the subtilties of the Jesuit?

CHAPTER CLXXV.

THE DOCTOR FOLLOWS UP HIS MEDITATIONS ON THE LETTER D., AND EXPECTS THAT THE READER WILL BE CONVINCED THAT IT IS A DYNAMIC LETTER, AND THAT THE HEBREWS DID NOT WITHOUT REASON CALL IT DALETH — THE DOOR — AS THOUGH IT WERE THE DOOR OF SPEECH. — THE MYSTIC TRIANGLE.

More authority, dear boy, name more; and sweet my child, let them be men of good repute and carriage.

LOVE'S LABOUR LOST.

THE Doctor, as I have said in the last Chapter, pronounced with peculiar emphasis the christian name of Daniel Defoe. Then taking up the auspicious word. — Is there not Daniel the prophet, in honour of whom my baptismal name was given, Daniel, if not the greatest of the prophets, yet for the matter of his prophecies the most important. Daniel the French historian, and Daniel the English poet; who reminds me of other poets in D, not less eminent. Donne, Dodsley, Drayton, Drummond, Douglas the Bishop of Dunkeld, Dunbar, Denham, Davenant, Dyer, Durfey, Dryden, and Stephen Duck; Democritus the wise Abderite, whom I especially honour for finding matter of jest, even in the profoundest thought, extracting mirth from philosophy, and joining in delightful matrimony wit with wisdom. Is there not Dollond the Optician? Dalembert and Diderot among those Encyclopedists with whose renown

— all Europe rings from side to side,

Derham the Astro-Physico — and Christo — Theologian, Dillenius the botanist, Dion who for his eloquence was called the golden-mouthed; Diagoras who boldly despising the false Gods of Greece, blindly and audaciously denied the God of Nature. Diocles who invented the cissoid, Deodati, Diodorus, and Dion Cassius. Thus rich was the letter D, even before the birth of Sir Humphrey Davy, and the catastrophe of Doctor Dodd: before Daniel Mendoza triumphed over Humphreys in the ring, and before Dionysius Lardner, Professor at the St——'niversity of London, projected the Cabinet Cyclopædia, Daniel O'Connell fought Mr. Peel, triumphed over the Duke of Wellington, bullied the British Government, and changed the British Constitution.

If we look to the fine arts, he pursued, the names of Douw, and Durer, Dolce and Dominichino instantly occur. In my own profession, among the ancients Dioscorides; among the moderns Dippel, whose marvellous oil is not more exquisitely curious in preparation than powerful in its use; Dover of the powder; Dalby of the Carminative; Daffy of the Elixir; Deventer by whom the important art of bringing men into the world has been so greatly improved; Douglas, who has rendered lithotomy so beautiful an operation, that he asserteth in his motto it may be done speedily, safely, and pleasantly; Dessault, now rising into fame among the Continental surgeons, and Dimsdale who is extending the blessings of inoculation. Of persons eminent for virtue or sanctity, who ever in friendship exceeded Damon, the friend of Pythias? Is there not St. John Damascenus, Dr. Doddridge, Deborah the Nurse of Rebekah, who was buried beneath Beth-el under an Oak, which was called Allon-bachuth, the Oak of Weeping, and Deborah the wife of Lapidoth, who dwelt under her palm-trees between Ramah and Beth-el in Mount Ephraim, where the children of Israel came up to her for judgment, for she was a mother in Israel; Demas for whom St. Paul greets the Colossians, and whom he calleth his fellow labourer; and Dorcas which being interpreted is in Hebrew Tabitha and in English Doe, who was full of good works and alms-deeds, whom therefore Peter raised from the dead, and whom the Greeks might indeed truly have placed among the Δευτερόποτμοι; Daniel already named, but never to be remembered too often, and Dan the father of his tribe. Grave writers there are, the Doctor would say, who hesitate not to affirm that Dan was the first King of Denmark, more properly called Danmark from his name, and that he instituted there the military order of Dannebrog. With the pretensions of these Danish Antiquaries, he pursued, I meddle not. There is surer authority for the merits of this my first namesake. "Dan shall judge his people, as one of the tribes of Israel. Dan shall be a serpent by the way, an adder in the path, that biteth the horse's heels, so that his rider shall fall backward." Daniel, quoth the Doctor, is commonly abbreviated into Dan, from whence doubtless it taketh its root; and the Daniel therefore who is not wise as a serpent, falsifieth the promise of the patriarch Jacob.

That this should have been the Dan who founded the kingdom of Denmark he deemed an idle fancy. King Dans in that country, however, there have been, and among them was King Dan called Mykelati or the Magnificent, with whom the Bruna Olld, or age of Combustion, ended in the North, and the Houghs Olld or age of barrows began, for he it was who introduced the custom of interment. But he considered it as indeed an honour to the name, that Death should have been called Δάνος by the Macedonians, not as a dialectic or provincial form of Θάνατος but from the Hebrew Dan, which signifies, says Jeremy Taylor, a Judge, as intimating that Judges are appointed to give sentence upon criminals in life and death.

Even if we look at the black side of the shield we still find that the D preserves its power: there is Dathan, who with Korah and Abiram went down alive into the pit, and the earth closed upon them; Dalila by whom Sampson was betrayed; Dionysius the acoustical tyrant; Domitian who like a true vice-gerent of Beelzebub tormented flies as well as men; Decius the fiercest of the persecutors; the inhuman Dunstan, and the devilish Dominic, after whom it seems all but an anticlimax to name the *ipsissimus* Diabolus, the Devil himself. And here let us remark through how many languages the name of the author of evil retains its characteristic initial, Διάβολος, Diabolus, Diavolo, Diablo, Diabo, Diable, in Dutch Duival, in Welsh Diawl, and though the Germans write him Teufel, it is because in their coarser articulation the D passes into the cognate sound of T, without offending their obtuser organs of hearing. Even in the appellations given him by familiar or vulgar irreverence, the same pregnant initial prevails, he is the Deuce, and Old Davy and Davy Jones. And it may be noted that in the various systems of false religion to which he hath given birth, the Delta is still a dominant inchoative. Witness Dagon of the Philistines, witness the Daggial of the Mahommedans, and the forgotten root from whence the Διός of the Greeks is derived. Why should I mention the Roman Diespiter, the Syrian Dirceto, Delius with his sister Delia, known also as Dictynna and the great Diana of the Ephesians. The Sicyonian Dia, Dione of whom Venus was born, Deiphobe the Cumæan Sybil who conducted Æneas in his descent to the infernal regions. Doris the mother of the Nereids, and Dorus father of the race of Pygmies. Why should I name the Dioscuri, Dice and Dionysus, the Earth, Mother Demeter, the Demiourgos, gloomy Dis, Demogorgon dread and Daphne whom the Gods converted into a Laurel to decorate the brows of Heroes and Poets.

Truly, he would say, it may be called a dynamic letter; and not without mystery did the Hebrews call it Daleth, the door, as though it were the door of speech. Then its form! how full of mysteries! The wise Egyptians represented it by three stars disposed in a triangle: it was their hieroglyphic of the Deity. In Greek it is the Delta.

Δ

In this form were the stupendous Pyramids built, when the sage Egyptians are thought to have emblematised the soul of man, which the Divine Plato supposed to be of this shape. This is the mysterious triangle, which the Pythagoreans called Pallas, because they said it sprang from the brain of Jupiter, and Tritogeneia, because if three right lines were drawn from its angles to meet in the centre, a triple birth of triangles was produced, each equal to the other.

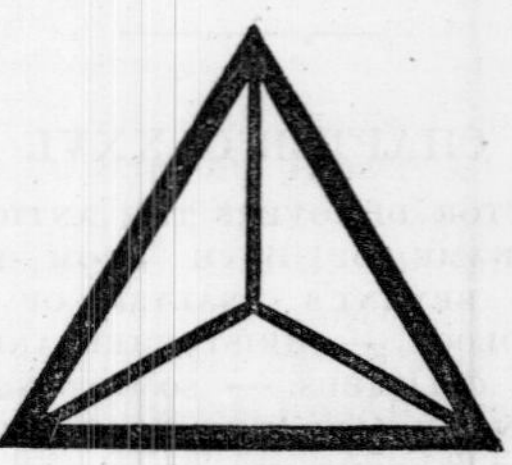

I pass reverently the diviner mysteries which have been illustrated from hence, and may perhaps be typified herein. Nor will I do more than touch upon the mechanical powers which we derive from a knowledge of the properties of the figures, and upon the science of Trigonometry. In its Roman and more familiar form, the Letter hath also sublime resemblances or prototypes. The Rainbow resting upon the earth describes its form. Yea, the Sky and the Earth represent a grand and immeasurable D; for when you stand upon a boundless plain, the space behind you and before in infinite longitude is the straight line, and the circle of the firmament which bends from infinite altitude to meet it, forms the bow.

For himself, he said, it was a never failing source of satisfaction when he reflected how richly his own destiny was endowed with Ds. The D was the star of his ascendant. There was in the accident of his life, — and he desired it to be understood as using the word accident in its scholastic acceptations, — a concatenation, a concentration. Yea he might venture to call it a constellation of Ds. Dove he was born; Daniel he was baptized; Daniel was the name of his father; Dinah of his mother, Deborah of his wife; Doctor was his title, Doncaster his dwelling-place; in the year of his marriage, which next to that of his birth was the most important of his life, D was the Dominical letter; and in the amorous and pastoral strains wherein he had made his passion known in the magazines, he had called himself Damon and his mistress Delia.

CHAPTER CLXXVI.

THE DOCTOR DISCOVERS THE ANTIQUITY OF THE NAME OF DOVE FROM PERUSING JACOB BRYANT'S ANALYSIS OF ANCIENT MYTHOLOGY. — CHRISTOPHER AND FERDINAND COLUMBUS. — SOMETHING ABOUT PIGEON-PIE, AND THE REASON WHY THE DOCTOR WAS INCLINED TO THINK FAVOURABLY OF THE SAMARITANS.

An I take the humour of a thing once, I am like your tailor's needle; I go through. BEN JONSON.

DOVE also was a name which abounded with mystical significations, and which derived peculiar significance from its mysterious conjunction with Daniel. Had it not been said, "Be ye wise as serpents and harmless as Doves?" To him the text was personally applicable in both parts. Dove he was by birth. Daniel by baptism or the second birth, and Daniel was Dan, and Dan shall be a serpent by the way.

But who can express his delight when in perusing Jacob Bryant's Analysis of ancient Mythology, he found that so many of the most illustrious personages of antiquity proved to be Doves, when their names were truly interpreted or properly understood! That erudite interpreter of hidden things taught him that the name of the Dove was Iön and Iönah, whence in immediate descent the Oän and Oannes of Berosus and Abydenus, and in longer but lineal deduction Æneas, Hannes, Hanno, Ionah, Ἰοάννης, Johannes, Janus, Eanus among the elder Romans, Giovanni among the later Italians, Juan, Joam, Jean, John, Jan, Iwain, Ivan, Ewan, Owen, Evan, Hans, Ann, Hannah, Nannette, Jane, Jeannette, Jeanne, Joanna and Joan; all who had ever borne these names, or any name derived from the same radical, as doubtless many there were in those languages of which he had no knowledge, nor any means of acquiring it, being virtually Doves. Did not Bryant expressly say that the prophet Jonah was probably so named as a messenger of the Deity, the mystic Dove having been from the days of Jonah regarded as a sacred symbol among all nations where any remembrance of the destruction and renovation of mankind was preserved! It followed therefore that the prophet Jonah, Hannibal, St. John, Owen Glendower, Joan of Arc, Queen Anne, Miss Hannah More, and Sir Watkin Williams Wynn, were all of them his namesakes, to pretermit or pass over Pope Joan, Little John, and Jack the Giantkiller. And this followed, not like the derivation of King Pepin from Ὥσπερ, by a jump in the process, such as that from Διάπερ to Napkin; nor like the equally well known identification of a Pigeon with an Eel Pye, in the logic of which the Doctor would have detected a fallacy, but in lawful etymology, and according to the strict interpretation of words. If he looked for the names through the thinner disguise of language there was Semiramis, who having been fed by Doves was named after them. What was Zurita the greatest historian of Arragon, but a young stock Dove? What were the three Palominos so properly enumerated in the Bibliotheca of Nicolas Antonio? Pedro the Benedictine in whose sermons a more than ordinary breathing of the spirit might not unreasonably be expected from his name; Francisco, who translated into Castillian the Psychomachia of the Christian poet Aurelius

Prudentius, and Diego the Prior of Xodar, whose *Liber de mutatione aeris, in quo assidua, et mirabilis mutationis temporum historia, cum suis causis, enarratur*, he so greatly regretted that he had never been able to procure; what were these Palominos? what but Doves? — Father Colombiere who framed the service for the Heart of Jesus, which was now so fashionable in Catholic countries, was clearly of the Dove genus. St. Columba was a decided Dove; three there were certainly, the Senonian, the Cordovan and the Cornish: and there is reason to believe that there was a fourth also, a female Dove, who held a high rank in St. Ursula's great army of virgins. Columbo the Anatomist, deservedly eminent as one of those who by their researches led the way for Harvey, he also was a Dove. Lastly, — and the Doctor in fine taste always reserved the greatest glory of the Dove name, for the conclusion of his discourse — lastly, there was Christopher Columbus, whom he used to call his famous namesake. And he never failed to commend Ferdinand Columbus for the wisdom and piety with which he had commented upon the mystery of the name, to remark that his father had conveyed the grace of the Holy Ghost to the New World, shewing to the people who knew him not who was God's beloved son, as the Holy Ghost had done in the figure of a Dove at the baptism of St. John, and bearing like Noah's Dove the Olive Branch, and the Oil of Baptism over the waters of the ocean.

And what would our onomatologist have said if he had learned to read these words in that curious book of the &c. family, the Oriental fragments of Major Edward Moor: "In respect to St. Columba, or Colomb, and other superstitious names and things in close relationship, I shall have in another place something to say. I shall try to connect *Col-omb*, with Kal-O'm, — those infinitely mysterious words of Hindu mythology: and with these, divers *Mythé*, converging into or diverging from O'M — A U M, — the Irish *Ogham*, — I A M, — *Amen*, ΙΛω — Il-Kolmkill, &c. &c. &c." Surely had the onomatologist lived to read this passage, he would forthwith have opened and corresponded with the benevolent and erudite etcæterarist of Bealings.

These things were said in his deeper moods. In the days of courtship he had said in song that Venus's car was drawn by Doves, regretting at the time that an allusion which came with such peculiar felicity from him, should appear to common readers to mean nothing more than what rhymers from time immemorial had said before him. After marriage he often called Mrs. Dove his Turtle, and in his playful humours, when the gracefulness of youth had gradually been superseded by a certain rotundity of form, he sometimes named her φάττα, his ring-dove. Then he would regret that she had not proved a stock-dove, — and if she frowned at him, or looked grave, she was his pouting pigeon.

One inconvenience, however, Mrs. Dove felt from his reverence for the name. He never suffered a pigeon-pie at his table. And when he read that the Samaritans were reproached with retaining a trace of Assyrian superstition because they held it unlawful to eat this bird, he was from that time inclined to think favourably of the schismatics of Mount Gerizim.

CHAPTER CLXXVII.

SOMETHING ON THE SCIENCE AND MYSTERY OF NUMBERS WHICH IS NOT ACCORDING TO COCKER. REVERIES OF JEAN D'ESPAGNE, MINISTER OF THE FRENCH - REFORMED CHURCH IN WESTMINSTER, AND OF MR. JOHN BELLAMY. A PITHY REMARK OF FULLER'S AND AN EXTRACT FROM HIS PISGAH SIGHT OF PALESTINE, TO RECREATE THE READER.

None are so surely caught, when they are catch'd,
As wit turn'd fool: folly, in wisdom hatch'd,
Hath wisdom's warrant, and the help of school,
And wit's own grace to grace a learned fool.

LOVE'S LABOUR LOST.

It may easily be supposed that the Doctor was versed in the science of numbers; not merely that common science which is taught at schools and may be learnt from Cocker's Arithmetic, but the more recondite mysteries which have in all ages delighted minds like his; and of which the richest specimens may be seen in the writings of the Hugonot Minister Jean de l'Espagne, and in those of our contemporary Mr. John Bellamy, author of the Ophion, of various papers in the Classical Journal, and defender of the Old and New Testament.

Cet auteur est assez digne d'etre lu, says Bayle of Jean de l'Espagne, and he says it in some unaccountable humour, too gravely for a jest. The writer who is thus recommended was Minister of the Reformed French Church in Westminster, which met at that time in Somerset Chapel, and his friend Dr. De Garencieres, who wrote commendatory verses upon him in French, Latin and Greek, calls him

Belle lumière des Pasteurs,
Ornement du Siecle ou nous sommes,
Qui trouve des admirateurs
Par tout ou il y a des hommes.

He was one of those men to whom the Bible comes as a book of problems and riddles, a mine in which they are always at work, thinking that whatever they can throw up must needs be gold. Among the various observations which he gave the world without any other order, as he says, than that in which they presented themselves to his memory, there may be found good, bad and indifferent. He thought the English Church had improperly appointed a Clerk to say Amen for the people. Amen being intended, among other reasons, as a mark whereby to distinguish those who believed with the officiating Priest from Idolaters and Heretics. He thought it was not expedient that Jews should be allowed to reside in England, for a Jew would perceive in the number of our tolerated sects, a confusion worse than that of Babel; and as the multitude here are always susceptible of every folly which is offered, and the more monstrous the faith, to them the better mystery, it was to be feared, he said, that for the sake of converting two or three Jews we were exposing a million Christians to the danger of Judaising; or at least that we should see new religions start up, compounded of Judaism with Christianity. He was of opinion, in opposition to what was then generally thought in England, that one might innocently say God bless you, to a person who sneezed, though he candidly admitted that there was no example either in the Old or New Testament, and that in all the Scriptures only one person is mentioned as having sneezed, to wit the Shunamite's son. He thought it more probable from certain texts that the Soul at death departs by way of the nostrils, than by way of the mouth according to the vulgar notion:—had he previously ascertained which way it came in, he would have had no difficulty in deciding which way it went out. And he propounded and resolved a question concerning Jephtha which no person but himself ever thought of asking: *Pourquoy Dieu voulant delivrer les Israelites, leur donna pour liberateur, voire pour Chef et Gouverneur perpetuel, un fils d'une paillarde?* "O Jephtha, Judge of Israel," that a Frenchman should call thee in filthy French *fils d'une putain!*

But the peculiar talent of the *Belle Lumière des Pasteurs* was for cabalistic researches concerning numbers, or what he calls *L'Harmonie du Temps*. Numbers, he held, (and every generation, every family, every individual was marked with one,) were not the causes of what came to pass, but they were marks or impresses which God set upon his works, distinguishing them by the difference of these their cyphers. And he laid it down as a rule that in doubtful points of computation, the one wherein some mystery could be discovered was always to be preferred. QUOY?—(think how triumphantly his mouth opened and his nose was erected and his nostrils were dilated, when he pronounced that interrogation)—QUOY? *la varieté de nos opinions qui provient d'imperfection, aneantira-t-elle les merveilles de Dieu?* In the course of his Scriptural computations he discovered that when the Sun stood still at the command of Joshua, it was precisely 2555 years after the Creation, that is seven years of years, a solar week, after which it had been preordained that the Sun should thus have its sabbath of rest: *Ceci n'est-il pas admirable?* It was on the tenth year of the tenth year of the years that the Sun went back ten degrees, which was done to show the chronology: *ou est le stupide qui ne soit ravi en admiration d'une si celeste harmonie?* With equal sagacity and equal triumph he discovered how the generations from Adam to Christ went by twenty-twos; and the generations of Christ by sevens, being 77 in all, and that from the time the promise of the Seed was given till its fulfilment there elapsed a week of years, seven times seventy years, seventy weeks of years, and seven times seventy weeks of years, by which beautiful geometry, if he might be permitted to use so inadequate a term, the fullness of time was made up.

What wonderful significations also hath Mr. Bellamy in his kindred pursuits discovered and darkly pointed out! Doth he not tell us of seven steps, seven days, seven priests, seven rams, seven bullocks, seven trumpets, seven shepherds, seven stars, seven spirits, seven eyes, seven lamps, seven pipes, seven heads, four wings, four beasts, four kings, four kingdoms, four carpenters; the number three he has left unimproved, — but for two, —

which number Nature framed
In the most useful faculties of man,
To strengthen mutually and relieve each other,
Two eyes, two ears, two arms, two legs and feet,
That where one failed the other might supply,

for this number Mr. Bellamy has two cherubims, two calves, two turtles, two birds alive, two *, two baskets of figs, two olive trees, two women grinding, two men in the fields, two woes, two witnesses, two candlesticks; and when he descends to the unit, he tells us of one tree, one heart, one stick, one fold, one pearl, — to which we must add one Mr. John Bellamy the Pearl of Commentators.

But what is this to the exquisite manner in which he elucidates the polytheism of the Greeks and Romans, showing us that the inferior Gods of their mythology were in their origin only men who had exercised certain departments in the state, a discovery which he illustrates in a manner the most familiar, and at the same time the most striking for its originality. Thus, he says, if the Greeks and Romans had been Englishmen, or if we Englishmen of the present day were Greeks and Romans, we should call our Secretary at War, Lord Bathurst for instance, Mars; the Lord Chancellor (Lord Eldon to wit) Mercury, — as being at the head of the department for eloquence. — (But as Mercury is also the God of thieves may not Mr. Bellamy, grave as he is, be suspected of insinuating here that the Gentlemen of the Long Robe are the most dextrous of pickpockets?) — The first Lord of the Admiralty, Neptune. The President of the College of Physicians, Apollo. The President of the Board of Agriculture, Janus. Because with one face he looked forward to the new year, while at the same time he looked back with the other on the good or bad management of the agriculture of the last, wherefore he was symbolically represented with a second face at the back of his head. Again Mr. Bellamy seems to be malicious, in thus typifying or seeming to typify Sir John Sinclair between two administrations with a face for both. The ranger of the forests, he proceeds, would be denominated Diana. The Archbishop of Canterbury, Minerva; — Minerva in a Bishop's wig! The first Lord of the Treasury, Juno; and the Society of Suppression of Vice, — Reader, lay thy watch upon the table, and guess for three whole minutes what the Society for the Suppression of Vice would be called upon this ingenious scheme, if the Greeks and Romans were Englishmen of the present generation, or if we of the present generation were heathen Greeks and Romans. I leave a *carte blanche* before this, lest thine eye outrunning thy judgment, should deprive thee of that proper satisfaction which thou wilt feel if thou shouldst guess aright. But exceed not the time which I have affixed for thee, for if thou dost not

* The blank is in the MS.

guess aright in three minutes, thou wouldest not in as many years.

Venus. Yes, Reader. By Cyprus and Paphos and the Groves of Idalia, — by the little God Cupid, — by all the Loves and Doves, — and by the lobbies of the London theatres — he calls the Society for the Suppression of Vice, Venus !

Fancy, says Fuller, runs riot when spurred with superstition. This is his marginal remark upon a characteristic paragraph concerning the Chambers about Solomon's Temple, with which I will here recreate the reader. "As for the mystical meaning of these chambers, Bede no doubt, thought he hit the very mark — when finding therein the three conditions of life, all belonging to God's Church : in the ground chamber, such as live in marriage ; in the middle chamber such as contract ; but in the *excelsis* or third story, such as have attained to the sublimity of perpetual virginity. Rupertus in the lowest chamber lodgeth those of practical lives with Noah ; in the middle — those of mixed lives with Job ; and in the highest — such as spend their days with Daniel in holy speculations. But is not this rather *lusus*, than *allusio*, sporting with, than expounding of scriptures ? Thus when the gates of the Oracle are made *five square*, Ribera therein reads our conquest over the five senses, and when those of the door of the Temple are said to be *four square*, therein saith he is denoted the *quaternion* of Evangelists. After this rate, Hiram (though no doubt dexterous in his art) could not so soon fit a pillar with a fashion as a Friar can fit that fashion with a mystery. If made three square, then the Trinity of Persons : four square, the cardinal virtues : five square, the *Pentateuch of Moses :* six square, the *Petitions* or the *Lord's Prayer :* seven square, their *Sacraments :* eight square, the *Beatitudes :* nine square, the Orders of Angels : ten square, the Commandments : eleven square, the moral virtues : twelve square, the articles of the creed are therein contained. In a word — for matter of numbers — fancy is never at a loss — like a beggar, never out of her way, but hath some haunts where to repose itself. But such as in expounding scriptures reap more than God did sow there, never eat what they reap themselves, because such grainless husks, when seriously thrashed out, vanish all into chaff.*

CHAPTER CLXXVIII.

THE MYSTERY OF NUMBERS PURSUED, AND CERTAIN CALCULATIONS GIVEN WHICH MAY REMIND THE READER OF OTHER CALCULATIONS EQUALLY CORRECT. ANAGRAMMATISING OF NAMES, AND THE DOCTOR'S SUCCESS THEREIN.

"There is no efficacy in numbers, said the wiser Philosophers ; and very truly," — saith Bishop Hacket in repeating this sentence ; but he continues — "some numbers are apt to enforce a reverent esteem towards them, by considering miraculous occurrences which fell out in *holy Scripture* on such and such a number. — *Non potest fortuitò fieri, quod tam sæpe fit*, says Maldonatus, whom I never find superstitious in this matter. It falls out too often to be called contingent ; and the oftener it falls out, the more to be attended." †

This choice morsel hath led us from the science of numbers. Great account hath been made of that science in old times. There was an epigrammatist who discovering that the name of his enemy Damagoras amounted in numerical letters to the same sum as Λοιμὸς the plague, inferred from thence that Damagoras and the Plague were one and the same thing ; a stingless jest serving, like many satires of the present age, to show the malice and not the wit of the

* Pisgah Sight of Palestine, Book iii. c. vii.

† On referring to Bishop Hacket's Sermons I find this Motto is not copied out *Verbatim*. See p. 245.

satirist. But there were those among the ancients who believed that stronger influences existed in the number of a name, and that because of their arithmetical inferiority in this point, Patroclus was slain by Hector, and Hector by Achilles. Diviners grounded upon this a science which they called Onomantia or Arithmomantia. When Maurice of Saxony, to the great fear of those who were most attached to him, engaged in war against Charles V., some one encouraged his desponding friends by this augury, and said that if the initials of the two names were considered, it would be seen that the fortunes of Maurice preponderated over those of Charles in the proportion of a thousand to a hundred.

A science like this could not be without attractions for the Doctor; and it was with no little satisfaction that he discovered in the three Ds with which his spoons and his house linen were marked, by considering them as so many capital Deltas, the figures 444, combining the complex virtues of the four thrice told. But he discovered greater secrets in the names of himself and his wife when taken at full length. He tried them in Latin, and could obtain no satisfactory result; nor had he any better success in Greek when he observed the proper orthography of Δανιὴλ and Δεββῶρα.* But anagrammatists are above the rules of orthography, just as Kings, Divines and Lawyers are privileged, if it pleases them, to dispense with the rules of grammar. Taking these words therefore letter by letter according to the common pronunciation (for who said he pronounces them Danieel and Deboarah?) and writing the surname in Greek letters instead of translating it, the sum which it thus produced was equal to his most sanguine wishes, for thus it proved

Daniel and Deborah Dove.

Δανιὲλ Δεβόρα Δοὺε.

Δανιὲλ.	
Δ	4
α	1
ν	50
ι	10
ε	5
λ	30
Daniel	100

Δεβόρα	
Δ	4
ε	5
β	2
ο	70
ρ	100
α	1
Deborah	182

Δοὺε	
Δ	4
ο	70
υ	400
ε	5
Dove	479

The whole being added together gave the following product

Daniel	100
Deborah	182
Dove	479
	761

Here was the number 761 found in fair addition, without any arbitrary change of letters, or licentious innovation in orthography. And herein was mystery. The number 761 is a prime number; from hence the Doctor inferred that, as the number was indivisible, there could be no division between himself and Mrs. Dove; an inference which the harmony of their lives fully warranted. And this alone would have amply rewarded his researches. But a richer dis-

* Δεβόῤῥα Gen. xxxv. 8., Δεββῶρα Judges iv. 4. The double ῥ will not affect the mystery !

covery flashed upon him. The year 1761 was the year of his marriage, and to make up the deficient thousand there was M for marriage and matrimony. These things, he would say, must never be too explicit; their mysterious character would be lost if they lay upon the surface; like precious metals and precious stones you must dig to find them.

He had bestowed equal attention and even more diligence in anagrammatising the names. His own indeed furnished him at first with a startling and by no means agreeable result; for, upon transposing the component letters of Daniel Dove, there appeared the words *Leaden void!* Nor was he more fortunate in a Latin attempt, which gave him *Dan vile Deo*. *Vel dona Dei*, as far as it bore a semblance of meaning, was better; but when, after repeated dislocations and juxta-positions, there came forth the words *Dead in love*, Joshua Sylvester was not more delighted at finding that Jacobus Stuart made *justa scrutabo*, and James Stuart *A just Master*, than the Doctor,—for it was in the May days of his courtship. In the course of these anagrammatical experiments he had a glimpse of success, which made him feel for a moment like a man whose lottery ticket is next in number to the £20,000 prize. Dove failed only in one letter of being Ovid. In old times they did not stand upon trifles in these things, and John Bunyan was perfectly satisfied with extracting from his name the words *Nu hony in a B*,—a sentence of which the orthography and the import are worthy of each other. But although the Doctor was contented with a very small sufficit of meaning, he could not depart so violently from the letters here. The disappointment was severe, though momentary: it was, as we before observed, in the days of his courtship; and could he thus have made out his claim to be called Ovid, he had as clear a right to add Naso as the poet of Sulmo himself, or any of the Nasonic race, for he had been at the promontory, "and why indeed Naso," as Holofernes has said?—Why not merely for that reason "looking toward Damascus," which may be found in the second volume of this work, in the sixty-third chapter and at the two hundred and thirtieth page*, but also "for smelling out the odoriferous flowers of fancy, the jerks of invention?"†

Thus much for his own name. After marriage he added his wife's with the conjunction copulative, and then came out *Dear Delia had bound one:* nothing could be more felicitous, Delia, as has already been noticed, having been the poetical name by which he addressed the object of his affections. Another result was, *I hadden a dear bond-love*, but having some doubts as to the syntax of the verb, and some secret dislike to its obsolete appearance, he altered it into *Ned, I had a dear bond-love*, as though he was addressing his friend Dr. Miller the organist, whose name was Edward.

CHAPTER CLXXIX.

THE SUBJECT OF ANAGRAMS CONTINUED; A TRUE OBSERVATION WHICH MANY FOR WANT OF OBSERVATION WILL NOT DISCOVER TO BE SUCH, VIZ., THAT THERE IS A LATENT SUPERSTITION IN THE MOST RATIONAL OF MEN. LUCKY AND UNLUCKY — FITTING AND UNFITTING — ANAGRAMS, AND HOW THE DOCTOR'S TASTE IN THIS LINE WAS DERIVED FROM OUR OLD ACQUAINTANCE JOSHUA SYLVESTER.

> Ha gran forza una vecchia opinione;
> E bisogna grand' arte, e gran fatica,
> A cavarla del capo alle persone.
>
> BRONZINO PITTORE.

ANAGRAMS are not likely ever again to hold so high a place among the prevalent pursuits of literature as they did in the seventeenth century, when Louis XIII. appointed the Provençal Thomas Billen to be his Royal Anagrammatist, and granted him a salary of 1200 *livres*. But no person will ever hit upon an apt one without feeling that degree of pleasure and surprise with which any odd

* This refers to the 8vo. Edition. See page 134. of this Edition.

† Love's Labour Lost, Act iv. Sc. ii.

coincidence is remarked. Has any one who knows Johnny the Bear heard his name thus anagrammatised without a smile? We may be sure he smiled and growled at the same time when he first heard it himself.

Might not Father Salvator Mile, and Father Louis Almerat, who were both musicians, have supposed themselves as clearly predestinated to be musical, as ever seventh son of a Septimus thought himself born for the medical profession, if they had remarked what Penrose discovered for them, that their respective names, with the F for Friar prefixed, each contained the letters of the six musical notes *ut*, *re*, *mi*, *fa*, *sol*, *la*, and not a letter more or less?

There is, and always hath been, and ever will be, a latent superstition in the most rational of men. It belongs to the weakness and dependence of human nature. Believing, as the Scriptures teach us to believe, that signs and tokens have been vouchsafed in many cases, is it to be wondered at that we seek for them sometimes in our moods of fancy, or that they suggest themselves to us in our fears and our distress? Men may cast off religion and extinguish their conscience without ridding themselves of this innate and inherent tendency.

Proper names have all in their origin been significant in all languages. It was easy for men who brooded over their own imaginations, to conceive that they might contain in their elements a more recondite, and perhaps, fatidical signification; and the same turn or twist of mind which led the Cabbalists to their extravagant speculations have taken this direction, when confined within the limits of languages which have no supernatural pretensions. But no serious importance was attached to such things, except by persons whose intellects were in some degree deranged. They were sought for chiefly as an acceptable form of compliment, sometimes in self-complacency of the most inoffensive kind, and sometimes for the sting which they might carry with them. Lycophron is said to have been the inventor of this trifling.

The Rules for the true discovery of perfect anagrams, as laid down by Mrs. Mary Fage*, allowed as convenient a licence in orthography as the Doctor availed himself of in Greek.

E may most-what conclude an English word,
And so a letter at a need afford.
H is an aspiration and no letter;
It may be had or left which we think better.
I may be I or Y as need require;
Q ever after doth a U desire;
Two Vs may be a double U; and then
A double U may be two Vs again.
X may divided be, and S and C
May by that letter comprehended be.
Z a double S may comprehend:
And lastly an apostrophe may ease
Sometimes a letter when it doth not please.

Two of the luckiest hits which anagrammatists have made were on the Attorney General William Noy, *I moyl in law;* and Sir Edmundbury Godfrey, *I find murdered by rogues.* Before Felton's execution it was observed that his anagram was *No, flie not.*

A less fortunate one made the Lady Davies mad, or rather fixed the character of her madness. She was the widow of Sir John Davies, the statesman and poet, and having anagrammatised Eleanor Davies into Reveal O Daniel, she was crazy enough to fancy that the spirit of the Prophet Daniel was incorporated in her. The Doctor mentioned the case with tenderness and a kind of sympathy. "Though the anagram, says Dr. Heylyn, had too much by an L and too little by an S, yet she found Daniel and Reveal in it, and that served her turn." Setting up for a Prophetess upon this conceit, and venturing upon political predictions in sore times, she was brought before the Court of High Commission, where serious pains were preposterously bestowed in endeavouring to reason her out of an opinion founded on insanity. All, as might have been expected, and ought to have been foreseen, would not do, "till Lamb, then Dean of the Arches, shot her through and through with an arrow borrowed from her own quiver." For while the Divines were reasoning the point with her out of Scripture,

* In her Fames Roule, or the names of King Charles, his Queen and his most hopeful posterity; together with the names of the Dukes, Marquisses, &c., anagrammatized, and expressed by acrostick lines on their lives. London, 1637. — *R. S.*

he took a pen into his hand, and presently finding that the letters of her name might be assorted to her purpose, said to her, Madam, I see that you build much on anagrams, and I have found out one which I hope will fit you: Dame Eleanor Davies,— *Never so mad a Ladie!* He then put it into her hands in writing, "which happy fancy brought that grave Court into such a laughter, and the poor woman thereupon into such a confusion, that afterwards she either grew wiser, or was less regarded."— This is a case in which it may be admitted that ridicule was a fair test of truth.

When Henri IV. sent for Marshal Biron to court, with an assurance of full pardon if he would reveal without reserve the whole of his negociations and practices, that rash and guilty man resolved to go and brave all dangers, because certain Astrologers had assured him that his ascendant commanded that of the King, and in confirmation of this some flattering friend discovered in his name *Henri de Bourbon* this anagram, *De Biron Bonheur. Comme ainsi fust*, says one of his contemporaries, *qu'il en fist gloire, quelque Gentilhomme bien advisé là present — dit tout bas à l'oreille d'un sien amy, s'il le pense ainsi il n'est pas sage, et trouvera qu'il y a du* Robin *dedans* Biron. *Robin* was a name used at that time by the French as synonymous with simpleton. But of unfitting anagrams none were ever more curiously unfit than those which were discovered in Marguerite de Valois, the profligate Queen of Navarre; *Salve, Virgo Mater Dei; ou, de vertu royal image!* The Doctor derived his taste for anagrams from the poet with whose rhymes and fancies he had been so well embued in his boyhood, old Joshua Sylvester, who, as the translator of Du Bartas, signed himself to the King in anagrammatical French *Voy Sire Saluste*, and was himself addressed in anagrammatical Latin as *Vere Os Salustii.*

"Except Eteostiques," says Drummond of Hawthornden, "I think the Anagram the most idle study in the world of learning. Their maker must be *homo miserrimæ patientiæ*, and when he is done, what is it but *magno conatu nugas magnas agere!* you may of one and the same name make both good and evil. So did my Uncle find in Anna Regina, *Ingannare*, as well as of Anna Britannorum Regina, *Anna Regnantium Arbor:* as he who in Charles de Valois found *Chasse la dure loy*, and after the massacre found *Chasseur desloyal.* Often they are most false, as Henri de Bourbon, *Bonheur de Biron.* Of all the anagrammatists and with least pain, he was the best who, out of his own name, being Jacques de la Chamber, found *La Chamber de Jacques*, and rested there: and next to him, here at home, a Gentleman whose mistress's name being Anna Grame, he found it an *Anagrame* already."

CHAPTER CLXXX.

THE DOCTOR'S IDEAS OF LUCK, CHANCE, ACCIDENT, FORTUNE, AND MISFORTUNE. THE DUCHESS OF NEWCASTLE'S DISTINCTION BETWEEN CHANCE AND FORTUNE, WHEREIN NO-MEANING IS MISTAKEN FOR MEANING. AGREEMENT IN OPINION BETWEEN THE PHILOSOPHER OF DONCASTER AND THE PHILOSOPHER OF NORWICH. DISTINCTION BETWEEN UNFORTUNATELY UGLY, AND WICKEDLY UGLY. DANGER OF PERSONAL CHARMS.

Ἔστι γὰρ ὡς ἀληθῶς ἐπίφθεγμα τὸ αὐτόματον, ἀνθρώπων ὡς ἔτυχε καὶ ἀλογίστως φρονούντων, καὶ τὸν μὲν λόγον αὐτῶν μὴ καταλαμβανόντων, διὰ δὲ τὴν ἀσθένειαν τῆς καταλήψεως, ἀλόγως οἰομένων διατετάχθαι ταῦτα, ὧν τὸν λόγον εἰπεῖν οὐκ ἔχουσιν. CONSTANT. ORAT. AD SANCT. CÆT. C. VII.

"Deformity is either natural, voluntary, or adventitious, being either caused by *God's unseen Providence*, (*by men nick-named, chance*,) or by men's cruelty."
FULLER'S HOLY STATE, B. iii c. 15.

IT may readily be inferred from what has already been said of our Philosopher's way of thinking, that he was not likely to use the words luck, chance, accident, fortune or misfortune, with as little reflection as is ordinarily shown in applying them. The distinction which that fantastic — and yet most likeable person — Margaret Duchess of Newcastle, makes between Chance and Fortune was far from satisfying him. "Fortune," says her Grace (she might have been called her Beauty too), "is only various corporeal motions of several creatures — designed to one creature, or more creatures; either to *that* creature, or *those* creatures' advantage, or disadvantage; if advantage, man names it Good Fortune; if disadvantage, man names it Ill Fortune. As for Chance, it is the visible effects of some hidden cause, and Fortune, a sufficient cause to produce such effects; for the conjunction of sufficient causes, doth produce such or such effects, which effects could not be produced — if any of those causes were wanting: so that Chances are but the effects of Fortune."

The Duchess had just thought enough about this to fancy that she had a meaning, and if she had thought a little more she might have discovered that she had none.

The Doctor looked more accurately both to his meaning and his words; but keeping as he did, in my poor judgment, the golden mean between superstition and impiety, there was nothing in this that savoured of preciseness or weakness, nor of that scrupulosity which is a compound of both. He did not suppose that trifles and floccinaucities of which neither the causes nor consequences are of the slightest import, were predestined; as, for example — whether he had beef or mutton for dinner, wore a blue coat or a brown — or took off his wig with his right hand or with his left. He knew that all things are under the direction of almighty and omniscient Goodness; but as he never was unmindful of that Providence in its dispensations of mercy and of justice, so he never disparaged it.

Herein the Philosopher of Doncaster agreed with the Philosopher of Norwich who saith, "let not fortune — which hath no name in Scripture, have any in thy divinity. Let providence, not chance, have the honour of thy acknowledgements, and be thy Œdipus on contingences. Mark well the paths and winding ways thereof; but be not too wise in the construction, or sudden in the application. The hand of Providence writes often by abbreviatures, hieroglyphics or short characters, which, like the laconism on the wall, are not to be made out but by a hint or key from that spirit which indicted them."*

Some ill, he thought, was produced in human affairs by applying the term unfortunate to circumstances which were brought about by imprudence. A man was unfortunate, if being thrown from his horse on a journey, he broke arm or leg, but not if he broke his neck in steeple-hunting, or when in full cry after a fox; if he were impoverished by the misconduct of others, not if he were ruined by his own folly and extravagance; if he suffered in any way by the villainy of another, not if he were transported, or hanged for his own.

Neither would he allow that either man or woman could with propriety be called, as we not unfrequently hear in common speech, *unfortunately* ugly. *Wickedly* ugly, he said, they might be, and too often were; and in such cases the greater their pretensions to beauty, the uglier they were. But goodness has a beauty of its own, which is not dependent upon form and features, and which makes itself felt and acknowledged, however otherwise ill-favoured the face may be in which it is set. He might have said with Seneca, *errare mihi visus est qui dixit*

Gratior est pulchro veniens e corpore virtus;

nullo enim honestamento eget; ipsa et magnum sui decus est, et corpus suum consecret. None, he would say with great earnestness, appeared so ugly to his instinctive perception as some of those persons whom the world accounted handsome, but upon whom pride, or haughtiness, or conceit had set its stamp, or who bore in their countenances what no countenance can conceal, the habitual expression of any reigning vice, whether it were sensuality and selfishness, or envy, hatred, malice, and uncharitableness. Nor could he regard with any satisfaction a fine

* The Readers of Jeremy Taylor will not fail to remember the passage following from his Great Exemplar. "God's Judgments are like *the writing upon the wall*, which was a missive of anger from God upon Belshazzar. It came upon an errand of revenge, and yet was writ in so dark characters that none could read it but a prophet." — Disc. xviii. *Of the Causes and Manner of the Divine Judgments.*

face which had no ill expression, if it wanted a good one: he had no pleasure in beholding mere formal and superficial beauty, that which lies no deeper than the skin, and depends wholly upon "a set of features and complexion." He had more delight, he said, in looking at one of the statues in Mr. Weddel's collection, than at a beautiful woman if he read in her face that she was as little susceptible of any virtuous emotion as the marble. While, therefore, he would not allow that any person could be unfortunately ugly, he thought that many were unfortunately handsome, and that no wise parent would wish his daughter to be eminently beautiful, lest what in her childhood was naturally and allowably the pride of his eye— should, when she grew up, become the grief of his heart. It requires no wide range of observation to discover that the woman who is married for her beauty has little better chance of happiness than she who is married for her fortune. "I have known very few women in my life," said Mrs. Montagu, "whom extraordinary charms and accomplishments did not make unhappy."

CHAPTER CLXXXI.

NO DEGREE OF UGLINESS REALLY UNFORTUNATE. FIDUS CORNELIUS COMPARED TO A PLUCKED OSTRICH. WILKES' CLAIM TO UGLINESS CONSIDERED AND NEGATIVED BY DOCTOR JOHNSON, NOTWITHSTANDING HOGARTH'S PORTRAIT. CAST OF THE EYE À LA MONTMORENCY. ST. EVREMOND AND TURENNE. WILLIAM BLAKE THE PAINTER, AND THE WELSH TRIADS. CURIOUS EXTRACT FROM THAT VERY CURIOUS AND RARE BOOK, THE DESCRIPTIVE CATALOGUE OF HIS OWN PICTURES, — AND A PAINFUL ONE FROM HIS POETICAL SKETCHES.

"*If thou beest not so handsome as thou wouldst have been, thank God thou art not more unhandsome than thou art.* 'Tis His mercy thou art not the mark for passenger's fingers to point at, an Heteroclite in nature, with some member defective or redundant. Be glad that thy clay cottage hath all the necessary forms thereto belonging, though the outside be not so fairly plaistered as some others." FULLER'S HOLY STATE, iii. c. 15.

I ASKED him once if there was not a degree of ugliness which might be deemed unfortunate, because a consciousness of it affected the ill-favoured individual so as to excite in him discontent and envy, and other evil feelings. He admitted that in an evil disposition it might have this tendency; but he said a disposition which was injuriously affected by such a cause, would have had other propensities quite as injurious in themselves and in their direction, evolved and brought into full action by an opposite cause. To exemplify this he instanced the two brothers Edward IV. and Richard III.

Fidus Cornelius burst into tears in the Roman Senate, because Corbulo called him a plucked ostrich: *Adversus alia maledicta mores et vitam convulnerantia, frontis illi firmitas constitit; adversus hoc tam absurdum lacrimæ prociderunt; tanta animorum imbecillitas est ubi ratio discessit.* But instances of such weakness, the Doctor said, are as rare as they are ridiculous. Most people see themselves in the most favourable light. "Ugly!" a very ugly, but a very conceited fellow, exclaimed one day when he contemplated himself in a looking-glass; "ugly! and yet there's something genteel in the face!" There are more coxcombs in the world than there are vain women; in the one sex there is a weakness for which time soon brings a certain cure, in the other it deserves a harsher appellation.

As to ugliness, not only in this respect do we make large allowances for ourselves, but our friends make large allowances for us also. Some one praised Palisson to Madame de Sevigné for the elegance of his manners, the magnanimity, the rectitude, and other virtues which he ought to have possessed; *hé bien*, she replied, *pour moi je ne connois que sa laideur; qu'on me le dedouble donc.* Wilkes, who pretended as little to beauty, as he did to public virtue, when he was off the stage used to say, that in winning the good graces of a lady there was not more than three days' difference between himself and the handsomest man in England. One of his female partizans praised him for his agreeable person, and being reminded of his squinting, she replied indignantly, that it was not more than a gentleman ought to squint. So rightly has Madame de Villedieu observed that

En mille occasions l'amour a sçeu prouver
Que tout devient pour luy, matiere à sympathie,
Quand il fait tant que d'en vouloir trouver.

She no doubt spoke sincerely, according to the light wherein, in the obliquity of her intellectual eyesight, she beheld him. Just as that prince of republican and unbelieving bigots, Thomas Holles, said of the same person, "I am sorry for the irregularities of Wilkes; they are, however, only as spots in the sun!" "It is the weakness of the many," says a once noted Journalist, "that when they have taken a fancy to a man, or to the name of a man, they take a fancy even to his failings." But there must have been no ordinary charm in the manners of John Wilkes, who in one interview overcame Johnson's well-founded and vehement dislike. The good nature of his countenance, and its vivacity and cleverness, made its physical ugliness be overlooked; and probably his cast of the eye, which was a squint of the first water, seemed only a peculiarity which gave effect to the sallies of his wit.

Hogarth's portrait of him he treated with characteristic good humour, and allowed it "to be an excellent compound caricature, or a caricature of what Nature had already caricatured. I know but one short apology, said he, to be made for this gentleman, or, to speak more properly, for the *person* of Mr. Wilkes; it is, that he did not make himself; and that he never was solicitous about the *case* (as Shakespeare calls it) only so far as to keep it clean and in health. I never heard that he ever hung over the glassy stream, like another Narcissus, admiring the image in it; nor that he ever stole an amorous look at his counterfeit in a side mirror. His form, such as it is, ought to give him no pain, while it is capable of giving so much pleasure to others. I believe he finds himself tolerably happy in the clay cottage to which he is tenant for life, because he has learned to keep it in pretty good order. While the share of health and animal spirits which heaven has given out should hold out, I can scarcely imagine he will be one moment peevish about the outside of so precarious, so temporary a habitation; or will ever be brought to our *Ingenium Galbæ malè habitat:—Monsieur, est mal logé.*" This was part of a note for his intended edition of Churchill.

Squinting, according to a French writer, is not unpleasing, when it is not in excess. He is probably right in this observation. A slight obliquity of vision sometimes gives an archness of expression, and always adds to the countenance a peculiarity, which, when the countenance has once become agreeable to the beholder, renders it more so. But when the eye-balls recede from each other to the outer verge of their orbits, or approach so closely that nothing but the intervention of the nose seems to prevent their meeting, a sense of distortion is produced, and consequently of pain. *Il y a des gens*, says Vigneul Marville, *qui ne sauroient regarder des louches sans en sentir quelque douleur aux yeux. Je suis des ceux-la.* This is because the deformity is catching, which it is well known to be in children; the tendency to imitation is easily excited in a highly sensitive frame — as in them; and the pain felt in the eyes gives warning that this action, which is safe only while it is unconscious and unobserved, is in danger of being deranged.

A cast of the eye *à la Montmorency* was much admired at the Court of Louis XIII., where the representative of that illustrious family had rendered it fashionable by his example. Descartes is said to have liked all persons who squinted for his nurse's sake, and the anecdote tells equally in favour of her and of him.

St. Evremond says in writing the Eulogy of Turenne, *Je ne m'amuserai point à depeindre tous les traits de son visage. Les caractères des Grands Hommes n'ont rien de commun avec les portraits des belles femmes. Mais je puis dire en gros qu'il avoit quelque chose d'auguste et d'agréable; quelque chose en sa physionomie qui faisoit concevoir je ne sai quoi de grand en son ame, et en son esprit. On pouvoit juger à le voir, que par un disposition particulière la Nature l'avoit pré-*

paré à faire tout ce qu'il a fait. If Turenne had not been an ill-looking man, the skilful eulogist would not thus have excused himself from giving any description of his countenance; a countenance from which indeed, if portraits belie it not, it might be inferred that nature had prepared him to change his party during the civil wars, as lightly as he would have changed his seat at a card-table, — to renounce the Protestant faith, and to ravage the Palatinate. *Ne souvenez-vous pas de la physionomie funeste de ce grand homme*, says Bussy Rabutin to Madame de Sevigné. An Italian bravo said, *che non teneva specchio in camera, perche quando si crucciava diveniva tanto terribile nell' aspetto, che veggendosi haria fatto troppo gran paura a se stesso.**

Queen Elizabeth could not endure the sight of deformity; when she went into public her guards, it is said, removed all misshapen and hideous persons out of her way.

Extreme ugliness has once proved as advantageous to its possessor as extreme beauty, if there be truth in those Triads wherein the Three Men are recorded who escaped from the battle of Camlan. They were Morvran ab Teged, in consequence of being so ugly, that every body thinking him to be a Demon out of Hell fled from him; Sandde Bryd-Angel, or Angel-aspect, in consequence of being so fine of form, so beautiful and fair, that no one raised a hand against him — for he was thought to be an Angel from Heaven: and Glewlwyd Gavaelvawr, or Great-grasp, (King Arthur's porter,) from his size and strength, so that none stood in his way, and every body ran before him; excepting these three, none escaped from Camlan, — that fatal field where King Arthur fell with all his chivalry.

That painter of great but insane genius, William Blake, of whom Allan Cunningham has written so interesting a memoir, took this Triad for the subject of a picture, which he called the Ancient Britons. It was one of his worst pictures, — which is saying much; and he has illustrated it with one of the most curious commentaries, in his very curious and very rare descriptive Catalogue of his own Pictures.

It begins with a translation from the Welsh, supplied to him, no doubt, by that good simple-hearted, Welsh-headed man, William Owen, whose memory is the great store-house of all Cymric tradition and lore of every kind.

"In the last battle of King Arthur only Three Britons escaped; these were the Strongest Man, the Beautifullest Man, and the Ugliest Man. These Three marched through the field unsubdued as Gods; and the Sun of Britain set, but shall arise again with tenfold splendour, when Arthur shall awake from sleep, and resume his dominion over earth and ocean.

"The three general classes of men," says the painter, "who are represented by the most Beautiful, the most Strong, and the most Ugly, could not be represented by any historical facts but those of our own countrymen, the Ancient Britons, without violating costumes. The Britons (say historians) were naked civilised men, learned, studious, abstruse in thought and contemplation; naked, simple, plain in their acts and manners; wiser than after ages. They were overwhelmed by brutal arms, all but a small remnant. Strength, Beauty, and Ugliness escaped the wreck, and remain for ever unsubdued, age after age.

"The British Antiquities are now in the Artist's hands; all his visionary contemplations relating to his own country and its ancient glory, when it was, as it again shall be, the source of learning and inspiration. He has in his hands poems of the highest antiquity. Adam was a Druid, and Noah. Also Abraham was called to succeed the Druidical age, which began to turn allegoric and mental signification into corporeal command; whereby human sacrifice would have depopulated the earth. All these things are written in Eden. The artist is an inhabitant of that happy country; and if everything goes on as it has begun, the work of vegetation and generation may

* Il Cortegiano, 27.

expect to be opened again to Heaven, through Eden, as it was in the beginning.

"The Strong Man represents the human sublime. The Beautiful Man represents the human pathetic, which was in the ban of Eden divided into male and female. The Ugly Man represents the human reason. They were originally one man, who was fourfold: he was self-divided and his real humanity drawn on the stems of generation: and the form of the fourth was like the Son of God. How he became divided is a subject of great sublimity and pathos. The Artist has written it under inspiration, and will, if God please, publish it. It is voluminous, and contains the ancient history of Britain, and the world of Satan and of Adam.

"In the mean time he has painted this picture, which supposes that in the reign of that British Prince, who lived in the fifth century, there were remains of those naked heroes in the Welsh mountains. They are now. Gray saw them in the person of his Bard on Snowdon; there they dwell in naked simplicity; happy is he who can see and converse with them, above the shadows of generation and death. In this picture, believing with Milton the ancient British history, Mr. Blake has done as all the ancients did, and as all the moderns who are worthy of fame, given the historical fact in its poetical vigour; so as it always happens; and not in that dull way that some historians pretend, who being weakly organised themselves, cannot see either miracle or prodigy. All is to them a dull round of probabilities and possibilities; but the history of all times and places is nothing else but improbabilities and impossibilities, — what we should say was impossible, if we did not see it always before our eyes.

"The antiquities of every nation under Heaven are no less sacred than those of the Jews; they are the same thing, as Jacob Bryant and all antiquaries have proved. How other antiquities came to be neglected and disbelieved, while those of the Jews are collected and arranged, is an enquiry worthy of both the Antiquarian and the Divine. All had originally one language, and one religion. This was the religion of Jesus, the everlasting Gospel. Antiquity preached the Gospel of Jesus. The reasoning historian, turner and twister of courses and consequences, such as Hume, Gibbon, and Voltaire, cannot, with all their artifice, turn or twist one fact, or disarrange self-evident action and reality. Reasons and opinions concerning acts are not history. Acts themselves alone are history, and they are neither the exclusive property of Hume, Gibbon, and Voltaire, Echard, Rapin, Plutarch, nor Herodotus. Tell me the acts, O historian, and leave me to reason upon them as I please; away with your reasoning and your rubbish. All that is not action is not worth reading. Tell me the What; I do not want you to tell me the Why, and the How; I can find that out myself, as well as you can, and I will not be fooled by you into opinions, that you please to impose, to disbelieve what you think improbable, or impossible. His opinion, who does not see spiritual agency, is not worth any man's reading; he who rejects a fact because it is improbable, must reject all History, and retain doubts only.

"It has been said to the Artist, take the Apollo for the model of your beautiful man, and the Hercules for your strong man, and the Dancing Fawn for your ugly man. Now he comes to his trial. He knows that what he does is not inferior to the grandest antiques. Superior they cannot be, for human power cannot go beyond either what he does, or what they have done. It is the gift of God; it is inspiration and vision. He had resolved to emulate those precious remains of antiquity. He has done so, and the result you behold. His ideas of strength and beauty have not been greatly different. Poetry as it exists now on earth in the various remains of ancient authors, Music as it exists in old tunes or melodies, Painting and Sculpture as it exists in the remains of antiquity and in the works of more modern genius, is Inspiration, and cannot be surpassed; it is perfect and eternal: Milton, Shakspeare, Michael Angelo, Rafael, the finest specimens of ancient Sculpture and

Painting, and Architecture, Gothic, Grecian, Hindoo, and Egyptian are the extent of the human mind. The human mind cannot go beyond the gift of God, the Holy Ghost. To suppose that Art can go beyond the finest specimens of Art that are now in the world, is not knowing what Art is; it is being blind to the gifts of the Spirit.

"It will be necessary for the Painter to say something concerning his ideas of Beauty, Strength, and Ugliness.

"The beauty that is annexed and appended to folly, is a lamentable accident and error of the mortal and perishing life; it does but seldom happen; but with this unnatural mixture the sublime Artist can have nothing to do; it is fit for the burlesque. The beauty proper for sublime Art, is lineaments, or forms and features that are capable of being the receptacle of intellect; accordingly the Painter has given in his beautiful man, his own idea of intellectual Beauty. The face and limbs (?) that deviates or alters least, from infancy to old age, is the face and limbs (?) of greatest Beauty and Perfection.

"The Ugly likewise, when accompanied and annexed to imbecillity and disease, is a subject for burlesque and not for historical grandeur; the artist has imagined the Ugly man; one approaching to the beast in features and form, his forehead small, without frontals; his nose high on the ridge, and narrow; his chest and the stamina of his make, comparatively little, and his joints and his extremities large; his eyes with scarce any whites, narrow and cunning, and everything tending toward what is truly ugly; the incapability of intellect.

"The Artist has considered his strong man as a receptacle of Wisdom, a sublime energizer; his features and limbs do not spindle out into length, without strength, nor are they too large and unwieldy for his brain and bosom. Strength consists in accumulation of power to the principal seat, and from thence a regular gradation and subordination; strength in compactness, not extent nor bulk.

"The strong man acts from conscious superiority, and marches on in fearless dependence on the divine decrees, raging with the inspirations of a prophetic mind. The Beautiful man acts from duty, and anxious solicitude for the fates of those for whom he combats. The Ugly man acts from love of carnage, and delight in the savage barbarities of war, rushing with sportive precipitation into the very teeth of the affrighted enemy.

"The Roman Soldiers rolled together in a heap before them: 'like the rolling thing before the whirlwind:' each shew a different character, and a different expression of fear, or revenge, or envy, or blank horror, or amazement, or devout wonder and unresisting awe.

"The dead and the dying, Britons naked, mingled with armed Romans, strew the field beneath. Amongst these, the last of the Bards who were capable of attending warlike deeds, is seen falling, outstretched among the dead and the dying; singing to his harp in the pains of death.

"Distant among the mountains are Druid Temples, similar to Stone Henge. The sun sets behind the mountains, bloody with the day of battle.

"The flush of health in flesh, exposed to the open air, nourished by the spirits of forests and floods, in that ancient happy period, which history has recorded, cannot be like the sickly daubs of Titian or Rubens. Where will the copier of nature, as it now is, find a civilized man, who has been accustomed to go naked? Imagination only can furnish us with colouring appropriate, such as is found in the frescoes of Rafael and Michael Angelo: the disposition of forms always directs colouring in works of true art. As to a modern man, stripped from his load of clothing, he is like a dead corpse. Hence Rubens, Titian, Correggio, and all of that class, are like leather and chalk; their men are like leather, and their women like chalk, for the disposition of their forms will not admit of grand colouring; in Mr. B.'s Britons, the blood is seen to circulate in their limbs; he defies competition in colouring."

My regard for thee, dear Reader, would

not permit me to leave untranscribed this very curious and original piece of composition. Probably thou hast never seen, and art never likely to see either the "Descriptive Catalogue" or the "Poetical Sketches" of this insane and erratic genius, I will therefore end the chapter with the *Mad Song* from the latter, — premising only *Dificultosa provincia es la que emprendo, y à muchos parecerà escusada; mas para la entereza desta historia, ha parecido no omitir aquesta parte.**

The wild winds weep,
  And the night is a-cold;
Come hither, Sleep,
  And my griefs unfold:
But lo! the morning peeps
  Over the eastern steep;
And the rustling birds of dawn
  The earth do scorn.

Lo! to the vault
  Of paved heaven,
With sorrow fraught
  My notes are driven:
They strike the ear of night,
  Make weep the eyes of day;
They make mad the roaring winds,
  And with tempests play.

Like a fiend in a cloud
  With howling woe,
After night I do croud
  And with night will go;
I turn my back to the east,
  From whence comforts have increas'd;
For light doth seize my brain
  With frantic pain.

CHAPTER CLXXXII.

AN IMPROVEMENT IN THE FORM OF THE HUMAN LEG SUGGESTED BY A PHYSICIAN. THE DOCTOR'S CURE OF A BROKEN SHIN AND INVENTION OF A SHIN-SHIELD.

Res fisci est, ubicunque natat. Whatsoever swims upon any water, belongs to this exchequer.
JEREMY TAYLOR. *Preface to the Duct. Dub.*

SOME Dr. Moreton is said to have advanced this extraordinary opinion in a treatise upon the beauty of the human structure, that had the calf of the leg been providentially set before, instead of being preposterously placed behind, it would have been evidently better, for as much as the shin-bone could not then have been so easily broken.

I have no better authority for this than a magazine extract. But there have been men of science silly enough to entertain opinions quite as absurd, and presumptuous enough to think themselves wiser than their Maker.

Supposing the said Dr. Moreton has not been unfairly dealt with in this statement, it would have been a most appropriate reward for his sagacity, if some one of the thousand and one wonder-working Saints of the Pope's Calendar had reversed his own calves for him, placed them in front, conformably to his own notion of the fitness of things, and then left him to regulate their motions as well as he could. The *Gastrocnemius* and the *Solæus* would have found themselves in a new and curious relation to the *Rectus femoris* and the two *Vasti*, and the anatomical reformer would have learned feelingly to understand the term of antagonising muscles in a manner peculiar to himself.

The use to which this notable philosopher would have made the calf of the leg serve, reminds me of a circumstance that occurred in our friend's practice. An old man hard upon threescore and ten broke his shin one day by stumbling over a chair; and although a hale person who seemed likely to attain a great age by virtue of a vigorous constitution, which had never been impaired through ill habits or excesses of any kind, the hurt that had been thought little of at first became so serious in its consequences, that a mortification was feared. Daniel Dove was not one of those practitioners who would let a patient die under their superintendence *secundum artem*, rather than incur the risque of being censured for trying in desperate cases any method not in the regular course of practice: and recollecting what he had heard when a boy, that a man whose leg and life were in danger from just such an accident had been saved by applying yeast to the wound, he tried the application. The dangerous symptoms were presently removed by it; a kindly process was induced,

* LUIS MUÑOZ, VIDA DEL P. L. DE GRANADA.

the wound healed, and the man became whole again.

Dove was then a young man; and so many years have elapsed since old Joseph Todhunter was gathered to his fathers, that it would now require an antiquarian's patience to make out the letters of his name upon his mouldering headstone. All remembrance of him (except among his descendants, if any there now be) will doubtless have passed away, unless he should be recollected in Doncaster by the means which Dr. Dove devised for securing him against another such accident.

The Doctor knew that the same remedy was not to be relied on a second time, when there would be less ability left in the system to second its effect. He knew that in old age the tendency of Nature is to dissolution, and that accidents which are trifling in youth, or middle age, become fatal at a time when Death is ready to enter at any breach, and Life to steal out through the first flaw in its poor crazy tenement. So, having warned Todhunter of this, and told him that he was likely to enjoy many years of life, if he kept a whole skin on his shins, he persuaded him to wear spatterdashes, quilted in front and protected there with whalebone, charging him to look upon them as the most necessary part of his clothing, and to let them be the last things which he doffed at night, and the first which he donned in the morning.

The old man followed this advice; lived to the great age of eighty-five, enjoyed his faculties to the last; and then died so easily, that it might truly be said he fell asleep.

My friend loved to talk of this case; for Joseph Todhunter had borne so excellent a character through life, and was so cheerful and so happy, as well as so venerable an old man, that it was a satisfaction for the Doctor to think he had been the means of prolonging his days.

CHAPTER CLXXXIII.

VIEWS OF OLD AGE. MONTAIGNE, DANIEL CORNEILLE, LANGUET, PASQUIER, DR. JOHNSON, LORD CHESTERFIELD, ST. EVREMOND.

> What is age
> But the holy place of life, the chapel of ease
> For all men's wearied miseries?
>
> MASSINGER.

MONTAIGNE takes an uncomfortable view of old age. *Il me semble,* he says, *qu'en la vieillesse, nos ames sont subjectes à des maladies et imperfections plus importunes qu'en la jeunesse. Je le disois estant jeune, lors on me donnoit de mon menton par le nez; je le dis encore à cette heure, que mon poil gris me donne le credit. Nous appellons sagesse la difficulté de nos humeurs, le desgoust des choses presentes: mais à la verité, nous ne quittons pas tant les vices, comme nous les changeons; et, à mon opinion, en pis. Outre une sotte et caduque fierté, un babil ennuyeux, ces humeures espineuses et inassociables, et la superstition, et un soin ridicule des richesses, lors que l'usage en est perdu, j'y trouve plus d'envie, d'injustice, et de malignité. Elle nous attache plus de rides en l'esprit qu'au visage: et ne se void point d'ames ou fort rares, qui en vieillissant ne sentent l'aigre, et le moisi.*

Take this extract, my worthy friends who are not skilled in French, or know no more of it than a Governess may have taught you,—in the English of John Florio, Reader of the Italian tongue unto the Sovereign Majesty of Anna, Queen of England, Scotland, &c., and one of the gentlemen of her Royal privy chamber; the same Florio whom some commentators, upon very insufficient grounds, have supposed to have been designed by Shakespeare in the Holofernes of Love's Labour's Lost.

"Methinks our souls in age are subject unto more importunate diseases and imperfections than they are in youth. I said so being young, when my beardless chin was upbraided me, and I say it again, now that my gray beard gives me authority. We entitle wisdom, the frowardness of our humours, and the distaste of present things;

but in truth we abandon not vices so much as we change them; and in mine opinion for the worse. Besides a silly and ruinous pride, cumbersome tattle, wayward and unsociable humours, superstition, and a ridiculous carking for wealth, when the use of it is well nigh lost. I find the more envy, injustice, and malignity in it. It sets more wrinkles in our minds than in our foreheads; nor are there any spirits, or very rare ones, which in growing old taste not sourly and mustily."

In the same spirit, recollecting perhaps this very passage of the delightful old Gascon, one of our own poets says,

Old age doth give by too long space,
Our souls as many wrinkles as our face;

and the same thing, no doubt in imitation of Montaigne, has been said by Corneille in a poem of thanks addressed to Louis XIV., when that King had ordered some of his plays to be represented during the winter of 1685, though he had ceased to be a popular writer,

Je vieillis, ou du moins, ils se le persuadent;
Pour bien écrire encor j'ai trop long tems écrit,
Et les rides du front passent jusqu' à l'esprit.

The opinion proceeded not in the poet Daniel from perverted philosophy, or sourness of natural disposition, for all his affections were kindly, and he was a tenderhearted, wise, good man. But he wrote this in the evening of his days, when he had

out lived the date
Of former grace, acceptance and delight;

when,

those bright stars from whence
He had his light, were set for evermore;

and when he complained that years had done to him

this wrong,
To make him write too much, and live too long;

so that this comfortless opinion may be ascribed in him rather to a dejected state of mind, than to a clear untroubled judgment. But Hubert Languet must have written more from observation and reflection than from feeling, when he said, in one of his letters to Sir Philip Sidney, "you are mistaken if you believe that men are made better by age; for it is very rarely so. They become indeed more cautious, and learn to conceal their faults and their evil inclinations; so that if you have known any old man in whom you think some probity were still remaining, be assured that he must have been excellently virtuous in his youth." *Erras si credis homines fieri ætate meliores; id nam est rarissimum. Fiunt quidem cautiores, et vitia animi, ac pravos suos affectus occultare discunt: quod si quem senem novisti in quo aliquid probitatis superesse judices, crede eum in adolescentiâ fuisse optimum.*

Languet spoke of its effects upon others. Old Estienne Pasquier, in that uncomfortable portion of his *Jeux Poëtiques* which he entitles *Vieillesse Rechignée*, writes as a self-observer, and his picture is not more favourable.

Je ne nourry dans moy qu'une humeur noire,
Chagrin, fascheux, melancholic, hagard,
Grongneux, despit, presomptueux, langard,
Je fay l'amour au bon vin et au boire.

But the bottle seems not to have put him in good humour either with others or himself.

Toute la monde me put; je vy de telle sort,
Que je ne fay meshuy que tousser et cracher,
Que de fascher autruy, et d'autruy me fascher;
Je ne supporte nul, et nul ne me supporte.
Un mal de corps je sens, un mal d'esprit je porte;
Foible de corps je veux, mais je ne puis marcher;
Foible d'esprit je n'oze à mon argent toucher,
Voilà les beaux effects que la vieillesse apporte!
O combien est heureux celuy qui, de ses ans
Jeune, ne passe point la fleur de son printans,
Ou celuy qui venu s'en retourne aussi vite!
Non: je m'abuze; ainçois ces maux ce sont appas
Qui me feront un jour trouver doux mon trespas,
Quand il plaira à Dieu que ce monde je quitte.

The miserable life I lead is such,
That now the world loathes me and I loathe it;
What do I do all day but cough and spit,
Annoying others, and annoyed as much!
My limbs no longer serve me, and the wealth
Which I have heap'd, I want the will to spend.
So mind and body both are out of health,
Behold the blessings that on age attend!
Happy whose fate is not to overlive
The joys which youth, and only youth can give,
But in his prime is taken, happy he!
Alas, that thought is of an erring heart,
These evils make me willing to depart
When it shall please the Lord to summon me.

The Rustic, in Hammerlein's curious dialogues *de Nobilitate et Rusticitate*, describes his old age in colours as dark as Pasquier's: *plenus dierum*, he says, *ymmo senex valde, id* *est, octogenarius, et senio confractus, et heri et nudiustercius, ymmo plerisque revolutionibus annorum temporibus, corporis statera recurvatus, singulto, tussito, sterto, ossito, sternuto, balbutio, catharizo, mussico, paraleso, gargariso, cretico, tremo, sudo, titillo, digitis sæpe geliso, et insuper (quod deterius est) cor meum affligitur, et caput excutitur, languet spiritus, fetet anhelitus, caligant oculi et facillant** *articuli, nares confluunt, crines defluunt, tremunt tactus et deperit actus, dentes putrescunt et aures surdescunt; de facili ad iram provocor, difficili revocor, cito credo, tarde discedo.*

The effects of age are described in language not less characteristic by the Conte Baldessar Castiglione in his Cortegiano. He is explaining wherefore the old man is always *laudator temporis acti;* and thus he accounts for the universal propensity;— *Gli anni fuggendo se ne portan seco molte commodità, e tra l' altre levano dal sangue gran parte de gli spiriti vitali; onde la complession si muta, e divengon debili gli organi, per i quali l' anima opera le sue virtù. Però de i cori nostri in quel tempo, come allo autunno le fogli de gli arbori, caggiono i soavi fiori di contento; e nel loco de i sereni et chiari pensieri, entra la nubilosa e turbida tristitia di mille calamità compagnata, di modo che non solamente il corpo, ma l' animo anchora è infermo; ne de i passati piaceri reserva altro che una tenace memoria, e la imagine di quel caro tempo della tenera eta, nella quale quando ci troviamo, ci pare che sempre il cielo, e la terra, e ogni cosa faccia festa, e rida imtorno à gli occhi nostri e nel pensiero, come in un delitioso et vago giardino, fiorisca la dolce primavera d' allegrezza: onde forse saria utile, quando gia nella fredda stagione comincia il sole della nostra vita, spogliandoci de quei piaceri, andarsene verso l' occaso, perdere insieme con essi anchor la lor memoria, e trovar (come disse Temistocle) un' arte, che a scordar insegnasse; perche tanto sono fallaci i sensi del corpo nostro, che spesso ingannano anchora il giudicio della mente. Però parmi che i vecchi siano alla condition di quelli, che partendosi dal porto, tengon gli occhi in terra, e par loro che la nave stia ferma, e la riva si parta; e pur è il contrario; che il porto, e medesimamente il tempo, e i piaceri restano nel suo stato, e noi con la nave della mortalità fuggendo n' andiamo, l' un dopo l' altro, per quel procelloso mare che ogni cosa assorbe et devora; ne mai piu pigliar terra ci è concesso; anzi sempre da contrarii venti combattuti, al fine in qualche scoglio la nave rompemo.*

Take this passage, gentle reader, as Master Thomas Hoby has translated it to my hand. "Years wearing away carry also with them many commodities, and among others take away from the blood a great part of the lively spirits; that altereth the complection, and the instruments wax feeble whereby the soul worketh his effects. Therefore the sweet flowers of delight vade * away in that season out of our hearts, as the leaves fall from the trees after harvest; and instead of open and clear thoughts, there entereth cloudy and troublous heaviness, accompanied with a thousand heart griefs: so that not only the blood, but the mind is also feeble, neither of the former pleasures retaineth it any thing else but a fast memory, and the print of the beloved time of tender age, which when we have upon us, the heaven, the earth and each thing to our seeming rejoiceth and laugheth always about our eyes, and in thought (as in a savoury and pleasant garden) flourisheth the sweet spring time of mirth: So that, peradventure, it were not unprofitable when now, in the cold season, the sun of our life, taking away from us our delights, beginneth to draw toward the West, to lose therewithall the mindfulness of them, and to find out as Themistocles saith, an art

---

* *Facillant* is here evidently the same as *vacillant.* For the real meaning of *facillo* the reader is referred to Du Cange in v. or to Martinius' Lexicon.

† "Vade" is no doubt the true word here. The double sense of it,—that is, to *fade*, or to *go away*,—may be seen in Todd's Johnson and in Nares' Glossary. Neither of them quote the following lines from the Earl of Surrey's Poems. They occur in his Ecclesiastes.

We, that live on the earth, draw toward our decay,
Our children fill our place awhile, and then they vade away.

And again,

New fancies daily spring, which vade, returning mo.

Jewel commonly writes "vade." See vol. i. pp. 141. 154. Ed. Jelf.

to teach us to forget; for the senses of our body are so deceivable, that they beguile many times also the judgement of the mind. Therefore, methinks, old men be like unto them that sailing in a vessel out of an haven, behold the ground with their eyes, and the vessel to their seeming standeth still, and the shore goeth; and yet is it clean contrary, for the haven, and likewise the time and pleasures, continue still in their estate, and we with the vessel of mortality flying away, go one after another through the tempestuous sea that swalloweth up and devoureth all things, neither is it granted us at any time to come on shore again; but, always beaten with contrary winds, at the end we break our vessel at some rock."

"Why Sir," said Dr. Johnson, "a man grows better humoured as he grows older. He improves by experience. When young he thinks himself of great consequence, and every thing of importance. As he advances in life, he learns to think himself of no consequence, and little things of little importance, and so he becomes more patient and better pleased." This was the observation of a wise and good man, who felt in himself, as he grew old, the effect of Christian principles upon a kind heart and a vigorous understanding. One of a very different stamp came to the same conclusion before him; *Crescit ætate pulchritudo animorum*, says Antonio Perez, *quantum minuitur eorundem corporum venustas*.

One more of these dark pictures. "The heart," says Lord Chesterfield, "never grows better by age; I fear rather worse; always harder. A young liar will be an old one; and a young knave will only be a greater knave as he grows older. But should a bad young heart, accompanied with a good head, (which by the way very seldom is the case) really reform, in a more advanced age, from a consciousness of its folly, as well as of its guilt, such a conversion would only be thought prudential and political, but never sincere."

It is remarkable that Johnson, though, as has just been seen, he felt in himself and saw in other good men, that the natural effect of time was to sear away asperities of character,

> Till the smooth temper of their age should be
> Like the high leaves upon the Holly Tree,

yet he expressed an opinion closely agreeing with this of Lord Chesterfield. "A man," he said, "commonly grew wicked as he grew older, at least he but changed the vices of youth, head-strong passion and wild temerity, for treacherous caution and desire to circumvent." These he can only have meant of wicked men. But what follows seems to imply a mournful conviction that the tendency of society is to foster our evil propensities, and counteract our better ones; "I am always," he said, "on the young people's side, when there is a dispute between them and the old ones; for you have at least a charm for virtue, till age has withered its very root." Alas, this is true of the irreligious and worldly minded, and it is generally true because they composed the majority of our corrupt contemporaries.

But Johnson knew that good men became better as they grew older, because his philosophy was that of the Gospel. Something of a philosopher Lord Chesterfield was, and had he lived in the days of Trajan or Hadrian, might have done honour to the school of Epicurus. But if he had not in the pride of his poor philosophy, shut both his understanding and his heart against the truths of revealed religion, in how different a light would the evening of his life have closed.

Une raison essentielle, says the Epicurean Saint Evremond, *qui nous oblige à nous retirer quand nous sommes vieux, c'est qu'il faut prevenir le ridicule où l'age nous fait tomber presque toujours.* And in another place he says, *certes le plus honnête-homme dont personne n'a besoin, a de la peine à s'exempter du ridicule en vieillissant.* This was the opinion of a courtier, a sensualist, and a Frenchman.

I cannot more appositely conclude this chapter than by a quotation ascribed, whether truly or not, to St. Bernard. *Maledictum caput canum et cor vanum, caput tremulum et cor emulum, canities in vertice et pernicies in mente: facies rugosa et lingua nugosa, cutis sicca et fides ficta; visus caligans et caritas claudicans: labium pendens et dens detrahens; virtus debilis et vita flebilis; dies uberes et fructus steriles, amici multi, et actus stulti.*

CHAPTER CLXXXIV.

FURTHER OBSERVATIONS CONCERNING OLD AGE. BISHOP REYNOLDS. OPINION OF THE DOCTOR CONCERNING BEASTS AND MEN. M. DE CUSTINE. THE WORLD IS TOO MUCH WITH US. WORDSWORTH. SIR WALTER RALEIGH.

In these reflections, which are of a serious, and somewhat of a melancholy cast, it is best to indulge; because it is always of use to be serious, and not unprofitable sometimes to be melancholy. FREEMAN'S SERMONS.

"As usurers," says Bishop Reynolds, "before the whole debt is paid, do fetch away some good parts of it for the loan, so before the debt of death be paid by the whole body, old age doth by little and little take away sometimes one sense, sometimes another; this year one limb, the next another; and causeth a man as it were to die daily. No one can dispel the clouds and sorrows of old age, but Christ, who is the sun of righteousness and the bright morning star."

Yet our Lord and Saviour hath not left those who are in darkness and the shadow of death, without the light of a heavenly hope at their departure, if their ways have not wilfully been evil,—if they have done their duty according to that law of nature which is written in the heart of man. It is the pride of presumptuous wisdom (itself the worst of follies) that has robbed the natural man of his consolation in old age, and of his hope in death, and exacts the forfeit of that hope from the infidel as the consequence and punishment of his sin. Thus it was in heathen times, as it now is in countries that are called christian. When Cicero speaks of those things which depend upon opinion, he says, *hujusmodi sunt probabilia; impiis apud inferos pœnas esse præparatas; eos, qui philosophiæ dent operam, non arbitrari Deos esse.* Hence it appears he regarded it as equally probable that there was an account to be rendered after death; and that those who professed philosophy would disbelieve this as a vulgar delusion, live therefore without religion, and die without hope, like the beasts that perish!

"*If* they perish," the Doctor used always reverently to say when he talked upon this subject. O Reader, it would have done you good as it has done me, if you had heard him speak upon it, in his own beautiful old age! "*If* they perish," he would say. "That the beasts die without hope we may conclude; death being to them like falling asleep, an act of which the mind is not cognisant! But that they live without religion, he would not say,—that they might not have some sense of it according to their kind; nor that all things animate, and seemingly inanimate, did not actually praise the Lord, as they are called upon to do by the Psalmist, and in the *Benedicite!*"

It is a pious fancy of the good old lexicographist Adam Littleton that our Lord took up his first lodging in a stable amongst the cattle, as if he had come to be the Saviour of them as well as of men; being, by one perfect oblation of himself, to put an end to all other sacrifices, as well as to take away sins. This, he adds, the Psalmist fears not to affirm, speaking of God's mercy. "Thou savest," says he, "both man and beast."

The text may lead us further than Adam Littleton's interpretation.

Qu'on ne me parle plus de NATURE MORTE, says M. de Custine, in his youth and enthusiasm, writing from Mont-Auvert; *on sent ici que la Divinité est partout, et que les pierres sont pénétrées comme nous-mêmes d'une puissance créatrice! Quand on me dit que les rochers sont insensibles, je crois entendre un enfant soutenir que l'aiguille d'une montre ne marche pas, parce qu'il ne la voit pas se mouvoir.*

Do not, said our Philosopher, when he threw out a thought like this, do not ask me how this can be! I guess at everything, and can account for nothing. It is more comprehensible to me that stocks and stones should have a sense of devotion, than that men should be without it. I could much more easily persuade myself that the birds in the air and the beasts in the field have souls to be saved, than I can believe that very many of my fellow bipeds have any more soul than, as some of our divines have said, serves to keep their bodies from putrefaction. "God forgive me, worm that I am! for the sinful thought of which I am too often conscious, — that of the greater part of the human race, the souls are not worth saving!" — I have not forgotten the look which accompanied these words, and the tone in which he uttered them, dropping his voice toward the close.

"We must of necessity," said he, "become better or worse as we advance in years. Unless we endeavour to spiritualise ourselves, and supplicate in this endeavour for that Grace which is never withheld when it is sincerely and earnestly sought, age bodilises us more and more, and the older we grow the more we are embruted and debased: so manifestly is the awful text verified which warns us that 'unto every one which hath shall be given, and from him that hath not, even that he hath shall be taken away from him.' In some the soul seems gradually to be absorbed and extinguished in its crust of clay; in others as if it purified and sublimed the vehicle to which it was united. *Viget animus, et gaudet non multum sibi esse cum corpore; magnam oneris partem sui posuit.** Nothing therefore is more beautiful than a wise and religious old age; nothing so pitiable as the latter stages of mortal existence — when the World and the Flesh, and that false philosophy which is of the Devil, have secured the victory for the Grave!"

"He that hath led a holy life," says one of our old Bishops, "is like a man which hath travelled over a beautiful valley, and being on the top of a hill, turneth about with delight, to take a view of it again." The retrospect is delightful, and perhaps it is even more grateful if his journey has been by a rough and difficult way. But whatever may have been his fortune on the road, the Pilgrim who has reached the Delectable Mountains looks back with thankfulness and forward with delight.

And wherefore is it not always thus? Wherefore, but because, as Wordsworth has said,

> The World is too much with us, late and soon
> Getting and spending, we lay waste our powers.

"Though our own eyes," says Sir Walter Raleigh, "do every where behold the sudden and resistless assaults of Death, and Nature assureth us by never failing experience, and Reason by infallible demonstration, that our times upon the earth have neither certainty nor durability, that our bodies are but the anvils of pain and diseases, and our minds the hives of unnumbered cares, sorrows and passions; and that when we are most glorified, we are but those painted posts against which Envy and Fortune direct their darts; yet such is the true unhappiness of our condition, and the dark ignorance which covereth the eyes of our understanding, that we only prize, pamper, and exalt this vassal and slave of death, and forget altogether, or only remember at our cast-away leisure, the imprisoned immortal Soul, which can neither die with the reprobate, nor perish with the mortal parts of virtuous men; seeing God's justice in the one, and his goodness in the other, is exercised for evermore, as the ever-living subjects of his reward and punishment. But when is it that we examine this great account? Never, while we have one vanity left us to spend! We plead for titles till our breath fail us; dig for riches whilst our strength enableth us; exercise malice while we can revenge; and then when time hath beaten from us both youth, pleasure and health, and that Nature itself hateth the house of Old Age, we remember with Job that 'we must go the way from whence we shall not return, and that our bed is made ready for us in the dark.' And then I say, looking over-late into the bottom of our conscience, which Pleasure and Ambition had locked up from us all our lives, we behold therein the fearful images of our actions past, and withal this terrible inscription that 'God will bring every work into judgement that man hath done under the Sun.'

* SENECA.

"But what examples have ever moved us? what persuasions reformed us? or what threatenings made us afraid? We behold other men's tragedies played before us; we hear what is promised and threatened; but the world's bright glory hath put out the eyes of our minds; and these betraying lights, with which we only see, do neither look up towards termless joys, nor down towards endless sorrows, till we neither know, nor can look for anything else at the world's hands. — But let us not flatter our immortal Souls herein! For to neglect God all our lives, and know that we neglect Him; to offend God voluntarily, and know that we offend Him, casting our hopes on the peace which we trust to make at parting, is no other than a rebellious presumption, and that which is the worst of all, even a contemptuous laughing to scorn and deriding of God, his laws and precepts. *Frustrà sperant qui sic de misericordiâ Dei sibi blandiuntur;* they hope in vain, saith Bernard, which in this sort flatter themselves with God's mercy."

CHAPTER CLXXXV.

EVOLVEMENTS. ANALOGIES. ANTICIPATIONS.

I have heard, how true
I know not, most physicians as they grow
Greater in skill, grow less in their religion;
Attributing so much to natural causes,
That they have little faith in that they cannot
Deliver reason for: this Doctor steers
Another course. MASSINGER.

I FORGET what poet it is, who, speaking of old age, says that

The Soul's dark mansion, battered and decayed,
Lets in new light through chinks that time has made;

a strange conceit, imputing to the decay of our nature that which results from its maturation.*

As the ancients found in the butterfly a beautiful emblem of the immortality of the Soul, my true philosopher and friend looked, in like manner, upon the chrysalis as a type of old age. The gradual impairment of the senses and of the bodily powers, and the diminution of the whole frame as it shrinks and contracts itself in age, afforded analogy enough for a mind like his to work on, which quickly apprehended remote similitudes and delighted in remarking them. The sense of flying in our sleep might probably, he thought, be the anticipation or forefeeling of an unevolved power, like an aurelia's dream of butterfly motion.

The tadpole has no intermediate state of torpor. This merriest of all creatures, if mirth may be measured by motion, puts out legs before it discards its tail and commences frog. It was not in our outward frame that the Doctor could discern any resemblance to this process; but he found it in that expansion of the intellectual faculties, those aspirations of the spiritual part, wherein the Soul seems to feel its wings and to imp them for future flight.

One has always something for which to look forward, some change for the better. The boy in petticoats longs to be dressed in the masculine gender. Little boys wish to be big ones. In youth we are eager to attain manhood, and in manhood matrimony becomes the next natural step of our desires. "Days then should speak, and multitude of years should teach wisdom;" and teach it they will, if man will but learn; for nature brings the heart into a state for receiving it.

Jucundissima est ætas devexa jam, non tamen præceps; et illam quoque in extremâ regulâ stantem, judico habere suas voluptates; aut hoc ipsum succedit in locum voluptatum, nullis egere. Quam dulce est cupiditates fatigasse ac reliquisse!† This was not Dr. Dove's philosophy: he thought the stage of senescence a happy one, not because we outgrow the desires and enjoyments of youth and manhood, but because wiser desires, more permanent enjoyments, and holier hopes succeed to them, — because time in its course

* There is more true philosophy in what Wordsworth says,

—"The wiser mind
Mourns less for what age takes away,
Than what it leaves behind."
The Fountain.

† SENECA.

brings us nearer to eternity, and as earth recedes Heaven opens upon our prospect.

"It is the will of God and nature," says Franklin, "that these mortal bodies be laid aside, when the soul is to enter into real life. This is rather an embryo state, a preparation for living. A man is not completely born until he be dead. Why, then, should we grieve that a new child is born among the immortals, a new member added to their happy society? We are spirits. That bodies should be lent us, while they can afford us pleasure, assist us in acquiring knowledge, or in doing good to our fellow-creatures, is a kind and benevolent act of God. When they become unfit for these purposes, and afford us pain instead of pleasure, instead of an aid become an encumbrance, and answer none of the intentions for which they were given, it is equally kind and benevolent, that a way is provided by which we may get rid of them. Death is that way."

"God," says Fuller, "sends his servants to bed when they have done their work."

This is a subject upon which even Sir Richard Blackmore could write with a poet's feeling.

Thou dost, O Death, a peaceful harbour lie
Upon the margin of Eternity;
Where the rough waves of Time's impetuous tide
Their motion lose, and quietly subside:
Weary, they roll their drousy heads asleep
At the dark entrance of Duration's deep.
Hither our vessels in their turn retreat;
Here still they find a safe untroubled seat,
When worn with adverse passions, furious strife,
And the hard passage of tempestuous life.

Thou dost to man unfeigned compassion show,
Soothe all his grief, and solace all his woe.
Thy spiceries with noble drugs abound,
That every sickness cure and every wound.
That which anoints the corpse will only prove
The sovereign balm our anguish to remove.
The cooling draught administered by thee,
O Death! from all our sufferings sets us free.
Impetuous life is by thy force subdued,
Life, the most lasting fever of the blood.
The weary in thy arms lie down to rest,
No more with breath's laborious task opprest.
Hear, how the men that long life-ridden lie,
In constant pain, for thy assistance cry,
Hear how they beg and pray for leave to die.
For vagabonds that o'er the country roam,
Forlorn, unpitied and without a home,
Thy friendly care provides a lodging-room.
The comfortless, the naked, and the poor,
Much pinch'd with cold, with grievous hunger more,
Thy subterranean hospitals receive,
Assuage their anguish and their wants relieve.
Cripples with aches and with age opprest,
Crawl on their crutches to the Grave for rest.
Exhausted travellers that have undergone
The scorching heats of life's intemperate zone,
Haste for refreshment to their beds beneath,
And stretch themselves in the cool shades of death.
Poor labourers who their daily task repeat,
Tired with their still returning toil and sweat,
Lie down at last; and at the wish'd for close
Of life's long day, enjoy a sweet repose.

Thy realms, indulgent Death, have still possest
Profound tranquillity and unmolested rest.
No raging tempests, which the living dread,
Beat on the silent regions of the dead:
Proud Princes ne'er excite with war's alarms
Thy subterranean colonies to arms.
They undisturbed their peaceful mansions keep,
And earthquakes only rock them in their sleep.

Much has been omitted which may be found in the original, and one couplet removed from its place; but the whole is Blackmore's.

CHAPTER CLXXXVI.

LEONE HEBREO'S DIALOGI DE AMORE. THE ELIXIR OF LIFE NO OBSTACLE TO DEATH. PARACELSUS. VAN HELMONT AND JAN MASS. DR. DOVE'S OPINION OF A BIOGRAPHER'S DUTIES.

> There's a lean fellow beats all conquerors!
>
> OLD FORTUNATUS.

In Leone Hebreo's Dialogi de Amore, one of the interlocutors says, *Vediamo che gli huomini naturalmente desiano di mai non morire; laqual cosa è impossibile, manifesta, e senza speranza.* To which the other replies, *Coloro chel desiano, non credeno interamente che sia impossibile, et hanno inteso per le historie legali, che Enoc, et Elia, et ancor Santo Giovanni Evangelista sono immortali in corpo, et anima: se ben veggono essere stato per miracolo: onde ciascuno pensa che à loro Dio potria fare simil miracolo. E però con questa possibilita si gionta qualche remota speranza, laquale incita un lento desiderio, massimamente per essere la morte horribile, e la corruttione propria odiosa à chi si vuole, et il desiderio non è d' acquistare cosa nuova, ma di non perdere la vita, che si truova; laquale havendosi di presente, è facil cosa ingannarsi l' huomo à desiare che non si perda; se ben naturalmente è impossibile: chel desiderio di ciò è talmente lento, che può essere di cosa impossibile et imaginabile, essendo di tanta importantia al desiderante. Et ancora ti dirò chel fondamento di questo desiderio non è vano in se, se bene è alquanto ingannoso, però chel desiderio dell' huomo d' essere immortale è veramente possibile; perche l' esentia dell' huomo, (come rettamente Platon vuole,) non è altro che la sua anima intellettiva, laquale per la virtu, sapientia, cognitione, et amore divino si fa gloriosa et immortale.*

Paracelsus used to boast that he would not die till he thought proper so to do; thus wishing it to be understood that he had discovered the Elixir of life. He died suddenly, and at a time when he seemed to be in full health; and hence arose a report, that he had made a compact with the Devil, who enabled him to perform all his cures, but came for him as soon as the term of their agreement was up.

Wherefore indeed should he have died by any natural means who so well understood the mysteries of life and of death? What, says he, is life? *Nihil meherclè vita est aliud, nisi Mumia quædam Balsamita conservans mortale corpus à mortalibus vermibus, et eschara cum impressâ liquoris salium commisturâ.* What is Death? *Nihil certe aliud quam Balsami dominium, Mumiæ interitus, salium ultima materia.* Do you understand this, Reader? If you do, I do not.

But he is intelligible when he tells us that Life may be likened to Fire, and that all we want is to discover the fuel for keeping it up, — the true Lignum Vitæ. "It is not against nature," he contends, "that we should live till the renovation of all things; it is only against our knowledge, and beyond it. But there are medicaments for prolonging life; and none but the foolish or the ignorant would ask why then is it that Princes and Kings who can afford to purchase them, die nevertheless like other people." "The reason," says the great Bombast von Hohenheim, "is, that their physicians know less about medicine than the very boors, and moreover that Princes and Kings lead dissolute lives." And if it be asked why no one, except Hermes Trismegistus, has used such medicaments; he replies that others have used them, but have not let it be known.

Van Helmont was once of opinion that no metallic preparation could contain in itself the blessing of the Tree of Life, though that the Philosopher's stone had been discovered was a fact that consisted with his own sure knowledge. This opinion, however, was in part changed, in consequence of some experiments made with an aurific powder, given him by a stranger after a single evening's acquaintance; (*vir peregrinus, unius vesperi amicus:*) these experiments convinced him that the stone partook of what he calls Zoophyte life, as distinguished both from vegetative and sensitive. But the true secret, he thought, must be derived from the vegetable world, and he sought for it in the Cedar, induced, as it seems, by the frequent mention of that tree in the Old Testament. He says much concerning the cedar, — among other things, that when all other plants were destroyed by the Deluge, and their kinds preserved only in their seed, the Cedars of Lebanon remained uninjured under the waters. However, when he comes to the main point, he makes a full stop, saying, *Cætera autem quæ de Cedro sunt mecum sepelientur: nam mundus non capax est.* It is not unlikely that if his mysticism had been expressed in the language of intelligible speculation, it might have been found to accord with some of Berkeley's theories in the *Siris*. But for his reticence upon this subject, as if the world were not worthy of his discoveries, he ought to have been deprived of his two remaining talents. Five, he tells us, he had received for his portion, but because instead of improving them he had shown himself unworthy of so large a trust, he by whom they were given had taken from him three. *Ago illi gratias, quod cum contulisset in me quinque talenta, fecissemque me indignum, et hactenus repudium coram eo factus essem, placuit divinæ bonitati, auferre à me tria, et relinquere adhuc bina, ut me sic ad meliorem frugem exspectaret. Maluit, inquam, me depauperare et tolerare, ut non essem utilis plurimis, modò me salvaret ab hujus mundi periculis. Sit ipsi æterna sanctificatio.*

He has, however, informed posterity of the means by which he prolonged the life of a man to extreme old age. This person, whose name was Jan Mass, was in the service of Martin Rythovius, the first Bishop of Ypres, when that prelate, by desire of the illustrious sufferers, assisted at the execution of Counts Egmond and Horn. Mass was then in the twenty-fifth year of his age. When he was fifty-eight, being poor, and having a large family of young children, he came to Van Helmont, and entreated him to prolong his life if he could, for the sake of these children, who would be left destitute in case of his death, and must have to beg their bread from door to door. Van Helmont, then a young man, was moved by such an application, and considering what might be the likeliest means of sustaining life in its decay, he called to mind the fact that wine is preserved from corruption by the fumes of burnt brimstone; it then occurred to him that the acid liquor of sulphur, *acidum sulfuris stagma*, (it is better so to translate his words than to call it the sulphuric acid,) must of necessity contain the fumes and odour of sulphur, being, according to his chemistry, nothing but those fumes of sulphur, combined with, or imbibed in, its mercurial salt. The next step in his reasoning was to regard the blood as the wine of life; if this could be kept sound, though longevity might not be the necessary consequence, life would at least be preserved from the many maladies which arose from its corruption, and the sanity, and immunity from such diseases, and from the sufferings consequent thereon, must certainly tend to its prolongation. He gave Mass therefore a stone bottle of the distilled liquor of sulphur, and taught him also how to prepare this oil from burnt sulphur. And he ordered him at every meal to take two drops of it in his first draught of beer; and not lightly to exceed that; two drops, he thought, contained enough of the fumes for a sufficient dose. This was in the year 1600; and now, says Helmont, in 1641, the old man still walks about the streets of Brussels. And what is still better, (*quodque augustius est,*) in all these forty years, he has never been confined by any illness, except that by a fall upon the ice he once broke his leg near the knee; and he has constantly been free from fever, remaining a slender and lean man, and always poor.

Jan Mass had nearly reached his hundredth year when this was written, and it is no wonder that Van Helmont, who upon a fantastic analogy had really prescribed an efficient tonic, should have accounted, by the virtue of his prescription, for the health and vigour which a strong constitution had retained to that extraordinary age. There is no reason for doubting the truth of his statement; but if Van Helmont relied upon his theory he must have made further experiments; it is probable therefore that he either distrusted his own hypothesis, or found, upon subsequent trials, that the result disappointed him.

Van Helmont's works were collected and edited by his son Francis Mercurius, who styles himself *Philosophus per Unum in quo Omnia Eremita peregrinans*, and who dedicated the collection as a holocaust to the ineffable Hebrew Name. The Vita Authoris which he prefixed to it relates to his own life, not to his father's, and little can be learned from it, except that he is the more mystical and least intelligible of the two. The most curious circumstances concerning the father are what he has himself communicated in the treatise entitled his Confession, into which the writer of his life in Aikin's Biography seems not to have looked, nor indeed into any of his works, the articles in that as in our other Biographies, being generally compiled from compilations, so as to present the most superficial information, with the least possible trouble to the writer, and the least possible profit to the reader,—skimming for him not the cream of knowledge but the scum.

Dr. Dove used to say that whoever wrote the life of an author without carefully perusing his works acted as iniquitously as a

Judge who should pronounce sentence in a cause without hearing the evidence; nay, he maintained, the case was even worse, because there was an even chance that the Judge might deliver a right sentence; but it was impossible that a life so composed should be otherwise than grievously imperfect, if not grossly erroneous. For all the ordinary business of the medical profession he thought it sufficient that a practitioner should thoroughly understand the practice of his art, and proceed empirically: God help the patients, he would say, if it were not so! and indeed without God's help they would fare badly at the best. But he was of opinion that no one could take a lively and at the same time a worthy interest in any art or science without as it were identifying himself with it, and seeking to make himself well acquainted with its history: a Physician therefore, according to his way of thinking, ought to be as curious concerning the writings of his more eminent predecessors, and as well read in the most illustrious of them, as a general in the wars of Hannibal, Cæsar, the Black Prince, the Prince of Parma, Gustavus Adolphus, and Marlborough. How carefully he had perused Van Helmont was shown by the little landmarks whereby, after an interval of — alas how many years, — I have followed him through the volume, — *haud passibus æquis.*

CHAPTER CLXXXVII.

VAN HELMONT'S WORKS, AND CERTAIN SPECIALITIES IN HIS LIFE.

Voilà mon conte. — Je ne sçay s'il est vray; mais, je l'ay ainsi ouy conter. — Possible que cela est faux, possible que non. — Je m'en rapporte à ce qui en est. Il ne sera pas damné qui le croira, ou décroira. BRANTÔME.

"THE works of Van Helmont," Dr. Aikin says, "are now only consulted as curiosities: but with much error and jargon, they contain many shrewd remarks, and curious speculations."

How little would any reader suppose from this account of them, or indeed from anything which Dr. Aikin has said concerning this once celebrated person, that Van Helmont might as fitly be classed among enthusiasts as among physicians, and with philosophers as with either; and that, like most enthusiasts, it is sometimes not easy to determine whether he was deceived himself, or intended to deceive others.

He was born at Brussels in the year 1577, and of noble family. In his Treatise entitled *Tumulus Pestis* (to which strange title a stranger* explanation is annexed) he gives a sketch of his own history, saying, *imitemini, si quid forte boni in eâ occurrerit.* He was a devourer of books, and digested into common places for his own use whatever he thought most remarkable in them, so that few exceeded him in diligence, but most, he says, in judgment. At the age of seventeen he was appointed by the Professors Thomas Fyenus, Gerard de Velleers, and Stornius, to read surgical lectures in the Medical College at Louvain. *Eheu*, he exclaims, *præsumsi docere, quæ ipse nesciebam!* and his presumption was increased because the Professors of their own accord appointed him to this Lectureship, attended to hear him, and were the Censors of what he delivered. The writers from whom he compiled his discourses were Holerius, Tagaultius, Guido, Vigo, Ægineta, and "the whole tribe of Arabian authors." But then he began, and in good time, to marvel at his own temerity and inconsiderateness in thinking that by mere reading he could be qualified to teach what could be learned only by seeing, and by operating, and by long practice, and by careful observation: and this distrust in himself was increased, when he discovered that the

---

* Lector, titulus quem legis, terror lugubris, foribus affixus,
intus mortem, mortis genus, et hominum
nunciat flagrum. Sta, et inquire, quid hoc?
Mirare. Quid sibi vult
Tumuli Epigraphe Pestis?
Sub anatome abii, non obii; quamdiu malesuada invidia
Momi, et hominum ignara cupido,
me fovebunt.
Ergo heic
Non funus, non cadaver, non mors, non sceleton,
non luctus, non contagium.
ÆTERNO DA GLORIAM
Quod Pestis jam desiit, sub Anatomes proprio supplicio.

Professors could give him no further light than books had done. However, at the age of twenty-two he was created Doctor of Medicine in the same University.

Very soon he began to repent that he, who was by birth noble, should have been the first of his family to choose the medical profession, and this against the will of his mother, and without the knowledge of his other relations. "I lamented," he says, "with tears the sin of my disobedience, and regretted the time and labour which had been thus vainly expended: and often with a sorrowful heart I intreated the Lord that he would be pleased to lead me to a vocation not of my own choice, but in which I might best perform his will; and I made a vow that to whatever way of life he might call me I would follow it, and do my utmost endeavour therein to serve him. Then, as if I had tasted of the forbidden fruit, I discovered my own nakedness. I saw that there was neither truth nor knowledge in my putative learning; and thought it cruel to derive money from the sufferings of others; and unfitting that an art, founded upon charity, and conferred upon the condition of exercising compassion, should be converted into a means of lucre."

These reflections were promoted if not induced by his having caught a disorder which, as it is not mentionable in polite circles, may be described by intimating that the symptom from which it derives its name is alleviated by what Johnson defines tearing or rubbing with the nails. It was communicated to him by a young lady's glove, into which, in an evil minute of sportive gallantry, he had insinuated his hand. The physicians treated him, *secundum artem*, in entire ignorance of the disease; they bled him to cool the liver, and they purged him to carry off the torrid choler and the salt phlegm; they repeated this clearance again and again, till from a hale strong and active man they had reduced him to extreme leanness and debility without in the slightest degree abating the cutaneous disease. He then persuaded himself that the humours which the Galenists were so triumphantly expelling from his poor carcase had not pre-existed there in that state, but were produced by the action of their drugs. Some one cured him easily by brimstone, and this is said to have made him feelingly perceive the inefficiency of the scholastic practice which he had hitherto pursued.

In this state of mind he made over his inheritance to a widowed sister, who stood in need of it, gave up his profession, and left his own country with an intention of never returning to it. The world was all before him, and he began his travels with as little fore-knowledge whither he was going, and as little fore-thought of what he should do, as Adam himself when the gate of Paradise was closed upon him; but he went with the hope that God would direct his course by His good pleasure to some good end. It so happened that he who had renounced the profession of medicine, as founded on delusion and imposture, was thrown into the way of practising it, by falling in company with a man who had no learning, but who understood the practical part of chemistry, or pyrotechny, as he calls it. The new world which Columbus discovered did not open a wider or more alluring field to ambition and rapacity than this science presented to Van Helmont's enthusiastic and inquiring mind. "Then," says he, "when by means of fire I beheld the *penetrale*, the inward or secret part of certain bodies, I comprehended the separations of many, which were not then taught in books, and some of which are still unknown." He pursued his experiments with increasing ardour, and in the course of two years acquired such reputation by the cures which he performed, that because of his reputation he was sent for by the Elector of Cologne. Then indeed he became more ashamed of his late and learned ignorance, and renouncing all books because they sung only the same cuckoo note, perceived that he profited more by fire, and by conceptions acquired in praying. "And then," says he, "I clearly knew that I had missed the entrance of true philosophy. On all sides obstacles and obscurities and difficulties appeared, which neither labour, nor time, nor vigils, nor expenditure of money could overcome and disperse, but only the mere goodness of God. Neither women nor social meetings deprived me then of even a single hour, but continual labour and watching were the thieves of my time; for I willingly cured the poor and those of mean estate, being more moved by human compassion, and a moral love of giving, than by pure universal charity reflected in the Fountain of Life."

INTERCHAPTER XX.

ST. PANTALEON OF NICOMEDIA IN BITHYNIA — HIS HISTORY, AND SOME FURTHER PARTICULARS NOT TO BE FOUND ELSEWHERE.

Non dicea le cose senza il quia ;
Che il dritto distingueva dal mancino,
E dicea pane al pane, e vino al vino.

BERTOLDO.

THIS Interchapter is dedicated to St. Pantaleon, of Nicomedia in Bithynia, student in medicine and practitioner in miracles, whose martyrdom is commemorated by the Church of Rome on the 27th of July.

SANCTE PANTALEON, ORA PRO NOBIS!

This I say to be on the safe side; though between ourselves, reader, Nicephorus, and Usuardus, and Vincentius, and St. Antoninus (notwithstanding his sanctity) have written so many lies concerning him, that it is very doubtful whether there ever was such a person, and still more doubtful whether there be such a Saint. However the body which is venerated under his name is just as venerable as if it had really belonged to him, and works miracles as well.

It is a tradition in Corsica that when St. Pantaleon was beheaded the executioner's sword was converted into a wax taper, and the weapons of all his attendants into snuffers, and that the head rose from the block and sung. In honour of this miracle the Corsicans, as late as the year 1775, used to have their swords consecrated, or charmed,—by laying them on the altar while a mass was performed to St. Pantaleon.

But what have I, who am writing in January instead of July, and who am no papist, and who have the happiness of living in a protestant country, and was baptized moreover by a right old English name,—what have I to do with St. Pantaleon? Simply this, —my new pantaloons are just come home, and that they derive their name from the aforesaid Saint is as certain,—as that it was high time I should have a new pair.

St. Pantaleon, though the tutelary Saint of Oporto, (which city boasteth of his relics,) was in more especial fashion at Venice: and so many of the grave Venetians were in consequence named after him, that the other Italians called them generally Pantaloni in derision,—as an Irishman is called Pat, and as Sawney is with us synonymous with Scotchman, or Taffy for a son of Cadwallader and votary of St. David and his leek. Now the Venetians wore long small clothes; these as being the national dress were called Pantaloni also; and when the trunk-hose of Elizabeth's days went out of fashion, we received them from France, with the name of pantaloons.

Pantaloons then, as of Venetian and Magnifico parentage, and under the patronage of an eminent Saint, are doubtless an honourable garb. They are also of honourable extraction, being clearly of the Braccæ family. For it is this part of our dress by which we are more particularly distinguished from the Oriental and inferior nations, and also from the abominable Romans, whom our ancestors, Heaven be praised! subdued. Under the miserable reign of Honorius and Arcadius, these Lords of the World thought proper to expel the Braccarii, or breeches-makers, from their capitals, and to prohibit the use of this garment, thinking it a thing unworthy that the Romans should wear the habit of Barbarians:—and truly it was not fit that so effeminate a race should wear the breeches.

The Pantaloons are of this good Gothic family. The fashion having been disused for more than a century was re-introduced some five and twenty years ago, and still prevails so much—that I who like to go with the stream, and am therefore content to have fashions thrust upon me, have just received a new pair from London.

The coming of a box from the Great City is an event which is always looked to by the juveniles of this family with some degree of impatience. In the present case there was especial cause for such joyful expectation; for the package was to contain no less a treasure than the story of the Lioness and the Exeter Mail, with appropriate engravings representing the whole of that remarkable history, and those engravings emblazoned in appropriate colours. This adventure had excited an extraordinary degree of interest among us, when it was related in the newspapers: and no sooner had a book upon the subject been advertised, than the young ones, one and all, were in an uproar, and tumultuously petitioned that I would send for it,—to which, thinking the prayer of the petitioners reasonable, I graciously assented. And moreover there was expected, among other things *ejusdem generis*, one of those very few perquisites which the all-annihilating hand of Modern Reform has not retrenched in our public offices,—an Almanac or Pocket-Book for the year, curiously bound and gilt, three only being made up in this magnificent manner for three magnificent personages, from one of whom this was a present to my lawful Governess. Poor Mr. Bankes! the very hairs of his wig will stand erect,

Like quills upon the fretful porcupine,

when he reads of this flagrant misapplication of public money; and Mr. Whitbread would have founded a motion upon it, had he survived the battle of Waterloo.

There are few things in which so many vexatious delays are continually occurring, and so many rascally frauds are systematically practised, as in the carriage of parcels. It is indeed much to be wished that Government could take into its hands the conveyance of goods as well as letters; for in this country whatever is done by Government is done punctually and honourably;—what corruption there is lies among the people themselves, among whom honesty is certainly less general than it was half a century ago. Three or four days elapsed, on each of which the box ought to have arrived. "Will it come to-day, Papa?" was the morning question: "why does not it come?" was the complaint at noon; and "when will it come?" was the query at night. But in childhood the delay of hope is only the prolongation of enjoyment; and through life indeed, hope, if it be of the right kind, is the best food of happiness. "The House of Hope," says Hafiz, "is built upon a weak foundation." If it be so, I say, the fault is in the builder: Build it upon a Rock, and it will stand.

Expectata dies,—long looked for, at length it came. The box was brought into the parlour, the ripping-chisel was produced, the nails were easily forced, the cover was lifted, and the paper which lay beneath it was removed. "There's the pantaloons!" was the first exclamation. The clothes being taken out, there appeared below a paper parcel, secured with a string. As I never encourage any undue impatience, the string was deliberately and carefully untied. Behold, the splendid Pocket-Book, and the history of the Lioness and the Exeter Mail,—had been forgotten!

O St. Peter! St. Peter!

"Pray, Sir," says the Reader, "as I perceive you are a person who have a reason for everything you say, may I ask wherefore you call upon St. Peter on this occasion?"

You may, Sir.

A reason there is, and a valid one. But what that reason is, I shall leave the commentators to discover; observing only, for the sake of lessening their difficulty, that the Peter upon whom I have called is not St. Peter of Verona, he having been an Inquisitor, one of the Devil's Saints, and therefore in no condition at this time to help anybody who invokes him.

"Well, Papa, you must write about them, and they must come in the next parcel," said the children. Job never behaved better, who was a scriptural Epictetus: nor Epictetus, who was a heathen Job.

I kissed the little philosophers; and gave

them the Bellman's verses, which happened to come in the box, with horrific cuts of the Marriage at Cana, the Ascension, and other portions of gospel history, and the Bellman himself; — so it was not altogether a blank. We agreed that the disappointment should be an adjourned pleasure, and then I turned to inspect the pantaloons.

I cannot approve the colour. It hath too much of the purple; not that imperial die by which ranks were discriminated at Constantinople, nor the more sober tint which Episcopacy affecteth. Nor is it the bloom of the plum; — still less can it be said to resemble the purple light of love. No! it is rather a hue brushed from the raven's wing, a black purple; not Night and Aurora meeting, which would make the darkness blush; but Erebus and Ultramarine.

Doubtless it hath been selected for me because of its alamodality, — a good and pregnant word, on the fitness of which some German, whose name appears to be erroneously as well as uncouthly written Geamoenus, is said to have composed a dissertation. Be pleased, Mr. Todd, to insert it in the interleaved copy of your dictionary!

Thankful I am that they are not like Jean de Bart's full-dress breeches; for when that famous sailor went to court he is said to have worn breeches of cloth of gold, most uncomfortably as well as splendidly lined with cloth of silver.

He would never have worn them, had he read Lampridius, and seen the opinion of the Emperor Alexander Severus, as by that historian recorded: *in lineâ autem aurum mitti etiam dementiam judicabat, cum asperitati adderetur rigor*.

The word breeches has, I am well aware, been deemed ineffable, and therefore not to be written — because not to be read. But I am encouraged to use it by the high and mighty authority of the Anti-Jacobin Review. Mr. Stephens having in his Memoirs of Horne Tooke used the word small-clothes is thus reprehended for it by the indignant Censor.

"His *breeches* he calls *small-clothes*; — the first time we have seen this bastard term, the offspring of gross ideas and disgusting affectation in print, in anything like a book. It is scandalous to see men of education thus employing the most vulgar language, and corrupting their native tongue by the introduction of illegitimate words. But this is the age of affectation. Even our fishwomen and milkmaids affect to blush at the only word which can express this part of a man's dress, and lisp *small-clothes* with as many airs as a would-be woman of fashion is accustomed to display. That this folly is indebted for its birth to grossness of imagination in those who evince it, will not admit of a doubt. From the same source arises the ridiculous and too frequent use of a French word for a part of female dress; as if the mere change of language could operate a change either in the thing expressed, or in the idea annexed to the expression! Surely, surely, English women, who are justly celebrated for good sense and decorous manners, should rise superior to such pitiful, such paltry, such low-minded affectation."

Here I must observe that one of these redoubtable critics is thought to have a partiality for breeches of the Dutch make. It is said also that he likes to cut them out for himself, and to have pockets of capacious size, wide and deep; and a large fob, and a large allowance of lining.

The Critic who so very much dislikes the word small-clothes, and argues so vehemently in behalf of breeches, uses no doubt that edition of the scriptures that is known by the name of the Breeches Bible.*

I ought to be grateful to the Anti-Jacobin Review. It assists in teaching me my duty to my neighbour, and enabling me to live in charity with all men. For I might perhaps think that nothing could be so wrong-headed as Leigh Hunt, so wrong-hearted as Cob-

* The Bible here alluded to was the Genevan one, by Rowland Hall, A. D. 1560. It was for many years the most popular one in England, and the notes were great favourites with the religious public, insomuch so that they were attached to a copy of King James' Translation as late as 1715. From the peculiar rendering of Genesis, iii. 7., the Editions of this translation have been commonly known by the name of "Breeches Bibles." — See Cotton's Various Editions of the Bible, p. 14., and Ames and Herbert, Ed. Dibdin, vol. iv. p. 410.

bett, so foolish as one, so blackguard as the other, so impudently conceited as both, — if it were not for the Anti-Jacobin. I might believe that nothing could be so bad as the coarse, bloody and brutal spirit of the vulgar Jacobin, — if it were not for the Anti-Jacobin.

Blessings on the man for his love of pure English! It is to be expected that he will make great progress in it, through his familiarity with fishwomen and milkmaids; for it implies no common degree of familiarity with those interesting classes to talk to them about breeches, and discover that they prefer to call them small-clothes.

But wherefore did he not instruct us by which monosyllable he would express the female garment, "which is indeed the sister to a shirt," — as an old poet says, and which he hath left unnamed, — for there are two by which it is denominated. Such a discussion would be worthy both of his good sense and his decorous style.

For my part, instead of expelling the word *chemise* from use I would have it fairly naturalised.

Many plans have been proposed for reducing our orthography to some regular system, and improving our language in various ways. Mr. Elphinstone, Mr. Pinkerton, and Mr. Spence, the founder of the Spencean Philanthropists, have distinguished themselves in these useful and patriotic projects, and Mr. Pytches is at present in like manner laudably employed,— though that gentleman contents himself with reforming what these bolder spirits would revolutionise. I also would fain contribute to so desirable an end.

We agree that in spelling words it is proper to discard all reference to their etymology. The political reformer would confine the attention of the Government exclusively to what are called truly British objects; and the philological reformers in like manner are desirous of establishing a truly British language.

Upon this principle, I would anglicise the orthography of *chemise;* and by improving upon the hint which the word would then offer in its English appearance, we might introduce into our language a distinction of genders — in which it has hitherto been defective. For example,

Hemise and Shemise.

Here, without the use of an article or any change of termination, we have the needful distinction made more perspicuously than by ὁ and ἡ, *hic* and *hæc*, *le* and *la*, or other articles serving for no other purpose.

Again. In letter-writing, every person knows that male and female letters have a distinct sexual character; they should therefore be generally distinguished thus,

Hepistle and Shepistle.

And as there is the same marked difference in the writing of the two sexes I would propose

Penmanship and Penwomanship.

Erroneous opinions in religion being promulgated in this country by women as well as men, the teachers of such false doctrines may be divided into

Heresiarchs and Sheresiarchs,

so that we should speak of

the Heresy of the Quakers,
the Sheresy of Joanna Southcote's people.

The troublesome affection of the diaphragm, which every person has experienced, is, upon the same principle, to be called according to the sex of the patient

Hecups or Shecups,

which, upon the principle of making our language truly British, is better than the more classical form of

Hiccups and Hæccups.

In its objective use the word becomes

Hiscups or Hercups;

and in like manner Histerics should be altered into Herterics, the complaint never being masculine.

So also instead of making such words as agreeable, comfortable, &c. adjectives of one termination, I would propose,

Masculine agreeabeau,	Feminine agreeabelle
comfortabeau	comfortabelle
miserabeau	miserabelle,
	&c. &c.

These things are suggested as hints to Mr. Pytches, to be by him perpended in his improvement of our Dictionary. I beg leave also to point out for his critical notice the remarkable difference in the meaning of the word misfortune, as applied to man, woman, or child: a peculiarity for which perhaps no parallel is to be found in any other language.

But to return from these philological speculations to the Anti-Jacobin by whom we have been led to them, how is it that this critic, great master as he is of the vulgar tongue, should affirm that breeches is the only word by which this part of a man's dress can be expressed? Had he forgotten that there was such a word as galligaskins? — to say nothing of inexpressibles and dontmention 'ems. Why also did he forget pantaloons? — and thus the Chapter like a rondeau comes round to St. Pantaleon with whom it began,

SANCTE PANTALEON, ORA PRO NOBIS!

"HERE is another Chapter without a heading," — the Compositor would have said, when he came to this part of the Manuscript, if he had not seen at a glance, that in my great consideration I had said it for him.

Yes, Mr. Compositor! Because of the matter whereon it has to treat, we must, if you please, entitle this an

ARCH-CHAPTER.

A Frenchman once, who was not ashamed of appearing ignorant on such a subject, asked another who with some reputation for classical attainments had not the same rare virtue, what was the difference between Dryads and Hamadryads; and the man of erudition gravely replied that it was much the same as that between Bishops and Archbishops.

I have dignified this Arch-Chapter in its designation, because it relates to the King.

Dr. Gooch, you are hereby requested to order this book for his Majesty's library,

C'est une rare pièce, et digne sur ma foi,
*Qu'on en fasse présent au cabinet d'un roi.**

Dr. Gooch, I have a great respect for you. At the time when there was an intention of bringing a bill into Parliament for emancipating the Plague from the Quarantine Laws, and allowing to the people of Great Britain their long withheld right of having this disease as freely as the small pox, measles and any other infectious malady, you wrote a paper, and published it in the Quarterly Review, against that insane intention; proving its insanity so fully by matter of fact, and so conclusively by force of reasoning, that your arguments carried conviction with them, and put an end, for the time, to that part of the emancipating and free trade system.

Dr. Gooch, you have also written a volume of medical treatises of which I cannot speak more highly than by saying, sure I am that if the excellent subject of these my reminiscences were living, he would, for his admiration of those treatises have solicited the pleasure and honour of your acquaintance.

Dr. Gooch, comply with this humble request of a sincere, though unknown admirer, for the sake of your departed brother-in-physic, who, like yourself, brought to the study of the healing art a fertile mind, a searching intellect, and a benevolent heart. More, Dr. G., I might say, and more I would say, but —

Should I say more, you well might censure me
(What yet I never was) a flatterer.†

When the King (God bless his Majesty!) shall peruse this book, and be well-pleased therewith, if it should enter into his royal mind to call for his Librarian, and ask of him what honour and dignity hath been done to the author of it, for having delighted the heart of the King, and of so many of his

---

* MOLIERE.

† BEAUMONT AND FLETCHER.

liege subjects, and you shall have replied unto his Majesty, "there is nothing done for him;" then Dr. Gooch when the King shall take it into consideration how to testify his satisfaction with the book and to manifest his bounty toward the author, you are requested to bear in mind my thoughts upon this weighty matter, of which I shall now proceed to put you in possession.

Should he generously think of conferring upon me the honour of knighthood, or a baronetcy, or a peerage, (Lord Doncaster the title,) or a step in the peerage, according to my station in life, of which you, Dr. Gooch, can give him no information; or should he meditate the institution of an Order of Merit for men of letters, with an intention of nominating me among the original members, worthy as such intentions would be of his royal goodness, I should nevertheless, for reasons which it is not necessary to explain, deem it prudent to decline any of these honours.

Far be it from me, Dr. Gooch, to wish that the royal apparel should be brought which the King useth to wear, and the horse that the King rideth upon, and the crown royal which is set upon his head; and that this apparel and horse should be delivered to the hand of one of the King's most noble princes, that he might array me withal; and bring me on horseback through the streets of London, and proclaim before me, thus shall it be done to the man whom the King delighteth to honour! Such an exhibition would neither accord with this age, nor with the manners of this nation, nor with my humility.

As little should I desire that his Majesty should give orders for me to be clothed in purple, to drink in gold and to sleep upon gold, and to ride in a chariot with bridles of gold, and to have an head-tire of fine linen, and a chain about my neck, and to eat next the King, because of my wisdom, and to be called the King's cousin. For purple garments, Dr. Gooch, are not among the *propria quæ maribus* in England at this time; it is better to drink in glass than in gold, and to sleep upon a feather bed than upon a golden one; the only head-tire which I wear is my night-cap. I care not therefore for the fineness of its materials; and I dislike for myself chains of any kind.

That his Majesty should think of sending for me to sit next him because of my wisdom, is what he in his wisdom will not do; and what, if he were to do, would not be agreeable to me, in mine. But should the King desire to have me called his Cousin, accompanying that of course with such an appanage as would be seemly for its support, and should he notify that most gracious intention to you his Librarian, and give order that it should be by you inserted in the Gazette, — to the end that the secret which assuredly no sagacity can divine, and no indiscretion will betray, should incontinently thereupon be communicated through you to the royal ear; and that in future editions of this work the name of the thus honoured author should appear with the illustrious designation, in golden letters, of "by special command of his Majesty,

Cousin to the King."

A gracious mandate of this nature, Dr. Gooch, would require a severe sacrifice from my loyal and dutiful obedience. Not that the respectful deference which is due to the royal and noble house of Gloucester should withhold me from accepting the proffered honour; to that house it could be nothing derogatory; the value of their consanguinity would rather be the more manifest, when the designation alone, unaccompanied with rank, was thus rendered by special command purely and singularly honourable. Still less should I be influenced by any apprehension of being confounded in cousinship with Olive, calling herself Princess of Cumberland. Nevertheless let me say, Dr. Gooch, while I am free to say it, — while I am treating of it paulo-post-futuratively, as of a possible case, not as a question brought before me for my prompt and irrevocable answer, — let me humbly say that I prefer the incognito even to this title. It is not necessary, and would not be proper to enter into my reasons for that preference: suffice it that it is my humour (speaking be it observed respectfully, and using that word in its critical and finer sense,) that it is the idiosyncrasy of my disposition, the familiar way in which it pleases me innocently to exercise my privilege of free will. It is not a secret which every body knows, which nobody could help knowing and which was the more notoriously known, because of its presumed secresy. Incognito I am and wish to be, and incognoscible it is in my power to remain:

> He deserves small trust,
> Who is not privy councillor to himself;

but my secret, (being my own,) is like my life (if that were needed) at the King's service, and at his alone;

> Τοῖς κυρίοις γὰρ πάντα χρὴ δηλοῦν λόγον.*

Be pleased therefore, Dr. Gooch, if his Majesty most graciously and most considerately should ask, what may be done for the man (—meaning me,—) whom the King delighteth to honour; — be pleased, good Dr. Gooch, to represent that the allowance which is usually granted to a retired Envoy, would content his wishes, make his fortunes easy, and gladden his heart; — (Dr. Gooch you will forgive the liberty thus taken with you!) — that "where the word of a King is, there is power," — that an ostensible reason for granting it may easily be found, a sealed communication from the unknown being made through your hands; — that many Envoys have not deserved it better, and many secret services which have been as largely rewarded have not afforded to the King so much satisfaction; — finally, that this instance of royal bounty will not have the effect of directing public suspicion toward the object of that bounty, nor be likely to be barked at by Joseph Hume, Colonel Davies, and Daniel Whittle Harvey!

* SOPHOCLES.

CHAPTER CLXXXVIII.

FOLLY IN PRINT, REFERRED TO, BUT (N.B.) NOT EXEMPLIFIED. THE FAIR MAID OF DONCASTER. DOUBTS CONCERNING THE AUTHENTICITY OF HER STORY. THEVENARD, AND LOVE ON A NEW FOOTING. STARS AND GARTERS. A MONITORY ANECDOTE FOR OUR SEX, AND A WHOLESOME NOVELTY IN DRESS RECOMMENDED TO BOTH.

> They be at hand, Sir, with stick and fiddle,
> They can play a new dance, Sir, called hey, diddle, diddle.
>
> KING CAMBYSES.

YOU have in the earlier chapters of this Opus, gentle Reader, heard much of the musical history of Doncaster; not indeed as it would have been related by that thoroughly good, fine-ear'd, kind-hearted, openhanded, happiest of musicians and men, Dr. Burney the first; and yet I hope thou mayest have found something in this relation which has been to thy pleasure in reading, and which, if it should be little to thy profit in remembrance, will be nothing to thy hurt. From music to dancing is an easy transition; but do not be afraid that I shall take thee to a Ball, — for I would rather go to the Treading Mill myself.

What I have to say of Doncaster dancing relates to times long before those to which my reminiscences belong.

In a collection of Poems entitled "Folly in Print" — (which title might be sufficiently appropriate for many such collections) — or a book of Rhymes, printed in 1667, there is a Ballad called the Northern Lass, or the Fair Maid of Doncaster. Neither book or ballad has ever fallen in my way, nor has that comedy of Richard Broome's, which from its name Oldys supposed to have been founded upon the same story. I learn, however, in a recent and voluminous account of the English Stage from the Revolution, (by a gentleman profoundly learned in the most worthless of all literature, and for whom that literature seems to have been quite good enough,) that Broome's play has no connection with the ballad, or with Doncaster. But the note in which Oldys mentions it has made me acquainted with this Fair Maid's propensity for dancing, and with the consequences that it brought upon her. Her name was Betty Maddox; a modern ballad writer would call her Elizabeth, if he adopted the style of the Elizabethan age; or Eliza, if his taste inclined to the refinements of modern euphony. When an hundred horsemen wooed her, says Oldys, she conditioned that she would marry the one of them who could dance her down;

> You shall decide your quarrel by a dance,*

but she wearied them all; and they left her a maid for her pains.

> *Legiadria suos fervebat tanta per artus,*
> *Ut quæcunque potest fieri saltatio per nos*
> *Humanos, agili motu fiebat ab illâ.*†

At that dancing match they must have footed it till, as is said in an old Comedy, a good country lass's capermonger might have been able to copy the figure of the dance from the impressions on the pavement.

For my own part I do not believe it to be a true story; they who please may. Was there one of the horsemen but would have said on such occasion, with the dancing Peruvians in one of Davenant's operatic dramas,

> Still round and round and round,
> Let us compass the ground.
> What man is he who feels
> Any weight at his heels,
> Since our hearts are so light, that, all weigh'd together,
> Agree to a grain, and they weigh not a feather.

I disbelieve it altogether, and not for its want of verisimilitude alone, but because when I was young there was no tradition of any such thing in the town where the venue of the action is laid; and therefore I conjecture that it is altogether a fictitious story, and may peradventure have been composed as a lesson for some young spinster whose indefatigable feet made her the terror of all partners.

The Welsh have a saying that if a woman were as quick with her feet as her tongue, she would catch lightning enough to kindle the fire in the morning; it is a fanciful saying, as many of the Welsh sayings are. But if Miss Maddox had been as quick with her tongue as her feet, instead of dancing an hundred horsemen down, she might have talked their hundred horses to death.

Why it was a greater feat than that of Kempe the actor, who in the age of odd performance danced from London to Norwich. He was nine days in dancing the journey, and published an account of it under the title of his "Nine Days Wonder."‡ It could have been no "light fantastic toe" that went through such work; but one fit for the roughest game at football. At sight of the awful foot to which it belonged, Cupid would have fled with as much reason as the Dragon of Wantley had for turning tail when Moor of Moor Hall with his spiked shoe-armour pursued him. He would have fled before marriage, for fear of being kicked out of the house after it. They must have been feet that instead of gliding and swimming and treading the grass so trim, went, as the old Comedy says, lumperdee, clumperdee.§

The Northern Lass was in this respect no Cinderella. Nor would any one, short of an Irish Giant, have fallen in love with her slipper, as Thevenard the singer did with that which he saw by accident at a shoemaker's, and inquiring for what enchanting person it was made, and judging of this earthly Venus as the proportions of Hercules have been estimated *ex pede*, sought her out, for love of her foot, commenced his addresses to her, and obtained her hand in marriage.

The story of Thevenard is true; at least it has been related and received as such; this of the Fair Maid of Doncaster is not even *ben trovato*. Who indeed shall persuade me, or who indeed will be persuaded, that if she had wished to drop the title of spinster, and take her matrimonial degree, she would not have found some good excuse for putting an end to the dance when she had found a partner to her liking? A little of that wit which seldom fails a woman when it is

* Dryden.

† Macaronica.

‡ Webster's Westward Ho. Act. v. Sc. i. — Anno 1600. — *R. S.* Since this note was written by the lamented author, the Dancing Journey has been republished by Mr. Dyce.

§ Ralph Roister Doister.

needed, would have taught her how to do this with a grace, and make it appear that she was still an invincible dancer, though the Stars had decreed that in this instance she should lose the honour of the dance. Some accident might have been feigned like those by which the ancient epic poets and their imitators contrive in their Games to disappoint those who are on the point of gaining the prize which is contended for.

If the Stars had favoured her, they might have predestined her to meet with such an accident as befel a young lady in the age of minuets. She was led out in a large assembly by her partner, the object of all eyes; and when the music began and the dance should have began also, and he was in motion, she found herself unable to move from the spot, she remained motionless for a few seconds, her colour changed from rose to ruby, presently she seemed about to faint, fell into the arms of those who ran to support her, and was carried out of the room. The fit may have been real, for though nothing ailed her, yet what had happened was enough to make any young woman faint in such a place. It was something far more embarrassing than the mishap against which Soame Jenyns cautions the ladies when he says,

> No waving lappets should the dancing fair,
> Nor ruffles edged with dangling fringes wear;
> Oft will the cobweb ornaments catch hold
> On the approaching button, rough with gold;
> Nor force nor art can then the bonds divide,
> When once the entangled Gordian knot is tied.
> So the unhappy pair, by Hymen's power
> Together joined in some ill-fated hour,
> The more they strive their freedom to regain,
> The faster binds the indissoluble chain.

It was worse than this in the position in which she had placed herself according to rule; for beginning the minuet, she was fastened not by a spell, not by the influence of her malignant Stars, but by the hooks and eyes of her garters. The Countess of Salisbury's misfortune was as much less embarrassing as it was more celebrated.

No such misfortunes could have happened to that Countess who has been rendered illustrious thereby, nor to the once fair danceress, who would have dreaded nothing more than that her ridiculous distress should become publicly known, if they had worn *genouillères*, that is to say, knee-pieces. A necessary part of a suit of armour was distinguished by this name in the days of chivalry; and the article of dress which corresponds to it may be called kneelets, if for a new article we strike a new word in that mint of analogy, from which whatever is lawfully coined comes forth as the King's English. Dress and cookery are both great means of civilisation; indeed they are among the greatest; both in their abuse are made subservient to luxury and extravagance, and so become productive of great evils, moral and physical; and with regard to both the physician may sometimes interfere with effect, when the moralist would fail. In diet the physician has more frequently to oppose the inclinations of his patient, than to gratify them; and it is not often that his advice in matters of dress meets with willing ears, although in these things the maxim will generally hold good, that whatever is wholesome is comfortable, and that whatever causes discomfort or uneasiness is more or less injurious to health. But he may recommend kneelets without having any objection raised on the score of fashion, or of vanity; and old and young may be thankful for the recommendation. Mr. Ready-to-halt would have found that they supported his weak joints, and rendered him less liable to rheumatic attacks; and his daughter Much-afraid, if she had worn them when she "footed it handsomely," might have danced without any fear of such accidents as happened to the Countess of old, or the heroine of the minuet in later times.

Begin therefore forthwith, dear Lady-readers, to knit *genouillères* for yourselves, and for those whom you love. You will like them better, I know, by their French name, though English comes best from English lips; but so you knit and wear them, call them what you will.

CHAPTER CLXXXIX.

THE DOCTOR'S OPINION OF LATE HOURS. DANCING. FANATICAL OBJECTION OF THE ALBIGENSES; INJURIOUS EFFECT OF THAT OPINION WHEN TRANSMITTED TO THE FRENCH PROTESTANTS. SIR JOHN DAVIES AND BURTON QUOTED TO SHOW THAT IT CAN BE NO DISPARAGEMENT TO SAY THAT ALL THE WORLD'S A STAGE, WHEN ALL THE SKY'S A BALL-ROOM.

I could be pleased with any one
Who entertained my sight with such gay shows,
As men and women moving here and there,
That coursing one another in their steps
Have made their feet a tune. DRYDEN.

THE Doctor was no dancer. He had no inclination for this pastime even in what the song calls "our dancing days," partly because his activity lay more in his head than in his heels, and partly perhaps from an apprehension of awkwardness, the consequence of his rustic breeding. In middle and later life he had strong professional objections, not to the act of dancing, but to the crowded and heated rooms wherein it was carried on, and to the late hours to which it was continued. In such rooms and at such assemblies, the Devil, as an old dramatist says, "takes delight to hang at a woman's girdle, like a rusty watch, that she cannot discern how the time passes."* Bishop Hall, in our friend's opinion, spake wisely when, drawing an ideal picture of the Christian, he said of him, "in a due season he betakes himself to his rest. He presumes not to alter the ordinance of day and night; nor dares confound, where distinctions are made by his Maker."

Concerning late hours indeed he was much of the same opinion as the man in the old play, who thought that "if any thing was to be damned, it would be Twelve o'clock at night."

These should be hours for necessities,
Not for delights; times to repair our nature
With comforting repose, and not for us
To waste these times.†

He used to say that whenever he heard of a ball carried on far into the night, or more properly speaking, far into the morning, it reminded him, with too much reason, of the Dance of Death.

Rise with the lark, and with the lark to bed:
The breath of night's destructive to the hue
Of ev'ry flow'r that blows. Go to the field,
And ask the humble daisy why it sleeps
Soon as the sun departs? Why close the eyes
Of blossoms infinite, long ere the moon
Her oriental veil puts off? Think why,
Nor let the sweetest blossom Nature boasts
Be thus exposed to night's unkindly damp.
Well may it droop, and all its freshness lose,
Compell'd to taste the rank and pois'nous steam
Of midnight theatre, and morning ball.
Give to repose the solemn hour she claims,
And from the forehead of the morning steal
The sweet occasion. O there is a charm
Which morning has, that gives the brow of age
A smack of earth, and makes the lip of youth
Shed perfume exquisite. Expect it not,
Ye who till noon upon a down-bed lie,
Indulging feverous sleep.‡

The reader need not be told that his objections were not puritanical, but physical. The moralist who cautioned his friend to refrain from dancing, because it was owing to a dance that John the Baptist lost his head, talked, he said, like a fool. Nor would he have formed a much more favourable opinion of the Missionary in South Africa, who told the Hottentots that dancing is a work of darkness, and that a fiddle is Satan's own instrument. At such an assertion he would have exclaimed — a fiddlestick! § — Why and how that word has become an interjection of contempt, I must leave those to explain who can. The Albigenses and the Vaudois are said to have believed that a dance is the Devil's procession, in which they who dance break the promise and vow which their sponsors made for them at their baptism, that they should renounce the Devil and all his works, the pomps and vanities of this wicked world,—(not to proceed further,) — this being one of his works, and undeniably one of the aforesaid vanities and

* WEBSTER.

† SHAKESPEARE.

‡ HURDIS' VILLAGE CURATE.

§ The explanation following is given in Grose's Classical Dictionary of the Vulgar Tongue. FIDDLESTICK'S END. Nothing: the ends of the ancient fiddlesticks ending in a point: hence metaphorically used to express a thing terminating in nothing.

pomps. They break, moreover, all the ten commandments, according to these fanatics; for fanatics they must be deemed who said this; and the manner in which they attempted to prove the assertion, by exemplifying it through the decalogue, shows that the fermentation of their minds was in the acetous stage.

Unfortunately for France, this opinion descended to the Huguenots; and the progress of the Reformation in that country was not so much promoted by Marot's psalms, as it was obstructed by this prejudice, — a prejudice directly opposed to the temperament and habits of a mercurial people. "Dancing," says Peter Heylyn, "is a sport to which they are so generally affected, that were it not so much enveighed against by their straight-laced Ministers, it is thought that many more of the French Catholicks had been of the Reformed Religion. For so extremely are they bent upon this disport, that neither Age nor Sickness, no nor poverty itself, can make them keep their heels still, when they hear the Music. Such as can hardly walk abroad without their Crutches, or go as if they were troubled all day with a Sciatica, and perchance have their rags hang so loose about them, that one would think a swift Galliard might shake them into their nakedness, will to the Dancing Green howsoever, and be there as eager at the sport, as if they had left their several infirmities and wants behind them. What makes their Ministers (and indeed all that follow the Genevian Discipline) enveigh so bitterly against Dancing, and punish it with such severity when they find it used? I am not able to determine, nor doth it any way belong unto this discourse. But being, as it is, a Recreation which this people are so given unto, and such a one as cannot be followed but in a great deal of company, and before many witnesses and spectators of their carriage in it; I must needs think the Ministers of the French Church more nice than wise, if they choose rather to deter men from their Congregations, by so strict a Stoicism, than indulge anything unto the jollity and natural gaiety of this people, in matters not offensive, but by accident only." *

Sweet recreation barr'd, what doth ensue,
But moody and dull melancholy,
Kinsman to grim and comfortless despair;
And at their heels, a huge infectious troop
Of pale distemperatures and foes to life.†

It is a good-natured Roman Catholic who says, "that the obliging vices of some people are better than the sour and austere virtues of others." The fallacy is more in his language than in his morality; for virtue is never sour, and in proportion as it is austere we may be sure that it is adulterated. Before a certain monk of St. Gal, Iso by name, was born, his mother dreamed that she was delivered of a hedgehog; her dream was fulfilled in the character which he lived to obtain of being bristled with virtues like one. Methinks no one would like to come in contact with a person of this description. Yet among the qualities which pass with a part of the world for virtues, there are some of a soft and greasy kind, from which I should shrink with the same instinctive dislike. I remember to have met somewhere with this eulogium passed upon one dissenting minister by another, that he was a lump of piety! I prefer the hedgehog.

A dance, according to that teacher of the Albigenses whose diatribe has been preserved, is the service of the Devil, and the fiddler, whom Ben Jonson calls Tom Tickle-foot, is the Devil's minister. If he had known what Plato had said he would have referred to it in confirmation of this opinion; for Plato says that the Gods, compassionating the laborious life to which mankind were doomed, sent Apollo, Bacchus and the Muses to teach them to sing, to drink, and to dance. And the old Puritan would, to his own entire satisfaction, have identified Apollo with Apollyon.

"But shall we make the welkin dance indeed?" ‡

* The Rector of a Parish once complained to Fenelon of the practice of the villagers in dancing on Sunday evenings. "My good friend," replied the prelate, "you and I should not dance; but allowance must be made to the poor people, who have only one day in the week to forget their misfortunes."

† Shakespeare.

‡ Ibid.

Sir John Davies, who holds an honourable and permanent station among English statesmen and poets, deduces Dancing, in a youthful poem of extraordinary merit, from the Creation, saying that it

then began to be
When the first seeds whereof the world did spring,
The fire, air, earth, and water did agree,
By Love's persuasion, Nature's mighty king,
To leave their first disordered combating;
And in a dance such measure to observe,
As all the world their motion should preserve.

He says that it with the world

in point of time begun:
Yea Time itself, (whose birth Jove never knew,
And which indeed is elder than the Sun,)
Had not one moment of his age outrun,
When out leapt Dancing from the heap of things,
And lightly rode upon his nimble wings.

For that brave Sun, the father of the day,
Doth love this Earth, the mother of the Night,
And like a reveller in rich array,
Doth dance his galliard in his leman's sight.

* * * *

Who doth not see the measures of the Moon,
Which thirteen times she danceth every year?
And ends her pavin thirteen times as soon
As doth her brother, of whose golden hair
She borroweth part, and proudly doth it wear;
Then doth she coyly turn her face aside,
That half her cheek is scarce sometimes descried.

And lo! the Sea that fleets about the land,
And like a girdle clips her solid waist,
Music and measure both doth understand:
For his great crystal eye is always cast
Up to the Moon, and on her fixed fast;
And as she danceth in her pallid sphere,
So danceth he about the centre here.

This is lofty poetry, and one cannot but regret that the poet should have put it in the mouth of so unworthy a person as one of Penelope's suitors, though the best of them has been chosen. The moral application which he makes to matrimony conveys a wholesome lesson:

If they whom sacred love hath link'd in one,
Do, as they dance, in all their course of life;
Never shall burning grief, nor bitter moan,
Nor factious difference, nor unkind strife,
Arise betwixt the husband and the wife;
For whether forth, or back, or round he go,
As the man doth, so must the woman do.

What if, by often interchange of place
Sometimes the woman gets the upper hand?
That is but done for more delightful grace;
For on that part she doth not ever stand;
But as the measure's law doth her command,
She wheels about, and ere the dance doth end,
Into her former place she doth transcend.*

This poem of Sir John Davies could not have been unknown to Burton, for Burton read everything; but it must have escaped his memory; otherwise he who delighted in quotations and quoted so well, would have introduced some of his stanzas, when he himself was treating of the same subject, and illustrated it with some of the same similitudes. "The Sun and Moon, some say," (says he,) "dance about the earth; the three upper planets about the Sun as their centre, now stationary, now direct, now retrograde, now *in apogæo*, then *in perigæo*, now swift, then slow; occidental, oriental, they turn round, jump and trace ♀ and ☿ about the Sun, with those thirty-three *Maculæ* or Burbonian planets, *circa Solem saltantes cytharedum*, saith Fromundus. Four Medicean stars dance about Jupiter, two Austrian about Saturn, &c., and all belike to the music of the spheres."

Sir Thomas Browne had probably this passage in his mind, when he said "acquaint thyself with the *choragium* of the stars."

"The whole matter of the Universe and all the parts thereof," says Henry More, "are ever upon motion, and in such a dance as whose traces backwards and forwards take a vast compass; and what seems to have made the longest stand, must again move, according to the modulations and accents of that Music, that is indeed out of the hearing of the acutest ears, but yet perceptible by the purest minds, and the sharpest wits. The truth whereof none would dare to oppose, if the breath of the gainsayer could but tell its own story, and declare through how many Stars and Vortices it has been strained, before the particles thereof met, to be abused to the framing of so rash a contradiction."

---

* It is remarkable that Sir John Davies should have written this Poem, which he entitled the Orchestra, and that very remarkable and beautiful one on the Immortality of the Soul.

CHAPTER CXC.

DANCING PROSCRIBED BY THE METHODISTS. ADAM CLARKE. BURCHELL'S REMARKS ON THE UNIVERSALITY OF THIS PRACTICE. HOW IT IS REGARDED IN THE COLUMBIAN PHILOSOPHY.

Non vi par adunque che habbiamo ragionato a bastanza di questo? A bastanza parmi, rispose il Signor Gasparo; pur desidero io d' intendere qualche particolarità anchor.

IL CORTEGIANO.

THE Methodist Preachers in the first Conference (that is Convocation or Yearly Meeting) after Mr. Wesley's death, passed a law for the public over which their authority extends, or, in their own language, made a rule, that "schoolmasters and schoolmistresses who received dancing-masters into their schools, and parents also who employed dancing-masters for their children, should be no longer members of the Methodist Society." Many arguments were urged against this rule, and therefore it was defended in the Magazine, which is the authorised organ of the Conference, by the most learned and the most judicious of their members, Adam Clarke. There was, however, a sad want of judgment in some of the arguments which he employed. He quoted the injunction of St. Paul, "whatsoever ye do in word or deed, do all in the name of the Lord Jesus, giving thanks to God and the Father by him," and he applied the text thus. Can any person, can any Christian *dance* in the name of the Lord Jesus? Or, through him, give thanks to God the Father for such an employment?

Another text also appeared to him decisive against dancing and its inseparable concomitants; "woe unto them who chaunt unto the sound of the viol, and invent unto themselves instruments of music, as did David." The original word, which we translate *chaunt*, signifies, according to him, *to quaver*, *to divide*, *to articulate*, and may, he says, as well be applied to the management of the feet, as to the modulations of the voice. This interpretation is supported by the Septuagint, and by the Arabic version; but suppose it be disputed, he says, "yet this much will not be denied, that the text is pointedly enough against that without which dancing cannot well be carried on, I mean, instrumental music." He might have read in Burton that "nothing was so familiar in France as for citizens' wives and maids to dance a round in the streets, and often too for want of better instruments to make good music of their own voices, and dance after it." Ben Jonson says truly "that measure is the soul of a dance, and Tune the tickle-foot thereof;" but in case of need the mouth can supply its own music.

It is true the Scripture says "there is a time to dance;" but this he explains as simply meaning "that human life is a variegated scene." Simple readers must they be who can simply understand it thus, to the exclusion of the literal sense. Adam Clarke has not remembered here that the Psalms enjoin us to praise the Lord with tabret and harp and lute, the strings and the pipe, and the trumpet and the loud cymbals, and to praise his name in the dance, and that David danced before the Ark. And though he might argue that Jewish observances are no longer binding, and that some things which were *permitted* under the Jewish dispensation are no longer lawful, he certainly would not have maintained that anything which was *enjoined* among its religious solemnities can now in itself be sinful.

I grant, he says, "that a number of motions and steps, circumscribed by a certain given space, and changed in certain quantities of time, may be destitute of physical and moral evil. But it is not against these things abstractedly that I speak. It is against their concomitant and consequent circumstances; the undue, the improper mixture of the sexes; the occasions and opportunities afforded of bringing forth those fruits of death which destroy their own souls, and bring the hoary heads of their too indulgent parents with sorrow to the grave.

So good a man as Adam Clarke is not to be suspected of acting like an Advocate here, and adducing arguments which he knew to be fallacious, in support of a cause not tenable by fair reasoning. And how so wise a man could have reasoned so weakly, is explained by a passage in his most interesting and most valuable autobiography. "*Malâ ave*, when about twelve or thirteen years of age, I learned to *dance*. I long resisted all solicitations to this employment; but at last I suffered myself to be overcome; and learnt, and profited beyond most of my fellows. I grew passionately fond of it, would scarcely walk but in *measured time*, and was continually *tripping*, moving, and *shuffling* in all times and places. I began now to value myself, which, as far as I can recollect, I had never thought of before. I grew impatient of control, was fond of company, wished to mingle more than I had ever done with young people. I got also a passion for *better clothing* than that which fell to my lot in life, was discontented when I found a neighbour's son *dressed better* than myself. I lost the spirit of *subordination*, and did not *love work*, imbibed a spirit of *idleness*, and, in short, drunk in all the brain-sickening effluvia of *pleasure*. Dancing and company took the place of *reading* and *study;* and the authority of my parents was feared indeed, but not respected; and few serious impressions could prevail in a mind imbued now with frivolity and the love of pleasure; yet I entered into no disreputable assembly, and in no one case ever kept any improper company. I formed no illegal connection, nor associated with any whose characters were either tarnished or suspicious. Nevertheless *dancing* was to me a *perverting influence*, an *unmixed moral evil;* for although, by the mercy of God, it led me not to depravity of manners, it greatly weakened the *moral principle*, drowned the voice of a well instructed conscience, and was the first cause of impelling me *to seek my happiness in this life*. Everything yielded to the disposition it had produced, and everything was absorbed by it. I have it justly in abhorrence for the moral injury it did me; and I can testify, (as far as my own observations have extended, and they have had a pretty wide range,) I have known it to produce the same evil in others that it produced in me. I consider it therefore as a branch of that *worldly education*, which leads from heaven to earth, from things spiritual to things sensual, and from God to Satan. Let them plead for it who will; I know it to be *evil*, and that *only*. They who bring up their children in this way, or send them to these schools where *dancing* is taught, are consecrating them to the service of Moloch, and cultivating the passions, so as to cause them to bring forth the weeds of a fallen nature, with an additional rankness, deep-rooted inveteracy, and inexhaustible fertility. *Nemo sobrius saltat*, 'no man in his senses will dance,' said Cicero, a heathen; shame on those Christians who advocate a cause by which many *sons* have become profligate, and many *daughters* have been ruined." Such was the experience of Adam Clarke in *dancing*, and such was his opinion of the practice.*

An opinion not less unfavourable is expressed in homely old verse by the translator of the Ship of Fools, Alexander Barclay.

Than it in the earth no game is more damnable;
 It seemeth no peace, but battle openly,
They that it use of minds seem unstable,
 As mad folk running with clamour, shout and cry
 What place is void of this furious folly?
None; so that I doubt within a while
These fools the holy Church shall defile.

Of people what sort or order may we find,
 Rich or poor, high or low of name,
But by their foolishness and wanton mind,
 Of each sort some are given unto the same.
 The priests and clerks to dance have no shame.
The friar or monk, in his frock and cowl,
Must dance in his dortour, leaping to play the fool.

To it comes children, maids, and wives,
 And flattering young men to see to have their prey;
The hand-in-hand great falsehood oft contrives.
 The old quean also this madness will assay;
 And the old dotard, though he scantly may
For age and lameness stir either foot or hand,
Yet playeth he the fool, with others in the band.

* It is old Fuller's observation, that "people over strait-laced in one part will hardly fail to grow awry in another." Over against the observations of Adam Clarke may be set the following, from the life of that excellent man — Sir William Jones. "Nor was he so indifferent to slighter accomplishments as not to avail himself of the instructions of a celebrated dancing-master at Aix-la-Chapelle. He had before taken lessons from Gallini in that trifling art.' — Carey's Lives of English Poets. Sir William Jones, p. 359.

Then leap they about as folk past their mind,
With madness amazed running in compace;
He most is commended that can most lewdness find,
Or can most quickly run about the place,
There are all manners used that lack grace,
Moving their bodies in signs full of shame,
Which doth their hearts to sin right sore inflame.

Do away your dances, ye people much unwise!
Desist your foolish pleasure of travayle!
It is methinks an unwise use and guise
To take such labour and pain without avayle.
And who that suspecteth his maid or wives tayle,
Let him not suffer them in the dance to be;
For in that game though size or cinque them fayle,
The dice oft runneth upon the chance of three.

The principle upon which such reasoning rests is one against which the Doctor expressed a strong opinion, whenever he heard it introduced. Nothing, he thought, could be more unreasonable than that the use of what is no ways hurtful or unlawful in itself, should be prohibited because it was liable to abuse. If that principle be once admitted, where is it to stop? There was a Persian tyrant, who having committed some horrible atrocity in one of his fits of drunkenness, ordered all the wine in his dominions to be spilt as soon as he became sober, and was conscious of what he had done; and in this he acted rightly, under a sense of duty as well as remorse; for it was enjoining obedience to a law of his religion, and enforcing it in a manner the most effectual. But a Christian government, which because drunkenness is a common sin shall prohibit all spirituous liquors, would by so doing subject the far greater and better part of the community to an unjust and hurtful privation; thus punishing the sober, the inoffensive, and the industrious, for the sake of the idle, the worthless, and the profligate.

Jones of Nayland regarded these things with no puritanical feeling. "In joy and thanksgiving," says that good and true minister of the Church of England, "the tongue is not content with speaking; it must evoke and utter a song, while the feet are also disposed to dance to the measures of music, as was the custom in sacred celebrities of old among the people of God, before the World and its vanities had engrossed to themselves all the expressions of mirth and festivity. They have now left nothing of that kind to religion, which must sit by in gloomy solemnity, and see the World with the Flesh and the Devil assume to themselves the sole power of distributing social happiness."

"Dancing," says Mr. Burchell, "appears to have been in all ages of the world, and perhaps in all nations, a custom so natural, so pleasing, and even useful, that we may readily conclude it will continue to exist as long as mankind shall continue to people the earth. We see it practised as much by the savage as by the civilised, as much by the lowest as by the highest classes of society; and as it is a recreation purely corporeal, and perfectly independent of mental qualification, or refinement, all are equally fitted for enjoying it: it is this probably which has occasioned it to become universal. All attempts therefore at rendering any exertion of the mind necessary to its performance, are an unnatural distortion of its proper and original features. Grace and ease of motion are the extent of its perfection; because these are the natural perfections of the human body. Every circumstance and object by which man is surrounded may be viewed in a philosophical light; and thus viewed, dancing appears to be a recreative mode of exercising the body and keeping it in health, the means of shaking off spleen, and of expanding one of the best characters of the heart, — the social feeling. When it does not affect this, the fault is not in the dance, but in the dancer; a perverse mind makes all things like itself. Dancing and music, which appear to be of equal antiquity, and equally general among mankind, are connected together only by a community of purpose: what one is for the body, the other is for the mind."

The Doctor had come to a conclusion not unlike this traveller's concerning dancing,— he believed it to be a manifestation of that instinct by which the young are excited to wholesome exercise, and by which in riper years harmless employment is afforded for superfluous strength and restless activity. The delight which girls as well as boys take in riotous sports were proof enough, he said, that Nature had not given so universal an inclination without some wise purpose. An infant of six months will ply its arms and legs in the cradle, with all its might and main, for joy, — this being the mode of dancing at that stage of life. Nay, he said, he could produce grave authorities on which casuists would pronounce that a probable belief might be sustained, to prove that it is an innate propensity, and of all propensities the one which has been developed in the earliest part of mortal existence; for it is recorded of certain Saints, that on certain holidays, dedicated either to the mystery, or to the heavenly patron under whose particular patronage they were placed, they danced before they were born, a sure token or presage of their future holiness and canonisation, and a not less certain proof that the love of dancing is an innate principle.

> Lovest thou Music?
> Oh, 'tis sweet!
> What's dancing?
> E'en the mirth of feet.*

CHAPTER CXCI.

A SERIOUS WORD IN SAD APOLOGY FOR ONE OF THE MANY FOOLISH WAYS IN WHICH TIME IS MIS-SPENT.

> Time, as he passes us, has a dove's wing,
> Unsoil'd, and swift, and of a silken sound;
> But the World's Time, is Time in masquerade!
> Their's, should I paint him, has his pinions fledged,
> With motley plumes; and where the peacock shews
> His azure eyes, is tinctured black and red
> With spots quadrangular of diamond form,
> Ensanguined hearts, clubs typical of strife,
> And spades, the emblem of untimely graves.
>
> COWPER.

HUNTING, gaming, and dancing are three propensities to which men are inclined equally in the savage and in the civilised, — in all stages of society from the rudest to the most refined, and in all its grades; the Doctor used to say they might be called semi-intellectual. The uses of hunting are obvious, wherever there are wild animals which may be killed for food, or beasts of prey which for our own security it is expedient to destroy.

Indeed because hunting, hawking, and fishing, (all which according to Gwillim and Plato are comprised in the term Venation,) tend to the providing of sustenance for man, Farnesius doth therefore account them all a species of agriculture. The great heraldic author approves of this comprehensive classification. But because the more heroic hunting, in which danger is incurred from the strength and ferocity of the animals pursued, hath a resemblance of military practice, he delivers his opinion that "this noble kind of venation is privileged from the title of an Illiberal Art, being a princely and generous exercise; and those only, who use it for a trade of life, to make sure thereof, are to be marshalled in the rank of mechanics and illiberal artizans." The Doctor admired the refinement of these authors; but he thought that neither lawful sporting nor poaching could conveniently be denominated agricultural pursuits.

He found it not so easy to connect the love of gaming with any beneficial effect; some kind of mental emotion however, he argued, was required for rendering life bearable by creatures with whom sleep is not so completely an act of volition, that like dogs they can lie down and fall asleep when they like. For those persons, therefore, who are disposed either by education, capacity, or inclination to make any worthier exertion of their intellectual faculties, gaming, though infinitely dangerous as a passion, may be useful as a pastime. It has indeed a strong tendency to assume a dangerous type, and to induce as furious an excitement as drunkenness in its most ferocious form; but among the great card-playing public of all nations, long experience has produced an effect in mitigating it, analogous to what the practice of inoculation has effected upon the small-pox. Vaccination would have afforded our philosopher a better illustration, if it had been brought into notice during his life.

Pope has assigned to those women who neither toil or spin, "an old age of cards,"

* From a Masque quoted by D'ISRAELI.

after "a youth of pleasure." This, perhaps, is not now so generally the course of female life, in a certain class and under certain circumstances, as it was in his days and in the Doctor's. The Doctor certainly was of opinion that if the senescent spinsters and dowagers within the circle of his little world had not their cards as duly as their food, many of them would have taken to something worse in their stead. They would have sought for the excitement which they now found at the whist or quadrille table from the bottle, or at the Methodist Meeting. In some way or other, spiritual or spirituous, they must have had it *; and the more scandalous of these ways was not always that which would occasion the greatest domestic discomfort, or lead to the most injurious consequences. Others would have applied to him for relief from maladies which, by whatever names they might be called, were neither more nor less than the effect of that *tædium vitæ* which besets those who having no necessary employment have not devised any for themselves. And when he regarded the question in this light he almost doubted whether the invention of cards had not been more beneficial than injurious to mankind.

It was not with an unkind or uncharitable feeling, still less with a contemptuous one, that Anne Seward mentioning the death of a lady "long invalid and far advanced in life," described her as "a civil social being, whose care was never to offend; who had the spirit of a gentlewoman in never doing a mean thing, whose mite was never withheld from the poor; and whose inferiority of understanding and knowledge found sanctuary at the card-table, that universal leveller of intellectual distinctions." Let not such persons be despised in the pride of intellect! Let them not be condemned in the pride of self-righteousness!

"Our law," says the Puritan Matthew Mead, "supposes all to be of some calling, not only men but women, and the young ladies too; and therefore it calls them during their virgin state spinsters. But alas, the viciousness and degeneracy of this age hath forfeited the title. Many can *card*, but few can spin; and therefore you may write them *carders*, *dancers*, *painters*, *ranters*, *spenders*, rather than spinsters. Industry is worn out by pride and delicacy; the comb and the looking-glass possess the place and the hours of the spindle and the distaff; and their great business is to curl the locks, instead of twisting wool and flax. So that both males and females are prepared for all ill impressions by the mischief of an idle education."

"There is something strange in it," says Sterne, "that life should appear so short *in the gross*, and yet so long *in the detail.* Misery may make it so, you'll say; — but we will exclude it, — and still you'll find, though we all complain of the shortness of life, what numbers there are who seem quite overstocked with the days and hours of it, and are constantly sending out into the highways and streets of the city, to compel guests to come in, and take it off their hands: to do this with ingenuity and forecast, is not one of the least arts and business of life itself; and they who cannot succeed in it, carry as many marks of distress about them, as bankruptcy itself could wear. Be as careless as we may, we shall not always have the power, — nor shall we always be in a temper to let the account run thus. When the blood is cooled, and the spirits which have hurried us on through half our days before we have numbered one of them, are beginning to retire; — then wisdom will press a moment to be heard, — afflictions, or a bed of sickness will find their hours of persuasion: — and should they fail, there is something yet behind: — old age will overtake us at the last, and with its trembling hand, hold up the glass to us."

---

* It happened during one of the lamented Southey's visits here at the Vicarage, West-Tarring, that a cargo of spirits was run close by. His remark was — "Better spirituous smuggling than spiritual pride."

CHAPTER CXCII.

MORE OF THE DOCTOR'S PHILOSOPHY, WHICH WILL AND WILL NOT BE LIKED BY THE LADIES, AND SOME OF THE AUTHOR'S WHICH WILL AND WILL NOT BY THE GENTLEMEN. THE READER IS INTRODUCED TO COUNT CASTIGLIONE, AND TO SIR JOHN CHEKE.

Ou tend l'auteur à cette heure?
Que fait-il? Revient-il? Va-t-il? Ou s'il demeure?
L'AUTEUR.
Non, je ne reviens pas, car je n'ai pas été;
Je ne vais pas aussi, car je suis arrêté;
Et ne demeure point, car, tout de ce pas même
Je pretens m'en aller. MOLIERE.

THE passage with which the preceding Chapter is concluded, is extracted from Sterne's Sermons, one of those discourses in which he tried the experiment of adapting the style of Tristram Shandy to the pulpit; — an experiment which proved as unsuccessful as it deserved to be. Gray, however, thought these sermons were in the style which in his opinion was most proper for the pulpit, and that they showed "a very strong imagination and a sensible head. But you see him," he adds, "often tottering on the verge of laughter, and ready to throw his perriwig in the face of his audience."

The extract which has been set before the reader is one of those passages which bear out Gray's judgment; it is of a good kind, and in its kind so good, that I would not weaken its effect, by inserting too near it the following Epigram from an old Magazine, addressed to a lady passionately fond of cards.

Thou, whom at length incessant gaming dubs,
Thrice honourable title! Queen of Clubs,
Say what vast joys each winning card imparts,
And that, too justly, called the King of Hearts.
Say, when you mourn of cash and jewels spoil'd,
May not the thief be Knave of Diamonds stil'd?
One friend, howe'er, when deep remorse invades,
Awaits thee, Lady; 'tis the Ace of Spades!

It has been seen that the Doctor looked upon the love of gaming as a propensity given us to counteract that indolence which, if not thus amused, would breed for itself both real and imaginary evils. And dancing he thought was just as useful in counteracting the factitious inactivity of women in their youth, as cards are for occupying the vacuity of their minds at a later period. Of the three semi-intellectual propensities, as he called them, which men are born with, those for hunting and gaming are useful only in proportion as the earth is uncultivated, and those by whom it is inhabited. In a well-ordered society there would be no gamblers, and the Nimrods of such a society must, like the heroes in Tongataboo, be contented with no higher sport than rat-catching: but dancing will still retain its uses. It will always be the most graceful exercise for children at an age when all that they do is graceful; and it will always be that exercise which can best be regulated for them, without danger of their exerting themselves too much, or continuing in it too long. And for young women in a certain rank, or rather region of life, — the temperate zone of society, — those who are above the necessity of labour, and below the station in which they have the command of carriages and horses, — that is for the great majority of the middle class, — it is the only exercise which can animate them to such animal exertion as may suffice

To give the blood its natural spring and play.*

Mr. Coleridge says (in his Table Talk) "that the fondness for dancing in English women is the reaction of their reserved manners: it is the only way in which they can throw themselves forth in natural liberty." But the women are not more fond of it in this country, than they are in France and Spain. There can be no healthier pastime for them, — (as certainly there is none so exhilarating, and exercise unless it be exhilarating is rarely healthful) — provided, — and upon this the Doctor always insisted, — provided it be neither carried on in hot rooms, nor prolonged to late hours. They order these things, he used to say, better in France; they order them better indeed anywhere than in England, and there was a time when they were ordered better among ourselves.

"The youth of this city," says the honest

* SOUTHEY.

old chronicler and historian of the metropolis his native place, "used on holidays, after evening prayers, to exercise their basters and bucklers, at their master's doors; and the maidens, one of them playing on a timbrel, to dance for garlands hanged athwart the streets, which open pastimes in my youth, being now suppressed, worser practises within doors are to be feared."

Every one who is conversant with the Middle Ages, and with the literature of the reigns of Elizabeth, James and Charles I. must have perceived in how much kindlier relations the different classes of society existed toward each other in those days than they have since done. The very word independence had hardly found a place in the English language, or was known only as denoting a mischievous heresy. It is indeed, as one of our most thoughtful contemporaries has well said, an "unscriptural word,"—and "when applied to man, it directly contradicts the first and supreme laws of our nature; the very essence of which is universal dependence upon God, and universal interdependence on one another."

The Great Rebellion dislocated the relations which had for some centuries thus happily subsisted; and the money-getting system which has long been the moving principle of British society, has, aided by other injurious influences, effectually prevented the recovery which time, and the sense of mutual interest, and mutual duty, might otherwise have brought about. It was one characteristic of those old times, which in this respect deserve to be called good, that the different classes participated in the enjoyments of each other. There were the religious spectacles, which, instead of being reformed and rendered eminently useful as they might have been, were destroyed by the brutal spirit of puritanism. There were the Church festivals, till that same odious spirit endeavoured to separate, and has gone far toward separating, all festivity from religion. There were tournaments and city pageants at which all ranks were brought together; they are now brought together only upon the race-course. Christmas Mummers have long ceased to be heard of. The Morris dancers have all but disappeared even in the remotest parts of the kingdom. I know not whether a Maypole is now to be seen. What between manufactures and methodism England is no longer the merry England which it was once a happiness and an honour to call our country. Akenside's words "To the Country Gentlemen of England," may be well remembered.

And yet full oft your anxious tongues complain
That lawless tumult prompts the rustic throng;
That the rude Village-inmates now disdain
Those homely ties which rul'd their fathers long.
Alas! your fathers did by other arts
Draw those kind ties around their simple hearts,
And led in other paths their ductile will;
By succour, faithful counsel, courteous cheer,
Won them their ancient manners to revere,
To prize their country's peace and heaven's due rites fulfil.

My friend saw enough of this change in its progress to excite in him many melancholy forebodings in the latter part of his life. He knew how much local attachment was strengthened by the recollection of youthful sports and old customs; and he well understood how little men can be expected to love their country, who have no particular affection for any part of it. Holidays he knew attached people to the Church, which enjoined their observance; but he very much doubted whether Sunday Schools would have the same effect.

In Beaumont and Fletcher's Play of the Prophetess, the countrymen discourse concerning the abdicated Emperor who has come to reside among them. One says to the other,

Do you think this great man will continue here?

The answer is

Continue here? what else? he has bought the great farm;
A great man * with a great inheritance
And all the ground about it, all the woods too,
And stock'd it like an Emperor. Now all our sports again
And all our merry gambols, our May Ladies,
Our evening dances on the green, our songs,
Our holiday good cheer; our bagpipes now, boys,
Shall make the wanton lasses skip again,
Our sheep-shearings and all our knacks.

* Southey has inserted a query here. "Qy Manor or Mansion." It is usually printed as in the text.—See Act v. Sc. iii.

It is said, however, in the *Cortegiano*; — *Che non saria conveniente che un gentilhuomo andasse ad honorare con la persona sua una festa di contado, dove i spettatori, et i compagni fussero gente ignobile.* What follows is curious to the history of manners. *Disse allhor' il S. Gasparo Pallavicino, nel paese nostro di Lombardia non s' hanno queste rispetti: anzi molti gentil' huomini giovani trovansi, che le feste ballano tuttol' di nel Sole co i villani, et con esti giocano a lanciar la barra, lottare, correre et saltare; et io non credo che sia male, perche ivi non si fa paragone della nobiltà, ma della forza, e destrezza, nelle quai cose spesso gli huomini di villa non vaglion meno che i nobili; et par che que quella domestichezza habbia in se una certa liberalità amabile.*— An objection is made to this; *Quel ballar nel Sole, rispose M. Federico, a me non piace per modo alcuno; ne so che guadagno vi si trovi. Ma chi vuol pur lottar, correr et saltar co i villani, dee (al parer mio) farlo in modo di provarsi, et (come si suol dir) per gentilezza, non per contender con loro, et dee l' huomo esser quasi sicuro di vincere; altramente non vi si metta; perche sta troppo male, et troppo è brutta cosa, et fuor de la dignità vedere un gentilhuomo vinto da un villano, et massimamente alla lotta; però credo io che sia ben astenersi almano in presentia di molti, perche il guadagno nel vincere è pochissimo, et la perdita nell' esse vinto è grandissima.*

That is, in the old version of Master Thomas Hoby; — "It were not meet that a gentleman should be present in person, and a doer in such a matter in the country, where the lookers-on and the doers were of a base sort. Then said the Lord Gasper Pallavicino, in our country of Lombardy these matters are not passed upon; for you shall see there young gentlemen, upon the holydays, come dance all the day long in the sun with them of the country, and pass the time with them in casting the bar, in wrestling, running and leaping. And I believe it is not ill done; for no comparison is there made of nobleness of birth, but of force and sleight; in which things many times the men of the country are not a whit inferior to gentlemen: and it seemeth this familiar conversation containeth in it a certain lovely freeness." "The dancing in the sun," answered Sir Frederick, "can I in no case away withal; and I cannot see what a man shall gain by it. But whoso will wrestle, run and leap with men of the country, ought, in my judgment, to do it after a sort; to prove himself, and (as they are wont to say) for courtesy, not to try mastery with them. And a man ought (in a manner) to be assured to get the upper hand, else let him not meddle withal; for it is too ill a sight, and too foul a matter, and without estimation, to see a gentleman overcome by a carter, and especially in wrestling. Therefore I believe it is well done to abstain from it, at the leastwise in the presence of many; if he be overcome, his gain is small, and his loss in being overcome very great."

This translation is remarkable for having a Sonnet, or more correctly speaking a quatorzain by Sackville prefixed to it, and at the end of the volume a letter of Sir John Cheke's to the translator, curious for its peculiar spelling, and for the opinion expressed in it that our language ought as much as possible to be kept pure and unmixed.

"I have taken sum pain," he says, "at your request, cheflie in your preface; not in the reading of it, for that was pleasaunt unto me, boath for the roundnes of your saienges and welspeakinges of the saam, but in changing certein wordes which might verie wel be let aloan, but that I am verie curious in mi freendes matters, not to determijn, but to debaat what is best. Whearin I seek not the bestnes haplie bi truth, but bi mijn own phansie and sheo of goodnes.

"I am of this opinion that our own tung shold be written cleane and pure, unmixt and unmangeled with borowing of other tunges; wherein if we take not heed bi tijm, ever borowing and never payeng, she shall be fain to keep her house as bankrupt. For then doth our tung naturallie and praiseablie utter her meaning, when she boroweth no conterfectness of other tunges to attire her self withall, but useth plainlie her own with such shift as nature, craft, experiens, and folowing of other excellent doth lead her unto; and if she went at ani tijm (as being unperfight she must) yet let her borow with suche bashfulnes, that it mai appear, that if either the mould of our own tung could serve us to fascion a woord of our own, or if the old denisoned wordes could content and ease this neede, we wold not boldly venture of unknoven wordes. This I say, not for reproof of you, who have scarslie and necessarily used, whear occasion serveth, a strange word so, as it seemeth to grow out of the matter and not to be sought for; but for mijn our defens, who might be counted overstraight a deemer of thinges, if I gave not thys accompt to you, my freend and wijs, of mi marring this your handiwork.

"But I am called awai. I prai you pardon mi shortnes; the rest of my saienges should be but praise and exhortacion in this your doinges, which at moar leisor I shold do better.

From my house in Wood street
the 16 of July 1557.

Yours assured
JOAN CHEEK."

Sir John Cheke died about two months after the date of this letter: and Hoby's translation was not published till 1561, because "there were certain places in it, which of late years being misliked of some that had the perusing of it, the Author thought it much better to keep it in darkness a while, then to put it in light, unperfect, and in piecemeal, to serve the time." The book itself had been put in the list of prohibited works, and it was not till 1576 that the Conte Camillo Castiglione, the author's son, obtained permission to amend the obnoxious passages and publish an expurgated edition.

It would have vexed Sir John if he had seen with how little care the printer, and his loving friend Master Hoby observed his system of orthography, in this letter. For he never used the final e unless when it is sounded, which he denoted then by doubling it; he rejected the y, wrote u when it was long, with a long stroke over it, doubled the other vowels when they were long, and threw out all letters that were not pronounced. No better system of the kind has been proposed, and many worse. Little good would have been done by its adoption, and much evil, if the translators of the Bible had been required to proceed upon his principle of using no words but such as were true English of Saxon original. His dislike of the translation for corrupting as he thought the language into vocables of foreign growth, made him begin to translate the New Testament in his own way. The Manuscript in his own hand, as far as it had proceeded, is still preserved at Bene't College*, and it shows that he found it impracticable to observe his own rule. But though as a precisian he would have cramped and impoverished the language, he has been praised for introducing a short and expressive style, avoiding long and intricate periods, and for bringing "fair and graceful writing into vogue." He wrote an excellent hand himself, and it is said that all the best scholars in those times followed his example, "so that fair writing and good learning seemed to commence together."

O Soul of Sir John Cheke, thou wouldst have led me out of my way, if that had been possible,—if my ubiety did not so nearly resemble ubiquity, that in Anywhereness and Everywhereness I know where I am, and can never be lost till I get out of Whereness itself into Nowhere.

---

* This has been since printed with a good Glossary by the Rev. James Goodwin, Fellow and Tutor of Corpus Christi Coll. Cambridge, and is very curious. All that remains is the Gospel according to St. Matthew, and part of the first chapter of the Gospel according to St. Mark. As an instance of Cheke's Englishisms I may refer to the rendering of προσήλυτον in c. xxiii. v. 15. by *freschman*. Some little of the MS. is lost. — See Preface, p. 10.

CHAPTER CXCIII.

MASTER THOMAS MACE, AND THE TWO HISTORIANS OF HIS SCIENCE, SIR JOHN HAWKINS AND DR. BURNEY. SOME ACCOUNT OF THE OLD LUTANIST AND OF HIS "MUSIC'S MONUMENT."

> This Man of Music hath more in his head
> Than mere crotchets. SIR W. DAVENANT.

THOU wast informed, gentle Reader, in the third Volume, and at the two hundred and sixth* page of this much-hereafter-to-be-esteemed Opus, that a *Tattle de Moy* was a new-fashioned thing in the Year of our Lord 1676. This was on the authority of the good old Lutanist, whom, I then told you, I took leave of but for a while, bethinking me of Pope's well-known lines,

> But all our praises why should Lords engross?
> Rise, honest Muse! and sing the MAN OF ROSS.

And now, gentle reader, seeing that whether with a consciousness of second sight or not, Master Mace, praiseworthy as the Man of Ross, has so clearly typified my Preludes and Voluntaries, my grave Pavines and graver Galliards, my Corantoes and Serabands, my Chichonas, and above all my Tattle-de-Moys, am I not bound in gratitude to revive the memory of Master Mace; or rather to extend it and make him more fully and more generally known than he has been made by the two historians of his science Sir John Hawkins and Dr. Burney? It is to the honour of both these eminent men, who have rendered such good services to that science, and to the literature of their country, that they should have relished the peculiarities of this simple-hearted old lutanist. But it might have been expected from both; for Dr. Burney was as simple-hearted himself, and as earnestly devoted to the art: and Sir John, who delighted in Ignoramus and in Izaak Walton, could not fail to have a liking for Thomas Mace.

"Under whom he was educated," says Sir John, "or by what means he became possessed of so much skill in the science of music, as to be able to furnish out matter for a folio volume, he has nowhere informed us; nevertheless his book contains so many particulars respecting himself, and so many traits of an original and singular character, that a very good judgment may be formed both of his temper and ability. With regard to the first, he appears to have been an enthusiastic lover of his art; of a very devout and serious turn of mind; and cheerful and good-humoured under the infirmities of age, and the pressure of misfortunes. As to the latter his knowledge of music seems to have been confined to the practice of his own instrument; and so much of the principles of the science as enabled him to compose for it; but for his style in writing he certainly never had his fellow."

This is not strictly just as relating either to his proficiency in music, or his style as an author. Mace says of himself, "having said so much concerning the lute, as also taken so much pains in laying open all the hidden secrets thereof, it may be thought I am so great a lover of it, that I make light esteem of any other instrument besides; which truly I do not; but love the viol in a very high degree; yea close unto the lute; and have done much more, and made very many more good and able proficients upon it, than ever I have done upon the lute. And this I shall presume to say, that if I excel in either, it is most certainly upon the viol. And as to other instruments, I can as truly say, I value every one that is in use, according to its due place; as knowing and often saying, that all God's creatures are good; and all ingenuities done by man, are signs, tokens, and testimonies of the wisdom of God bestowed upon man."

So also though it is true that Thomas Mace stands distinguished among the writers on Music, yet it could be easy to find many fellows for him as far as regards peculiarity of style. A humourist who should collect odd books might form as numerous a library, as the man of fastidious taste who should confine his collection to such works only as in their respective languages were esteemed classical. "The singularity of his style,"

---

* P. 213. of this Edition.

says Sir John, "remarkable for a profusion of epithets and words of his own invention, and tautology without end, is apt to disgust such as attend less to the matter than manner of his book; but in others it has a different effect; as it exhibits, without the least reserve, all the particulars of the author's character, which was not less amiable than singular." — "The vein of humour that runs through it presents a lively portraiture of a good-natured, gossipping old man, virtuous and kind-hearted." — The anxious "precision with which he constantly delivers himself, is not more remarkable than his eager desire to communicate to others all the knowledge he was possessed of, even to the most hidden secrets." — "The book breathes throughout a spirit of devotion; and, agreeable to his sentiments of music is a kind of proof that his temper was improved by the exercise of his profession." — There is no pursuit by which, if it be harmless in itself, a man may not be improved in his moral as well as in his intellectual nature, provided it be followed for its own sake: but most assuredly there is none however intrinsically good, or beneficial to mankind, from which he can desire any moral improvement, if his motive be either worldly ambition, or the love of gain. — *Ἀδύνατον ἐκ φαύλης ἀφορμῆς ἐπὶ τὸ τέλος εὐδραμεῖν.**

To give an account of "Music's Monument," which Dr. Burney calls a matchless book, not to be forgotten among the curiosities of the seventeenth century! will be to give the character of Thomas Mace himself, for no author ever more compleatly embodied his own spirit in his writings.

It is introduced with an Epistle Dedicatory, which by an easy misrepresentation has been made to appear profane.

To Thee, One-Only-Oneness, I direct
My weak desires and works.
Thou only art The Able True Protector;
Oh be my shield, defender and director,
Then sure we shall be safe.
Thou know'st, O Searcher of all hearts how I,
With right, downright, sincere sincerity,
Have longed long to do some little good,
(According to the best I understood)
With thy rich talent, though by me made poor,
For which I grieve, and will do so no more,
By thy good Grace assisting, which I do
Most humbly beg for. Oh, adjoin it to
My longing ardent soul; and have respect
To this my weak endeavour, and accept,
In thy great mercy, both of it and me,
Even as we dedicate ourselves to Thee.

An Epistle, in verse, follows, "to all Divine Readers, especially those of the Dissenting Ministry, or Clergy, who want not only skill, but good will to this most excelling part of divine service, viz. singing of psalms, hymns and spiritual songs, to the praise of the Almighty, in the public Assemblies of his Saints: and yet more particularly, to all great and high Persons, Supervisors, Masters, or Governors of the Church, (if any such there should be,) wanting skill, or good will thereunto."

He says to those "high men of honoûr," that

Example is the thing;
There's but one way, which is yourselves to sing.
This sure will do it; for when the vulgar see
Such worthy presidents their leaders be,
Who exercise therein and lead the van,
They will be brought to't, do they what they can.
But otherwise for want of such example,
Tis meanly valued, and on it they trample;
And by that great defect, so long unsought,
Our best Church Music's well-nigh brought to nought.
Besides,
No robes adorn high persons like to it;
No ornaments for pure Divines more fit.

That Counsel given by the Apostle Paul
Does certainly extend to Christians all.
Colossians the third, the sixteenth verse;
(Turn to the place:) that text will thus rehearse,
Let the word of Christ dwell in you plenteously,
(What follows? Music in its excellency.)
Admonishing yourselves, in sweet accord,
In singing psalms with grace unto the Lord,
Sed sine arte, that cannot be done,
Et sine arte, better let alone.

Having thus "fronted this Book with the divine part, and preached his little short sermon" upon the last of St. Paul, he says that his first and chief design in writing this book was only to discover the occult mysteries of the noble lute, and to shew the great worthiness of that too much neglected and abused instrument, and his good will to all the true lovers of it, in making it plain and easy, giving the true reasons why it has been formerly a very hard instrument to play well upon, and also why now it is

* Iamblichus.

become so easy and familiarly pleasant. "And I believe," says he, "that whosoever will but trouble himself to read those reasons, — and join his own reason, with the reasonableness of those reasons, will not be able to find the least reason to contradict those reasons."

He professed that by his directions "any person, young or old, should be able to perform so much and so well upon it, in so much or so little time, towards a full and satisfactory delight and pleasure, (yea, if it were but only to play common toys, jigs or tunes,) as upon any instrument whatever; yet with this most notable and admirable exception, (for the respectable commendation of the lute,) that they may, besides such ordinary and common contentments, study and practice it all the days of their lives, and yet find new improvements, yea doubtless if they should live unto the age of Methusalem, ten times over; for there is no limitation to its vast bounds and bravery." It appears that the merit of this book in this respect is not overstated: one of his sons attained to great proficiency on this instrument by studying the book without any assistance from his father; and Sir John Hawkins affirms on his own knowledge that Mr. John Immyns, lutanist to the Chapel Royal, has the like experience of it. "This person who had practised on sundry instruments for many years, and was able to sing his part at sight, at the age of forty took to the lute, and by the help of Mace's book alone, became enabled to play thorough base, and also easy lessons on it; and by practice had rendered the tablature as familiar to him, as the notes of the scale."

The notation called the tablature is minutely explained in the work. It has not the least relation to the musical character; the six strings of the lute are represented by as many lines, "and the several frets or stops by the letters a, b, c, d, e, f, g, h, y, (a preference to i as being more conspicuous,) k; the letter *a* ever signifying the open string in all positions." Many persons have been good performers on the lute, and at the same time totally ignorant of the notes of the Gamut. His printer, he said, "had outdone all music work in this kind ever before printed in this nation; and was indeed the only fit person to do the like, he only having those new materials, the like to which was never had made before in England." They might have been more distinct, and more consistent; — five being common English characters, the *c* more resembling the third letter in the Greek alphabet than any thing else, the *b* reversed serving for *g*, and the *d* in like manner for *e*.

The characters for the time of notes he compares to money, as supposing that most people would be ready enough to count them the better for that. Considering therefore the semi-breve as a groat, the minim becomes two pence, the crotchet a penny, the quaver a half-penny, and the semi-quaver a farthing. "Trouble not yourself for the demi-quaver," he says, "till you have a quick hand, it being half a semi-quaver."

But besides these, there are marks in his notation for the fifteen graces which may be used upon the lute, though few or none used them all. They are the Shake, the Beat, the Back-fall, the Half-fall, the Whole-fall, the Elevation, the Single Relish, the Double Relish, the Slur, the Slide, the Spinger, the Sting, the Tutt, the Pause and the Soft and Loud Play, "which is as great and good a grace as any other whatever."

"Some," says Master Mace, "there are, and many I have met with, who have such a natural agility in their nerves, and aptitude to that performance, that before they could do any thing else to purpose, they would make a shake rarely well. And some again can scarcely ever gain a good shake, by reason of the unaptness of their nerves to that action, but yet otherwise come to play very well. I, for my own part, have had occasion to break both my arms; by reason of which, I cannot make the nerve-shake well, nor strong; yet by a certain motion of my arm, I have gained such a contentive shake, that sometimes my scholars will ask me, how they shall do to get the like. I have then no better answer for them, than to tell them, they must first break their arm, as I have done; and so possibly after that, by practice, they may get my manner of Shake."

Rules are given for all these graces, but observe, he says, "that whatever your grace be, you must in your farewell express the true note perfectly, or else your pretended grace, will prove a disgrace."

"The Spinger is a grace very neat and curious, for some sort of notes, and is done thus: After you have hit your note, you must just as you intend to part with it, dab one of your rest fingers lightly upon the same string, a fret or two frets below, (according to the air,) as if you did intend to stop the string, in that place, yet so gently, that you do not cause the string to sound, in that stop, so dab'd; but only so that it may suddenly take away that sound which you last struck, yet give some small tincture of a new note, but not distinctly to be heard as a note; which grace, if well done and properly, is very taking and pleasant."

The Sting is "another very neat and pretty grace," it makes the sound seem to swell with pretty unexpected humour, and gives much contentment upon cases.

The Tut is easily done, and always with the right hand. "When you would perform this grace, it is but to strike your letter which you intend shall be so graced, with one of your fingers, and immediately clap on your next striking finger upon the string which you struck; in which doing, you suddenly take away the sound of the letter; and if you do it clearly, it will seem to speak the word, *Tut*, so plainly, as if it were a living creature, speakable!"

While, however, the pupil was intent upon exhibiting these graces, the zealous master exhorted him not to be unmindful of his own, but to regard his postures, for a good posture is comely, creditable and praiseworthy, and moreover advantageous as to good performance. "Set yourself down against a table, in as becoming a posture, as you would choose to do for your best reputation. Sit upright and straight; then take up your lute, and lay the body of it in your lap across. Let the lower part of it lie upon your right thigh, the head erected against your left shoulder and ear; lay your left hand down upon the table, and your right arm over the lute, so that you may set your little finger down upon the belly of the lute, just under the bridge, against the treble, or second string: and then keep your lute stiff, and strongly set with its lower edge against the table-edge; and so, leaning your breast something hard against its ribs, cause it to stand steady and strong, so that a bystander cannot easily draw it from your breast, table, and arm. This is the most becoming, steady and beneficial posture."

"Your left hand thus upon the table, your lute firmly fixed, yourself and it in your true postures, — bring up your left hand from the table, bended, just like the balance of a hook, all excepting your thumb, which must stand straight and span'd out; your fingers also, all divided out from the other in an equal and handsome order; and in this posture, place your thumb under the neck of the lute, a little above the fret, just in the midst of the breadth of the neck; all your four-fingers in this posture, being held close over the strings on the other side, so that each finger may be in a readiness to stop down upon any fret. And now in this lively and exact posture, I would have your posture drawn, which is the most becoming posture I can direct unto for a lutanist."

"Know that an old lute is better than a new one." Old instruments indeed are found by experience to be far the best, the reasons for which Master Mace could no further dive into than to say, he apprehended, "that by extreme age, the wood and those other adjuncts, glue, parchment, paper, linings of cloth, (as some used,) but above all the varnish, are by time very much dried, limped, made gentle, rarified, or to say better, even airified; so that that stiffness, stubbornness, or *clunguiness* which is natural to such bodies, are so debilitated and made pliable, that the pores of the wood have a more free liberty to move, stir or secretly vibrate; by which means the air, (which is the life of all things both animate and inanimate,) has a more free and easy recourse to pass and repass, &c. Whether I have hit upon the right cause I know not, but sure I am that age adds goodness to instruments."

The Venice lutes were commonly good; and the most esteemed maker was Laux Malles, whose name was always written in text letters. Mace had seen two of his lutes, "pitiful, old, battered, cracked things;" yet for one of these, which Mr. Gootiere the famous lutanist in his time showed him, the King paid an hundred pounds. The other belonged to Mr. Edward Jones, one of Gootiere's scholars; and he relates this "true story" of it; that a merchant bargained with the owner to take it with him in his travels, on trial; if he liked it, he was on his return to give an hundred pounds for it; otherwise he was to return it safe, and pay twenty pounds "for his experience and use of it."—He had often seen lutes of three or four pounds a-piece "more illustrious and taking to a common eye."

The best shape was the Pearl mould, both for sound and comeliness, and convenience in holding. The best wood for the ribs was what he calls air-wood, this was absolutely the best; English maple next. There were very good ones, however, of plum, pear, yew, rosemary-air, and ash. Ebony and ivory, though most costly and taking to a common eye, were the worst. For the belly the finest grained wood was required, free from knots or obstructions; cypress was very good, but the best was called Cullen's-cliff, being no other than the finest sort of fir, and the choicest part of that fir. To try whether the bars within, to strengthen and keep it straight and tight, were all fast, you were gently to knock the belly all along, round about, and then in the midst, with one of your knuckles; "if any thing be either loose in it, or about it, you may easily perceive it, by a little fuzzing or hizzing; but if all be sound, you shall hear nothing but a tight plump and twanking knock."

Among the aspersions against the lute which Master Mace indignantly repelled, one was that it cost as much in keeping as a horse. "I do confess," said he, "that those who will be prodigal and extraordinary curious, may spend as much as may maintain two or three horses, and men to ride upon them too if they please. But he never charged more than ten shillings for first stringing one, and five shillings a quarter for maintaining it with strings."

The strings were of three sorts, minikins, Venice Catlins, and Lyons, for the basses; but the very best for the basses were called Pistoy Basses; these, which were smooth and well-twisted strings, but hard to come by, he supposes to be none others than thick Venice Catlins, and commonly dyed of a deep dark red. The red strings, however, were commonly rotten, so were the yellow; the green sometimes very good; the clear blue the best. But good strings might be spoilt in a quarter of an hour, if they were exposed to any wet, or moist air. Therefore they were to be bound close together, and wrapt closely up either in an oiled paper, a bladder, or a piece of sere cloth, "such as often comes over with them," and then to be kept in some close box, or cupboard, but not amongst linen, (for that gives moisture,) and in a room where is usually a fire. And when at any time you open them for your use, take heed they lie not too long open, nor in a dark window, nor moist place; for moisture is the worst enemy to your strings.

"How to choose and find a true string, which is the most curious piece of skill in stringing, is both a pretty curiosity to do, and also necessary. First, draw out a length, or more; then take the end, and measure the length it must be of, within an inch or two, (for it will stretch so much at least in the winding up,) and hold that length in both hands, extended to reasonable stiffness: then, with one of your fingers strike it; giving it so much liberty in slackness as you may see it vibrate, or open itself. If it be true, it will appear to the eye just as if they were two strings; but if it shows more than two, it is false, and will sound unpleasantly upon your instrument, nor will it ever be well in tune, either stopt or open, but snarl." Sir John Hawkins observes that this direction is given by Adrian Le Roy in his instructions for the lute, and is adopted both by Mersennus and Kircher. Indeed this experiment is the only known test of a true string, and for that reason is practised by such as are curious at this day.

In his directions for playing, Master Mace says, "take notice that you strike not your strings with your nails, as some do, who maintain it the best way of play; but I do not; and for this reason; because the nail cannot draw so sweet a sound from the lute as the nibble end of the flesh can do. I confess in a concert it might do well enough, where the mellowness, (which is the most excellent satisfaction from a lute,) is lost in the crowd; but alone, I could never receive so good content from the nail as from the flesh."

Mace considered it to be absolutely necessary that all persons who kept lutes should know how to repair them; for he had known a lute "sent fifty or sixty miles to be mended of a very small mischance, (scarce worth twelve pence for the mending,) which besides the trouble and cost of carriage, had been broken all to pieces in the return, and so farewell lute and all the cost." One of the necessary tools for this work is "a little working knife, such as are most commonly made of pieces of broken good blades, fastened into a pretty thick haft of wood or bone, leaving the blade out about two or three inches;" "grind it down upon the back," he says, "to a sharp point, and set to a good edge; it will serve you for many good uses, either in cutting, carving, making pins, &c."

His directions for this work are exceedingly minute; but when the lute was in order, it was of no slight importance to keep it so, and for this also he offers some choice observations. "You shall do well, ever when you lay it by in the day-time, to put it into a bed that is constantly used, between the rug and blanket, but never between the sheets, because they may be moist." "This is the most absolute and best place to keep it in always." There are many great commodities in so doing; it will save your strings from breaking, it will keep your lute in good order, so that you shall have but small trouble in tuning it; it will sound more brisk and lively, and give you pleasure in the very handling of it; if you have any occasion extraordinary to set up your lute at a higher pitch, you may do it safely, which otherwise you cannot so well do, without danger to your instrument and strings: it will be a great safety to your instrument, in keeping it from decay, it will prevent much trouble in keeping the bars from flying loose and the belly from sinking: and these six conveniences considered all together, must needs create a seventh, which is, that lute-playing must certainly be very much facilitated, and made more delightful thereby. Only no person must be so inconsiderate as to tumble down upon the bed whilst the lute is there, for I have known," said he, "several good lutes spoilt with such a trick."

I will not say of the reader, who after the foregoing specimens of Music's Monument has no liking for Master Mace and his book, that he

Is fit for treasons, stratagems, and spoil,

but I cannot but suspect that he has no taste for caviare, dislikes laver, would as willingly drink new hock as old, and more willingly the base compound which passes for champagne, than either. Nay I could even suspect that he does not love those "three things which persons loving, love what they ought, — the whistling of the wind, the dashing of the waves, and the rolling of thunder:" and that he comes under the commination of this other triad, "let no one love such as dislike the scent of cloves, the taste of milk, and the song of birds." My Welsh friends shall have the pleasure of reading these true sayings, in their own ancient, venerable, and rich language.

Tri dyn o garu tri pheth à garant à ddylaint; gorddyan y gwgnt, boran y tònau, ac angerdd y daran.

Tri pheth ma chared neb a 'u hanghara: rhogleu y meillion, blâs llaeth, a chân adar.

CHAPTER CXCIV.

A MUSIC LESSON FROM MASTER THOMAS MACE TO BE PLAYED BY LADY FAIR:— A STORY, THAN WHICH THERE IS NONE PRETTIER IN THE HISTORY OF MUSIC.

What shall I say? Or shall I say no more?
I must go on! I'm brim-full, running o'er.
But yet I'll hold, because I judge ye wise;
And few words unto such may well suffice.
But much—much more than this I could declare;
Yet for some certain reasons I'll forbear.
But less than this I could not say; because,
If saying less, I should neglect my cause,
For 'tis the Doctor's cause I plead so strong for,
And 'tis his cause compleated that I long for,
And 'tis true doctrine certainly I preach,
And 'tis that doctrine every priest should teach.

THOMAS MACE, TO ALL DIVINE READERS.

O LADY fair, before we say,

Now cease my lute; this is the last
Labour that thou and I shall waste,
And ended is that we begun;
My lute be still, for I have done:*

before we say this, O Lady fair, play I pray you the following lesson by good Master Mace. It will put you in tune for the story "not impertinent" concerning it, which he thought fit to relate, although, he said, many might choose to smile at it. You may thank Sir John Hawkins for having rendered it from tablature into the characters of musical notation.

* SIR THOMAS WYAT.

"This Lesson," says Master Mace, "I call my Mistress, and I shall not think it impertinent to detain you here a little longer than ordinary in speaking something of it, the occasion of it, and why I give it that name. And I doubt not, but the relation I shall give may conduce to your advantage in several respects, but chiefly in respect of Invention.

"You must first know, That it is a lesson, though old; yet I never knew it disrelished by any, nor is there any one lesson in this Book of that age, as it is; yet I do esteem it (in its kind) with the best Lesson in the Book, for several good reasons, which I shall here set down.

"It is, this very winter, just forty years since I made it — and yet it is new, because all like it, — and then when I was past being a suitor to my best beloved, dearest, and sweetest living Mistress, but not married, yet contriving the best, and readiest way towards it; And thus it was,

"That very night, in which I was thus agitated in my mind concerning her, my living Mistress, — she being in Yorkshire, and myself at Cambridge, close shut up in my chamber, still and quiet, about ten or eleven o'clock at night, musing and writing letters to her, her Mother, and some other Friends, in summing up and determining the whole matter concerning our Marriage. You may conceive I might have very intent thoughts all that time, and might meet with some difficulties, for as yet I had not gained her Mother's consent, — so that in my writings I was sometimes put to my studyings. At which times, my Lute lying upon my table, I sometimes took it up, and walked about my chamber, letting my fancy drive which way it would, — (for I studied nothing, at that time, as to Music,) — yet my secret genius or fancy prompted my fingers, do what I could, into this very humour. So that every time I walked, and took up my Lute, in the interim, betwixt writing and studying, this Air would needs offer itself unto me continually; insomuch that, at the last, (liking it well, and lest it should be lost,) I took paper and set it down, taking no further notice of it at that time. But afterwards it passed abroad for a very pleasant and delightful Air amongst all. Yet I gave it no name till a long time after, nor taking more notice of it, in any particular kind, than of any other my Composures of that nature.

"But after I was married, and had brought my wife home to Cambridge, it so fell out that one rainy morning I stay'd within, and in my chamber my wife and I were all alone, she intent upon her needlework, and I playing upon my Lute, at the table by her. She sat very still and quiet, listening to all I played without a word a long time, till at last, I hapned to play this lesson; which, so soon as I had once played, she earnestly desired me to play it again, 'for,' said she, 'That shall be called my Lesson.'

"From which words, so spoken, with emphasis and accent, it presently came into my remembrance, the time when, and the occasion of its being produced, and I returned her this answer, viz., That it may very properly be called your Lesson, for when I composed it you were wholly in my fancy, and the chief object and ruler of my thoughts; telling her how, and when it was made. And therefore, ever after, I thus called it My Mistress, and most of my scholars since call it Mrs. Mace, to this day.

"Thus I have detained you, (I hope not too long,) with this short relation; nor should I have been so seemingly vain, as to have inserted it, but that I have an intended purpose by it, to give some advantage to the reader, and doubt not but to do it to those who will rightly consider what here I shall further set down concerning it.

"Now in reference to the occasion of it, &c. It is worth taking notice, That there are times and particular seasons, in which the ablest Master of his Art shall not be able to command his Invention or produce things so to his content or liking, as he shall at other times; but he shall be (as it were) stupid, dull, and shut up, as to any neat, spruce, or curious Invention.

"But again, at other times, he will have Inventions come flowing in upon him, with so much ease and freedom, that his greatest trouble will be to retain, remember, or set them down, in good order.

"Yet more particularly, as to the occasion of this Lesson, I would have you take notice, that as it was at such a time, when I was wholly and intimately possessed with the true and perfect idea of my living Mistress, who was at that time lovely, fair, comely, sweet, debonair, uniformly-neat, and every way compleat; how could, possibly, my fancy run upon anything at that time, but upon the very simile, form, or likeness, of the same substantial thing?

"And that this Lesson doth represent, and shadow forth such a true relation, as here I have made, I desire you to take notice of it, in every particular; which I assure myself may be of benefit to any, who shall observe it well.

"First, therefore, observe the two first Bars of it, which will give you the Fugue; which Fugue is maintained quite through the whole lesson.

"Secondly, observe the Form, and Shape of the whole lesson, which consists of two uniform, and equal strains; both strains having the same number of Bars.

"Thirdly, observe the humour of it; which you may perceive (by the marks and directions) is not common.

"These three terms, or things, ought to be considered in all compositions, and performances of this nature, viz. Ayres, or the like.

"The Fugue is lively, ayrey, neat, curious, and sweet, like my Mistress.

"The Form is uniform, comely, substantial, grave, and lovely, like my Mistress.

"The humour is singularly spruce, amiable, pleasant, obliging, and innocent, like my Mistress.

"This relation to some may seem odd, strange, humorous, and impertinent; but to others (I presume) it may be intelligible and useful; in that I know, by good experience, that in Music, all these significations, (and vastly many more,) may, by an experienced and understanding Artist, be clearly, and most significantly expressed; yea, even as by language itself, if not much more effectually. And also, in that I know, that as a person is affected or disposed in his temper, or humour, by reason of what object of his mind soever, he shall at that time produce matter, (if he be put to it,) answerable to that temper, disposition, or humour, in which he is.

"Therefore I would give this as a caveat, or caution, to any, who do attempt to exercise their fancies in such matters of Invention, that they observe times, and seasons, and never force themselves to anything, when they perceive an indisposition; but wait for a fitter, and more hopeful season, for what comes most compleatly, comes most familiarly, naturally, and easily, without pumping for, as we use to say.

"Strive therefore to be in a good, cheerful, and pleasant humour always when you would compose or invent, and then, such will your productions be; or, to say better, chuse for your time of Study, and Invention, if you may, that time wherein you are so disposed, as I have declared. And doubtless, as it is in the study and productions of Music, so must it needs be in all other studies, where the use and exercise of fancy is requirable.

"I will, therefore, take a little more pains than ordinary, to give such directions, as you shall no ways wrong, or injure my Mistress, but do her all the right you can, according to her true deserts.

"First, therefore, observe to play *soft*, and *loud*, as you see it marked quite through the Lesson.

"Secondly, use *that Grace*, which I call the *Sting*, where you see it set, and the *Spinger* after it.

"And then, in the last four strains, observe the *Slides*, and *Slurs*, and you cannot fail to know my *Mistress's Humour*, provided you keep *true time*, which you must be extremely careful to do in all lessons: For Time is the one half of Music.

"And now, I hope I shall not be very hard put to it, to obtain my pardon for all this trouble I have thus put you to, in the exercise of your patience; especially from those, who are so ingenious and good-natured, as to prize, and value, such singular and choice endowments, as I have here made mention of in so absolute and compleat a subject."

My Mistress or Mrs. Mace.

Thomas Mace.

There is no prettier story in the history of Music than this; and what a loving, loveable, happy creature must he have been who could thus in his old age have related it!

CHAPTER CXCV.

ANOTHER LESSON, WITH THE STORY AND MANNER OF ITS PRODUCTION.

Οὐδεὶς ἐρεῖ ποθ', ὡς ὑπόβλητον λόγον,
——ἔλεξας, ἀλλὰ τῆς σαυτοῦ φρενός.

SOPHOCLES.

MASTER Mace has another lesson which he calls Hab-Nab; it "has neither fugue, nor very good form," he says, "yet a humour, although none of the best;" and his "story of the manner and occasion of Hab-Nab's production," affords a remarkable counterpart to that of his favourite lesson.

"View every bar in it," he says, "and you will find not any one Bar like another, nor any affinity in the least kind betwixt strain and strain, yet the Air pleaseth some sort of people well enough; but for my own part, I never was pleased with it; yet because some liked it, I retained it. Nor can I tell how it came to pass that I thus made it, only I very well remember the time, manner, and occasion of its production, (which was on a sudden,) without the least premeditation, or study, and merely accidentally; and, as we use to say, *ex tempore*, in the *tuning of a lute*.

"And the occasion, I conceive, might possibly contribute something towards it, which was this.

"I had, at that very instant, when I made it, an agitation in hand, viz., the stringing up, and tuning of a Lute, for a person of an ununiform, and inharmonical disposition, (as to Music,) yet in herself well proportioned, comely, and handsome enough, and ingenious for other things, but to Music very unapt, and learned it only to please her friends, who had a great desire she should be brought to it, if possible, but never could, to the least good purpose; so that at the last we both grew weary; *for there is no striving against such a stream.*

"I say, this occasion possibly might be the cause of this so inartificial a piece, in regard that that person, at that time, was the chief object of my mind and thoughts. I call it inartificial, because the chief observation (as to good performance) is wholly wanting. Yet it is true Music, and has such a form and humour, as may pass, and give content to many. Yet I shall never advise any to make things thus by hab-nab*, without any design, as was this. And therefore I give it that name.

"There are abundance of such things to be met with, and from the hands of some, who fain would pass for good composers; yet most of them may be traced, and upon examination, their things found only to be snaps and catches; which they,—having been long conversant in Music, and can command an Instrument, through great and long practice, some of them very well,—have taken here and there, (hab-nab,) from several airs and things of other men's works, and put them handsomely together, which then pass for their own compositions.

"Yet I say, it is no affront, offence, or injury, to any Master, for another to take his Fugue, or Point to work upon, nor dishonour for any Artist so to do, provided he shew by his Workmanship, a different Discourse, Form, or Humour. But it is rather a credit and a repute for him so to do; for by his works he shall be known. It being observable, That great Master Composers may all along be as well known by their Compositions, or their own compositions known to be of them, as the great and learned writers may be known by their styles and works."

---

* *Hab-Nab* is a good old English word, derived from the Anglo-Saxon. Skinner is correct enough. "Temerè, sine consilio *ab* AS. *Habban* Habere, *Nabban*, non Habere, addito scilicet *na*, non, cum apostropho." Will-nill, i. e. Will ye, or will ye not, is a parallel form. Every one will recollect the lines of Hudibras, (Part ii. Canto iii.)

> With that he circles draws, and squares,
> With cyphers, astral characters:
> Then looks 'em o'er to understand 'em
> Although set down, *hab nab*, at random.

Dr. Grey illustrates the expression from Don Quixote: "Let every man," says Sancho Pancha, "take care what he talks or how he writes of other men, and not set down *at random*, *hab-nab*, *higgledy-piggledy*, what comes into his noddle." Part ii c. iii.

On referring to the original it will be seen that the Translator has used three words for one. "Cada uno mire como habla ó como escriba de las presonas, y no ponga *á troche moche* lo primero que le viene al magin."

CHAPTER CXCVI.

FURTHER ACCOUNT OF MASTER THOMAS MACE, — HIS LIGHT HEART, HIS SORROWS, AND HIS POVERTY,—"POORLY, POOR MAN, HE LIVED, POORLY, POOR MAN, HE DIED" — PHINEAS FLETCHER.

The sweet and the sour,
The nettle and the flower,
The thorn and the rose,
This garland compose.
SMALL GARLAND OF PIOUS AND GODLY SONGS.

LITTLE more is known of Thomas Mace than can be gathered from his book. By a good portrait of him in his sixty-third year, it appears that he was born in 1613, and by his arms that he was of gentle blood. And as he had more subscribers to his book in York than in any other place, (Cambridge excepted,) and the name of Henry Mace, Clerk, occurs among them, it may be presumed that he was a native of that city, or of that county. This is the more likely, because when he was established at Cambridge in his youth, his true love was in Yorkshire; and at that time his travels are likely to have been confined between the place of his birth and of his residence.

The price of his book was twelve shillings in sheets; and as he obtained about three hundred subscribers, he considered this fair encouragement to publish. But when the work was completed and the accounts cast up, he discovered that "in regard of his unexpected great charge, besides his unconceivable care and pains to have it compleatly done, it could not be well afforded at that price, to render him any tolerable or reasonable requital." He gave notice therefore, that after it should have been published three months, the price must be raised; "adding thus much, (as being bold to say) that there were several pages, yea several lessons in this book, (according to the ordinary value, esteem, or way of procuring such things,) which were every one of them of more value than the price of the whole book by far."

It might be truly said of him, that

Poorly, poor man, he lived, poorly, poor man, he died,*

for he never attained to any higher preferment than that of being "one of the Clerks of Trinity College." But it may be doubted whether any of those who partook more largely of the endowment of that noble establishment, enjoyed so large a portion of real happiness. We find him in the sixty-third year of his age, and the fortieth of his marriage, not rich, not what the world calls fortunate, but a contented, cheerful old man; even though "Time had done to him this wrong" that it had half deprived him of his highest gratification, for he had become so deaf that he could not hear his own lute. When Homer says of his own blind bard that the Muse gave him good and evil, depriving him of his eyes, but giving him the gift of song, we understand the compensation;

Τὸν πέρι Μοῦσ' ἐφίλησε, δίδου δ' ἀγαθόν τε κακόν τε,
'Οφθαλμῶν μὲν ἄμερσε, δίδου δ' ἡδεῖαν ἀοιδήν·

but what can compensate a musician for the loss of hearing! There is no inward ear to be the bliss of solitude. He could not, like Pythagoras, ἀῤῥήτῳ τινὶ καὶ δυσεπινοήτῳ θειότητι χρώμενος, by an effort of ineffable and hardly conceivable divinity retire into the depths of his own being, and there listen to that heavenly harmony of the spheres which to him alone of all the human race was made audible; —'Εαυτῷ γὰρ μόνῳ τῶν ἐπὶ γῆς ἁπάντων συνετὰ καὶ ἐπήκοα τὰ κοσμικὰ φθέγματα ἐνόμιζεν ἀπ' αὐτῆς τῆς φυσικῆς πηγῆς καὶ ῥίζης.† Master Mace had no such supernatural faculty, and no such opinion of himself. But the happy old man devises a means of overcoming to a certain degree his defect by inventing what he called a Dyphone, or Double Lute of fifty strings, a representation of which is given in his book, as "the one only instrument in being of that kind, then lately invented by himself, and made with his own hands in the year 1672."

"The occasion of its production was my necessity; viz. my great defect in hearing; adjoined with my unsatiable love and desire

* PHINEAS FLETCHER.
† IAMBLICHI Liber de Pythagoricâ Vitâ, c. xv.

after the Lute. It being an instrument so soft, and past my reach of hearing, I did imagine it was possible to contrive a louder Lute, than ever any yet had been; whereupon, after divers casts and contrivances, I pitched upon this order, the which has (in a great degree) answered my expectation, it being absolutely the lustiest or loudest Lute that I ever yet heard. For although I cannot hear the least twang of any other Lute, when I play upon it, yet I can hear this in a very good measure, yet not so loud as to distinguish every thing I play, without the help of my teeth, which when I lay close to the edge of it, (there, where the lace is fixed,) I hear all I play distinctly. So that it is to me (I thank God!) one of the principal refreshments and contentments I enjoy in this world. What it may prove to others in its use and service, (if any shall think fit to make the like,) I know not, but I conceive it may be very useful, because of the several conveniences and advantages it has of all other Lutes."

This instrument was on the one side a Theorboe, on the other lute, having on the former part twenty-six strings, twenty-four on the latter. It had a fuller, plumper, and lustier sound, he said, than any other lute, because the concave was almost as long again, being hollow from neck to mouth. "This is one augmentation of sound; there is yet another; which is from the strange and wonderful secret, which lies in the nature of sympathy, in unities, or the uniting of harmonical sounds, the one always augmenting the other. For let two several instruments lie asunder at any reasonable distance, when you play upon one, the other shall sound, provided they be both exactly tuned in unisons to each other; otherwise not. This is known to all curious inspectors into such mysteries. If this therefore be true, it must needs be granted, that when the strings of these two twins, accordingly put on, are tuned in unities and set up to a stiff lusty pitch, they cannot but more augment and advantage one the other."

Some allowances he begged for it, because it was a new-made instrument and could not yet speak so well as it would do, when it came to age and ripeness, though it already gave forth "a very free, brisk, trouling, plump and sweet sound," and because it was made by a hand that never before attempted the making of any instrument. He concludes his description of it, with what he calls a Recreative Fancy: saying, "because it is my beloved darling, I seemed, like an old doting body, to be fond of it; so that when I finished it, I bedecked it with these five rhymes following, fairly written upon each belly.

"First, round the Theorboe knot, thus,

> I am of old, and of Great Britain's fame,
> Theorboe was my name.

Then next, about the French Lute knot, thus,

> I'm not so old; yet grave, and much acute;
> My name was the French lute.

Then from thence along the sides, from one knot to the other, thus,

> But since we are thus joined both in one,
> Henceforth our name shall be the Lute Dyphone.

Then again cross-wise under the Theorboe-knot, thus,

> Lo here a perfect emblem seen in me,
> Of England and of France, their unity;
> Likewise that year they did each other aid,
> I was contrived, and thus compleatly made.

viz. when they united both against the Dutch and beat them soundly, A. D. 1672.

"Then lastly, under the French Lute-knot, thus,

> Long have we been divided, now made one,
> We sang in sevenths; now in full unison.
> In this firm union, long may we agree,
> No unison is like Lute's harmony.
>
> Thus in its body, tis trim, spruce and fine
> But in its sp'rit, tis like a thing divine."

Poor Mace formed the plan of a Music-room, and hoped to have erected it himself; "but it pleased God," says he, "to disappoint and discourage me several ways, for such a work; as chiefly by the loss of my hearing, and by that means the emptiness of my purse, (my meaning may easily be guessed at,) I only wanted money enough but no good will thereunto." However he engraved his plan, and annexed a description of it, "in hopes that at one time or other, there might arise some honourable and truly nobly-spirited person, or persons, who may consider the great good use and benefit of such a necessary convenience, and also find in his heart to become a benefactor to such an eminent good work, — for the promotion of the art and encouragement of the true lovers of it; there being great need of such a thing, in reference to the compleating and illustrating of the University Schools."

What he designed was a room six yards square, having on each side three galleries for spectators, each something more than three yards deep. These were to be one story from the ground, "both for advantage of sound, and also to avoid the moisture of the earth, which is very bad, both for instrument and strings;" and the building was to be "in a clear and very delightful dry place, both free from water, the overhanging of trees, and common noises." The room was for the performers, and it was to be "one step higher on the floor than the galleries the better to convey the sound to the auditors:" — being thus clear and free from company, all inconvenience of talking, crowding, sweating and blustering, &c. are taken away; the sound has its free and uninterrupted passage; the performers are no ways hindered; and the instruments will stand more steadily in tune, (for no lutes, viols, pedals, harpsicons, &c., will stand in tune at such a time; no, nor voices themselves;) "For I have known," says he, "an excellent voice, well prepared for a solemn performance, who has been put up in a crowd, that when he has been to perform his part, could hardly speak, and by no other cause but the very distemper received by that crowd and overheat."

The twelve galleries, though but little, would hold two hundred persons very well; and thus the uneasy and unhandsome accommodation, which has often happened to persons of quality, being crowded up, squeezed and sweated among persons of an inferior rank, might be avoided, "which thing alone, having such distinct reception for persons of different qualities, must needs be accounted a great conveniency." But there was a scientific convenience included in the arrangement; for the lower walls were to be "wainscoted, hollow from the wall, and without any kind of carved, bossed, or rugged work, so that the sound might run glib and smooth all about, without the least interruption. And through that wainscot there must be several conveyances all out of the room — by grooves, or pipes to certain auditor's seats, where the hearer, as he sate, might at a small passage, or little hole, receive the pent-up sound, which let it be never so weak in the music-room, he, (though at the furthest end of the gallery,) should hear as distinctly as any who were close by it." The inlets into these pipes should be pretty large, a foot square at least, yet the larger the better, without all doubt, and so the conveyance to run proportionably narrower, till it came to the ear of the auditor, where it need not be above the wideness of one's finger end. "It cannot," says he, "be easily imagined, what a wonderful advantage such a contrivance must needs be, for the exact and distinct hearing of music; without doubt far beyond all that ever has yet been used. For there is no instrument of touch, be it never so sweet, and touched with the most curious hand that can be, but in the very touch, if you be near unto it, you may perceive the touch to be heard; especially of viols and violins: but if you be at a distance, that harshness is lost, and conveyed unto the air, and you receive nothing but the pure sweetness of the instrument; so as I may properly say, you lose the body, but enjoy the soul or spirit thereof."

Such a necessary, ample and most convenient erection would become, he thought, any nobleman, or gentleman's house; and there might be built together with it as convenient rooms for all services of a family, as by any other contrivance whatever, and as magnificently stately. Were it but once experienced, he doubted not, but that the advantages would apparently show themselves, and be esteemed far beyond what he had written, or that others could conceive.

The last notice which we have of good Master Mace is an advertisement, dated London, 1690, fourteen years after the publication of his book. Dr. Burney found it in the British Museum, in a collection of title-pages, devices and advertisements. It is addressed "to all Lovers of the best sort of Music."

Men say the times are strange;—tis true;
'Cause many strange things hap to be.
Let it not then seem strange to you
That here one strange thing more you see.

That is, in Devereux Court, next the Grecian Coffee House, at the Temple back gate, there is a deaf person teacheth music to perfection; who by reason of his great age, viz. seventy-seven, is come to town, with his whole stock of rich musical furniture; viz. instruments and books, to put off, to whomsoever delights in such choice things; for he has nothing light or vain, but all substantial and solid Music. Some particulars do here follow.

"First, There is a late invented Organ, which, for private use, exceeds all other fashioned organs whatever; and for which, substantial artificial reasons will be given; and, for its beauty, it may become a nobleman's dining-room.

"Second, There belongs to it a pair of fair, large-sized consort viols, chiefly fitted and suited for that, or consort use; and 'tis great pity they should be parted.

"Third, There is a pedal harpsicon, (the absolute best sort of consort harpsicon that has been invented; there being in it more than twenty varieties, most of them to come in with the foot of the player; without the least hindrance of play,) exceedingly pleasant.

"Fourth, Is a single harpsicon.

"Fifth, A new invented instrument, called a Dyphone, viz. a double lute; it is both theorboe and French lute compleat; and as easy to play upon as any other lute.

"Sixth, Several other theorboes, lutes and viols, very good.

"Seventh, Great store of choice collections of the works of the most famous composers that have lived in these last hundred years, as Latin, English, Italian and some French.

"Eighth, There is the publishers own Music's Monument; some few copies thereof he has still by him to put off, it being a subscribed book, and not exposed to common sale. All these will be sold at very easy rates, for the reasons aforesaid; and because, indeed, he cannot stay in town longer than four months, exactly."

He further adds, "if any be desirous to partake of his experimental skill in this high noble art, during his stay in town, he is ready to assist them; and haply, they may obtain that from him, which they may not meet withal elsewhere. He teacheth these five things; viz. the theorboe, the French lute, and the viol, in all their excellent ways and uses; as also composition, together with the knack of procuring invention to young composers, (the general and greatest difficulty they meet withal;) this last thing not being attempted by any author, (as he knows of,) yet may be done, though some have been so wise, or otherwise to contradict it:

Sed experientia docuit.

Any of these five things may be learned so understandingly, in this little time he stays, by such general rules as he gives, together with Music's Monument, (written principally to such purposes,) as that any, aptly inclined, may, for the future, teach themselves, without any other help."

This is the last notice of poor Mace: poor he may be called, when at the age of seventy-seven he is found in London upon the forlorn hope of selling his instruments and his books, and getting pupils during this stay. It may be inferred that he had lost the son of whose musical proficiency he formerly spoke with so much pleasure; for otherwise this professional collection and stock in trade would hardly have been exposed to sale, but it appears that the good old man retained his mental faculties, and his happy and contented spirit.

Dr. Burney recommends the perusal of what he calls his matchless book "to all who have taste for excessive simplicity and quaintness, and can extract pleasure from the sincere and undissembled happiness of an author, who with exalted notions of his subject and abilities, discloses to his readers every inward working of self-approbation in as undisguised a manner, as if he were communing with himself in all the plenitude of mental comfort and privacy."

CHAPTER CXCVII.

QUESTION PROPOSED, WHETHER A MAN BE MAGNIFIED OR MINIFIED BY CONSIDERING HIMSELF UNDER THE INFLUENCE OF THE HEAVENLY BODIES, AND ANSWERED WITH LEARNING AND DISCRETION.

I find by experience that Writing is like Building, wherein the undertaker, to supply some defect, or serve some convenience which at first he foresaw not, is usually forced to exceed his first model and proposal, and many times to double the charge and expence of it.

Dr. John Scott.

Is man magnified or minified by considering himself as under the influence of the heavenly bodies, — not simply as being

Moved round in earth's dismal course
With rocks and stones and trees *;

but as affected by them in his constitution bodily and mental, and dependent on them for weal or woe, for good or evil fortune; as subjected, that is, according to astrological belief to

The Stars, who, by I know not what strange right,
Preside o'er mortals in their own despite,
Who without reason, govern those who most,
(How truly, judge from thence!) of reason boast;
And by some mighty magic, yet unknown,
Our actions guide, yet cannot guide their own.†

Apart from what one of our Platonic divines calls "the power of astral necessity, and uncontrollable impressions arising from the subordination and mental sympathy and dependence of all mundane causes," which is the Platonist's and Stoic's "proper notion of fate ‡;" apart, I say, from this, and from the Calvinist's doctrine of predestination, is it a humiliating, or an elevating consideration, that the same celestial movements which cause the flux and reflux of the ocean, should be felt in the pulse of a patient suffering with a fever: and that the eternal laws which regulate the stars in their courses should decide the lot of an individual?

Here again a distinction must be made, — between the physical theory and the pseudo-science. The former is but a question of more or less; for that men are affected by atmospherical influence is proved by every endemic disease; and invalids feel in themselves a change of weather as decidedly as they perceive its effect upon the weather-glass, the hygrometer, or the strings of a musical instrument. The sense of our weakness in this respect, — of our dependence upon causes over which we have no control, and which in their operation and nature are inexplicable by us, must have a humbling and therefore a beneficial tendency in every mind disposed to goodness. It is in the order of Providence that we should learn from sickness and adversity lessons which health and prosperity never teach.

Some of the old theoretical physicians went far beyond this. Sachs von Lewenheimb compared the microcosm of man with the macrocosm in which he exists. "The heart in the one," he said, "is what the ocean is in the other, the blood has its ebbing and flowing like the tide, and as the ocean receives its impulse from the moon and the winds, the brain and the vital spirits act in like manner upon the heart." Baillet has noticed for censure the title of his book in his chapter *Des prejugés des Titres des Livres;* it is *Oceanus Macro-Micro-cosmicus.* Peder Severinsen carrying into his medical studies a fanciful habit of mind which he might better have indulged in his younger days when he was a Professor of Poetry, found in the little world of the human body, antitypes of everything in the great world, its mountains and its valleys, its rivers and its lakes, its minerals and its vegetables, its elements and its spheres. According to him the stars are living creatures, subject to the same diseases as ourselves. Ours indeed

* Wordsworth.
† Churchill.
‡ John Smith.

are derived from them by sympathy, or astral influence, and can be remedied only by those medicines, the application of which is denoted by their apparent qualities, or by the authentic signature of nature.

This fancy concerning the origin of diseases is less intelligible than the mythology of those Rosicrucians who held that they were caused by evil demons rulers of the respective planets, or by the Spirits of the Firmament and the Air. A mythology this may more properly be called than a theory; and it would belong rather to the history of Manicheism than of medicine, were it not that in all ages fanaticism and imposture have, in greater or less degree, connected themselves with the art of healing.

But however dignified, or super-celestial the theoretical causes of disease, its effect is always the same in bringing home, even to the proudest heart, a sense of mortal weakness: whereas the belief which places man in relation with the Stars, and links his petty concerns and fortunes of a day with the movements of the heavenly bodies, and the great chain of events, tends to exalt him in his own conceit. The thriftless man in middle or low life who says, in common phrase, that he was born under a threepenny planet, and therefore shall never be worth a groat, finds some satisfaction in imputing his unprosperity to the Stars, and casting upon them the blame which he ought to take upon himself. In vain did an old Almanack-maker say to such men of the Creator, in a better strain than was often attained by the professors of his craft.

He made the Stars to be an aid unto us,
Not (as is fondly dream'd) to help undo us:
Much less without our fault to ruinate
By doom of irrecoverable Fate.
And if our best endeavours use we will,
These glorious Creatures will be helpful still
In all our honest ways: for they do stand
To help, not hinder us, in God's command,
Who doth not only rule them by his powers
But makes their glory servant unto ours.
Be wise in Him, and if just cause there be
The Sun and Moon shall stand and wait on thee.

On the other hand the lucky adventurer proceeds with superstitious confidence in his Fortune; and the ambitious in many instances have devoted themselves, or been deceived to their own destruction. It is found accordingly that the professors of astrology generally in their private practice addressed themselves to the cupidity or the vanity of those by whom they were employed. Honest professors there were who framed their schemes faithfully upon their own rules; but the greater number were those who consulted their own advantage only, and these men being well acquainted with human nature in its ordinary character, always took this course. — Their character has changed as little as human nature itself in the course of two thousand years since Ennius expressed his contempt for them, in a passage preserved by Cicero.

Non habeo denique nauci Marsum augurem,
Non vicanos haruspices, non de circo astrologos,
Non Isiacos conjectores, non interpretes somnium.
Non enim sunt ii aut scientiâ aut arte divini,
Sed superstitiosi vates, impudentesque harioli,
Aut inertes, aut insani, aut quibus egestas imperat:
Qui sibi semitam non sapiunt, alteri monstrant viam.
Quibus divitias pollicentur, ab iis drachmam ipsi petunt.
De his divitiis sibi deducant drachmam, reddant cætera.

Pompey, Crassus, and Cæsar were each assured by the Chaldæans that he should die in his own house, in prosperity, and in a good old age. Cicero tells us this upon his own knowledge: *Quam multa ego Pompeio, quam multa Crasso, quam multa huic ipsi Cæsari à Chaldæis dicta memini, neminem eorum nisi senectute, nisi domi, nisi cum claritate esse moriturum! ut mihi ermirum videatur, quemquam extare, qui etiam nunc credat iis, quorum prædicta quotidie videat re et eventis refelli.*

And before the age of Ennius, Euripides had in the person of Tiresias shown how surely any such profession, if the professor believed in his own art, must lead to martyrdom, or falsehood. When the blind old Prophet turns away from Creon, he says, in words worthy of Milton's favourite poet,

Τὰ μὲν παρ' ἡμῶν πάντ' ἔχεις· ἡγοῦ, τέκνον,
Πρὸς οἶκον· ὅστις δ' ἐμπύρῳ χρῆται τέχνῃ,
Μάταιος· ἢν μὲν ἐχθρὰ σημήνας τύχῃ,
Πικρὸς καθέστηκ', οἷς ἂν οἰωνοσκοπῇ,
Ψευδῆ δ' ὑπ' οἴκτου τοῖσι χρωμένοις λέγων,
'Αδικεῖ τὰ τῶν θεῶν. Φοῖβον ἀνθρώποις μόνον
Χρῆν θεσπιωδεῖν, ὃς δέδοικεν οὐδένα.

The sagacity of the poet will be seen by those who are versed in the history of the

Old Testament; and for those who are not versed in it, the sooner they cease to be ignorant in what so nearly concerns them, the better it may be for themselves.

Jeremy Taylor says that he reproves those who practised judicial astrology, and pretended to deliver genethliacal predictions, "not because their reason is against religion, for certainly," said he, "it cannot be; but because they have not reason enough in what they say; they go upon weak principles which they cannot prove; they reduce them to practice by impossible mediums; they argue about things with which they have little conversation. Although the art may be very lawful if the stars were upon the earth, or the men were in heaven, if they had skill in what they profess, and reason in all their pretences, and after all that their principles were certain, and that the stars did really signify future events, and that those events were not overruled by everything in heaven and in earth, by God, and by our own will and wisdom,—yet because here is so little reason and less certainty, and nothing but confidence and illusion, therefore it is that religion permits them not; and it is not the reason in this art that is against religion, but the folly or the knavery of it; and the dangerous and horrid consequents which they feel that run a-whoring after such idols of imagination."

In our days most of those persons who can afford to employ the greater part of their thoughts upon themselves fall at a certain age under the influence either of a physical or a spiritual director, for Protestantism has its *Directeurs* as well as Popery, less to its advantage and as little to its credit. The spiritual professors have the most extensive practice, because they, like their patients, are of all grades, and are employed quite as much among the sound as the sick. The astrologer no longer contests the ascendancy with either. That calling is now followed by none but such low impostors, that they are only heard of when one of them is brought before a magistrate for defrauding some poor credulous creature in the humblest walks of life. So low has that cunning fallen, which in the seventeenth century introduced its professors into the cabinets of kings, and more powerful ministers. An astrologer was present at the birth of Louis XIV., that he might mark with all possible precision the exact moment of his nativity. After the massacre of St. Bartholomew's day, Catherine de Medici, deep in blood as she was, hesitated about putting to death the King of Navarre and the Prince of Condé, and the person of whom she took counsel was an astrologer,—had she gone to her Confessor their death would have been certain. Cosmo Ruggieri was an unprincipled adventurer, but on this occasion he made a pious use of his craft, and when the Queen inquired of him what the nativities of these Princes prognosticated, he assured her that he had calculated them with the utmost exactness, and that according to the principles of his art, the State had nothing to apprehend from either of them. He let them know this as soon as he could, and told them that he had given this answer purely from regard for them, not from any result of his schemes, the matter being in its nature undiscoverable by astrology.

The Imperial astrologers in China excused themselves once for a notable failure in their art, with more notable address. The error indeed was harmless, except in its probable consequences to themselves; they had predicted an eclipse, and no eclipse took place. But instead of being abashed at this proof of their incapacity the ready rogues complimented the Emperor, and congratulated him upon so wonderful and auspicious an event. The eclipse, they said, portended evil, and therefore in regard to him the Gods had put it by.

An Asiatic Emperor who calls himself Brother to the Sun and Moon might well believe that his relations would go a little out of their way to oblige him, if the Queen of Navarre could with apparent sincerity declare her belief that special revelations are made to the Great, as one of the privileges of their high estate, and that her mother, that Catherine de Medici whose name is for ever infamous, was thus miraculously forewarned of every remarkable event that befell her husband and her children, nor was she herself without her share in this privilege, though her character was not more spotless in one point than her mother's in another. *De ces divins advertissemens,* she says, *je ne me veux estimer digne, toutesfois pour ne me taire comme ingrate des graces que j'ay receües de Dieu, que je dois et veux confesser toute ma vie, pour luy en rendre grace, et que chacun le loue aux merveilles des effets de sa puissance, bonté, et miséricorde, qu'il luy a plû faire en moy, j'advoueray n'avoir jamais esté proche de quelques signalez accidens, ou sinistres, ou heureux, que j'en aye eu quelque advertissement ou en songe, ou autrement; et puis bien dire ce vers,*

De mon bien ou mon mal, mon esprit m'est oracle.

CHAPTER CXCVIII.

PETER HOPKINS' VIEWS OF ASTROLOGY. HIS SKILL IN CHIROMANCY, PALMISTRY, OR MANUAL DIVINATION WISELY TEMPERED. SPANISH PROVERB AND SONNET BY BARTOLOME LEONARDO DE ARGENSOLA. TIPPOO SULTAN. MAHOMETAN SUPERSTITION. W. Y. PLAYTES' PROSPECTUS FOR THE HORN BOOK FOR THE REMEMBRANCE OF THE SIGNS OF SALVATION.

Seguite dunque con la mente lieta,
Seguite, Monsignor, che com' io dico,
Presto presto sarete in su la meta.
LUDOVICO DOLCE.

PETER HOPKINS had believed in astrology when he studied it in early life with his friend Gray; his faith in it had been overthrown by observation and reflection, and the unperceived influence of the opinions of the learned and scientific public; but there was more latent doubt in his incredulity than had ever lurked at the root of his belief.

He was not less skilled in the kindred, though more trivial art of Chiromancy, Palmistry, or Manual Divination, for the divine origin of which a verse in the Book of Job was adduced as scriptural proof; "He sealeth up the hand of every man, that all men may know his work." The text appears more chiromantical in the Vulgate: *Qui in manu omnium hominum signa posuit:* Who has placed signs in the hand of all men. The uses of the science were represented to be such, as to justify this opinion of its origination: "For hereby," says Fabian Withers, "thou shalt perceive and see the secret works of Nature, how aptly and necessarily she hath compounded and knit each member with other, giving unto the hand, as unto a table, certain signs and tokens whereby to discern and know the inward motions and affections of the mind and heart, with the inward state of the whole body: as also our inclination and aptness to all our external actions and doings. For what more profitable thing may be supposed or thought, than when a man in himself may foresee and know his proper and fatal accidents, and thereby to embrace and follow that which is good, and to avoid and eschew the evils which are imminent unto him, for the better understanding and knowledge thereof?"

But cautioning his readers against the error of those who perverted their belief in palmistry and astrology, and used it as a refuge or sanctuary for all their evil deeds, "we ought," said he, "to know and understand that the Stars do not provoke or force us to anything, but only make us apt and prone; and being so disposed, allure as it were, and draw us forward to our natural inclination. In the which if we follow the rule of Reason, taking it to be our only guide and governor, they lose all the force, power and effect which they by any means may have in and upon us: contrariwise, if we give ourselves over to follow our own sensuality and natural dispositions, they work even the same effect on us—that they do in brute beasts."

Farther he admonishes all "which should read or take any fruit of his small treatise, to use such moderation in perusing of the same that they do not by and by take in hand to give judgment either of their own, or other men's estates or nativities, without diligent circumspection and taking heed; weighing and considering how many ways a man may be deceived; as by the providence and discretion of the person on whom he gives judgment, also, the dispensation of God, and our fallible and uncertain speculation." "Wherefore," he continues, "let all men in seeking hereby to foresee their own fortune, take heed that by the promise of good, they be not elate, or high-minded, giving themselves over to otiosity or idleness, and trusting altogether to the Natural Influences; neither yet by any signs or tokens of adversity, to be dejected or cast down, but to take and weigh all things with such equality and moderation, directing their state of life and living to all perfectness and goodness, that they may be ready to embrace and follow all that which is good and profitable; and also not only to eschew and avoid, but to withstand and set at nought all evil and adverse fortune, whensoever it may happen unto them."

Whoever studies the history of opinions, that is, of the aberrations, caprices, and extravagances of the human mind, may find some consolation in reflecting upon the practical morality which has been preached not only by men of the most erroneous faith, but even by fanatics, impostors and hypocrites, as if it were in the order of Providence that there should be no poison which had not also some medicinal virtue. The books of palmistry have been so worn by perusal that one in decent preservation is now among the rarities of literature; and it may be hoped that of the credulous numbers who have pored over them, many have derived more benefit from the wholesome lessons which were thus unexpectedly brought home to them, than they suffered detriment from giving ear to the profession of a fallacious art.

The lesson was so obvious that the Spaniards expressed it in one of their pithy proverbs, *es nuestra alma en nuestra palma.* The thought has been expanded into a sonnet by Bartolome Leonardo de Argensola, a poet whose strains of manly morality have not been exceeded in that language.

Fabio, pensar que el Padre soberano
En esas rayas de la palma diestra
(Que son arrugas de la piel) te muestra
Los accidentes del discurso humano;
Es beber con el vulgo el error vano
De la ignorancia, su comun maestra.
Bien te confieso, que la suerte nuestra.
Mala, o buena, la puso en nuestra mano.
Di, quién te estorvará el ser Rey, si vives
Sin envidiar la suerte de los Reyes,
Tan contento y pacifico en la tuya,
Que estén ociosas para ti sus leyes;
Y qualquier novedad que el Cielo influya,
Como cosa ordinaria la recibes?

Fabius to think that God hath interlined
The human hand like some prophetic page,
And in the wrinkles of the palm defined
As in a map, our mortal pilgrimage,
This is to follow, with the multitude,
Error and Ignorance, their common guides,
Yet heaven hath placed, for evil or for good,
Our fate in our own hands, whate'er betides,
Being as we make it. Art thou not a king
Thyself my friend, when envying not the lot
Of thrones, ambition hath for thee no sting,
Laws are to thee as they existed not,
And in thy harmless station no event
Can shake the calm of its assured content.

"Nature," says a Cheirologist, "was a careful workman in the creation of the human body. She hath set in the hand of man certain signs and tokens of the heart, brain and liver, because in them it is that the life of man chiefly consists, but she hath not done so of the eyes, ears, mouth, hands and feet, because those parts of the body seem rather to be made for a comeliness or beauty, than for any necessity." What he meant to say was that any accident which threatened the three vital parts was betokened in the lines of the palm, but that the same fashioning was not necessary in relation to parts which might be injured without inducing the loss of life. Therefore every man's palm has in it the lines relating to the three noble parts; the more minute lines are only found on subjects of finer texture, and if they originally existed in husbandmen and others whose hands are rendered callous by their employments, they are effaced.

It was only cheirologically speaking that he disparaged what sailors in their emphatic language so truly call our precious eyes and limbs, not that he estimated them like Tippoo Sultan, who in one of his letters says, that if people persisted in visiting a certain person who was under his displeasure, "their ears and noses should be dispensed with." This strange tyrant wrote odes in praise of himself, and describes the effect of his just government to be such, that in the security of his protection "the deer of the forest made their pillow of the lion and the tyger, and their mattress of the leopard and the panther."

Tippoo did not consider ears and noses to be superfluities when in that wanton wickedness which seldom fails to accompany the possession of irresponsible power he spoke of dispensing with them. But in one instance arms and legs were regarded as worse than superfluous. Some years ago a man was exhibited who was born without either, and in that condition had found a woman base enough to marry him. Having got some money together, she one day set this wretched creature upon a chimney-piece, from whence he could not move, and went off with another man, stripping him of everything that she could carry away. The first words he uttered, when some one came into the room and took him down, were an imprecation upon those people who had legs and arms, because, he said, they were always in mischief!

The Mahommedans believe that every man's fate is written on his forehead, but that it can be read by those only whose eyes have been opened. The Brahmins say that the sutures of the skull describe in like manner the owner's destined fortune, but neither can this mysterious writing be seen by any one during his life, nor decyphered after his death. Both these notions are mere fancies which afford a foundation for nothing worse than fable. Something more extraordinary has been excogitated by W. Y. Playtes, Lecturer upon the Signs of the light of the Understanding. He announces to mankind that the prints of the nails of the Cross which our Lord showed Thomas are printed in the roots of the nails of the hands and feet of every man that is born into the world, for witnesses, and for leading us to believe in the truth of all the signs, and graven images and pictures that are seen in the Heavenly Looking Glass of Reflection, in the Sun and the Moon and the Stars. This Theosophist has published a short Prospectus of his intended work entitled the Horn Book for the remembrance of the Signs of Salvation, which Horn Book is (should subscriptions be forthcoming) to be published in one hundred and forty-four numbers, forming twelve octavo volumes of six hundred pages each, with fifty plates, maps and tables, and 365,000 marginal references, — being one thousand for every day in the year. Wonder not, reader, at the extent of this projected work; for, says the author, "the Cow of the Church of Truth giveth abundance of milk, for the Babes of Knowledge." But for palmistry there was a plausible theory which made it applicable to the purposes of fraud.

Among the odd persons with whom Peter Hopkins had become acquainted in the course of his earlier pursuits, was a sincere student of the occult sciences, who, being a more refined and curious artist, whenever he cast the nativity of any one, took an impression from the palm of the hand, as from an engraved plate, or block. He had thus a fac-simile of what he wanted. According to Sir Thomas Browne, the variety in the lines is so great, that there is almost no strict conformity. Bewick in one of his works has in this manner printed his own thumb. There are French deeds of the 15th century which are signed by the imprint of five fingers dipt in ink, underwritten *Ce est la griffe de monseigneur*.*

Hopkins himself did not retain any lurking inclination to believe in this art. You could know without it, he said, whether a person were open-handed, or close-fisted, and this was a more useful knowledge than palmistry could give us. But the Doctor sometimes made use of it to amuse children, and gave them at the same time playful admonition, and wholesome encouragement.

* The Reader, who is curious in such matters, may turn to Ames and Herbert, (Dibdin, ii. 380.) for the hands in Holt's Lac Puerorum, emprynted at London by Wynkyn de Worde.

CHAPTER CXCIX.

CONCERNING THE GREAT HONOURS TO WHICH CERTAIN HORSES HAVE ATTAINED, AND THE ROYAL MERITS OF NOBS.

Siento para contarlas que me llama
El á mi, yo á mi pluma, ella á la fama.

BALBUENA.

There have been great and good horses whose merits have been recorded in history and in immortal song as they well deserved to be. Who has not heard of Bucephalus? of whom Pulteney said that he questioned whether Alexander himself had pushed his conquests half so far, if Bucephalus had not stooped to take him on his back. Statius hath sung of Arion, who when he carried Neptune left the winds panting behind him, and who was the best horse that ever has been heard of for taking the water.

Sæpe per Ionium Libycumque natantibus ire
Interjunctus equis, omnesque assuetus in oras
Cæruleum deferre patrem.

Tramp, tramp across the land he went,
Splash, splash across the sea.

But he was a dangerous horse in a gig. Hercules found it difficult to hold him in, and Polynices when he attempted to drive him made almost as bad a figure as the Taylor upon his ever-memorable excursion to Brentford.

The virtues of Caligula's horse, whom that Emperor invited to sup with him, whom he made a Priest, and whom he intended to make Consul, have not been described by those historians who have transmitted to us the account of his extraordinary fortune; and when we consider of what materials, even in our days, both Priests and Senators are sometimes made, we may be allowed to demur at any proposition which might include an admission that dignity is to be considered an unequivocal mark of desert. More certain it is that Borysthenes was a good horse, for the Emperor Adrian erected a monument to his memory, and it was recorded in his epitaph that he used to fly over the plains and marshes and Etrurian hills, hunting Pannonian boars; he appears by his name to have been, like Nobs, of Tartaric race.

Bavieca was a holy and happy horse, — I borrow the epithets from the Bishop of Chalons's sermon upon the Bells. Gil Diaz deserved to be buried in the same grave with him. And there is an anonymous Horse, of whom honourable mention is made in the Roman Catholic Breviary, for his religious merits, because after a Pope had once ridden him, he never would suffer himself to be unhallowed by carrying a woman on his back. These latter are both Roman Catholic Houyhnhnms, but among the Mahometans also, quadrupedism is not considered an obstacle to a certain kind of canonisation. Seven of the Emperor of Morocco's horses have been Saints, or Marabouts, as the Moors would call it; and some there were who enjoyed that honour in the year 1721 when Windus was at Mequinez. One had been thus distinguished for saving the Emperor's life; "and if a man," says the Traveller, "should kill one of his children, and lay hold of this horse, he is safe. This horse has saved the lives of some of the captives, and is fed with *cuscuru* and camel's milk. After the Emperor has drank, and the horse after him, some of his favourites are suffered to drink out of the same bowl." This was probably the horse who had a Christian slave appointed to hold up his tail when he was led abroad, and to carry a vessel and towel, — "for use unmeet to tell."

I have discovered only one Houyhnhnm who was a martyr, excepting those who are sometimes burnt with the rest of the family by Captain Rock's people in Ireland. This was poor Morocco, the learned horse of Queen Elizabeth's days: he and his master Banks, having been in some danger of being put to death at Orleans, were both burnt alive by the Inquisition at Rome, as magicians. — The word martyr is here used in its religious acceptation: for the victims of avarice and barbarity who are destroyed by hard driving and cruel usage are numerous enough to make a frightful account among the sins of this nation.

Fabretti the antiquary had a horse which, when he carried his master on an antiquarian excursion, assisted him in his researches; for this sagacious horse had been so much accustomed to stop where there were ruins, and probably had found so much satisfaction in grazing, or cropping the boughs among them at his pleasure, that he was become a sort of antiquary himself; and sometimes by stopping and as it were pointing like a setter, gave his master notice of some curious and half-hidden objects which he might otherwise have passed by unperceived.

How often has a drunken rider been carried to his own door by a sure-footed beast, sensible enough to understand that his master was in no condition either to guide him, or to take care of himself. How often has a stage coach been brought safely to its inn after the coachman had fallen from the box. Nay, was there not a mare at Ennis races in Ireland (Atalanta was her name) who, having thrown her rider, kept the course with a perfect understanding of what was expected from her, looked back and quickened her speed as the other horses approached her, won the race, trotted a few paces beyond the post, then wheeled round, and came up to the scale as usual? And did not Hurleyburley do the same thing at the Goodwood races?

That Nobs was the best horse in the world I will not affirm. Best is indeed a bold word to whatever it be applied, and yet in the shopkeeper's vocabulary it is at the bottom of his scale of superlatives. A haberdasher in a certain great city is still remembered, whose lowest priced gloves were what he called Best, but then he had five degrees of optimism; Best, Better than Best, Best of all, Better than Best of all, and the Real Best. It may be said of Nobs, then, that he was one of the Real Best: equal to any that Spain could have produced to compare with him, though concerning Spanish horses, the antiquary and historian Morales, (properly and as it were prophetically baptized Ambrosio, because his name ought ever to be in ambrosial odour among his countrymen,) concerning Spanish horses, I say, that judicious author has said, *la estima que agora se hace en todo el mundo de un caballo Español es la mas solemne cosa que puede haber en animales.*

Neither will I assert that there could not have been a better horse than Nobs, because I remember how Roger Williams tells us, "one of the chiefest Doctors of England was wont to say concerning strawberries, that God could have made a better berry, but he never did." Calling this to mind, I venture to say as that chiefest Doctor might, and we may believe would have said upon the present occasion, that a better horse than Nobs there might have been, — but there never was.

The Duchess of Newcastle tells us that her Lord, than whom no man could be a more competent judge, preferred barbs and Spanish to all others, for barbs, he said, were like gentlemen in their kind, and Spanish horses like Princes. This saying would have pleased the Doctor, as coinciding entirely with his own opinions. He was no believer in equality either among men or beasts; and he used to say, that in a state of nature Nobs would have been the king of his kind.

And why not? If I do not show you sufficient precedents for it call me Fimbul Fambi.

CHAPTER CC.

A CHAPTER OF KINGS.

> Fimbul-Fambi *heitr*
> *Sá er fatt kann segia,*
> *That er ósnotvrs athal.*
>
> *Fimbul-fambi (fatuus) vocatur*
> *Qui pauca novit narrare:*
> *Ea est hominis insciti proprietas.*
>
> Edda, *Hava Mál.*

There are other monarchies in the inferior world, besides that of the Bees, though they have not been registered by Naturalists, nor studied by them.

For example, the King of the Fleas keeps his court at Tiberias, as Dr. Clarke discovered to his cost, and as Mr. Cripps will testify for him.

The King of the Crocodiles resides in Upper Egypt; he has no tail, but Dr. Southey has made one for him.

The Queen Muscle may be found at the Falkland Islands.

The Oysters also have their King according to Pliny. Theirs seems to be a sort of patriarchical monarchy, the King, or peradventure the Queen, Oyster being distinguished by its size and age, perhaps therefore the parent of the bed; for every bed, if Pliny err not, has its sovereign. In Pliny's time the diver made it his first business to catch the royal Oyster, because his or her Majesty being of great age and experience, was also possessed of marvellous sagacity, which was exercised for the safety of the commonweal; but if this were taken the others might be caught without difficulty, just as a swarm of Bees may be secured after the Queen is made prisoner. Seeing, however, that his Oyster Majesty is not to be heard of now at any of the Oyster shops in London, nor known at Colchester or Milton, it may be that liberal opinions have, in the march of intellect, extended to the race of Oysters, that monarchy has been abolished among them, and that republicanism prevails at this day throughout all Oysterdom, or at least in those parts of it which be near the British shores. It has been observed also by a judicious author that no such King of the Oysters has been found in the West Indian Pearl fisheries.

The King of the Bears rules over a territory which is on the way to the desert of Hawaida, and Hatim Tai married his daughter, though the said Hatim was long unwilling to become a Mac Mahon by marriage.

"I was told by the Sheikh Othman and his son, two pious and credible persons," says the traveller Ibn Batista, "that the Monkies have a leader whom they follow as if he were their King (this was in Ceylon). About his head is tied a turban composed of the leaves of trees, (for a crown,) and he reclines upon a staff, (which is his sceptre). At his right and left hand are four Monkies with rods in their hands, (gold sticks,) all of which stand at his head whenever the leading Monkey (his Majesty) sits. His wives and children are daily brought in on these occasions, and sit down before him; then comes a number of Monkies (his privy council), which sit and form an assembly about him. After this each of them comes with a nut, a lemon or some of the mountain fruit, which he throws down before the leader. He then eats (dining in public, like the King of France,) together with his wives, and children, and the four principal Monkies: they then all disperse. One of the Jogres also told me, that he once saw the four Monkies standing in the presence of the leader, and beating another Monkey with rods; after which they plucked off all his hair."

The Lion is the King of Beasts. Hutchinson, however, opines that Bulls may be ranked in a higher class; for helmets are fortified with their horns, which is a symbol of pre-eminence. Certainly he says, both the Bull and Lion discover the King, but the Bull is a better and more significant representative of a King than the Lion. But neither Bull nor Lion is King of all Beasts, for a certain person whose name being anagrammatised rendereth Johnny the Bear, is notoriously the King of the Bears at this time: even Ursa Major would not dispute his title. And a certain honourable member of the House of Commons would by the tottle of that whole House be voted King of the Bores.

The King of the Codfish frequents the shores of Finmark. He has a sort of chubbed head, rising in the shape of a crown, his forehead is broad, and the lower jaw bone projects a little; in other parts he resembles his subjects, whom he leads and directs in their migrations. The Laplanders believe that the fisherman who takes him will from that time forth be fortunate, especially in fishing; and they show their respect for his Cod-Majesty, when he is taken, by hanging him up whole to dry, instead of cutting off his head as they do to the common fish.

In Japan the Tai, which the Dutch call

Steenbrassem, is the King of Fish, because it is sacred to their sea-god Jebis, and because of its splendid colours, and also, perhaps, because of its exorbitant price, it being so scarce, that for a court entertainment, or on other extraordinary occasions, one is not to be had under a thousand cobangs.

Among the Gangas or Priests of Congo is one whose official title is Mutuin, and who calls himself King of the Water, for by water alone he professes to heal all diseases. At certain times all who need his aid are assembled on the banks of a river. He throws an empty vessel in, repeats some mysterious words, then takes it out full and distributes the water as an universal medicine.

The Herring has been called the King of Fish, because of its excellence, the Herring, as all Dutchmen know, and as all other men ought to know, exceeding every other fish in goodness. Therefore it may have been that the first dish which used to be brought to table in this country on Easter Day, was a Red Herring on horseback, set in a corn sallad.

Others have called the Whale, King of Fish. But Abraham Rees, D.D. and F.R.S. of Cyclopædian celebrity, assures us that the whale, notwithstanding its piscine appearance, and its residence in the waters, has no claim to a place among fishes. Uncle Toby would have whistled Lillabullero at being told that the Whale was not a fish. The said Abraham Rees, however, of the double Dees, who is, as the advertisement on the cover of his own Cyclopædia informs us, "of acknowledged learning and industry, and of unquestionable experience in this (the Cyclopædian) department of literary labour," candidly admits that the Ancients may surely be excused for thinking Whales were fish. But how can Abraham Rees be excused for denying the Whale's claim to a place among the inhabitants of the Great Deep, — which was appointed for him at the Creation?

But the Great Fish, who is undoubtedly the King of Fish, and of all creatures that exist in the sea, Whales, Mermen-and-Maids included, is the fish Arez, which Ormuzd created, and placed in the water that surrounds Hom, the King of Trees, to protect that sacred arboreal Majesty against the Great Toad sent there by Ahriman to destroy it.

It is related in the same archives of cosmogony that the King of the Goats is a White Goat, who carries his head in a melancholy and cogitabund position, regarding the ground, — weighed down perhaps by the cares of royalty; that the King of the Sheep has his left ear white, — from whence it may appear that the Royal Mutton is a black sheep, which the Royal Ram of the Fairy Tales is not: that the King of the Camels has two white ears: and that the King of the Bulls is neither Apis, nor John Bull, but a Black Bull with yellow ears. According to the same archives, a White Horse with yellow ears and full eyes is King of the Horses; — doubtless the Mythological Horse King would acknowledge Nobs for his Vicegerent. The Ass King is also white: his Asinine Majesty has no Vicegerent. The number of competitors being so great that he has appointed a regency.

The King of Dogs is yellow. The King of Hares red.

There are Kings among the Otters in the Highland waters, and also among their relations the Sea Otters. The royal Otter is larger than his subjects, and has a white spot upon the breast. He shuns observation, which it is sometimes provident for Kings to do, especially under such circumstances as his, for his skin is in great request, among soldiers and sailors; it is supposed to ensure victory, to secure the wearer from being wounded, to be a prophylactic in times of contagious sickness, and a preservative in shipwreck. But it is not easy to find an Otter King, and when found there is danger in the act of regicide, for he bears a charmed life. The moment in which he is killed proves fatal to some other creature, either man or beast, whose mortal existence is mysteriously linked with his. The nature of the Otter monarchy has not been described: it is evident, however, that his ministers have no loaves to dispose of, — but then they have plenty of fishes.

The Ant, who, when Solomon entered the Valley of Ants with his armies of Genii and men and birds, spoke to the nation of Ants, saying, "O Ants, enter ye not your habitations, lest Solomon and his host tread you under foot, and perceive it not," — that wise pismire is said by certain commentators upon the Koran to have been the Queen of the Ants.

Men have held the Eagle to be the King of Birds; but, notwithstanding the authority of Horace, the Gods know otherwise, for they appointed the Tchamrosch to that dignity, at the beginning. Some writers indeed would have the Eagle to be Queen, upon the extraordinary ground that all Eagles are hens; though in what manner the species is perpetuated these persons have not attempted to show.

The Carrion Crows of Guiana have their King, who is a White Crow (*rara avis in terris*) and has wings tipt with black. When a flight of these birds arrive at the prey which they have scented from afar, however ravenous they may be, they keep at a respectful distance from the banquet, till his Carrion Majesty has satisfied himself. But there is another Bird, in South America, whom all the Birds of prey of every species acknowledge for their natural sovereign, and carry food to him in his nest, as their tribute.

The King of the Elks is so huge an elk that other elks look like pismires beside him. His legs are so long, and his strength withal such, that when the snow lies eight feet deep it does not in the least impede his pace. He has an arm growing out of his shoulder, and a large suite who attend upon him wherever he goes, and render him all the service he requires.

I have never heard anything concerning the King of the Crickets except in a rodomontade of Matthew Merrygreeks, who, said Ralph Roister Doister,

> Bet him on Christmas day
> That he crept in a hole, and had not a word to say.

Among the many images of Baal, one was the form or representation of a Fly, and hence, says Master Perkins, he is called Baalzebub the Lord of Flies, because he was thought to be the chiefest Fly in the world. That is he was held to be the King of the Flies. I wish the King of the Spiders would catch him.

The King of the Peacocks may be read of in the Fairy Tales. The Japanese name for a crane is Tsuri, and the common people in that country always give that bird the same title which is given to their first secular Emperor, Tsiri-sama — my great Lord Crane.

The Basilisk, or crowned Cockatrice, who is the chief of a Cock's egg, is accounted the King of Serpents. And as it has been said that there is no Cock Eagle, so upon more probable cause it is affirmed that there is no female Basilisk, that is no Henatrice, the Cock laying only male eggs. But the most venomous of this kind is only an earthly and mortal vicegerent, for the true King of Serpents is named Sanc-ha-naga, and formerly held his court in Chacragiri, a mountain in the remote parts of the East, where he and his serpentine subjects were oppressed by the Rational Eagle Garuda. In the spirit of an imperial Eagle, Garuda required from them a serpent every day for his dinner, which was regarded by the serpents as a most unpleasant tribute, especially by such as were full grown and in good condition; for the Rational Eagle being large and strong enough to carry Vishnu on his back, expected always a good substantial snake sufficient for a meal. Sanc-ha-naga, like a Patriot King, endeavoured to deliver his liege subjects from this consuming tyranny; the attempt drew upon him the wrath of Garuda, which would soon have been followed by his vengeance, and the King of Serpents must have been devoured himself, if he and all the snakes had not retired, as fast as they could wriggle, to Sanc-ha-vana, in Sanc-ha-dwip, which is between Cali and the Sea; there they found an asylum near the palace of Carticeya, son of the mountain goddess Parvats, and Commander of the Celestial Armies. Carticeya is more powerful than Garuda, and therefore the divine

Eagle is too rational to invade them while they are under his protection. It would have been more fortunate for the world if the King of Serpents had not found any one to protect him; for whatever his merits may be towards his subjects, he is a most pestilent Potentate, the breath of his nostrils is a fiery wind which destroys and consumes all creatures and all herbs within an hundred *yojanas* of his abode, and which, in fact, is the Simoom, so fatal to those who travel in the deserts. The sage Agastya for a time put a stop to this evil, for he, by the virtue of his self-inflection, obtained such power, that he caught Sanc-ha-naga, and carried him about in an earthen vessel. That vessel, however, must have been broken in some unhappy hour, for the fiery and poisonous wind is now as frequent as ever in the deserts.

The Hindoos say that whoever performs yearly and daily rites in honour of the King of the Serpents will acquire immense riches. *This* King of the Serpents, I say, to wit Sanc'-ha-naga, — (or Sanc' ha-mucha, as he is also called from the shape of his mouth resembling that of a shell,) — because there is another King of the Serpents, Karkotaka by name, whom the sage Narada for deceiving him punished once by casting him into a great fire, and confining him there by a curse till he was delivered in the manner which the reader may find related in the 14th book of Nela and Damarante, as translated by Mr. Milman from the Sanscrit.

The Locusts according to Agur in the Book of Proverbs have no King, although they go forth all of them by bands. Perhaps their form of government has changed, for the Moors of Morocco inform us that they have a sovereign, who leads forth their innumerable armies; and as his nation belongs to the Mahometan world, his title is Sultan Jereed.

The Rose is the Queen of the Garden:

Plebei cedite flores;
Hortorum regina suos ostendit honores. *

Bampfield Moore Carew was King of the Beggars; and James Bosvill was King of the Gypsies. He lies buried in Rossington Churchyard, near Doncaster, and for many years the gypsies from the south visited his grave annually, and among other rites poured a flagon of ale upon it.

There was a personage at Oxford who bore in that University the distinguished title of Rex Rafforum. After taking his degree he exchanged it for that of the Reverend.

The *Scurræ*, — (we have no word in our language which designates men who profess and delight in indulging an ill-mannered and worse-minded buffoonery,) — the *Scurræ* also have their King. He bears a Baron's coronet.

The throne of the Dandies has been vacant since the resignation of the personage dignified and distinguished by the title of Beau Brummel.

By an advertisement in the Times of Friday, June 18. 1830, I learn that the beautiful and stupendous Bradwell Ox is at present the "truly wonderful King of the Pastures," the said King Ox measuring fourteen feet in girth, and sixteen feet in length, being eighteen hands high, and five years and a half old, and weighing four thousand five hundred pounds, or more than five hundred and sixty stone, which is nearly double the size of large oxen in general.

Under the Twelve Cæsars (and probably it might deserve the title long after them), the Via Appia was called the Queen of Roads. That from Hyde Park Corner is *Regina viarum* in the 19th century.

Easter Sunday has been called the King of Days, though Christmas Day might dispute the sovereignty, being in Greek the Queen day of the Kalendar. Ἡ βασιλίσσα ἡμέρα Justin Martyr calls it.

Who is King of the Booksellers? There is no King among them at this time, but there is a Directory of five Members, Longman, Rees, Orme, Brown and Green in the East: the Emperor Murraylemagne, whom Byron used to call the Grand Murray, reigned alone in the West, till Henry Colburn divided his empire, and supported the sta-

* Rapin.

tion which he had assumed by an army of trumpeters which he keeps in constant pay.

If the Books had a King that monarchy must needs be an elective one, and the reader of these volumes knows where the election would fall. But literature being a Republic, this cannot be the King of Books. Suffice it that it is a Book for a King, or, for our Sovereign Lady the Queen.

INTERCHAPTER XXI.

MEASURE FOR MEASURE.

Le Plebe è bestia
Di cento teste, e non rinchiude in loro
Pur oncia di saper. Chiabrera.

The Public, will, I very well know, make free with me *more suo*, as it thinks it has a right to do with any one who comes before it with anything designed for its service, whether it be for its amusement, its use, or its instruction. Now, my Public, I will *more meo* make free with you — that we may be so far upon equal terms:

Οὐδὲν δεῖ παραμπέχειν λόγους.*

You have seldom or never had the truth spoken to you when you have been directly addressed. You have been called the enlightened Public, the generous Public, the judicious Public, the liberal Public, the discerning Public, and so forth. Nay your bare title the Public oftentimes stands alone *par excellence* in its plain majesty like that of the king, as if needing no affix to denote its inherent and pre-eminent importance. But I will speak truth to you, my Public.

Be not deceived! I have no bended knees,
No supple tongue, no speeches steep'd in oil,
No candied flattery, nor honied words! †

I must speak the truth to you, my Public,

Sincera verità non vuol tacersi.‡

Where your enlightenedness (if there be such a word) consists, and your generosity, and your judgment, and your liberality, and your discernment, and your majesty to boot, — to express myself as Whitfield or Rowland Hill would have done in such a case (for they knew the force of language) — I must say, it would puzzle the Devil to tell. *Il faut librement avec verité francher ce mot, sans en estre repris; ou si l'on est, c'est très-mal à propos.*§

I will tell you what you are; you are a great, ugly, many-headed beast, with a great many ears which are long, hairy, ticklish, moveable, erect, and never at rest.

Look at your picture in Southey's Hexameters, — that poem in which his laureated Doctorship writes verses by the yard instead of the foot, — he describes you as "many-headed and monstrous,"

with numberless faces,
Numberless bestial ears, erect to all rumours, and restless,
And with numberless mouths which are fill'd with lies as with arrows.

Look at that Picture, my Public! — It is very like you!

For individual readers I profess just as much respect as they individually deserve. There are a few persons in every generation for whose approbation, — rather let it be said for whose gratitude and love, — it is worth while "to live laborious days," and for these readers of this generation and the generations that are to follow, — for these

Such as will join their profit with their pleasure,
And come to feed their understanding parts; —
For these I'll prodigally spend myself,
And speak away my spirit into air;
For these I'll melt my brain into invention,
Coin new conceits, and hang my richest words
As polished jewels in their bounteous ears.‖

Such readers, they who to their learning add knowledge, and to their knowledge wisdom, and to their wisdom benevolence, will say to me,

Ὦ καλὰ λέγων, πολὺ δ' ἄμεινον' ἔτι τῶν λόγων
ἐργασάμεν', εἴθ' ἐπέλ-
θοις ἅπαντά μοι σαφῶς·
ὡς ἐγώ μοι δοκῶ
κἂν μακρὰν ὁδὸν διελθεῖν ὥστ' ἀκοῦσαι.
πρὸς τάδ' ὦ βέλτιστε θαῤῥήσας λέγ', ὡς ἅ-
παντες ἡδόμεσθά σοι.¶

But such readers are very few. Walter Landor said that if ten such persons should

* Euripides. † Randolph's Aristippus. ‡ Chiabrera.

§ Brantome. ‖ Ben Jonson. ¶ Aristophanes.

approve his writings, he would call for a division and count a majority. To please them is to obtain an earnest of enduring fame; for which, if it be worth anything, no price can be too great. But for the aggregate anything is good enough. Yes, my Public, Mr. Hume's arithmetic, and Mr. Brougham's logic, Lord Castlereagh's syntax, Mr. Irving's religion, and Mr. Carlisle's irreligion, the politics of the Edinburgh Review, and the criticism of the Quarterly, Thames water, Brewers' beer, Spanish loans, old jokes, new constitutions, Irish eloquence, Scotch metaphysics, Tom and Jerry, Zimmerman on Solitude, Chancery Equity and Old Bailey Law, Parliamentary wit, the patriotism of a Whig Borough-monger, and the consistency of a British cabinet; *Et s'il y a encore quelque chose à dire, je le tiens pour dit.* —

Yes, my Public,

> Nor would I you should look for other looks,
> Gesture, or compliment from me. *

Minus dico quam vellem, et verba omninò frigidiora hæc quam ut satis exprimant quod concipio †: these and anything worse than these, — if worse than what is worse can be imagined, will do for you. If there be anything in infinite possibility more worthless than these, more floccical-naucical, nihilishpilish, assisal-teruncial, more good for nothing than good for nothingness itself, it is good enough for you.

INTERCHAPTER XXII.

VARIETY OF STILES.

> *Qualis vir, talis oratio.*
>
> ERASMI ADAGIA.

AUTHORS are often classed, like painters, according to the school in which they have been trained, or to which they have attached themselves. But it is not so easy to ascertain this in literature as it is in painting; and if some of the critics who have thus endeavoured to class them were sent to school themselves, and there whipt into a little more learning, so many silly classifications of this kind would not mislead those readers who suppose, in the simplicity of their own good faith, that no man presumes to write upon a subject which he does not understand.

Stiles may with more accuracy be classed, and for this purpose metals might be used in literature as they are in heraldry. We might speak of the golden stile, the silver, the iron, the leaden, the pinchbeck and the bronze.

Others there are which cannot be brought under any of these appellations. There is the Cyclopean stile, of which Johnson is the great example; the sparkling, or micacious, possessed by Hazlitt, and much affected in Reviews and Magazines; the oleaginous, in which Mr. Charles Butler bears the palm, or more appropriately the olive branch: the fulminating — which is Walter Landor's, whose conversation has been compared to thunder and lightning; the impenetrable — which is sometimes used by Mr. Coleridge; and the Jeremy-Benthamite, which cannot with propriety be distinguished by any other name than one derived from its unparalleled and unparallelable author.

Ex stilo, says Erasmus, *perpendimus ingenium cujusque, omnemque mentis habitum ex ipsâ dictionis ratione conjectamus. Est enim tumidi, stilus turgidus; abjecti, humilis, exanguis; asperi, scaber; amarulenti, tristis ac maledicus; deliciis affluentis, picturatus ac dissolutus; Breviter, omne vitæ simulacrum, omnis animi vis, in oratione perinde ut in speculo repræsentatur, ac vel intima pectoris, arcanis quibusdam vestigiis, deprehenduntur.*

There is the lean stile, of which Nathaniel Lardner, and William Coxe may be held up as examples; and there is the larded one, exemplified in Bishop Andrewes, and in Burton, the Anatomist of Melancholy; Jeremy Taylor's is both a flowery and a fruitful stile: Harvey the Meditationist's a weedy one. There are the hard and dry; the weak and watery; the manly and the womanly; the juvenile and the anile; the round and the pointed; the flashy and the fiery; the lucid and the opaque; the lumi-

* BEN JONSON. † PICUS MIRANDULA.

nous and the tenebrous; the continuous and the disjointed. The washy and the slap-dash are both much in vogue, especially in magazines and reviews; so are the barbed and the venomed. The High-Slang stile is exhibited in the Court Journal and in Mr. Colburn's novels; the Low-Slang in Tom and Jerry, Bell's Life in London, and most Magazines, those especially which are of most pretensions.

The flatulent stile, the feverish, the aguish, and the atrabilious, are all as common as the diseases of body from which they take their name, and of mind in which they originate; and not less common than either is the dyspeptic stile, proceeding from a weakness in the digestive faculty.

Learned, or if not learned, Dear Reader, I had much to say of stile, but the under written passage from that beautiful book, Xenophon's Memorabilia Socratis, has induced me, as the Latins say, *stilum vertere*, and to erase a paragraph written with ink in which the gall predominated.

Ἐγὼ δ' οὖν καὶ αὐτὸς, ὦ Ἀντιφῶν, ὥσπερ ἄλλός τις ἢ ἵππῳ ἀγαθῷ ἢ κυνὶ ἢ ὄρνιθι ἥδεται, οὕτω καὶ ἔτι μᾶλλον ἥδομαι τοῖς φίλοις ἀγαθοῖς· καὶ, ἐάν τι σχῶ ἀγαθὸν διδάσκω, καὶ ἄλλοις σύνιστημι, παρ' ὧν ἂν ἡγῶμαι ὠφελήσεσθαί τι αὐτοὺς εἰς ἀρετήν· καὶ τοὺς θησαυροὺς τῶν πάλαι σοφῶν ἀνδρῶν, οὓς ἐκεῖνοι κατέλιπον ἐν βιβλίοις γράφεντες, ἀνελίττων κοινῇ σὺν τοῖς φίλοις διέρχομαι· καὶ ἄν τι ὁρῶμεν ἀγαθὸν, ἐκλεγόμεθα, καὶ μέγα νομίζομεν κέρδος, ἐὰν ἀλλήλοις ὠφέλιμοι γιγνώμεθα.

INTERCHAPTER XXIII.

A LITTLE ADVICE BESTOWED UPON THE SCORNFUL READER IN A SHORT INTERCHAPTER.

No man is so foolish but may give another good counsel sometimes; and no man is so wise, but may easily err, if he will take no other's counsel but his own.

BEN JONSON.

I WILL now bestow a little advice upon the scornful reader.

"And who the Devil are you," exclaims that reader, "who are impertinent enough to offer your advice, and fool enough to suppose that I shall listen to it?"

"Whatever your opinion may be, Sir, concerning an Evil Principle, whether you hold with the thorough-paced Liberals, that there is no Principle at all, (and in one sense, exemplify this in your own conduct,) or with the Unitarians that there is no Evil one; or whether you incline to the Manichean scheme of Two Principles, which is said to have its advocates,—in either case the diabolical expletive in your speech is alike reprehensible: you deserve a reprimand for it; and you are hereby reprimanded accordingly.—Having discharged this duty, I answer your question in the words of Terence, with which I doubt not you are acquainted, because they are to be found in the Eton grammar: *Homo sum, nihil humani à me alienum puto.*"

"And what the Devil have the words of Terence to do with my query?"

"You are again reprimanded, Sir. If it be a bad thing to have the Devil at one's elbow, it cannot be a good one to have him at one's tongue's end. The sentence is sufficiently applicable. It is a humane thing to offer advice where it is wanted, and a very humane thing to write and publish a book which is intended to be either useful or delightful to those who read it."

"A humane thing to write a book!—Martin of Galway's humanity is not a better joke than that!"

"Martin of Galway's humanity is no joke, Sir. He has begun a good work, and will be remembered for it with that honour which is due to all who have endeavoured to lessen the sum of suffering and wickedness in this wicked world."

"Answer me one question, Mr. Author, if you please. If your book is intended to be either useful or delightful, why have you filled it with such a parcel of nonsense?"

"What you are pleased to call by that name, Mr. Reader, may be either sense or nonsense according to the understanding which it meets with. *Quicquid recipitur, recipitur in modum recipientis.* Look in the seventh Chapter of the second book of Esdras, and at the twenty-fifth verse you will find the solution of your demand."

"And do you suppose I shall take the trouble of looking into the Bible to please the humour of such a fellow as you?"

"If you do not, Sir, there are others who will; and more good may arise from looking into that book,—even upon such an occasion,—than either they or I can anticipate."

And so, scornful reader, wishing thee a better mind, and an enlightened understanding, I bid thee gladly and heartily farewell!

PREFACE TO THE SEVENTH VOLUME.*

INVENIAS ETIAM DISJECTI MEMBRA POETÆ.

THE present Volume contains all that it is thought advisable to publish of the Papers and Fragments for THE DOCTOR, &c. Some of these Papers, as in the former Volume, were written out fair and ready for Publication—but the order, and the arrangement intended is altogether unknown.

I have taken care to examine the different extracts,—and occasionally I have added a note or an explanation, where such seemed to be needed. The whole has been printed with scrupulous exactness from the MSS. The Epilude of Mottoes is a selection from such as had not been used in the body of the work. Some of them may possibly have been quoted before—but if so, it has escaped my recollection.—

Mihi dulces
Ignoscent, si quid peccâro stultus, amici,
Inque vicem illorum patiar delicta libenter.

JOHN WOOD WARTER.

Vicarage, West-Tarring, Sussex.
Sept. 14th, 1847.

CHAPTER CCI.

QUESTION CONCERNING THE USE OF TONGUES. THE ATHANASIAN CONFESSORS. GIBBON'S RELATION OF THE SUPPOSED MIRACLE OF TONGUES. THE FACTS SHOWN TO BE TRUE, THE MIRACLE IMAGINARY, AND THE HISTORIAN THE DUPE OF HIS OWN UNBELIEF.

Perseveremus, peractis quæ rem continebant, scrutari etiam ea quæ, si vis verum, connexa sunt, non cohærentia; quæ quisquis diligenter inspicit, nec facit operæ prætium, nec tamen perdit operam. SENECA.

FOR what use were our tongues given us? "To speak with, to be sure," will be the immediate reply of many a reader. But Master, Mistress, Miss or Master Speaker, (whichever you may happen to be,) I beg leave to observe that this is only one of the uses for which that member was formed, and that for this alone it has deserved to be called an unruly member; it is not its primary, nor by any means its most important use. For what use was it given to thy labourer the ox, thy servant the horse, thy friend,—if thou deservest to have such a friend,—the dog,—thy playfellow the kitten,—and thy cousin the monkey? †

In another place I shall answer my own question, which was asked in this place, because it is for my present purpose to make it appear that the tongue, although a very convenient instrument of speech, is not necessary for it.

It is related in Gibbon's great history, a work which can never be too highly praised for its ability, nor too severely condemned for the false philosophy which pervades it, that the Catholics, inhabitants of Tipasa, a maritime colony of Mauritania, were by command of the Arian King, Hunneric, Genseric's detestable son and successor, assembled on the forum, and there deprived of their right hands and their tongues. "But the holy confessors," he proceeds to say, "continued to speak without tongues;

* This refers to Vol. vii. of the edition in 8vo.

† Simia quam similis, turpissima bestia notis. ENNIUS.

and this miracle is attested by Victor, an African bishop, who published an history of the persecution within two years after the event. 'If any one,' says Victor, 'should doubt of the truth, let him repair to Constantinople, and listen to the clear and perfect language of Restitutus, the subdeacon, one of these glorious sufferers, who is now lodged in the palace of the Emperor Zeno, and is respected by the devout Empress.' At Constantinople we are astonished to find a cool, a learned, an unexceptionable witness, without interest and without passion. Æneas of Gaza, a Platonic philosopher, has accurately described his own observations on these African sufferers. 'I saw them myself: I heard them speak: I diligently inquired by what means such an articulate voice could be formed without any organ of speech: I used my eyes to examine the report of my ears: I opened their mouth, and saw that the whole tongue had been completely torn away by the roots; an operation which the physicians generally suppose to be mortal.' The testimony of Æneas of Gaza might be confirmed by the superfluous evidence of the Emperor Justinian, in a perpetual edict; of Count Marcellinus in his Chronicles of the times; and of Pope Gregory the First, who had resided at Constantinople as the minister of the Roman Pontiff. They all lived within the compass of a century, and they all appeal to their personal knowledge, or the public notoriety, for the truth of a miracle, which was repeated in several instances, displayed on the greatest theatre of the world, and submitted during a series of years, to the calm examination of the senses." He adds in a note that "the miracle is enhanced by the singular instance of a boy who had *never* spoken before his tongue was cut out."

Now comes the unbelieving historian's comment. He says, "this supernatural gift of the African confessors, who spoke without tongues, will command the assent of those, and of those only, who already believe, that their language was pure and orthodox. But the stubborn mind of an infidel is guarded by secret, incurable suspicion; and the Arian, or Socinian, who has seriously rejected the doctrines of the Trinity, will not be shaken by the most plausible evidence of an Athanasian miracle."

Well has the sceptical historian applied the epithet stubborn to a mind affected with the same disease as his own.

Oh dear unbelief
How wealthy dost thou make thy owner's wit!
Thou train of knowledge, what a privilege
Thou givest to thy possessor! anchorest him
From floating with the tide of vulgar faith,
From being damn'd with multitudes! *

Gibbon would not believe the story because it had been adduced as a miracle in confirmation of the Catholic doctrine as opposed to the Arian heresy. He might probably have questioned the relation between the alleged miracle and the doctrine: and if he had argued that it is not consistent with the plan of revelation (so far as we may presume to reason upon it) for a miracle to be wrought in proof of a doctrinal point, a Christian who believes sincerely in that very doctrine might agree with him.

But the circumstances are attested, as he fairly admits, by the most ample and unexceptionable testimony; and like the Platonic philosopher whose evidence he quotes, he ought to have considered the matter of fact, without regard to the application which the Catholics, in perfect good faith, made of it. The story is true, but it is not miraculous.

Cases which demonstrate the latter part of this question were known to physiologists before a book was published at Paris in the year 1765, the title of which I find in Mr. D'Israeli's Curiosities of Literature, thus translated; "The Christian Religion proved by a single fact; or a Dissertation in which is shown that those Catholics whose tongues Hunneric King of the Vandals cut out, spoke miraculously all the remainder of their days: from whence is deduced the consequence of the miracle against the Arians, the Socinians and the Deists, and particularly against the author of Emilius,

* Marston.

by solving their difficulties." It bears this motto, *Ecce Ego admirationem facio populo huic, miraculo grandi et stupendo.* And Mr. D'Israeli closes his notice of the Book by saying "there needs no farther account of it than the title." That gentleman, who has contributed so much to the instruction and entertainment of his contemporaries, will I am sure be pleased at perusing the facts in disproof of the alleged miracle, brought together here by one who as a Christian believes in miracles and that they have not ceased, and that they never will cease.

In the Philosophical Transactions, and in the Gentleman's Magazine, is an account of a woman, Margaret Cutting by name, who about the middle of the last century was living at Wickham Market in Suffolk. When she was four years of age "a cancer ate off her tongue at the root, yet she never lost the power of speech, and could both read distinctly afterwards and sing." Her speech was very intelligible, but it was a little through the nose owing to the want of the uvula; and her voice was low. In this case a new tongue had been formed, about an inch and half in length and half an inch broad; but this did not grow till some years after the cure.

Upon the publication of this case it was observed that some few instances of a like nature had been recorded; and one in particular by Tulpius of a man whom he had himself examined, who, having had his tongue cut out by the Turks, could after three years speak distinctly. One of the persons who published an account of this woman saw several men upon whom the same act of cruelty had been committed by these barbarians or by the Algerines: "one of them," says he, "aged thirty-three, wrote a good hand, and by that means answered my questions. He informed me that he could not pronounce a syllable, nor make any articulate sound; though he had often observed that those who suffered that treatment when they were very young, were some years after able to speak; and that their tongues might be observed to grow in proportion to the other parts of the body: but that if they were adults, or full-grown persons, at the time of the operation, they were never able to utter a syllable. The truth of this observation was confirmed to me by the two following cases. Patrick Strainer and his son-in-law came to Harwich, in their way to Holland, the third of this month. I made it my business to see and examine them. The father told me he had his tongue cut out by the Algerines, when he was seven years of age: and that some time after he was able to pronounce many syllables, and can now speak most words tolerably well; his tongue, he said, was grown at least half an inch. The son-in-law, who is about thirty years of age, was taken by the Turks, who cut out his tongue; he cannot pronounce a syllable; nor is his tongue grown at all since the operation; which was more than five years ago."

Sir John Malcolm, in one of his visits to Persia, became acquainted with Zâl Khan of Khist, who "was long distinguished as one of the bravest and most attached followers of the Zend family. When the death of Lootf Ali Khan terminated its powers, he, along with the other governors of provinces and districts in Furs, submitted to Aza Mahomed Khan. That cautious and cruel monarch, dreading the ability, and doubtful of the allegiance of this chief, ordered his eyes to be put out. An appeal for the recall of the sentence being treated with disdain, Zâl Khan loaded the tyrant with curses. 'Cut out his tongue,' was the second order. The mandate was imperfectly executed, and the loss of half this member deprived him of speech. Being afterwards persuaded that its being cut close to the root would enable him to speak so as to be understood, he submitted to the operation; and the effect has been, that his voice, though indistinct and thick, is yet intelligible to persons accustomed to converse with him. This I experienced from daily intercourse. He often spoke to me of his sufferings and of the humanity of the present King, who had restored him to his situation as head of his tribe, and governor of Khist. — I am not an anatomist," Sir John adds, "and cannot therefore give a reason why a man, who could not articulate with half a tongue, should speak when he had none at all. But the facts are as stated; and I had them from the very best authority, old Zâl Khan himself." *

A case occurred in the household of that Dr. Mark Duncan whom our James I. would have engaged as his Physician in ordinary, but Duncan having married at Saumur and settled in that city declined the invitation, because his wife was unwilling to leave her friends and relations and her native place. Yielding therefore, as became him, to her natural and reasonable reluctance, he passed the remainder of his useful and honourable life at Saumur. It is noticed as a remarkable circumstance that the five persons of whom his family consisted died and were interred in as many different kingdoms, one in France, another at Naples, a third at Stockholm, a fourth in London, and the fifth in Ireland. A son of Duncan's valet, in his thirteenth year, lost his tongue by the effects of the small-pox, the root being so consumed by this dreadful disease, that in a fit of coughing it came away. The boy's speech was no otherwise affected by the loss than that he found it difficult to pronounce the letter r. He was exhibited throughout Europe, and lived long afterwards. A surgeon at Saumur composed a treatise upon the case, and Duncan, who was then Principal of the College in that city, supplied him with this title for it Aglossostomographie. A rival physician published a dissertation to prove that it ought to be Aglossostomatographie, and he placed these verses at the conclusion of this odd treatise.

Lecteur, tu t'esmerveilleras
Qu'un garçon qui n'a point de langue,
Prononce bien une harangue;
Mais bien plus tu t'estonneras
Qu'un barbier que ne sçait pas lire
Le grec, se mesle d'en escrire.
Que si ce plaisant épigramme,
Doux fruit d'un penser de mon âme
Te semble n'aller pas tant mal,
C'est que je l'ai fait à cheval.

Quelques gens malins changerent le dernier vers dans les exemplaires qu'ils purent trouver, et y mirent — C'est que je l'ai fait en *cheval.*

The reader who thinks upon what he reads, will find some materials for thinking on, in what has here been collected for him. First as to the physical facts:— they show that the power of reproduction exists in the human body, in a greater degree than has been commonly supposed. But it is probable that this power would be found only in young subjects, or in adults whose constitutions were unusually healthful and vigorous. A very small proportion of the snails which have been decapitated by experimental physiologists have reproduced their heads; though the fact of such reproduction is certainly established.

Rhazes records two cases which had fallen under his own observation; in one of which the tibia, in the other the under-jaw, had been reproduced; neither acquired the consistency of the other bones. The Doctor used to adduce these cases in support of a favourite theory of his own, with which the reader will in due time be made acquainted.

Secondly, there is a moral inference to be drawn from the effect which the story produced upon Gibbon. He could not invalidate, or dispute the testimony upon which it came before him; but he chose to disbelieve it. For he was ignorant that the facts might be physically true, and he would not on any evidence give credit to what appeared miraculous. A stubborn mind conduces as little to wisdom, or even to knowledge, as a stubborn temper to happiness.

* This account of Zâl Khan (Mrs. Southey writes me word) was farther confirmed by the testimony of Mr. Bruce, her relative, who knew him and had *looked* into the tongue-less mouth. Mr. Bruce was well acquainted with another person who had undergone the same cruel punishment. Being a wealthy man, he bribed the executioner to spare a considerable portion of the tongue; but finding that he could not articulate a word with the imperfect member, he had it entirely extracted — root and all, and then spoke almost as intelligibly as before his punishment.

This person was well known at Calcutta, as well as at Bushire and Shiraz — where Mr. Bruce first became acquainted with him. He was a man of some consequence and received as such in the first circles at Calcutta, and it was in one of those — a dinner party — that on the question being warmly argued — as to the possibility of articulation after the extraction of the tongue, he opened his mouth and desired the company assembled to look into it, and so set their doubts on the matter for ever at rest.

CHAPTER CCII.

A LAW OF ALFRED'S AGAINST LYING TONGUES. OBSERVATIONS ON LAX ONES.

As I have gained no small satisfaction to myself, — so I am desirous that nothing that occurs here may occasion the least dissatisfaction to others. And I think it will be impossible anything should, if they will be but pleased to take notice of my design. HENRY MORE.

If the laws of our great Alfred, whose memory is held in such veneration by all who are well acquainted with his history, and his extraordinary virtues, and whose name has been so often taken in vain by speculative reformers who were ignorant of the one, and incapable of estimating the other; — if the laws of Alfred, I say, had continued in use, everything relating to the reproduction of human tongues would long before this time have been thoroughly understood; for by those laws any one who broached a public falsehood, and persisted in it, was to have his tongue cut out; and this punishment might not be commuted for any smaller fine than that at which the life of the criminal would have been rated.

The words of the law are these:

DE RUMORIBUS FICTITIIS.

Si quis publicum mendacium confingat, et ille in eo firmetur, nullâ levi re hoc emendet, sed lingua ei excidatur; nec minori precio redimi liceat, quam juxta capitis æstimationem censebatur.

What a wholesome effect might such a law have produced upon orators at public meetings, upon the periodical press, and upon the debates in Parliament.

"I am charmed," says Lady M. W. Montague, "with many points of the Turkish law, to our shame be it spoken, better designed and better executed than ours; particularly the punishment of convicted liars (triumphant criminals in our country, God knows!): they are burnt in the forehead with a hot iron, when they are proved the authors of any notorious falsehoods. How many white foreheads should we see disfigured, how many fine gentlemen would be forced to wear their wigs as low as their eyebrows, were this law in practice with us!"

But who can expect that human laws should correct that propensity in the wicked tongue! They who have "the poison of asps under their lips," and "which have said with our tongues will we prevail; we are they that ought to speak: who is lord over us?" — they who "love to speak all words that may do hurt, and who cut with lies like a sharp razor" — what would they care for enactments which they would think either to evade by their subtlety, or to defy in the confidence of their numbers and their strength? Is it to be expected that those men should regard the laws of their country, who set at nought the denunciations of scripture, and will not "keep their tongues from evil, and their lips that they speak no guile," though they have been told that it is "he who hath used no deceit in his tongue and hath not slandered his neighbour, who shall dwell in the tabernacle of the Lord, and rest upon his holy hill!"

Leave we them to their reward, which is as certain as that men shall be judged according to their deeds. Our business is with the follies of the unruly member, not with its sins: with loquacious speakers and verbose writers, those whose "tongues are gentelmen-ushers to their wit, and still go before it,"* who never having studied the *exponibilia*, practise the art of battology by intuition; and in a discourse which might make the woeful hearer begin to fear that he had entered unawares upon eternity, bring forth, "as a man would say in a word of two syllables, nothing."* The West Britons had in their own Cornish language this good proverbial rhyme, (the — graphy whereof, be it ortho or not is Mr. Polwhele's,)

An lavor goth ewe lavar gwir,
Ne vedn nevera doaz vas a tavaz re hir.
The old saying is a true saying,
Never will come good from a tongue too long.

Oh it is a grievous thing to listen, or seem to listen as one is constrained to do, some-

* BEN JONSON.

times by the courtesy of society, and sometimes by "the law of sermon," to an unmerciful manufacturer of speech, who before he ever arrives at the empty matter of his discourse,

> *no puede — dexar — de decir*
> *— antes, — siguiera*
> *quatro, o cinco mil palabras!* *

Vossius mentions three authors, who, to use Bayle's language, — for in Bayle the extract is found, *enfermaient de grands riens dans une grande multitude de paroles.* Anaximenes the orator was one; when he was about to speak, Theocritus of Chios said, "here begins a river of words and a drop of sense," — Ἄρχεται λέξεων μὲν ποταμὸς, νοῦ δὲ σταλαγμός. Longolius, an orator of the Lower Empire, was the second. The third was Faustus Andrelinus, Professor of Poetry at Paris, and *Poeta Laureatus:* of him Erasmus *dicitur dixisse,* — is said to have said, — that there was but one thing wanting in all his poems, and that thing was comprised in one word of one syllable, ΝΟΥΣ.

It were better to be remembered as Bayle has remembered Petrus Carmilianus, because of the profound obscurity in which this pitiful poet was buried, than thus to be thought worthy of remembrance only for having produced a great deal that deserved to be forgotten. There is, or was, an officer of the Exchequer called Clericus Nihilorum, or Clerk of the Nihils. If there were a High Court of Literature with such an officer on its establishment, it would be no sinecure office for him in these, or in any days, to register the names of those authors who have written to no purpose, and the titles of those books from which nothing is to be learned.

On ne vid jamais, says the Sieur de Brocourt, *homme qui ne die plustost trop, que moins qu'il ne doit; et jamais parole proferée ne servit tant, comme plusieurs teuës ont profite; car tousjours pouvons-nous bien dire ce qu'avons teu, et non pas taire ce qu'avons publié.* The latter part of this remark is true; the former is far too general. For more harm is done in public life by the reticence of well-informed men, than by the loquacity of sciolists; more by the timidity and caution of those who desire at heart the good of their country, than by the audacity of those who labour to overthrow its constitutions. It was said in the days of old, that "a man full of words shall not prosper upon the earth." *Mais nous avons changé tout cela.*†

Even in literature a leafy style, if there be any fruit under the foliage, is preferable to a knotty one, however fine the grain. Whipt cream is a good thing; and better still when it covers and adorns that amiable combination of sweetmeats and ratafia cakes soaked in wine, to which Cowper likened his delightful poem, when he thus described the "Task." "It is a medley of many things, some that may be useful, and some that, for aught I know, may be very diverting. I am merry that I may decoy people into my company, and grave that they may be the better for it. Now and then I put on the garb of a philosopher, and take the opportunity that disguise procures me, to drop a word in favour of religion. In short, there is some froth, and here and there a bit of sweetmeat, which seems to entitle it justly to the name of a certain dish the ladies call a Trifle." But in Task or Trifle unless the ingredients were good, the whole were nought. They who should present to their deceived guests whipt white of egg would deserve to be whipt themselves.

If there be any one who begins to suspect that in tasking myself, and trifling with my reader, my intent is not unlike Cowper's, he will allow me to say to him, "by your leave, Master Critic, you must give me licence to flourish my phrases, to embellish my lines, to adorn my oratory, to embroider my speeches, to interlace my words, to draw out my sayings, and to bombard the whole suit of the business for the time of your wearing."‡

* Calderon.

† See Remarks on Mr. Evans's Third Series of Scripture Biography: "Moses," p. 43.

‡ Taylor, the Water Poet.

CHAPTER CCIII.

WHETHER A MAN AND HIMSELF BE TWO. MAXIM OF BAYLE'S. ADAM LITTLETON'S SERMONS, — A RIGHT-HEARTED OLD DIVINE WITH WHOM THE AUTHOR HOPES TO BE BETTER ACQUAINTED IN A BETTER WORLD. THE READER REFERRED TO HIM FOR EDIFICATION. WHY THE AUTHOR PURCHASED HIS SERMONS.

Parolles. Go to, thou art a witty fool, I have found thee.

Clown. Did you find me in yourself, Sir? or were you taught to find me? The search, Sir, was profitable; and much fool may you find in you, even to the world's pleasure and the increase of laughter.

ALL'S WELL THAT ENDS WELL.

"WHETHER this author means to make his Doctor more fool or philosopher, is more than I can discover," says a grave reader, who lays down the open book, and knits his brow while he considers the question.

Make him, good Reader! I, *make* him! — make "the noblest work of ——" But as the Spaniards say, *el creer es cortesia*, and it is at your pleasure either to believe the veracity of these biographical sketches, or to regard them as altogether fictitious. It is at your pleasure, I say; not at your peril: but take heed how you exercise that pleasure in cases which are perilous! The worst that can happen to you for disbelief in this matter is, that I shall give you little credit for courtesy, and less for discrimination; and in Doncaster you will be laughed to scorn. You might as well proclaim at Coventry your disbelief in the history of Lady Godiva and Peeping Tom; or tell the Swiss that their tale of shooting the apple on the child's head was an old story before William Tell was born.

But perhaps you did not mean to express any such groundless incredulity, your doubt may be whether I represent or consider my friend as having in his character a larger portion of folly or of philosophy?

This you might determine, Reader, for yourself, if I could succeed in delineating him to the life, — the inner I mean, not the outward man,

Et en peu de papier, comme sur un tableau,
*Vous pourtraire au naïf tout son bon, et son beau.**

He was the soul of goodness,
And all our praises of him are like streams
Drawn from a spring, that still rise full, and leave
The part remaining greatest.

But the Duchess of Newcastle hath decided in her philosophy that it is not possible for any one person thoroughly to understand the character of another. In her own words, "if the Mind was not joined and mixed with the sensitive and inanimate parts, and had not interior as well as exterior parts, the whole Mind of one man might perceive the whole Mind of another man; but that being not possible — one whole Mind cannot perceive another whole Mind." By which observation we may perceive there are no Platonic Lovers in Nature. An odd conclusion of her Grace's, and from odd premises. But she was an odd personage.

So far, however, the beautiful and fanciful as well as fantastic Duchess is right, that the more congenial the disposition of two persons who stand upon the same intellectual level, the better they understand each other. The lower any one is sunk in animal life, the less is he capable of apprehending the motives and views of those who have cultivated the better part of their nature.

If I am so unfortunate as to fail in producing the moral likeness which I am endeavouring to pourtray, it will not be owing to any want of sympathy with the subject in some of the most marked features of his character.

It is a maxim of Bayle's, *Qu'il n'y a point de grand esprit dans le caractère du quel il n'entre un peu de folie.* And he named Diogenes as one proof of this. Think indeed somewhat more than a little upon the words folly and philosophy, and if you can see any way into a mist, or a stone wall, you will perceive that the same radicals are found in both.

This sort of mixed character was never more whimsically described than by Andrew

* PASQUIER.

Erskine in one of his letters to Boswell, in which he tells him, "since I saw you I received a letter from Mr. D——; it is filled with encomiums upon you; he says there is a great deal of humility in your vanity, a great deal of tallness in your shortness, and a great deal of whiteness in your black complexion. He says there's a great deal of poetry in your prose, and a great deal of prose in your poetry. He says that as to your late publication, there is a great deal of Ode in your Dedication, and a great deal of Dedication in your Ode. He says there is a great deal of coat in your waistcoat, and a great deal of waistcoat in your coat, that there is a great deal of liveliness in your stupidity, and a great deal of stupidity in your liveliness. But to write you all he says would require rather more fire in my grate than there is at present, and my fingers would undoubtedly be numbed, for there is a great deal of snow in this frost, and a great deal of frost in this snow."

The Marquis de Custine in a book which in all its parts, wise or foolish, strikingly characterises its author, describes himself thus: *J'ai un mélange de gravité et de légèreté qui m'empêchera de devenir autre chose qu'un vieil enfant bien triste. Si je suis destiné à éprouver de grands malheurs, j'aurai l'occasion de remercier Dieu de m'avoir fait naitre avec cette disposition à la fois sérieuse et frivole : le sérieux m'aidera à me passer du monde — l'enfantillage à supporter le douleur. C'est à quoi il réussit mieux que la raison.*

Un peu de folie there certainly was in the *grand esprit* of my dear master, and more than *un peu* there is in his faithful pupil. But I shall not enter into a discussion whether the gravity of which the Marquis speaks preponderated in his character, or whether it was more than counterpoised by the levity. Enough of the latter, thank Heaven! enters into my own composition not only to preserve me from becoming *un vieil enfant bien triste*, but to entitle me in all innocent acceptance of the phrase to the appellation of a merry old boy, that is to say, merry at becoming times, there being a time for all things. I shall not enter into the discussion as it concerns my guide, philosopher and friend, because it would be altogether unnecessary; he carried ballast enough, whatever I may do. The elements were so happily mixed in him that though Nature did not stand up and say to all the world "this is a man," because such a miracle could neither be in the order of Nature or of Providence; — I have thought it my duty to sit down and say to the public this was a Doctor.

There is another reason why I shall refrain from any such inquiry; and that reason may be aptly given in the words of a right-hearted old divine, with whom certain congenialities would lead my friend to become acquainted in that world, where I also hope in due season to meet and converse with him.

"People," says Adam Littleton, "are generally too forward in examining others, and are so taken up with impertinence and things that do not concern them, that they have no time to be acquainted with themselves; like idle travellers, that can tell you a world of stories concerning foreign countries, and are very strangers at home. Study of ourselves is the most useful knowledge, as that without which we can know neither God nor anything else aright, as we should know them.

"And it highly concerns us to know ourselves well; nor will our ignorance be pardonable, but prove an everlasting reproach, in that we and ourselves are to be inseparable companions in bliss or torment to all eternity; and if we, through neglect of ourselves here, do not in time provide for that eternity, so as to secure for ourselves future happiness, God will at last make us know ourselves, when it will be too late to make any good use of that knowledge, but a remediless repentance that we and ourselves ever met in company; when poor ruined self shall curse negligent sinful self to all ages, and wish direful imprecations upon that day and hour that first joined them together.

"Again, God has given man that advantage above all other creatures, that he can with reflex acts look back and pass judgment upon himself. But seeing examination here supposes two persons, the one to examine, the other to be examined, and yet seems to name but one, a man to examine himself; unless a man and himself be two, and thus every one of us have two selfs in him; let us first examine who 'tis here is to execute the office of examinant, and then who 'tis that is to be the party examined.

"Does the whole man in this action go over himself by parts? Or does the regenerate part call the unregenerate part to account? Or if there be a divided self in every man, does one self examine the other self, as to wit, the spiritual self, the carnal self? Or is it some one faculty in a man, by which a man brings all his other faculties and parts to trial, — such a one as the conscience may be? If so, how then is conscience itself tried, having no Peers to be tried by, as being superior to all other human powers, and calling them all to the bar?"

Here let me interpose a remark. Whether a man and himself be two must be all one in the end; but woe to that house in which the man and his wife are!

> The end of love is to have two made one
> In will, and in affection.*

The old Lexicographer answers his own question thus: "Why, yes; I do think 'tis the conscience of a man which examines the man, and every part of him, both spiritual and carnal, as well regenerate as unregenerate, and itself and all. For hence it was called *conscientia*, as being that faculty by which a man becomes conscious to himself, and is made knowing together with himself of all that good and evil that lies working in his nature, and has been brought forth in his actions. And this is not only the Register, and Witness and Judge of all parts of man, and of all that they do, but is so impartial an officer also, that it will give a strict account of all itself at any time does, *accusing* or *excusing* even itself in every motion of its own."

Reader I would proceed with this extract, were it not for its length. The application which immediately follows it, is eloquently and forcibly made, and I exhort thee if ever thou comest into a library where Adam Littleton's Sermons are upon the shelf,

> look
> Not *on*, but *in* this Thee-concerning book! †

Take down the goodly tome, and turn to the sermon of Self-Examination, preached before the (Royal) Family at Whitehall, March 3, 1677–8. You will find this passage in the eighty-sixth page of the second paging, and I advise you to proceed with it to the end of the Discourse.

I will tell the reader for what reason I purchased that goodly tome. It was because of my grateful liking for the author, from the end of whose dictionary I, like Daniel in his boyhood, derived more entertainment and information to boot, than from any other book which, in those days, came within the walls of a school. That he was a truly learned man no one who ever used that dictionary could doubt, and if there had not been oddity enough in him to give his learning a zest, he never could have compounded an appellation for the Monument, commemorating in what he calls an heptastic vocable, — which may be interpreted a seven-leagued word, — the seven Lord Mayors of London under whose mayoralties the construction of that lying pillar went on from its commencement to its completion. He called it the Fordo-Watermanno-Hansono-Hookero-Vinero-Sheldono-Davisian pillar.

I bought the book for the author's sake, — which in the case of a living author is a proper and meritorious motive, and in the case of one who is dead, may generally be presumed to be a wise one. It proved so in this instance. For though there is nothing that bears the stamp of oddity in his sermons, there is much that is sterling. They have a merit of their own, and it is of no mean

* Ben Jonson.

† Sir William Denny.

degree. Their manner is neither Latimerist nor Andrewesian, nor Fullerish, nor Cotton-Matherish, nor Jeremy Taylorish, nor Barrowish, nor Southish, but Littletonian. They are full of learning, of wisdom, of sound doctrine, and of benevolence, and of earnest and persuasive piety. No one who had ears to hear could have slept under them, and few could have listened to them without improvement.

CHAPTER CCIV.

ADAM LITTLETON'S STATEMENT THAT EVERY MAN IS MADE UP OF THREE EGOS. DEAN YOUNG — DISTANCE BETWEEN A MAN'S HEAD AND HIS HEART.

Perhaps when the Reader considers the copiousness of the argument, he will rather blame me for being too brief than too tedious. DR. JOHN SCOTT.

In the passage quoted from Adam Littleton in the preceding chapter, that good old divine inquired whether a man and himself were two. A Moorish prince in the most extravagant of Dryden's extravagant tragedies, (they do not deserve to be called romantic,) agrees with him, and exclaims to his confidential friend,

> Assist me, Zulema, if thou wouldst be
> The friend thou seem'st, assist me against me.

Machiavel says of Cosmo de Medici that whoever considered his gravity and his levity might say there were two distinct persons in him.

"There is often times," says Dean Young, (father of the poet,) "a prodigious distance betwixt a man's head and his heart; such a distance that they seem not to have any correspondence; not to belong to the same person, not to converse in the same world. Our heads are sometimes in Heaven, contemplating the nature of God, the blessedness of Saints, the state of eternity; while our hearts are held captive below in a conversation earthly, sensual, devilish. 'Tis possible we may sometimes commend virtue convincingly, unanswerably; and yet our own hearts be never affected by our own arguments; we may represent vice in her native dress of horror, and yet our hearts be not at all startled with their own menaces. We may study and acquaint ourselves with all the truths of religion, and yet all this out of curiosity, or hypocrisy, or ostentation; not out of the power of godliness, or the serious purpose of good living. All which is a sufficient proof that the consent of the Head and of the Heart are two different things."

Dean Young may seem in this passage to have answered Adam the Lexicographist's query in the affirmative, by showing that the head belongs sometimes to one Self and the heart to the other. Yet these two Selves, notwithstanding this continual discord, are so united in matrimony, and so inseparably made one flesh, that it becomes another query whether death itself can part them.

The aforesaid Dean concludes one of his Discourses with the advice of an honest heathen. *Learn to be one Man;* that is, learn to live and act alike. "For," says he, "while we act from contrary principles; sometimes give, and sometimes defraud; sometimes love, and sometimes betray; sometimes are devout, and sometimes careless of God; this is to be *two* Men, which is a foolish aim, and always ends in loss of pains. 'No,' says wise Epictetus, '*Learn to be one Man,*' thou mayest be a good man; or thou mayest be a bad man, and that to the purpose; but it is impossible that thou shouldst be both. And here the Philosopher had the happiness to fall in exactly with the notion of my text. *We cannot serve two Masters.*"

But in another sermon Adam Littleton says that "every man is made of three Egos, and has three Selfs in him;" and that this "appears in the reflection of Conscience upon actions of a dubious nature; whilst one Self accuses, another Self defends, and the third Self passes judgment upon what hath been so done by the man!" This he adduced as among various "means and unworthy comparisons, whereby to show that though the mysterious doctrine of the Trinity" far exceeds our reason, there want not natural instances to illustrate it. But he adds most properly that we should neither "say or think aught of God in this kind," without a preface of reverence and asking pardon; "for it is sufficient for us and most suitable to the mystery, so to conceive, so to discourse of God, as He himself has been pleased to make Himself known to us in his Word."

If all theologians had been as wise, as humble, and as devout as Adam Littleton, from how many heresies and evils might Christendom have been spared!

In the Doctor's own days the proposition was advanced, and not as a paradox, that a man might be in several places at the same time. *Presence corporelle de l'homme en plusieurs lieux prouvée possible par les principes de la bonne Philosophie* is the title of a treatise by the Abbé de Lignac, who having been first a Jesuit, and then an Oratorian, secularised himself without departing from the principles in which he had been trained up. The object of his treatise was to show that there is nothing absurd in the doctrine of Transubstantiation. He made a distinction between man and his body, the body being always in a state of change, the man remaining the while identically the same. But how his argument that because a worm may be divided and live, the life which animated it while it was whole continues a single life when it animates all the parts into which the body may have separated, proves his proposition, or how his proposition, if proved, could prove the hyper-mysterious figment of the Romish Church to be no figment, but a divine truth capable of philosophical demonstration, Œdipus himself were he raised from the dead would be unable to explain.

CHAPTER CCV.

EQUALITY OF THE SEXES, — A POINT ON WHICH IT WAS NOT EASY TO COLLECT THE DOCTOR'S OPINION. THE SALIC LAW. DANIEL ROGERS'S TREATISE OF MATRIMONIAL HONOUR. MISS HATFIELD'S LETTERS ON THE IMPORTANCE OF THE FEMALE SEX, AND LODOVICO DOMENICHI'S DIALOGUE UPON THE NOBLENESS OF WOMEN.

Mirths and toys
To cozen time withal: for o' my troth, Sir,
I can love, — I think well too, — well enough;
And think as well of women as they are,—
Pretty fantastic things, some more regardful,
And some few worth a service. I'm so honest
I wish 'em all in Heaven, and you know how hard, Sir,
'Twill be to get in there with their great farthingals.

BEAUMONT AND FLETCHER.

And not much easier now with their great sleeves.

AUTHOR, A. D. 1830.

THE question concerning the equality of the sexes, which was discussed so warmly some thirty years ago in Magazines and Debating Societies, was one upon which it was not easy to collect the Doctor's real opinion. His manner indeed was frequently sportive when his meaning was most serious, and as frequently the thoughts and speculations with which he merely played, and which were sports or exercitations of intellect and humour, were advanced with apparent gravity. The propensity, however, was always retained within due bounds, for he had treasured up his father's lessons in his heart, and would have regarded it as a crime ever to have trifled with his principles or feelings. But this question concerning the sexes was a subject which he was fond of introducing before his female acquaintance; it was like hitting the right note for a dog when you play the flute, he said. The sort of half anger, and the indignation, and the astonishment, and the merriment withal, which he excited when he enlarged upon this fertile theme, amused him greatly, and moreover he had a secret pleasure in observing the invincible good-humour of his wife, even when she thought it necessary for the honour of her sex to put on a semblance of wrath at the notions which he repeated, and the comments with which he accompanied them.

He used to rest his opinion of male superiority upon divinity, law, grammar, natural history, and the universal consent of nations. Noting also by the way, that in the noble science of heraldry, it is laid down as a rule "that amongst things sensitive the males are of more worthy bearing than the females." *

The Salic law he looked upon as in this respect the Law of Nature. And therefore he thought it was wisely appointed in France, that the royal Midwife should receive a fee of five hundred crowns upon the birth of a boy, and only three hundred if it were a female child. This the famous Louise Bourgeois has stated to be the custom, who for the edification of posterity, the advancement of her own science, and the use of French historians, published a *Recit veritable de la naissance de Messieurs et Dames les enfans de France*, containing minute details of every royal parturition at which she had officiated.

But he dwelt with more force on the theological grounds of his position. "The wife is the weaker vessel. Wives submit yourselves to your husbands: be in subjection to them. The Husband is the head. Sarah obeyed Abraham, calling him Lord." And here he had recourse to the authority of Daniel Rogers, (whom he liked the better for his name's sake,) who in his Treatise of Matrimonial Honour teaches that the duty of subjection is woman's chief commandment; and that she is properly made subject by the Law of Creation and by the Law of Penalty. As thus. All other creatures were created male and female at the same time; man and woman were not so, for the Man was first created — as a perfect creature, and afterwards the woman was thought of. Moreover she was not made of the same matter, equally, with man, — but of him, of a rib taken from him, and thirdly, she was made for his use and benefit as a meet helpmate, "three weighty reasons and grounds of the woman's subjection to the man, and that from the purpose of the Creator; who might have done otherwise, that is, have yielded to the Woman co-equal beginning, sameness of generation, or relation of usefulness; for he might have made her without any such precedency of matter, without any dependency upon him, and equally for her good as for his. All show at ennobling the Man as the Head and more excellent, not that the Man might upbraid her, but that she might in all these read her lesson of subjection. And doubtless, as Malachi speaks, herein is wisdom, for God hath left nothing to be bettered by our invention.

"The woman, being so created by God in the integrity of Nature had a most divine honour and partnership of his image, put upon her in her creation; yea, such as (without prejudice of those three respects) might have held full and sweet correspondence with her husband. But her sin still augmented her inequality, and brought her lower and lower in her prerogative. For since she would take upon her, as a woman, without respect to the order, dependence and use of her creation, to enterprise so sad a business, as to jangle and demur with the Devil about so weighty a point as her husband's freehold, and of her own brain to lay him and it under foot, without the least parley and consent of his, obeying Satan before him, — so that till she had put all beyond question and past amendment, and eaten, she brought not the fruit to him, therefore the Lord stript her of this robe of her honour, and smote into the heart of Eve an instinct of inferiority, a confessed yielding up of her insufficient self to depend wholly upon her husband."

This being a favourite commentary with the Doctor upon the first transgression, what would he have said if he had lived to read an Apology for Eve by one of her daughters? — yes, an Apology for her and a Defence, showing that she acted meritoriously in eating the Apple. It is a choice passage, and the reader shall have it from Miss Hatfield's Letters on the Importance of the Female Sex.

"By the creation of woman, the great design was accomplished, — the universal system was harmonised. Happiness and in-

* Gwillim.

nocence reigned together. But unacquainted with the nature or existence of evil, — conscious only of good and imagining that all were of that essence around her; without the advantages of the tradition of forefathers to relate, or of ancient records to hand down, Eve was fatally and necessarily ignorant of the rebellious disobedience of the fallen Angels, and of their invisible vigilance and combination to accomplish the destruction of the new favourites of Heaven.

"In so momentous an event as that which has ever been exclusively imputed to her, neither her virtue nor her prudence ought to be suspected; and there is little reason to doubt, that if the same temptations had been offered to her husband under the same appearances, but he also would have acquiesced in the commission of this act of disobedience.

"Eve's attention was attracted by the manner in which the Serpent first made his attack: he had the gift of speech, which she must have observed to be a faculty peculiar to themselves. This appeared an evidence of something supernatural. The wily tempter chose also the form of the serpent to assist his design, as not only in wisdom and sagacity that creature surpassed all others, but his figure was also erect and beautiful, for it was not until the offended justice of God denounced the curse, that the Serpent's crest was humbled to the dust.

"During this extraordinary interview, it is evident that Eve felt a full impression of the divine command, which she repeated to the tempter at the time of his solicitations. She told him they were not to eat of *that* Tree. — But the Serpent opposed her arguments with sophistry and promises. He said unto the Woman, ye shall not surely die—but shall be as Gods. What an idea to a mortal! — Such an image astonished her! — It was not the gross impulses of greedy appetite that urged her, but a nobler motive had induced her to examine the consequences of the act. — She was to be better and happier; — to exchange a mortal for an angelic nature. Her motive was great, — virtuous, — irresistible. Might she not have felt herself awed and inspired with a belief of a divine order? —Upon examination she found it was to produce a greater good than as mortals they could enjoy; this impression excited a desire to possess that good; and that desire determined her will and the future destiny of a World!"

It must be allowed that this Lady Authoress has succeeded in what might have been supposed the most difficult of all attempts, that of starting a new heresy, — her followers in which may aptly be denominated Eveites.

The novelty consists not in excusing the mother of mankind, but in representing her transgression as a great and meritorious act. An excuse has been advanced for her in Lodovico Domenichi's Dialogue upon the Nobleness of Women. It is there pleaded that the fruit of the fatal tree had not been forbidden to Eve, because she was not created when the prohibition was laid on. Adam it was who sinned in eating it, not Eve, and it is in Adam that we have all sinned, and all die. Her offence was in tempting him to eat, *et questo anchora senza intention cattiva, essendo stata tentata dal Diavolo. L'huomo adunque peccò per certa scientia, et la Donna ignorantemente, et ingannata.*

I know not whether this special pleading be Domenichi's own; but he must have been conscious that there is a flaw in it, and could not have been in earnest, as Miss Hatfield is. The Veronese lady Isotta Nogarola thought differently; *essendo studiosa molto di Theologia et di Philosophia*, she composed a Dialogue wherein the question whether Adam or Eve in the primal transgression had committed the greater sin. How she determined it I cannot say, never having seen her works.

Domenichi makes another assertion in honour of womankind which Miss Hatfield would undoubtedly consider it an honour for herself to have disproved in her own person, that no heresy, or error in the faith, ever originated with a woman.

Had this Lady, most ambitious of Eve's daughters, been contemporary with Doctor Dove, how pleasant it would have been to have witnessed a debate between them upon the subject! He would have wound her up to the highest pitch of indignation, and she would have opened the flood-gates of female oratory upon his head.

CHAPTER CCVI.

THE SUBJECT CONTINUED. OPINIONS OF THE RABBIS. ANECDOTE OF LADY JEKYLL AND A TART REPLY OF WILLIAM WHISTON'S. JEAN D'ESPAGNE. QUEEN ELIZABETH OF THE QUORUM QUARUM QUORUM GENDER. THE SOCIETY OF GENTLEMEN AGREE WITH MAHOMET IN SUPPOSING THAT WOMEN HAVE NO SOULS, BUT ARE OF OPINION THAT THE DEVIL IS AN HERMAPHRODITE.

Sing of the nature of women, and then the song shall be surely full of variety, old crotchets, and most sweet closes: It shall be humourous, grave, fantastic, amorous, melancholy, sprightly, one in all and all in one. MARSTON.

THE Doctor had other theological arguments in aid of the opinion which he was pleased to support. The remark has been made which is curious, or in the language of Jeremy Taylor's age, *considerable*, that we read in Genesis how when God saw everything else which he had made he pronounced that it was very good, but he did not say this of the woman.

There are indeed certain Rabbis who affirm that Eve was not taken out of Adam's side: but that Adam had originally been created with a tail, (herein agreeing with the well-known theory of Lord Monboddo,) and that among the various experiments and improvements which were made in his form and organisation before he was finished, the tail was removed as an inconvenient appendage, and of the excrescence or superfluous part which was then lopped off, the Woman was formed.

"We are not bound to believe the Rabbis in everything," the Doctor would say; "and yet it cannot be denied that they have preserved some valuable traditions which ought to be regarded with much respect." And then by a gentle inclination of the head, and a peculiar glance of the eye, he let it be understood that this was one of those traditions which were entitled to consideration. "It was not impossible," he said, "but that a different reading in the original text might support such an interpretation: the same word in Hebrew frequently signified different things, and rib and tail might in that language be as near each other in sound or as easily miswritten by a hasty hand, or misread by an inaccurate eye, as *costa* and *cauda* in Latin." He did not pretend that this was the case — but that it might be so. And by a like corruption (for to such corruptions all written and even all printed books are liable) the text may have represented that Eve was taken from the side of her husband instead of from that part of the back where the tail grew. The dropping of a syllable might occasion it.

"And this view of the question," he said, "derived strong support from that well-known and indubitable text wherein the Husband is called the Head; for although that expression is in itself most clear and significative in its own substantive meaning, it becomes still more beautifully and emphatically appropriate when considered as referring to this interpretation and tradition, and implying as a direct and necessary converse that the Wife is the Tail."

There is another legend relating to a like but even less worthy formation of the first helpmate, and this also is ascribed to the Rabbis. According to this mythos the rib which had been taken from Adam was for a moment laid down, and in that moment a monkey stole it and ran off with it full speed. An Angel pursued, and though not in league with the Monkey he could have been no good Angel; for overtaking him, he caught him by the Tail, brought it maliciously back instead of the Rib, and of that Tail was Woman made. What became of the Rib, with which the Monkey got clear off, "was never to mortal known."

However the Doctor admitted that on the whole the received opinion was the more probable. And after making this admission he related an anecdote of Lady Jekyll, who was fond of puzzling herself and others with such questions as had been common enough a generation before her, in the days of the Athenian Oracle. She asked William Whiston of berhymed name and eccentric memory, one day at her husband's table, to resolve a difficulty which occurred to her in the Mosaic account of the creation. "Since it pleased God, Sir," said she, "to create the Woman out of the Man, why did he form her out of the rib rather than any other part?" Whiston scratched his head and answered: "Indeed, Madam, I do not know, unless it be that the rib is the most crooked part of the body." "There!" said her husband, "you have it now: I hope you are satisfied!"

He had found in the writings of the Huguenot divine, Jean D'Espagne, that Women have never had either the gift of tongues, or of miracle; the latter gift, according to this theologian, being withheld from them because it properly accompanies preaching, and women are forbidden to be preachers. A reason for the former exception the Doctor supplied; he said it was because one tongue was quite enough for them: and he entirely agreed with the Frenchman that it must be so, because there could have been no peace on earth had it been otherwise. But whether the sex worked miracles or not was a point which he left the Catholics to contend. Female Saints there certainly had been,—"the Lord," as Daniel Rogers said, "had gifted and graced many women above some men especially with holy affections; I know not," says that divine, "why he should do it else (for he is wise and not superfluous in needless things) save that as a Pearl shining through a chrystal glass, so her excellency shining through her weakness of sex, might show the glory of the workman." He quoted also what the biographer of one of the St. Catharines says, "that such a woman ought not to be called a woman, but rather an earthly Angel, or a heavenly homo: *hæc fœmina, sed potius Angelus terrestris, vel si malueris, homo cœlestis dicenda erat, quam fœmina.*" In like manner the Hungarians thinking it infamous for a nation to be governed by a woman—and yet perceiving the great advantage of preserving the succession, when the crown fell to a female, they called her King Mary, instead of Queen.

And Queen Elizabeth, rather than be accounted of the feminine gender, claimed it as her prerogative to be of all three. "A prime officer with a White Staff coming into her presence" she willed him to bestow a place then vacant upon a person whom she named. "May it please your Highness Madam," said the Lord, "the disposal of that place pertaineth to me by virtue of this White Staff." "True," replied the Queen, "yet I never gave you your office so absolutely, but that I still reserved myself of the *Quorum*." "Of the *Quarum*, Madam," returned the Lord, presuming, somewhat too far, upon her favour.—Whereat she snatched the staff in some anger out of his hand, and told him "he should acknowledge her of the *Quorum, Quarum, Quorum* before he had it again."

It was well known indeed to Philosophers, he said, that the female is an imperfection or default in nature, whose constant design is to form a male; but where strength and temperament are wanting—a defective production is the result. Aristotle therefore calls Woman a Monster, and Plato makes it a question whether she ought not to be ranked among irrational creatures. There were Greek Philosophers, who (rightly in his judgment) derived the name of Ἀθηνῆ from Θῆλυς and *alpha privativa*, as implying that the Goddess of wisdom, though Goddess, was nevertheless no female, having nothing of female imperfection. And a book unjustly ascribed to the learned Acidalius was published in Latin, and afterwards in French, to prove that women were not reasonable creatures, but distinguished from men by this specific difference, as well as in sex.

Mahomet too was not the only person who has supposed that women have no souls. In this Christian and reformed country, the question was propounded to the British Apollo whether there is now, or will be at the resurrection any females in Heaven—since, says the questioner, there seems to be no need of them there! The Society of Gentlemen who, (in imitation of John Dunton, his brother-in-law the elder Wesley, and their coadjutors,) had undertaken in this Journal to answer all questions, returned a grave reply, that sexes being corporeal distinctions there could be no such distinction among the souls which are now in bliss; neither could it exist after the resurrection, for they who partook of eternal life neither marry nor are given in marriage.

That same Society supposed the Devil to be an Hermaphrodite, for though by his roughness they said he might be thought of the masculine gender, they were led to that opinion because he appeared so often in petticoats.

CHAPTER CCVII.

FRACAS WITH THE GENDER FEMININE. THE DOCTOR'S DEFENCE.

If there sit twelve women at the table, let a dozen of them be—as they are. TIMON OF ATHENS.

"PĀPP-PĀAH!" says my daughter.

"You intolerable man!" says my wife.

"You abominable creature!" says my wife's eldest sister, "you wicked wretch!"

"Oh Mr. Author," says Miss Graveairs, "I did not expect this from you."

"Very well, Sir, very well! This is like you!" says the Bow-Begum.

"Was there ever such an atrocious libel upon the sex?" says the Lady President of the Celestial Blues.

The Ladies of the Stocking unanimously agree in the sentence of condemnation.

Let me see, who do I know among them? There is Mrs. Lapis Lazuli and her daughter Miss Ultramarine,—there is Mrs. Bluestone, the most caustic of female critics, and her friend Miss Gentian,—Heaven protect me from the bitterness of her remarks,—there is Lady Turquoise, Lady Celestina Sky, the widow Bluebeard, Miss Mazarine, and that pretty creature Serena Cerulean, it does me good to look at her, she is the blue-bell of the party. There is Miss Sapphire, Miss Priscilla Prussian, Mrs. Indigo, and the Widow Woad. And Heaven knows who beside. Mercy on me—it were better to be detected at the mysteries of the Bona Dea, than be found here! Hear them how they open in succession—

"Infamous!"

"Shameful!"

"Intolerable!"

"This is too bad."

"He has heaped together all the slanderous and odious things that could be collected from musty books."

"Talk of his Wife and Daughter. I do not believe any one who had wife and daughter would have composed such a Chapter as that. An old bachelor I warrant him, and mustier than his books."

"Pedant!"

"Satirist!"

"Libeller!"

"Wretch!"

"Monster!"

And Miss Virginia Vinegar compleats the climax by exclaiming with peculiar emphasis, "Man!"

All Indigo-land is in commotion; and Urgand the Unknown would be in as much danger *proh-Jupiter!* from the Stockingers, if he fell into their hands, as Orpheus from the Mænades. *Tantæne animis cælestibus iræ?*

"Why Ladies! dear Ladies! good Ladies! gentle Ladies! merciful Ladies! hear me,—hear me! In justice, in compassion, in charity, hear me! For your own sakes, and for the honour of feminality, hear me!"

"What has the wretch to say?"

"What *can* he say?"

"What indeed *can be said?* Nevertheless let us hear him, so bad a case must always be made worse by any attempt at defending it."

"Hear him! hear him!"

"Englishwomen, countrywomen, and lovelies,—lovelies, I certainly may call you, if it be not lawful for me to say lovers,—hear me for your honour, and have respect to your honour that you may believe, censure me in your wisdom, and awake your senses that you may be better judges. Who is here so unfeminine that would be a male creature? if any, speak; for her have I offended. Who is here so coarse that would not be a woman? if any, speak; for her have I offended. Who is here so vile that will not love her sex? if any speak; for her have I offended. I can have offended none but those who are ashamed of their womanhood, if any such there be, which I am far from thinking."

Gentle Ladies, do you in your conscience believe that any reasonable person could possibly think the worse of womankind, for any of the strange and preposterous opinions which my lamented and excellent friend used to repeat in the playfulness of an eccentric fancy? Do you suppose that he was more in earnest when he brought forward these learned fooleries, than the Devil's Advocate when pleading against a suit for canonisation in the Papal Court?

Questo negro inchiostro, ch' io dispenzo
Non fu per dare, o donne, a i vostri nasi,
*Ingrato odore, o d' altro che d' incenzo.**

Hear but to the end, and I promise you on the faith of a true man, a Red Letter Chapter in your praise; not a mere panegyric in the manner of those who flatter while they despise you, but such an honest estimate as will bear a scrutiny, — and which you will not like the worse because it may perhaps be found profitable as well as pleasing.

Forgive me, sacred sex of woman, that,
In thought or syllable, I have declaim'd
Against your goodness; and I will redeem it
With such religious honouring your names,
That when I die, some never thought-stain'd virgin
Shall make a relic of my dust, and throw
My ashes, like a charm, upon those men
Whose faiths they hold suspected.†

---

* Mauro.

† Shirley.

CHAPTER CCVIII.

VALUE OF WOMEN AMONG THE AFGHAUNS. LIGON'S HISTORY OF BARBADOES, AND A FAVOURITE STORY OF THE DOCTOR'S THEREFROM. CLAUDE SEISSEL, AND THE SALIC LAW. JEWISH THANKSGIVING. ETYMOLOGY OF MULIER, WOMAN, AND LASS; — FROM WHICH IT MAY BE GUESSED HOW MUCH IS CONTAINED IN THE LIMBO OF ETYMOLOGY.

If thy name were known that writest in this sort,
By womankind, unnaturally, giving evil report,
Whom all men ought, both young and old, defend with all their might,
Considering what they do deserve of every living wight,
I wish thou should exiled be from women more and less,
And not without just cause thou must thyself confess.

Edward More.

It would have pleased the Doctor when he was upon this topic if he had known how exactly the value of women was fixed among the Afghauns, by whose laws twelve young women are given as a compensation for the slaughter of one man, six for cutting off a hand, an ear, or a nose; three for breaking a tooth, and one for a wound of the scalp.

By the laws of the Venetians as well as of certain Oriental people, the testimony of two women was made equivalent to that of one man. And in those of the Welsh King Hywel Dda, or Howel Dha, "the satisfaction for the murder of a woman, whether she be married or not, is half that of her brother," which is upon the same standard of relative value. By the same laws a woman was not to be admitted as bail for a man, nor as witness against him.

He knew that a French Antiquarian (Claude Seissel) had derived the name of the Salic law from the Latin word *Sal*, *comme une loy pleine de sel, c'est à dire pleine de sapience* ‡, and this the Doctor thought a far more rational etymology than what some one proposed either seriously or in sport, that the law was called *Salique* because the words *Si aliquis* and *Si aliqua* were of such frequent occurrence in it. "To be born a man-child," says that learned author who first composed an Art of Rhetoric in the English

---

‡ Brantôme.

tongue, "declares a courage, gravity and constancy. To be born a woman, declares weakness of spirit, neshenes of body, and fickleness of mind."* Justin Martyr, after saying that the Demons by whom according to him the system of heathen mythology was composed, spake of Minerva as the first Intelligence and the daughter of Jupiter, makes this observation; "now this we consider most absurd, to carry about the image of Intelligence in a female form!" The Father said this as thinking with the great French comic poet that a woman never could be anything more than a woman.

Car, voyez-vous, la femme est, comme on dit, mon maître,
Un certain animal difficile à connoître,
Et de qui la nature est fort encline au mal;
Et comme un animal est toujours animal.
Et ne sera jamais qu'animal, quand sa vie
Dureroit cent mille ans; aussi, sans repartie,
La femme est toujours femme, et jamais ne sera
Que femme, tant qu'entier le monde durera.

A favourite anecdote with our Philosopher was of the Barbadoes Planters, one of whom agreed to exchange an English maid servant with the other for a bacon pig, weight for weight, four-pence per pound to be paid for the overplus, if the balance should be in favour of the pig, sixpence if it were on the Maid's side. But when they were weighed in the scales, Honour who was "extreme fat, lazy and good for nothing," so far outweighed the pig, that the pig's owner repented of his improvident bargain, and refused to stand to it. Such a case Ligon observes, when he records this notable story, seldom happened; but the Doctor cited it as showing what had been the relative value of women and pork in the West Indies. And observe, he would say, of white women, English, Christian women,—not of poor heathen blacks, who are considered as brutes, bought and sold like brutes, worked like brutes—and treated worse than any Government ought to permit even brutes to be treated.

However, that women were in some respects better than men, he did not deny. He doubted not but that Cannibals thought them so; for we know by the testimony of such Cannibals as happen to have tried both, that white men are considered better meat than negroes, and Englishmen than Frenchmen, and there could be little doubt that, for the same reason, women would be preferred to men. Yet this was not the case with animals, as was proved by buck venison, ox beef, and wether mutton. The tallow of the female goat would not make as good candles as that of the male. Nature takes more pains in elaborating her nobler work; and that the male, as being the nobler, was that which Nature finished with greatest care must be evident, he thought, to any one who called to mind the difference between cock and hen birds, a difference discoverable even in the egg, the larger and finer eggs, with a denser white and a richer yolk, containing male chicks. Other and more curious observations had been made tending to the same conclusion, but he omitted them, as not perhaps suited for general conversation, and not exactly capable of the same degree of proof. It was enough to hint at them.

The great Ambrose Parey, (the John Hunter and the Baron Larrey of the sixteenth century,) has brought forward many instances wherein women have been changed into men, instances which are not fabulous: but he observes, "you shall find in no history, men that have degenerated into women; for nature always intends and goes from the imperfect to the more perfect, but never basely from the more perfect to the imperfect." It was a rule in the Roman law, that when husband and wife overtaken by some common calamity perished at the same time, and it could not be ascertained which had lived the longest, the woman should be presumed to have expired the first, as being by nature the feeblest. And for the same reason if it had not been noted whether brother or sister being twins came first in the world, the legal conclusion was that the boy being the stronger was the first born.

And from all these facts he thought the writer must be a judicious person who published a poem entitled the Great Birth of Man, or Excellence of his Creation over Woman.

* Wilson.

Therefore according to the Bramins, the widow who burns herself with the body of her husband, will in her next state be born a male; but the widow, who refuses to make this self-sacrifice, will never be anything better than a woman, let her be born again as often as she may.

Therefore it is that the Jew at this day begins his public prayer with a thanksgiving to his Maker, for not having made him a woman; — an escape for which the Greek philosopher was thankful. One of the things which shocked a Moor who visited England was to see dogs, women, and dirty shoes, permitted to enter a place of worship, the Mahometans, as is well known, excluding all three from their Mosques. Not that all Mahometans believe that women have no souls. There are some who think it more probable they have, and these more liberal Mussulmen hold that there is a separate Paradise for them, because they say, if the women were admitted into the Men's Paradise, it would cease to be Paradise, — there would be an end of all peace there. It was probably the same reason which induced Origen to advance an opinion that after the day of Judgment women will be turned into men. The opinion has been condemned among his heresies; but the Doctor maintained that it was a reasonable one, and almost demonstrable upon the supposition that we are all to be progressive in a future state. "There was, however," he said, "according to the Jews a peculiar privilege and happiness reserved for them, that is for all those of their chosen nation, during the temporal reign of the Messiah, for every Jewish woman is then to lie in every day!"

"I never," says Bishop Reynolds, "read of more dangerous falls in the Saints than were Adam's, Samson's, David's, Solomon's, and Peter's; and behold in all these, either the first enticers, or the first occasioners, are women. A weak creature may be a strong tempter: nothing too impotent or useless for the Devil's service." Fuller among his Good Thoughts has this paragraph: — "I find the natural Philosopher making a character of the Lion's disposition, amongst other his qualities, reporteth, first, that the Lion feedeth on men, and afterwards (if forced with extremity of hunger, on women. Satan is a roaring Lion seeking whom he may devour. Only he inverts the method, and in his bill of fare takes the second first. Ever since he over-tempted our grandmother Eve, encouraged with success he hath preyed first on the weaker sex."

"Sit not in the midst of women," saith the son of Sirach in his Wisdom, "for from garments cometh a moth, and from women wickedness." "Behold, this have I found, saith the Preacher, counting one by one to find out the account; which yet my soul seeketh, but I find not: one man among a thousand have I found; but a woman among all those have I not found."

"It is a bad thing," said St. Augustine, "to look upon a woman, a worse to speak to her, and to touch her is worst of all." John Bunyan admired the wisdom of God for making him shy of the sex, and boasted that it was a rare thing to see him "carry it pleasant towards a woman." "The common salutation of women," said he, "I abhor, their company alone I cannot away with!" John, the great Tinker, thought with the son of Sirach, that "better is the churlishness of a man, than a courteous woman, a woman which bringeth shame and reproach." And Menu the lawgiver of the Hindoos hath written that "it is the nature of women in this world to cause the seduction of men." And John Moody in the play, says, "I ha' seen a little of them, and I find that the best, when she's minded, won't ha' much goodness to spare." A wife has been called a daily calamity, and they who thought least unfavourably of the sex have pronounced it a necessary evil.

"*Mulier*, quasi *mollior*," saith Varro *; a derivation upon which Dr. Featley thus commenteth: "Women take their name in

* The Soothsayer in Cymbeline was of a like opinion with Varro!

> The piece of tender air, thy virtuous daughter,
> Which we call *mollis aer;* and *mollis aer*
> We term it *mulier*.

Southey's favourite play upon the stage was Cymbeline, and next to it, As you like it.

Latin from tenderness or softness, because they are usually of a softer temper than men, and much more subject to passions, especially of fear, grief, love, and longing; their fear is almost perpetual, their grief immoderate, their love ardent, and their longing most vehement. They are the weaker vessels, not only weaker in body than men, and less able to resist violence, but also weaker in mind and less able to hold out in temptations; and therefore the Devil first set upon the woman as conceiving it a matter of more facility to supplant her than the man." And they are such dissemblers, says the Poet,

As if their mother had been made
Only of all the falsehood of the man,
Disposed into that rib.

"Look indeed at the very name," said the Doctor, putting on his gravest look of provocation to the ladies. —"Look at the very name — *Woman*, evidently meaning either *man's woe* — or abbreviated from *woe to man*, because by woman was woe brought into the world."

And when a girl is called a lass, who does not perceive how that common word must have arisen? Who does not see that it may be directly traced to a mournful interjection, *alas!* breathed sorrowfully forth at the thought the girl, the lovely and innocent creature upon whom the beholder has fixed his meditative eye, would in time become a woman, — a woe to man!

There are other tongues in which the name is not less significant. The two most notoriously obstinate things in the world are a mule and a pig. Now there is one language in which *pige* means a young woman: and another in which woman is denoted by the word *mulier:* which word, whatever grammarians may pretend, is plainly a comparative, applied exclusively and with peculiar force to denote the only creature in nature which is more mulish than a mule. *Comment*, says a Frenchman, *pourroit-on aymer les* Dames, *puis qu'elles se nomment ainsi du* dam *et* dommage *qu'elles apportent aux hommes!* *

* Bouchet.

INTERCHAPTER XXIV.

A TRUE STORY OF THE TERRIBLE KNITTERS E' DENT WHICH WILL BE READ WITH INTEREST BY HUMANE MANUFACTURERS, AND BY MASTERS OF SPINNING JENNIES WITH A SMILE. BETTY YEWDALE. THE EXCURSION — AN EXTRACT FROM, AND AN ILLUSTRATION OF.

O voi ch' avete gl' intelletti sani,
Mirate la dottrina, che s' asconde
Sotto 'l velame degli versi strani. — Dante.†

"It was about six an' fifty year sen, in June, when a woman cam fra' Dent at see a Nebbor of ours e' Langdon.‡ They er terrible knitters e' Dent § — sea my Fadder an' Mudder sent me an' my lile Sister, Sally, back we' her at larn at knit. I was between sebben an' eight year auld, an' Sally twea year younger — T' Woman reade on ya Horse, we Sally afore her — an' I on anudder, we a man walking beside me — whiles he gat up behint an' reade — Ee' them Days Fwoak dud'nt gang e' Carts — but Carts er t'best — I'd rader ride e' yan than e' onny Carriage — I us't at think if I was t' Leady, here at t' Ho ‖,' how I wad tear about int' rwoads — but sen I hae ridden in a Chaise I hate t' nwotion ont' warst of ought — for t' Trees gang fleeing by o' ya side, an t' Wa'as ¶ on tudder, an' gars yan be as seek as a peeate.**

"Weel, we dud'nt like Dent at a' — nut that they wer bad tull us — but ther way o' leeving — it was round Meal — an' they *stoult* it int' frying pan, e' keaeks as thick as my fing-er. — Then we wer *stawed* †† we' sae

† By an oversight, this quotation has occurred before. See p. 410.

‡ The valley of Langdale, near Ambleside. The Langdale Pikes are known to all tourists.

§ Dent is a chapelry in the Parish and Union of Sedbergh, W. Division of the wapentake of Staincliffe and Ewcross, W. Riding of the County of York, sixteen miles E. from Kendal. — *Lewis's Topog. Dict.*

‖ i. e. at the Hall.

¶ Wa'as, i. e. Walls, as in p. 560.

** Quære, does this mean pet, as in the Taming of the Shrew?

—"A pretty *peat!* 'tis best
Put finger in the eye, — an we knew why."
Act. i. *Sc.* 1.

†† i. e. cloyed, saturated, fatigued. Brockett's Glossary of North Country words.

mickle knitting—We went to a *Skeul* about a mile off—ther was a Maister an' Mistress—they larnt us our Lessons, yan a piece—an' then we o' knit as hard as we cud drive, striving whilk cud knit t' hardest yan again anudder—we hed our *Darracks* * set afore we com fra' Heam int' mwornin; an' if we dud'nt git them duun we warrant to gang to our dinners—They hed o' macks o' contrivances to larn us to knit swift—T' Maister wad wind 3 or 4 clues togedder, for 3 or 4 Bairns to knitt off—*that*' at knit slawest raffled tudders yarn, an' than she gat weel thumpt (but ther was baith Lasses an' Lads 'at learnt at knit)—Than we ust at sing a mack of a sang, whilk we wer at git at t'end on at every needle, ca'ing ower t' Neams of o' t' fwoak in t' Deaal—but Sally an me wad never ca' *Dent* Fwoak—sea we ca'ed Langdon Fwoak—T' Sang was—

Sally an' I, Sally an' I,
For a good pudding pye,
Taa hoaf wheat, an' tudder hoaf rye,
Sally an' I, for a good pudding pye.

We sang this (altering t' neams) at every needle: and when we com at t' end cried "off" an' began again, an' sea we strave on o' t' day through.

"We wer *stawed*, as I telt yea—o' t' pleser we hed was when we went out a bit to beat t' fire for a nebbor 'at was baking—that was a grand day for us!—At Kursmas teea, ther was t' maskers—an' on Kursmas day at mworn they gav' us sum reed stuff to' t' Breakfast—I think it maun ha' been Jocklat—but we dud'nt like 't at a', 't ommost puzzened us!—an' we cared for nought but how we wer to git back to Langdon—Neet an' Day ther was nought but *this* knitting! T' Nebbors ust at gang about fra' house to house, we' ther wark,—than yan fire dud, ye knaw, an' they cud hev a better—they hed girt lang black peeats—an' set them up an hed in a girt round we' a whol at top—an a' t' Fwoak sat about it. When ony o' them gat into a hubble we' ther wark, they shouted out "*turn a Peeat*"—an' *them* 'at sat naarest t' fire turnt yan, an' meaad a *low*†—for they nivver hed onny cannal.—We knat quorse wosset stockings—some gloves—an' some neet caps, an' wastecwoat breests, an' petticwoats. I yance knat a stocking, for mysell, e' six hours—Sally yan e' sebben—an' t'woman's Doughter, 'at was aulder than us e' eight—an' they sent a nwote to our Fwoak e' Langdon at tell them.

"Sally an' me, when we wer by our sells, wer always contrivin how we wer at git away, when we sleept by oursells we talk't of nought else—but when t' woman's Doughter sleept we' us we wer *qwhite* mum—summat or udder always happent at hinder us, till yan day, between Kursmas an' Cannalmas, when t' woman's Doughter stait at heaam, we teuk off. Our house was four mile on 'todder side o' Dent's Town—whor, efter we hed pass t' Skeul, we axed t' way to Kendal—It hed been a hard frost, an' ther was snaw on t' grund—but it was beginnin to thow, an' was varra sloshy an' cauld—but we *poted* alang leaving our lile footings behint us—we hed our cloggs on—for we durst'nt change them for our shoon for fear o' being fund out—an' we had nought on but our hats, an' bits o' blue bedgowns, an' brats—see ye may think we cuddent be varra heeat—I hed a sixpence e' my pocket, an' we hed three or four shilling mare in our box, 'at our Fwoak hed ge'en us to keep our pocket we'—but, lile mafflins‡ as we wer, we thought it wad be misst an' durst'nt tak ony mare.

"Afore we gat to Sebber§ we fell hungry; an' ther was a fine, girt, reed house nut far off t' rwoad, whar we went an' begged for a bit o' breead—but they wadd'nt give us ought—sea we trampt on, an com to a lile theakt house, an' I said—'Sally thou

* i. e. *Days-works*. So the Derwent is called the Darron.

† i. e. *a flame;* it is an Icelandic word. See Haldorson's Lexicon. *At loga, ardere,* and *Loga, flamma.* So in St. George for England,

As timorous larks amazed are
With light, and with a *low*-bell.

‡ *Maffling—a state of perplexity.*—BROCKETT. Maffled, mazed, and maisled (as used a little further on) have all a like sense.

§ i. e. Sedbergh.

sall beg t' neesht — thou's less than me, an' mappen they'll sarra us'— an' they dud — an' gav us a girt shive* o' breead — at last we gat to *Scotch Jins*, as they ca' t' public House about three mile fra Sebber (o' this side) — a Scotch woman keept it. — It was amaist dark, sea we axt her at let us stay o' neet — she teuk us in, an' gav us sum boilt milk and breead — an' suun put us to bed — we telt her our taael; an' she sed we wer int' reet at run away.

"Neesht mwornin she gav us sum mare milk an' breead, an' we gav her our sixpence — an' then went off-sledding away amangt' snaw, ower that cauld moor (ye ken' 't weel enough) naarly starved to deeath, an' maisled — sea we gat on varra slawly, as ye may think — an' 't rain'd tua. We begged again at anudder lile theakt house, on t' Hay Fell — there was a woman an' a heap of raggeltly Bairns stannin round a Teable — an' she gave us a few of their poddish, an' put a lock of sugar into a sup of cauld tea tull them.

"Then we trailed on again till we com to t' Peeat Lane Turnpike Yat — they teuk us in there, an' let us warm oursells, an' gav us a bit o' breead. They sed had duun re'et to com away; for Dent was t' poorest plaace in t' warld, and we wer seafe to ha' been hungert — an' at last we gat to Kendal, when 't was naar dark — as we went up t' streat we met a woman, an' axt t' way to Tom Posts — (*that* was t' man at ust te bring t' Letters fra' Kendal to Ammelsid an' Hawksheead yance a week — an' baited at his house when we com fra' Langdon) — she telt us t' way an' we creept on, but we leaked back at her twea or three times — an' she was still stanning, leuking at us — then she com back an' *quiesed* us a deal, an' sed we sud gang heam with her — We telt her whor we hed cum fra' an' o' about our Tramp 'at we hed hed. — She teuk us to her house — it was a varra poor yan — down beside t' brig at we had cum ower into t' Town — Ther was nea fire on — but she went out, an' brought in sam *eilding*† (for they can buy a pennerth, or sea, o' quols or Peeats at onny time there) an' she set on a good fire — an' put on t' kettle — then laited‡ up sum of her awn claes, an' tiet them on us as weel as she cud, an' dried ours — for they wer as wet as thack — it hed rained a' t' way — Then she meead us sum tea — an' as she hedden't a bed for us in her awn house she teuk us to a nebbors — Ther was an auld woman in a Bed naar us that flaed us sadly — for she teuk a fit int' neet an' her feace turnt as black as a cwol — we laid trimmiling, an' hutched oursells ower heead e' bed — Fwoks com an' steud round her — an' we heeard them say 'at we wer asleep — sea we meade as if we wer asleep, because we thought if we wer asleep they waddn't kill us — an' we wisht oursells e' t' streets again, or onny whor — an' wad ha' been fain to ha' been ligging under a Dyke.

"Neesht mwornin we hed our Brekfast, an' t' woman gav us baith a hopenny Keack beside (that was as big as a penny 'an now) to eat as we went — an' she set us to t' top o' t' House o' Correction Hill — It was freezing again, an' t' rwoad was terrible slape; sea we gat on varra badly — an' afore we com to Staavley (an' that was but a lile bit o' t' rwoad) we fell hung'ry an' began on our keacks — then we sed we wad walk sea far, an' then tak a bite — an' then on again an' tak anudder — and afore we gat to t' Ings Chapel they wer o' gane — Every now an' than we stopped at reest — an' sat down, an' grat §, under a hedge or wa'a crudled up togedder, taking haud o' yan anudder's hands at try at warm them, for we were fairly maizled wi' t' cauld — an' when we saw onny body cumming we gat up an' walked away

* i. e. a slice. So in Titus Andronicus.

"Easy it is
Of a cut loaf to steal a *shive* we know."

† *Fire-elding*, — the common term for fuel. *Ild* in Danish is *fire*. Such words were to be expected in Cumberland. The commencement of Landor's lines to Southey, 1833, will explain why —

Indweller of a peaceful vale,
Ravaged erewhile by white-hair'd Dane, &c.

‡ To *late* or *leat* is to seek out. See BROCKETT. It is from the Icelandic *at leyta*, quærere. Cf. Haldorson in v.

§ i. e. wept, from the old word *greet*, common to all the Northern languages. Chaucer, Spenser, &c., use it. See Specimen Glossarii in Edda Sæmundar hinns Froda V. *Grætr, ploratus, at græta, plorare:* hence *grief*, &c.

— but we duddn't meet monny Fwoak — I dunnat think Fwoak warr sea mickle in t' rwoads e' them Days.

"We scraffled* on t' this fashion — an' it was quite dark afore we gat to Ammelsid Yat — our feet warr sare an' we warr naarly dune for — an' when we turnt round Windermer Watter heead, T' waves blasht sea dowly † that we *warr* fairly heart-brossen — we sat down on a cauld steane an' grat sare — but when we hed hed our belly-full o' greeting we gat up, an feelt better ‡ fort' an' sea dreed on again — slaw enough ye may be sure — but we warr e' *kent* rwoads — an' now when I gang that gait I can nwote o' t' sports whor we reested — for them lile bye lwoans erent sea micklealtert, as t' girt rwoads, fra what they warr. At Clappersgait t' Fwoak wad ha' knawn us, if it heddent been dark, an' o' ther duirs steeked §, an geen us a relief, if we hed begged there — but we began at be flate ‖ 'at my Fadder an' Mudder wad be angert at us for running away.

"It was twea o'clock int' mworning when we gat to our awn Duir — I c'aed out 'Fadder! Fadder! — Mudder! Mudder!' ower an' ower again — She hard us, an' sed —'That's our Betty's voice' — 'Thou's nought but fancies, lig still,' said my Fadder — but she waddent; an' sea gat up, an' opent' Duir and there warr we stanning doddering ¶ — an' daized we' cauld, as deer deead as macks nea matter — When she so us she was mare flate than we — She brast out a crying — an' we grat — an' my Fadder grat an' a' — an' they duddent flight **, nor said nought tull us, for cumming away, — they warrant a bit angert — an' my Fadder sed we sud nivver gang back again.

"T' Fwoaks e' Dent nivver mist us, tilt' Neet — because they thought 'at we hed been keept at dinner time 'at finish our tasks — but when neet com, an' we duddent cum heam, they set off efter us to Kendal — an' mun ha' gane by Scotch Jins when we warr there — how they satisfied thersells, I knan't, but they suppwosed we hed gane heam — and sea they went back — My Fadder wasn't lang, ye may be seur, o' finding out' T' Woman at Kendal 'at was sea good tull us — an' my Mudder put her doun a pot o' Butter, an' meead her a lile cheese an' sent her."

Interpolation.

The above affecting and very simple story, Reader, was taken down from the mouth of Betty Yewdale herself, the elder of the two children, — at that time an old woman, but with a bright black eye that lacked no lustre. A shrewd and masculine woman, Reader, was Betty Yewdale, — fond of the Nicotian weed and a short pipe so as to have the full flavour of its essence, — somewhat, sooth be said, too fond of it, for the pressure of the pipe produced a cancer in her mouth, which caused her death. — Knowest thou, gentle Reader, that most curious of all curious books — (we stop not to inquire whether Scarron be indebted to it, or it to Scarron) — the Anatomy of Melancholy by Democritus Junior, old Burton to wit? — Curious if thou art, it cannot fail, but that thou knowest it well, — curious or not, hear what he says of Tobacco, poor Betty Yewdale's bane!

"Tobacco, divine, rare, super-excellent tobacco, which goes far beyond all their panaceas, potable gold, and philosopher's stones, a sovereign remedy to all diseases. A good vomit, I confesse, a vertuous herb, if it be well qualified, opportunely taken, and medicinally used; but, as it is commonly abused by most men, which take it as tinkers do ale, 'tis a plague, a mischief, a violent purger of goods, lands, health, hellish, devilish and damned tobacco, the ruine and overthrow of body and soul.'

---

* i. e. struggled on. Brockett in v.

† i. e. lonely, melancholy. *Ibid.*

‡ The scholar will call to mind the ὀλοοῖο τεταρπώμεσθα γόοιο of the Iliad, xxiii. 98., with like expressions in the Odyssey, e. g. xi. 211, xix. 213, and the reader of the Pseudo Ossian will remember the words of Fingal: "Strike the harp in my hall, and let Fingal hear the song. *Pleasant is the joy of grief.*" See Adam Littleton's Sermons: part ii. p. 263.

§ "Steek the heck," — i. e. shut the door. Brockett.

‖ From the verb "Flay," *to frighten.*

¶ We still speak of *Dodder* or *Quaker's* grass, — a word, by the way, older than the Sect.

** A. S. *Flitan* — to scold.

Gentle Reader! if thou knowest not the pages of honest old Burton — we speak not of his melancholy end, which melancholy may have wrought, but of his honesty of purpose, and of his life, — thou wilt not be unacquainted with that excellent Poem of Wordsworth's, — "The Excursion, being a Portion of the Recluse." — *If any know not the wisdom contained in it, forthwith let them study it!* — Acquainted with it or not, it is Betty Yewdale that is described in the following lines, as holding the lanthorn to guide the steps of old Jonathan, her husband, on his return from working in the quarries, if at any time he chanced to be beyond his usual hour. They are given at length; — for who will not be pleased to read them *decies repetita?*

Much was I pleased, the grey-haired wanderer said,
When to those shining fields our notice first
You turned; and yet more pleased have from your lips,
Gathered this fair report of them who dwell
In that retirement; whither, by such course
Of evil hap and good as oft awaits
A lone wayfaring man, I once was brought.
Dark on my road the autumnal evening fell
While I was traversing yon mountain pass,
And night succeeded with unusual gloom;
So that my feet and hands at length became
Guides better than mine eyes — until a light
High in the gloom appeared, too high, methought,
For human habitation, but I longed
To reach it destitute of other hope.
I looked with steadiness as sailors look,
On the north-star, or watch-tower's distant lamp,
And saw the light — now fixed — and shifting, now —
Not like a dancing meteor; but in line
Of never varying motion, to and fro.
It is no night fire of the naked hills,
Thought I, some friendly covert must be near.
With this persuasion thitherward my steps
I turn, and reach at last the guiding light;
Joy to myself! but to the heart of Her
Who there was standing on the open hill,
(The same kind Matron whom your tongue hath praised)
Alarm and disappointment! The alarm
Ceased, when she learned through what mishap I came,
And by what help had gained those distant fields.
Drawn from her Cottage, on that open height,
Bearing a lantern in her hand she stood
Or paced the ground, — to guide her husband home,
By that unwearied signal, kenned afar;
An anxious duty! which the lofty Site,
Traversed but by a few irregular paths,
Imposes, whensoe'er untoward chance
Detains him after his accustomed hour
When night lies black upon the hills. 'But come,
Come,' said the Matron, — 'to our poor abode;
Those dark rocks hide it! Entering, I beheld
A blazing fire — beside a cleanly hearth
Sate down; and to her office, with leave asked,
The Dame returned. — Or ere that glowing pile
Of mountain turf required the builder's hand
Its wasted splendour to repair, the door
Opened, and she re-entered with glad looks,
Her Helpmate following. Hospitable fare,
Frank conversation, make the evening's treat:
Need a bewildered Traveller wish for more?
But more was given; I studied as we sate
By the bright fire, the good Man's face — composed
Of features elegant; an open brow
Of undisturbed humanity; a cheek
Suffused with something of a feminine hue;
Eyes beaming courtesy and mild regard:
But in the quicker turns of his discourse,
Expression slowly varying, that evinced
A tardy apprehension. From a fount
Lost, thought I, in the obscurities of time,
But honour'd once, those features and that mien
May have descended, though I see them here,
In such a man, so gentle and subdued,
Withal so graceful in his gentleness.
A race illustrious for heroic deeds,
Humbled, but not degraded, may expire.
This pleasing fancy (cherished and upheld
By sundry recollections of such fall
From high to low, ascent from low to high,
As books record, and even the careless mind
Cannot but notice among men and things,)
Went with me to the place of my repose.

BOOK V. THE PASTOR.

*** Miss Sarah Hutchinson, Mrs. Wordsworth's sister, and Mrs. Warter took down the story from the old woman's lips, and Southey laid it by for the Doctor, &c. She then lived in a cottage at Rydal, where I afterwards saw her. Of the old man it was told me — (for I did not see him) — "He is a perfect picture, — like those we meet with in the better copies of Saints in our old Prayer Books."

There was another comical History intended for an Interchapter to the Doctor, &c. of a runaway match to Gretna Green by two people in humble life, — but it was not handed over to me with the MS. materials. It was taken down from the mouth of the old woman who was one of the parties — and it would probably date back some sixty or seventy years.

CHAPTER CCIX.

EARLY APPROXIMATION TO THE DOCTOR'S THEORY. GEORGE FOX. ZACHARIAH BEN MOHAMMED. COWPER. INSTITUTES OF MENU. BARDIC PHILOSOPHY. MILTON. SIR THOMAS BROWNE.

There are distinct degrees of Being as there are degrees of Sound; and the whole world is but as it were a greater Gamut, or scale of music.

NORRIS.

CERTAIN theologians, and certain theosophists, as men who fancy themselves inspired sometimes affect to be called, had approached so nearly to the Doctor's hypothesis of progressive life, and propensities continued in the ascending scale, that he appealed to them as authorities for its support. They saw the truth, he said, as far as they went; but it was only to a certain point: a step farther and the beautiful theory would have opened upon them. "How can we choose, said one, but remember the mercy of God in this our land in this particular, that no ravenous dangerous beasts do range in our nation, if men themselves would not be wolves, and bears, and lions one to another!" And why are they so, observed the Doctor commenting upon the words of the old Divine; why are they so, but because they have actually been lions, and bears, and wolves? Why are they so, but because, as the wise heathen speaks, more truly than he was conscious of speaking, *sub hominum effigie latet ferinus animus.* The temper is congenital, the propensity innate; it is bred in the bone; and what Theologians call the old Adam, or the old Man, should physiologically, and perhaps therefore preferably, be called the old Beast.

That wise and good man William Jones, of Nayland, has, in his sermon upon the nature and œconomy of Beasts and Cattle, a passage which, in elucidating a remarkable part of the Law of Moses, may serve also as a glose or commentary upon the Doctor's theory.

"The Law of *Moses*, in the xith chapter of *Leviticus*, divides the brute creation into two grand parties, from the fashion of their feet, and their manner of feeding, that is, from the *parting of the hoof*, and the *chewing of the cud;* which properties are indications of their general characters, as *wild* or *tame.* For the dividing of the hoof and the chewing of the cud are peculiar to those cattle which are serviceable to man's life, as sheep, oxen, goats, deer, and their several kinds. These are shod by the Creator for a peaceable and inoffensive progress through life; as the Scripture exhorts us to be *shod* in like manner *with the preparation of the Gospel of Peace.* They live temperately upon herbage, the diet of students and saints; and after the taking of their food, chew it deliberately over again for better digestion; in which act they have all the appearance a brute can assume of pensiveness or meditation; which is, metaphorically, called *rumination* *, with reference to this property of certain animals.

"Such are these: but when we compare the beasts of the field and the forest, they, instead of the harmless hoof, have feet which are *swift to shed blood,* (Rom. iii. 15.) sharp claws to seize upon their prey, and teeth to devour it; such as lions, tigers, leopards, wolves, foxes, and smaller vermin.

"Where one of the Mosaic marks is found, and the other is wanting, such creatures are of a middle character between the wild and the tame; as the swine, the hare, and some others. Those that part the hoof afford us wholesome nourishment; those that are shod with any kind of hoof may be made useful to man; as the camel, the horse, the ass, the mule; all of which are fit to travel and carry burdens. But when the foot is divided into many parts, and armed with claws, there is but small hope of the manners; such creatures being in general either murderers, or hunters, or thieves; the malefactors and felons of the brute creation: though among the wild there are all the possible gradations of ferocity and evil temper.

"Who can review the creatures of God, as they arrange themselves under the two great denominations of wild and tame, without wondering at their different dispositions and ways of life! sheep and oxen lead a sociable as well as a peaceful life; they are formed into flocks and herds; and as they live honestly they walk openly in the day. The time of darkness is to them, as to the virtuous and sober amongst men, a time of rest. But the beast of prey goeth about in

* Pallentes *ruminat* herbas. — VIRGIL.

Dum jacet, et lentè revocatas *ruminat* herbas. — OVID.

It were hardly necessary to recal to an English reader's recollection the words of Brutus to Cassius,

Till then, my noble friend, *chew* upon this, —
JULIUS CÆSAR.

or those of Agrippa in Antony and Cleopatra,

Pardon what I have spoke;
For 'tis a studied, not a present thought,
By duty *ruminated.*

solitude; the time of darkness is to him the time of action; then he visits the folds of sheep, and stalls of oxen, thirsting for their blood; as the thief and the murderer visits the habitations of men, for an opportunity of robbing, and destroying, under the concealment of the night. When the sun ariseth the beast of prey retires to the covert of the forest; and while the cattle are spreading themselves over a thousand hills in search of pasture, the tyrant of the desert is laying himself down in his den, to sleep off the fumes of his bloody meal. The ways of men are not less different than the ways of beasts; and here we may see them represented as on a glass; for, as the quietness of the pasture, in which the cattle spend their day, is to the howlings of a wilderness at night, such is the virtuous life of honest labour to the life of the thief, the oppressor, the murderer, and the midnight gamester, who live upon the losses and sufferings of other men."

But how would the Doctor have delighted in the first Lesson of that excellent man's Book of Nature, — a book more likely to be useful than any other that has yet been written with the same good intent.

The Beasts.

"The ass hath very long ears, and yet he hath no sense of music, but brayeth with a frightful noise. He is obstinate and unruly, and will go his own way, even though he is severely beaten. The child who will not be taught is but little better; he has no delight in learning, but talketh of his own folly, and disturbeth others with his noise.

"The dog barketh all the night long, and thinks it no trouble to rob honest people of their rest.

"The fox is a cunning thief, and men, when they do not fear God, are crafty and deceitful. The wolf is cruel and bloodthirsty. As he devoureth the lamb, so do bad men oppress and tear the innocent and helpless.

"The adder is a poisonous snake, and hath a forked double tongue; and so men speak lies, and utter slanders against their neighbours, when *the poison of asps is under their lips*. The devil, who deceiveth with lies, and would destroy all mankind, is the *old serpent*, who brought death into the world by the venom of his bite. He would kill me, and all the children that are born, if God would let him; but Jesus Christ came to save us from his power, and to *destroy the works of the Devil.*

"Lord, thou hast made me a man for thy service: O let me not dishonour thy work, by turning myself into the likeness of some evil beast: let me not be as the fox, who is a thief and a robber: let me never be cruel, as a wolf, to any of thy creatures; especially to my dear fellow-creatures, and my dearer fellow Christians; but let me be harmless as the lamb; quiet and submissive as the sheep; that so I may be fit to live, and be fed on thy pasture, under the good shepherd, Jesus Christ. It is far better to be the poorest of his flock, than to be proud and cruel, as the lion or the tiger, who go about seeking what they may devour."

The Questions.

"*Q.* What is the child that will not learn?

"*A.* An ass, which is ignorant and unruly.

"*Q.* What are wicked men, who hurt and cheat others?

"*A.* They are wolves, and foxes, and blood-thirsty lions.

"*Q.* What are ill-natured people, who trouble their neighbours and rail at them?

"*A.* They are dogs, who bark at everybody.

"*Q.* But what are good and peaceable people?

"*A.* They are harmless sheep; and little children under the grace of God, are innocent lambs.

"*Q.* But what are liars?

"*A.* They are snakes and vipers, with double tongues and poison under their lips.

"*Q.* Who is the good shepherd?

"*A.* Jesus Christ."

There is a passage not less apposite in Donne's Epistle to Sir Edward, afterwards Lord Herbert of Cherbury.

Man is a lump where all beasts kneaded be;
Wisdom makes him an Ark where all agree.
The fool in whom these beasts do live at jar,
Is sport to others and a theatre;
Nor 'scapes he so, but is himself their prey,
All that was man in him is ate away;
And now his beasts on one another feed,
Yet couple in anger and new monsters breed.
How happy he which hath due place assign'd
To his beasts, and disaforested his mind,
Empaled himself to keep them out, not in;
Can sow and dares trust corn where they have been,
Can use his horse, goat, wolf and every beast,
And is not ass himself to all the rest.

To this purport the Patriarch of the Quakers writes, where he saith "now some men have the nature of Swine, wallowing in the mire: and some men have the nature of Dogs, to bite both the sheep and one another: and some men have the nature of Lions, to tear, devour, and destroy: and some men have the nature of Wolves, to tear and devour the lambs and sheep of Christ: and some men have the nature of the Serpent (that old destroyer) to sting, evenom, and poison. *He that hath an ear to hear, let him hear*, and learn these things within himself. And some men have the natures of other beasts and creatures, minding nothing but earthly and visible things, and feeding without the fear of God. Some men have the nature of a Horse, to prance and vapour in their strength, and to be swift in doing evil. And some men have the nature of tall sturdy Oaks, to flourish and spread in wisdom and strength, who are strong in evil, which must perish and come to the fire. Thus the Evil one is but *one in all*, but worketh many ways; and whatsoever a Man's or Woman's nature is addicted to that is outward, the Evil one will fit him with that, and will please his nature and appetite, to keep his mind in his inventions, and in the creatures from the Creator."

To this purport the so-called Clemens writes in the Apostolical Constitutions when he complains that the flock of Christ was devoured by Demons and wicked men, or rather not men, but wild beasts in the shape of men, πονηροῖς ἀνθρώποις, μᾶλλον δὲ οὐκ ἀνθρώποις, ἀλλὰ θηρίοις ἀνθρωποείδεσιν, by Heathens, Jews and godless heretics.

With equal triumph, too, did he read a passage in one of the numbers of the Connoisseur, which made him wonder that the writer, from whom it proceeded in levity, should not have been led on by it to the clear perception of a great truth. "The affinity," says that writer, who is now known to have been no less a person than the author of the Task, "the affinity between chatterers and monkeys, and praters and parrots, is too obvious not to occur at once. Grunters and growlers may be justly compared to hogs. Snarlers are curs that continually shew their teeth, but never bite; and the spit-fire passionate are a sort of wild cats, that will not bear stroking, but will purr when they are pleased. Complainers are screech-owls; and story-tellers, always repeating the same dull note, are cuckoos. Poets, that prick up their ears at their own hideous braying, are no better than asses; critics in general are venomous serpents, that delight in hissing; and some of them, who have got by heart a few technical terms, without knowing their meaning, are no better than magpies."

So, too, the polyonomous Arabian philosopher Zechariah Ben Mohammed Ben Mahmud Al Camuni Al Cazvini. "Man," he says, "partakes of the nature of vegetables, because, like them, he grows and is nourished; he stands in this further relation to the irrational animals, that he feels and moves; by his intellectual faculties he resembles the higher orders of intelligences, and he partakes more or less of these various classes, as his inclination leads him. If his sole wish be to satisfy the wants of existence, then he is content to vegetate. If he partakes more of the animal than the vegetable nature, we find him fierce as the lion, greedy as the bull, impure as the hog, cruel as the leopard, or cunning as the fox; and if, as is sometimes the case, he possesses all these bad qualities, he is then a demon in human shape."

Gratifying as these passages were to him, some of them being mere sports of wit, and others only the produce of fancy, he would have been indeed delighted if he had known what was in his days known by no European scholar, that in the Institutes of Menu, his notion is distinctly declared as a revealed truth; there it is said, "In whatever occupation the Supreme Lord first employed any vital soul, to that occupation the same soul attaches itself spontaneously, when it receives a new body again and again. Whatever quality, noxious or innocent, harsh or mild, unjust or just, false or true, he conferred on any being at its creation, the same quality enters it of course on its future births." *

Still more would it have gratified him if he had known (as has before been cursorily observed) how entirely his own theory coincided with the Druidical philosophy, a philosophy which he would rather have traced to the Patriarchs, than to the Canaanites. Their doctrine, as explained by the Welsh translator of the Paradise Lost, in the sketch of Bardism which he has prefixed to the poems of Llywarc the Aged, was that "the whole animated creation originated in the lowest point of existence, and arrived by a regular train of gradations at the probationary state of humanity, the intermediate stages being all necessarily evil, but more or less so as they were removed from the beginning, which was evil in the extreme. In the state of humanity, good and evil were equally balanced, consequently it was a state of liberty, in which, if the conduct of the free agent preponderated towards evil, death gave but an awful passage whereby he returned to animal life, in a condition below humanity equal to the degree of turpitude to which he had debased himself, when free to choose between good and evil: and if his life were desperately wicked, it was possible for him to fall to his original vileness, in the lowest point of existence, there to recommence his painful progression through the ascending series of brute being. But if he had acted well in this his stage of probation, death was then to the soul thus tried and approved, what the word by which in the language of the Druids it is denoted, literally means, enlargement. The soul was removed from the sphere wherein evil hath any place, into a state necessarily good; not to continue there in one eternal condition of blessedness, eternity being what no inferior existence could endure, but to pass from one gradation to another, gaining at every ascent increase of knowledge, and retaining the consciousness of its whole preceding progress through all. For the good of the human race, such a soul might again be sent on earth, but the human being of which it then formed the life, was incapable of falling." In this fancy the Bardic system approached that of the Bramins, this Celtic avatar of a happy soul, corresponding to the twice-born man of the Hindus. And the Doctor would have extracted some confirmation for the ground of the theory from that verse of the Psalm which speaks of us as "curiously wrought in the lowest parts of the earth."

* Sir W. Jones.

Young, he used to say, expressed unconsciously this system of progressive life, when he spoke of man as a creature

> From different natures marvellously mix'd;
> Connection exquisite of distant worlds;
> Distinguish'd link in being's endless chain,
> Midway from nothing to the Deity.

It was more distinctly enounced by Akenside.

> The same paternal hand
> From the mute shell-fish gasping on the shore
> To men, to angels, to celestial minds
> Will ever lead the generations on
> Through higher scenes of being: while, supplied
> From day to day with his enlivening breath,
> Inferior orders in succession rise
> To fill the void below. As flame ascends,
> As vapours to the earth in showers return,
> As the pois'd ocean toward the attracting moon
> Swells, and the ever listening planets charmed
> By the Sun's call their onward pace incline,
> So all things which have life aspire to God,
> Exhaustless fount of intellectual day!
> Centre of souls! nor doth the mastering voice
> Of nature cease within to prompt aright
> Their steps; nor is the care of heaven withheld
> From sending to the toil external aid,
> That in their stations all may persevere
> To climb the ascent of being, and approach
> For ever nearer to the Life Divine.

The Bardic system bears in itself intrinsic evidence of its antiquity; for no such philosophy could have been devised among any Celtic people in later ages; nor could the

Britons have derived any part of it from any nation with whom they had any opportunity of intercourse, at any time within reach of history. The Druids, or rather the Bards, (for these, according to those by whom their traditionary wisdom has been preserved, were the superior order,) deduced as corollaries from the theory of Progressive Existence, these beautiful Triads.*

"There are three Circles of Existence; the Circle of Infinity, where there is nothing but God, of living or dead, and none but God can traverse it; the Circle of Inchoation, where all things are by nature derived from Death, — this Circle hath been traversed by man; and the Circle of happiness, where all things spring from life, — this man shall traverse in heaven.

"Animated beings having three states of Existence; that of Inchoation in the Great Deep, or lowest point of Existence; that of Liberty in the State of Humanity; and that of Love, which is the Happiness of Heaven.

"All animated Beings are subject to three Necessities; beginning in the Great Deep; Progression in the Circle of Inchoation; and Plenitude in the Circle of Happiness. Without these things nothing can possibly exist but God.

"Three things are necessary in the Circle of Inchoation; the least of all, Animation, and thence beginning; the materials of all things, and thence Increase, which cannot take place in any other state; the formation of all things out of the dead mass, and thence Discriminate Individuality.

"Three things cannot but exist towards all animated Beings from the nature of Divine Justice: Co-sufferance in the Circle of Inchoation, because without that none could attain to the perfect knowledge of anything; Co-participation in the Divine Love; and Co-ultimity from the nature of God's Power, and its attributes of Justice and Mercy.

"There are three necessary occasions of Inchoation: to collect the materials and properties of every nature; to collect the knowledge of everything; and to collect power towards subduing the Adverse and the Devastative, and for the divestation of Evil. Without this traversing every mode of animated existence, no state of animation, or of anything in nature, can attain to plenitude."

"By the knowledge of three things will all Evil and Death be diminished and subdued; their nature, their cause, and their operation. This knowledge will be obtained in the Circle of Happiness."

"The three Plenitudes of Happiness: — Participation of every nature, with a plenitude of One predominant; conformity to every cast of genius and character, possessing superior excellence in one: the love of all Beings and Existences, but chiefly concentred in one object, which is God; and in the predominant One of each of these, will the Plenitude of Happiness consist."

Triads, it may be observed, are found in the Proverbs of Solomon: so that to the evidence of antiquity which these Bardic remains present in their doctrines, a presumption is to be added from the peculiar form in which they are conveyed.

Whether Sir Philip Sydney had any such theory in his mind or not, there is an approach to it in that fable which he says old Lanquet taught him of the Beasts desiring from Jupiter, a King, Jupiter consented, but on condition that they should contribute the

* Originally quoted in the notes to Madoc to illustrate the lines which follow.

"Let the Bard,
Exclaim'd the King, give his accustom'd lay:
For sweet, I know, to Madoc is the song
He loved in earlier years.
Then strong of voice,
The officer proclaim'd the sovereign will,
Bidding the hall be silent; loud he spake
And smote the sounding pillar with his wand
And hush'd the banqueters. The chief of Bards
Then raised the ancient lay.
Thee, Lord, he sung,
O Father! Thee, whose wisdom, Thee, whose power,
Whose love, — all love, all power, all wisdom, Thou!
Tongue cannot utter, nor can heart conceive.
He in the lowest depth of Being framed
The imperishable mind; in every change
Through the great circle of progressive life,
He guides and guards, till evil shall be known,
And being known as evil cease to be;
And the pure soul emancipate by death,
The Enlarger, shall attain its end predoom'd,
The eternal newness of eternal joy.

qualities convenient for the new and superior creature.

Full glad they were, and took the naked sprite,
  Which straight the Earth yclothed in her clay;
The Lion heart, the Ounce gave active might;
  The Horse, good shape; the Sparrow lust to play;
  Nightingale, voice enticing songs to say;
Elephant gave a perfect memory,
And Parrot, ready tongue that to apply.

The Fox gave craft; the Dog gave flattery;
  Ass, patience; the Mole, a working thought;
Eagle, high look; Wolf, secret cruelty;
  Monkey, sweet breath; the Cow, her fair eyes brought:
  The Ermine, whitest skin, spotted with nought.
The Sheep, mild-seeming face; climbing the Bear,
The Stag did give his harm-eschewing fear.

The Hare, her slights; the Cat, her melancholy;
  Ant, industry; and Coney, skill to build;
Cranes, order; Storks, to be appearing holy;
  Cameleons, ease to change; Duck, ease to yield;
  Crocodile, tears which might be falsely spill'd;
Ape, great thing gave, tho' he did mowing stand,
The instrument of instruments, the hand.

Thus Man was made, thus Man their Lord became.

At such a system he thought Milton glanced when his Satan speaks of the influences of the heavenly bodies, as

Productive in herb, plant, and nobler birth
Of creatures animate with gradual life
Of growth, sense, reason, all summ'd up in man:

for that the lines, though capable of another interpretation, ought to be interpreted as referring to a scheme of progressive life, appears by this fuller developement in the speech of Rafaël;

O Adam, one Almighty is, from whom
All things proceed, and up to him return,
If not deprav'd from good, created all
Such to perfection, one first matter all,
Indued with various forms, various degrees
Of substance, and in things that live, of life;
But more refin'd, more spiritous, and pure,
As nearer to him plac'd, or nearer tending
Each in their several active spheres assign'd,
Till body up to spirit work, in bounds
Proportion'd to each kind. So from the root
Springs lighter the green stalk, from thence the leaves
More aery, last the bright consummate flower
Spirits odorous breathes: flow'rs and their fruit,
Man's nourishment, by gradual scale sublimed,
To vital spirits aspire, to animal,
To intellectual; give both life and sense
Fancy and understanding; whence the soul
Reason received, and reason is her being
Discursive, or intuitive; discourse
Is oftest yours, the latter most is ours,
Differing but in degree, of kind the same.*

Whether that true philosopher, in the exact import of the word, Sir Thomas Browne, had formed a system of this kind, or only threw out a seminal idea from which it might be evolved, the Doctor, who dearly loved the writings of this most meditative author, would not say. But that Sir Thomas had opened the same vein of thought appears in what Dr. Johnson censured in "a very fanciful and indefensible section" of his Christian Morals; for there, and not among his Pseudodoxia Epidemica, that is to say, Vulgar Errors, the passage is found. Our Doctor would not only have deemed it defensible, but would have proved it to be so by defending it. "Since the brow," says the Philosopher of Norwich, "speaks often truth, since eyes and noses have tongues, and the countenance proclaims the heart and inclinations; let observation so far instruct thee in physiognomical lines, as to be some rule for thy distinction, and guide for thy affection unto such as look most like men. Mankind, methinks, is comprehended in a few faces, if we exclude all visages which any way participate of symmetries and schemes of look common unto other animals. For as though man were the extract of the world, in whom all were in *coagulato*, which in their forms were *in soluto*, and at extension, we often observe that men do most act those creatures whose constitution, parts and complexion, do most predominate in their mixtures. This is a corner-stone in physiognomy, and holds some truth, not only in particular persons, but also in whole nations." †

But Dr. Johnson must cordially have assented to Sir Thomas Browne's inferential admonition. "Live," says that Religious Physician and Christian Moralist, — "live unto the dignity of thy nature, and leave it not disputable at last whether thou hast

* Spenser in his "Hymne of Heavenly Beautie" falls into a similar train of thought, as is observed by Thyer:—

By view whereof it plainly may appeare
That still as every thing doth upward tend,
And further is from earth, so still more cleare
And faire it grows, till to his perfect end
Of purest beautie it at last ascend;
Ayre more than water, fire much more than ayre,
And heaven than fire, appeares more pure and fayre.

But these are somewhat of Pythagorean speculations — caught up by Lucretius and Virgil.

† Part ii. Section 9.

been a man, or since thou art a composition of man and beast, how thou hast predominantly passed thy days, to state the denomination. Un-man not, therefore, thyself by a bestial transformation, nor realize old fables. Expose not thyself by fourfooted manners unto monstrous draughts and caricature representations. Think not after the old Pythagorean concert what beast thou mayest be after death. Be not under any brutal metempsychosis while thou livest and walkest about erectly under that scheme of man. In thine own circumference, as in that of the earth, let the rational horizon be larger than the sensible, and the circle of reason than of sense: let the divine part be upward, and the region of beast below: otherwise it is but to live invertedly, and with thy head unto the heels of thy antipodes. Desert not thy title to a divine particle and union with invisibles. Let true knowledge and virtue tell the lower world thou art a part of the higher. Let thy thoughts be of things which have not entered into the hearts of beasts; think of things long past, and long to come; acquaint thyself with the choragium of the stars, and consider the vast expansion beyond them. Let intellectual tubes give thee a glance of things which visive organs reach not. Have a glimpse of incomprehensible, and thoughts of things, which thoughts but tenderly touch. Lodge immaterials in thy head, ascend unto invisibles; fill thy spirit with spirituals, with the mysteries of faith, the magnalities of religion, and thy life with the honour of God; without which, though giants in wealth and dignity, we are but dwarfs and pygmies in humanity, and may hold a pitiful rank in that triple division of mankind into heroes, men and beasts. For though human souls are said to be equal, yet is there no small inequality in their operations; some maintain the allowable station of men, many are far below it; and some have been so divine as to approach the apogeum of their natures, and to be in the confinium of spirits."

CHAPTER CCX.

A QUOTATION FROM BISHOP BERKELEY, AND A HIT AT THE SMALL CRITICS.

Plusieurs blameront l'entassement de passages que l'on vient de voir; j'ai prévu leurs dédains, leurs dégoûts, et leurs censures magistrales; et n'ai pas voulu y avoir égard. BAYLE.

HERE I shall inform the small critic, what it is, "a thousand pounds to one penny," as the nursery song says, or as the newspaper reporters of the Ring have it, Lombard Street to a China Orange, — no small critic already knows, whether he be diurnal, hebdomadal, monthly or trimestral, — that a notion of progressive Life is mentioned in Bishop Berkeley's Minute Philosopher, not as derived from any old system of philosophy or religion, but as the original speculation of one who belonged to a club of Freethinkers. Another member of that worshipful society explains the system of his acquaintance, thus:

"He made a threefold partition of the human species into Birds, Beasts and Fishes, being of opinion that the Road of Life lies upwards in a perpetual ascent, through the scale of Being: in such sort, that the souls of insects after death make their second appearance in the shape of perfect animals, Birds, Beasts or Fishes; which upon their death are preferred into human bodies, and in the next stage into Beings of a higher and more perfect kind. This man we considered at first as a sort of heretic, because his scheme seemed not to consist with our fundamental tenet, the Mortality of the Soul: but he justified the notion to be innocent, inasmuch as it included nothing of reward or punishment, and was not proved by any argument which supposed or implied either incorporeal spirit, or Providence, being only inferred, by way of analogy, from what he had observed in human affairs, the Court, the Church, and the Army, wherein the tendency is always upwards, from lower posts to higher. According to this system, the Fishes are those men who swim in pleasure, such as *petits maitres*, *bons vivans*, and honest fellows. The Beasts are dry, drudging, covetous, rapacious folk, and all those addicted to care and business like oxen, and other dry land animals, which spend their lives in labour and fatigue. The Birds are airy, notional men, Enthusiasts, Projectors, Philosophers, and such like; in each species every individual retaining a tincture of his former state, which constitutes what is called genius."

The quiet reader who sometimes lifts his eyes from the page (and closes them perhaps) to meditate upon what he has been reading, will perhaps ask himself wherefore I consider it to be as certain that no small critic should have read the Minute Philosopher, as that children cannot be drowned while "sliding on dry ground?"—My reason for so thinking is, that small critics never read anything so good. Like town ducks they dabble in the gutter, but never purify themselves in clear streams, nor take to the deep waters.

CHAPTER CCXI.

SOMETHING IN HONOUR OF BISHOP WATSON. CUDWORTH. JACKSON OF OXFORD AND NEWCASTLE. A BAXTERIAN SCRUPLE.

S'il y a des lecteurs qui se soucient peu de cela, on les prie de se souvenir qu'un auteur n'est pas obligé à ne rien dire que ce qui est de leur goût. BAYLE.

HAD my ever-by-me-to-be-lamented friend, and from this time forth, I trust, ever-by-the-public-to-be-honoured philosopher, been a Welshman; or had he lived to become acquainted with the treasures of Welsh lore which Edward Williams, William Owen, and Edward Davies, the Curate of Olveston, have brought to light; he would have believed in the Bardic system as heartily as the Glamorganshire and Merionethshire Bards themselves, and have fitted it, without any apprehension of heresy, to his own religious creed. And although he would have perceived with the Curate of Olveston (worthy of the best Welsh Bishoprick for his labours; O George the Third, why did no one tell thee that he was so, when he dedicated to thee his Celtic Researches?),—although (I say) he would have perceived that certain of the Druidical rites were derived from an accursed origin,—a fact authenticated by their abominations, and rendered certain by the historical proof that the Celtic language affords in both those dialects wherein any genuine remains have been preserved,—that knowledge would still have left him at liberty to adopt such other parts of the system as harmonised with his own speculations, and were not incompatible with the Christian faith. How he would have reconciled them shall be explained when I have taken this opportunity of relating something of the late Right Reverend Father in God, Richard Watson, Lord Bishop of Llandaff, which is more to his honour than anything that he has related of himself. He gave the Curate of Olveston, upon George Hardinge's recommendation, a Welsh Rectory, which, though no splendid preferment, placed that patient, and learned, and able and meritorious *poor* man, in a respectable station, and conferred upon him (as he gratefully acknowledged) the comfort of independence.

My friend had been led by Cudworth to this reasonable conclusion that there was a theology of divine tradition, or revelation, or a divine cabala, amongst the Hebrews first, and from them afterward communicated to the Egyptians and other nations. He had learned also from that greater theologian Jackson of Corpus (whom the Laureate Southey (himself to be commended for so doing) loses no opportunity of commending) * that divine communion was not confined to the Israelites before their distinction from other nations, and that "idolatry and superstition could not have increased so much in the old world, unless there had been evident documents of a divine power in ages precedent;" for "strange fables and lying

* Since Southey's death, Jackson's Works, to the much satisfaction of all sound theologians, have been reprinted at the Clarendon Press. I once heard Mr. Parker the Bookseller—the uncle of the present Mr. Parker—say, that he recollected the sheets of the Folio Edition being used as wrappers in the shops! Alexander's dust as a bung to a beer-barrel, quotha!

wonders receive being from notable and admirable decayed truths, as baser creatures do life from the dissolution of more noble bodies." These were the deliberate opinions of men not more distinguished among their contemporaries and eminent above their successors, for the extent of their erudition, than remarkable for capacity of mind and sobriety of judgment. And with these the history of the Druidical system entirely accords. It arose "from the gradual or accidental corruption of the patriarchal religion, by the abuse of certain commemorative honours which were paid to the ancestors of the human race, and by the admixture of Sabæan idolatry;" and on the religion thus corrupted some Canaanite abominations were engrafted by the Phœnicians. But as in other apostacies, a portion of original truth was retained in it.

Indeed just as remains of the antediluvian world are found everywhere in the bowels of the earth, so are traces not of scriptural history alone, but of primæval truths, to be discovered in the tradition of savages, their wild fables, and their bewildered belief; as well as in the elaborate systems of heathen mythology and the principles of what may deserve to be called divine philosophy. The farther our researches are extended, the more of these collateral proofs are collected, and consequently the stronger their collective force becomes. Research and reflection lead also to conclusions as congenial to the truly christian heart as they may seem startling to that which is christian in everything except in charity. Impostors acting only for their own purposes have enunciated holy truths, which in many of their followers have brought forth fruits of holiness. True miracles have been worked in false religions. Nor ought it to be doubted that prayers which have been directed to false Gods in erring, but innocent, because unavoidable misbelief, have been heard and accepted by that most merciful Father, whose eye is over all his creatures, and who hateth nothing that he hath made. — Here, be it remarked, that Baxter has protested against this fine expression in that paper of exceptions against the Common Prayer which he prepared for the Savoy Meeting, and which his colleagues were prudent enough to set aside, lest it should give offence, they said, but probably because the more moderate of them were ashamed of its frivolous and captious cavillings; the Collect in which it occurs, he said, hath no reason for appropriation to the first day of Lent, and this part of it is unhandsomely said, being true only in a formal sense *quâ talis*, for "he hateth all the works of iniquity." Thus did he make iniquity the work of God, a blasphemy from which he would have revolted with just abhorrence if it had been advanced by another person: but dissent had become in him a cachexy of the intellect.

CHAPTER CCXII.

SPECULATIONS CONNECTED WITH THE DOCTOR'S THEORY. DOUBTS AND DIFFICULTIES.

Voilà bien des mystères, dira-t-on ; j'en conviens ; aussi le sujet le mérite-t-il bien. Au reste, il est certain que ces mystères ne cachent rien de mauvais. GOMGAM.

BUT although the conformity of the Bardic system to his own notions of progressive existence would have appeared to the Doctor

— confirmation strong
As proof of holy writ,—

he would have assented to that system no farther than such preceding conformity extended. Holding it only as the result of his own speculations, — as hypothesis, — a mere fancy, — a toy of the mind, — a plaything for the intellect in its lighter moments, and sometimes in its graver ones the subject of a dream, — he valued it accordingly. And yet the more he sported with it, and the farther he pursued it in his reveries, the more plausible it appeared, and the better did it seem to explain some of the physical phenomena, and some of the else seemingly inexplicable varieties of human nature. It was Henry More's opinion that the Pre-existence of the Soul, which is so explicit and frequent a doctrine of the Platonists, "was a tenet for which there are many plausible reasons, and against which there is nothing considerable to be alleged; being a key," he said, "for some main mysteries of Providence which no other can so handsomely unlock." More however, the Doctor thought, might be advanced against that tenet, than against his own scheme, for to that no valid objection could be opposed. But the metempsychosis in a descending scale as a scheme of punishment would have been regarded by him as one of those corruptions which the Bards derived from the vain philosophy or false religions of the Levant.

Not that this part of their scheme was without a certain plausibility on the surface, which might recommend it to inconsiderate minds. He himself would have thought that no Judge ever pronounced a more just decision than the three Infernal Lord Chancellors of the dead would do, if they condemned his townsman the pettyfogger to skulk upon earth again as a pole-cat, creep into holes as an earwig, and be flattened again between the thumbnails of a London chambermaid, or exposed to the fatal lotion of Mr. Tiffin, bug-destroyer to his Majesty. It was fitting, he thought, that every keen sportsman, for once at least, should take the part of the inferior creature in those amusements of the field which he had followed so joyously, and that he should be winged in the shape of a partridge, run down in the form of a hare by the hounds, and Actæonised in a stag: that the winner of a Welsh main should be the cock of one, and die of the wounds received in the last fight; that the merciless postmaster should become a post-horse at his own inn; and that they who have devised, or practised, or knowingly permitted any wanton cruelty for the sake of pampering their appetites, should in the next stage of their existence feel in their own person the effect of those devices, which in their human state they had only tasted. And not being addicted himself to "the most honest, ingenuous, quiet, and harmless art of angling," (forgive him Sir Humphrey Davy! forgive him Chantrey! forgive him, thou best of all publishers, John Major, who mightest write *Ne plus ultra* upon thy edition of any book which thou delightest to honour,) he allowed that even Izaak Walton of blessed memory could not have shown cause for mitigation of the sentence, if Rhadamanthus and his colleagues in the Court below, had condemned him to be spitted upon the hook of some dear lover and ornament of the art, in the shape of "a black snail with his belly slit to shew the white;" or of a perch, which of fish, he tells us, is the longest lived on a hook; or sewed him metempsycho-sized into a frog, to the arming iron, with a fine needle and silk, with only one stitch, using him in so doing, according to his own minute directions, as if he loved him, that is, harming him as little as he possibly might, that he might live the longer.

This would be fitting, he thought, and there would have been enough of purgatory in it to satisfy the sense of vindictive justice, if any scheme of purgatory had been reconcilable with his scriptural belief. Bishop Hall has a passage in his Choice Helps for a Pious Spirit, which might be taken in the sense of this opinion, though certainly no such meaning was intended by the writer. "Man," he says, "as he consists of a double nature, flesh and spirit, so is he placed in a middle rank, betwixt an angel, which is a spirit, and a beast, which is flesh: partaking of the qualities and performing the acts of both. He is angelical in his understanding, in his sensual affections bestial; and to whether of these he most incline and comforteth himself, that part wins more of the other, and gives a denomination to him; so as he that was before half angel, half beast, if he be drowned in sensuality, hath lost the angel and is become a beast; if he be wholly taken up with heavenly meditations, he hath quit the beast, and is improved angelical. It is hard to hold an equal temper, either he must degenerate into a beast, or be advanced to an angel."

Had the Doctor held this opinion according to the letter, and believed that those who brutalised their nature in the stage of humanity, were degraded to the condition of brutes after death, he could even have persuaded himself that intelligible indications of such a transmigration might be discovered in the eyes of a dog when he looks to some hard master for mercy, or to some kind one for notice, and as it were for a recognition of the feelings and thoughts which had no other means of expression. But he could not have endured to think it possible that the spaniel who stood beside him in mute supplication, with half-erected ears, looking for a morsel of food, might be a friend or relation; and that in making a troublesome or a thievish cur slink away with his tail between his legs, he might be hurting the feelings of an old acquaintance.

And indeed on the whole it would have disturbed his sense of order, to think that while some inferior creatures were innocently and unconsciously ascending in the scale of existence through their appointed gradations, others were being degraded to a condition below humanity for their sins committed in the human state. Punishment such degradation could not be deemed, unless the soul so punished retained its consciousness; and such consciousness would make it a different being from those who were externally of its fellow kind, and thus would the harmony of nature be destroyed: and to introduce discord there were to bring back Chaos Bad enough, as he saw, is the inequality which prevails among mankind, though without it men would soon be all upon the dead level of animal and ferine life: But what is it to that which would appear in the lower world, if in the same species some individuals were guided only by their own proper instincts, and others endued with the consciousness of a human and reasonable mind?

The consequences also of such a doctrine where it was believed could not but lead to pitiable follies, and melancholy superstitions. Has humanity ever been put to a viler use than by the Banians at Surat, who support a hospital for vermin in that city, and regale the souls of their friends who are undergoing penance in the shape of fleas, or in loathsome pedicular form, by hiring beggars to go in among them, and afford them pasture for the night!

Even from his own system consequences followed which he could not reconcile to his wishes. Fond as he was of animals, it would have been a delight to him if he could have believed with the certainty of faith that he should have with him in Heaven all that he had loved on earth. But if they were only so many vehicles of the living spirit during its ascent to humanity, — only the egg, the caterpillar and the aurelia from which the human but immortal Psyche was to come forth at last, then must their uses be at an end in this earthly state: and Paradise he was sometimes tempted to think would want something if there were no beautiful insects to hover about its flowers, no birds to warble in its groves or glide upon its waters, — would not be the Paradise he longed for unless the lion were there to lie down with the lamb, and the antelope reclined its gentle head upon the leopard's breast. Fitting, and desirable, and necessary he considered the extinction of all noxious kinds, all which were connected with corruption, and might strictly be said to be of the earth earthly. But in his Paradise he would fain have whatever had been in Eden, before Paradise was lost, except the serpent.

"I can hardly," says an English officer who was encamped in India near a lake overstocked with fish, "I can hardly censure the taste of the Indians, who banish from a consecrated pond the net of the fisher, the angler's hook and the fowler's gun. Shoals of large fish giving life to the clear water of a large lake covered with flocks of aquatic birds, afford to the sight a gratification which would be ill exchanged for the momentary indulgence of appetite." My excellent friend would heartily have agreed with this Englishman; but in the waters of Paradise he would have thought, neither did the fish prey upon each other, nor the birds upon them, death not being necessary there as the means of providing aliment for life.

That there are waters in the Regions of the Blessed, Bede, it is said, assures us for this reason, that they are necessary there to temper the heat of the Sun. And Cornelius à Lapide has found out a most admirable use for them above the firmament, — which is to make rivers, and fountains, and water-works for the recreation of the souls in bliss, whose seat is in the Empyrean Heaven.

"If an herd of kine," says Fuller, "should meet together to fancy and define happiness, — (that is to imagine a Paradise for themselves,) — they would place it to consist in fine pastures, sweet grass, clear water, shadowy groves, constant summer; but if any winter, then warm shelter and dainty hay, with company after their kind, counting these low things the highest happiness, because their conceit can reach no higher. Little better do the heathen poets describe Heaven, paving it with pearl and roofing it with stars, filling it with Gods and Goddesses, and allowing them to drink, (as if without it, no poet's Paradise,) nectar and ambrosia."

CHAPTER CCXIII.

BIRDS OF PARADISE. THE ZIZ. STORY OF THE ABBOT OF ST. SALVADOR DE VILLAR. HOLY COLETTE'S NONDESCRIPT PET. THE ANIMALCULAR WORLD. GIORDANO BRUNO.

> And so I came to Fancy's meadows, strow'd
> With many a flower;
> Fain would I here have made abode,
> But I was quickened by my hour. HERBERT.

HINDOOS and Mahommedans have stocked their heavens not only with mythological monsters but with beautiful birds of celestial kind. They who have read Thalaba will remember the

> Green warbler of the bowers of Paradise:

and they who will read the history of the Nella-Rajah, — which whosoever reads or relates shall (according to the author) enjoy all manner of happiness and planetary bliss, — that is to say, all the good fortune that can be bestowed by the nine great luminaries which influence human events, — they who read that amusing story will find that in the world of Daivers, or Genii, there are milk-white birds called Aunnays, remarkable for the gracefulness of their walk, wonderfully endowed with knowledge and speech, incapable of deceit, and having power to look into the thoughts of men.

These creatures of imagination are conceived in better taste than the Rabbis have displayed in the invention of their great bird Ziz, whose head when he stands in the deep sea reaches up to Heaven; whose wings when they are extended darken the sun; and one of whose eggs happening to fall crushed three hundred cedars, and breaking in the fall, drowned sixty cities in its yolk. That fowl is reserved for the dinner of the Jews in heaven, at which Leviathan is to be the fish, and Behemoth the roast meat. There will be cut and come again at all of them; and the carvers, of whatever rank in the hierarchy they may be, will have no sinecure office that day.

The monks have given us a prettier tale; — praise be to him who composed, — but the liar's portion to those who made it pass for truth. There was an Abbot of S. Salvador de Villar who lived in times when piety flourished, and Saints on earth enjoyed a visible communion with Heaven. This holy man used in the intervals of his liturgical duties to recreate himself by walking in a pine forest near his monastery, employing his thoughts the while in divine meditations. One day when thus engaged during his customary walk, a bird in size and appearance resembling a blackbird alighted before him on one of the trees, and began so sweet a song, that in the delight of listening the good Abbot lost all sense of time and place, and of all earthly things, remaining motionless and in extasy. He returned not to the Convent at his accustomed hour, and the Monks supposed that he had withdrawn to some secret solitude; and would resume his office when his intended devotion there should have been compleated. So long a time elapsed without his reappearance that it was necessary to appoint a substitute for him *pro tempore;* his disappearance and the forms observed upon this occasion being duly registered. Seventy years passed by, during all which time no one who entered the pine forest ever lighted upon the Abbot, nor did he think of anything but the bird before him, nor hear anything but the song which filled his soul with contentment, nor eat, nor drink, nor sleep, nor feel either want, or weariness, or exhaustion. The bird at length ceased to sing and took flight: and the Abbot then, as if he had remained there only a few minutes, returned to the monastery. He marvelled as he approached at certain alterations about the place, and still more when upon entering the house, he knew none of the brethren whom he saw, nor did any one appear to know him. The matter was soon explained, his name being well known, and the manner of his disappearance matter of tradition there as well as of record: miracles were not so uncommon then as to render any proof of identity necessary, and they proposed to reinstate him in his office. But the holy man was sensible that after so great a favour had been vouchsafed him, he was not to remain a sojourner upon earth; so he exhorted them to live in peace with one another, and in the fear of God, and in the strict observance of their rule, and to let him end his days in quietness; and in a few days, even as he expected, it came to pass, and he fell asleep in the Lord.

The dishonest monks who, for the honour of their Convent and the lucre of gain, palmed this lay (for such in its origin it was) upon their neighbours as a true legend, added to it, that the holy Abbot was interred in the cloisters; that so long as the brethren continued in the observance of their rule, and the place of his interment was devoutly visited, the earth about it proved a certain cure for many maladies, but that in process of time both church and cloisters became so dilapidated through decay of devotion, that cattle strayed into them, till the monks and the people of the vicinity were awakened to a sense of their sin and of their duty, by observing that every animal which trod upon the Abbot's grave fell and broke its leg.* The relics therefore were translated with due solemnity, and deposited in a new monument, on which the story of the miracle, *in perpetuam rei memoriam*, was represented in bas-relief.

The Welsh have a tradition concerning the Birds of Rhianon, — a female personage who hath a principal part in carrying on the spells in Gwlad yr Hud, or the Enchanted Land of Pembrokeshire. Whoso happened to hear the singing of her birds stood seven years listening, though he supposed the while that only an hour or two had elapsed. Owen Pughe could have told us more of these Birds.

Some Romish legends speak of birds which were of no species known on earth and who by the place and manner of their appearances were concluded to have come from Paradise, or to have been celestial spirits in that form. Holy Colette of portentous sanctify, the Reformeress of the Poor Clares, and from whom a short-lived variety of the Franciscans were called Colettines, was favoured, according to her biographers, with frequent visits by a four-footed pet, which was no mortal creature. It was small, resembling a squirrel in agility, and an ermine in the snowy whiteness of its skin, but not in other respects like either; and it had this advantage over all earthly pets, that it was sweetly and singularly fragrant. It would play about the saint, and invite her attention by its gambols. Colette felt a peculiar and mysterious kind of pleasure when it showed itself; and for awhile not supposing that there was anything supernatural in its appearance, endeavoured to catch it, for she delighted in having lambs and innocent birds to fondle: but though the Nuns closed the door, and used every art and effort to entice or catch it, the little nondescript always either eluded them, or vanished; and it never tasted of any food which they set before it. This miracle being unique in its kind is related with becoming admiration by the chroniclers of the Seraphic Order; as it well may, for, for a monastic writer to invent a new

* Superstition is confined to no country, but is spread, more or less, over all. The classical reader will call to mind what Herodotus tells happened in the territory of Agyllæi. *Clio. c.* 167, ἐγίνετο διάστροφα καὶ ἔμπηρα καὶ ἀπόπληκτα, ὁμοίως πρόβατα καὶ ὑποζύγια καὶ ἄνθρωποι.

miracle of any kind evinces no ordinary power of invention.

If this story be true, and true it must be unless holy Colette's reverend Roman Catholic biographers are liars, its truth cannot be admitted *sans tirer à consequence;* and it would follow as a corollary not to be disputed, that there are animals in the world of Angels. And on the whole it accorded with the general bearing of the Doctor's notions (notions rather than opinions he liked to call them where they were merely speculative) to suppose that there may be as much difference between the zoology of that world, and of this, as is found in the zoology and botany of widely distant regions here, according to different circumstances of climate: and rather to imagine that there were celestial birds, beasts, fishes, and insects, exempt from evil, and each happy in its kind to the full measure of its capacity for happiness, than to hold the immortality of brutes. Cudworth's authority had some weight with him on this subject, where the Platonical divine says that as "human souls could not possibly be generated out of matter, but were some time or other created by the Almighty out of nothing preexisting, either in generations, or before them," so if it be admitted that brute animals are "not mere machines, or *automata*, (as some seem inclinable to believe,) but conscious and thinking beings; then, from the same principle of reason, it will likewise follow, that their souls cannot be generated out of matter neither, and therefore must be derived from the fountain of all life, and created out of nothing by Him; who, since he can as easily annihilate as create, and does all for the best, no man need at all to trouble himself about their permanency, or immortality."

Now though the Doctor would have been pleased to think, with the rude Indian, that when he was in a state of existence wherein no evil could enter,

His faithful dog should bear him company,

he felt the force of this reasoning; and he perceived also that something analogous to the annihilation there intended might be discerned in his own hypothesis. For in what may be called the visible creation he found nothing resembling that animalcular world which the microscope has placed within reach of our senses; nothing like those monstrous and prodigious forms which Leeuwenhoeck, it must be believed, has faithfully delineated. — Bishop has a beautiful epigram upon the theme καλὰ πέφανται:

When thro' a chink *, a darkened room
Admits the solar beam,
Down the long light that breaks the gloom,
Millions of atoms stream.

In sparkling agitation bright,
Alternate dyes they bear;
Too small for any sense but sight,
Or any sight, but *there*.

Nature reveals not all her store
To human search, or skill;
And when she deigns to shew us more
She shows us Beauty still.

But the microscopic world affords us exceptions to this great moral truth. The forms which are there discovered might well be called

Abominable, inutterable, and worse
Than fables yet have feign'd, or fear conceiv'd,
Gorgons and Hydras, and Chimæras dire.

Such verily they would be, if they were in magnitude equal to the common animals by which we are surrounded. But Nature has left all these seemingly misformed creatures in the lowest stage of existence,—the circle of inchoation; neither are any of the hideous forms of insects repeated in the higher grades of animal life; the sea indeed contains creatures marvellously uncouth and ugly, *beaucoup plus de monstres, sans comparaison, que la terre*, and the Sieur de Brocourt, who was as curious in collecting the opinions of men as our philosopher, though no man could

* The reader may not be displeased to read the following beautiful passage from Jeremy Taylor.

"If God is glorified in the sun and moon, in the rare fabric of the honeycombs, in the discipline of bees, in the economy of pismires, in the little houses of birds, in the curiosity of an eye, God being pleased to delight in those little images and reflexes of himself from those pretty mirrors, which, *like a crevice in the wall, through a narrow perspective, transmit the species of a vast excellency:* much rather shall God be pleased to behold himself in the glasses of our obedience, in the emissions of our will and understanding; these being rational and apt instruments to express him, far better than the natural, as being near communications of himself." — *Invalidity of a late or Death-bed Repentance*, vol. v. p. 464.

make more dissimilar uses of their knowledge, explains it *à cause de la facilité de la generation qui est en elle, dont se procreent si diverses figures, à raison de la grande chaleur qui se trouve en la mer, l'humeur y estant gras, et l'aliment abondant; toute generation se faisant par chaleur et humidité, qui produisent toutes choses.* With such reasoning our Doctor was little satisfied; it was enough to know that as the sea produces monsters, so the sea covers them, and that fish are evidently lower in the scale of being than the creatures of earth and air. It is the system of Nature then that whatever is unseemly should be left in the earliest and lowest stages; that life as it ascends should cast off all deformity, as the butterfly leaves its *exuviæ* when its perfect form is developed; and finally, that whatever is imperfect should be thrown off, and nothing survive in immortality but what is beautiful as well as good.

He was not acquainted with the speculation, or conception (as the Philotheistic philosopher himself called it) of Giordano Bruno, that *deformium animalium formæ, formosæ sunt in cœlo.* Nor would he have assented to some of the other opinions which that pious and high-minded victim of papal intolerance connected with it. That *metallorum in se non lucentium formæ, lucent in planetis suis*, he might have supposed, if he had believed in the relationship between metals and planets. And if Bruno's remark applied to the Planets only, as so many other worlds, and did not regard the future state of the creatures of this our globe, the Doctor might then have agreed to his assertion that *non enim homo, nec animalia, nec metalla ut hic sunt, illic existunt.* But the Philotheist of Nola, in the remaining part of this his twelfth *Conceptus Idearum* soared above the Doctor's pitch: *Quod nempe hic discurrit*, he says, *illic actu viget, discursione superiori. Virtutes enim quæ versus materiam explicantur: versus actum primum uniuntur, et complicantur. Unde patet quod dicunt Platonici, ideam quamlibet rerum etiam non viventium, vitam esse et intelligentiam quandam. Item et in Primâ Mente unam esse rerum omnium ideam. Illuminando igitur, vivificando, et uniendo est quod te superioribus agentibus conformans, in conceptionem et retentionem specierum efferaris.* Here the Philosopher of Doncaster would have found himself in the dark, but whether because "blinded by excess of light," or because the subject is within the confines of uttermost darkness, is not for me his biographer to determine.

CHAPTER CCXIV.

FURTHER DIFFICULTIES. QUESTION CONCERNING INFERIOR APPARITIONS. BLAKE THE PAINTER, AND THE GHOST OF A FLEA.

In amplissimâ causâ, quasi magno mari, pluribus ventis sumus vecti. PLINY.

THERE was another argument against the immortality of brutes, to which, it may be, he allowed the more weight, because it was of his own excogitating. Often as he had heard of apparitions in animal forms, all such tales were of some spirit or hobgoblin which had assumed that appearance; as, for instance, that *simulacrum admodum monstruosum*, that portentous figure in which Pope Gregory the Ninth after his death was met roaming about the woods by a holy hermit: it was in the form of a wild beast with the head of an ass, the body of a bear, and the tail of a cat. Well might the good hermit fortify himself with making the sign of the cross when he beheld this monster: he approved himself a courageous man by speaking to the apparition, which certainly was not "in such a questionable shape" as to invite discourse: and we are beholden to him for having transmitted to posterity the bestial Pope's confession, that because he had lived an unreasonable and lawless life, it was the will of God and of St. Peter whose chair he had defiled by all kinds of abominations, that he should thus wander about in a form of ferine monstrosity.

He had read of such apparitions, and been sufficiently afraid of meeting a barguest* in

* A northern word, used in Cumberland and Yorkshire. Brocket and Grose neither of them seem aware that this

his boyish days; but in no instance had he ever heard of the ghost of an animal. Yet if the immaterial part of such creatures survived in a separate state of consciousness, why should not their spirits sometimes have been seen as well as those of our departed fellow creatures? No cock or hen ghost ever haunted its own barn door; no child was ever alarmed by the spirit of its pet lamb; no dog or cat ever came like a shadow to visit the hearth on which it rested when living. It is laid down as a certain truth deduced from the surest principles of demonology by the Jesuit Thyræus, who had profoundly studied that science, that whenever the apparition of a brute beast or monster was seen, it was a Devil in that shape. *Quotiescumque sub brutorum animantium forma conspiciuntur spiritus, quotiescumque monstra exhibentur dubium non est,* autoprosopos *adesse Dæmoniorum spiritus.* For such forms were not suitable for human spirits, but for evil Demons they were in many respects peculiarly so: and such apparitions were frequent.

Thus the Jesuit reasoned, the possibility that the spirit of a brute might appear never occurring to him, because he would have deemed it heretical to allow that there was anything in the brute creation partaking of immortality. No such objection occurred to the Doctor in his reasonings upon this point. His was a more comprehensive creed; the doubt which he felt was not concerning the spirit of brute animals, but whether it ever existed in a separate state after death, which the Ghost of one, were there but one such appearance well attested, would sufficiently prove.

He admitted, indeed, that for every authenticated case of an apparition, a peculiar cause was to be assigned, or presumed; but that for the apparition of an inferior animal, there could in general be no such cause. Yet cases are imaginable wherein there might be such peculiar cause, and some final purpose only to be brought about by such preternatural means. The strong affection which leads a dog to die upon his master's grave, might bring back the spirit of a dog to watch for the safety of a living master. That no animal ghosts should have been seen afforded, therefore, in this judgment no weak presumption against their existence.

O Dove, "my guide, philosopher, and friend!" that thou hadst lived to see what I have seen, the portrait of the Ghost of a Flea, engraved by Varley, from the original by Blake! The engraver was present when the likeness was taken, and relates the circumstances thus in his Treatise on Zodiacal Physiognomy.

"This spirit visited his imagination in such a figure as he never anticipated in an insect. As I was anxious to make the most correct investigation in my power of the truth of these visions, on hearing of this spiritual apparition of a Flea, I asked him if he could draw for me the resemblance of what he saw. He instantly said, 'I see him now before me.' I therefore gave him paper and a pencil, with which he drew the portrait of which a fac-simile is given in this number. I felt convinced by his mode of proceeding, that he had a real image before him; for he left off, and began on another part of the paper to make a separate drawing of the mouth of the Flea, which the spirit having opened, he was prevented from proceeding with the first sketch till he had closed it. During the time occupied in compleating the drawing, the Flea told him that all fleas were inhabited by the souls of such men as were by nature blood-thirsty to excess, and were therefore providentially confined to the size and form of insects; otherwise, were he himself, for instance, the size of a horse, he would depopulate a great portion of the country. He added that if in attempting to leap from one island to another he should fall into the sea, he could swim, and should not be lost."

The Ghost of the Flea spoke truly when he said what a formidable beast he should be, if with such power of leg and of pro-

spirit or dæmon had the form of the beast. Their derivations are severally "*Berg*, a hill, and *geest*, ghost;"—"*Bar*, a gate or style, and *gheist*."

The locality of the spirit will suggest a reference to the Icelandic *Berserkr*. In that language *Bera* and *Bersi* both signify a *bear*.

boscis, and such an appetite for blood, he were as large as a horse. And if all things came by chance, it would necessarily follow from the laws of chance that such monsters there would be: but because all things are wisely and mercifully ordered, it is, that these varieties of form and power which would be hideous, and beyond measure destructive upon a larger scale, are left in the lower stages of being; the existence of such deformity and such means of destruction there, and their non-existence as the scale of life ascends, alike tending to prove the wisdom and the benevolence of the Almighty Creator.

CHAPTER CCXV.

FACTS AND FANCIES CONNECTING THE DOCTOR'S THEORY WITH THE VEGETABLE WORLD.

> We will not be too peremptory herein: and build standing structures of bold assertions on so uncertain a foundation; rather with the Rechabites we will live in tents of conjecture, which on better reason we may easily alter and remove.
> FULLER.

It may have been observed by the attentive reader — (and all my readers will be attentive, except those who are in love,) — that although the Doctor traced many of his acquaintance to their prior allotments in the vegetable creation, he did not discover such symptoms in any of them as led him to infer that the object of his speculations had existed in the form of a tree; — crabbed tempers, sour plums, cherry-cheeks, and hearts of oak being nothing more than metaphorical expressions of similitude. But it would be a rash and untenable deduction were we to conclude from the apparent omission that the arboreal world was excluded from his system. On the contrary, the analogies between animal and vegetable life led him to believe that the Archeus of the human frame received no unimportant part of his preparatory education in the woods.

Steele in a playful allegory has observed "that there is a sort of vegetable principle in the mind of every man when he comes into the world. In infants, the seeds lie buried and undiscovered, till after a while they sprout forth in a kind of rational leaves, which are words; and in due season the flowers begin to appear in variety of beautiful colours, and all the gay pictures of youthful fancy and imagination; at last the fruit knits and is formed, which is green perhaps at first, sour and unpleasant to the taste, and not fit to be gathered; till, ripened by due care and application, it discovers itself in all the noble productions of philosophy, mathematics, close reasoning, and handsome argumentation. I reflected further on the intellectual leaves before mentioned, and found almost as great a variety among them as in the vegetable world." In this passage, though written only as a sport of fancy, there was more, our speculator thought, than was dreamed of in Steele's philosophy.

Empedocles, if the fragment which is ascribed to him be genuine, pretended to remember that he had pre-existed not only in the forms of maiden and youth, fowl and fish, but of a shrub also;

> Ἤδη γάρ ποτ' ἐγὼ γενόμην κούρη τε κόρος τε,
> Θάμνος τ', οἰωνός τε, καὶ εἰν ἅλι ἔλλοπος ἰχθῦς.

But upon such authority the Doctor placed as little reliance as upon the pretended recollections of Pythagoras, whether really asserted by that philosopher or falsely imputed to him by fablers in prose or verse. When man shall have effected his passage from the mortal and terrestrial state into the sphere where there is nothing that is impure, nothing that is evil, nothing that is perishable, then indeed it is a probable supposition that he may look back into the lowest deep from whence he hath ascended, recal to mind his progress step by step, through every stage of the ascent, and understand the process by which it had been appointed for him, (applying to Plato's words a different meaning from that in which they were intended,) ἐκ πολλῶν ἕνα γεγονότα εὐδαίμονα ἔσεσθαι, to become of many creatures, one happy one. In that sphere such a retrospect would enlarge the knowledge, and consequently the happiness also, of the soul which has there attained the perfection of its nature — the end for which it was created and redeemed. But any such consciousness of pre-existence would in this stage of our mortal being be so incompatible with the condition of humanity, that the opinion itself can be held only as a speculation, of which no certainty can ever have been made known to man, because that alone has been revealed, the knowledge of which is necessary: the philosophers therefore who pretended to it, if they were sincere in the pretension (which may be doubted) are entitled to no more credit, than the poor hypochondriac who fancies himself a bottle or a tea-pot.

Thus our philosopher reasoned, who either in earnest or in jest, or in serious sportiveness, *παίζων καὶ σπουδάζων ἅμα*, was careful never to lean more upon an argument than it would bear. Sometimes he pressed the lame and halt into his service, but it was with a clear perception of their defects, and he placed them always in positions where they were efficient for the service required for them, and where more valid ones would not have been more available. He formed, therefore, no system of dendranthropology, nor attempted any classification in it; there were not facts enough whereon to found one. Yet in more than one circumstance which observant writers have recorded, something he thought might be discerned which bore upon this part of the theory, — some traces of

> those first affections,
> Those shadowy recollections,

on which Wordsworth (in whose mystic strains he would have delighted) dwells. Thus he inferred that the soul of Xerxes must once have animated a plane tree, and retained a vivid feeling connected with his arboreal existence, when he read in Evelyn how that great king "stopped his prodigious army of seventeen hundred thousand soldiers to admire the pulchritude and procerity of one of those goodly trees; and became so fond of it, that spoiling both himself, his concubines, and great persons of all their jewels, he covered it with gold, gems, necklaces, scarfs and bracelets, and infinite riches; in sum, was so enamoured of it, that for some days, neither the concernment of his grand expedition, nor interest of honour, nor the necessary motion of his portentous army, could persuade him from it. He stiled it his mistress, his minion, his goddess; and when he was forced to part from it, he caused the figure of it to be stamped on a medal of gold, which he continually wore about him."

"That prudent Consul Passianus Crispus" must have been influenced by a like feeling, when he "fell in love with a prodigious beech of a wonderful age and stature, used to sleep under it, and would sometimes refresh it with pouring wine at the root." Certainly, as Evelyn has observed, "a goodly tree was a powerful attractive" to this person. The practice of regaling trees with such libations was not uncommon among the wealthy Romans; they seem to have supposed that because wine gladdened their own hearts, it must in like manner comfort the root of a tree: and Pliny assures us that it did so, *compertum id maximè prodesse radicibus*, he says, *docuimusque etiam arbores vina potare*. If this were so, the Doctor reasoned that there would be a peculiar fitness in fertilising the vine with its own generous juice, which it might be expected to return with increase in richer and more abundant clusters: forgetting, ignoring, or disregarding this opinion which John Lily has recorded that the vine watered (as he calls it) with wine is soon withered. He was not wealthy enough to afford such an experiment upon that which clothed the garden-front of his house, for this is not a land flowing with wine and oil; but he indulged a favourite apple-tree (it was a Ribstone pippin) with cider; and when no sensible improvement in the produce could be perceived, he imputed the disappointment rather to the parsimonious allowance of that congenial liquor, than to any error in the theory.

But this has led me astray, and I must return to Xerxes the Great King. The predilection or passion which he discovered for the plane, the sage of Doncaster explained by deriving it from a dim reminiscence of his former existence in a tree of the same kind; or which was not less likely in the wanton ivy which had clasped one, or in the wild vine which had festooned its branches with greener leaves, or even in the agaric which had grown out of its decaying substance. And he would have quoted Wordsworth if the Sage of Rydal had not been of a later generation:

> Our birth is but a sleep and a forgetting;
> The soul that rises with us, our life's star,
> Hath had elsewhere its setting,
> And cometh from afar.

Other examples of men who have doated upon particular trees he accounted for by the same philosophy. But in the case of the Consul Crispus he was more inclined to hold the first supposition, — to wit, that he had been a beech himself, and that the tree which he loved so dearly had sprung from his own mast, so that the feeling with which he regarded it was a parental one. For that man should thus unconsciously afford proof of his relationship to tree, was rendered more probable by a singular, though peradventure single fact, in which a tree so entirely recognised its affinity with man, that a slip accidentally grafted on the human subject, took root in the body, grew there, flourished, blossomed and produced fruit after its kind. "A shepherd of Tarragon had fallen into a sloe tree, and a sharp point thereof having run into his breast, in two years time it took such root, that, after many branches had been cut off, there sprang up some at last which bare both flowers and fruit." "Peiresc," as Gassendi the writer of his life assures us, "would never be quiet till Cardinal Barberino procured the Archbishop of that place to testify the truth of the story; and Putean the knight received not only letters testifying the same, but also certain branches thereof, which he sent unto him."

CHAPTER CCXVI.

A SPANISH AUTHORESS. HOW THE DOCTOR OBTAINED HER WORKS FROM MADRID. THE PLEASURE AND ADVANTAGES WHICH THE AUTHOR DERIVES FROM HIS LANDMARKS IN THE BOOKS WHICH HE HAD PERUSED.

> ALEX. *Quel es D. Diego aquel Arbol,*
> *que tiene la copa en tierra*
> *y las raizes arriba?*
> DIEG. *El hombre.* EL LETRADO DEL CIELO.

> MAN is a Tree that hath no top in cares,
> No root in comforts.*

This is one of the many poetical passages in which the sound is better than the sense;— yet it is not without its beauty. The same similitude has been presented by Henry More in lines which please the ear less, but satisfy the understanding.

> The lower man is nought but a fair plant
> Whose grosser matter is from the base ground.

"A plant," says Jones of Nayland, "is a system of life, but insensitive and fixed to a certain spot. An animal hath voluntary motion, sense, or perception, and is capable of pain and pleasure. Yet in the construction of each there are some general principles which very obviously connect them. It is literally as well as metaphorically true, that trees have limbs, and an animal body branches. A vascular system is also common to both, in the channels of which life is maintained and circulated. When the trachea, with its branches in the lungs, or the veins and arteries, or the nerves, are separately represented, we have the figure of a tree. The leaves of trees have a fibrous and fleshy part; their bark is a covering which answers to the skin in animals. An active vapour pervades them both, and perspires from both, which is necessary for the preservation of health and vigour. The *vis vitæ*, or involuntary, mechanical force of animal life, is kept up by the same elements which act upon plants for their growth and support." †

* CHAPMAN.

† The reader of Berkeley will naturally turn to the

"Plants," says Novalis, "are Children of the Earth; we are Children of the Æther. Our lungs are properly our root; we live when we breathe; we begin our life with breathing." Plato also compared man to a Tree, but his was a physical similitude, he likened the human vegetable to a tree inverted, with the root above and the branches below. Antonio Perez allegorised the similitude in one of his epistles to Essex, thus, *Unde credis hominem inversam arborem appellari? Inversam nostris oculis humanis et terrenis; rectam verò verè, viridemque, si radicem defixam habuerit in suo naturali loco, cœlo, unde orta.* And Rabelais pursues the resemblance farther, saying that trees differ from beasts in this, *Qu'elles ont la teste, c'est le tronc, en bas; les cheveulx, ce sont les racines, en terre; et les pieds, ce sont les rameaulx, contremont; comme si un homme faisoit le chesne fourchu.*

The thought that man is like a tree arose in the Doctor's mind more naturally when he first saw the representation of the veins and arteries in the old translation of Ambrose Paré's works. And when in course of time he became a curious inquirer into the history of her art, he was less disposed to smile at any of the fancies into which Doña Oliva Sabuco Barrera had been led by this resemblance, than to admire the novelty and ingenuity of the theory which she deduced from it.

Bless ye the memory of this Spanish Lady, all ye who bear, or aspire to, the honour of the bloody hand as Knights of Esculapius! For from her, according to Father Feyjoo, the English first, and afterwards the physicians of other countries, learned the theory of nervous diseases; — never, therefore, did any other individual contribute so largely to the gratification of fee-feeling fingers!

Feyjoo has properly enumerated her among the women who have done honour to their country: and later Spaniards have called her the immortal glory not of Spain alone, but of all Europe. She was born, and dwelt in the city of Alcaraz, and flourished in the reign of Philip II. to whom she dedicated in 1587 her "New Philosophy of the Nature of Man," * appealing to the ancient law of chivalry, whereby great Lords and high-born Knights were bound always to favour women in their adventures. In placing under the eagle wings of his Catholic Majesty this child which she had engendered, she told the King that he was then receiving from a woman greater service than any that men had rendered him, with whatever zeal and success they had exerted themselves to serve him. The work which she laid before him would better the world, she said, in many things, and if he could not attend to it, those who came after him peradventure would. For though there were already all too-many books in the world, yet this one was wanting.

The brief and imperfect notices of this Lady's system, which the Doctor had met with in the course of his reading, made him very desirous of procuring her works: this it would not be easy to do in England at this time, and then it was impossible. He obtained them, however, through the kindness of Mason's friend, Mr. Burgh, whom he used to meet at Mr. Copley's at Netterhall, and who in great or in little things was always ready to render any good office in his power to any person. Burgh procured the book through the Rev. Edward Clarke, (father of Dr. Clarke the traveller,) then Chaplain to the British Embassador in Spain. The volume came with the despatches from Madrid, it was forwarded to Mr. Burgh in an official frank, and the Doctor marked with a white stone the day on which the York carrier delivered it at his house. That precious copy is now in my possession †; my friend has noted in it,

Siris of that author — called by Southey in his life of Wesley "one of the best, wisest, and greatest men whom Ireland, with all its fertility of genius, has produced." Vol. ii. 260., 2nd Edit.

* It should seem by her name, as suffixed to the Carta Dedicatorie, that she was of French or Breton extraction, for she signs herself, Oliva de Nantes, Sabuco Barera. — *R. S.*

† This curious book I unluckily missed at the Sale of Southey's Library. I was absent at the time, and it passed into private hands. It sold for thirteen shillings

as was his custom, every passage that seemed worthy of observation, with the initial of his own name — a small capital, neatly written in red ink. Such of his books as I have been able to collect are full of these marks, showing how carefully he had read them. These notations have been of much use to me in my perusal, leading me to pause where he had paused, to observe what he had noted, and to consider what had to him seemed worthy of consideration. And though I must of necessity more frequently have failed to connect the passages so noted with my previous knowledge as he had done, and for that reason to see their bearings in the same point of view, yet undoubtedly I have often thus been guided into the same track of thought which he had pursued before me. Long will it be before some of these volumes meet with a third reader; never with one in whom these vestiges of their former owner can awaken a feeling like that which they never fail to excite in me!

But the red letters in this volume have led me from its contents; and before I proceed to enter upon them in another chapter, I will conclude this, recurring to the similitude at its commencement, with an extract from one of Yorick's Sermons. "It is very remarkable," he says, "that the Apostle St. Paul calls a bad man a wild olive *tree*, not barely a branch," — (as in the opposite case where our Saviour told his disciples that He was the vine, and that they were only branches,) — "but a Tree, which having a root of its own supports itself, and stands in its own strength, and brings forth its own fruit. And so does every bad man in respect of the wild and sour fruit of a vicious and corrupt heart. According to the resemblance, if the Apostle intended it, he is a Tree, — has a root of his own, and fruitfulness such as it is, with a power to bring it forth without help. But in respect of religion and the moral improvements of virtue and goodness, the Apostle calls us, and reason tells us, we are no more than a *branch*, and all our fruitfulness, and all our support, depend so much upon the influence and communications of God, that without Him we can do nothing, as our Saviour declares."

only. See Catalogue, No. 3453. The title is as follows: — *Sabuco (Olivia) Nueva Filosofia de la Naturaleza del hombre, no conocida ni alcançada de los Grandes Filosofos Antiguos.* First Edition. *Madrid*, 1587.

CHAPTER CCXVII.

SOME ACCOUNT OF D. OLIVA SABUCO'S MEDICAL THEORIES AND PRACTICE.

Yo — volveré
A nueva diligencia y paso largo,
Que es breve el tiempo, 's grande la memoria
Que para darla al mundo está á mi cargo.

Balbuena.

Carew the poet speaking metaphorically of his mistress calls her foot,

the precious root
On which the goodly cedar grows.

Doña Oliva on the contrary thought that the human body might be called a tree reversed, the brain being the root, and the other the bark. She did not know what great authority there is for thinking that trees stand upon their heads, for though we use vulgarly but improperly to call the uppermost of the branches the top of a tree, we are corrected, the learned John Gregory tells us, by Aristotle in his books *De Animâ**, where we are taught to call the root the head, and the top the feet.

The *pia mater* according to her theory diffuses through this bark by the nerves that substance, moisture, sap, or white chyle which, when it flows in its proper course, preserves the human vegetable in a state of well being, but when its course is reverted it becomes the cause of diseases. This nervous fluid, the brain derived principally from the air, which she held to be water in a state of rarefaction, air being the chyle of the upper world, water of the inferior, and the Moon with air and water, as with milk, feeding like a nursing mother, all

* Quære? Lib. ii. c. ii. § 6. *αἱ δὲ ῥίζαι τῷ στόματι ἀνάλογον κ. τ. ἑ.*

sublunary creatures, and imparting moisture for their increase, as the Sun imparteth heat and life. Clouds are the milk of the Moon, from which, if she may so express herself, she says it rains air and wind as well as water, wind being air, or rarefied water rarefied still farther. The mutation or rarefaction of water into air takes place by day, the remutation or condensation of air into water by night: this is shown by the dew, and by this the ebbing and flowing of the sea are caused.

In the brain, as in the root of the animal tree, all diseases, according to Doña Oliva, had their origin. From this theory she deduced a mode of practice, which if it did not facilitate the patient's recovery, was at least not likely to retard it; and tended in no way to counteract, or interfere with the restorative efforts of nature. And although fanciful in its foundation, it was always so humane, and generally so reasonable, as in a great degree to justify the confidence with which she advanced it. She requested that a board of learned men might be appointed, before whom she might defend her system of philosophy and of therapeutics, and that her practice might be tried for one year, that of Hippocrates and Galen having been tried for two thousand, with what effect was daily and miserably seen, when of a thousand persons there were scarcely three who reached the proper termination of life and died by natural decay, the rest being cut off by some violent disease. For, according to her, the natural termination of life is produced by the exhaustion of the radical moisture, which in the course of nature is dried, or consumed, gradually and imperceptibly; death therefore, when that course is not disturbed, being an easy passage to eternity. This gradual desiccation it is which gives to old age the perfection of judgment that distinguishes it; and for the same reason the children of old men are more judicious than others, young men being deficient in judgment by reason of the excess of radical moisture, children still more so.

She had never studied medicine, she said; but it was clear as the light of day that the old system was erroneous, and must needs be so, because its founders were ignorant of the nature of man, upon which being rightly understood the true system must, of necessity, be founded. Hope is what supports health and life; fear, the worst enemy of both. Among the best preservatives and restoratives she recommended therefore cheerfulness, sweet odours, music, the country, the sound of woods and waters, agreeable conversation, and pleasant pastimes. Music, of all external things, she held to be that which tends most to comfort, rejoice and strengthen the brain, being as it were a spiritual pleasure in which the mind sympathises; and the first of all remedies, in this, her true system of medicine, was to bring the mind and body into unison, removing thus that discord which is occasioned when they are ill at ease; this was to be done by administering cheerfulness, content, and hope to the mind, and in such words and actions as produced these, the best medicine was contained. Next to this it imported to comfort the stomach, and to cherish the root of man, that is to say the brain, with its proper corroborants, especially with sweet odours and with music. For music was so good a remedy for melancholy, so great an alleviator of pain, such a soother of uneasy emotions, and of passion, that she marvelled wherefore so excellent a medicine should not be more in use, seeing that undoubtedly many grievous diseases, as for example epilepsy, might be disarmed and cured by it; and it would operate with the more effect if accompanied with hopeful words and with grateful odours, for Doña Oliva thought with Solomon that "pleasant words are as an honeycomb, sweet to the soul, and health to the bones."

Consequently unpleasant sounds and ill smells were, according to her philosophy, injurious. The latter she confounded with noxious air, which was an error to be expected in those days, when nothing concerning the composition of the atmosphere had been discovered. Thus she thought it was by their ill odour that limekilns and charcoal-fires occasioned death; and that owing to the same cause horses were frequently killed when the filth of a stable was removed, and men who were employed in cleaning vaults. Upon the same principle, in recommending perfumes as alexipharmic, she fell in with the usual practice. The plague, according to her, might be received not by the breath alone, but the eyes also, for through the sight there was ready access to the brain; it was prudent therefore to close the nostrils when there might be reason to apprehend that the air was tainted; and when conversing with an infected person, not to talk face to face, but to avert the countenance. In changing the air, with the hope of escaping an endemic disease, the place to go to should be that from whence the pestilence had come, rather than one whither it might be going.

Ill sounds were noxious in like manner, though not in like degree, because no discord can be so grating as to prove fatal; but any sound which is at once loud and discordant she held to be unwholesome, and that to hear any one sing badly, read ill, or talk importunately like a fool was sufficient to cause a defluxion from the brain; if this latter opinion were well founded, no Speaker of the House of Commons could hold his office for a single Session without being talked to death. With these she classed the sound of a hiccup, the whetting of a saw, and the cry of bitter lamentation.

Doña Oliva, it may be presumed, was endued with a sensitive ear and a quick perception of odours, as well as with a cheerful temper, and an active mind. Her whole course of practice was intended to cheer and comfort the patient, if that was possible. She allowed the free use of water, and fresh air, and recommended that the apartments of the sick should be well ventilated. She prescribed refreshing odours, among others that of bread fresh from the oven, and that wine should be placed near the pillow, in order to induce sleep. She even thought that cheerful apparel conduced to health, and that the fashion of wearing black, which prevailed in her time, was repugnant to reason. Pursuing her theory that the brain was the original seat of disease, she advised that the excessive moisture which would otherwise take a wrong course from thence should be drawn off through the natural channels by sneezing powders, or by pungent odours which provoke a discharge from the eyes and nostrils, by sudorifics also, exercise, and whatever might cause a diversion to the skin. When any part was wounded, or painful, or there was a tumour, she recommended compression above the part affected, with a woollen bandage, tightly bound, but not so as to occasion pain. And to comfort the root of the animal tree she prescribes scratching the head with the fingers, or combing it with an ivory comb, — a general and admirable remedy she calls this, against which some former possessor of the book, who seems to have been a practitioner upon the old system, and has frequently entered his protest against the medical heresies of the authoress, has written in the margin "bad advice." She recommended also cutting the hair, and washing the head with white wine, which as it were renovated the skin, and improved the vegetation.

But Doña Oliva did not reject more active remedies; on the contrary she advised all such as men had learned from animals, and this included a powerful list, for she seems to have believed all the fables with which natural history in old times abounded, and of which indeed it may almost be said to have consisted. More reasonably she observed that animals might teach us the utility of exercise, seeing how the young lambs sported in the field, and dogs played with each other, and birds rejoiced in the air. When the stomach required clearing she prescribed a rough practice, that the patient should drink copiously of weak wine and water, and of tepid water with a few drops of vinegar and an infusion of camomile flowers; and that he should eat also things difficult of digestion, such as radishes, figs, carrots, onions, anchovies, oil and vinegar, with plenty of Indian pepper, and with something acid the better to cut the phlegm which was to be got rid of; having thus stored the stomach well for the expenditure which was to be required from it, the patient was then to lay himself on a pillow across a chair, and produce the desired effect either by his fingers or by feathers dipped in oil. After this rude operation, which was to refresh the brain and elevate the pia mater, the stomach was to be comforted.

To bathe the whole body with white wine was another mode of invigorating the pia mater; for there it was that all maladies originated, none from the liver; the nature of the liver, said she, is that it cannot err; *es docta sin doctor*.

The latter treatises in her book are in Latin, but she not unfrequently passes, as if unconsciously, into her own language, writing always livelily and forcibly, with a clear perception of the fallacy of the established system, and with a confidence, not so well founded, that she had discovered the real nature of man, and thereby laid the foundation of a rational practice, conformable to it.

CHAPTER CCXVIII.

THE MUNDANE SYSTEM AS COMMONLY HELD IN D. OLIVA'S AGE. MODERN OBJECTIONS TO A PLURALITY OF WORLDS BY THE REV. JAMES MILLER.

Un cerchio immaginatoci bisogna,
A voler ben la spera contemplare;
Cosi chi intender questa storia agogna
Conviensi altro per altro immaginare;
Perchè qui non si canta, e finge, e sogna;
Venuto è il tempo da filosofare. PULCI.

ONE of Doña Oliva's treatises is upon the *Compostura del Mundo*, which may best be interpreted the Mundane System; herein she laid no claim to the merit of discovery, only to that of briefly explaining what had been treated of by many before her. The mundane system she illustrates by comparing it to a large ostrich's egg, with three whites and eleven shells, our earth being the yolk. The water, which according to this theory surrounded the globe, she likened to the first or innermost *albumen;* the second and more extensive was the air; the third and much the largest consisted of fire. The eleven shells were so many leaves one inclosing the other, circle within circle, like a nest of boxes. The first of these was the first heaven, wherein the Moon hath her appointed place, the second that of the planet Mercury, the third that of Venus; the fourth was the circle of the Sun; Mars, Jupiter and Saturn moved in the fifth, sixth and seventh; the eighth was the starry sky; the ninth the chrystalline; the tenth the *primum mobile*, which imparted motion to all; and the eleventh was the *immobile*, or empyreum, surrounding all, containing all, and bounding all; for beyond this there was no created thing, either good or evil.

A living writer of no ordinary powers agrees in this conclusion with the old philosophers whom Doña Oliva followed; and in declaring his opinion he treats the men of science with as much contempt as they bestow upon their unscientific predecessors in astronomy.

Reader, if thou art capable of receiving pleasure from such speculations, (and if thou art not, thou art little better than an Oran-Otang,) send for a little book entitled the "Progress of the Human Mind, its objects, conditions and issue: with the relation which the Progress of Religion bears to the general growth of mind; by the Rev. James Miller." Send also for the "Sibyl's Leaves, or the Fancies, Sentiments and Opinions of Silvanus, miscellaneous, moral and religious," by the same author, the former published in 1823, the latter in 1829. Very probably you may never have heard of either: but if you are a buyer of books, I say unto you, buy them both.

"Infinity," says this very able and original thinker, "is the retirement in which perfect love and wisdom only dwell with God.

"In Infinity and Eternity the sceptic sees an abyss in which all is lost: I see in them the residence of Almighty Power, in which my reason and my wishes find equally a firm support. — Here holding by the pillars of Heaven, I exist — I stand fast.

"Surround our material system with a

void, and mind itself becoming blind and impotent in attempting to travel through it, will return to our little lights, like the dove which found no rest for the sole of her foot. But when I find Infinity filled with light, and life, and love, I will come back to you with my olive branch: follow me, or farewell! you shall shut me up in your cabins no more.

"In stretching our view through the wide expanse which surrounds us, we perceive a system of bodies receding behind one another, till they are lost in immeasureable distance. This region beyond, though to us dark and unexplored, from the impossibility of a limit, yet gives us its infinity as the most unquestionable of all principles. But though the actual extent to which this infinite region is occupied by the bodies of which the universe is composed, is far beyond our measure and our view, and though there be nothing without to compel us anywhere to stop in enlarging its bounds, Nature herself gives us other principles not less certain, which prove that she must have limits, and that it is impossible her frame can fill the abyss which surrounds her. Her different parts have each their fixed place, their stated distance. You may as well measure infinity by mile-stones as fill it with stars. To remove any one from an infinite distance from another, you must, in fixing their place, set limits to the infinity you assume. You can advance from unity as far as you please, but there is no actual number at an infinite distance from it. You may, in the same manner, add world to world as long as you please, only because no number of them can fill infinity, or approach nearer to fill it. We have the doctrine of Nature's abhorrence of a *vacuum;* it is from a *plenum* like this she shrinks, as from a region in which all her substance would be dissipated into nothing. Her frame is composed of parts which have each their certain proportion and relation. It subsists by mutual attractions and repulsions, lessening and increasing with distance; by a circulation which, actually passing through every part, rejects the idea of a space which it could never pervade. Infinity cannot revolve; the circulation of Nature cannot pervade infinity. The globe we inhabit, and all its kindred planets, revolve in orbits which embrace a common power in the centre which animates and regulates their motions, and on the influence of which their internal energies evidently depend. That we may not be lost in looking for it in the boundless regions without, our great physical power is all within, in the bosom of our own circle; and the same facts which prove the greatness of this power to uphold, to penetrate, to enliven at such a distance, shew in what manner it might at last become weak,—become nothing. Whatever relations we may have to bodies without, or whatever they may have to one another, their influence is all directed to particular points,—to given distances. Material Nature has no substance, can make no effort, capable of pervading infinity. The light itself of all her powers the most expansive, in diffusing itself through her own frame, shews most of all her incapacity to occupy the region beyond, in which (as the necessary result of its own effort) it soon sinks, feeble and faint, where all its motion is but as rest, in an extent to which the utmost possible magnitude of Nature is but a point."

The reader will now be prepared for the remarks of this free thinker upon the Plurality of Worlds. Observe I call him free thinker not in disparagement, but in honour; he belongs to that service in which alone is perfect freedom.

"Perceiving," he says, "as it is easy to do, the imperfection of our present system, instead of contemplating the immense prospect opened to our view in the progress of man, in the powers and the means he possesses, the philosopher sees through his telescope worlds and scales of being to his liking. By means of these, without the least reference to the Bible, or the human heart, Pope, the pretty talking parrot of Bolingbroke, with the assistance of his pampered goose, finds it easy to justify the ways of God to man. From worlds he never saw, he proves ours is as it should be.

"To form the children of God for himself, to raise them to a capacity to converse with him, to enjoy all his love, this grand scenery is not unnecessary, — not extravagant. A smaller exhibition would not have demonstrated his wisdom and power. You would make an orrery serve perhaps! By a plurality of Gods, error degraded the Supreme Being in early ages; by a plurality of worlds it would now degrade his children, deprive them of their inheritance.

"What are they doing in these planets? Peeping at us through telescopes? We may be their Venus or Jupiter. They are perhaps praying to us, sending up clouds of incense to regale our nostrils. Hear them, far-seeing Herschel! gauger of stars. I will pray to One only, who is above them all; and if your worlds come between me and Him, I will kick them out of my way. In banishing your new ones, I put more into the old than is worth them all put together.

"These expanding heavens, the residence of so many luminous bodies of immeasurable distance and magnitude, and which the philosopher thinks must be a desert if devoted to man, at present possessing but so small a portion of his own globe, shall yet be too little for him, — the womb only in which the infant was inclosed, incapable of containing the mature birth.

"We shall yet explore all these celestial bodies more perfectly than we have hitherto done our own globe, analyse them better than the substances we can shut up in our retorts, count their number, tell their measure.

"As nature grows, mind grows. It grows to God, and in union with him shall fill, possess all.

"Our rank among worlds is indeed insignificant if we are to receive it from the magnitude of our globe compared with others, compared with space. Put Herschel with his telescope on Saturn, he would scarcely think us worthy of the name of even a German prince. We may well be the sport of Jupiter, the little spot round which Mars and Venus coquette with one another. Little as it is, however, — pepper-corn, clod of clay as it is, with its solitary satellite, and all its spots and vapours, I prefer it to them all. I am glad I was born in it, I love its men, and its women, and its laws. It's people shall be my people; it's God shall be my God. Here I am content to lodge and here to be buried. What Abanas and Pharphars may flow in these planets I know not: here is Jordan, here is the river of life. From this world I shall take possession of all these; while those, who in quest of strange worlds have forsaken God, shall be desolate.

"This globe is large enough to contain man; man will yet grow large enough to fill Heaven.

"Fear not, there is no empty space in the universe, none in eternity: nothing lost. God possesses all, and there is room for nothing but the objects of his affections."

CHAPTER CCXIX.

THE ARGUMENT AGAINST CHRISTIANITY DRAWN FROM A PLURALITY OF WORLDS SHOWN TO BE FUTILE: REMARKS ON THE OPPOSITE DISPOSITIONS BY WHICH MEN ARE TEMPTED TO INFIDELITY.

— ascolta
Siccome suomo di verace lingua;
E porgimi l'orecchio. CHIABRERA.

THE extracts with which the preceding Chapter concludes will have put thee in a thoughtful mood, Reader, if thou art one of those persons whose brains are occasionally applied to the purpose of thinking upon such subjects as are worthy of grave consideration. Since then I have thee in this mood, let us be serious together. Egregiously is he mistaken who supposes that this book consists of nothing more than

Fond Fancy's scum, and dregs of scattered thought.*

Everywhere I have set before thee what Bishop Reynolds calls *verba desiderii*, — "pleasant, delightful, acceptable words, such as are worthy of all entertainment, and may minister (not a few of them) comfort and refreshment to the hearers." I now come

* SIR P. SIDNEY.

to thee with *verba rectitudinis* — "equal and right words; not loose, fabulous, amorous, impertinent, which should satisfy the itch of ear, or tickle only a wanton fancy; but profitable and wholesome words, — so to please men as that it may be unto edification and for their profit: words written to make men sound and upright; — to make their paths direct and straight, without falseness or hypocrisy." Yea they shall be *verba veritatis*, — "words of truth, which will not deceive or misguide those that yield up themselves to the direction of them: a truth which is sanctifying and saving, and in these respects most worthy of our attention and belief."

Make up your mind then to be Tremayned in this chapter.

The benevolent reader will willingly do this, he I mean who is benevolent to himself as well as towards me. The so-called philosopher or man of liberal opinions, who cannot be so inimical in thought to me, as they are indeed to themselves, will frown at it; one such exclaims pshaw, or pish, according as he may affect the *forté* manner, or the fine, of interjecting his contemptuous displeasure; another already winces, feeling himself by anticipation touched upon a sore place. To such readers it were hopeless to say *favete*, *Numquid æger laudat medicum secantem?* But I shall say with the Roman Philosopher of old, who is well entitled to that then honourable designation, *tacete*, — *et præbete vos curationi: etiam si exclamaveritis, non aliter audiam, quam si ad tactum vitiorum vestrorum ingemiscatis.**

My own observation has led me to believe with Mr. Miller, that some persons are brought by speculating upon a Plurality of Worlds to reason themselves out of their belief in Christianity: such Christianity indeed it is as has no root, because the soil on which it has fallen is shallow, and though the seed which has been sown there springs up, it soon withers away. Thus the first system of superstition, and the latest pretext for unbelief, have both been derived from the contemplation of the heavenly bodies. The former was the far more pardonable error, being one to which men, in the first ages, among whom the patriarchal religion had not been carefully preserved, were led by natural piety. The latter is less imputable to the prevalence of unnatural impiety, than to that weakness of mind and want of thought which renders men as easily the dupe of the infidel propagandist in one age, as of the juggling friar in another. These objectors proceed upon the gratuitous assumption that other worlds are inhabited by beings of the same kind as ourselves, and moreover in the same condition; that is having fallen, and being therefore in need of a Redeemer. Ask of them upon what grounds they assume this, and they can make no reply.

Too many, alas! there are who part with their heavenly birth-right at a viler price than Esau! It is humiliating to see by what poor sophistries they are deluded, — by what pitiable vanity they are led astray! And it is curious to note how the same evil effect is produced by causes the most opposite. The drunken pride of intellect makes one man deny his Saviour and his God: another, under the humiliating sense of mortal insignificancy, feels as though he were "a worm and no man," and therefore concludes that men are beneath the notice, still more beneath the care of the Almighty. "When I consider thy Heavens, the work of thy fingers, the Moon and the Stars, which thou hast ordained; what is man that thou art mindful of him? and the son of man that thou visitest him?" Of those who pursue this feeling to a consequence as false as it is unhappy, there is yet hope; for the same arguments (and they are all-sufficient) by which the existence of the Deity is proved, prove also his infinite goodness; and he who believes in that goodness, if he but feelingly believe, is not far from trusting in it,

> — σύ δέ κεν ῥεα πάντ' ἐσορήσαις
> Αἴ κεν ἴδης αὐτόν.†

It is a good remark of Mr. Riland's, in his

* Seneca.

† Orpheus.

Estimate of the Religion of the Times, that men quarrel with the Decalogue rather than with the Creed. But the quarrel that begins with one, generally extends to the other; we may indeed often perceive how manifestly men have made their doctrines conform to their inclinations: Αἱ ἀκροάσεις κατὰ τὰ ἔθη συμβαίνουσιν· ὡς γὰρ εἰώθαμεν, οὕτως ἀξιοῦμεν λέγεσθαι.* They listen only to what they like, as Aristotle has observed, and would be instructed to walk on those ways only which they choose for themselves. But if there be many who thus make their creed conform to their conduct, and are led by an immoral life into irreligious opinions, there are not a few whose error begins in the intellect, and from thence proceeds to their practice in their domestic and daily concerns. Thus if unbelief begins not in the evil heart, it settles there. But perhaps it is not so difficult to deal with an infidel who is in either of these predicaments, as with one whose disposition is naturally good, whose course of life is in no other respect blameless, or meritorious, but who, owing to unhappy circumstances, has either been allowed to grow up carelessly in unbelief, or trained in it systematically, or driven to seek for shelter in it from the gross impostures of popery, or the revolting tenets of Calvinism, the cant of hypocrisy, or the crudities of cold Socinianism. Such persons supposing themselves whole conclude that they have no need of a physician, and are thus in the fearful condition of those righteous ones of whom our Lord said that he came not to call them to repentance! The sinner, brave it as he may, feels inwardly the want of a Saviour, and this is much, though not enough to say with the poet

Pars sanitatis velle sanari fuit; †

nor with the philosopher, *Et hoc multum est velle servari:* nor with the Father, Ὁ τὸ πρῶτον δοὺς καὶ το δεύτερον δώσει. For if this be rejected, then comes that "penal induration, as the consequent of voluntary and contracted induration," which one of our own great Christian philosophers pronounces to be "the sorest judgement next to hell itself." Nevertheless it is much to feel this self-condemnation and this want. But he who confides in the rectitude of his intentions, and in his good works, and in that confidence rejects so great salvation, is in a more aweful state, just as there is more hope of him who suffers under an acute disease, than of a patient stricken with the dead palsy.

* Bp. Reynolds quotes this same passage in his Sermon on "Brotherly Reconciliation," and applies it in the same way. Works, vol. v. p. 158.

† Seneca in Hippol.

CHAPTER CCXX.

DOÑA OLIVA'S PHILOSOPHY, AND VIEWS OF POLITICAL REFORMATION.

Non vi par adunque che habbiamo ragionato a bastanza di questo? — A bastanza parmi, rispose il Signor Gaspar; par desidero io d'intendere qualche particolarita anchor.

CASTIGLIONE.

According to Doña Oliva's philosophy, the quantity of water is ten times greater than that of earth, air in like manner exceeding water in a tenfold degree, and fire in the same proportion out-measuring air. From the centre of the earth to the first heaven the distance by her computation is 36,292 leagues of three miles each and two thousand paces to the mile. From the surface of the earth to its centre, that centre being also the central point of the Infernal regions, her computed distance is 117,472 leagues. How far it is to the confines has not been ascertained by discovery, and cannot be computed from any known data.

Pliny has preserved an anecdote in geological history, which relates to this point, and which, not without reason, he calls *exemplum vanitatis Græcæ maximum.* It relates to a certain philosopher, Dionysiodorus by name, who was celebrated for his mathematical attainments, and who it seems retained his attachment to that science after death, and continued the pursuit of it. For having died in a good old age, and received all fitting sepulchral rites, he wrote a letter from Hades to the female relations who had succeeded to his property, and who probably were addicted to the same studies as himself, for otherwise he would not have communicated with them upon such a subject. They found the letter in his sepulchre, wherein he had deposited it as at a post-office "till called for;" and whither he knew they would repair for the due performance of certain ceremonies, among others that of pouring libations through the perforated floor of the Tomb-chamber upon the dust below. The purport of his writing was not to inform them of his condition in the Shades, nor to communicate any information concerning the World of Spirits, but simply to state the scientific fact, that having arrived in the depths of the earth, he had found the distance from the surface to be 42,000 stadia. The philosophers to whom this *post-mortem* communication was imparted, reasonably inferred that he had reached the very centre, and measured from that point; they calculated upon the data thus afforded them, and ascertained that the globe was exactly 250,000 stadia in circumference. Pliny, however, thought that this measurement was 12,000 stadia short of the true amount. *Harmonica ratio*, he says, *quæ cogit rerum naturam sibi ipsam congruere, addit huic mensuræ stadia xii. millia; terramque nonagesimam sextam totius mundi partem facit.*

"What is the centre of the earth?" says the melancholy Burton. "Is it pure element only as Aristotle decrees? Inhabited, as Paracelsus thinks, with creatures whose chaos is the earth? Or with Faeries, as the woods and waters, according to him, are with Nymphs? Or, as the air, with Spirits? Dionysiodorus," he adds, "might have done well to have satisfied all these doubts."

But the reason, according to Doña Oliva, wherefore the place of punishment for sinful souls has been appointed in the centre of this our habitable earth, is this; the soul being in its essence lighter than air, fire, or any of the ten spheres, has its natural place in the Empyreum or Heaven of Heavens, where the Celestial Court is fixed, and whither it would naturally ascend when set free from the body, as to its natural and proper place of rest. The punishment, therefore, is appropriately appointed in the place which is most remote from its native region, and most repugnant to its own nature; the pain, therefore, must needs be *fort et dure* which it endures when confined within that core of the earth, to which all things that are heaviest gravitate.

In these fancies she only followed or applied the received opinions of the middle ages. A more remarkable part of her works, considering the time and place in which they were composed, is a Colloquy* upon the means by which the World and the Governments thereof might be improved. Having in her former treatises laid down a better system for treating the infirmities of the human microcosm, she enters nothing loth, and nothing doubting her own capacity, upon the maladies of the body politic.

The first evils which occurred to her were those of the law, its uncertainty and its delays, by which properties were wasted, families ruined, and hearts broken. "What barbarity it is," she says, "that a cause should continue forty years in the Courts! that one Counsellor should tell you the right is on your side, and another should say the same thing to your adversary; that one decision should be given in one place, and another to revoke it in that; and in a third a different one from either, and all three perhaps equally wide of the truth and justice of the case, and yet each such as can be maintained by legal arguments, and supported by legal authorities!" The cause of all this she ascribes to the multiplicity of laws and of legal books, which were more than enough to load twenty carts, and yet more were continually added, and all were in Latin. Could any folly exceed that of those law-givers who presumed to prescribe laws for all possible contingencies, and for the whole course of future generations! She was therefore for reducing the written laws to a few fundamentals in the vernacular tongue, and leaving everything else to be decided

* *Colloquio de las Cosas que mejoraran este Mundo y sus Republicas.*—R.S.

by men of good conscience and sincere understanding; by which the study of jurisprudence as a science would be abolished, and there might be an end to those numerous costly professorships for which so many chairs and universities had been founded. Ten short commandments comprised the law of God; but human laws by their number and by the manner in which they were administered occasioned more hurt to the souls of men than even to their lives and fortunes; for in courts of law it was customary, even if not openly permitted, to bear false witness against your neighbour, to calumniate him in writing, and to seek his destruction or his death. Laws which touched the life ought to be written, because in capital cases no man ought to be left to an uncertain sentence, nor to the will of a Judge, but all other cases should be left to the Judges, who ought always to be chosen from Monasteries, or some other course of retired life, and selected for their religious character. This she thought, with the imposition of a heavy fine for any direct falsehood, or false representation advanced either in evidence, or in pleading, and for denying the truth, or suppressing it, would produce the desired reformation.

Next she considered the condition of the agricultural labourers, a class which had greatly diminished, and which it was most desirable to increase. Their condition was to be bettered by raising their wages and consequently the price of produce, and exempting their cattle, their stores and their persons from being taken in execution. She would also have them protected against their own imprudence, by preventing them from obtaining credit for wedding-garments, that being one of the most prevalent and ruinous modes of extravagance in her days. In this rank of life it sometimes happened, that a shopkeeper not only seized the garments themselves, but the peasant's cattle also, to make up the payment of a debt thus contracted.

She thought it a strange want of policy that in a country where the corn failed for want of rain, the waters with which all brooks and rivers were filled in winter should be allowed to run to waste. Therefore she advised that great tanks and reservoirs should be formed for the purposes of irrigation, and that they should be rendered doubly profitable by stocking them with fish, such as shad, tench and trout. She advised also that the seed should frequently be changed, and crops raised in succession, because the soil loved to embrace new products: and that new plants should be introduced from the Indies; where hitherto the Spaniards had been more intent upon introducing their own, than in bringing home from thence others to enrich their own country; the cacao in particular she recommended, noticing that this nut for its excellence had even been used as money.

Duels she thought the Christian Princes and the Pope might easily prevent, by erecting a Jurisdiction which should take cognisance of all affairs of honour. She would have had them also open the road to distinction for all who deserved it, so that no person should be debarred by his birth from attaining to any office or rank; "this," she said, "wast he way to have more Rolands and Cids, more Great Captains, more Hannibals and Tamerlanes."

Such were Doña Oliva's views of political reformation, the wretched state of law and of medicine explaining satisfactorily to her most of the evils with which Spain was afflicted in the reign of Philip II. She considered Law and Physic as the two great plagues of human life, according to the Spanish proverb,

A quien yo quiero mal,
De le Dios pleyto y orinal.

Upon these subjects and such as these the Spanish lady might speculate freely; if she had any opinions which "savoured of the frying-pan," she kept them to herself.

CHAPTER CCXXI.

THE DOCTOR'S OPINION OF DOÑA OLIVA'S PRACTICE AND HUMANITY.

Anchor dir si potrebber cose assai
Che la materia è tanto piena et folta,
Che non se ne verrebbe à capo mai,
Dunque fia buono ch' io suoni à raccolta.

FR. SANSOVINO.

THE Doctor's opinion of Doña Oliva's practice was that no one would be killed by it, but that many would be allowed to die whom a more active treatment might have saved. It would generally fail to help the patient, but it would never exasperate the disease; and therefore in her age it was an improvement, for better is an inert treatment than a mischievous one.

He liked her similitude of the tree, but wondered that she had not noted as much resemblance to the trunk and branches in the bones and muscles, as in the vascular system. He admired the rational part of her practice, and was disposed to think some parts of it not irrational which might seem merely fanciful to merely practical men.

She was of opinion that more persons were killed by affections of the mind, than by intemperance, or by the sword: this she attempts to explain by some weak reasoning from a baseless theory; but the proofs which she adduces in support of the assertion are curious. "Many persons," she says, "who in her own time had fallen under the King's displeasure, or even received a harsh word from him, had taken to their beds and died." It was not uncommon for wives who loved their husbands dearly, to die a few days after them; two such instances had occurred within the same week in the town in which she resided: and she adds the more affecting fact that the female slaves of the better kind (*esclavas abiles*), meaning perhaps those upon whom any care had been bestowed, were frequently observed to pine away as they grew up, and perish; and that this was still more frequent with those who had a child born to an inheritance of slavery. Mortified ambition, irremediable grief, and hopeless misery, had within her observation produced the same fatal effect. The general fact is supported by Harvey's testimony. That eminent man said to Bishop Hacket that during the Great Rebellion, more persons whom he had seen in the course of his practice died of grief of mind than of any other disease. In France it was observed not only that nervous diseases of every kind became much more frequent during the revolution but cases of cancer also, — moral causes producing in women a predisposition to that most dreadful disease.

Our friend was fortunate enough to live in peaceful times, when there were no public calamities to increase the sum of human suffering. Yet even then, and within the limits of his own not extensive circle, he saw cases enough to teach him that it is difficult to minister to a mind diseased, but that for a worm in the core there is no remedy within the power of man.

He liked Doña Oliva for the humanity which her observations upon this subject implies. He liked her also for following the indications of nature in part of her practice; much the better he liked her for prescribing all soothing circumstances and all inducements to cheerfulness that were possible; and nothing the worse for having carried some of her notions to a whimsical extent. He had built an Infirmary in the air himself, "others," he said, "might build Castles there."

It was not such an Infirmary as the great Hospital at Malta, where the Knights attended in rotation and administered to the patients, and where every culinary utensil was made of solid silver, such was the ostentatious magnificence of the establishment. The doctor provided better attendance, for he had also built a Beguinage in the air, as an auxiliary institution; and as to the utensils, he was of opinion that careful neatness was very much better than useless splendour. But here he would have given Doña Oliva's soothing system a fair trial, and have surrounded the patients with all circumstances that could minister to the comfort or alleviation of either a body or a mind diseased. "The principal remedy in true medicine," said that Lady practitioner, "is to reconcile the mind and body, or to bring them in accord with each other, — (*componer el anima con el cuerpo:*) to effect this you must administer contentment and pleasure to the mind, and comfort to the stomach and to the brain: the mind can only be reached by judicious discourse and pleasing objects; the stomach is to be comforted by restoratives; the brain by sweet odours and sweet sounds." The prospect of groves and gardens, the shade of trees, the flowing of water, or its gentle fall, music and cheerful conversation, were things which she especially advised. How little these circumstances would avail in the fiercer forms of acute diseases, or in the protracted evils of chronic suffering, the Doctor knew but too well. But he knew also that medical art was humanely and worthily employed, when it alleviated what no human skill could cure.

"So great," says Dr. Currie, "are the difficulties of tracing out the hidden causes of the disorders to which this frame of ours is subject, that the most candid of the profession have allowed and lamented how unavoidably they are in the dark; so that the best medicines, administered by the wisest heads, shall often do the mischief they intend to prevent." There are more reasons for this than Dr. Currie has here assigned. For not only are many of the diseases which flesh is heir to, obscure in their causes, difficultly distinguishable by their symptoms, and altogether mysterious in their effect upon the system, but constitutions may be as different as tempers, and their varieties may be as many and as great as those of the human countenance. Thus it is explained wherefore the treatment which proves successful with one patient should fail with another, though precisely in the same stage of the same disease. Another and not unfrequent cause of failure is that the life of a patient may depend as much upon administering the right remedy at the right point of time, as the success of an alchemist was supposed to do upon seizing the moment of projection. And where constant attendance is not possible, or where skill is wanting, it must often happen that the opportunity is lost. This cause would not exist in the Columbian Infirmary, where the ablest Physicians would be always within instant call, and where the Beguines in constant attendance would have sufficient skill to know when that call became necessary.

"A ship-captain," the Doctor used to say, "when he approaches the coast of France from the Bay of Biscay, or draws near the mouth of the British Channel, sends down the lead into the sea, and from the appearance of the sand which adheres to its tallowed bottom, he is enabled to find upon the chart where he is, with sufficient precision for directing his course. Think," he would say, "what an apparently impossible accumulation of experience there must have been, before the bottom of that sea everywhere within soundings could be so accurately known, as to be marked on charts which may be relied on with perfect confidence! No formal series of experiments was ever instituted for acquiring this knowledge; and there is nothing in history which can lead us to conjecture about what time sailors first began to trust to it. The boasted astronomy of the Hindoos and Egyptians affords a feebler apparent proof in favour of the false antiquity of the world, than might be inferred from this practice. Now if experience in the Art of Healing had been treasured up with equal care, it is not too much to say that therapeutics might have been as much advanced, as navigation has been by preserving the collective knowledge of so many generations." *

Fragments.

— The prince
Of Poets, Homer, sang long since,
A skilful leech is better far
Than half a hundred men of war.

Such prescriptions as were composed of any part of the human body were repro-

* The following fragments belong to the chapters which were to have treated on the Medical Science. They may therefore appropriately be appended to these chapters on Doña Oliva. I have only prefixed a motto from Butler.

bated by Galen, and he severely condemned Xenocrates for having introduced them, as being worse than useless in themselves, and wicked in their consequences. Yet these abominable ingredients continued in use till what may be called the Reformation of medicine in the Seventeenth century. Human bones were administered internally as a cure for ulcers, and the bones were to be those of the part affected. A preparation called Aqua Divina was made by cutting in pieces the body of a healthy man who had died a violent death, and distilling it with the bones and intestines. Human blood was prescribed for epilepsy, by great authorities, but others equally great with better reason condemned the practice, for this among other causes, that it might communicate the diseases of the person from whom it was taken. Ignorant surgeons when they bled a patient used to make him drink the warm blood that he might not lose the life which it contained. The heart dried, and taken in powder, was thought good in fevers; but conscientious practitioners were of opinion that it ought not to be used, because of the dangerous consequences which might be expected if such a remedy were in demand. It is not long since a Physician at Heidelberg prescribed human brains to be taken inwardly in violent fevers, and boasted of wonderful cures. And another German administered cat's entrails as a panacea!

The Egyptian physicians, each being confined to the study and treatment of one part of the body, or one disease, were bound to proceed in all cases according to the prescribed rules of their art. If the patient died under this treatment, no blame attached to the physician; but woe to the rash practitioner who ventured to save a life by any means out of the regular routine; the success of the experiment was not admitted as an excuse for the transgression, and he was punished with death; for the law presumed that in every case the treatment enjoined was such as by common consent of the most learned professors had been approved, because by long experience it had been found beneficial. The laws had some right to interfere because physicians received a public stipend.

Something like this prevails at this day in China. It is enacted in the Ta Tsing Leu Lee, that "when unskilful practitioners of medicine or surgery administer drugs, or perform operations with the puncturing needle, contrary to the established rules and practice, and thereby kill the patient, the Magistrates shall call in other practitioners to examine the nature of the medicine, or of the wound, as the case may be, which proved mortal; and if it shall appear upon the whole to have been simply an error without any design to injure the patient, the practitioner shall be allowed to redeem himself from the punishment of homicide, as in cases purely accidental, but shall be obliged to quit his profession for ever. If it shall appear that a medical practitioner intentionally deviates from the established rules and practice, and while pretending to remove the disease of his patient, aggravates the complaint, in order to extort more money for its cure, the money so extorted shall be considered to have been stolen, and punishment inflicted accordingly, in proportion to the amount. If the patient dies, the medical practitioner who is convicted of designedly employing improper medicines, or otherwise contriving to injure his patient, shall suffer death by being beheaded after the usual period of confinement."

No man ever entertained a higher opinion of medical science, and the dignity of a Physician, than Van Helmont. What has been said of the Poet ought, in his opinion, to be said of the Physician also, *Nascitur, non fit;* and in his relation to the Creator, he was more Poet, or Prophet, whom the word VATES brings under one predicament, — more than Priest. *Scilicet Pater Misericordiarum, qui Medicum ab initio, ceu Mediatorem inter Deum et hominem, constituit, immo sibi in deliciis posuit, à Medico vinci velle, nimirum, ad hoc se creasse peculiari elogio, et elegisse testatur. Ita est sane. Non enim citius hominem punit Deus, infirmat, aut interimere minatur, sibi quam optet opponentem Medicum, ut se Omnipotentem, etiam meritas immittendo pœnas, vincat propriis clementiæ suæ donis. Ejusmodi autem Medici sunt in ventre matris præparati, — suo fungentes munere, nullius lucri intuitu, nudèque reflectuntur super beneplacitum* (*immo mandatum*) *illius, qui solus, verè misericors, nos jubet, sub indictione pœnæ infernalis, fore Patri suo similes.* — Obedite præpositis *præceptum quidem: sed* honora parentes, honora Medicum, *angustius est quam obedire, cum cogamur etiam obedire minoribus. Medicus enim Mediator inter Vitæ Principem et Mortem.*

"To wit," — this done into English by J. C. sometime of M. H. Oxon. — "the Father of mercies, he who appointed a Physician, or Mediator between God and man from the beginning, yea He made it his delight that he would be overcome by a Physician, indeed he testifieth that he created and chose him to this end — for a peculiar testimony of his praise. It is so in truth. For no sooner doth He punish, weaken, and threaten to kill man, but he desireth a Physician opposing himself, that He may conquer himself, being Omnipotent, and even in sending deserved punishments, by the proper gifts of his clemency. — Of this sort are Physicians, which are fitted from their Mothers' wombs, exercise their gift with respect to no gain; and they are nakedly cast upon the good pleasure — yea the command — of him, who alone being truly merciful commands us that, under pain of infernal punishment, we be like to his father. — *Obey those that sit over you*, is a precept indeed; but honour thy Parents, honour the Physician, is more strict than to obey, seeing we are constrained even to obey our youngers. For the Physician is a Mediator between the Prince of life and Death."

Some of the Floridian tribes had a high opinion of medical virtue. They buried all their dead, except the Doctors; them they burned, reduced their bones to powder, and drank it in water.

A century ago the Lions in the Tower were named after the different Sovereigns then reigning, "and it has been observed that when a King dies, the Lion of that name dies also."

In the great Place at Delhi the poor Astrologers sit, as well Mahometan as Heathen. These Doctors, forsooth, sit there in the sun upon a piece of tapestry, all covered with dust, having about them some old mathematical instruments, which they make show of to draw passengers, and a great open book representing the animals of the Zodiac. These men are the oracles of the vulgar, to whom they pretend to give for one *Payssa*, that is a penny, good luck, and they are they that looking upon the hands and face, turning over their books and making a show of calculation, determine the fortunate moment when a business is to be begun, to make it successful. The mean women, wrapped up in a white sheet from head to foot, come to find them out, telling them in their ear their most secret concerns, as if they were their confessors, and intreat them to render the stars propitious to them, and suitable to their designs, as if they could absolutely dispose of their influences.

The most ridiculous of all these astrologers, in my opinion, was a mongrel Portugueze from Goa, who sat with much gravity upon his piece of tapestry, like the rest, and had a great deal of custom, though he could neither read nor write; and as for instruments and books was furnished with nothing but an old sea-compass, and an old Romish prayer-book in the Portugueze language, of which he showed the pictures for figures of the Zodiac. "*As taes bestias, tal Astrologo*, — for such beasts, such an Astrologer," said he to father Buze, a Jesuit, who met him there.

M. Rondeau in 1780 opened a large tumour which had grown behind a woman's left ear, at Brussels, and found in it a stone, in form and size like a pigeon's egg, which all the experiments to which it was subject proved to be a real Bezoar, of the same colour, structure, taste and substance with the oriental and occidental Bezoars. This, however, was a fact which the Doctor could not exactly accommodate to his theory, though it clearly belonged to it; the difficulty was not in this, that there are those animals in which the Bezoar is produced, the goat, in which it is most frequent, the cow, in which it is of less value, and the ape, in which it is very seldom found, but is of most efficacy. Through either of these forms the Archeus might have passed. But how the Bezoar, which is formed in the stomach of these animals, should have concreted in a sort of wen upon the woman's head was a circumstance altogether anomalous.

At Mistra, a town built from the ruins of Sparta, the sick are daily brought and laid at the doors of the metropolitan Church, as at the gates of the ancient temples, that those who repair thither to worship may indicate to them the remedies by which their health may be recovered.

It is well remarked of the Spaniards by the Abbé de Vayrac, *Que d'un trop grand attachement pour les Anciens en matière de Philosophie et de Medecine, et de trop de negligence pour eux en matière de Poësie, il arrive presque toujours qu'ils ne sont ni bons Philosophes, ni bons Medecins, ni bons Poëtes.*

The desire of having something on which to rely, as dogmatical truths, "as it appears," says Donne, "in all sciences, so most manifestly in Physic, which for a long time considering nothing but plain curing, and that by example and precedent, the world at last longed for some certain canons and rules how these cures might be accomplished: and when men are inflamed with this desire, and that such a fire breaks out, it rages and consumes infinitely by heat of argument, except some of authority interpose. This produced Hippocrates his Aphorisms; and the world slumbered, or took breath, in his resolution divers hundreds of years. And then in Galen's time, which was not satisfied with the effect of curing, nor with the knowledge how to cure, broke out another desire of finding out the causes why those simples wrought those effects. Then Galen, rather to stay their stomachs than that he gave them enough, taught them the qualities of the four Elements, and arrested them upon this, that all differences of qualities proceeded from them. And after, (not much before our time,) men perceiving that all effects in physic could not be derived from these beggarly and impotent properties of the Elements, and that therefore they were driven often to that miserable refuge of specific form, and of antipathy and sympathy, we see the world hath turned upon new principles, which are attributed to Paracelsus, but indeed too much to his honour."

"This indenture made 26 Apr. 18 Hen. 8, between Sir Walter Strickland, knight, of one part, and Alexander Kenet, Doctor of Physic, on the other part, witnesseth, that the said Alexander permitteth, granteth, and by these presents bindeth him, that he will, with the grace and help of God, render and bring the said Sir Walter Strickland to perfect health of all his infirmities and diseases contained in his person, and especially stomach and lungs and breast, wherein he has most disease and grief; and over to minister such medicines truly to the said Sir Walter Strickland, in such manner and ways as the said Master Alexander may make the said Sir Walter heal of all infirmities and diseases, in as short time as possible may be, with the grace and help of God. And also the said Master Alexander granteth he shall not depart at no time from the said Sir Walter without his license, unto the time the said Sir Walter be perfect heal, with the grace and help of God. For the which care the said Sir Walter Strictland granteth by these presents, binding himself to pay or cause to be paid to the said Mr. Alexander or his assigns £20. sterling monies of good and lawful money of England, in manner and form following: that is, five marks to be paid upon the first day of May next ensuing, and all the residue of the said sum of £20. to be paid parcel by parcel as shall please the said Sir Walter, as he thinks necessary to be delivered and paid in the time of his disease, for sustaining such charges as the said Mr. Alexander must use in medicine for reducing the said Sir Walter to health; and so the said payment continued and made, to the time the whole sum of £20. aforesaid be fully contented and paid. In witness whereof, either to these present indentures have interchangeably set their seals, the day and year above mentioned."

Sir Walter, however, died on the 9th of January following.

Je voudrois de bon cœur, says an interlocutor in one of the evening conversation parties of Guillaume Bouchet, Sieur de Brocourt, *qu'il y eust des Medecins pour remedier aux ennuis et maladies de l'esprit, ne plus ne moins qu'il en y a qui guerissent les maladies et douleurs du corps; comme il se trouve qu'il y en avoit en Grece; car il est escrit que Xenophon ayant faict bastir une maison à Corinthe, il mit en un billet sur la porte, qu'il faisoit profession, et avoit le moyen de guerir de paroles ceux qui estoient ennuyez et faschez; et leur demandant les causes de leurs ennuis, il les guerissoit, les recomfortant, et consolant de leurs douleurs et ennuis.*

Under barbarous governments the most atrocious practices are still in use. It was reported in India that when Hyder Aly was suffering with a malignant bile on his back common in that country, and which occasioned his death, an infant's liver was applied to it every day. An Englishman in the service of Phizal Beg Cawn was on an embassy at Madras when this story was current; the Governor asked him whether he thought it likely to be true, and he acknowledged his belief in it, giving this sufficient reason, that his master Phizal Beg had tried the same remedy, but then he begged leave to affirm, in behalf of his master, that the infants killed for his use were slaves, and his own property.

Of odd notions concerning virginity I do not remember a more curious one than that virgin mummy was preferred in medicine.

INTERCHAPTER XXV.

A WISHING INTERCHAPTER WHICH IS SHORTLY TERMINATED, ON SUDDENLY RECOLLECTING THE WORDS OF CLEOPATRA, — "WISHERS WERE EVER FOOLS."

> Begin betimes, occasion's bald behind,
> Stop not thine opportunity, for fear too late
> Thou seek'st for much, but canst not compass it.
>
> MARLOWE.

Plust a Dieu que j'eusse presentement cent soixante et dixhuit millions d'or! says a personage in Rabelais: *ho, comment je triumpherois!*

It was a good, honest, large, capacious wish; and in wishing, it is as well to wish for enough. By enough, in the way of riches, a man is said to mean always something more than he has. Without exposing myself to any such censorious remark, I will, like the person above quoted, limit my desires to a positive sum, and wish for just one million a-year.

"And what would you do with it?" says Mr. Sobersides.

"*Attendez encores un peu, avec demie once de patience.*"

> I now esteem my venerable self
> As brave a fellow, as if all that pelf
> Were sure mine own; and I have thought a way
> Already how to spend.

And first, for my private expenditure, I would either buy a house to my mind, or build one; and it should be such as a house ought to be, which I once heard a glorious agriculturist define "a house that should have in it everything that is voluptuous, and necessary and right." In my acceptation of that felicitous definition, I request the reader to understand that everything which is right is intended, and nothing but what is perfectly so: that is to say I mean every possible accommodation conducive to health and comfort. It should be large enough for my friends, and not so large as to serve as an hotel for my acquaintance, and I would live in it at the rate of five thousand a-year, beyond which no real and reasonable enjoyment is to be obtained by money.

I would neither keep hounds, nor hunters, nor running horses.

I would neither solicit nor accept a peerage. I would not go into Parliament. I would take no part whatever in what is called public life, farther than to give my vote at an election against a Whig, or against any one who would give his in favour of the Catholic Question.

I would not wear my coat quite so threadbare as I do at present: but I would still keep to my old shoes, as long as they would keep to me.

But stop — Cleopatra adopted some wizard's words when she said "Wishers were ever fools!"

CHAPTER CCXXII.

ETYMOLOGY. UN TOUR DE MAÎTRE GONIN. ROMAN DE VAUDEMONT AND THE LETTER C. SHENSTONE. THE DOCTOR'S USE OF CHRISTIAN NAMES.

Πρᾶγμα, πρᾶγμα μέγα κεκίνηται, μέγα.

ARISTOPHANES.

Magnus thesaurus latet in nominibus, said Strafford, then Lord Deputy Wentworth, when noticing a most unwise scheme which was supposed to proceed from Sir Abraham Dawes, he observes, it appeared most plainly that he had not his name for nothing! In another letter, he says, "I begin to hope I may in time as well understand these customs as Sir Abraham Dawes. Why should I fear it? for I have a name less ominous than his."

Gonin, Court de Gebelin says, is a French word or rather name which exists only in these proverbial phrases, *Maître Gonin,* — *un tour de Maître Gonin;* it designates *un Maître passé en ruses et artifices; un homme fin et rusé.* The origin of the word, says he, was altogether unknown. Menage rejects with the utmost contempt the opinion of those who derive it from the Hebrew עונן, *Gwunen*, a diviner, an enchanter. It is true that this etymology has been advanced too lightly, and without proofs: Menage, however, ought to have been less contemptuous, because he could substitute nothing in its place.

It is remarkable that neither Menage nor Court de Gebelin should have known that Maistre Gounin was a French conjuror, as well known in his day as Katterfelto and Jonas, or the Sieur Ingleby Emperor of Conjurors in later times. He flourished in the days of Francis the First, before whom he is said to have made a private exhibition of his art in a manner perfectly characteristic of that licentious King and his profligate court. Thus he effected *par ses inventions, illusions et sorcelleries et enchantements,* — *car il estoit un homme fort expert et subtil en son art*, says Brantôme; *et son petit-fils, que nous avons veu, n'y entendoit rien au prix de luy.* Grandfather and grandson having been at the head of their worshipful profession, the name passed into a proverbial expression, and survived all memory of the men.

Court de Gebelin traced its etymology far and wide. He says, it is incontestable that this word is common to us with the ancient Hebrews, though it does not come to us from them. We are indebted for it to the English. Cunning *designe chez eux un homme adroit, fin, rusé.* Master Cunning *a fait Maître Gonin.* This word comes from the primitive *Cen* pronounced *Ken*, which signifies ability, (*habilité,*) art, power. The Irish have made from it *Kanu*, I know; *Kunna*, to know; *Kenning*, knowledge, (*science*); *Kenni*-mann, wise men (*hommes savans,*) Doctors, Priests.

It is a word common to all the dialects of the Celtic and Teutonic; to the Greek in which *Konne-ein** signifies to know (*savoir*), to be intelligent and able, &c., to the Tartar languages, &c.

---

* So in the MS.

Les Anglois, associant Cunning *avec* Man, *homme, en font le mot* Cunning-Man, *qui signifie Devin, Enchanteur, homme qui fait de grandes choses, et qui est habile : c'est donc le correspondant du mot Hebreu* Gwunen, *Enchanteur, Devin;* Gwuna, *Magicienne, Devineresse; d'où le verbe* Gwunen, *deviner, observer les Augures, faire des prestiges. Ne soyons pas étonnés*, says the author, bringing this example to bear upon his system, *de voir ce mot commun à tant de Peuples, et si ancien : il vint chez tous d'une source commune, de la haute Asie, berceau de tous ces Peuples et de leur Langue.*

If Mr. Canning had met with the foregoing passage towards the close of his political life, when he had attained the summit of his wishes, how would it have affected him in his sober mind? Would it have tickled his vanity, or stung his conscience? Would he have been flattered by seeing his ability prefigured in his name? or would he have been mortified at the truth conveyed in the proverbial French application of it, and have acknowledged in his secret heart that cunning is as incompatible with self-esteem as it is with uprightness, with magnanimity, and with true greatness?

His name was unlucky not only in its signification, but according to Roman de Vaudemont, in its initial.

Maudit est nom qui par C se commence,
Coquin, cornard, caignard, coqu, caphard :
Aussi par B, badaud, badin, bavard,
Mais pire est C, si j'ay bien remembrance.

Much as the Doctor insisted upon the virtues of what he called the divine initial, he reprehended the uncharitable sentiment of these verses, and thought that the author never could have played at "I love my Love with an A," or that the said game perhaps was not known among the French; for you must get to x, y, and z before you find it difficult to praise her in any letter in the alphabet, and to dispraise her in the same.

Initials therefore, he thought, (always with one exception,) of no other consequence than as they pleased the ear, and combined gracefully in a cypher, upon a seal or ring. But in names themselves a great deal more presents itself to a reflecting mind.

Shenstone used to bless his good fortune that his name was not obnoxious to a pun. He would not have liked to have been complimented in the same strain as a certain Mr. Pegge was by an old epigrammatist.

What wonder if my friendship's force doth last
Firm to your goodness? You have pegg'd it fast.

Little could he foresee, as Dr. Southey has observed, that it was obnoxious to a rhyme in French English. In the gardens of Ermenonville M. * placed this inscription to his honour.

This plain stone
To William Shenstone.
In his writings he display'd
A mind natural;
At Leasowes he laid
Arcadian greens rural.

Poor Shenstone hardly appears more ridiculous in the frontispiece to his own works, where, in the heroic attitude of a poet who has won the prize and is about to receive the crown, he stands before Apollo in a shirt and boa, as destitute of another less dispensable part of dress as Adam in Eden; but like Adam when innocent, not ashamed: while the shirtless God holding a lyre in one hand prepares with the other to place a wreath of bay upon the brow of his delighted votary.

The father of Sir Joshua Reynolds fancied that if he gave his son an uncommon Christian name, it might be the means of bettering his fortune; and therefore he had him christened Joshua. It does not appear, however, that the name ever proved as convenient to the great painter as it did to Joshua Barnes. He to whose Barnesian labours Homer and Queen Esther, and King Edward III. bear witness, was a good man and a good scholar, and a rich widow who not imprudently inferred that he would make a good husband, gave him an opportunity by observing to him one day that Joshua made the Sun and Moon stand still, and significantly adding that nothing could resist Joshua. The hint was not thrown

* So in the MS.

away; — and he never had cause to repent that he had taken, nor she that she had given it.

A Spanish gentleman who made it his pastime to write books of chivalry, being to bring into his work a furious Giant, went many days devising a name which might in all points be answerable to his fierceness; neither could he light upon any; till playing one day at cards in his friend's house, he heard the master of the house say to the boy — muchacho — *tra qui tantos*. As soon as he heard Traquitantos he laid down his cards, and said that now he had found a name which would fit well for his Giant.*

I know not whether it was the happy-minded author of the Worthies and the Church History of Britain who proposed as an Epitaph for himself the words "Fuller's Earth," or whether some one proposed it for him. But it is in his own style of thought and feeling.

Nor has it any unbeseeming levity, like this which is among Browne's poems.

Here lieth in sooth
Honest John Tooth,
Whom Death on a day
From us drew away.

Or this upon a Mr. Button,

Here lieth one, God rest his soul,
Whose grave is but a button-hole.

No one was ever punned to death, nor, though Ditton is said to have died in consequence of "the unhappy effect" which Swift's verses produced upon him, can I believe that any one was ever rhymed to death.

A man may with better reason bless his godfathers and godmothers if they chuse for him a name which is neither too common nor too peculiar.†

It is not a good thing to be Tom'd or Bob'd, Jack'd or Jim'd, Sam'd or Ben'd, Natty'd or Batty'd, Neddy'd or Teddy'd, Will'd or Bill'd, Dick'd or Nick'd, Joe'd or Jerry'd, as you go through the world. And yet it is worse to have a christian name, that for its oddity shall be in every body's mouth when you are spoken of, as if it were pinned upon your back, or labelled upon your forehead: — Quintin Dick, for example, which would have been still more unlucky if Mr. Dick had happened to have a cast in his eye. The Report on Parochial Registration contains a singular example of the inconvenience which may arise from giving a child an uncouth christian name. A gentleman called Anketil Gray had occasion for a certificate of his baptism: it was known at what church he had been baptized, but on searching the register there no such name could be found; some mistake was presumed therefore not in the entry, but in the recollection of the parties, and many other registers were examined without success. At length the first register was again recurred to, and then upon a closer investigation they found him entered as Miss Ann Kettle Grey.

Souvent, says Brantôme, ceux qui portent le nom de leurs ayeuls, leur *ressemblent volontiers, comme je l'ay veu observer et en discourir à aucuns philosophes.* He makes this remark after observing that the Emperor Ferdinand was named after his grandfather Ferdinand of Arragon, and Charles V. after his great-grandfather Charles the Bold. But such resemblances are, as Brantôme implies, imitational where they exist. And Mr. Keightley's observation, that "a man's name and his occupation have often a most curious coincidence," rests perhaps on a similar ground, men being sometimes designated by their names for the way of life which they are to pursue. Many a boy has been called Nelson in our own days, and Rodney in our father's, because he was intended for the sea service, and many a seventh son has been christened Luke, in the hope that he might live to be a physician. In what other business than that of lottery-office would the name Goodluck so surely have brought business to the house? Captain Death could never have practised medicine or surgery, unless under an *alias;* but there would be no better name with which to meet an enemy

* Huarte.

† It is said of an eccentric individual that he never forgave his Godfathers and Godmother for giving him the name of Moses, for which the short is Mo.

in battle. Dr. Damman was an eminent physician and royal professor of midwifery at Ghent in the latter part of the last century. He ought to have been a Calvinistic divine.

The Ancients paid so great a regard to names, that whenever a number of men were to be examined on suspicion, they began by putting to the torture the one whose name was esteemed the vilest. And this must not be supposed to have had its origin in any reasonable probability, such as might be against a man who, being apprehended for a riot, should say his name was Patrick Murphy, or Dennis O'Connor, or Thady O'Callaghan; or against a Moses Levi, or a Daniel Abrahams for uttering bad money; it was for the import of the name itself, and the evidence of a base and servile origin which it implied.

J'ai été tousjours fort etonné, says Bayle, *que les familles qui portent un nom odieux ou ridicule, ne le quitent pas.* The Leatherheads and Shufflebottoms, the Higgenses and Huggenses, the Scroggses and the Scraggses, Sheepshanks and Ramsbottoms, Taylors and Barbers, and worse than all, Butchers, would have been to Bayle as abominable as they were to Dr. Dove. "I ought," the Doctor would say, "to have a more natural dislike to the names of Kite, Hawk, Falcon and Eagle; and yet they are to me (the first excepted) less odious than names like these: and even preferable to Bull, Bear, Pig, Hog, Fox or Wolf."

"What a name," he would say, "is Lamb for a soldier, Joy for an undertaker, Rich for a pauper, or Noble for a taylor: Big for a lean and little person, and Small for one who is broad in the rear and abdominous in the van. Short for a fellow six feet without his shoes, or Long for him whose high heels hardly elevate him to the height of five. Sweet for one who has either a vinegar face, or a foxey complexion. Younghusband for an old bachelor. Merryweather for any one in November and February, a black spring, a cold summer or a wet autumn. Goodenough for a person no better than he should be: Toogood for any human creature, and Best for a subject who is perhaps too bad to be endured."

Custom having given to every Christian name its *alias*, he always used either the baptismal name or its substitute as it happened to suit his fancy, careless of what others might do. Thus he never called any woman Mary, though *Mare* he said being the sea was in many respects but too emblematic of the sex. It was better to use a synonyme of better omen, and Molly therefore was to be preferred as being soft. If he accosted a vixen of that name in her worst temper he *mollyfied* her. On the contrary he never could be induced to substitute Sally for Sarah. — Sally he said had a salacious sound, and moreover it reminded him of rovers, which women ought not to be. Martha he called Patty, because it came pat to the tongue. Dorothy remained Dorothy, because it was neither fitting that women should be made Dolls nor Idols. Susan with him was always Sue, because women were to be sued, and Winifred Winny because they were to be won.

CHAPTER CCXXIII.

TRUE PRONUNCIATION OF THE NAME OF DOVE. DIFFICULTIES OF PRONUNCIATION AND PROSODY. A TRUE AND PERFECT RHYME HIT UPON.

> *Tal nombre, que a los siglos extendido,*
> *Se olvide de olvidarsele al Olvido.* LOPE DE VEGA.

CONSIDERING the many mysteries which our Doctor discovered in the name of Dove, and not knowing but that many more may be concealed in it which will in due time be brought to light, I am particularly desirous, — I am solicitous, — I am anxious, — I wish (which is as much as if a Quaker were to say "I am moved," or "it is upon my mind,") to fix for posterity, if possible, the true pronunciation of that name. *If possible*, I say, because whatever those readers may think, who have never before had the sub ject presented to their thoughts, it is exceedingly difficult. My solicitude upon this point will not appear groundless, if it be recollected to what strange changes pronunciation is liable, not from lapse of time alone, but from caprice and fashion. Who in the present generation knows not how John Kemble was persecuted about his *a-ches*, a point wherein, right as he was, he was proved to be wrong by a new *norma loquendi*. Our allies are no longer iambic as they were wont to be, but pure trochees now, like Alley Croker and Mr. Alley the counsellor. *Beta* is at this day called *Veta* in Greece, to the confusion of Sir John Cheke, to the triumph of Bishop Gardiner, and in contempt of the whole ovine race. Nay, to bring these observations home to the immediate purport of this chapter, the modern Greeks when they read this book will call the person, on whose history it relates, Thaniel Thove! and the Thoctor! their Delta having undergone as great a change as the Delta in Egypt. Have I not reason then for my solicitude?

Whoever examines that very rare and curious book, *Lesclarcissement de la langue françoyse*, printed by Johan Haukyns, 1530, (which is the oldest French grammar in our language, and older than any that the French possess in their own,) will find indubitable proof that the pronunciation of both nations is greatly altered in the course of the last three hundred years.

Neither the Spaniards nor Portuguese retain in their speech that strong Rhotacism which they denoted by the double *rr*, and which Camden and Fuller notice as peculiar to the people of Carlton in Leicestershire. Lily has not enumerated it among those *isms* from which boys are by all means to be deterred; a most heinous *ism*, however, it is. A strange uncouth wharling Fuller called it, and Camden describes it as a harsh and ungrateful manner of speech with a guttural and difficult pronunciation. They were perhaps a colony from Durham or Northumberland in whom the *burr* had become hereditary.

Is the poetry of the Greeks and Romans ever read as they themselves read it? Have we not altered the very metre of the pentameter by our manner of reading it? Is it not at this day doubtful whether Cæsar was called Kæsar, Chæsar, or as we pronounce his name? And whether Cicero ought not to be called Chichero* or Kikero? Have I not therefore cause to apprehend that there may come a time when the true pronunciation of Dove may be lost or doubtful? Major Jardine has justly observed that in the great and complicated art of alphabetical writing, which is rendered so easy and familiar by habit, we are not always aware of the limits of its powers.

"Alphabetical writing," says that always speculative writer, "was doubtless a wonderful and important discovery. Its greatest merit, I think, was that of distinguishing sounds from articulations, a degree of perfection to which the eastern languages have not yet arrived; and that defect may be, with those nations, one of the chief causes of their limited progress in many other things. You know they have no vowels, except some that have the *a*, but always joined to some articulation: their attempt to supply that defect by points give them but very imperfect and indistinct ideas of vocal and articulate sounds, and of their important distinction. But even languages most alphabetical, if the expression may be allowed, could not probably transmit by writing a compleat idea of their own sounds and pronunciation from any one age or people to another. Sounds are to us infinite and variable, and we cannot transmit by one sense the ideas and objects of another. We shall be convinced of this when we recollect the innumerable qualities of tone in human voices, so as to enable us to distinguish all

---

* The well-known verses of Catullus would be against C*h*ic*h*ero, at least.

> *C*h*ommoda dicebat, si quando commoda vellet*
> *Dicere, et* h*insidias Arrius insidias:*
> *Et tum mirificè sperabat se esse locutum,*
> *Cum quantum poterat, dixerat* h*insidias, &c.*
>
> CARM. LXXXIV.

The *h* appears to have been an old Shibboleth, and not restricted either to Shropshire or Warwickshire. Mr. Evans' verses will occur to many readers of "The Doctor, &c."

our acquaintances, though the number should amount to many hundreds, or perhaps thousands. With attention we might discover a different quality of tone in every instrument; for all these there never can be a sufficient number of adequate terms in any written language; and when that variety comes to be compounded with a like variety of articulations, it becomes infinite to us. The varieties only upon the seven notes in music, varied only as to pitch and modulation throughout the audible scale, combined with those of time, are not yet probably half exhausted by the constant labour of so many ages. So that the idea of Mr. Steel and others, of representing to the eye the tune and time only of the sounds in any language, will probably ever prove inadequate to the end proposed, even without attempting the kinds and qualities of tones and articulations which would render it infinite and quite impossible."

Lowth asserts that "the true pronunciation of Hebrew is lost,—lost to a degree far beyond what can ever be the case of any European language preserved only in writing; for the Hebrew language, like most of the other Oriental languages, expressing only the consonants, and being destitute of its vowels, has lain now for two thousand years in a manner mute and incapable of utterance, the number of syllables is in a great many words uncertain, the quantity and accent wholly unknown."

In the pronouncing Dictionary of John Walker, (that great benefactor to all ladies employed in the task of education,) the word is written *Duv*, with a figure of 2 over the vowel, designating that what he calls the short simple *u* is intended, as in the English *tub*, *cup*, *sup*, and the French *veuf*, *neuf*. How Sheridan gives it, or how it would have been, as Mr. Southey would say, *uglyographised* by Elphinstone and the other whimsical persons who have laboured so disinterestedly in the vain attempt of regulating our spelling by our pronunciation, I know not, for none of their books are at hand. My public will forgive me that I have not taken the trouble to procure them. It has not been neglected from idleness, nor for the sake of sparing myself any pains which ought to have been taken. Would I spare any pains in the service of my Public!

I have not sought for those books because their authority would have added nothing to Walker's: nor if they had differed from him, would any additional assistance have been obtained. They are in fact all equally inefficient for the object here required, which is so to describe and fix the true pronunciation of a particular word, that there shall be no danger of it ever being mistaken, and that when this book shall be as old as the Iliad, there may be no dispute concerning the name of its principal personage, though more places should vie with each other for the honour of having given birth to Urgand the Unknown, than contended for the birth of Homer. Now that cannot be done by literal notation. If you think it may, "I beseech you, Sir, paint me a voice! Make a sound visible if you can! Teach mine ears to see, and mine eyes to hear!"

The prosody of the ancients enables us to ascertain whether a syllable be long or short. Our language is so much more flexible in verse that our poetry will not enable the people of the third and fourth millenniums even to do this, without a very laborious collation, which would after all in many instances leave the point doubtful. Nor will rhyme decide the question; for to a foreigner who understands English only by book (and the people of the third and fourth millenniums may be in this state) Dove and Glove, Rove and Grove, Move and Prove, must all appear legitimate and interchangeable rhymes.

I must therefore have given up the matter in despair had it not been for a most fortunate and felicitous circumstance. There is one word in the English language which, happen what may, will never be out of use, and of which the true pronunciation, like the true meaning, is sure to pass down uninterruptedly and unaltered from generation to generation. That word, that one and only word which must remain immutable wherever English is spoken, whatever other mutations the speech may undergo, till the language itself be lost in the wreck of all things, — that word (Youths and Maidens ye anticipate it now!) that one and only word —

> Τόδε μὲν οὐκέτι στόματος ἐν πύλαις
> Καθέξω· *

that dear delicious monosyllable LOVE, — that word is a true and perfect rhyme to the name of our Doctor.

> Speak but one rhyme and I am satisfied;
> . . . pronounce but Love and Dove.†

CHAPTER CCXXIV.

CHARLEMAGNE, CASIMIR THE POET, MARGARET DUCHESS OF NEWCASTLE, NOCTURNAL REMEMBRANCER. THE DOCTOR NOT AMBITIOUS OF FAME. THE AUTHOR IS INDUCED BY MR. FOSBROOKE AND NORRIS OF BEMERTON TO EJACULATE A HEATHEN PRAYER IN BEHALF OF HIS BRETHREN.

> *Tutte le cose son rose et viole*
> *Ch' io dico ò ch' io dirò de la virtute.*
>
> FR. SANSOVINO.

IT is recorded of Charlemagne by his secretary Eginhart, that he had always pen, ink and parchment beside his pillow, for the purpose of noting down any thoughts which might occur to him during the night: and lest upon waking he should find himself in darkness, a part of the wall, within reach from the bed, was prepared, like the leaf of a tablet, with wax, on which he might indent his memoranda with a style.

The Jesuit poet Casimir had a black tablet always by his bedside, and a piece of chalk, with which to secure a thought, or a poetical expression that might occur to him, *si quid insomnis noctu non infeliciter cogitabat ne id sibi periret.* In like manner it is related of Margaret Duchess of Newcastle that some of her young ladies always slept within call, ready to rise at any hour in the night, and take down her thoughts, lest she should forget them before morning.

Some threescore years ago a little instrument was sold by the name of the Nocturnal Remembrancer; it consisted merely of some leaves of what is called asses-skin, in a leathern case wherein there was one aperture from side to side, by aid of which a straight line could be pencilled in the dark: the leaf might be drawn up and fixed at measured distances, till it was written on from top to bottom.

Our Doctor, (—now that thou art so well acquainted with him and likest him so cordially, Reader, it would be ungenerous in me to call him mine)—*our* Doctor needed no such contrivances. He used to say that he "laid aside all his cares when he put off his wig, and that never any were to be found under his night-cap." Happy man, from whom this might be believed! but so even had been the smooth and noiseless tenour of his life that he could say it truly. Anxiety and bereavements had brought to him no sleepless nights, no dreams more distressful than even the realities that produce and blend with them. Neither had worldly cares or ambitious hopes and projects ever disquieted him, and made him misuse in midnight musings the hours which belong to sleep. He had laid up in his mind an inexhaustible store of facts and fancies, and delighted in nothing more than in adding to these intellectual treasures; but as he gathered knowledge only for its own sake, and for the pleasure of the pursuit, not with any emulous feelings, or aspiring intent

> —to be for ever known,
> And make the years to come his own,

he never said, with the studious Elder Brother in Fletcher's comedy,

> —the children
> Which I will leave to all posterity,
> Begot and brought up by my painful studies
> Shall be my living issue.

And therefore — *voilà un homme qui était fort savant et fort éloquent, et néanmoins* — (altering a little the words of Bayle,) — *il n'est pas connu dans la république des lettres, et il y a eu une infinité de gens beaucoup moins habile que lui, qui sont cent fois plus connus; c'est qu'ils ont publié des livres, et que la presse n'a point roulé sur ses productions. Il importe extrêmement aux hommes doctes,*

---

* EURIPIDES. † ROMEO AND JULIET.

qui ne veulent pas tomber dans l'oubli après leur mort, de s'ériger en auteurs; sans cela leur nom ne passe guère la première génération; res erat unius ætatis. Le commun des lecteurs ne prend point garde au nom des savans qu'ils ne connaissent que par le témoignage d'autrui; on oublie bientôt un homme, lorsque l'éloge qu'en font les autres finit par — le public n'a rien ou de lui.

Bayle makes an exception of men who like Peiresc distinguish themselves *d'un façon singulière.*

"I am not sure," says Sir Egerton Brydges, "that the life of an author is a happy life; but yet, if the seeds of authorship be in him, he will not be happy except in the indulgence of this occupation. Without the culture and free air which these seeds require they will wither and turn to poison." It is no desirable thing, according to this representation, to be born with such a predisposition to the most dangerous of all callings. But still more pitiable is the condition of such a person, if Mr. Fosbrooke has described it truly: "the mind of a man of genius," says he, (who beyond all question is a man of genius himself,) "is always in a state of pregnancy, or parturition; and its power of bearing offspring is bounded only by supervening disease, or by death." Those who are a degree lower in genius are in a yet worse predicament; such a sort of man, as Norris of Bemerton describes, who, "although he conceives often, yet by some chance or other he always miscarries, and the issue proves abortive."

JUNO LUCINA *fer opem!*

This invocation the Doctor never made metaphorically for himself, whatever serious and secret prayers he may have preferred for others, when exercising one branch of his tripartite profession.

Bernardin de Saint Pierre says in one of his letters, when his *Etudes de la Nature* were in the press, *Je suis a present dans les douleurs de l'enfantement, car il n'y a point de mère qui souffre autant en mettant un enfant au monde, et qui craigne plus qu'on ne l'écorche ou qu'on ne les crève un œil, qu'un auteur qui revoit les épreuves de son ouvrage.*

CHAPTER CCXXV.

TWO QUESTIONS GROWING OUT OF THE PRECEDING CHAPTER.

A Taylor who has no objection to wear motley, may make himself a great coat with half a yard of his own stuff, by eking it out with cabbage from every piece that comes in his way. ROBERT SOUTHEY.

BUT here two questions arise:

Ought Dr. Dove, or ought he not, to have been an author?

Was he, or was he not, the happier, for not being one?

"Not to leave the reader," as Lightfoot says, "in a *bivium* of irresolutions," I will examine each of these questions, *Escriviendo algunos breves reglones, sobre lo mucho que dezir y escrivir se podria en esto; — moviendo me principalmente a ello la grande ignorancia que sobre esta matheria veo manifiestamente entre las gentes de nuestro siglo.**

"I am and have been," says Robert Wilmot "(if there be in me any soundness of judgement,) of this opinion, that whatsoever is committed to the press is commended to eternity; and it shall stand a lively witness with our conscience, to our comfort or confusion, in the reckoning of that great day. Advisedly therefore was that proverb used of our elder Philosopher, *Manum a Tabulâ;* withhold thy hand from the paper, and thy papers from the print, or light of the world."

Robert Wilmot *says*, I say, using the present tense in setting his words before the reader, because of an author it may truly be said that "being dead he yet speaketh." Obscure as this old author now is, for his name and his existing works are known only to those who love to pore among the tombs and the ruins of literature, yet by those who will always be enough "to make a few," his name will continue to be known, long after many of those bubbles which now glitter as they float upon the stream of popularity are "gone for ever;" and his remains are safe for the next half millennium, if the globe

* GARIBAY.

should last so long without some cataclasm which shall involve its creatures and its works in one common destruction.

Wilmot is right in saying that whatever is written for the public, is, as regards the individual responsibility of the writer, written for eternity, however brief may be its earthly duration; — an aweful consideration for the authors of wicked books, and for those who by becoming instrumental in circulating such books involve themselves in the author's guilt as accessaries after the fact, and thereby bring themselves deservedly under the same condemnation.

Looking at the first question in this point of view, it may be answered without hesitation, the Doctor was so pure in heart, and consequently so innocent in mind, that there was no moral reason why he ought not to have been an author. He would have written nothing but what, religiously speaking, might have been accounted among his good works, — so far as, so speaking, any works may deserve to be called good.

But the question has two handles, and we must now take it by the other.

An author, more obscure in the literature of his own country than Wilmot, (unless indeed some Spanish or Italian Haslewood may have disinterred his name,) has expressed an opinion directly the reverse of Wilmot's concerning authorship. Ye who understand the noble language which the Emperor Charles V. ranked above all other living tongues may have the satisfaction of here reading it in the original.

*Muchos son los que del loable y fructuoso trabajo de escrevir, rehuir suelen; unos por no saber, a los quales su ignorancia en alguna manera escusa; otros por negligencia, que teniendo habilidad y disposicion par ello no lo hazen; y a estos es menester que Dios los perdone en lo passado, y emiende en lo por venir; otros dexan de hazello por temor de los detractores y que mal acostumbran dezir; los quales a mi parecer de toda reprehension son dignos, pues siendo el acto en si virtuoso, dexan de usarlo por temor. Mayormente que todos, o los mas que este exercicio usan, o con buen ingenio escriven, o con buen desseo querrian escrevir. Si con buen ingenio hazen buena obra, cierto es que dese ser alabada. Y së el defecto de mas no alcanzar algo, la haze diminuta de lo que mejor pudiera ser, deve se loar lo que el tal quisiera hazer, si mas supiera, o la invencion y fantasia de la obra, por que fue, o porque desseo ser bueno. De manere que es mucho mejor escrevir como quiera que se pueda hazer, que no por algun temor dexar de hazerlo.**

"Many," says this author, "are they who are wont to eschew the meritorious and fruitful labour of writing, some for want of knowledge, whom their ignorance in some manner excuses; others for negligence, who having ability and fitness for this nevertheless do it not, and need there is for them, that God should forgive them for the past, and amend them for the time to come; others forbear writing, for fear of detractors and of those who accustom themselves to speak ill; and these in my opinion are worthy of all reprehension, because the act being in itself so virtuous they are withheld by fear from performing it. Moreover it is to be considered that all, or most of those who practise this art, either write with a good genius, or a good desire of writing well. If having a good genius they produce a good work, certes that work deserves to be commended. And if for want of genius it falls short of this, and of what it might better have been, still he ought to be praised, who would have made his work praiseworthy if he had been able, and the invention and fancy of the work, either because it is or because he wished it to be so. So that it is much better for a man to write whatever his ability may be, than to be withheld from the attempt by fear."

A very different opinion was expressed by one of the most learned of men, *Ego multos studiosos quotidie video, paucos doctos; in doctis paucos ingeniosos; in semidoctis nullos bonos; atque adeo literæ generis humani unicum solamen, jam pestis et perniciei maximæ loco sunt.*†

M. Cornet used to say, *Que pour faire des*

---

* Question de Amor. Prologo. † Scaliger.

livres, il faloit être ou bien fou ou bien sage, que pour lui, comme il ne se croïoit pas assez sage pour faire un bon livre, ni assez fou pour en faire un méchant, il avoit pris le parti de ne point écrire.

Pour lui, the Docteur of the Sorbonne: *pour moi*, — every reader will, in the exercise of that sovereign judgment whereof every reader is possessed, determine for himself whether in composing the present work I am to be deemed *bien sage* or *bien fou*. I know what Mr. Dulman thinks upon this point, and that Mr. Slapdash agrees with him. To the former I shall say nothing; but to the latter, and to Slenderwit, Midge, Wasp, Dandeprat, Brisk and Blueman, I shall let Cordara the Jesuit speak for me.

O quanti, o quanti sono, a cui dispiace
Vedere un uom contento; sol per questo
Lo pungono con stile acre e mordace,
Per questi versi miei chi sa che presto
Qualche zanzara contro me non s'armi,
E non prenda di qui qualche pretesto.
Io certo me l' aspetto, che oltraggiarmi
Talun pretenderà sol perchè pare,
Che di lieti pensier' sappia occuparmi.
Ma canti pur, lo lascerò cantare
E per mostrargli quanto me ne prendo,
Tornerò, se bisogna, a verseggiare.

Leaving the aforesaid *litterateurs* to construe and apply this, I shall proceed in due course to examine and decide whether Dr. Daniel Dove ought or ought not to have been an author, — being the first of two questions, propounded in the present chapter, as arising out of the last.

CHAPTER CCXXVI.

THE AUTHOR DIGRESSES A LITTLE, AND TAKES UP A STITCH WHICH WAS DROPPED IN THE EARLIER PART OF THIS OPUS. NOTICES CONCERNING LITERARY AND DRAMATIC HISTORY, BUT PERTINENT TO THIS PART OF OUR SUBJECT.

Jam paululum digressus a spectantibus,
Doctis loquar, qui non adeo spectare quam
Audire gestiunt, logosque ponderant,
Examinant, dijudicantque pro suo
Candore vel livore; non latum tamen
Culmum (quod aiunt) dum loquar sapientibus
Loco movebor. MACROPEDIUS.

THE boy and his schoolmaster were not mistaken in thinking that some of Textor's Moralities would have delighted the people of Ingleton as much as any of Rowland Dixon's stock pieces. Such dramas have been popular wherever they have been presented in the vernacular tongue. The progress from them to the regular drama was slow, perhaps not so much on account of the then rude state of most modern languages, as because of the yet ruder taste of the people. I know not whether it has been observed in literary history how much more rapid it was in schools, where the Latin language was used, and consequently fit audience was found, though few.

George von Langeveldt, or Macropedius, as he called himself, according to the fashion of learned men in that age, was contemporary with Textor, and like him one of the pioneers of literature, but he was a person of more learning and greater intellectual powers. He was born about the year 1475, of a good family in the little town or village of Gemert, at no great distance from Bois-le-Duc. As soon as his juvenile studies were compleated he entered among the *Fratres Vitæ Communis*; they employed him in education, first as Rector in their college at Bois-le-duc, then at Liege, and afterwards at Utrecht, from whence in 1552, being infirm and grievously afflicted with gout, he returned to Bois-le-duc, there to pass the remainder of his days, as one whose work was done. Old and enfeebled, however, as he was, he lived till the year 1558, and then died not of old age but of a pestilential fever.

There is an engraved portrait of him in the hideous hood and habit of his order; the countenance is that of a good-natured, intelligent, merry old man: underneath are these verses by Sanderus the topographer.

Tu Seneca, et nostri potes esse Terentius ævi,
Seu struis ad faciles viva theatra pedes,
Seu ploras tragicas, Macropedi, carmine clades,
Materiam sanctis adsimilante modis.
Desine jam Latios mirari Roma cothurnos;
Nescio quid majus Belgica scena dabit.

Macropedius published Rudiments both of the Greek and Latin languages; he had studied the Hebrew and Chaldee; had some skill in mathematics, and amused his leisure in making mathematical instruments, a branch of art in which he is said to have been an excellent workman. Most of the men who distinguished themselves as scholars in that part of the Low Countries, toward the latter part of the 16th century, had been his pupils: for he was not more remarkable for his own acquirements than for the earnest delight which he took in instructing others. There is some reason for thinking that he was a severe disciplinarian, perhaps a cruel one. Herein he differed widely from Textor, who took every opportunity for expressing his abhorrence of magisterial cruelty. In one of these Dialogues with which Guy and young Daniel were so well acquainted, two schoolmasters after death are brought before Rhadamanthus for judgment; one for his inhumanity is sent to be tormented in Tartarus, part of his punishment, in addition to those more peculiarly belonging to the region, being that

Verbera quæ pueris intulit, ipse ferat:

the other who indulged his boys and never maltreated them is ordered to Elysium, the Judge saying to him

— tua te in pueros clementia salvum
Reddit, et æternis persimilem superis.

That Textor's description of the cruelty exercised by the pedagogues of his age was not overcharged, Macropedius himself might be quoted to prove, even when he is vindicating and recommending such discipline as Dr. Parr would have done. I wish Parr had heard an expression which fell from the honest lips of Isaac Reid, when a school, noted at that time for its consumption of birch, was the subject of conversation;—the words would have burned themselves in. I must not commit them to the press; but this I may say, that the Recording Angel entered them on the creditor side of that kind-hearted old man's account.

Macropedius, like Textor, composed dramatic pieces for his pupils to represent. The latter, as has been shown in a former chapter, though he did not exactly take the Moralities for his model, produced pieces of the same kind, and adapted his conceptions to the popular facts, while he clothed them in the language of the classics. His aim at improvement proceeded no farther, and he never attempted to construct a dramatic fable. That advance was made by Macropedius, who in one of his dedicatory epistles laments that among the many learned men who were then flourishing, no Menander, no Terence was to be found; their species of writing, he says, had been almost extinct since the time of Terence himself, or at least of Lucilius. He regretted this because comedy might be rendered useful to persons of all ages, *quid enim plus pueris ad eruditionem, plus adolescentibus ad honesta studia, plus provectioribus, immò omnibus in commune ad virtutem conducat?*

Reuchlin, or Capnio, (as he who was one of the lights of his generation was misnamed and misnamed himself,) who had with his other great and eminent merits that of restoring or rather introducing into Germany the study of Hebrew, revived the lost art of comedy. If any one had preceded him in this revival, Macropedius was ignorant of it; and by the example and advice of this great man he was induced to follow him, not only as a student of Hebrew, but as a comic writer. Hrosvitha indeed, a nun of Gandersheim in Saxony, who lived in the tenth century and in the reign of Otho II., composed six Latin comedies *in emulation* of Terence, but in praise of virginity; and these with other of her poems were printed at Nuremburg in the year 1501. The book I have never seen, nor had De Bure, nor had he been able (such is its rarity) to procure any account of it farther than enabled him to give its title. The name of Conrad Celtes, the first German upon whom the degree of Poet Laureate was conferred, appears in the title, as if he had discovered the manuscript; *Conrado Celte inventore.* De Bure says the volume was *attribué au même Conradus Celtes.* It is rash for any one to form an opinion of a book which he has never examined, unless he is well acquainted with the character and capacity of its author; nevertheless I may venture to observe that nothing can be less in unison with the life and conversation of this Latin poet, as far as these may be judged of by his acknowledged poems, than the subjects of the pieces published under Hrosvitha's name; and no reason can be imagined why, if he had written them himself, he should have palmed them upon the public as her composition.

It is remarkable that Macropedius, when he spoke of Reuchlin's comedies, should not have alluded to these, for that he must have seen them there can be little or no doubt. One of Reuchlin's is said to have been imitated from *la Farce de Pathelin*, which, under the title of the Village Lawyer, has succeeded on our own stage, and which was so deservedly popular that the French have drawn from it more than one proverbial saying. The French Editor who affirms this says that Pathelin was printed in 1474, four years before the representation of Reuchlin's comedy; but the story is one of those good travellers which are found in all countries, and Reuchlin may have dramatised it without any reference to the French drama, the existence of which may very probably have been unknown to him, as well as to Macropedius. Both his pieces are satirical. His disciple began with a scriptural drama upon the Prodigal Son; Asotus is its title. It must have been written early in the century, for about 1520 he laid it aside as a juvenile performance, and faulty as much because of the then comparatively rude state of learning, as of his own inexperience.

Scripsi olim adolescens, trimetris versibus,
Et tetrametris, eâ phrasi et facundiâ
Quæ tum per adolescentiam et mala tempora
Licebat, evangelicum Asotum aut Prodigum
Omnis quidem mei laboris initium.

After it had lain among his papers for thirty years, he brought it to light, and published it. In the prologue he intreats the spectators not to be offended that he had put his sickle into the field of the Gospel, and exhorts them, while they are amused with the comic parts of the dialogue, still to bear in mind the meaning of the parable.

Sed orat author carminis vos res duas :
Ne ægre feratis, quod levem falcem tulit
Sementem in evangelicam, eamque quod audeat
Tractare majestatem Iambo et Tribracho ;
Neve insuper nimis hæreatis ludicris
Ludisque comicis, sed animum advortite
Hic abdito mysterio, quod eruam.

After these lines he proceeds succinctly to expound the parable.

Although the grossest representations were not merely tolerated at that time in the Miracle Plays, and Mysteries, but performed with the sanction and with the assistance of the clergy, it appears that objections were raised against the sacred dramas of this author. They were composed for a learned audience, — which is indeed the reason why the Latin, or as it may more properly be called the Collegiate drama, appeared at first in a regular and respectable form, and received little or no subsequent improvement. The only excuse which could be offered for the popular exhibitions of this kind, was that they were, if not necessary, yet greatly useful, by exciting and keeping up the lively faith of an ignorant, but all-believing people. That apology failed where no such use was needed. But Macropedius easily vindicated himself from charges which in truth were not relevant to his case; for he perceived what scriptural subjects might without impropriety be represented as he treated them, and he carefully distinguished them from those upon which no fiction could be engrafted without apparent profanation. In the prologue to his Lazarus he makes this distinction between the Lazarus of the parable, and the Lazarus of the Gospel History: the former might be thus treated for edification, the latter was too sacred a theme,

— quod is sine
Filii Dei persona agi non possiet.

Upon this distinction he defends himself, and carefully declares what were the bounds which ought not to be overpassed.

Fortassis objectabit illi quispiam
Quod audeat sacerrimam rem, et serio
Nostræ saluti a Christo Jesu proditam
Tractare comicè, et facere rem ludicram.
Fatetur ingenuè, quod eadem ratio se
Sæpenumero deterruit, ne quid suum,
Vel ab aliis quantumlibet scriptum, piè
Doctève, quod personam haberet Christi Jesu
Agentis, histrionibus seu ludiis
Populo exhibendum ex pulpito committeret.

From this passage I am induced to suspect that the Jesus Scholasticus, and the tragedy De Passione Christi, which are named in the list of his works, have been erroneously ascribed to him. No date of time or place is affixed to either by the biographers. After his judicious declaration concerning such subjects it cannot be thought he would have written these tragedies ; nor that if he had written them before he seriously considered the question of their propriety, he would afterwards have allowed them to appear. It is more probable that they were published without an author's name, and ascribed to him, because of his reputation. No inference can be drawn from their not appearing in the two volumes of his plays; because that collection is entitled *Omnes Georgii Macropedii Fabulæ* Comicæ, and though it contains pieces which are deeply serious, that title would certainly preclude the insertion of a tragedy. But a piece upon the story of Susanna which the biographers have also ascribed to him is not in the collection * ; the book was printed after his retirement to Bois-le-duc, when from his age and infirmities he was most unlikely to have composed it, and therefore I conclude that, like the tragedies, it is not his work.

Macropedius was careful to guard against anything which might give offence, and therefore he apologises for speaking of the *fable* of his Nama :

Mirabitur fortasse vestrûm quispiam,
Quod fabulam rem sacrosanctam dixerim.
Verum sibi is persuasum habebit, omne quod
Tragico artificio comicovè scribitur,
Dici poetis fabulam ; quod utique non
Tam historia veri texitur, quod proprium est,
Quam imago veri fingitur, quod artis est.
Nam comicus non propria personis solet,
Sed apta tribuere atque verisimilia, ut
Quæ pro loco vel tempore potuere agi
Vel dicier.

For a very different reason he withdrew from one of these dramas certain passages, by the advice of his friends ; he says, *qui rem seriam fabulosius tractandum dissuaserunt.* These it seems related to the first chapter of St. Luke, but contained circumstances derived not from that Gospel, but from the legends engrafted upon it, and therefore he rejects them as *citra scripturæ authoritatem.*

From the scrupulousness with which Macropedius in this instance distinguishes between the facts of the Gospel history and the fables of man's invention, it may be suspected that he was not averse at heart to those hopes of a reformation in the church which were at that time entertained. This is still further indicated in the drama called Hecastus (Ἕκαστος — Every one,) in which he represents a sinner as saved by faith in Christ and repentance. He found it necessary to protest against the suspicion which he had thus incurred, and to declare that he held works of repentance and the sacraments appointed by the Church necessary for salvation.†

Hecastus is a rich man, given over to the pomps and vanities of the world, and Epicuria his wife is of the same disposition. They have prepared a great feast, when Nomodidascalus arrives with a summons for him to appear before the Great King for judgement. Hecastus calls upon his son Philomathes, who is learned in the law, for counsel; the son is horror-stricken, and confesses his ignorance of the language in which the summons is written :

Horror, pater, me invadit, anxietas quoque
Non mediocris ; nam elementa quanquam barbara
Miram Dei potentiam præ se ferunt,
Humaniores literas scio ; barbaras
Neque legere, neque intelligere, pater, queo.

The father is incensed that a son who had been bred to the law for the purpose of

* This must be a comic drama. — *R. S.*

† Hecastus was represented by the schoolboys in 1538, *non sine magno spectantium plausu.* It was printed in the ensuing year ; and upon reprinting it, in 1550, the author offers his apology. He says, *Fuere multi quibus (fabulæ scopo recte considerato) per omnia placuit ; fuere quibus in ea nonnulla offenderunt ; fuere quoque, quibus omnino displicuit, ob hoc præcipue, quod erroribus quibusdam nostri temporis connivere et suffragari videretur. Inprimis illi, quod citra pœnitentiæ opera (satisfactionem dicimus) et ecclesiæ sacramenta, per solam in Christum fidem et cordis contritionem, condonationem criminum docere, vel asserere videretur : et quod quisque certo se fore servendum credere teneretur : Id quod nequaquam nec mente concepi, nec unquam docere volui, licet quibusdam fortassis fabulæ scopum non exactè considerantibus, primâ (quod aiunt) fronte sic videri potuerit. Si enim rei scopum, quem in argumento indicabam, penitus observassent, secus fortassis judicaturi fuissent.* — *R. S.*

pleading his cause at any time should fail him thus; but Nomodidascalus vindicates the young man, and reads a severe lecture to Hecastus, in which Hebrew words of aweful admonishment are introduced and interpreted. The guests arrive; he tells them what has happened, and entreats them to accompany him, and assist him when he appears before the Judge; they plead other engagements, and excuse themselves. He has no better success with his kinsmen; though they promise to look after his affairs, and say that they will make a point of attending him with due honour as far as the gate. He then calls upon his two sons to go with him unto the unknown country whereto he has been summoned. The elder is willing to fight for his father, but not to enter upon such a journey; the lawyer does not understand the practice of those courts, and can be of no use to him there; but he advises his father to take his servants with him, and plenty of money.

Madam Epicuria, who is not the most affectionate of wives, refuses to accompany him upon this unpleasant expedient, and moreover requests that her maids may be left with her; let him take his man servants with him, and gold and silver in abundance. The servants bring out his wealth. Plutus, *ex arcâ loquens*, is one of the Dramatis Personæ, and the said Plutus, when brought upon the stage in a chest, or strong box, complains that he is shaken to pieces by being thus moved. Hecastus tells him he must go with him to the other world and help him there, which Plutus flatly refuses. If he will not go of his own accord he shall be carried whether he will or no, Hecastus says. Plutus stands stiffly to his refusal.

Non transferent; prius quidem
Artus et ilia ruperint, quam transferant.
In morte nemini opitulor usquam gentium,
Quin magis ad alienum dominum transeo.

Hecastus on his part is equally firm, and orders his men to fetch some strong poles, and carry off the chest, Plutus and all. Having sent them forward, he takes leave of his family, and Epicuria protests that she remains like a widowed dove, and his neighbours promise to accompany him as far as the gate.

Death comes behind him now:

Horrenda imago, larva abominabilis,
Figura tam execranda, ut atrum dæmona
*Putetis obvium.**

This dreadful personage is with much difficulty entreated to allow him the respite of one short hour, after which Death declares he will return, and take him, will he or nill he before the Judge, and then to the infernal regions. During this interval who should come up but an old and long-neglected friend of Hecastus, Virtue by name; a poor emaciated person, in mean attire, in no condition to appear with him before the Judge, and altogether unfit to plead his desperate cause. She promises, however, to send him a Priest to his assistance, and says moreover that she will speak to her sister Faith, and endeavour to persuade her to visit him.

Meantime the learned son predicts from certain appearances the approaching end of his father.

Actum Philocrate, de patris salute, uti
Plane recenti ex lotio prejudico,
Nam cerulea si tendit ad nigredinem
Urina mortem proximam denunciat.

He has been called on, he says, too late,

Sero meam medentis admisit manum.

The brothers begin to dispute about their inheritance, and declare law against each other; but they suspend the dispute when Hieronymus the Priest arrives, that they may look after him lest he should prevail

* The reader should by all means consult Mr. Sharpe's "Dissertation on the Pageants or Dramatic Mysteries, anciently performed in Coventry." "The Devil," he observes, "was a very favourite and prominent character in our Religious Mysteries, wherein he was introduced as often as was practicable, and considerable pains taken to furnish him with appropriate habiliments, &c." p. 31. also pp. 57-60. There are several plates of "*Hell-Mought and Sir Sathanas*," which will not escape the examination of the curious. The bloody Herod was a character almost as famous as "*Sir Sathanas*;" hence the expression "*to out-herod Herod*," *e.g.* in Hamlet, Act iii. Sc. ii. With reference to the same personage Charmian says to the Soothsayer in Antony and Cleopatra, "Let me have a child at fifty, to whom *Herod of Jewry* may do homage," Act i. Sc. ii.; and Mrs. Page asks in the Merry Wives of Windsor, "What *Herod of Jewry* is this?" Act ii. Sc. i.

upon the dying to dispose of too large a part of his property in charitable purposes.

Id cautum oportet maximè. Novimus enim
Quàm tum sibi, tum cæteris quibus favent,
Legata larga extorqueat id hominum genus,
Cum morte ditem terminandum viderint.

Virtue arrives at this time with his sister Faith; they follow Hieronymus into the chamber into which Hecastus has been borne; and as they go in up comes Satan to the door, and takes his seat there to draw up a bill of indictment against the dying man: he must do it carefully, he says, that there may be no flaw in it.

Causam meam scripturus absolutius
Adversum Hecastum, hic paululum desedero;
Ne si quid insit falsitatis maximis
Facinoribus, res tota veniat in gravem
Fœdamque controversiam. Abstinete vos,
Quotquot theatro adestis, à petulantiâ,
Nisi si velitis et hos cachinnos scribier.

Then he begins to draw up the indictment, speaking as he writes,

Primum omnium superbus est et arrogans,—
Superbus est et arrogans,—et arrogans;—
Tum in ædibus,—tum in ædibus; tum in vestibus,—
Tum in vestibus. Jam reliqua tacitus scripsero,
Loquaculi ne exaudiant et deferant.

While Satan is thus employed at the door, the priest Hieronymus within is questioning the patient concerning his religion. Hecastus possesses a very sound and firm historical belief. But this the Priest tells him is not enough, for the Devils themselves believe and tremble, and he will not admit Faith into the chamber till Hecastus be better instructed in the true nature of a saving belief.

Credis quod omnia quæ patravit Filius
Dei unicus, tibi redimendo gesserit?
Tibi natus est? tibi vixerit? tibi mortuus
Sit? tibi sepultus? et tibi surrexerit?
Mortemque tibi devicerit?

Hecastus confesses in reply that he is a most miserable sinner, unworthy of forgiveness; and having brought him into this state of penitence the Priest calls Fides in.

Then says Fides,

Hæc tria quidem, cognitio nempe criminis,
Horror gehennæ, et pœnitentia, læta sunt
Veræ salutis omnium primordia,
Jam perge, ut in Deum excites fiduciam.

When this trust has been given him, and he has declared his full belief, he confesses that still he is in fear,

— est quod adhuc parit mihi scrupulum;
Mors horrida, atque aspectus atri Dæmonis,
Queis terribilius (inquiunt) nil hominibus,
Post paululum quos adfuturos arbitros.

But Hieronymus assures him that Fides and Virtus will defend him from all danger, and under their protection he leaves him.

The scene is now again at the door: Mors arrives. Satan abuses her for having made him wait so long, and the *improba bestia* in return reproaches him for his ingratitude and imprudence. However they make up their quarrel. Satan goes into the house expecting to have a long controversy with his intended victim, and Mors amuses herself in the mean time with sharpening her dart. Satan, however, finds that his controversy is not to be with Hecastus himself, but with his two advocates Fides and Virtus; and they plead their cause so provokingly that the old Lawyer tears his bill, and sculks into a corner to see how Mors will come off.

Now comes his son the Doctor, and prognosticates speedy dissolution *ex pulsu et atro lotio.* And having more professional pride than filial feeling, he would fain persuade the Acolyte, who is about to assist in administering extreme unction, that he has chosen a thankless calling, and would do wisely if he forsook it for more gainful studies. The youth makes a good defence for his choice, and remains master in the argument; for the Doctor getting sight of Death brandishing the sharpened dart takes fright and runs off. Having put the Doctor to flight, Death enters the sick chamber, and finding Fides there calls in Satan as an ally: their joint force avails nothing against Virtus, Fides, and Hieronymus; and these dismiss the departing Spirit under a convoy of Angels to Abraham's bosom.

Three supplementary scenes conclude the two dramas; in the two first the widow and the sons and kinsmen lament the dead, and declare their intention of putting themselves all in mourning, and giving a funeral worthy of his rank. But Hieronymus reproves them for the excess of their grief, and for the manner by which they intended to show their respect for the dead. The elder son is convinced by his discourse, and replies

Recte mones vir omnium piissime,
Linquamus omnem hunc apparatum splendidum,
Linquamus hæcce cuncta in usum pauperum,
Linquamus omnem luctum inanem et lachrymas ;
Moresque nostros corrigamus pristinos.
Si multo amœniora vitæ munia,
Post hanc calamitatem, morantur in fide
Spe ut charitate mortuos, quid residuum est
Nisi et hunc diem cum patre agamus mortuo
Lætissimum ? non in cibis et poculis
Gravioribus, natura quam poposcerit ;
Nec tympanis et organis, sed maximas
Deo exhibendo gratias. Viro pio
Congaudeamus intimis affectibus ;
Et absque pompâ inutili exequias pias
Patri paremus mortuo.

The Steward then concludes the drama by dismissing the audience in these lines :

Vos qui advolastis impigri ad
Nostra hæc theatra, tum viri, tum fœminæ,
Adite nunc vestras domos sine remorâ.
Nam Hecastus hic quem Morte cæsum exhibuimus,
Non ante tertium diem tumulandus est,
Valete cuncti, et, si placuimus, plaudite.

We have in our own language a dramatic piece upon the same subject, and of the same age. It was published early in Henry the Eighth's reign, and is well known to English philologists by the name of Every Man. The title page says, "Here begynneth a treatyse how the hye Fader of Heven sendeth Dethe to somon every creature to come and gyve a counte of theyr lyves in this worlde, and is in maner of a moralle Playe."

The subject is briefly stated in a prologue by a person in the character of a Messenger, who exhorts the spectators to hear with reverence.

This mater is wonders precyous ;
But the extent of it is more gracyous,
And swete to bere awaye.
The story sayth, Man, in the begynnynge
Loke well and take good heed to the endynge,
Be you never so gay.

God (the Son) speaketh at the opening of the piece, and saying that the more He forbears the worse the people be from year to year, declares his intention to have a reckoning in all haste of every man's person, and do justice on every man living.

Where art thou, Deth, thou mighty messengere ?

DETHE.

Almighty God, I am here at your wyll
Your commaundement to fulfyll.

GOD.

Go thou to Every-man
And shewe hym in my name,
A pylgrymage he must on hym take,
Whiche he in no wyse may escape :
And that he brynge with him a sure rekenynge,
Without delay or ony taryenge.

DETHE.

Lorde, I wyll in the world go renne over all
And cruelly out serche bothe grete and small.

The first person whom Death meets is Every-man himself, and he summons him in God's name to take forthwith a long journey, and bring with him his book of accounts. Every-man offers a thousand pounds to be spared, and says that if he may but have twelve years allowed him, he will make his accounts so clear that he shall have no need to fear the reckoning. Not even till to-morrow is granted him. He then asks if he may not have some of his acquaintances to accompany him on the way, and is told yes, if he can get them. The first to whom he applies is his old boon-companion Fellowship, who promises to go with him anywhere, — till he hears what the journey is on which Every-man is summoned : he then declares that he would eat, drink and drab with him, or lend him a hand to kill anybody, but upon such a business as this he will not stir a foot ; and with that bidding him God speed, he departs as fast as he can.

Alack, exclaims Every-man, when thus deserted,

Felawship herebefore with me wolde mery make,
And now lytell sorowe for me dooth he take.
Now wheder for socoure shall I flee
Syth that Felawship hath forsaken me ?
To my kynnesmen I wyll truely,
Prayenge them to helpe me in my necessyte.
I byleve that they wyll do so ;
For kynde wyll crepe where it may not go.

But one and all make their excuses ; they have reckonings of their own which are not ready, and they cannot and will not go with him. Thus again disappointed he breaks out in more lamentations ; and then catches at another fallacious hope.

Yet in my mynde a thynge there is ;
All my lyfe I have loved Ryches ;

If that my good now helpe me myght
He wolde make me herte full lyght.
I wyll speke to hym in this distresse,
Where art thou, my Goodes, and Ryches?

GOODES.

Who calleth me? Every-man? What hast thou haste?
I lye here in corners, trussed and pyled so hye,
And in chestes I am locked so fast,
Also sacked in bagges, thou mayst se with thyn eye
I cannot styrre; in packes low I lye.
What wolde ye have? lightly me saye.—
Syr, an ye in the worlde have sorowe or adversyte
That can I helpe you to remedy shortly.

EVERY-MAN.

In this world it is not, I tell thee so,
I am sent for an other way to go,
To gyve a strayte counte generall
Before the hyest Jupiter of all:
And all my life I have had joye and pleasure in the,
Therefore, I pray the, go with me:
For paraventure, thou mayst before God Almighty
My rekenynge helpe to clene and puryfye;
For it is said ever amonge
That money maketh all ryght that is wrong.

GOODES.

Nay, Every-man, I synge an other songe;
I folowe no man in such vyages.
For an I wente with the,
Thou sholdes fare moche the worse for me.

Goodes then exults in having beguiled him, laughs at his situation, and leaves him. Of whom shall he take counsel? He bethinks him of Good Dedes.

But alas she is so weke
That she can nother go nor speke.
Yet wyll I venter on her now
My Good Dedes, where be you?

GOOD DEDES.

Here I lye colde on the grounde,
Thy sinnes hath me sore bounde
That I cannot stere.

EVERY-MAN.

I pray you that ye wyll go with me.

GOOD DEDES.

I wolde full fayne, but I can not stand veryly.

EVERY-MAN.

Why, is there any thynge on you fall?

GOOD DEDES.

Ye, Sir; I may thanke you of all.
If ye had parfytely sheved me,
Your boke of counte full redy had be.
Loke, the bokes of your workes and dedes eke,
A! se how they lye under the fete,
To your soules hevynes.

EVERY-MAN.

Our Lorde Jesus helpe me,
For one letter here I cannot se!

GOOD DEDES.

There is a blynde rekenynge in tyme of dystres!

EVERY-MAN.

Good-Dedes, I pray you, helpe me in this nede,
Or elles I am for ever dampned in dede.

Good Dedes calls in Knowledge to help him to make his reckoning; and Knowledge takes him lovingly to that holy man Confession; and Confession gives him a precious jewel called Penance, in the form of a scourge.

When with the scourge of Penance man doth hym bynde,
The oyl of forgyvenes than shall he fynde,—
Now may you make your rekenynge sure.

EVERY-MAN.

In the name of the holy Trynyte,
My body sore punyshed shall be.
Take this, Body, for the synne of the flesshe!
Also thou delytest to go gay and fresshe,
And in the way of dampnacyon thou dyd me brynge,
Therefore suffre now strokes of punysshynge.
Now of penaunce I wyll wede the water clere
To save me from Purgatory, that sharpe fyre.

GOOD DEDES.

I thanke God, now I can walke and go;
And am delyvered of my sykenesse and wo,
Therfore with Every-man I wyll go and not spare;
His good workes I wyll helpe hym to declare.

KNOWLEGE.

Now Every-man, be mery and glad,
Your Good Dedes cometh now, ye may not be sad.
Now is your Good Dedes hole and sounde,
Goynge upryght upon the grounde.

EVERY-MAN.

My herte is lyght, and shall be evermore,
Nor wyll I smyte faster than I dyde before.

Knowledge then makes him put on the garment of sorrow called contrition, and makes him call for his friends Discretion, Strength, and Beauty, to help him on his pilgrimage, and his Five Wits to counsel him. They come at his call, and promise faithfully to help him.

STRENGTH.

I Strength wyll by you stande in dystres,
Though thou wolde in batayle fyght on the grownde.

FYVE-WYTTES.

And thought it were thrugh the world rounde,
We wyll not depart for swete ne soure.

BEAUTE.

No more wyll I unto dethes howre,
Watsoever therof befall.

He makes his testament, and gives half his goods in charity. Discretion and Knowledge send him to receive the holy sacrament and extreme unction, and Five-Wits expatiates upon the authority of the Priesthood. To the Priest he says,

God hath—more power given
Than to ony Aungell that is in Heven,
With five wordes he may consecrate
Goddes body in flesshe and blode to make,
And handeleth his maker bytwene his handes.
The preest byndeth and unbyndeth all bandes
Both in erthe and in heven.—
No remedy we fynde under God
But all-onely preesthode.

— God gave Preest that dygnyte,
And setteth them in his stede among us to be:
Thus they be above Aungelles in degree.

Having received his viaticum Every-man sets out upon this mortal journey: his comrades renew their protestations of remaining with him; till when he grows faint on the way, and his limbs fail, — they fail him also.

EVERY-MAN.
— into this cave must I crepe,
And tourne to erth, and there to slepe.

What, says Beauty; into this Grave?

— adewe by saynt Johan,
I take my tappe in my lappe and am gone.

Strength in like manner forsakes him; and Discretion says that "when Strength goeth before, he follows after ever more." And Fyve-Wyttes, whom he took for his best friend, bid him, "farewell and then an end."

EVERY-MAN.
O Jesu, helpe! all hath forsaken me!

GOOD DEDES.
Nay, Every-man, I wyll byde with the,
I wyll not forsake the in dede;
Thou shalt fynde me a good frende at nede.

Knowledge also abides him till the last; the song of the Angel who receives his spirit is heard, and a Doctour concludes the piece with an application to the audience.

This morall men may have in mynde,
— forsake Pryde for he deceyveth you in the ende,
And remembre Beaute, Fyve-Wyttes, Strength and Dyscrecyon,
They all at the last do Every-man forsake,
Save his Good Dedes, these doth he take:
But be ware, an they be small,
Before God he hath no helpe at all! *

CHAPTER CCXXVII.

SYSTEM OF PROGRESSION MARRED ONLY BY MAN'S INTERFERENCE. THE DOCTOR SPEAKS SERIOUSLY AND HUMANELY, AND QUOTES JUVENAL.

MONTENEGRO. How now, are thy arrows feathered?
VELASCO. Well enough for roving.
MONTENEGRO. Shoot home then. SHIRLEY.

IT is only when Man interferes, that the system of progression, which the All Father has established throughout the living and sentient world, is interrupted, and Man, our Philosopher would sorrowfully observe, has interrupted it, not only for himself, but for such of the inferior creatures as are under his control. He has degraded the instincts of some, and in others, perhaps it may not be too much to say that he has corrupted that moral sense of which even the brute creation partakes in its degree; and has inoculated them with his own vices. Thus the decoy duck is made a traitor to her own species, and so are all those smaller birds which the bird-catcher trains to assist him in ensnaring others. The Rat, who is one of the bravest of created things, is in like manner rendered a villain.

Upon hunting and hawking the Doctor laid little stress, because both dogs and falcons in their natural state would have hunted and fowled on their own account. These sports, according to his "poor way of thinking," tended to deprave not so much the animals, as the human beings employed in them; for when they ceased to be necessary for the support or protection of man, they became culpable. But to train dogs for war, and flesh them upon living prisoners, as the Spaniards did, (and as, long since the decease of my venerable friend, Buonaparte's officers did in St. Domingo,) — to make horses, gentle and harmless as well as noble in their disposition as they are, take a part in our senseless political contentions, charge a body of men, and trample over their broken limbs and palpitating bodies, — to convert the Elephant, whom Pope, he said, had wronged by only calling him half-reasoning, the mild, the thoughtful, the magnanimous Elephant, into a wilful, and deliberate, and cruel executioner,—these, he thought, were acts of high treason against humanity, and of impiety against universal nature. Grievous indeed it is, he said, to know that the whole creation groaneth and travaileth in pain; but more grievous to consider that man, who by his original sin was the guilty cause of their general depravation, should continue by repeated sins to aggravate it; — to which he added that the lines of the Roman Satirist, though not exactly true, were yet humiliating and instructive.

* The reader who may wish to see EVERY-MAN complete will find it in the first volume of Thomas Hawkins' "Origin of the English Drama," &c.

Mundi
Principio indulsit communis conditor illis
Tantum animas, nobis animum quoque, mutuus ut nos
Adfectus petere auxilium et præstare juberet,
Dispersos trahere in populum, migrare vetusto
De nemore, et proavis habitatas linquere silvas;
Ædificare domos, Laribus conjungere nostris
Tectum aliud, tutos vicino limine somnos
Ut conlata daret fiducia; protegere armis
Labsum, aut ingenti nutantem vulnere civem,
Communi dare signa tubâ, defendier isdem
Turribus, atque unâ portarum clave teneri.
Sed jam serpentum major concordia; parcit
Cognatis maculis similis fera; quando leoni
Fortior eripuit vitam leo? quo nemore unquam
Expiravit aper majoris dentibus apri?
Indica tigris agit rabidâ cum tigride pacem
Perpetuam: sævis inter se convenit ursis.
Ast homini ferrum lethale incude nefandâ
Produxisse parum est; quum rastra et sarcula tantum
Adsueti coquere, et marris ac vomere lassi
Nescierint primi gladios excudere fabri.
Adspicimus populos, quorum non sufficit iræ
Occidisse aliquem: sed pectora, brachia, vultum
Crediderint genus esse cibi. Quid diceret ergo
Vel quo non fugerit, si nunc hæc monstra videret
Pythagoras: cunctis animalibus abstinuit qui
*Tanquam homine, et ventri indulsit non omne legumen.**

CHAPTER CCXXVIII.

RATS. PLAN OF THE LAUREATE SOUTHEY FOR LESSENING THEIR NUMBER. THE DOCTOR'S HUMANITY IN REFUSING TO SELL POISON TO KILL VERMIN, AFTER THE EXAMPLE OF PETER HOPKINS HIS MASTER. POLITICAL RATS NOT ALLUDED TO. RECIPE FOR KILLING RATS.

I know that nothing can be so innocently writ, or carried, but may be made obnoxious to construction; marry, whilst I bear mine innocence about me, I fear it not.
BEN JONSON.

THE Laureate Southey proposed some years ago in one of his numerous and multifarious books, three methods for lessening the number of rats, one of which was to inoculate some of these creatures with the small-pox or any other infectious disease, and turn them loose. Experiments, he said, should first be made, lest the disease should assume in them so new a form, as to be capable of being returned to us with interest. If it succeeded, man has means in his hand which would thin the hyenas, wolves, jackals and all gregarious beasts of prey.

Considering the direction which the March of his Intellect has long been taking, it would surprise me greatly if the Laureate were now to recommend or justify any such plan. For setting aside the contemplated possibility of physical danger, there are moral and religious considerations which ought to deter us from making use of any such means, even for an allowable end.

Dr. Dove, like his master and benefactor Peter Hopkins before him, never would sell poison for destroying vermin. Hopkins came to that resolution in consequence of having been called as a witness upon a trial for poisoning at York. The arsenic had not been bought at his shop; but to prevent the possibility of being innocently instrumental to the commission of such a crime, he made it from that time a rule for himself, irrevocable as the laws of the Medes and Persians, that to no person whatever, on any account, would he supply ingredients which by carelessness or even by unavoidable accident might be so fatally applied.

To this rule his pupil and successor, our Doctor, religiously adhered. And when any one not acquainted with the rule of the shop, came there on such an errand, he used always, if he was on the spot, to recommend other methods, adapting his arguments to what he knew of the person's character, or judged of it from his physiognomy. To an ill-conditioned and ill-looking applicant he simply recommended certain ways of entrapping rats as more convenient, and more likely to prove efficacious: but to those of whom he entertained a more favourable opinion, he would

* The reader may call to mind the commencement of the Third Canto of Rokeby.

The hunting tribes of air and earth
Respect the brethren of their birth;
Nature, who loves the claim of kind,
Less cruel, chase to each assigned.
The falcon, poised on soaring wing,
Watches the wild-duck by the spring;
The slow-hound wakes the fox's lair;
The greyhound presses on the hare;
The eagle pounces on the lamb;
The wolf devours the fleecy dam:
Even tiger fell and sullen bear
Their likeness and their lineage spare.
Man, only, mars kind Nature's plan
And turns the fierce pursuit on man;
Plying war's desultory trade,
Incursion, flight, and ambuscade,
Since Nimrod, Cush's mighty son,
At first the bloody game begun.

hint at the cruelty of using poison, observing that though we exercised a clear natural right in destroying noxious creatures, we were not without sin if in so doing we inflicted upon them any suffering more than what must needs accompany a violent death.

Some good-natured reader who is pestered with rats in his house, his warehouses, or his barns, will perhaps, when he comes to this part of our book, wish to be informed in what manner our Zoophilist would have advised him to rid himself of these vermin.

There are two things to be considered here, first how to catch rats, and secondly, how to destroy them when caught. And the first of these questions is a delicate one, when a greater catch has recently been made than any that was ever heard of before, except in the famous adventure of the Pied Piper at Hammel. Jack Robinson had some reputation in his day for his professional talents in this line, but he was a bungler in comparison with Mr. Peel.

The second belongs to a science which Jeremy the thrice illustrious Bentham calls Phthisozoics, or the art of destruction applied to noxious animals, a science which the said Jeremy proposes should form part of the course of studies in his Chrestomathic school. There are no other animals in this country who do so much mischief now as the disciples of Jeremy himself.

But leaving this pestilent set, as one of the plagues with which Great Britain is afflicted for its sins; and intending no offence to any particular Bishop, Peer, Baronet, Peer-expectant, or public man whatever, and protesting against any application of what may here be said to any person who is, has been, or may be included under any of the forementioned denominations, I shall satisfy the good-natured reader's desires, and inform him in what manner our Philosopher and Zoophilist, (philanthropist is a word which would poorly express the extent of his benevolence,) advised those who consulted him as to the best manner of taking and destroying rats. Protesting therefore once more, as is needful in these ticklish times, that I am speaking not of the Pro-papist or Anti-Hanoverian rat, which is a new species of the Parliament rat, but of the old Norway or Hanoverian one, which in the last century effected the conquest of our island by extirpating the original British breed, I inform the humane reader that the Doctor recommended nothing more than the common rat-catcher's receipt, which is to lure them into a cage by oil of carraways, or of rhodium, and that when entrapped, the speediest and easiest death which can be inflicted is by sinking the cage in water.

Here Mr. Slenderwit, critic in ordinary to an established journal, wherein he is licensed to sink, burn and destroy any book in which his publisher has not a particular interest, turns down the corners of his mouth in contemptuous admiration, and calling to mind the anecdote of Grainger's invocation repeats in a tone of the softest self-complacence, "Now Muse, let's sing of Rats!" And Mr. Slapdash, who holds a similar appointment in a rival periodical, slaps his thigh in exultation upon finding so good an opportunity for a stroke at the anonymous author. But let the one simper in accompaniment to the other's snarl. I shall say out my say in disregard of both. Ay, Gentlemen,

> For if a Humble Bee should kill a Whale
> With the butt end of the Antarctic pole,
> 'Tis nothing to the mark at which we aim.

CHAPTER CCXXIX.

RATS LIKE LEARNED MEN LIABLE TO BE LED BY THE NOSE. THE ATTENDANT UPON THE STEPS OF MAN, AND A SORT OF INSEPARABLE ACCIDENT. SEIGNEUR DE HUMESESNE AND PANTAGRUEL.

> Where my pen hath offended,
> I pray you it may be amended
> By discrete consideration
> Of your wise reformation:
> I have not offended, I trust,
> If it be sadly discust.
>
> SKELTON.

MARVEL not, reader, that rats, though they are among the most sagacious of all animals, should be led by the nose. It has been the fate of many great men, many learned men, most weak ones, and some cunning ones.

When we regard the comparative sagacity of animals, it should always be remembered that every creature, from the lowest point of sentient existence upward, till we arrive at man, is endued with sagacity sufficient to provide for its own well-being, and for the continuance of its kind. They are gifted with greater endowments as they ascend in the scale of being, and those who lead a life of danger, and at the same time of enterprise, have their faculties improved by practice, take lessons from experience, and draw rational conclusions upon matters within their sphere of intellect and of action, more sagaciously than nine tenths of the human race can do.

Now no other animal is placed in circumstances which tend so continually to sharpen its wits — (were I writing to the learned only, I should perhaps say to acuate its faculties, or to develope its intellectual powers,) — as the rat, nor does any other appear to be of a more improvable nature. He is of a most intelligent family, being related to the Beaver. And in civilised countries he is not a wild creature, for he follows the progress of civilisation, and adapts his own habits of life to it, so as to avail himself of its benefits.

The "pampered Goose" who in Pope's Essay retorts upon man, and says that man was made for the use of Geese, must have been forgetful of plucking-time, as well as ignorant of the rites that are celebrated in all old-fashioned families on St. Michael's day. But the Rat might with more apparent reason support such an assertion: he is not mistaken in thinking than corn-stacks are as much for his use as for the farmer's; that barns and granaries are his winter magazines; that the Miller is his acting partner, the Cheesemonger his purveyor, and the Storekeeper his steward. He places himself in relation with man, not as his dependent like the dog, nor like the cat as his ally, nor like the sheep as his property, nor like the ox as his servant, nor like horse and ass as his slaves, nor like poultry who are to "come and be killed" when Mrs. Bond invites them; but as his enemy, a bold borderer, a Johnnie Armstrong or Rob Roy, who acknowledge no right of property in others, and live by spoil.

Wheresoever man goes, Rat follows, or accompanies him. Town or country are equally agreeable to him. He enters upon your house as a tenant-at-will, (his own, not yours,) works out for himself a covered way in your walls, ascends by it from one story to another, and leaving you the larger apartments, takes possession of the space between floor and ceiling, as an entresol for himself. There he has his parties, and his revels, and his gallopades, (merry ones they are,) when you would be asleep, if it were not for the spirit with which the youth and belles of Rat-land keep up the ball over your head. And you are more fortunate than most of your neighbours, if he does not prepare for himself a mausoleum behind your chimney-piece or under your hearth-stone*, retire into it when he is about to die, and very soon afford you full proof that though he may have lived like a hermit, his relics are not in the odour of sanctity. You have then the additional comfort of knowing that the spot so appropriated will thenceforth be used either as a common cemetery, or a family vault. In this respect, as in many others, nearer approaches are made to us by inferior creatures than are dreamt of in our philosophy.

The adventurous merchant ships a cargo for some distant port, Rat goes with it. Great Britain plants a colony in Botany Bay, Van Diemen's Land, or at the Swan River, Rat takes the opportunity for colonising also. Ships are sent out upon a voyage of discovery, Rat embarks as a volunteer. He doubled the Stormy Cape with Diaz, arrived at Malabar in the first European vessel with Gama, discovered the

* Southey alludes here to an incident which occurred in his own house. On taking up the hearth-stone in the dining-room at Keswick, it was found that the mice had made underneath it a Campo Santo, — a depository for their dead.

new world with Columbus and took possession of it at the same time, and circumnavigated the globe with Magellan, and with Drake, and with Cook.

After all, the Seigneur de Humesesne, whatever were the merits of that great case which he pleaded before Pantagruel at Paris, had reasonable grounds for his assertion when he said, *Monsieur et Messieurs, si l'iniquité des hommes estoit aussi facilement vuë en jugement categorique, comme on connoit mousches en lait, le monde quatre bœufs ne seroit tant mangé de Rats comme il est.*

The Doctor thought there was no creature to which you could trace back so many persons in civilised society by the indications which they afforded of habits acquired in their prænatal professional education. In what other vehicle, during its ascent, could the Archeus of the Sailor have acquired the innate courage, the constant presence of mind, and the inexhaustible resources, which characterise a true seaman? Through this link too, on his progress towards humanity, the good soldier has passed, who is brave, alert and vigilant, cautious never to give his enemy an opportunity of advantage, and watchful to lose the occasion that presents itself. From the Rat our Philosopher traced the engineer, the miner, the lawyer, the thief, and the thief-taker, — that is, generally speaking: some of these might have pre-existed in the same state as moles or ferrets; but those who excelled in their respective professions had most probably been trained as rats.

The judicious reader will do me the justice to observe that as I am only faithfully representing the opinions and fancies of my venerable friend, I add neither M. P., Dean, Bishop nor Peer to the list, nor any of those public men who are known to hanker after candle-ends and cheese-parings.

Indeed, it is a strange-disposed time;
But men may construe things after their fashion,
Clean from the purpose of the things themselves.*

It behoves me to refrain more especially upon this subject from anything which the malicious might interpret as scandal: for the word itself σκάνδαλον, the Greek grammarians tell us, and the great Anglo-Latin Lexicographist tells me, properly signifies that little piece of wood in a mouse-trap or pit-fall, which bears up the trap, and being touched lets it fall.

* Shakspeare.

CHAPTER CCXXX.

DISTINCTION BETWEEN YOUNG ANGELS AND YOUNG YAHOOS. FAIRIES, KILLCROPS, AND CHANGELINGS. LUTHER'S OPINIONS ON THE SUBJECT. HIS COLLOQUIA MENSALIA. DIFFERENCE BETWEEN THE OLD AND NEW EDITION.

I think it not impertinent sometimes to relate such accidents as may seem no better than mere trifles; for even by trifles are the qualities of great persons as well disclosed as by their great actions; because in matters of importance they commonly strain themselves to the observance of general commended rules; in lesser things they follow the current of their own natures.

Sir Walter Raleigh.

It may easily be inferred from some of the Doctor's peculiar opinions, or fancies, as he in unaffected humility would call them, that though a dear lover of children, his love of them was not indiscriminate. He made a great distinction between young angels and young yahoos, and thought it might very early be discovered whether the angel or the brute part predominated.

This is sometimes so strongly marked and so soon developed as to excite observation even in the most incurious; and hence the well-known superstition concerning Changelings.

In the heroic ages a divine origin is ascribed to such persons as were most remarkable for their endowments either of body or of mind; but this may far more probably be traced to adulation in the poets, than to contemporary belief at any time prevailing among the people; whereas the opposite superstition was really believed in the middle ages, and traces of it are still to be found.

It is remarkable that the Fairies, who in

the popular belief of this country are never represented as malignant upon any other occasion, act an evil part in the supposed case of Changelings. So it is with the Trolls also of our Scandinavian kinsmen, (though this race of beings is in worse repute:) the children whom they substitute for those whom they steal are always a plague to the nurse and to the parents. In Germany such children were held to be young Devils, but whether Mac-Incubi, Mac-Succubi, or O'Devils by the whole blood is not clearly to be collected from Martin Luther, who is the great authority upon this subject. He is explicit upon the fact that the Nix or Water Fiend increases the population by a mixed breed; but concerning the Killcrops, as his countrymen the Saxons call them, whom the Devil leaves in exchange, when he steals children for purposes best known to himself, Luther does not express any definite opinion, farther than that they are of a devilish nature: how fathered, how mothered, the reader is left to conjecture as he pleases.

"Eight years since," said Luther, at "Dessaw I did see and touch a changed child, which was twelve years of age; he had his eyes and all members like another child; he did nothing but feed, and would eat as much as two clowns or threshers were able to eat. When one touched it, then it cried out. When any evil happened in the house, then it laughed, and was joyful; but when all went well, then it cried, and was very sad. I told the Prince of Anhalt, that if I were Prince of that country, so would I venture *homicidium* thereon, and would throw it into the river Moldaw. I admonished the people dwelling in that place devoutly to pray to God to take away the Devil; the same was done accordingly, and the second year after the Changeling died.

"In Saxonia, near unto Halberstad, was a man that also had a Killcrop, who sucked the mother and five other women dry, and besides devoured very much. This man was advised that he should in his pilgrimage at Halberstad make a promise of the Killcrop to the Virgin Mary, and should cause him there to be rocked. This advice the man followed, and carried the Changeling thither in a basket. But going over a river, being upon the bridge, another Devil that was below in the river called, and said, Killcrop! Killcrop! Then the child in the basket, (which never before spake one word,) answered Ho, ho! The Devil in the water asked further, whither art thou going? The child in the basket said, 'I am going towards Halberstad to our Loving Mother, to be rocked.' The man being much affrighted thereat, threw the child with the basket over the bridge into the water. Whereupon the two Devils flew away together, and cried, ho, ho, ha! tumbling themselves one over another and so vanished.

"Such Changelings and Killcrops," said Luther, "*supponit Satan in locum verorum filiorum;* for the Devil hath this power, that he changeth children, and instead thereof layeth Devils in the cradles, which thrive not, only they feed and suck: but such Changelings live not above eighteen or nineteen years. It oftentimes falleth out that the children of women in child-bed are thus changed, and Devils laid in their stead, one of which more fouleth itself than ten other children do, so that the parents are much therewith disquieted; and the mothers in such sort are sucked out, that afterwards they are able to give suck no more. Such Changelings," said Luther, "are baptized, in regard that they cannot be known the first year, but are known only by sucking the mothers dry."

Mr. Cottle has made this the subject of a lively eclogue; but if that gentleman had happened upon the modern edition of Luther's *Colloquia Mensalia*, or Divine Discourses at his Table, instead of the old one, this pleasant poem would never have been written, the account of the Killcrops being one of the passages which the modern editor thought proper to omit. His omissions are reprehensible, because no notice is given that any such liberty has been taken; and indeed a paragraph in the introductory life which is prefixed to the edition might lead the reader to conclude that it is a faithful reprint; that paragraph saying there are many things which, for the credit of Luther, might as well have been left out, and proceeding to say, "but then it must be considered that such Discourses must not be brought to the test of our present refined age; that all what a man of Luther's name and character spoke, particularly at the latter part of his life, was thought by his friends worth the press, though himself meant it only for the recreation of the company; that he altered many opinions in his progress from darkness to light; and that it is with a work of this kind, as with the publishing of letters which were never intended for the press; the Author speaks his sentiments more freely, and you are able to form a true idea of his character, by looking, as it were, into his heart." Nevertheless there are considerable omissions, and as may be supposed of parts which are curious, and in a certain sense valuable because they are characteristic. But the reprint was the speculation of a low publisher, put forth in numbers, and intended only for a certain class of purchasers, who would read the book for edification. The work itself deserves farther notice, and that notice is the more properly and willingly bestowed upon it here, because the original edition is one of the few volumes belonging to my venerable friend which have passed into my possession, and his mark occurs frequently in its margin.

"I will make no long excursion here, but a short apology for one that deserved well of the *reformed* Religion. Many of our adversaries have aspersed *Luther*, with ill words, but none so violent as our *English* fugitives, because he doth confess it that the *Devil* did encounter him very frequently, and familiarly, when he first put pen to paper against the corruptions of the *Church of Rome*. In whose behalf I answer: much of that which is objected I cannot find in the *Latin Editions* of his works which himself corrected, although it appears by the quotations some such things were in his first writings set forth in the Dutch language. 2. I say no more than he confesseth ingenuously of himself in an epistle to *Brentius*, his meaning was good, but his words came from him very unskilfully, and his style was most rough and unsavoury. St. Paul says of himself, that he was *rudis sermone*, *rude in speech*. But Luther was not so much ἰδιώτης τῷ λόγῳ, the word used in Saint Paul, as ἄγροικος, after his *Dutch Monastical* breeding, and his own hot freedom. By nature he had a boisterous clownish expression; but for the most part very good jewels of doctrine in the dunghills of his language. 3. If the Devil did employ himself to delude and vex that heroical servant of God, who took such a task upon him, being a simple Monk, to inveigh against errors and superstitions which had so long prevailed, why should it seem strange to any man? *Ribadaneira* sticks it among the praises of his founder *Ignatius Loiola*, that the Devil did declaim and cry out against him, (believe it every one of you at your leisure,) and why might not the Devil draw near to vex *Luther*, as well as roar out a great way off against *Loiola?* I have digrest a little with your patience, to make *Luther's* case appear to be no outrageous thing, that weak ones may not be offended when they hear such stuff objected out of *Parsons*, or *Barclay*, or *Walsingham*, or out of *Bellarmine* himself. If *Beelzebub* was busy with the *Master*, what will he be with the *Servants?* When Christ did begin to lay the first corner stone of the *Gospel*, *then he walked into the wilderness to be tempted of the Devil*."*

---

* Hacket's Sermons.

CHAPTER CCXXXI.

QUESTION AS TO WHETHER BOOKS UNDER THE TERMINATION OF "ANA" HAVE BEEN SERVICEABLE OR INJURIOUS TO LITERATURE CONSIDERED IN CONNECTION WITH LUTHER'S TABLE TALK. HISTORY OF THE EARLY ENGLISH TRANSLATION OF THAT BOOK, OF ITS WONDERFUL PRESERVATION, AND OF THE MARVELLOUS AND UNIMPEACHABLE VERACITY OF CAPTAIN HENRY BELL.

Prophecies, predictions,
Stories and fictions,
Allegories, rhymes,
And serious pastimes
For all manner men,
Without regard when,
Or where they abide,
On this or that side,
Or under the mid line
Of the Holland sheets fine,
Or in the tropics fair
Of sunshine and clear air,
Or under the pole
Of chimney and sea coal:
Read they that list; understand they that can;
Verbum satis est to a wise man.

Book of Riddles.

Luther's Table Talk is probably the earliest of that class of books, which, under the termination of *ana*, became frequent in the two succeeding centuries, and of which it may be questioned whether they have been more serviceable or injurious to literature. For though they have preserved much that is valuable, and that otherwise might probably have been lost, on the other hand they have introduced into literary history not a little that is either false, or of suspicious authority; some of their contents have been obtained by breach of confidence; many sayings are ascribed in them to persons by whom they were never uttered, and many things have been fabricated for them.

The Collection concerning Luther bears this title in the English translation: "Doctoris Martini Lutheri Colloquia Mensalia: or, Dr. Martin Luther's Divine Discourses at his Table, &c., which in his lifetime he held with divers learned men, (such as were Philip Melancthon, Casparus Cruciger, Justus Jonas, Paulus Eberus, Vitus Dietericus, Joannes Bugenhagen, Joannes Forsterus, and others:) containing Questions and Answers touching Religion, and other main Points of Doctrine; as also many notable Histories, and all sorts of Learning, Comforts, Advices, Prophecies, Admonitions, Directions and Instructions. Collected first together by Dr. Antonius Lauterbach, and afterwards disposed into certain Commonplaces by John Aurifaber, Doctor in Divinity. Translated out of the High German into the English tongue, by Captain Henry Bell.

John vi. 12. Gather up the fragments that nothing be lost.

1 Cor. x. 31. Whether therefore ye eat or drink, or whatsoever ye do, do all to the Glory of God.

Tertull. Apologet. cap. 39. The primitive Christians ate and drank to satisfy nature, and discoursed at their Tables of the Holy Scriptures, or otherwise, as became those that knew God did hear them, *ut non tam cœnam cœnaverint, quam disciplinam.*

Ancient Writers, Councils, and our University College Statutes require *sacra ad mensam.*

Luther in Gen. 2. *Sermones vera sunt condimenta ciborum.*

Melchior Adamus in Vita Lutheri. *Inter prandendum et cœnandum non raró conciones aliis dictavit.*

London, Printed by William Du Gard, dwelling in Suffolk-lane, near London-stone, 1652."

The original Collection was first published three-and-thirty years after Luther's death, consequently not till most of those persons from whose reminiscences it professes to be compiled had passed away. The book therefore is far from carrying with it any such stamp of authenticity as Boswell's Life of Johnson, which in that respect, as well as for its intrinsic worth, is the Ana of all Anas. But though it may have been undertaken upon book-making motives, there seems no reason to suppose that the task was not performed faithfully by the Doctors Clearstream and Goldsmith, according to their judgement, and that much which had lightly or carelessly fallen from such a man as Luther was likely to be carefully preserved, and come into their hands. Many parts indeed authenticate themselves, bearing so strong a likeness that no one can hesitate at filiating them upon the ipsissimus Luther. The editor of the modern English edition, John Gottlieb Burckhardt, D. D., who was Minister of the German Lutheran Congregation in the Savoy, says, "the Book made a great noise at its first appearance in 1569. Some indeed have called its authenticity in question; but there is no reason to doubt of the testimony of Dr. John Aurifaber; and indeed the full character of Luther's free manner of speaking and thinking is seen almost in every line. The same manly, open, bold and generous spirit breathes through the whole, as is felt in reading the compositions which he published himself in his lifetime. There is a pleasing variety of matters contained in these discourses, and many fundamental truths are proposed in a familiar, careless dress, and in Luther's own witty, acute manner; for which reason it is as much entertaining to popular capacities as to men of genius. Many good Christians have found it to be of great benefit for establishing their souls in the knowledge and practice of truth, and of the good old way; and since many weeds grow up from time to time in the Church, this book handed down to posterity, will be a standing test of sound doctrines, which our forefathers believed, and of such wise principles on which they acted at, and after the Reformation." On the other hand the book afforded as much gratification to the enemies of Luther, as to his admirers. Bayle after noticing some of the monstrous calumnies with which the Papists assailed his memory, proceeds to say, *La plûpart de ces medisances sont fondées sur quelques paroles d'un certain livre publié par les amis de Luther, ausquelles on donne un sens tres-malin, et fort éloigné de la pensée de ce Ministre. Ce n'est pas qu'il ne faille convenir qu'il y eut une très-grande imprudence à publier une telle compilation. Ce fut l'effet d'un zèle inconsideré, ou plutôt d'une preoccupation excessive, qui empêchoit de conoître les defauts de ce grand homme.* In like manner Seckendorf, whom Bayle quotes, says it was compiled with little prudence, and incautiously published, but upon its authenticity, (as far as any such collection can be deemed authentic,) he casts no suspicion.

Something worse than want of prudence may be suspected in those who set forth the English translation. The translator introduced it by "a Narrative of the miraculous preserving" of the book, and "how by God's Providence it was discovered lying under the ground where it had lain hid fifty-two years:" "I, Capt. Henry Bell," he says, "do hereby declare both to the present age and also to posterity, that being employed beyond the seas in state affairs divers years together, both by King James, and also by the late King Charles, in Germany I did hear and understand in all places, great bewailing and lamentation made, by reason of the destroying or burning of above fourscore thousand of Martin Luther's books, entituled his last Divine Discourses. For after such time as God stirred up the spirit of Martin Luther to detect the corruptions and abuses of Popery, and to preach Christ, and clearly to set forth the simplicity of the Gospel, many Kings, Princes and States, Imperial Cities, and Hanse-Towns, fell from the Popish Religion, and became Protestants as their posterities still are, and remain to this very day. And for the further advancement of the great work of Reformation then begun, the foresaid Princes and the rest did then order, that the said Divine Discourses of Luther should forthwith be printed, and that every Parish should have and receive one of the foresaid printed Books into every Church throughout all their principalities and dominions, to be chained up, for the common people to read therein. Upon which the Reformation was wonderfully promoted and increased, and spread both here in England and other countries beside. But afterwards it so fell out, that the Pope then living, viz. Gregory XIII., understanding what great hurt and prejudice he and his popish religion had already received by reason of the said Luther's Divine Discourses; and also fearing that the same might bring farther contempt and mischief upon himself, and upon the popish Church, he therefore, to prevent the same, did fiercely stir up and instigate the Emperor then in being, viz. Rudolphus II., to make an edict through the whole empire, that all the foresaid printed books should be burnt, and also that it should be *Death* for any person to have or keep a copy thereof, but also to burn the same: which edict was speedily put in execution accordingly, in so much that not one of all the said printed books, not so much as any one copy of the same, could be found out, nor heard of in any place."

Upon this it is to be observed that in the popish states of Germany such an edict was not required, and that in the Protestant ones it could not be enforced. There is therefore as little foundation for the statement, as for the assertion introduced in it that the Reformation was promoted in England by the publication of this book in German. The Book appears not to have been common, for Bayle had never seen it; but this was because few editions were printed, not because many copies were destroyed. The reader, however, will judge by what follows of the degree of credit which may be given to any statement of Capt. Henry Bell's.

"Yet it pleased God," the veracious Captain proceeds, "that anno 1626 a German Gentleman, named Casparus Van Sparr, (with whom, in the time of my staying in Germany about King James's business, I became very familiarly known and acquainted,) having occasion to build upon the old foundation of an house wherein his grandfather dwelt at that time when the said edict was published in Germany for the burning of the foresaid books, and digging deep into the ground under the said old foundation, one of the said original printed books was there happily found, lying in a deep obscure hole, being wrapt in a strong linen cloth, which was waxed all over with bees-wax both within and without, whereby the book was preserved fair without any blemish. And at the same time Ferdinandus II. being Emperor in Germany, who was a severe enemy and persecutor of the Protestant religion, the foresaid Gentleman and grandchild to him that had hidden the said Book in that obscure hole, fearing that if the said Emperor should get knowledge that one of the said Books was yet forthcoming and in his custody, thereby not only himself might be brought into trouble, but also the Book in danger to be destroyed, as all the rest were so long before; and also calling me to mind, and knowing that I had the High Dutch tongue very perfect, did send the said original Book over hither into England, unto me; and therewith did write unto me a letter, wherein he related the passages of the preserving and finding out of the said Book. And also he earnestly moved me in his letter, that for the advancement of God's glory, and of Christ's Church, I would take the pains to translate the said Book, to the end that that most excellent Divine Work of Luther might be brought again to light!

"Whereupon I took the said Book before me, and many times began to translate the same, but always I was hindered therein, being called upon about other business; insomuch that by no possible means I could remain by that work. Then about six weeks after I had received the said Book, it fell out, that I being in bed with my Wife, one night between twelve and one of the clock, she being asleep but myself yet awake, there appeared unto me an Antient Man, standing at my bed-side, arrayed all in white, having a long and broad white beard, hanging down to his girdle-stead; who, taking me by my right ear, spake these words following unto me. *Sirrah! Will not you take time to translate that Book which is sent unto you out of Germany? I will shortly provide for you both place and time to do it!* And then he vanished away out of my sight. Whereupon being much thereby affrighted, I fell into an extreme sweat, insomuch that my Wife awaking, and finding me all over wet, she asked me what I ailed; I told her what I had seen and heard; but I never did heed nor regard visions, nor dreams. And so the same fell soon out of my mind.

"Then, about a fortnight after I had seen

that Vision, I went to Whitehall to hear the Sermon; after which ended, I returned to my lodging, which was then in King Street at Westminster, and sitting down to dinner with my Wife, two Messengers were sent from the whole Council-Board, with a warrant to carry me to the Keeper of the Gate House, Westminster, there to be safely kept, until further order from the Lords of the Council; which was done without showing me any cause at all wherefore I was committed. Upon which said warrant I was kept there ten whole years close prisoner; where I spent five years thereof about the translating of the said Book: insomuch as I found the words very true which the old man in the foresaid Vision did say unto me, '*I will shortly provide for you both place and time to translate it.*'"

CHAPTER CCXXXII.

THE DOCTOR'S FAMILY FEELING.

It behoves the high
For their own sakes to do things worthily.
BEN JONSON.

No son ever regarded the memory of his father with more reverential affection than this last of the Doves. There never lived a man, he said, to whom the lines of Marcus Antonius Flaminius, (the sweetest of all Latin poets in modern times, or perhaps of any age,) could more truly be applied.

Vixisti, genitor, bene, ac beate,
Nec pauper, neque dives; eruditus
Satis, et satis eloquens; valente
Semper corpore, mente sanâ; amicis
Jucundus, pietate singulari.

"What if he could not with the Heveninghams of Suffolk count five and twenty knights of his family, or tell sixteen knights successively with the Tilneys of Norfolk, or with the Nauntons shew where his ancestors had seven hundred pounds a year before the conquest,"* he was, and with as much, or perhaps more reason, contented with his parentage. Indeed his family feeling was so strong, that, if he had been of an illustrious race, pride, he acknowledged, was the sin which would most easily have beset him; though on the other hand, to correct this tendency, he thought there could be no such persuasive preachers as old family portraits, and old monuments in the family church.

He was far, however, from thinking that those who are born to all the advantages, as they are commonly esteemed, of rank and fortune, are better placed for the improvement of their moral and intellectual nature, than those in a lower grade. *Fortunatos nimium sua si bona nôrint!* he used to say of this class, but this is a knowledge that they seldom possess; and it is rare indeed to find an instance in which the high privileges which hereditary wealth conveys are understood by the possessors, and rightly appreciated and put to their proper use. The one, and the two talents are,

(Oh! bright occasions of dispensing good
How seldom used, how little understood!†)

in general, more profitably occupied than the five; the five indeed are not often tied up in a napkin, but still less often are they faithfully employed in the service of that Lord from whom they are received in trust, and to whom an account of them must be rendered.

"A man of family and estate," said Johnson, "ought to consider himself as having the charge of a district over which he is to diffuse civility and happiness."—Are there fifty men of family and estate in the Three Kingdoms who feel and act as if this were their duty?—Are there five and forty?—Forty?—Thirty?—Twenty?—Or can it be said with any probability of belief that "peradventure Ten shall be found there?"

— in sangue illustre e signorile,
In uom d' alti parenti al mondo nato,
La viltà si raddoppia, e più si scorge
Che in coloro il cui grado alto non sorge.‡

Here in England stood a village, within the memory of man, — no matter where, —

---

* FULLER.

† COWPER.

‡ TASSO RINALDO.

close by the Castle of a noble proprietor, — no matter who:

— il figlio
Del tale, ed il nipote del cotale,
*Natò per madre della tale.**

It contained about threescore houses, and every cottager had ground enough for keeping one or two cows. The noble proprietor looked upon these humble tenements as an eye-sore; and one by one as opportunity offered, he purchased them, till at length he became owner of the whole, one field excepted, which belonged to an old Quaker. The old man resisted many offers, but at last he was induced to exchange it for a larger and better piece of land in another place. No sooner had this transaction been compleated, than the other occupants, who were now only tenants at will, received notice to quit; the houses were demolished, the inclosures levelled, hearthsteads and homesteads, the cottage garden and the cottage field disappeared, and the site was in part planted, in part thrown into the park. The Quaker, who unlike Naboth had parted with the inheritance of his fathers, was a native of the village; but he knew not how dearly he was attached to it, till he saw its demolition: it was his fault, he said; and if he had not exchanged his piece of ground, he should never have lived to see his native place destroyed. He took it deeply to heart; it preyed upon his mind, and he soon lost his senses and died.

I tell the story as it was related, within sight of the spot, by a husbandman who knew the place and the circumstances, and well remembered that many people used to come every morning from the adjacent parts to buy milk there, — "a quart of new milk for a half-penny, and a quart of old given with it."

Naboth has been named in relating this, but the reader will not suppose that I have any intention of comparing the great proprietor to Ahab, — or to William the Conqueror. There was nothing unjust in his proceedings, nothing iniquitous; and (though there may have been a great want of proper feeling) nothing cruel. I am not aware that any hardship was inflicted upon the families who were ejected, farther than the inconvenience of a removal. He acted as most persons in the same circumstances probably would have acted, and no doubt he thought that his magnificent habitation was greatly improved by the demolition of the poor dwellings which had neighboured it so closely. Farther it may be said in his justification, (for which I would leave nothing unsaid,) that very possibly the houses had not sufficient appearance of neatness and comfort to render them agreeable objects, that the people may have been in no better state of manners and morals than villagers commonly are, which is saying that they were bad enough; that the filth of their houses was thrown into the road, and that their pigs, and their children, who were almost as unclean, ran loose there. Add to this, if you please, that though they stood in fear of their great neighbour, there may have been no attachment to him, and little feeling of good-will. But I will tell you how Dr. Dove would have proceeded if he had been the hereditary Lord of that Castle and that domain.

He would have considered that this village was originally placed there for the sake of the security which the Castle afforded. Times had changed, and with them the relative duties of the Peer and of the Peasantry: he no longer required their feudal services, and they no longer stood in need of his protection. The more, therefore, according to his "way of thinking," was it to be desired, that other relations should be strengthened, and the bonds of mutual good-will be more closely intertwined. He would have looked upon these villagers as neighbours, in whose welfare and good conduct he was especially interested, and over whom it was in his power to exercise a most salutary and beneficial influence; and, having this power, he would have known that it was his duty so to use it. He would have established a school in the village, and have allowed no alehouse there. He would have taken his domestics preferably from thence. If there

* Chiabrera.

were a boy who, by his gentle disposition, his diligence, and his aptitude for learning, gave promise of those qualities which best become the clerical profession, he would have sent that boy to a grammar-school, and afterwards to college, supporting him there in part, or wholly, according to the parents' means, and placing him on his list for preferment, according to his deserts.

If there were any others who discovered a remarkable fitness for any other useful calling, in that calling he would have had them instructed, and given them his countenance and support, as long as they continued to deserve it. The Archbishop of Braga, Fray Bartolomen dos Martyres, added to his establishment a Physician for the poor. Our friend would, in like manner, have fixed a medical practitioner in the village,—one as like as he could find to a certain Doctor at Doncaster; and have allowed him such a fixed stipend as might have made him reasonably contented and independent of the little emolument which the practice of the place could afford, for he would not have wished his services to be gratuitous where there was no need. If the parish, to which the village belonged, was too extensive, or the parochial Minister unwilling, or unable, to look carefully after this part of his flock, his Domestic Chaplain, (for he would not have lived without one,) should have taken care of their religious instruction.

In his own family and his own person he would have set his neighbours an example of "whatsoever things are honest, whatsoever things are just, whatsoever things are pure, whatsoever things are lovely, whatsoever things are of good report." And as this example produced its sure effects, he would have left the Amateurs of Agriculture to vie with each other in their breeds of sheep and oxen, and in the costly cultivation of their farms. It would have been, not his boast, for he boasted of nothing; — not his pride, for he had none of

> that poor vice which only empty men
> Esteem a virtue — *

* Beaumont and Fletcher.

it was out of the root of Christian humility that all his virtues grew,— but his consolation and his delight, to know that nowhere in Great Britain was there a neater, a more comfortable village than close to his own mansion; nowhere a more orderly, a more moral, a more cheerful, or a happier people. And if his castle had stood upon an elevation commanding as rich a survey as Belvoir or Shobden, that village, when he looked from his windows, would still have been the most delightful object in the prospect.

I have not mentioned the name of the old Quaker in my story; but I will preserve it in these pages, because the story is to his honour. It was Joshua Dickson. If Quakers have (and certainly they have) the quality which is called modest assurance, in a superlative degree, that distinguishes them from any other class of men (it is of the *men* only that I speak), they are the only sect, who, as a sect, cultivate the sense of conscience. This was not a case of conscience, but of strong feeling, assuming that character under a tendency to madness.

When Lord Harcourt, about the same time, removed the village of Nuneham, an old widow, Barbara Wyat by name, earnestly intreated that she might be allowed to remain in her old habitation. The request, which it would have been most unfeeling to refuse, was granted; she ended her days there, and then the cottage was pulled down: but a tree, which grew beside it, and which she had planted in her youth, is still shown on the terrace at Nuneham, and called by her name. Near it is placed the following Inscription by that amiable man, the Laureate Whitehead. Like all his serious poems it may be read with pleasure and profit,— though the affecting circumstance, which gives the anecdote its highest interest, is related only in a note.

> This Tree was planted by a female hand,
> In the gay dawn of rustic beauty's glow;
> And fast beside it did her cottage stand,
> When age had clothed the matron's head with snow.
>
> To her, long used to nature's simple ways,
> This single spot was happiness compleat;
> Her tree could shield her from the noontide blaze,
> And from the tempest screen her little seat.

Here with her Colin oft the faithful maid
  Had led the dance, the envious youths among;
Here when his aged bones in earth were laid,
  The patient matron turned her wheel and sung.

She felt her loss, yet felt it as she ought,
  Nor dared 'gainst Nature's general law exclaim,
But checkt her tears and to her children taught
  That well-known truth their lot would be the same.

The Thames before her flowed, his farther shores
  She ne'er explored, contented with her own;
And distant Oxford, tho' she saw its towers,
  To her ambition was a world unknown.

Did dreadful tales the clowns from market bear
  Of kings and tumults and the courtier train,
She coldly listened with unheeding ear,
  And good Queen Anne, for aught she cared, might reign.

The sun her day, the seasons marked her year,
  She toiled, she slept, from care, from envy free;
For what had she to hope, or what to fear,
  Blest with her cottage, and her favourite Tree.

Hear this ye Great, whose proud possessions spread
  O'er earth's rich surface to no space confined!
Ye learn'd in arts, in men, in manners read,
  Who boast as wide an empire o'er the mind,

With reverence visit her august domain;
  To her unlettered memory bow the knee;
She found that happiness you seek in vain,
  Blest with a cottage, and a single Tree.*

Mason would have produced a better inscription upon this subject, in the same strain; Southey in a different one; Crabbe would have treated it with more strength; Bowles with a finer feeling; so would his kinswoman and namesake Caroline, than whom no author or authoress has ever written more touchingly, either in prose or verse. Wordsworth would have made a picture from it worthy of a place in the great Gallery of his Recluse. But Whitehead's is a remarkable poem, considering that it was produced during what has been not unjustly called the neap tide of English poetry: and the reader who should be less pleased with it than offended by its faults, may have cause to suspect that his refinement has injured his feelings in a greater degree than it has improved his taste.

* The Classical reader will be aware that the Author of these lines had Claudian's "Old Man of Verona" in his mind's eye, as Claudian had Virgil's "Corycian Old Man." — *Georg.* iv. 127.

CHAPTER CCXXXIII.

THE PETTY GERMAN PRINCES EXCELLENT PATRONS OF LITERATURE AND LEARNED MEN. THE DUKE OF SAXE WEIMAR. QUOTATION FROM BISHOP HACKET. AN OPINION OF THE EXCELLENT MR. BOYLE. A TENET OF THE DEAN OF CHALON, PIERRE DE ST. JULIEN, AND A VERITABLE PLANTAGENET.

Ita nati estis, ut bona malaque vestra ad Rempublicam pertineant. TACITUS.

"We have long been accustomed to laugh at the pride and poverty of petty German Princes," says one of the most sensible and right-minded travellers that ever published the result of his observations in Germany †; "but nothing," he proceeds, "can give a higher idea of the respectability which so small a people may assume, and the quantity of happiness which one of these insignificant monarchs may diffuse around him, than the example of the little state of Weimar, with a prince like the present ‡ Grand Duke at its head. The mere pride of sovereignty, frequently most prominent where there is only the title to justify it, is unknown to him; he is the most affable man in his dominions, not simply with the condescension which any prince can learn to practise as a useful quality, but from goodness of heart." The whole population of his state little if at all exceeds that of Leicestershire; his capital is smaller than a third or fourth rate country town; so in fact it scarcely deserves the name of a town; and the inhabitants, vain as they are of its well-earned reputation as the German Athens, take a pride in having it considered merely a large village: his revenue is less than that of many a British Peer, great Commoner, or commercial Millionist. Yet "while the treasures of more weighty potentates were insufficient to meet the necessities of their political relations, his confined revenues could give independence and careless leisure to the men who were gaining for Germany

† RUSSELL. ‡ A.D. 1822.

its intellectual reputation." It is not too much to say that for that intellectual reputation, high as it is, and lasting as it will be, Germany is little less beholden to the Duke of Weimar's well-bestowed patronage, than to the genius of Wieland, and Schiller, and Goëthe. "In these little principalities, the same goodness of disposition can work with more proportional effect than if it swayed the sceptre of an empire; it comes more easily and directly into contact with those towards whom it should be directed: the artificial world of courtly rank and wealth has neither sufficient glare nor body to shut out from the prince the more chequered world that lies below."

Alas no Prince either petty or great has followed the Duke of Saxe Weimar's example! "He dwells," says Mr. Downes, "like an estated gentleman, surrounded by his tenantry." Alas no British Peer, great Commoner, or commercial Millionist, has given to any portion of his ampler revenues a like beneficent direction.

A good old Bishop* quoting the text "not many wise men after the flesh, not many mighty, not many noble are called," cautions us against distorting the Scripture as if it pronounced nothing but confusion to the rulers of the earth: "let not the honourable person," said he, "hang down his head, as if power and wisdom, and noble blood, and dignity, were causes of rejection before God: no, beloved! Isaiah foretold that Kings should be nursing fathers, and Queens should be nursing mothers of the Church, but it is often seen that the benignity of nature and the liberality of fortune are made impediments to a better life; and, therefore, Nobles and Princes are more frequently threatened with judgment. I adjoin moreover that the Scriptures speak more flatly against illustrious Magistrates, than the common sort; for if God had left it to men, whose tongues are prostituted to flattery, they had scarce been told that their abominable sins would bring damnation."

When our philosopher considered the manner in which large incomes are expended, (one way he had opportunities enough of observing at Doncaster,) he thought that in these times high birth brought with it dangers and evils which in many or most instances more than counterbalanced its advantages.

That excellent person Mr. Boyle had formed a different opinion. To be the son of a Peer whose prosperity had found many admirers, but few parallels, and not to be his eldest son, was a happiness that he used to "mention with great expressions of gratitude; his birth, he said, so suiting his inclinations and designs, that, had he been permitted an election, his choice would scarce have altered God's assignment. For as on the one side, a lower birth would have too much exposed him to the inconveniences of a mean descent, which are too notorious to need specifying; so on the other side, to a person whose humour indisposes him to the distracting hurry of the world, the being born heir to a great family is but a glittering kind of slavery, whilst obliging him to a public entangled course of life, to support the credit of his family, and tying him from satisfying his dearest inclinations, it often forces him to build the advantages of his house upon the ruins of his own contentment."

"A man of mean extraction," he continues, "is seldom admitted to the privacy and secrets of great ones promiscuously, and scarce dares pretend to it, for fear of being censured saucy, or an intruder. And titular greatness is ever an impediment to the knowledge of many retired truths, that cannot be attained without familiarity with meaner persons, and such other condescensions, as fond opinion, in great men, disapproves and makes disgraceful." "But he himself," Mr. Boyle said, "was born in a condition that neither was high enough to prove a temptation to laziness, nor low enough to discourage him from aspiring." And certainly to a person that affected so much an universal knowledge, and arbitrary vicissitudes of quiet and employments, it could not be unwelcome to be of a quality that was a handsome

* Bishop Hacket.

stirrup to preferment, without an obligation to court it, and which might at once both protect his higher pretensions from the guilt of ambition, and secure his retiredness from contempt.

There would be more and higher advantages in high birth than Mr. Boyle apprehended, if the Dean of Chalon, Pierre de St. Julien, were right when he maintained *contre l'opinion des Philosophes, et l'ordinaire des Predicaments,—que la vraye Noblesse a sa source du sang, et est substancielle.*

Ces mots Gentilhomme de sang, et d'armes, de race genereuse, de bonne part, &c., says the well-born Dean, who in his title pages let us know that he was *de la maison de Balleurré,—sont termes non de qualité, ny d'habitude; ains importants substance de vray, comme il est bien dit,*

> *veniunt cum sanguine mores;*

et aillieurs,

> *Qui viret in foliis venit à radicibus humor;*
> *Sic patrum in natos abeunt cum semine mores.*

Et comme le sang est le vehicule, et porteur des esprits de vie, esquels est enclose la substance de l'âme; aussi est il le comme chariot, qui porte et soustient celle substance qui decoule des peres, et des ayeulx, par long ordre de generation, et provient aux enfants, qui, nez de bonne et gentille semence, sont (conformement à l'opinion du divin Philosophe Platon) rendu tels que leurs progeniteurs, par la vertu des esprits enclos en la semence.—Tellement qu'on ne peut nyer, que comme d'une bonne Ayre sortent de bons oyseaux, d'un bon Haras de bons chevaux, &c., aussi il importe beaucoup aux hommes d'estre nez de bons et valeureux parents; voire tant, que les mal nez, ennemys de ceste bien naissance, ne sont suffisants pour en juger.

Sir Robert Cotton once met with a man driving the plough, who was a true and undoubted Plantagenet. "That worthy Doctor," (Dr. Hervey) says that worthy Fuller, (*dignissimus* of being so styled himself,) "hath made many converts in physic to his seeming paradox, maintaining the circulation of blood running round about the body of man. Nor is it less true that gentle blood fetcheth a circuit in the body of a nation, running from Yeomanry, through Gentry to Nobility, and so retrograde, returning through Gentry to Yeomanry again."

Plust à Dieu, said Maistre François Rabelais, of facetious memory, *qu'un chacun saust aussi certainement*—(as Gargantua that is,)—*sa genealogie, depuis l'Arche de Noé, jusqu'à cet âge! Je pense que plusieurs sont aujourd'hui Empereurs, Roys, Ducs, Princes et Papes en la terre, lesquels sont descendus de quelques Porteurs de rogatons et de constrets. Comme au rebours plusieurs sont gueux de l'hostiere, souffreteux et miserables, lesquels sont descendus de sang et ligne de grands Roys et Empereurs; attends l'admirable transport des Regnes et Empires*

> *Des Assyriens, és Medes;*
> *Des Medes, és Perses;*
> *Des Perses, és Macédoniens;*
> *Des Macédoniens, és Grecs;*
> *Des Grecs, és Francois.*

Et pour vous donner à entendre de moy qui vous parle, je cuide que suis descendu de quelque riche Roy, ou Prince, au temps jadis; car oncques ne vistes homme qui eust plus grande affection d'estre Roy ou riche que moy, afin de faire grand chere, pas ne travailler, point ne me soucier et bien enrichir mes amis, et tous gens de bien et de sçavoir.

CHAPTER CCXXXIV.

OPINION OF A MODERN DIVINE UPON THE WHEREABOUT OF NEWLY-DEPARTED SPIRITS. ST. JOHN'S BURIAL, ONE RELIC ONLY OF THAT SAINT, AND WHEREFORE. A TALE CONCERNING ABRAHAM, ADAM AND EVE.

> *Je sçay qu'il y a plusieurs qui diront que je fais beaucoup de petits fats contes, dont je m'en passerois bien. Ouy, bien pour aucuns,—mais non pour moy, me contentant de m'en renouveller le souvenance, et en tirer autant de plaisir.* BRANTÔME.

WATTS, who came to the odd conclusion in his Philosophical Essay, that there may be Spirits which must be said in strict philosophy to be nowhere, endeavoured to explain what he called the *ubi* or *whereness* of those spirits which are in a more imaginable situation. While man is alive, the soul he thought might be said to be in his brain, because the seat of consciousness seems to be there; but as soon as it is dislodged from that local habitation by death, it finds itself at once in a heaven or hell of its own, and this "without any removal or relation to place, or change of distances." The shell is broken, the veil is withdrawn; it is where it was, but in a different mode of existence, in the pure intellectual, or separate world. "It reflects upon its own temper and actions in this life, it is conscious of its virtues, or its vices," and it has an endless spring of peace and joy within, or is tormented with the anguish of self-condemnation.

In his speculations the separation of soul from body is total, till their reunion at the day of judgement; and this unquestionably is the christian belief. The fablers of all religions have taken a different view, because at all times and in all countries they have accommodated their fictions to the notions of the people. The grave is with them a place of rest, or of suffering. If Young had been a Jew, a Mahommedan, or a Roman Catholic, he might be understood as speaking literally when he says,

How populous, how vital is the grave.

St. Augustine had been assured by what he considered no light testimony that St. John was not dead, but asleep in his sepulchre, and that the motion of his breast as he breathed might be perceived by a gentle movement of the earth. The words of our Lord after his Resurrection, concerning the beloved disciple, "If I will that he tarry till I come, what is that to thee," gave scope to conjecture concerning the fate of this Evangelist, and yet in some degree set bounds to that spirit of lying invention which in process of time annexed as many fables to corrupted Christianity as the Greek and Roman poets had engrafted upon their heathenism, or the Rabbis upon the Jewish faith. "Sinner that I am," said a French prelate with demure irony, when a head of St. John the Baptist was presented to him to kiss in some Church of which it was the choicest treasure, — "sinner that I am, this is the fourth head of the glorious Baptist that I have had the happiness of holding in these unworthy hands!" But while some half dozen or half score of these heads were produced, because it was certain that the Saint had been beheaded, no relic of St. John the Evangelist's person, nor of the Virgin Mary's, was ever invented. The story of the Assumption precluded any such invention in the one case, — and in St. John's the mysterious uncertainty of his fate had the same effect as this received tradition. The Benedictines of St. Claude's Monastery in the Jura exhibited his own manuscript of the Apocalypse, — (the most learned of that order in no unlearned age believed or affected to believe that it was his actual autograph,) — and they considered that it was greatly enhanced in value by its being the only relic of that Saint in existence.

The fable which St. Augustine seems to have believed was either parent or child of the story told under the name of Abdias, that when the Beloved Disciple had attained the postdiluvian age of ninety-seven, our Lord appeared to him, said unto him, "come unto me, that thou mayest partake at my feast with thy brethren," and fixed the next Sunday, being Easter, for his removal from this world. On that Sunday accordingly, the Evangelist, after having performed service in his own temple at Ephesus, and exhorted the people, told some of his chosen disciples to take with them two mattocks and spade, and accompany him therewith. They went to a place near the city, where he had been accustomed to pray; there he bade them dig a grave, and when they would have ceased from the work, he bade them dig it still deeper. Then taking off all his garments except a linen vestment, he spread them in the grave, laid himself down upon them, ordered his disciples to cover him up, and forthwith fell asleep in the Lord. Abdias proceeds no farther with the story; but other ecclesiastic romancers add that the evangelist enjoined them to open the grave on the day following; they did so and found nothing but his garments, for the Blessed Virgin, in recompence for the filial piety which he had manifested towards her in obedience to our Lord's injunctions from the cross, had obtained for him the privilege of an Assumption like her own. Baronius has no objection to believe this; but that St. John actually died is, he says, more than certain, — *certo certius;* and that his grave at Ephesus was proof of it, for *certe non nisi mortuorum solent esse sepulchra.*

Yet the Cardinal knew that the historian of his Church frequently represented the dead as sentient in their graves. The Jews have some remarkable legends founded upon the same notion. It is written in the book of Zohar, say the Rabbis, how when Abraham had made a covenant with the people of the land, and was about to make a feast for them, a calf, which was to be slaughtered on the occasion, broke loose and ran into the cave of Machpelah. Abraham followed, and, having entered the cave in pursuit, there he discovered the bodies of Adam and Eve, each on a bed, with lamps burning between them. They were sleeping the sleep of death, and there was a good odour around them, like the odour of repose. In consequence of having made this discovery it was that he desired to purchase the cave for his own burial-place; and when the sons of Jebus refused to sell it, he fell upon his knees, and bowed himself before them, till they were entreated. When he came to deposit the body of Sarah there, Adam and Eve rose up, and refused their consent. The reason which they gave for this unexpected prohibition was, that they were already in a state of reproach before the Lord, because of their transgression, and a farther reproach would be brought upon them by a comparison with his good deeds, if they allowed such company to be introduced into their resting-place. But Abraham took upon himself to answer for that; upon this they were satisfied with his assurances, and composed themselves again to their long sleep.

The Rabbis may be left to contend for the authority of the book of Zohar in this particular against the story of the Cabalists that Adam's bones were taken into the Ark, and divided afterwards by Noah among his sons. The skull fell to Shem's portion; he burnt it on the mountain, which, for that reason, obtained the name of Golgotha, or Calvary, — being interpreted, the place of a skull, and on that spot, for mystical signification, the cross whereon our Saviour suffered was erected; — a wild legend, on which as wild a fiction has been grafted, that a branch from the Tree of Life had been planted on Adam's grave, and from the wood which that branch had produced the cross was made.

And against either of these the authority of Rabbi Judas Bar Simon is to be opposed, for he affirms that the dust of Adam was washed away by the Deluge, and utterly dispersed.

The Rabbis have also to establish the credit of their own tradition against that of the Arabs, who, at this time, show Eve's grave near Jeddah; — about three days' journey east from that place, according to Bruce. He says it is covered with green sods, and about fifty yards in length. The Cashmerian traveller Abdulkurreem, who visited it in 1742, says that it measured an hundred and ninety-seven of his footsteps, which would make the mother of mankind much taller than Bruce's measurement. He likens it to a flower-bed; on the middle of the grave there was then a small dome, and the ends of it were enclosed with wooden pales. Burckhardt did not visit it; he was told that it was about two miles only, northward of the town, and that it was a rude structure of stone, some four feet in length, two or three in height, and as many in breadth, thus resembling the tomb of Noah, which is shown in the valley of Bekaa, in Syria. Thus widely do these modern travellers, on any one of whom reasonable reliance might have been placed, differ in the account of the same thing.

CHAPTER CCXXXV.

THE SHORTEST AND PLEASANTEST WAY FROM DONCASTER TO JEDDAH, WITH MANY MORE, TOO LONG.

Πόνος πόνῳ πόνον φέρει,
Πᾶ πᾶ γὰρ οὐκ ἔβαν ἔγω. SOPHOCLES.

We have got from the West Riding of Yorkshire, to the Eastern shore of the Red Sea, without the assistance of mail-coach, steam-packet, or air-balloon, the magical carpet, the wishing-cap, the shoes of swiftness, or the seven-leagued boots. From Mr. Bacon's vicarage we have got to Eve's grave, not *per saltum*, by any sudden, or violent transition; but by following the stream of thought. We shall get back in the same easy manner to that vicarage, and to the quiet churchyard wherein the remains of one of the sweetest and for the few latter years of her short life, one of the happiest of Eve's daughters, were deposited in sure and certain hope. If you are in the mood for a Chapter upon Churchyards, go, reader, to those which Caroline Bowles has written; you will find in them everything that can touch the heart, everything that can sanctify the affections, unalloyed by anything that can offend a pure taste and a masculine judgement.

But before we find our way back we must tarry awhile among the tombs, and converse with the fablers of old.

A young and lovely Frenchwoman after visiting the *Columbarium* near the Villa Albani, expressed her feelings strongly upon our custom of interring the dead, as compared with the urn-burial of the ancients. *Usage odieux*, said she, *qui rend la mort horrible! Si les anciens en avaient moins d'effroi, c'est que la coutume de brûler les corps dérobait au trépas tout ce qu'il a de hideux. Qu'il était consolant et doux de pouvoir pleurer sur des cendres chéries! Qu'il est épouvantable et déchirant aujourd'hui de penser que celui qu'on a tant aimé n'offre plus qu'une image affreuse et décharnée dont on ne pourrait supporter la vue.*

The lady in whose journal these lines were written lies buried in the Campo Santo at Milan, with the following inscription on her tomb; *Priez pour une jeune Française que la mort a frappée à vingt ans, comme elle allait, après un voyage de huit mois avec un epoux chéri, revoir son enfant, son père et sa mère, qui venaient joyeux au-devant d'elle.* Her husband wished to have her remains burnt, in conformity to her own opinion respecting the disposal of the dead, and to his own feelings at the time, that he might have carried her ashes to his own country, and piously have preserved them there, to weep over them, and bequeath them to his son; *mais les amis qui m'entouraient*, he says, *combattèrent mon désir, comme une inspiration insensée de la douleur.*

There can be no doubt that our ghastly personification of Death has been derived from the practice of interment; and that of all modes in which the dead have ever been disposed of, cremation is in some respects the best. But this mode, were it generally practicable, would in common use be accompanied with more revolting circumstances than that which has now become the Christian usage. Some abominations, however, it would have prevented, and though in place of those superstitions which it precluded others would undoubtedly have arisen, they would have been of a less loathsome character.

The Moors say that the dead are disturbed if their graves be trodden on by Christian feet; the Rabbis that they feel the worms devouring them.

On the south side of the city of Erzeroom is a mountain called Eyerli, from the same likeness which has obtained for one of the English mountains the unpoetical name of Saddleback. The Turkish traveller Evlia Effendi saw on the top of this mountain a tomb eighty paces in length, with two columns marking the place of the head and of the feet. "I was looking on the tomb," he says, "when a bad smell occurred very hurtfully to my nose, and to that of my servant who held the horses; and looking near, I then saw that the earth of the grave, which was greasy and black, was boiling, like gruel in a pan. I returned then, and having related my adventures in the evening in company with the Pashaw, Djaafer Effendi of Erzeroom, a learned man and an elegant writer, warned me not to visit the place again, for it was the grave of Balaam the son of Beor, who died an infidel, under the curse of Moses, and whose grave was kept always in this state by subterraneous fires."

When Wheler was at Constantinople, he noticed a monument in the fairest and largest street of that city, the cupola of which was covered with an iron grating. It was the tomb of Mahomet Cupriuli, father to the then Grand Vizier. He had not been scrupulous as to the means by which he settled the government during the Grand Seignior's minority, and carried it on afterwards, quelling the discontents and factions of the principal Agas, and the mutinies of the Janizaries. Concerning him after his decease, says this traveller, "being buried here, and having this stately monument of white marble covered with lead erected over his body, the Grand Seigneur and Vizier had this dream both in the same night, to wit, that he came to them and earnestly begged of them a little water to refresh him, being in a burning heat. Of this the Grand Seigneur and Vizier told each other in the morning, and thereupon thought fit to consult the Mufti what to do concerning it. The Mufti, according to their gross superstition, advised that the roof of his sepulchre should be uncovered, that the rain might descend on his body, thereby to quench the flames which were tormenting his soul. And this remedy the people who smarted under his oppression think he had great need of, supposing him to be tormented in the other world for his tyrannies and cruelties committed by him in this."

If Cupriuli had been a Russian instead of a Turk, his body would have been provided with a passport before it was committed to the grave. Peter Henry Bruce in his curious memoirs gives the form of one which in the reign of Peter the Great, always before the coffin of a Russian was closed, was put between the fingers of the corpse :—"We N. N. do certify by these presents that the bearer hereof hath always lived among us as became a good Christian, professing the Greek religion; and although he may have committed some sins, he hath confessed the same, whereupon he hath received absolution, and taken the communion for the remission of sins: That he hath honoured God and his Saints; that he hath not neglected his prayers; and hath fasted on the hours and days appointed by the Church: That he hath always behaved himself towards me, his Confessor, in such a manner that I have no reason to complain of him, or to refuse him the absolution of his sins. In witness whereof I have given him these testimonials, to the end that St. Peter upon sight of them, may not deny him the opening of the gate to eternal bliss!"

The custom evidently implies an opinion that though soul and body were disunited by death, they kept close company together till after the burial; otherwise a passport which the Soul was to present at Heaven's gate would not have been placed in the hands of the corpse. In the superstitions of the Romish church a re-union is frequently supposed, but that there is an immediate separation upon death is an article of faith, and it is represented by Sir Thomas More as one of the punishments for a sinful soul to be brought from Purgatory and made to attend, an unseen spectator, at the funeral of its own body, and feel the mockery of all the pomps and vanities used upon that occasion. The passage is in his Supplycacyon of Soulys. One of the Supplicants from Purgatory speaks:

"Some hath there of us, while we were in health, not so much studied how we might die penitent, and in good christian plight, as how we might solemnly be borne out to burying, have gay and goodly funerals, with heralds at our herses, and offering up our helmets, setting up our scutcheons and coat-armours on the wall, though there never came harness on our backs, nor never ancestor of ours ever bare arms before. Then devised we some Doctor to make a sermon at our mass in our month's mind, and then preach to our praise with some fond fantasy devised of our name; and after mass, much feasting, riotous and costly; and finally, like madmen, made men merry at our death, and take our burying for a brideale. For special punishment whereof, some of us have been by our Evil Angels brought forth full heavily, in full great despight to behold our own burying, and so, stand in great pain, invisible among the press, and made to look on our carrion corpse, carried out with great pomp, whereof our Lord knoweth we have taken heavy pleasure!"

In opposition to this there is a Rabbinical story which shows that though the Jews did not attribute so much importance to the rites of sepulture as the ancient Greeks, they nevertheless thought that a parsimonious interment occasioned some uncomfortable consequences to the dead.

A pious descendant of Abraham, whom his wife requited with a curtain lecture for having, as she thought improvidently, given alms to a poor person in a time of dearth, left his house, and went out to pass the remainder of the night among the tombs, that he might escape from her objurgations. There he overheard a conversation between the Spirits of two young women, not long deceased. The one said, "come let us go through the world, and then listen behind the curtain and hear what chastisements are decreed for it." The other made answer, "I cannot go, because I have been buried in a mat made of reeds, but go you, and bring me account of what you hear." Away went the Ghost whose grave-clothes were fit to appear in: and when she returned, "well friend, what have you heard behind the curtain?" said the ghost in the reed-mat. "I heard," replied the gad-about, "that whatever shall be sown in the first rains will be stricken with hail." Away went the alms-giver; and upon this intelligence, which was more certain than any prognostication in the Almanack, he waited till the second rains before he sowed his field; all other fields were struck with hail, but according as he had expected his crop escaped.

Next year, on the anniversary of the night which had proved so fortunate to him, he went again to the Tombs: and overheard another conversation between the same ghosts to the same purport. The well-dressed ghost went through the world, listened behind the curtain, and brought back information that whatever should be sown in the second rains would be smitten with rust. Away went the good man, and sowed his field in the first rains; all other crops were spoiled with the rust, and only his escaped. His wife then inquired of him how it had happened that in two successive years he had sown his fields at a different time from everybody else, and on both occasions his were the only crops that had been saved. He made no secret to her of his adventures, but told her how he had come to the knowledge which had proved so beneficial. Ere long his wife happened to quarrel with the mother of the poor ghost who was obliged to keep her sepulchre; and the woman of unruly tongue, among other insults, bade her go and look at her daughter, whom she had buried in a reed-mat! Another anniversary came round, and the good man went again to the Tomb; but he went this time in vain, for when the well-dressed Ghost repeated her invitation, the other made answer, "let me alone, my friend, the words which have passed between you and me have been heard among the living."

The learned Cistercian * to whom I owe this legend, expresses his contempt for it; nevertheless he infers from it that the spirits of the dead know what passes in this world; and that the doctrine of the Romish Church upon that point is proved by this tradition to have been that of the Synagogue also.

The Mahommedans, who adopted so many of the Rabbinical fables, dispensed in one case, for reasons of obvious convenience, with all ceremonies of sepulchral costume. For the funeral of their martyrs, by which appellation all Musselmen who fell in battle against the unbelievers were honoured, none of those preparations were required, which

* Bertolacci.

were necessary for those who die a natural death. A martyr needs not to be washed after his death, nor to be enveloped in grave-clothes; his own blood with which he is besmeared serves him for all legal purification, and he may be wrapped in his robe, and buried immediately after the funeral prayer, conformably to the order of the Prophet, who has said, "bury them as they are, in their garments, and in their blood! Wash them not, for their wounds will smell of musk on the Day of Judgement."

A man of Medina, taking leave of his wife as he was about to go to the wars, commended to the Lord her unborn babe. She died presently afterwards, and every night there appeared a brilliant light upon the middle of her tomb. The husband hearing of this upon his return, hastened to the place; the sepulchre opened of itself; the wife sate up in her winding-sheet, and holding out to him a boy in her arms, said to him take "that which thou commendedst to the Lord. Hadst thou commended us both, thou shouldest have found us both alive." So saying she delivered to him the living infant, and laid herself down, and the sepulchre closed over her.

* * * * *

PARS IMPERFECTA MANEBAT. — *Virg. Æn.*

The following materials, printed verbatim from the MS. Collection, were to have completed the Chapter. It has been thought advisable in the present instance to show how the lamented Southey worked up the collection of years. Each extract is on a separate slip of paper, and some of them appear to have been made from thirty to forty years ago, more or less.

And so the virtue of his youth before
Was in his age the ground of his delight.

JAMES I.

Ἔνθεν δὲ Σθενέλου τάφον ἔδρακον Ἀκτορίδαο
Ὅς ῥά τ' Ἀμαζονίδων πολυθαρσέος ἐκ πολέμοιο
Ἂψ ἀνιὼν (δὴ γὰρ συνανήλυθεν Ἡρακλῆϊ)
Βλήμενος ἰῷ κεῖθεν ἐτ' ἀγχιάλου θάνεν ἀκτῆς.
Οὐ μέν θην προτέρω ἀνεμέτρεον· ἧκε γὰρ αὐτὴ
Φερσεφόνη ψυχὴν πολυδάκρυον Ἀκτορίδαο
Λισσομένην, τυτθόν περ ὁμήθεας ἄνδρας ἰδέσθαι.
Τύμβου δὲ στεφάνης ἐπιβὰς σκοπιάζετο νῆα,
Τοῖος ἐὼν οἷος πόλεμον δ' ἴεν· ἀμφὶ δὲ καλὴ
Τετράφαλος φοίνικι λόφῳ ἐπελάμπετο πήληξ,
Καὶ ῥ' ὁ μὲν αὖτις ἔδυνε μέγαν ζόφον· οἱ δ' ἐσιδόντες
Θάμβησαν. τοῖς δ' ὦρσε θεοπροπέων ἐπικέλσαι
Ἀμπυκίδης Μόψος, λοιβῇσί τε μειλίξασθαι.
Οἳ δ' ἀνὰ μὲν κραιπνῶς λαῖφος σπάσαν, ἐκ δὲ βαλόντες
Πείσματ' ἐν αἰγιαλῷ Σθενέλου τάφον ἀμφεπένοντο,
Χύτλα τέ οἱ χεύαντο, καὶ ἥγνισαν ἔντομα μήλων.

APOLLONIUS RHODIUS.

The Abaza (a Circassian tribe) have a strange way of burying their Beys. They put the body in a coffin of wood, which they nail on the branches of some high trees and make a hole in the coffin by the head, that the Bey, as they say, may look unto Heaven. Bees enter the coffin, and make honey, and cover the body with their comb: If the season comes they open the coffin, take out the honey and sell it, therefore much caution is necessary against the honey of the Abazas. EVLIA EFFENDI.

Once in their life time, the Jews say, they are bound by the Law of Moses to go to the Holy Land, if they can, or be able, and the bones of many dead Jews are carried there, and there burnt. We were fraughted with wools from Constantinople to Sidon, in which sacks, as most certainly was told to me, were many Jew's bones put into little chests, but unknown to any of the ship. The Jews our Merchants told me of them at my return from Jerusalem to Saphet, but earnestly intreated me not to tell it, for fear of preventing them another time.

Going on, one of my companions said, if you will take the trouble of going a little out of the way, you will see a most remarkable thing. Well, said I, what should be the object of all pains taken in travelling, if it were not to admire the works of God. So we went on for an hour to the north, but not taking the great road leading to the Plain of Moosh, we advanced to a high rock that is a quarter of an hour out of the road. To this rock, high like a tower, a man was formerly chained, whose bones are yet preserved in the chains. Both bones and chains are in a high state of preservation. The bones of the arms are from seven to eight cubits in length, of an astonishing thickness. The skull is like the cupola of a bath, and a man may creep in and out without pain through the eye-holes. Eagles nestle in them. These bones are said to be those of a faithful man who in Abraham's time was chained by Nimrod to this rock, in order to be burnt by fire. The fire calcined part of his body, so that it melted in one part with the rock; but the arms and legs are stretching forth to the example of posterity. We have no doubt that they will rise again into life at the sound of the trumpet on the day of judgement. EVLIA EFFENDI.

The Magistrates of Leghorn have authority to issue out orders for killing dogs if they abound too much in the streets, and molest the inhabitants. The men entrusted with the execution of these orders go through the city in the night, and drop small bits of poisoned bread in the streets. These are eaten by the dogs and instantaneously kill them. Before sunrise the same men go through the streets with a cart, gather hundreds of the dead dogs, and carry them to the Jew's burying-ground without the town. HASSELQUIST.

In the ROMANCE OF MERLIN it is said that before the time of Christ, Adam and Eve and the whole ancient world were (not in Limbo) but actually in Hell. And that when the Prophets comforted the souls under their sufferings by telling them of the appointed Redeemer, the Devils for that reason tormented these Prophets more than others. The Devils themselves tell the story, *et les tourmentions plus que les autres. Et ilz faisoycnt semblant que nostre tourment ne les grevoit riens; ainçois comfortoyent les aultres pecheurs et disoyent. Le Saulveur de tout le monde viendra qui tous nous delivrera.*

At the time of the deluge the wife of Noah being pregnant, was through the hardships of the voyage delivered of a dead child to which the name of Tarh was given, because the letters of this word form the number 217, which was the number of days he was carried by his mother instead of the full time of 280 days, or nine months. This child was buried in the district now called Djezere Ibn Omar, the Island or Peninsula of the son of Omar, and this was the first burial on earth after the deluge. And Noah prayed unto the Lord, saying, Oh God, thou hast given me a thousand years of life, and this child is dead before it began to live on earth! And he begged of the Lord as a blessing given to the burial-place of his child, that the women of this town might never miscarry, which was granted; so that since that time women, and female animals of every kind in this town, are all blessed with births in due time and long living. The length of the grave of this untimely child of Noah is 40 feet and it is visited by pilgrims. EVLIA EFFENDI.

They suppose that a few souls are peculiarly gifted with the power of quitting their bodies, of mounting into the skies, visiting distant countries, and again returning and resuming them; they call the mystery of prayer by which this power is obtained, the *Mandiram*. CRAUFURD.

The plain of Kerbela is all desert, inhabited by none but by the dead, and by roving wild hounds, the race of the dogs which licked the blood of the martyrs, and which since are doomed to wander through the wilderness.
EVLIA EFFENDI.

Shi whang, the K. of Tsin becoming Emperor, he chose for his sepulchre the mountain Li, whose foundation he caused to dig, if we may so speak, even to the centre of the earth. On its surface he erected a mausoleum which might pass for a mountain. It was five hundred feet high, and at least half a league in circumference. On the outside was a vast tomb of stone, where one might walk as easily as in the largest hall. In the middle was a sumptuous coffin, and all around there were lamps and flambeaux, whose flames were fed by human fat. Within this tomb, there was upon one side a pond of quicksilver, upon which were scattered birds of gold and silver; on the other a compleat magazine of moveables and arms; here and there were the most precious jewels in thousands. DU HALDE.

Emududakel, the Messenger of Death, receives the Soul as 'tis breathed out of the body into a kind of a sack, and runs away with it through briars and thorns and burning whirlwinds, which torment the Soul very sensibly, till he arrives at the bank of a fiery current, through which he is to pass to the other side in order to deliver the soul to Emen, the God of the Dead.
LETTERS TO THE DANISH MISSIONARIES.

A curious story concerning the power which the Soul has been supposed to possess of leaving the body, in a visible form, may be found in the notes to the Vision of the Maid of Orleans. A more extraordinary one occurs in the singularly curious work of Evlia Effendi.

"Sultan Bajazet II. was a saint-monarch, like Sultan Orkhaun, or Sultan Mustapha I. There exist different works relating his miracles and deeds, but they are rare. The last seven years of his life he ate nothing which had blood and life. One day longing much to eat calf's or mutton's feet, he struggled long in that glorious contest with the Soul, and as at last a well-seasoned dish of feet was put before him, he said unto his Soul, "See my Soul, the feet are before thee, if thou wantest to enjoy them, leave the body and feed on them." In the same moment a living creature was seen to come out of his mouth, which drank of the juice in the dish and having satisfied its appetite, endeavoured to return into the mouth from whence it came. But Bajazet having prevented it with his hand to re-enter his mouth, it fell on the ground, and the Sultan ordered it to be beaten. The Pages arrived and kicked it dead on the ground. The Mufti of that time decided that as the Soul was an essential part of man, this dead Soul should be buried: prayers were performed over it, and the dead Soul was interred in a small tomb near Bajazet's tomb. This is the truth of the famous story of Bajazet II. having died twice and having been twice buried. After this murder of his own Soul, the Sultan remained melancholy in the corner of retirement, taking no part or interest in the affairs of government."

The same anecdote of the Soul coming out of the mouth to relish a most desired dish, had already happened to the Sheik Bajazet Bostaumi, who had much longed to eat *Mohallebi* (a milk-dish), but Bajazet Bostaumi permitted it to re-enter, and Sultan Bajazet killed it; notwithstanding which he continued to live for some time longer.

See *Josselyn* for a similar tale.

When Mohammed took his journey upon Alborach, Gabriel (said he) led me to the first Heaven, and the Angels in that Heaven graciously received me, and they beheld me with smiles and with joy, beseeching for me things prosperous and pleasant. One alone among the Angels there sat, who neither prayed for my prosperity, nor smiled; and Gabriel when I inquired of him who he was, replied, never hath that Angel smiled, nor will smile, he is the Keeper of the Fire; and I said to him is this the Angel who is called the well-beloved of God? and he replied, this is that Angel. Then said I bid him that he show me the Fire, and Gabriel requesting him, he removed the cover of the vessel of Fire, and the Fire ascending I feared lest all things whatever that I saw should be consumed, and I besought Gabriel that the Fire again might be covered. And so the fire returned to its place, and it seemed then as when the Sun sinks in the West, and the gloomy Angel, remaining the same, covered up the Fire.
RODERICI XIMENES, ARC. TOL. HIST. ARAB.

Should a Moslem when praying, feel himself disposed to gape, he is ordered to suppress the sensation as the work of the Devil, and to close his mouth, lest the father of iniquity should enter and take possession of his person. It is curious that this opinion prevails also among the Hindoos, who twirl their fingers close before their mouths when gaping, to prevent an evil spirit from getting in that way. GRIFFITHS.

In what part soever of the world they die and are buried, their bodies must all rise to judgement in the Holy Land, out of the valley of Jehosophat, which causeth that the greater and richer sort of them have their bones conveyed to some part hereof by their kindred or friends. By which means they are freed of a labour to scrape thither through the ground, which with their nails they hold they must, who are not there buried, nor conveyed thither by others. SANDERSON. PURCHAS.

The Russians in effecting a practicable road to China discovered in lat. 50 N., between the rivers Irtish and Obalet, a desert of very considerable extent, overspread in many parts with Tumuli, or Barrows, which have been also taken notice of by Mr. Bell and other writers. This desert constitutes the southern boundary of Siberia. It is said the borderers on the desert have, for many years, continued to dig for the treasure deposited in these tumuli, which still, however, remain unexhausted. We are told that they find considerable quantities of gold, silver and brass, and some precious stones, among ashes and remains of dead bodies: also hilts of swords, armour, ornaments for saddles and bridles, and other trappings, with the bones of those animals to which the trappings belonged, among which are the bones of elephants. The Russian Court, says Mr. Demidoff, being informed of these depredations, sent a principal officer, with sufficient troops, to open such of these tumuli, as were too large for the marauding parties to undertake and to secure their contents. This officer, on taking a survey of the numberless monuments of the dead spread over this great desert, concluded that the barrow of the largest dimensions most probably contained the remains of the prince or chief; and he was not mistaken; for, after removing a very deep covering of earth and stones, the workmen came to three vaults, constructed of stones, of rude workmanship; a view of which is exhibited in the engraving. That wherein the prince was deposited, which was in the centre, and the largest of the three, was easily distinguished by the sword, spear, bow, quiver and arrow which lay beside him. In the vault beyond him, towards which his feet lay, were his horse, bridle, saddle and stirrups. The body of the prince lay in a reclining posture on a sheet of pure gold, extending from head to foot, and another sheet of gold, of the like dimensions, was spread over him. He was wrapt in a rich mantle, bordered with gold and studded with rubies and emeralds. His head, neck, breast and arms naked, and without any ornament. In the lesser vault lay the princess, distinguished by her female ornaments. She was placed reclining against the wall, with a gold chain of many links, set with rubies, round her neck, and gold bracelets round her arms. The head, breast and arms were naked. The body was covered with a rich robe, but without any border of gold or jewels, and was laid on a sheet of fine gold, and covered over with another. The four sheets of gold weighed 40 lb. The robes of both looked fair and complete; but on touching, crumbled into dust. Many more of the tumuli were opened, but this was the most remarkable. In the others a great variety of curious articles were found.

MONTHLY REVIEW, Vol. 49

The following story I had from Mr. *Pierson*, factor here for the *African* company, who was sent here from *Cape Coree* to be second to Mr. *Smith* then chief factor. Soon after his arrival Mr. *Smith* fell very ill of the country malignant fever; and having little prospect of recovery, resigned his charge of the company's affairs to *Pierson*. This Mr. *Smith* had the character of an obliging, ingenious young gentleman, and was much esteemed by the King, who hearing of his desperate illness, sent his *Fatishman* to hinder him from dying; who coming to the factory went to Mr. *Smith's* bed-side, and told him, that his King had such a kindness for him, that he had sent to keep him alive, and that he should not die. Mr. *Smith* was in such a languishing condition, that he little regarded him. Then the Fatishman went from him to the hog-yard, where they bury the white men; and having carried with him some brandy, rum, oil, rice, &c., he cry'd out aloud, *O you dead white men that lie here, you have a mind to have this factor that is sick to you, but he is our king's friend and he loves him, and will not part with him as yet.* Then he went to captain *Wiburn's* grave who built the factory, and cry'd, *O you captain of all the dead white men that lie here, this is your doings; you would have this man from us to bear you company, because he is a good man, but our king will not part with him, nor you shall not have him yet.* Then making a hole in the ground over his grave, he poured in the brandy, rum, oil, rice, &c., telling him, *If he wanted those things, there they were for him, but the factor he must not expect, nor should not have*, with more such nonsense; then went to *Smith*, and assured him he should not die; but growing troublesome to the sick man, *Pierson* turned him out of the factory, and in two days after poor *Smith* made his *exit*.

Mr. Josiah Relph to Mr. Thomas Routh, in Castle Street, Carlisle. June 20, 1740.

* * * * *

"The following was sent me a few months ago by the minister of Kirklees in Yorkshire, the burying-place of Robin Hood. My correspondent tells me it was found among the papers of the late Dr. Gale of York, and is supposed to have been the genuine epitaph of that noted English outlaw. He adds that the grave-stone is yet to be seen, but the characters are now worn out.

Here undernead dis laitl Stean
Laiz Robert Earl of Huntingtun.
Nea Arcir ver az hie sa geud,
An Piple kauld im Robin Heud.
Sick utlawz az hi and is men
Vil england nivir si agen.
Obiit 24. Kal. Dehembris, 1247.

I am, dear Sir, your most faithful and humble Servant,
JOSIAH RELPH."

Note in Nichols. — See the stone engraved in the Sepulchral Monuments, vol. i. p. cviii. Mr. Gough says the inscription was never on it; and that the stone must have been brought from another place, as the ground under it, on being explored, was found to have been never before disturbed.*

Lord Dalmeny, son of the E. of Rosebery, married about eighty years ago a widow at Bath for her beauty. They went abroad, she sickened, and on her death-bed requested that she might be interred in some particular churchyard, either in Sussex or Suffolk, I forget which. The body was embalmed, but at the custom-house in the port where it was landed the officer suspected smuggling and insisted on opening it. They recognised the features of the wife of their own clergyman,— who having been married to him against her own inclination had eloped. Both husbands followed the body to the grave. The Grandfather of Dr. Smith of Norwich knew the Lord.

It was a melancholy notion of the Stoics that the condition of the Soul, and even its individual immortality, might be affected by the circumstances of death: for example, that if any person were killed by a great mass of earth falling upon him, or the ruins of a building, the Soul as well as the body would be crushed, and not being able to extricate itself would be extinguished there: *existimant animam hominis magno pondere extriti permeare non posse, et statim spargi, quia non fuerit illi exitus liber.*

Upon this belief, the satirical epitaph on Sir John Vanbrugh would convey what might indeed be called a heavy curse.

* On the disputed question of the genuineness of the above epitaph, see the Notes and Illustrations to Ritson's Robin Hood, pp. xliv — 1. Robin Hood's Death and Burial is the last Ballad in the second volume.

"And there they buried bold Robin Hood,
Near to the fair Kirkleys."

Some of the Greenlanders, for even in Greenland there are sects, suppose the soul to be so corporeal that it can increase or decrease, is divisible, may lose part of its substance, and have it restored again. On its way to Heaven, which is five days' dreadful journey, all the way down a rugged rock, which is so steep that they must slide down it, and so rough that their way is tracked with blood, they are liable to be destroyed, and this destruction, which they call the second death, is final, and therefore justly deemed of all things the most terrible. It is beyond the power of their Angekoks to remedy this evil ; but these impostors pretend to the art of repairing a maimed soul, bringing home a strayed or runaway one, and of changing away one that is sickly, for the sound and sprightly one of a hare, a rein-deer, a bird, or an infant.

" This is the peevishness of our humane wisdom, yea, rather of our humane folly, to yearn for tidings from the dead, as if a spirit departed could declare anything more evidently than the book of God, which is the sure oracle of life? This was Saul's practise, — neglect Samuel when he was alive, and seek after him when he was dead. What says the Prophet, *Should not a people seek unto their God? Should the living repair to the dead?* (*Isai. viij.* 19.) Among the works of Athanasius I find (though he be not the author of the questions to Antiochus,) a discourse full of reason, why God would not permit the soul of any of those that departed from hence to return back unto us again, and to declare the state of things in hell unto us. For what pestilent errors would arise from thence to seduce us? Devils would transform themselves into the shapes of men that were deceased, pretend that they were risen from the dead (for what will not the Father of lies feign?) and so spread in any false doctrines, or incite us to many barbarous actions, to our endless error and destruction. And admit they be not Phantasms, and delusions, but the very men, yet all men are liars, but God is truth. I told you what a Necromancer Saul was in the Old Testament, he would believe nothing unless a prophet rose from the grave to teach him. There is another as good as himself in the New Testament, and not another pattern in all the Scripture to my remembrance, Luke xvi. 27. The rich man in hell urged Abraham to send Lazarus to admonish his brethren of their wicked life ; Abraham refers to Moses and the Prophets. He that could not teach himself when he was alive, would teach Abraham himself being in hell, *Nay, Father Abraham, but if one went unto them from the dead, they will repent.*

" The mind is composed with quietness to hear the living ; the apparitions of dead men, beside the suspicion of delusion, would fill us with ghastly horror, and it were impossible we should be fit scholars to learn if such strong perturbation of fear should be upon us. How much better hath God ordained for our security, and tranquillity, *that the priest's lips should preserve knowledge?* I know, if God shall see it fit to have us disciplined by such means, he can stir up the spirits of the faithful departed to come among us : So, after Christ's resurrection, many dead bodies of the Saints which slept arose, and came out of their graves, and went into the Holy City, and appeared unto many. This was not upon a small matter, but upon a brave and renowned occasion : But for the Spirits of damnation, that are tied in chains of darkness, there is no re-passage for them, and it makes more to strengthen our belief that never any did return from hell to tell us their woeful tale, than if any should return. It is among the severe penalties of damnation that there is no indulgence for the smallest respite to come out of it. The heathen put that truth into this fable. The Lion asked the Fox, why he never came to visit him when he was sick : Says the Fox, because I can trace many beasts by the print of their foot that have gone toward your den, Sir Lion, but I cannot see the print of one foot that ever came back :

Quia me vestigia terrent
Omnia te advorsum spectantia, nulla retrorsum.

So there is a beaten, and a broad road that leads the reprobate to hell, but you do not find the print of one hoof that ever came back. When I have given you my judgment about apparitions of the dead in their descending from Heaven, or ascending from hell, I must tell you in the third place, I have met with a thousand stories in Pontifician writings concerning some that have had repassage from Purgatory to their familiars upon earth. Notwithstanding the reverence I bear to Gregory the Great, I cannot refrain to say ; He was much to blame to begin such fictions upon his credulity ; others have been more to blame that have invented such Legends ; and they are most to be derided that believe them. *O miserable Theology!* if thy tenets must be confirmed by sick men's dreams, and dead men's phantastical apparitions !"

Bp. Hackett.

" It is a morose humour in some, even ministers, that they will not give a due commendation to the deceased : whereby they not only offer a seeming unkindness to the dead, but do a real injury to the living, by discouraging virtue, and depriving us of the great instruments of piety, good examples : which usually are far more effective methods of instruction, than any precepts : These commonly urging only the necessity of those duties, while the other show the possibility and manner of performing.

" But then, 'tis a most unchristian and uncharitable mistake in those, that think it unlawful to commemorate the dead, and to celebrate their memories : whereas there is no one thing does so much uphold and keep up the honour and interest of religion amongst the multitude, as the due observance of those Anniversaries which the Church has, upon this account, scattered throughout the whole course of the year, would do : and indeed to our neglect of this in a great part the present decay of religion may rationally be imputed.

" Thus in this age of our's what Pliny saith of his, *Postquam desimus facere laudanda, laudari quoque ineptum putamus.* Since people have left off doing things that are praiseworthy, they look upon praise itself as a silly thing.

" And possibly the generality of hearers themselves are not free from this fault ; who peradventure may fancy their own life upbraided, when they hear another's commended.

" But that the servants of God, which depart this life in his faith and fear, may and must be praised, I shall endeavour to make good upon these three grounds.

" *In common justice to the deceased themselves.* Ordinary civility teaches us to speak well of the dead. *Nec quicquam sanctius habet reverentia superstitum, quàm ut amissos venerabiliter recordetur,* says Ausonius, and makes this the ground of the Parentalia, which had been ever since Numa's time.

" *Praise,* however it may become the living, is a just debt to the deserts of the dead, who are now got clear out of the reach of envy ; which, if it have anything of the generous in it, will scorn, vulture-like, to prey upon carcass.

" Besides, Christianity lays a greater obligation upon us ; *The Communion of Saints* is a *Tenet* of our faith. Now, as we ought not *pray* to or for them, so we may and must *praise* them.

" This is the least we can do in return for those great offices they did the Church Militant, while they were with us, and now do, they are with God: nor have we any other probable way of communicating with them.

"The Philosopher in his Morals makes it a question, whether the dead are in any way concerned in what befals them or their posterity after their decease; and whether those honours and reproaches, which survivors cast upon them, reach them or no? and he concludes it after a long debate in the affirmative; not so, he says, as to alter their state, but, συμβάλλεσθαί τι, to contribute somewhat to it.

"Tully, though not absolutely persuaded of an immortal soul, as speaking doubtfully and variously of it, yet is constant to this, that he takes a good name and a reputation, we leave behind us, to be a kind of immortality.

"But there is more in it than so. Our remembrance of the Saints may be a means to improve their bliss, and heighten their rewards to all eternity. Abraham, the Father of the Faithful, hath his bosom thus daily enlarged for new comers.

"Whether the heirs of the kingdom are, at their first admission, instated into a full possession of all their glory, and kept to that stint, I think may be a doubt. For if the faculty be perfected by the object, about which 'tis conversant; then the faculties of those blessed ones being continually employed upon an infinite object, must needs be infinitely perficible, and capable still of being more and more enlarged, and consequently of receiving still new and further additions of glory.

"Not only so, (this is in Heaven:) but even the influence of that example, they leave behind them on earth, drawing still more and more souls after them to God, will also add to those improvements to the end of the world, and bring in a revenue of accessory joys.

"And would it not be unjust in us then to deny them those glorious advantages which our commemoration and inclination may and ought to give them." *

Adam Littleton.

Circles and right lines limit and close all bodies, and the mortal right lined circle must conclude to shut up all. There is no Antidote against the Opinion of Time, which temporally considereth all things; Our Fathers find their Graves in our short memories and sadly tell us how we may be buried in our survivors. Grave-stones tell truth scarce forty years: Generations pass while some trees stand, and old families last not three oaks. To be read by bare Inscriptions like many in Gruter, to hope for Eternity by Ænigmatical Epithetes, or first Letters of our names to be studied by Antiquaries, who we were, and have new names given us like many of the Mummies, are cold consolations unto the students of perpetuity even by everlasting Languages.

Sir T. Browne.

---

* "Five Sermons formerly printed," p. 61., at the end of the volume. The one from which the above passage is extracted is that preached at the obsequies of the Right Honourable the Lady Jane Cheyne.

CHAPTER CCXXXVI.

CHARITY OF THE DOCTOR IN HIS OPINIONS. MASON THE POET. POLITICAL MEDICINE. SIR WILLIAM TEMPLE. CERVANTES. STATE PHYSICIANS. ADVANTAGE TO BE DERIVED FROM, WHETHER TO KING, CABINET, LORDS, OR COMMONS. EXAMPLES. PHILOSOPHY OF POPULAR EXPRESSIONS. COTTON MATHER. CLAUDE PAJON AND BARNABAS OLEY. TIMOTHY ROGERS AND MELANCHOLY.

Go to!
You are a subtile nation, you physicians,
And grown the only cabinets in court! B. Jonson.

The Doctor, who was charitable in all his opinions, used to account and apologise for many of the errors of men, by what he called the original sin of their constitution, using the term not theologically, but in a physico-philosophical sense. What an old French physician said concerning Charles VIII. was in entire accord with his speculations, — *ce corps étoit composé de mauvais pâte, et de matière cathareuse*. Men of hard hearts and heavy intellect, he said, were made of stony materials. For a drunkard, his qualifying censure was, — "poor fellow! bibulous clay — bibulous clay!" Your light-brained, light-hearted people, who are too giddy ever to be good, had not earth enough, he said, in their composition. Those upon whose ungrateful temper benefits were ill bestowed, and on whom the blessings of fortune were thrown away, he excused by saying that they were made from a sandy soil; — and for Mammon's muckworms, — their mould was taken from the dunghill.

Mason the poet was a man of ill-natured politics, out of humour with his country till the French Revolution startled him and brought him into a better state of feeling. This, however, was not while the Doctor lived, and till that time he could see nothing but tyranny and injustice in the proceedings of the British Government, and nothing but slavery and ruin to come for the nation. These opinions were the effects of Whiggery*

---

* See Vol. IV. p. 275. — p. 317. of this edition.

acting upon a sour stomach and a saturnine constitution. To think ill of the present and augur worse of the future has long been accounted a proof of patriotism among those who by an illustrious antiphrasis call themselves patriots. "What the Romans scorned to do after the battle of Cannæ," said Lord Keeper Finch in one of his solid and eloquent speeches, "what the Venetians never did when they had lost all their *terra firma*, that men are now taught to think a virtue and the sign of a wise and good man, *desperare de Republica:* and all this in a time of as much justice and peace at home, as good laws for the security of religion and liberty, as good execution of these laws, as great plenty of trade and commerce abroad, and as likely a conjuncture of affairs for the continuance of these blessings to us, as ever nation prospered under."

The Doctor, when he spoke of this part of Mason's character, explained it by saying that the elements had not been happily tempered in him — "cold and dry, Sir!" and then he shook his head and knit his brow with that sort of compassionate look which came naturally into his countenance when he was questioned concerning a patient whose state was unfavourable.

But though he believed that many of our sins and propensities are bred in the bone, he disputed the other part of the proverb, and maintained that they might be got out of the flesh. And then generalising with a rapidity worthy of Humboldt himself, he asserted that all political evils in modern ages and civilised states were mainly owing to a neglect of the medical art; — and that there would not, and could not be so many distempers in the body politic, if the *primæ viæ* were but attended to with proper care; an opinion in which he was fortified by the authority of Sir William Temple.

"I have observed the fate of *Campania*," says that eminent statesman, "determine contrary to all appearances, by the caution and conduct of a General, which was attributed by those that knew him to his age and infirmities, rather than his own true qualities, acknowledged otherwise to have been as great as most men of the age. I have seen the counsels of a noble country grow bold, or timorous, according to the fits of his good or ill-health that managed them, and the pulse of the Government beat high with that of the Governor; and this unequal conduct makes way for great accidents in the world. Nay, I have often reflected upon the counsels and fortunes of the greatest monarchies rising and decaying sensibly with the ages and healths of the Princes and chief officers that governed them. And I remember one great minister that confessed to me, when he fell into one of his usual fits of the gout, he was no longer able to bend his mind or thought to any public business, nor give audiences beyond two or three of his domestics, though it were to save a kingdom; and that this proceeded not from any violence of pain, but from a general languishing and faintness of spirits, which made him in those fits think nothing worth the trouble of one careful or solicitous thought. For the approaches, or lurkings of the Gout, the Spleen, or the Scurvy, nay the very fumes of indigestion, may indispose men to thought and to care, as well as diseases of danger and pain. Thus accidents of health grow to be accidents of State, and public constitutions come to depend in a great measure upon those of particular men; which makes it perhaps seem necessary in the choice of persons for great employments, (at least such as require constant application and pains,) to consider their bodies as well as their minds, and ages and health as well as their abilities."

Cervantes, according to the Doctor, clearly perceived this great truth, and went farther than Sir W. Temple, for he perceived also the practical application, though it was one of those truths which, because it might have been dangerous for him to propound them seriously, he was fain to bring forward in a comic guise, leaving it for the wise to discover his meaning, and for posterity to profit by it. He knew — (*Daniel loquitur*) — for what did not Cervantes know? — that if Philip II. had committed himself to the superintendence of a Physician instead of a Father Confessor, many of the crimes and miseries by which his reign is so infamously distinguished, might have been prevented. A man of his sad spirit and melancholy complexion to be dieted upon fish the whole forty days of Lent, two days in the week during the rest of the year, and on the eve of every holiday besides, — what could be expected but atrabilious thoughts, and cold-blooded resolutions? Therefore Cervantes appointed a Physician over Sancho in his Baratarian government: the humour of the scene was for all readers, the application for those who could penetrate beyond the veil, the benefit for happier ages when the art of Government should be better understood, and the science of medicine be raised to its proper station in the state.

Shakespeare intended to convey the same political lesson, when he said "take physic, pomp!" He used the word pomp instead of power, cautiously, for in those days it was a perilous thing to meddle with matters of state.

When the Philosopher Carneades undertook to confute Zeno the Stoic in public argument, (still, reader, *Daniel loquitur*,) how did he prepare himself for the arduous disputation? — by purging his head with hellebore, to the intent that the corrupt humours which ascended thither from the stomach should not disturb the seat of memory and judgement, and obscure his intellectual perception. The theory, Sir, was erroneous, but the principle is good. When we require best music from the instrument, ought we not first to be careful that all its parts are in good order, and if we find a string that jars, use our endeavours for tuning it?

It may have been the jest of a satirist that Dryden considered stewed prunes as the best means of putting his body into a state favourable for heroic composition; but that odd person George Wither tells us of himself that he usually watched and fasted when he composed, that his spirit was lost if at such times he tasted meat or drink, and that if he took a glass of wine he could not write a verse: — no wonder, therefore, that his verses were for the most part in a weak and watery vein.* Father Paul Sarpi had a still more extraordinary custom: it is not to an enemy, but to his friend and admirers that we are indebted for informing us with what care that excellent writer attended to physical circumstance as affecting his intellectual powers. For when he was either reading or writing, alone, "his manner," says Sir Henry Wotton, "was to sit fenced with a castle of paper about his chair, and over head; for he was of our Lord of St. Alban's opinion *that all air is predatory*, and especially hurtful when the spirits are most employed."

There should be a State Physician to the King, besides his Physicians ordinary and extraordinary, — one whose sole business should be to watch over the royal health as connected with the discharge of the royal functions, a head keeper of the King's health.

For the same reason there ought to be a Physician for the Cabinet, a Physician for the Privy Council, a Physician for the Bench of Bishops, a Physician for the twelve Judges, two for the House of Lords, four for the House of Commons, one for the Admiralty, one for the War Office, one for the Directors of the East India Company, (there was no Board of Control in the Doctor's days, or he would certainly have advised that a Physician should be placed upon that Establishment also): one for the Lord Mayor, two for the Common Council, four for the Livery. (He was speaking in the days of Wilkes and Liberty.) "How much mischief," said he, "might have been prevented by cupping the Lord Mayor, blistering a few of the Aldermen, administering salts and manna to lower the pulse of civic patriotism, and keeping the city orators upon a low regimen for a week before every public meeting."

Then in the Cabinet what evils might be averted by administering laxatives or corroborants as the case required.

---

* The Greek Proverb, adverted to by Horace in 1 Epist. xix., was in the Dcctor's thoughts:

ὕδωρ δὲ πίνων οὐδὲν ἂν τέκοι σοφόν.

In the Lords and Commons, by clearing away bile, evacuating ill-humours and occasionally by cutting for the simples.*

While men are what they are, weak, frail, inconstant, fallible, peccable, sinful creatures, — it is in vain to hope that Peers and Commoners will prepare themselves for the solemn exercise of their legislative functions by fasting and prayer, — that so they may be better fitted for retiring into themselves, and consulting upon momentous questions, the Urim and Thummim which God hath placed in the breast of every man. But even as Laws are necessary for keeping men within the limits of their duty when conscience fails, so in this case it should be part of the law of Parliament that what its Members will not do for themselves, the Physician should do for them. They should go through a preparatory course of medicine before every session, and be carefully attended as long as Parliament was sitting.

Traces of such a practice, as of many important and primeval truths, are found among savages, from whom the Doctor was of opinion that much might be learned, if their customs were diligently observed and their traditions carefully studied. In one of the bravest nations upon the Mississippi, the warriors before they set out upon an expedition always prepared themselves by taking the Medicine of War, which was an emetic, about a gallon in quantity for each man, and to be swallowed at one draught. There are other tribes in which the Beloved Women prepare a beverage at the Physic Dance, and it is taken to wash away sin.

"Here," said the Doctor, "are vestiges of early wisdom, probably patriarchal, and if so, revealed," — for he held that all needful knowledge was imparted to man at his creation. And the truth of the principle is shown in common language. There is often a philosophy in popular expressions and forms of speech, which escapes notice, because words are taken as they are uttered, at their current value, and we rest satisfied with their trivial acceptation. We take them in the husk and the shell, but sometimes it is worth while to look for the kernel. Do we not speak of *sound* and orthodox opinions, — *sound* principles, *sound* learning? *mens sana in corpore sano.* A sound mind is connected with a sound body, and sound and orthodox opinions result from the sanity of both. Unsound opinions are diseased ones, and therefore the factious, the heretical and the schismatic, ought to be put under the care of a physician.

"I have read of a gentleman," says Cotton Mather, "who had an humour of making singular and fanciful expositions of scripture; but one Doctor Sim gave him a dose of physic, which when it had wrought, the gentleman became orthodox immediately and expounded at the old rate no more."

Thus as the accurate, and moderate, and erudite Mosheim informs us, the French theologian Claude Pajon was of opinion that in order to produce that amendment of the heart which is called regeneration, nothing more is requisite than to put the body, if its habit is bad, into a sound state by the power of physic, and having done this, then to set truth and falsehood before the understanding, and virtue and vice before the will, clearly and distinctly in their genuine colours, so as that their nature and their properties may be fully apprehended. But the Doctor thought that Pajon carried his theory too far, and ought to have been physicked himself.

That learned and good man Barnabas Oley, the friend and biographer of the saintly Herbert, kept within the bounds of discretion, when he delivered an opinion of the same tendency. After showing what power is exercised by art over nature, 1st, in inanimate materials, 2dly, in vegetables, and 3dly, the largeness or latitude of its power over the memory, the imagination and locomotive faculties of sensitive creatures, he proceeds to the fourth rank, the rational, "which adds a diadem of excellency to the three degrees above mentioned, being an approach unto the nature angelical and divine." "Now," says he, "1st, in as much as the human body partly agrees with the

* The probable origin of this Proverb is given in Grose's Dictionary of the Vulgar Tongue.

first rank of materials inanimate, so can Art partly use it, as it uses them, to frame (rather to modify the frame of) it into great variety; the head thus, the nose so; and other ductile parts, as is seen and read, after other fashions. 2. Art can do something to the Body answerable to what Gardeners do to plants. If our Blessed Saviour's words (Matthew vi. 27.) deny all possibility of adding procerity or tallness to the stature, yet as the Lord Verulam notes, to make the Body dwarfish, crook-shouldered (as some Persians did) to recover straightness, or procure slenderness, is in the power of Art. But, 3. much more considerable authority has it over the humours, either so to impel and enrage them, that like furious streams they shall dash the Body (that bottom wherein the precious Soul is embarked) against dangerous rocks, or run it upon desperate sands; or so to attemper and tune them, that they shall become like calm waters or harmonious instruments for virtuous habits, introduced by wholesome moral precepts, to practise upon. It is scarce credible what services the *Noble Science of Physic* may do unto Moral, (*yea to Grace and Christian*,) virtue, by prescribing diet to prevent, or medicine to allay the fervours and eruptions of humours, of blood, and of that *irriguum concupiscentiæ*, or ὁ τροχὸς τῆς γενέσεως, especially if these jewels, their recipes, light into obedient ears. These helps of bettering nature are within her lowest and middle region of Diet and Medicine."

A sensible woman of the Doctor's acquaintance, (the mother of a young family,) entered so far into his views upon this subject, that she taught her children from their earliest childhood to consider ill-humour as a disorder which was to be cured by physic. Accordingly she had always small doses ready, and the little patients, whenever it was thought needful, took rhubarb *for the crossness*. No punishment was required. Peevishness or ill-temper and rhubarb were associated in their minds always as cause and effect.

There are Divines who have thought that melancholy may with advantage be treated in age, as fretfulness in this family was in childhood. Timothy Rogers, who having been long afflicted with Trouble of Mind and the Disease of Melancholy, wrote a discourse concerning both for the use of his fellow sufferers, says of Melancholy, that "it does generally indeed first begin at the body, and then conveys its venom to the mind; and if anything could be found that might keep the blood and spirits in their due temper and motion, this would obstruct its further progress, and in a great measure keep the soul clear. I pretend not" (he continues) "to tell you what medicines are proper to remove it, and I know of none, I leave you to advise with such as are learned in the profession of Physic." And then he quotes a passage from "old Mr. Greenham's Comfort for afflicted Consciences." "If a Man," saith old Mr. Greenham, "that is troubled in conscience come to a Minister, it may be he will look all to the Soul and nothing to the Body: if he come to a Physician he considereth the Body and neglecteth the Soul. For my part, I would never have the Physician's counsel despised, nor the labour of the Minister neglected: because the Soul and Body dwelling together,—it is convenient, that as the Soul should be cured by the Word, by Prayer, by Fasting, or by Comforting, so the Body must be brought into some temperature by physic, and diet, by harmless diversions and such like ways; providing always that it be so done in the fear of God, as not to think by these ordinary means quite to smother or evade our troubles, but to use them as preparatives, whereby our Souls may be made more capable of the spiritual methods which are to follow afterwards."

But Timothy Bright, Doctor of Physic, is the person who had the most profound reverence for the medical art. "No one," he said, "should touch so holy a thing that hath not passed the whole discipline of liberal sciences, and washed himself pure and clean in the waters of wisdom and understanding." "O Timothy Bright, Timothy Bright," said the Doctor, "rightly wert thou called Timothy Bright, for thou wert a Bright Timothy!" Nor art thou less deserving of praise, O Timothy Bright, say I, for having published an abridgement of the Book of Acts and Monuments of the Church, written by that Reverend Father Master John Fox, and by thee thus reduced into a more accessible form,—for such as either through want of leisure or ability have not the use of so necessary a history.

CHAPTER CCXXXVII.

MORE MALADIES THAN THE BEST PHYSICIANS CAN PREVENT BY REMEDIES. THE DOCTOR NOT GIVEN TO QUESTIONS, AND OF THE POCO-CURANTE SCHOOL AS TO ALL THE POLITICS OF THE DAY.

> A slight answer to an intricate and useless question is a fit cover to such a dish; a cabbage leaf is good enough to cover a pot of mushrooms. JEREMY TAYLOR.

YET in his serious moods the Doctor sadly confessed with that Sir George, whom the Scotch ungratefully call Bloody Mackenzie, that "as in the body natural, so likewise in the politic, Nature hath provided more diseases than the best of Physicians can prevent by remedies." He knew that kingdoms as well as individuals have their agues and calentures, are liable to plethora sometimes, and otherwhiles to atrophy, to fits of madness which no hellebore can cure, and to decay and dissolution which no human endeavours can avert. With the maladies of the State indeed he troubled himself not, for though a true-born Englishman, he was as to all politics of the day, of the Poco-curante school. But with those of the human frame his thoughts were continually employed; it was his business to deal with them; his duty and his earnest desire to heal them, under God's blessing, where healing was humanly possible, or to alleviate them, when anything more than alleviation was beyond the power of human skill.

The origin of evil was a question upon which he never ventured. Here, too, he said with Sir George Mackenzie, "as I am not able by the Jacob's Ladder of my merit to scale Heaven, so am I less able by the Jacob's Staff of my private ability to take up the true altitude of its mysteries:" and borrowing a play upon words from the same old Essayist, he thought the brain had too little *pia mater*, which was too curious in such inquiries. But the mysteries of his own profession afforded "ample room and verge enough" for his speculations, however wide and wild their excursions. Those mysteries are so many, so momentous, and so inscrutable, that he wondered not at any superstitions which have been excogitated by bewildered imagination, and implicitly followed by human weakness in its hopes and fears, its bodily and its mental sufferings.

As little did he wonder at the theories advanced by men who were, in their days, the Seraphic and Angelic and Irrefragable Doctors of the healing art:—the tartar of Paracelsus, the Blas and Gas of Van Helmont, nor in later times at the animalcular hypotheses of Langius and Paullinus; nor at the belief of elder nations, as the Jews, and of savages everywhere, that all maladies are the immediate work of evil spirits. But when he called to mind the frightful consequences to which the belief of this opinion has led, the cruelties which have been exercised, the crimes which have been perpetrated, the miseries which have been inflicted and endured, it made him shudder at perceiving that the most absurd error may produce the greatest mischief to society, if it be accompanied with presumption, and if any real or imaginary interest be connected with maintaining it.

The Doctor, like his Master and benefactor Peter Hopkins, was of the Poco-curante school in politics. He said that the Warwickshire gentleman who was going out with his hounds when the two armies were beginning to engage at Edge-hill, was not the worst Englishman who took the field that day.

Local circumstances favoured this tendency to political indifference. It was observed in the 34th Chapter of this Opus that one of the many reasons for which our Philosopher thought Doncaster a very likeable place of residence was, that it sent no Members to Parliament. And Yorkshire being too large a county for any of its great families to engage lightly in contesting it, the Election fever, however it might rage in other towns or other parts of the county, never prevailed there. But the constitution of the Doctor's mind secured him from all excitement of this nature. Even in the days of Wilkes and Liberty, when not a town in England escaped the general Influenza, he was not in the slightest degree affected by it, nor did he ever take up the Public Advertiser for the sake of one of Junius's Letters.

CHAPTER CCXXXVIII.

SIMONIDES. FUNERAL POEMS. UNFEELING OPINION IMPUTED TO THE GREEK POET, AND EXPRESSED BY MALHERBE. SENECA. JEREMY TAYLOR AND THE DOCTOR ON WHAT DEATH MIGHT HAVE BEEN, AND, WERE MEN WHAT CHRISTIANITY WOULD MAKE THEM, MIGHT BE.

Intendale chi può; che non è stretto
Alcuno a creder più di quel che vuole.
ORLANDO INNAMORATO.

AMONG the lost works of antiquity, there are few poems which I should so much rejoice in recovering, as those of Simonides. Landor has said of him that he and Pindar wrote nothing bad; that his characteristics were simplicity, brevity, tenderness, and an assiduous accuracy of description. "If I were to mention," he adds, "what I fancy would give an English reader the best idea of his manner, I should say, the book of Ruth."

One species of composition wherein he excelled was that which the Dutch in their straight-forward way call *Lykzangen* or *Lykdichten*, but for which we have no appropriate name, — poems in commemoration of the dead. Beautiful specimens are to be found in the poetry of all countries, and this might be expected, threnodial being as natural as amatory verse; and as the characteristic of the latter is passion with little reflection, that of the former is, as naturally, to be at the same time passionate and thoughtful.

Our own language was rich in such poems during the Elizabethan age, and that which followed it. Of foreign poets none has in this department exceeded Chiabrera.

There is a passage among the fragments of Simonides which is called by his old editor consolatory, παρηγορικόν: but were it not for the authority of Seneca, who undoubtedly was acquainted with the whole poem, I should not easily be persuaded that so thoughtful, so pensive, so moralising a poet would, in any mood of mind, have recommended such consolation:

Τοῦ μὲν θανόντος οὐκ ἂν ἐνθυμοίμεθα,
Εἴ τι φρονοῖμεν, πλεῖον ἡμέρας μιᾶς·

let us not call to mind the dead, if we think of him at all, more than a single day. Indeed I am not certain from what Seneca says, whether the poet was speaking in his own, or in an assumed character, nor whether he spoke seriously or satirically; or I cannot but suspect that the passage would appear very differently, if we saw it in its place. Malherbe gives the same sort of advice in his consolation to M. du Périer upon the death of a daughter.

Ne te lasse donc plus d'inutiles complaintes;
Mais sage à l'avenir,
Aime une ombre comme ombre, et des cendres éteintes
Eteins le souvenir;

such a feeling is much more in character with a Frenchman than with Simonides.

Seneca himself, Stoic though he was, gave no such advice, but accounted the remembrance of his departed friends among his solemn delights, not looking upon them as lost: *Mihi amicorum defunctorum cogitatio dulcis ac blanda est; habui enim illos, tanquam amissurus; amissi tanquam habeam.*

My venerable friend was not hardened by a profession, which has too often the effect of blunting the feelings, even if it does not harden the heart. His disposition and his happy education preserved him from that injury; and as his religion taught him that death was not in itself an evil, — that for him, and for those who believed with him, it had no sting, — the subject was as familiar to his meditations as to his professional practice. A speculation which Jeremy Taylor, without insisting on it, offers to the consideration of inquisitive and modest persons, appeared to him far more probable than the common opinion which Milton expresses when he says that the fruit of the Forbidden Tree brought death into the world. That, the Bishop argues, "which *would have been*, had there been no sin, and that which *remains* when the sin or guiltiness is gone, is not properly the punishment of the sin. But dissolution of the soul and body should have been, if Adam had not sinned; for the world would have been too little to have entertained those myriads of men, which must, in all reason, have been born from that blessing of 'Increase and multiply,' which was given at the first creation: and to have confined mankind to the pleasures of this world, in case he had not fallen, would have been a punishment of his innocence: but however, it *might have been*, though God had not been angry, and *shall still be*, even when the sin is taken off. The proper consequent of this will be, that when the Apostle says 'Death came in by Sin,' and that 'Death is the wages of Sin,' he primarily and literally means the solemnities, and causes, and infelicities, and untimeliness of temporal death; and not merely the dissolution, which is directly no evil, but an inlet to a better state."

As our friend agreed in this opinion with Bishop Taylor; and moreover as he read in Scriptures that Enoch and Elijah had been translated from this world without tasting of death; and as he deemed it probable at least, that St. John, the beloved disciple, had been favoured with a like exemption from the common lot, he thought that Asgill had been hardly dealt with in being expelled from Parliament for his "Argument," that according to the Covenant of Eternal Life, revealed in the Scriptures, man might be translated from hence, without passing through death. The opinion, Dr. Dove thought, might be enthusiastic, the reasoning wild, the conclusion untenable, and the manner of the book indecorous, or irreverent. But he had learned that much, which appears irreverent, and in reality is so, has not been irreverently intended; and the opinion, although groundless, seemed to him anything rather than profane.

But the exemptions which are recorded in the Bible could not, in his judgement, be considered as showing what would have been the common lot if our first parents had preserved their obedience. This he opined would more probably have been uthanasy than translation; death, not preceded by infirmity and decay, but as welcome, and perhaps as voluntary, as sleep.

Or possibly the transition from a corporeal to a spiritual,— or more accurately in our imperfect language,—from an earthly to a celestial state of being, might have been produced by some developement, some formal mutation as visible, (adverting to a favourite fancy of his own,) as that which in the butterfly was made by the ancients their emblem of immortality. Bishop Van Mildert shows us upon scriptural authority that "the degree of perfection at which we may arrive has no definite limits, but is to go on increasing as long as this state of probation continues." So in the paradisiacal, and possibly in the millennial state, he thought, that with such an intellectual and moral improvement, a corresponding organic evolution might keep pace; and that as the child expands into man, so man might mature into Angel.

CHAPTER CCXXXIX.

THE DOCTOR DISSENTS FROM A PROPOSITION OF WARBURTON'S, AND SHOWS IT TO BE FALLACIOUS. HUTCHINSON'S REMARKS ON THE POWERS OF BRUTES. LORD SHAFTESBURY QUOTED. APOLLONIUS AND THE KING OF BABYLON. DISTINCTION IN THE TALMUD BETWEEN AN INNOCENT BEAST AND A VICIOUS ONE. OPINION OF ISAAC LA PEYRESC. THE QUESTION DE ORIGINE ET NATURA ANIMARUM IN BRUTIS AS BROUGHT BEFORE THE THEOLOGIANS OF SEVEN PROTESTANT ACADEMIES IN THE YEAR 1635 BY DANIEL SENNERTUS.

Toutes veritez ne sont pas bonnes à dire serieusement.
GOMGAM.

WARBURTON has argued that "from the *nature* of any action morality cannot arise, nor from its effects;—not from the first, because being only reasonable or unreasonable, nothing follows but a fitness in doing one, and an absurdity in doing the other;—not from the second, because did the good or evil produced make the action *moral*, brutes, from whose actions proceed both good and evil, would have morality." But Warburton's proposition is fallacious, and his reasoning is inconclusive; there is an essential difference between right and wrong, upon which the moral law is founded; and in the *reductio ad absurdum* upon which he relies, there is no absurdity. The language of the people is sometimes true to nature and philosophy when that of the learned departs widely from the one, and is mistaken in the other. When we call a beast vicious, we mean strictly what the word implies; and if we never speak of one as virtuous, it is because man reserves the praise of virtue to his own kind. The word good supplies its place. A horse that has any vice in him is never called good.

"In this case alone it is," says Lord Shaftesbury, "we call any creature worthy or virtuous, when it can have the notion of a public interest, and can attain the speculation or science of what is morally good or ill, admirable or blameable, right or wrong. For though we may vulgarly call a horse *vicious*, yet we never say of a good one, nor of any mere beast, idiot, or changeling, though ever so good-natured, that he is *worthy* or *virtuous*.

"So that if a creature be generous, kind, constant, compassionate, yet if he cannot reflect on what he himself does, or sees others do, so as to take notice of what is *worthy* or *honest;* and make that notice or conception of *worth* and *honesty* to be an object of his affection, he has not the character of being virtuous; for thus, and no otherwise, he is capable of having a sense of right and wrong; a sentiment or judgement of what is done through just, equal and good affection, or the contrary."

The Jews upon this subject agree with the common and natural opinion; and the Talmud accordingly, when any mischief has been done by an animal, distinguishes between an innocent beast and a vicious one, the owner of an innocent one being required to pay only half the amount of an injury thus, as it was deemed, casually incurred. There have been cases in which the laws have considered a beast as guilty of a crime, and amenable therefore to penal justice. In the year 1403 Simon de Baudemont, Lieutenant at Meulont of Jhean Lord of Maintenon, the Bailiff of Mantes and Meulont, signed an attestation making known the expences which had been incurred in order to execute justice on a Sow that had eaten a child. "For expences with the jail the charge was 6 *sols*. Item, to the executioner who came from Paris to Meulont to put the sentence in execution by the command of our Lord the Bailiff and of the king's Attorney, 54 *sols*. Item, for the carriage that conveyed her to execution, 6 *sols*. Item, for ropes to tie and haul her up, 2 *sols*, 8 *deniers*. Item, for gloves 12 *deniers;* amounting in the whole to 69 *sols*, 8 *deniers*." It must be supposed the Executioner insisted upon the gloves, as a point of honour, that no one might reproach him with having sullied his hands by performing upon such a subject.

When Apollonius was introduced to the King of Babylon, the King invited him to sacrifice with him, for he was about to offer a Nisean horse to the Sun, selected for its beauty and adorned with all pomp for the occasion. But the Philosopher replied, "O King, do you sacrifice after your manner, and give me leave to sacrifice after mine." He then took frankincense, and prayed, saying, "O Sun, conduct me so far as it seemeth good to me and to thee. And let me become acquainted with virtuous men; but as for the wicked, let me neither know them nor they me." And throwing the frankincense in the fire he observed the smoke, how it ascended and which way it bent, and just touching the fire when it seemed that he had sacrificed enough, he said to the King that he had performed the rites of his country, and forthwith withdrew that he might have nothing to do with blood and slaughter. Afterwards when the King took him where were many lions, bears, and panthers reserved for sport, invited him to go with him and hunt them, Apollonius replied, "King, you should remember, that I did not choose to be present at your sacrifice, much less should I like to see animals wounded, and by the pain of their wounds rendered more ferocious than nature has made them."

Isaac la Peyresc thought differently from the Talmudists and the French Lawyers. He says, quoting the Apostle, *Ubi non est lex, neque prævaricatio est.* Where 'no law is, there is no transgression.' *Prævaricatio autem eadem est, quæ transgressio legis: illa ipsa proprie quæ peccatum imputationis labe infecit. Quod ut compingatur in oculos: pecudes actualiter et materialiter eadem faciunt, quæ transgrediuntur homines; incestant, rapiunt, occidunt; non erit tamen uspiam adeo supinus qui dicat, pecudes peccare ad similitudinem transgressionis hominum; quia pecudes quæ hæc peccant, sequuntur tantum suam naturam et suam materiam; neque legum transgrediuntur ullam, quia nulla eis data est cujus transgressione formetur in eis et imputetur peccatum.*

Yet it cannot be doubted that in such a case Peyresc himself, disregarding his own arguments, would have ordered the Sow to be put to death.

This author derives *peccatum* from *pecus*, for, says he, "as often as a man wilfully departs from that right reason which constitutes him man, — as often as under the impulse of that brute matter which he has in common with beasts, he commits any action fitting in a beast, but unworthy in man, so often he seems to fall below his own species, and sink into that of a brute." *Latini nomen peccati mutuati sunt à pecore. Quoties enim homo delirat à rectâ ratione illâ quæ hominem constituit; quoties impulsu materiæ suæ quam habet communem cum brutis, quid agit dignum pecore, et indignum homine, toties cadere videtur à specie suâ, et incidere in speciem pecoris sive bruti.*

Pecunia is known to be derived from *Pecus*, wealth, of which money is the representative, having originally consisted in cattle. As money is proverbially the root of all evil, this etymological connection might be remarkable enough to be deemed mysterious by those who are fond of discovering mysteries in words.

"Brutes," Hutchinson says, "are made in scripture objects to inculcate the duties in society, and even emblems of spiritual and divine perfections. Many of them are more strictly bound in pairs than is common between men and women; many, both males and females, take greater care and pains, and run greater risques for the education and defence of their young, than any of our species. Many of them excel us in instructing their young, so in policy, in industry, in mechanical arts and operations. And there are other species among them, examples to deter men from the vices in society." "The power in brutes," he says, "is by the same agent as that in the body of man, and they are made of the same species of dust; most of them are guided by what is called instinct; some of them are tamed and disciplined and their powers made serviceable to men, and all of them are subject to the immediate power of God, when he pleases to direct them. Mechanism is carried so far in them, that in the parts or degrees of sensation they excel man; that by every one of their actions man might see the *ne plus ultra* of sense, and know how to distinguish the difference between them and the decayed image in him, to value it accordingly, and excite a proportionate zeal in him to recover the first perfections in that image, and augment them to secure the pleasure of exercising them upon the most desirable objects to all eternity." So far so good, but this once influential writer makes an erroneous conclusion when he says, "if you allow anything farther than mechanism to Brutes, imagine that they have souls, or think, or act the part of souls: you either begin to think that you have no soul, or that it is, such as are in Brutes, mortal."

The question *de Origine et Naturâ Animarum in Brutis* was brought before the Theologians of seven Protestant Academies in the year 1635, by Daniel Sennertus, Professor of Medicine at Wittemberg, of whose Institutes Sir Thomas Browne says to a student in that art, "assure yourself that when you are a perfect master of them you will seldom meet with any point in physic to which you will not be able to speak like a man." It was the opinion of this very learned professor that what in scholastic language is called the *form* of every perfect thing, (distinguished from *figure*,—*forma est naturæ bonum, figura, artis opus*,) though it is not a soul, yet even in precious stones is something altogether different from the four elements, and that every soul, or living principle, is a certain quintessence; the wonderful operations in plants, and the more wonderful actions of brute creatures, far exceeding all power of the elements, had convinced him of this. But for asserting it, Freitagius the medical Professor at Groninghen attacked him fiercely as a blasphemer and a heretic. Sennertus being then an old man was more moved by this outrage than became one of his attainments and high character. So he laid the case before the Universities of Leipsic, Rostock, Basle, Marpurg, Konigsberg, Jena, Strasburg, and Altdorff, and he requested their opinion upon these two propositions, whether what he had affirmed, that the souls of brute creatures had been created at first from nothing by the Deity, and were not of an elementary nature, but of something different, was blasphemous and heretical, or whether it were not an ignorant opinion of his assailant, that brute animals consisted wholly of elementary matter, both as to their body and soul?

They all answered the questions more or less at large, the Leipsic Doctors saying, *Officii nostri duximus esse ut in timore Domini ea sub diligentem disquisitionem vocaremus.* They saw nothing irreligious in the opinion that God at the creation had formed the bodies of brutes from elementary matter, and created their souls *ex nihilo;* after which both were reproduced in the natural course of generation; these souls, however, were not immortal, nor so separable from the matter with which they were united, as to survive it, and exist without it, or return again into their bodies; but when the animals died, the animal soul died also. Thus the excellence of man was unimpaired, and the privilege of the human soul remained inviolate, the prerogative of man being that God had breathed into him the breath of life, whereby he became a living soul. Thus they fully acquitted Sennertus of the charge brought against him; and waiving any such direct condemnation of his accuser as he had desired, condemned in strong terms the insolent manner in which the accusation had been preferred.

The Theologians of Rostock replied more briefly. Dismissing at once the charge of blasphemy and heresy as absurd, they treated the question as purely philosophical, saying, *Quod de elementari naturâ animarum brutorum dicitur, de illo nostrum non est disserere. Arbitramur, hæc non solum Philosophorum, sed et libertati, super his modestè, veritatis inveniendæ studio, philosophantium permittenda; quos nimium constringere, et unius hominis, Aristotelis, alteriusve, velle alligare opinioni, pugnare videtur cum naturâ intellectus humani, quem nulli opinioni servum Deus esse voluit.* Concerning the second question, they were not willing, they said, to draw the saw of contention with any one; *Si tamen, quod sentimus dicendum est, respondemus, illum qui cœlum et terram ex nihilo creavit, non eguisse ullâ materiâ, ex quâ brutorum animas produceret; sed illi placuisse iis quæ Moses recitat verbis compellare terram et aquam, et ad solius Omnipotentis nutum et imperium, ex subjectis quæ compellârit, animas emersisse.* This answer Sennertus obtained through his friend Lauremberg the Horticulturist and Botanist, who advised him at the same time to disregard all invidious attacks; *Turbas tibi dari quòd liberè philosophari satagis, id ipse nôsti, neque novum esse, neque insolens, hâc ætate. Eandem tecum sortem experiuntur omnes eleganter et solidè eruditi, quibus qui paria facere non valet, invidet et oblatrat. Tu verò noli hoc nomine te quicquam macerare neu obtrectationem illam gravius vocare ad animum. Nota est orbi tua eruditio, tua virtus et ingenuitas, quæ ea propter nullam patietur jacturam. Tu modo, ut hactenus fecisti, pergito bene mereri de Republicâ literariâ, et mihi favere, certò tibi persuasus, habere te hîc loci hominem tui amantem, et observantem maxime.*

Zuinger answered more at large for the Faculty at Basle. They bade him not to marvel that he should be accused of heresy and blasphemy, seeing that the same charge has been brought against their Theologians, who when they taught according to Scripture that God alone was the Father of the spirits as their parents were of their bodies, and that the reasonable soul therefore was not derived from their parents, but infused and concreated θύραθεν *à Deo* ἀμέσως were accused either of Pelagianism, as if they had denied Original Sin, or of blasphemy, as if they had made God the author of sin. They admonished him to regard such calumnies more justly and quietly, for evil and invidious tongues could never detract from that estimation which he had won for him in the Republic of Letters. Nevertheless as he had asked for their opinion, they would freely deliver it.

First, then, as to the postulate which he had premised in the Epistle accompanying his Questions, that wherever there is creation, something is produced from nothing, (*ubicunque creatio est, ibi aliquid ex nihilo producitur*,) if by this he intended, that in no mode of creation, whether it were κτίσις, or ποίησις, or πλᾶσις, there was no substrate matter out of which something was made by the omnipotent virtue of the Deity, in that case they thought, that his opinion was contrary to Scripture, forasmuch as it plainly appeared in the book of Genesis, that neither the male nor female were created from nothing, but the man from the dust of the ground, and the woman from one of his ribs, *tanquam præcedentibus corporum materiebus*. But though it is indubitable that the creation of the soul in either parent was immediately *ex nihilo*, as was shown in the creation of Adam, we see nevertheless that the name of creation has been applied by Moses to the formation (*plasmationi*) of their bodies. But if Sennertus's words were to be understood as intending that wherever there was a creation, something was produced in this either *ex nihilo* absolutely, or relatively and κατά τι out of something, some preceding matter, which though certainly in itself something, yet relatively, — that which is made out of it, is nothing, (*nihil, aut non ens*,) because it hath in itself no power, liability, or aptitude that it should either be, or become that which God by his miraculous and omnipotent virtue makes it, they had no difficulty in assenting to this. As for example, the dust of which God formed the body of Adam was something and nothing. Something in itself, for it was earth; nothing in respect of that admirable work of the human body which God formed of it.

As for the question whether his opinion was blasphemous and heretical, it could be neither one nor the other, for it neither derogated from the glory of God, nor touched upon any fundamental article of faith. Some there were who opined that Chaos was created *ex nihilo*, which they understood by Tohu Vabohu, from which all things celestial and elementary were afterwards mediately created by God. Others exploding Chaos held that heaven, earth, water, and air, were created *ex nihilo*. But they did not charge each other with blasphemy and heresy because of this disagreement, and verily they who thought that the souls of brutes were originally created by God *ex nihilo* appeared no more to derogate from the might, majesty and glory of God, than those who held that brutes were wholly created from the element. The virtue of an omnipotent God became in either case presupposed.

There was no heresy, they said, in his assertion that the souls of brutes were not of an elementary nature, but of something different: provided that a just distinction were made between the rational soul and the brute soul, the difference being not merely specific but generic. For the rational soul is altogether of a spiritual nature and essence, *adeòque Ens uti vocant transcendens*, bearing the image of God in this, that properly speaking it is a spirit, as God is a Spirit. 2d.

The rational soul as such, as Aristotle himself testifies, has no bodily energies, or operations; its operations indeed are performed in the body but not by the body, nor by bodily organs; but the contrary is true concerning the souls of brutes. 3dly. The rational soul, though it be closely conjoined with the body and hypostatically united therewith, nevertheless is separable therefrom, so that ever out of the body *sit ὑφιστάμενον aliquod;* but the souls of brutes are immersed in matter and in bodies, so that they cannot subsist without them. Lastly, the rational soul alone hath the privilege of immortality, it being beyond all controversy that the souls of brutes are mortal and corruptible. These differences being admitted, and saving the due prerogative, excellence, and as it were divinity of the rational soul, the Theological Faculty of Basle thought it of little consequence if any one held that the souls of brutes were of something different from elementary matter.

They delivered no opinion in condemnation of his assailant's doctrine, upon the ground that the question was not within their province. *Certum est*, they said, *uti formas rerum omnium difficulter, et non nisi a posteriori, et per certas* περιστάσεις, *cognoscere possumus; ita omnium difficillimè Animarum naturam nos pervestigare posse, nostramque, uti in aliis, ita in hac materiâ, scientiam esse, ut scitè Scaliger loquitur, umbram in sole. Ac non dubium, Deum hic vagabundis contemplationibus nostris ponere voluisse, ut disceremus imbecillitatis et cæcitatis nostræ conscientiâ humiliari, cum stupore opera ejus admirari, atque cum modestia et sobrietate philosophari.* They declared, however, that the rational soul differed from that of brutes in its nature, essence, properties and actions, and that this was not to be doubted of by Christians: that the soul of brutes was not spiritual, not immaterial, that all its actions were merely material, and performed by corporeal organs, and they referred to Sennertus's own works as rightly affirming that it was partible, *et dividatur ad divisionem materiæ, ita ut cum corporis parte aliquid animæ possit avelli*, inferring here, as it seems from a false analogy, that animal life was like that of vegetables, *quæ ex parte a plantâ avulsâ propagantur.*

They entered also into some curious criticism metaphysical and philological upon certain texts pertinent to the questions before them. When the dust became lice throughout all the land of Egypt, the mutation of the dust into lice was to be understood: so too in the creation of Adam, and the formation of Eve, there could be no doubt concerning the matter from which both were made. But when water was miraculously produced from the rock, and from the hollow place in the jaw, *ibi sanè nemo sanus dicet, aquam è petrâ aut maxillâ à Deo ita fuisse productam, ut petra aut maxilla materiam aquæ huic præbuerit.*

The answer from Marpurg was short and satisfactory. There also the Professors waived the philosophical question, saying, *Nos falcem in alienam messem non mittemus, nec Morychi in alieno choro pedem nostrum ponemus, sed nostro modulo ac pede nos metiemur, nobis id etiam dictum putantes,* τὰ ὑπὲρ ἡμᾶς οὐδὲν πρὸς ἡμᾶς. *Nobis nostra vendicabimus, Philosophis philosophica relinquentes.* Tertullian, they said, had asserted that Philosophers were the Patriarchs of Heretics, nevertheless a philosophical opinion, while it keeps within its own circles, and does not interfere with the mysteries of faith, is no heresy. They adduced a subtle argument to show that upon the point in question there was no real difference between something and nothing. *Creatio ex nihilo intelligitur fieri tum ratione sui principii, quod est nihilum negativum; tum ratione indispositionis, ob quam materia, ex quâ aliquid fit, in productione pro nihilo habetur. Quamvis igitur animæ bestiarum dicerentur in Creatione ex potentiâ materiæ eductæ, nihilominus ob indispositionem materiæ quam formæ eductæ multum superant, ex nihilo creatæ essent.* And they agreed with Luther, and with those other Divines who held that the words in the first Chapter of Genesis whereby the Earth was bade to bring forth grass, herbs, trees, and living creatures after their kind, and the water to bring forth fishes, were to be strictly understood, the earth and the waters having, *ex Dei benedictione, activè et verè* produced them.

The answer from Konigsberg was not less favourable. The dispute which Freitagius had raised, *infelix illa σύῤῥαξις* they called it, ought to have been carried on by that Professor with more moderation. Granting that the souls of brutes were not created separately like human souls but conjointly with the body, it still remained doubtful *quomodo se habuerit divinum partim ad aquam et terram factum mandatum, partim simultanea brutalium animarum cum corporibus creatio.* For earth and water might here be variously considered, 1, as the element, 2, as the matter, 3, as the subject, and 4, *ut mater vel vivus uterus ad animalium productionem immediatâ Dei operatione exaltatus.* Water and earth themselves were first created, and on the fifth the vital and plastic power was communicated to them, in which by virtue of the omnipotent word they still consist. They were of opinion that the souls of brutes and of plants also were divinely raised above an elementary condition, it being always understood that the human soul far transcended them. The expression of Moses that formed every beast and every fowl out of the ground, proved not the matter whereof, but the place wherein they were formed.

The Faculty at Jena returned a shorter reply. The ingratitude of the world toward those who published their lucubrations upon such abstruse points, reminded them, they said, of Luther's complaint in one of his Prefaces: *Sæpe recordor boni Gersonis dubitantis num quid boni publicè scribendum et proferendum sit. Si scriptio omittitur, multæ animæ negliguntur, quæ liberari potuissent; si verò illa præstatur, statim Diabolus præstò est cum linguis pestiferis et calumniarum plenis, quæ omnia corrumpunt et inficiunt.* What was said of the production of fish, plants, and animals might be understood synecdochically, *salvâ verborum Mosaicorum integritate*, as the text also was to be understood concerning the creation of man, where it is said that the Lord formed him of the dust of the earth, and immediately afterwards that he breathed into his nostrils the breath of life.

The Strasburg Divines entered upon the subject so earnestly that their disquisition far exceeds in length the whole of the communications from the other Universities. Sennertus could not have wished for a more elaborate or a more gratifying reply. The Faculty at Altdorff said that the question was not a matter of faith, and therefore no one could be obnoxious to the charge of heresy for maintaining or controverting either of the opposite opinions. They seem, however, to have agreed with neither party; not with Freitagius, because they denied that brute souls were of an elementary nature; not with Sennertus, because they denied that they were created at first from nothing. It is manifest, said they, that they are not now created from nothing, because it would follow from thence that they subsist of themselves, and are not dependent upon matter, and are consequently immortal, which is absurd. It remained therefore that the souls of brutes, as they do not now receive their existence from mere nothing, so neither did they at the first creation, but from something presupposed, which the Peripatetics call the power of matter or of the subject, which from the beginning was nothing else, and still is nothing else, than its propension or inclination to this or that form. *Quæ forma multiplex, cum etiam in potentia primi subjecti passiva præcesserit, per miraculosam Dei actionem ex illa fuit educta, actumque essendi completum in variis animalium speciebus accepit.*

Sennertus either published these papers or prepared them for publication just before his death. They were printed in octavo at Wittenberg, with the title *De Origine et Natura Animarum in Brutis, Sententiæ Cl. Theologorum in aliquot Germaniæ Academiis,* 1638. Sprengel observes that none of the Historians of Philosophy have noticed,—

Cætera desunt.

CHAPTER CCXL.

THE JESUIT GARASSE'S CENSURE OF HUARTE AND BARCLAY. EXTRAORDINARY INVESTIGATION. THE TENDENCY OF NATURE TO PRESERVE ITS OWN ARCHETYPAL FORMS. THAT OF ART TO VARY THEM. PORTRAITS. MORAL AND PHYSICAL CADASTRE. PARISH CHRONICLER AND PARISH CLERK THE DOCTOR THOUGHT MIGHT BE WELL UNITED.

Is't you, Sir, that know things?
SOOTH. In nature's infinite book of secresy,
A little I can read. SHAKSPEARE.

THE Jesuit Garasse censured his contemporaries Huarte and Barclay for attempting, the one in his *Examen de los Ingenios*, the other in his *Icon Animorum*, to class men according to their intellectual characters: *ces deux Autheurs*, says he, *se sont rendus criminels contre l'esprit de l'homme, en ce qu'ils ont entrepris de ranger en cinq ou six cahiers, toutes les diversitez des esprits qui peuvent estre parmy les hommes, comme qui voudroit verser toute l'eau de la mer dans une coquille.* For his own part, he had learned, he said, *et par la lecture, et par l'experience, que les hommes sont plus dissemblables en esprit qu'en visage.*

Garasse was right; for there goes far more to the composition of an individual character, than of an individual face. It has sometimes happened that the portrait of one person has proved also to be a good likeness of another. Mr. Hazlitt recognised his own features and expression in one of Michael Angelo's devils. And in real life two faces, even though there be no relationship between the parties, may be all but indistinguishably alike, so that the one shall frequently be accosted for the other; yet no parity of character can be inferred from this resemblance. Poor Capt. Atkins, who was lost in the Defence off the coast of Jutland in 1811, had a double of this kind, that was the torment of his life; for this double was a swindler, who having discovered the lucky facsimileship, obtained goods, took up money, and at last married a wife in his name. Once when the real Capt. Atkins returned from a distant station, this poor woman, who was awaiting him at Plymouth, put off in a boat, boarded the ship as soon as it came to anchor, and ran to welcome him as her husband.

The following Extraordinary Investigation, cut out of a Journal of the day, would have excited our Doctor's curiosity, and have led him on to remoter speculations.

"On Tuesday afternoon an adjourned inquest was held at the Christchurch workhouse, Boundary-row, Blackfriars-road, before Mr. R. Carter, on the body of Eliza Baker, aged 17, who was found drowned at the steps of Blackfriars-bridge, on Saturday morning, by a police constable. Mr. Peter Wood, an eating-house-keeper, in the Bermondsey New-road, near the Bricklayers Arms, having seen a paragraph in one of the Sunday newspapers, that the body of a female had been taken out of the Thames on the previous day, and carried to the workhouse to be owned, and, from the description given, suspecting that it was the body of a young female who had lived in his service, but who had been discharged by his wife on account of jealousy, he went to the workhouse and recognised the body of the unfortunate girl. He was very much agitated, and he cut off a lock of her hair, and kissed the corpse. He immediately went to an undertaker, and gave orders for the funeral. He then went to the deceased's parents, who reside in Adelaide-place, Whitecross-street, Cripplegate, and informed them of the melancholy fate of their daughter. They also went to the workhouse, and, on being shown the body, were loud in their lamentations.

"On the Jury having assembled on Monday evening, they proceeded to view the body of the deceased, and, on their return, a number of witnesses were examined, mostly relations, who swore positively to the body. From the evidence it appeared that the deceased had lived with Mr. Wood as a servant for four months, but his wife being jealous, she was discharged about a month ago, since which time Mr. Wood had secretly supplied her with money, and kept her from want. Mrs. Baker, the mother of the deceased, and other relations, in giving their evidence, spoke in severe terms of the conduct of Mr. Wood, and said that they had no doubt but that he had seduced the unfortunate girl, which had caused her to commit suicide.

"The Jury appeared to be very indignant, and, after five hours' deliberation, it was agreed to adjourn the case until Tuesday afternoon, when they re-assembled. Mr. Wood, the alleged seducer, was now present, but he was so overcome by his feelings at the melancholy occurrence, that nothing could be made of him; in fact, he was like a man in a state of stupefaction. Mrs. Wood, the wife, was called in; she is twenty-eight years older than her husband, and shook her head at him, but nothing was elicited from her, her passion completely overcoming her reason.

"A Juryman.—'The more we dive into this affair the more mysterious it appears against Mr. Wood.'

"This remark was occasioned on account of some marks of violence on the body; there had been a violent blow on the nose, a black mark on the forehead, and a severe wound on the thigh. The Jury were commencing to deliberate on their verdict, when a drayman in the employ of Messrs. Whitbread and Co., brewers, walked into the jury-room, and said that he wished to speak to the Coroner and Jury.

"Mr. Carter.—'What is it you want?'

"Drayman.—'I comes to say, gentlemen, that Mrs. Baker's daughter, you are now holding an inquest on, is now alive and in good health.'

"The Coroner and Jury (in astonishment).—'What do you say?'

"Drayman.—'I'll swear that I met her to-day in the streets, and spoke to her.'

"The Coroner, Witnesses, and Jury were all struck with amazement, and asked the drayman if he could bring Eliza Baker forward, which he undertook to do in a short time.

"In the interim the Jury and Witnesses went again to view the body of the deceased. Mr. Wood shed tears over the corpse, and was greatly affected, as well as her relations: the drayman's story was treated as nonsense, but the Jury, although of the same opinion, were determined to await his return. In about a quarter of an hour the drayman returned, and introduced the real Eliza Baker, a fine looking young woman, and in full health. To depict the astonishment of the relations and of Mr. Wood is totally impossible, and at first they were afraid to touch her. She at last went forward, and took Mr. Wood by the hand (who stood motionless), and exclaimed, 'How could you make such a mistake as to take another body for mine? Do you think I would commit such an act?' Mr. Wood could not reply, but fell senseless in a fit, and it was with great difficulty that seven men could hold him. After some time he recovered, and walked away, to the astonishment of every one, with Eliza Baker, leaving his wife in the jury-room. Several of the Jurors remarked that they never saw such a strong likeness in their lives as there was between Eliza Baker and the deceased, which fully accounted for the mistake that the Witnesses had made.

"The whole scene was most extraordinary, and the countenances of Witnesses and Jurymen it is impossible to describe. There was no evidence to prove who the deceased was: and the Jury, after about eleven hours' investigation, returned a verdict of 'Found drowned,' but by what means the deceased came into the water there is no evidence to prove."

But in such likenesses, the resemblance is probably never so exact as to deceive an intimate friend, except upon a cursory glance, at first sight: even between twins, when any other persons might be perplexed, the parents readily distinguish. The varieties of countenances are far more minute, and consequently more numerous, than would appear upon light consideration. A shepherd knows the face of every sheep in his flock, though to an inexperienced eye they all seem like one another.

The tendency of Nature is to preserve its own archetypal forms, the tendency of art and of what is called accident being to vary them. The varieties which are produced in plants by mere circumstances of soil and situation are very numerous, but those which are produced by culture are almost endless. Moral and physical circumstances effect changes as great, both externally and internally, in man. Whoever consults the elaborate work of Dr. Prichard on the Physical History of Mankind, may there see it established by the most extensive research and the most satisfactory proofs, that the varieties of the human race, great and striking as they are, are all derived from one stock; philosophical inquiry here, when fully and fairly pursued, confirming the scriptural account, as it has done upon every subject which is within the scope of human investigation.

Dr. Dove, in the course of his professional practice, had frequent opportunities of observing the stamp of family features at those times when it is most apparent; at birth, and in the last stage of decline, — for the elementary lines of the countenance come forth as distinctly in death as they were shaped in the womb. It is one of the most affecting circumstances connected with our decay and dissolution, that all traces of individual character in the face should thus disappear, the natural countenance alone remaining, and that in this respect, the fresh corpse should resemble the new-born babe. He had, in the same way, opportunities for observing that there were family dispositions both of body and mind, some remaining latent till the course of time developed them, and others, till circumstances seemed as it were to quicken them into action. Whether these existed in most strength where the family likeness was strongest, was a point on which his own observation was not extensive enough for him to form an opinion. Speculatively he inclined to think that moral resemblances were likely to manifest themselves in the countenance, but that constitutional ones must often exist where there could be no outward indication of them. Thus a family heart, (metaphorically speaking,) may be recognised in the "life, conduct, and behaviour," though the face should be a false index; and hereditary tendencies in the great organs of life show themselves only in family diseases.

Under our Saxon Kings, a person was appointed in every great Monastery to record public events, register the deaths, promotions, &c. in the community, and enter in this current chronicle every occurrence in the neighbourhood which was thought worthy of notice. At the end of every reign, a summary record was compiled from these materials, — and to this we owe our Saxon Chronicle, the most ancient and authentic in Europe.

But he often regretted that in every generation so much knowledge was lost, and that so much experience was continually allowed to run to waste, many — very many of the evils which afflict mankind being occasioned by this neglect, and perpetuated by it. Especially he regretted this in his own art: and this regret would not have been removed if Medical Journals had been as numerous in his days as they are at present. His wishes went much farther.

We are told that in the sixteenth century the great Lords in France piqued themselves upon having able and learned men for their secretaries, and treated them as their friends. The principal business of such secretaries was to keep a journal of the most interesting events; and the masters having witnessed or borne a part in the business of state, were well able to inform them of the intrigues and tortuous policy of their own times. From such journals it is that most of those old Memoirs have been formed, in which French literature is so peculiarly rich. They usually include as much general history as is in any way connected with the personage whom the writer served.

Boswell, who if ever man went to Heaven for his good works, has gone there for his life of Johnson, — Boswell, I say, thought, and Johnson agreed with him, that there ought to be a chronicler kept in every considerable family, to preserve the characters and transactions of successive generations. In like manner, Milton's friend, Henry

More, the Platonist and Poet, would have had the stories of apparitions and witchcraft publicly recorded, as they occurred in every parish, thinking that this course would prove "one of the best antidotes against that earthly and cold disease of Sadducism and Atheism," which he said, "if not prevented might easily grow upon us, to the hazard of all religion and the best kinds of philosophy." Our philosopher had more comprehensive notions of what ought to be. He wished not only for such domestic chronicles, but that in every considerable family there should be a compleat set of portraits preserved in every generation, taken in so small a size that it might never be necessary to eject them in order to make room for others. When this had been done for some centuries, it might be seen how long a family likeness remains; whether Nature repeats her own forms at certain times, or after uncertain intervals; or whether she allows them to be continually modified, as families intermarry, till the original type at last may altogether be obliterated.

In China there are not only learned men, whose business it is to record everything remarkable that is either said or done by the reigning Emperor, (which is done for his own instruction, as well as for that of his successors,) but the great families have, in like manner, their records, and these are considered as the most precious part of the inheritance which descends from sire to son. All who aspire to any high office are required to be well acquainted with the history of their ancestors, and in that history their indispensable qualifications are examined.

That excellent good man Gilpin drew up a family record of his great-grandfather, grandfather, and father, who had all been "very valuable men." "I have often thought," said he, "such little records might be very useful in families; whether the subjects of them were good or bad. A lighthouse may serve equally the purpose of leading you into a haven, or deterring you from a rock."*

If it may stand with your soft blush, to hear
Yourself but told unto yourself, and see
In my character what your features be,
You will not from the paper slightly pass.
No lady, but at some time loves her glass.
And this shall be no false one, but as much
Removed, as you from need to have it such.†

There was once a German who, being a poet, physician, and physiognomist, saw in a vision of Paradise Physiognomy herself, and received from her a most gracious compliment, which lay buried among the Heidelberg Manuscripts in the Vatican, till Frederick Adelung, in the year 1799, brought it to light some centuries after the very name of the poet had perished. Read the compliment, reader, if thou canst, as given by the German antiquary, without note, comment, glossary, or punctuation. I can answer for the fidelity of my transcript, though not of his text.

Zu mir in gar glicher wise
Quam us hymels paradyse
Vil manich schöne frouwe name
Jeglicher wol die kron zam
Sie waren schöne und gecleit
Vrauwelicher zuchte mynnekeit
Sie ziert ine danne riche gewant
Mir wart iglicher name bekant
Wanne er in geschriben was
An ir vorgespan als ich las
PHISONOMIA *kunstenriche*
Gutlicht redt wider mich
Wir byden dich herre bescheiden
Das du in gottes geleiden
Dust machen myne lobelich kunst
So hastu mynneclichen gunst
Von mir und myner gespilen vil
Der igliche dich des bidden wil
Das du in erkennen gebest
Und du in unser früntschaft lebest
Alleine din cleit sy donne
Got wil dir geben solich wonne
Die mannich gelerter mane
Nummer mer gewynnen kan.

There was no truth in Physiognomy when she made this promise to her medico-poet. Yet he deserved her gratitude, for he taught that her unerring indications might be read not in the countenance alone, but in all the members of the human body.

In cases of disputed inheritance, when it is contended that the heir claimant is not the son of his reputed father, but a spurious or supposititious child, such a series of portraits would be witnesses, he thought,

* WARNER'S RECOLLECTIONS.

† BEN JONSON.

against whose evidence no exception could be taken. Indeed such evidence would have disproved the impudent story of the Warming Pan, if anything had depended upon legitimacy in that case; and in our times it might divest D. Miguel of all claim to the crown of Portugal, by right of birth.

But these legal and political uses he regarded as trifling, when compared with the physiological inferences which in process of time might be obtained, for on this subject Mr. Shandy's views were far short of Dr. Dove's. The improvement of noses would be only an incidental consequence of the knowledge that might be gathered from the joint materials of the family portrait gallery, and the family chronicle. From a comparison of these materials it might be inferred with what temperaments of mind and of body, with what qualities good or evil, certain forms of feature, and certain characters of countenance, were frequently found to be connected. And hence it might ultimately be learned how to neutralise evil tendencies by judicious intermarriages, how to sweeten the disposition, cool the temper, and improve the blood.

To be sure there were some difficulties in the way. You might expect from the family chronicler a faithful notice of the diseases which had proved dangerous or fatal; to this part of his duty there could be no objection. But to assure the same fidelity concerning moral and intellectual failings or vices, requires a degree of independence not to be hoped for from a writer so circumstanced. If it had still been the custom for great families to keep a Fool, as in old times, our Philosopher in his legislative character would have required that the Fool's more notable sayings should be recorded, well knowing that in his privileged freedom of speech, and the monitions and rebukes which he conveyed in a jest, the desiderated information would be contained. But in our present state of manners he could devise no better check upon the family historiographer,—no better provision against his sins, both of omission and of commission, than that of the village or parish chronicle; for in every village or parish he would have had every notable event that occurred within its boundaries duly and authentically recorded. And as it should be the Chronicler's duty to keep a Remembrancer as well as a Register, in which whatever he could gather from tradition, or from the recollections of old persons, was to be preserved, the real character which every person of local distinction had left behind him among his domestics and his neighbours would be found here, whatever might be recorded upon his monument.

By these means, one supplying the deficiencies of the other, our Philosopher thought a knowledge of the defects and excellencies of every considerable family might be obtained, sufficient for the purposes of physiology, and for the public good.

There was a man in the neighbouring village of Bentley, who, he used to say, would have made an excellent Parish Chronicler, an office which he thought might well be united with that of Parish Clerk.* This person went by the name of Billy Dutchman: he was a journeyman stone-mason, and kept a book wherein he inserted the name of every one by whom he had been employed, how many days he had worked in every week, and how many he had been idle, either owing to sickness or any other cause, and what money he had earned in each week, summing up the whole at the year's end. His earning in the course of nine and twenty years, beginning in 1767, amounts to £583 18*s.* 3*d.*, being, he said, upon an average, seven shillings and ninepence a-week.

The Doctor would have approved of Jacob Abbott's extension of his own plan and adaptation of it to a moral and religious

* Such a Chronicler is old James Long — now 77 years of age — 50 of which he has served in the capacity of Parish Clerk of West-Tarring, in the County of Sussex. There is no by-gone incident in this, or the neighbouring Parishes, — no mere-stone or balk — with which he is not acquainted. Aged and truthful Chronicler!

— Enjoy thy plainness
It nothing ill becomes thee. —

Since the above was written the old man has been gathered to his fathers. *Requiescat in pace!*

purpose. Jacob Abbott, without any view to the physical importance of such documents, advises that domestic journals should be kept: "Let three or four of the older brothers and sisters of a family agree to write a history of the family; any father would procure a book for this purpose, and if the writers are young, the articles intended for insertion in it might be written first on separate paper, and then corrected and transcribed. The subjects suitable to be recorded in such a book will suggest themselves to every one; a description of the place of residence at the time of commencing the book, with similar descriptions of other places from time to time, in case of removals; the journies or absences of the head of the family or its members; the sad scenes of sickness or death which may be witnessed, and the joyous ones of weddings, or festivities, or holydays; the manner in which the members are from time to time employed; and pictures of the scenes which the fire-side group exhibits in the long winter evening, or the conversation which is heard, and the plans formed at the supper table or in the morning walk.

"If a family, where it is first established, should commence with such a record of their own efforts and plans, and the various dealings of Providence towards them, the father and the mother carrying it on jointly until the children are old enough to take the pen, they would find the work a source of great improvement and pleasure. It would tend to keep distinctly in view the great objects for which they ought to live; and repeatedly recognizing, as they doubtless would do, the hand of God, they would feel more sensibly and more constantly their dependence upon him."

CHAPTER CCXLI.

THE DOCTOR'S UTOPIA DENOMINATED COLUMBIA. HIS SCHEME ENTERED UPON — BUT "LEFT HALF TOLD" LIKE "THE STORY OF CAMBUSCAN BOLD."

> I will to satisfy and please myself, make an Utopia of mine own, a new Atlantis, a poetical commonwealth of mine own, in which I will freely domineer, build cities, make laws, statutes, as I list myself. And why may I not?
>
> BURTON.

THE Doctor's plan would have provided materials for a moral and physiological Cadastre, or Domesday Book. This, indeed, is the place for stating what the reader, knowing as much as he knows of our Philosopher, will not be surprised to hear, that Dr. Dove had conceived an Utopia of his own. He fixed it an island, thinking the sea to be the best of all neighbours, and he called it Columbia, not as pretending that it had been discovered by his "famous namesake," but for a reason which the sagacious may divine.

The scheme of his government had undergone many changes, although from the beginning it was established upon the eternal and immutable principles of truth and justice. Every alteration was intended to be final; yet it so happened that, notwithstanding the proposed perpetuity of the structure, and the immutability of the materials, he frequently found cause to exercise the imperscriptible and inalienable right of altering and improving his own work. He justified this, as being himself sole legislator, and moreover the only person in existence whose acceptance of the new constitution was necessary for its full establishment; and no just objection, he said, could be advanced against any of these changes, if they were demonstrably for the better, not merely innovations, but improvements also; for no possible revolution, however great, or however suddenly effected, could occasion the slightest evil to his Commonwealth. Governments *in nubibus* being mended as easily as they are made, for which, as for many other reasons, they are so much better than any that are now actually existing, have existed, or ever will exist.

At first he denominated his Commonwealth an Iatrarchy, and made the Archiatros, or Chief Physician, head of the state. But upon after consideration he became convinced that the cares of general government, after all the divisions and subdivisions which could be made, were quite enough for any one head, however capacious and however strong, and however ably assisted. Columbia, therefore, was made an absolute monarchy, hereditary in the male line, according to the Salic law.

> How did he hold sweet dalliance with his crown,
> And wanton with dominion, how lay down,
> Without the sanction of a precedent,
> Rules of a most large and absolute extent,
> Rules which from sense of public virtue spring,
> And all at once commence a Patriot King! *

O Simon Bolivar, once called the Liberator, if thou couldst have followed the example of this less practical but more philosophical statesman, and made and maintained thyself as absolute monarch of thy Columbia, well had it been for thy Columbians and for thee! better still for thyself, it may be feared, if thou hadst never been born.

There was an order of hereditary nobles in the Doctor's Columbia; men were raised to that rank as a just reward for any signal service which they had rendered to the state; but on the other hand an individual might be degraded for any such course of conduct as evinced depravity in himself, or was considered as bringing disgrace upon his order. The chiefs of the Hierarchy, the Iatrarchy, the Nomarchy and the Hoplarchy, (under which title both sciences, naval and military, were comprised,) were, like our Bishops, Peers of the realm by virtue of their station, and for life only.

I do not remember what was the scheme of representation upon which his House of Commons was elected, farther than it commenced with universal suffrage and ascended through several stages, the lowest assembly choosing electors for the next above it, so that the choice ultimately rested with those who from their education and station of life might be presumed to exercise it with due discretion. Such schemes are easily drawn up; making and mending constitutions, to the entire satisfaction of the person so employed, being in truth among the easiest things in the world. But like most Utopianisers the legislator of this Columbia had placed his Absolute King and his free People under such strict laws, and given such functions to the local authorities, and established such compleat and precise order in every tything, that the duties of the legislative body were easy indeed; this its very name imported; for he called it the Conservative Assembly.

> Nor is Crown-wisdom any quintessence
> Of abstract truth, or art of Government,
> More than sweet sympathy, or counterpease
> Of humours, temper'd happily to please.†

The legislator of Columbia considered good policy as a very simple thing. He said to his King, his Three Estates and his collective nation, with the inspired lawgiver, "and now Israel what doth the Lord thy God require of thee, but to fear the Lord thy God, to walk in all his ways, and to love him, and to serve the Lord thy God with all thy heart and with all thy soul: to keep the commandments of the Lord and his statutes, which I command thee, this day, for thy good?" And he added with St. Paul, "now the end of the commandment is charity, out of a pure heart, and of a good conscience, and of faith unfeigned."

Take care of the pennies, says the frugal old Proverb, and the pounds will take care of themselves. *Les petites choses*, says M. de Custine, *sont tout ce qu'on* sent *de l'existence; les grandes se* savent, *ce qui est très-différent.* Take care of little things, was the Doctor's maxim as a legislator, and great ones will then proceed regularly and well. He was not ignorant that legislators as well as individuals might be penny-wise and pound foolish; proofs enough he had seen in the conduct of the English Government, and many more and more glaring ones he

* CHURCHILL

† LORD BROOKE.

would have seen if he had lived to behold the progress of œconomical reform and liberal legislation. He also knew that an over-attention to trifles was one sure indication of a little mind; but in legislation as in experimental philosophy, he argued, that circumstances which appeared trifling to the ignorant were sometimes in reality of essential importance, that those things are not trifles upon which the comfort of domestic life, the peace of a neighbourhood, and the stability of a state depend, and yet all these depend mainly upon things apparently so trifling as common schools and parochial government.

"I have ever observed it," says Ben Jonson, "to have been the office of a wise patriot, among the greatest affairs of the state, to take care of the commonwealth of learning. For schools they are the seminaries of state; and nothing is worthier the study of a statesman, than that part of the republic which we call the advancement of letters."

CHAPTER CCXLII.

FARTHER REMARKS UPON THE EFFECTS OF SCHISM, AND THE ADVANTAGES WHICH IT AFFORDS TO THE ROMISH CHURCH AND TO INFIDELITY.

— Io non ci ho interresso
Nessun, nè vi fui mai, ne manco chieggo
Per quel ch' io ne vò dir, d' esservi messo.
Vò dir, che senza passion eleggo,
E non forzato, e senza pigliar parte;
Di dirne tutto quel, ch' intendo e veggo.
BRONZINO PITTORE.

ONE cause why infidelity gained ground among the middle and the lower classes was, that owing to the increase of population, the growth of the metropolis, and the defects of our Church Establishment, no provision had been made for their religious instruction. Every one belonged to a parish, but in populous parishes a small part only of the parishioners belonged to the Clergyman's flock; his fold in very many places would not have contained half, and in some not a tenth of them; they were left therefore as stray sheep, for false shepherds and for the wolf. This was the main cause of the increase of dissenters among us, and their increase occasioned an increase of infidelity. Many of their ministers and more of their students, revolting against the monstrous doctrines of Calvinism, passed from one extreme to the other, more gradually indeed than their brethren have done in Germany, in Geneva, and in New England, for they halted awhile on Arian ground, before they pitched their tents in the debateable land of Socinianism, where not a few of them afterwards crossed the border. The principle of Nonconformity itself led naturally to this consequence; it scornfully rejected that reasonable and well-defined submission to authority required by the Church of England, which is the true Catholic Church; and thus it encouraged, and indeed invited, tutors and pupils at their Academies to make their own immature and ill-instructed reason the test of all truths. A good and wise man has well remarked that "what men take for, or at least assert to be, the dictates of their conscience, may often in fact be only the dictates of their pride." With equal truth also he has said that he who "decides for himself in rejecting what almost all others receive, has not shewn himself at least in one instance to be a 'wise man;'—he does not 'know that he is a fool.'"

This cause was continually operating upon their students and younger ministers during the latter half of the last century. It was suspended first by the missionary spirit, which called forth a high degree of enthusiasm, and gave that feeling its most useful direction, and secondly by the revival of political Puritanism, as soon as the successors of the Parliamentary Divines thought themselves strong enough to act as a party in the state, and declare war against the Establishment. But as in that time, so in a greater degree at present, the floating population, who by no fault of their own are extra-parochial as to all purposes of church-worship and religious instruction, are as much endangered by facility of change, as the students used to be by their boasted liberty of choice. Sectarian history might supply numerous examples; one may be related here for the extraordinary way in which it terminated. I know not from what community of Christians the hero of the tale strayed over to the Methodists, but he enjoyed for awhile the dream of perfection, and the privilege of assurance as one of their members. When this excitement had spent itself, he sought for quietness among the Quakers, *thee'd* his neighbour, wore drab, and would not have pulled off his hat to the King. After awhile, from considering, with them, that baptism was a beggarly element, he passed to the opposite extreme; it was not enough for him to have been sprinkled in his infancy, he must be dipped over head and ears in the water, and up he rose, rejoicing as he shook his dripping locks, that he was now a Baptist. His zeal then took another direction; he had a strong desire to convert the lost sheep of Israel; and off he sets from a remote part of the country to engage in single controversy with a learned Rabbi in one of the Midland counties. Tell it not in Duke's-Place! Publish it not in the Magazine of the Society for converting the Jews!—The Rabbi converted him: and if the victor in the dispute had thought proper to take the *spolia opima* which were fairly lost, the vanquished would have paid the penalty, as he conceived himself in honour and in conscience bound. He returned home glorying in his defeat, a Jew in everything but parentage and the outward and visible sign. The sons of the synagogue are not ambitious of making converts, and they did not choose to adopt him by performing the initiating rites. He obtained it, however, from a Christian surgeon, who, after many refusals, was induced at length in humanity to oblige him, lest, as he solemnly declared he would, he should perform it upon himself.

They who begin in enthusiasm, passing in its heat and giddiness from one sect to another, and cooling at every transition, generally settle in formalism, where they find some substantial worldly motives for becoming fixed; but where the worldly motives are wanting, it depends upon temperament and accident whether they run headlong into infidelity, or take refuge from it in the Roman Catholic church. The papal clergy in England have always known how to fish in troubled waters; and when the waters are still, there are few among them who have not been well instructed in the art of catching gudgeons. Our clergy have never been, in the same sense, fishers of men.

In an epigram written under the portrait of Gibbon, as unquotable at length, as it is unjust in part of the lines which may be quoted, the face is said to be

> — the likeness of one
> Who through every religion in Europe has run
> And ended at last in believing in none.

It was a base epigram which traduced the historian's political character for no other reason than that he was not a Whig; and it reproached him for that part of his conduct which was truly honourable,—the sincerity with which, when ill-instructed, he became a Roman Catholic, and the propriety with which, after full and patient investigation, he gave up the tenets of the Romish church as untenable. That he proceeded farther, and yielded that which can be maintained against the Gates of Hell, is to be lamented deeply for his own sake, and for those in whom he has sown the seeds of infidelity. But the process from change to change is a common one, and the cases are few wherein there is so much to extenuate the culpability of the individual. It was not in the self-sufficiency of empty ignorance that Gibbon and Bayle went astray; generally the danger is in proportion to the want of knowledge; there are more shipwrecks among the shallows than in the deep sea.

During the great Rebellion, when the wild beasts had trampled down the fences, broken into the vineyard and laid it waste, it is curious to observe the course taken by men who felt for various causes, according to their different characters, the necessity of attaching themselves to some religious communion. Cottington, being in Spain, found it convenient to be reconciled to the Romish church; the dominant religion being to him, as a politician, the best. Weak and plodding men like Father Cressey took the same turn in dull sincerity: Davenant, because he could not bear the misery of a state of doubt, and was glad to rest his head upon the pillow of authority; Goring from remorse; Digby (a little later) from ambition, and Lambert, because he was sick of the freaks and follies of the sectaries.

Their "opinions and contests," says Sir Philip Warwick, "flung all into chaos, and this gave the great advantages to the Romanists, who want not their differences among themselves, but better manage them; for they having retained a great part of primitive truths, and having to plead some antiquity for their many doctrinal errors and their ambitious and lucrative encroachments, and having the policy of flinging coloquintida into our pot, by our dissentions and follies, they have with the motion of the circle of the wheel, brought themselves who were at the Nadir, to be almost at the Zenith of our globe."

In no other age (except in our own and now from a totally different cause) did the Papists increase their numbers so greatly in this kingdom. And infidelity in all its grades kept pace with Popery. "Look but upon many of our Gentry," says Sanderson, (writing under the Commonwealth,) "what they are already grown to from what they were, within the compass of a few years: and then *ex pede Herculem;* by that, guess what a few years more may do. Do we not see some, and those not a few, that have strong natural parts, but little sense of religion turned (little better than professed) Atheists. And other some, nor those a few, that have good affections, but weak and unsettled judgements, or (which is still but the same weakness) an overweening opinion of their own understandings, either quite turned, or upon the point of turning Papists? These be sad things, God knoweth, and we all know, not visibly imputable to anything so much, as to those distractions, confusions, and uncertainties that in point of religion have broken in upon us, since the late changes that have happened among us in church affairs."

The Revolution by which the civil and religious liberties of the British nation were, at great cost, preserved, stopped the growth of Popery among us for nearly an hundred years: but infidelity meanwhile was little impeded in its progress by the occasional condemnation of a worthless book; and the excellent works which were written to expose the sophistry, the ignorance, and the misrepresentations of the infidel authors seldom found readers among the persons to whom they might have been most useful. It may be questioned whether any of Jeremy Bentham's misbelieving disciples has ever read Berkeley's Minute Philosopher, or the kindred work of Skelton which a London bookseller published upon Hume's *imprimatur.*

CHAPTER CCXLIII.

BREVITY BEING THE SOUL OF WIT THE AUTHOR STUDIES CONCISENESS.

You need not fear a surfeit, here is but little, and that light of digestion. QUARLES.

Who was Pompey?

"The Dog will have his day," says Shakespeare. And the Dog must have his Chapter, say I. But I will defer writing that Chapter till the Dog-days.

CHAPTER CCXLIV.

THE AUTHOR VENTURES TO SPEAK A WORD ON CHRISTIAN CHEERFULNESS: — QUOTES BEN SIRACH, SOLOMON, BISHOP HACKET, WALTER SAVAGE LANDOR, BISHOP REYNOLDS, MILTON, ETC.

—'Αλλὰ σὺ ταῦτα μαθὼν, βιότου ποτί τέρμα
Ψυχῇ τῶν ἀγαθῶν πλῆθι χαριζόμενος. SIMONIDES.

In the thirtieth chapter of the Book called Ecclesiasticus, and at the twenty-fifth verse, are these words

A cheerful and a good heart will have a care of his meat and diet.

This is not the text to a sermon, but the beginning of a Chapter. There is no reason why a chapter, as well as a sermon, should not be thus impressively introduced: and if this Chapter should neither be so long as a sermon, nor so dull as those discourses which perchance and (I fear) per-likelihood, it may be thy fortune to hear, O Reader, at thy parish church, or in phrase nonconformist, to sit under at the conventicle, it will be well for thee: for having began to read it, I dare say thou wilt peruse it orally, or ocularly, to the end.

A cheerful and a good heart the Doctor had; ay, as cheerful and good a one as ever man was blessed with. He held with Bishop Hacket, that melancholy was of all humours the fittest to make a bath for the Devil, and that cheerfulness and innocent pleasure preserve the mind from rust, and the body from putrifying with dulness and distempers; wherefore that Bishop of good and merry memory would sometimes say, he did not like to look upon a sour man at dinner, and if his guests were pleased within, would bid them hang out the white flag in their countenance.

Udite, udite amici, un cor giocondo
E Rey del Mondo.

And if the poet says true, (which I will be sworn he does,) our Doctor might be more truly King of the World, than Kehama after he had performed his sacrifice.

His cheerfulness he would not have exchanged for all the bank-bills which ever bore the signature of Abraham Newland, or his successor Henry Hase; he thanked his Maker for it; and that it had been kept from corruption, and made so far good as (with all Christian humility) to be self-approved; he thanked his heavenly Father also for the free grace vouchsafed him, and his earthly one for having trained him in the way that he should go.

Cheerful and grateful takers the Gods love,
And such as wait their pleasures with full hopes;
The doubtful and distrustful man Heaven frowns at.*

Being thus cheerful and good, he had that care of his meat and diet which the son of Sirach commends in the text, and notices as an indication of cheerfulness and goodness.

Understand me, Reader: and understand the author of the Wisdom. It was not such a care of his meat and diet as Apicius has been infamed for in ancient, and Darteneuf in modern times; not such as Lucullus was noted for, or Sir William Curtis, with whom Lucullus, had he been an English East Indian Governor, instead of a Roman Prætor, might have been well pleased to dine. Read Landor's conversation between Lucullus and Cæsar, if thou art a scholar, Reader, and if anything can make thee think with respect and admiration of Lucullus, it will be the beautiful strain of feeling and philosophy that thou wilt find there. Wouldst thou see another work of first-rate genius, not less masterly in its kind, go and see Chantrey's bust of Sir William Curtis; and when thou shalt have seen what he hath made of that countenance, thou wilt begin to think it not impossible that a silk purse may be made of a sow's ear. Shame on me that in speaking of those who have gained glory by giving good dinners, I should have omitted the name of Michael Angelo Taylor, he having been made immortal for this his great and singular merit!

Long before the son of Sirach, Solomon had spoken to the same effect: "there is nothing better for a man than that he should eat and drink, and that he should make his soul enjoy good in its labour. This also I saw that it was from the hand of God." "Go thy way," said the wisest of monarchs and of men, in his old age, when he took a more serious view of his past life; the honours, pleasures, wealth, wisdom, he had so abundantly enjoyed; the errors and miscarriages which he had fallen into; the large experience and many observations he had made, of things natural, moral, domestical: civil, sensual, divine: the curious and critical inquiry he had made after true happiness, and what contribution all things under the sun could afford thereunto: — "Go thy way," he said, "eat thy bread with joy, and drink thy wine with a merry heart!"

"Inasmuch," says Bishop Reynolds in his commentary upon this passage, "as the dead neither know, nor enjoy, any of these worldly blessings; and inasmuch as God gives them to his servants in love, and as comfortable refreshments unto them in the days of their

* Beaumont and Fletcher.

vanity, therefore he exhorteth unto a cheerful fruition of them, while we have time and liberty so to do; that so the many other sorrows and bitterness which they shall meet with in this life, may be mitigated and sweetened unto them. He speaketh not of sensual, epicurean, and brutish excess; but of an honest, decent, and cheerful enjoyment of blessings, with thankfulness, and in the fear of God." "A *merry* heart," the Bishop tells us, might in this text have been rendered a *good* one; as, in other parts of scripture, a *sad* heart is called an *evil* heart. "It is pleasing unto God," says the Bishop, "that when thou hast in the fear of his name, and in obedience to his ordinance, laboured, and by his blessing gotten thee thine appointed portion, then thou shouldst, after an honest, cheerful, decent and liberal manner, without further anxiety or solicitousness, enjoy the same. This is the principal boundary of our outward pleasures and delights, still to keep ourselves within such rules of piety and moderation, as that our ways may be pleasing unto God. And this shows us the true way to find sweetness in the creature, and to feel joy in the fruition thereof; namely, when our persons and our ways are pleasing unto God: for piety doth not exclude, but only moderate earthly delights; and so moderate them, that though they be not so excessive as the luxurious and sensual pleasures of foolish epicures, yet they are far more pure, sweet, and satisfactory, as having no guilt, no gall, no curse, nor inward sorrow and terrors attending on them."

Farther the Bishop observes, that food and raiment, being the substantiall of outward blessings, Solomon has directed unto cheerfulness in the one, and unto decency and comeliness in the other. He hath advised us also to let the head lack no ointment, such perfumes being an expression of joy used in feasts; "the meaning is," says the Bishop, "that we should lead our lives with as much freeness, cheerfulness, and sweet delight, in the liberal use of the good blessings of God, as the quality of our degree, the decency of our condition, and the rules of religious wisdom, and the fear of God, do allow us; not sordidly or frowardly denying ourselves the benefit of those good things which the bounty of God hath bestowed upon us."

It is the etiquette of the Chinese Court for the Emperor's physicians to apply the same epithet to his disease as to himself — so they talk of his most high and mighty diarrhœa.

At such a point of etiquette the Doctor would laugh — but he was all earnestness when one like Bishop Hacket said, "Do not disgrace the dignity of a Preacher, when every petty vain occasion doth challenge the honour of a sermon before it. If ever there were τὸ δέον οὐκ ἐν τῷ δεόντι, — a good work marred for being done unreasonably," — (in the Doctor's own words, *Grace before a sluttish meal, a dirty table-cloth*) — "now it is when grace before meat will not serve the turn, but every luxurious feast must have the benediction of a preacher's pains before it. *Quis te ferat cœnantem ut Lucullus, concionantem ut Cato?* Much less is it to be endured, that somebody must make a sermon, before Lucullus hath made a supper. It is such a flout upon our calling methinks, as the Chaldeans put upon the Jews in their captivity,— they in the height of their jollity must have *one of the Songs of Sion*."

The Doctor agreed in the main with Lord Chesterfield in his opinion upon political dieteticks.

"The Egyptians who were a wise nation," says that noble author, "thought so much depended upon diet, that they dieted their kings, and prescribed by law both the quality and quantity of their food. It is much to be lamented, that those bills of fare are not preserved to this time, since they might have been of singular use in all monarchical governments. But it is reasonably to be conjectured, from the wisdom of that people, that they allowed their kings no aliments of a bilious or a choleric nature, and only such as sweetened their juices, cooled their blood, and enlivened their faculties, — if they had any."

He then shows that what was deemed necessary for an Egyptian King is not less so for a British Parliament. For, "suppose," he says, "a number of persons, not over-lively at best, should meet of an evening to concert and deliberate upon public measures of the utmost consequence, grunting under the load and repletion of the strongest meats, panting almost in vain for breath, but quite in vain for thought, and reminded only of their existence by the unsavoury returns of an olio; what good could be expected from such a consultation? The best one could hope for would be, that they were only assembled for show, and not for use; not to propose or advise, but silently to submit to the orders of some one man there, who, feeding like a rational creature, might have the use of his understanding.

"I would therefore recommend it to the consideration of the legislature, whether it may not be necessary to pass an act, to restrain the licentiousness of eating, and assign certain diets to certain ranks and stations; I would humbly suggest the strict vegetable as the properest ministerial diet, being exceedingly tender of those faculties in which the public is so highly interested, and very unwilling they should be clogged or incumbered."

"The Earl of Carlisle," says Osborne, in his Traditional Memorials, "brought in the vanity of ante-suppers, not heard of in our forefathers' time, and for aught I have read, or at least remember, unpractised by the most luxurious tyrants. The manner of which was, to have the board covered at the first entrance of the guests, with dishes, as high as a tall man could well reach, filled with the choicest viands sea or land could afford: and all this once seen, and having feasted the eyes of the invited, was in a manner thrown away, and fresh set on to the same height, having only this advantage of the other, that it was hot.

"I cannot forget one of the attendants of the King, that at a feast made by this monster in excess, eats to his single share a whole pye, reckoned to my Lord at ten pounds, being composed of ambergreece, magisteriall of pearl, musk, &c., yet was so far, (as he told me,) from being sweet in the morning, that he almost poisoned his whole family, flying himself, like the Satyr, from his own stink. And after such suppers huge banquets no less profuse, a waiter returning his servant home with a cloak-bag full of dried sweetmeats and confects, valued to his Lordship at more than ten shillings the pound."

But, gentle and much esteemed Reader, and therefore esteemed because gentle, instead of surfeiting thy body, let me recreate thy mind, with the annexed two Sonnets of Milton, which tell of innocent mirth, and the festive but moderate enjoyment of the rational creature.

TO MR. LAWRENCE.

Lawrence, of virtuous father virtuous son,
Now that the fields are dank, and ways are mire,
Where shall we sometimes meet, and by the fire
Help waste a sullen day, what may be won
From the hard season, gaining? time will run
On smoother, till Favonius re-inspire
The frozen earth, and clothe in fresh attire
The lily and rose, that neither sow'd nor spun.
What neat repast shall feast us, light and choice,
Of Attic taste, with wine, whence we may rise
To hear the lute well touch'd, or artful voice
Warble immortal notes of Tuscan air?
He who of these delights can judge, and spare
To interpose them oft, is not unwise.

TO SYRIAC SKINNER.

Cyriac, whose grandsire on the royal bench
Of British Themis, with no mean applause
Pronounc'd, and in his volumes taught our laws,
Which others at their bar so often wrench;
To day deep thoughts resolve with me to drench
In mirth, that after no repenting draws:
Let Euclid rest, and Archimedes pause,
And what the Swede intends, and what the French.
To measure life learn thou betimes, and know
Toward solid good what leads the nearest way;
For other things mild Heav'n a time ordains,
And disapproves that care, though wise in show,
That with superfluous burden loads the day
And when God sends a cheerful hour refrains.

Thou canst cure the body and the mind,
Rare Doctor, with thy two-fold soundest art;
Hippocrates hath taught thee the one kind,
Apollo and the Muse the other part;
And both so well that thou well both dost please,
The mind with pleasure, and the corpse with ease.

Davies of Hereford.

FRAGMENTS TO THE DOCTOR.

LOVE FRAGMENT FOR THE LADIES, — INTRODUCED BY A CURIOUS INCIDENT WHICH THE AUTHOR BEGS THEY WILL EXCUSE.

Now will ye list a little space,
And I shall send you to solace;
You to solace and be blyth,
Hearken! ye shall hear belyve
A tale that is of verity.
ROSWALL AND LILLIAN.

A STORY was told me with an assurance that it was literally true, of a Gentleman who being in want of a wife, advertised for one, and at the place and time appointed was met by a Lady. Their stations in life entitled them to be so called, and the Gentleman as well as the Lady was in earnest. He, however, unluckily seemed to be of the same opinion as King Pedro was with regard to his wife Queen Mary of Aragon, that she was not so handsome as she might be good, so the meeting ended in their mutual disappointment. Cœlebs advertised a second time, appointing a different Square for the place of meeting, and varying the words of the advertisement. He met the same Lady, — they recognised each other, could not choose but smile at the recognition, and perhaps neither of them could choose but sigh. You will anticipate the event. The persevering Bachelor tried his lot a third time in the newspapers, and at the third place of appointment he met the equally persevering Spinster. At this meeting neither could help laughing. They began to converse in good humour, and the conversation became so agreeable on both sides, and the circumstance appeared so remarkable, that this third interview led to a marriage, and the marriage proved a happy one.

When Don Argentes Prince of Galdasse had been entrapped into the hands of a revengeful woman whose husband he had slain in fair combat, he said to two handsome widows who were charged every day to punish him with stripes, *que par raison là on se se voit une grande beauté n'a pas lieu la cruauté ou autre vice* — and the Chronicler of this generation of the house of Amadis, observes that this assertion *fut bien verifié en ces deux jeunes veufues douées de grande beauté, lesquelles considerans la beauté et disposition de ce jeune chevalier et la vertu de sa personne, presterent l'oreille aux raisons qu'il alleguoit pour son excuse, et aux louanges qu'il leur donnoit de rare et singuliere beauté, de maniere qu'elles eurent pitié de luy.*

"I can hardly forbear fancying," says Lord Shaftesbury, "that if we had a sort of Inquisition, or formal Court of Judicature, with grave Officers and Judges, erected to restrain poetical licence, and in general to suppress that fancy and humour of versification, but in particular that most extravagant passion of Love, as it is set out by Poets, in its heathenish dress of Venus's and Cupids; if the Poets, as ringleaders and teachers of this heresy, were under grievous penalties forbid to enchant the people by their vein of rhyming; and if the People, on the other side, were under proportionable penalties forbid to hearken to any such charm, or lend their attention to any love-tale, so much as in a play, a novel, or a ballad; we might perhaps see a new Arcadia arising out of this heavy persecution. Old people and young would be seized with a versifying spirit; we should have field conventicles of Lovers and Poets; forests would be filled with romantic Shepherds and Shepherdesses; and rocks resound with echoes of hymns and praises offered to the powers of Love. We might indeed have a fair chance, by this management, to bring back the whole train of Heathen Gods, and set our cold Northern Island burning with as many altars to Venus and Apollo, as were formerly in Cyprus, Delos, or any of those warmer Grecian climates."

But I promised you, dear Ladies, more upon that subject which of all subjects is and ought to be the most interesting to you, because it is the most important. You have not forgotten that promise, and the time has now come for fulfilling it.

Venus, unto thee for help, good Lady, I do call,
For thou wert wont to grant request unto thy servants all;
Even as thou didst help always Æneas thine own child,
Appeasing the God Jupiter with countenance so mild
That though that Juno to torment him on Jupiter did preace,
Yet for the love he bare to thee, did cause the winds to cease;
I pray thee pray the Muses all to help my memory,
That I may have ensamples good in defence of feminye.*

Something has been said upon various ways which lead to love and matrimony; but what I have to say concerning imaginative love was deferred till we should arrive at the proper place for entering upon it.

More or less, imagination enters into all loves and friendships, except those which have grown with our growth, and which therefore are likely to be the happiest because there can be no delusion in them. Cases of this kind would not be so frequent in old romances, if they did not occur more frequently in real life than unimaginative persons could be induced to believe, or made to understand.

Sir John Sinclair has related a remarkable instance in his Reminiscences. He was once invited by Adam Smith to meet Burke and Mr. Windham, who had arrived at Edinburgh with the intention of making a short tour in the Highlands. Sir John was consulted concerning their route; in the course of his directions he dwelt on the beauty of the road between Dunkeld and Blair;—and added, that instead of being cooped up in a post-chaise, they would do well to get out and walk through the woods and beautiful scenes through which the road passes, especially some miles beyond Dunkeld.

Some three years afterwards Mr. Windham came up to Sir John in the House of Commons, and requested to speak to him for a few moments behind the Speaker's chair. "Do you recollect," said he, "our meeting together at Adam Smith's at dinner?"—"Most certainly I do."

"Do you remember having given us directions for our Highland tour, and more especially to stroll through the woods between Dunkeld and Blair?"—"I do."

Mr. Windham then said, "In consequence of our adopting that advice, an event took place of which I must now inform you. Burke and I were strolling through the woods about ten miles from Dunkeld, when we saw a young female sitting under a tree, with a book in her hand. Burke immediately exclaimed, 'Let us have a little conversation with this solitary damsel, and see what she is about.' We accosted her accordingly and found that she was reading a recent novel from the London press. We asked her how she came to read novels, and how she got such books at so great a distance from the metropolis, and more especially one so recently published. She answered that she had been educated at a boarding-school at Perth, where novels might be had from the circulating library, and that she still procured them through the same channel. We carried on the conversation for some time, in the course of which she displayed a great deal of smartness and talent; and at last we were obliged, very reluctantly, to leave her, and proceed on our journey. We afterwards found that she was the daughter of a proprietor of that neighbourhood who was known under the name of the Baron Maclaren. I have never been able," continued Mr. Windham,

* Edward More.

"to get this beautiful mountain nymph out of my head; and I wish you to ascertain whether she is married or single." And he begged Sir John Sinclair to clear up this point as soon as possible, for much of his future happiness depended upon the result of the inquiry.

If not the most important communication that ever took place behind the Speaker's chair, this was probably the most curious one. Sir John lost no time in making the desired inquiry. He wrote to a most respectable clergyman in the neighbourhood where Miss Maclaren lived, the Rev. Dr. Stewart, minister of Moulin; and was informed in reply, that she was married to a medical gentleman in the East Indies of the name of Dick. "Upon communicating this to Mr. Windham," says Sir John, "he seemed very much agitated. He was soon afterwards married to the daughter of a half-pay officer. I have no doubt, however, that had Miss Maclaren continued single, he would have paid her his addresses."

This is an example of purely imaginative love. But before we proceed with that subject, the remainder of Sir John Sinclair's story must be given. Some years afterward he passed some days at Duneira in Perthshire, with the late Lord Melville, and in the course of conversation told him this anecdote of Mr. Windham. Upon which Lord Melville said, "I am more interested in that matter than you imagine. You must know that I was riding down from Blair to Dunkeld in company with some friend, and we called at Baron Maclaren's, where a most beautiful young woman desired to speak with me. We went accordingly to the bank of a river near her father's house, when she said, 'Mr. Dundas, I hear that you are a very great man, and what is much better, a very good man, I will venture therefore to tell you a secret. There is a young man in this neighbourhood who has a strong attachment to me, and to confess the truth, I have a great regard for him. His name is William Dick; he has been bred to the medical profession; and he says, that if he could get to be a surgeon in the East Indies, he could soon make his fortune there, and would send for me to marry him. Now I apply to you, Mr. Dundas, as a great and good man, in hopes that you can do something for us: and be assured that we shall be for ever grateful, if you will procure him an appointment.'"

Mr. Dundas was so much struck with the impressive manner of her address, that he took her by the hand and said, "My good girl, be assured that if an opportunity offers, I shall not forget your application." The promise was not forgotten. It was not long before an East India Director with whom he was dining, told him that he had then at his disposal an appointment of surgeon in the East India Company's service, and offered it to him for any one whom he would wish to serve in that line. Dundas immediately related his adventure, much to the amusement of the Director. Mr. Dick obtained the appointment, and was soon able to send for his betrothed. She had several offers in the course of the voyage and after her arrival, but she refused to listen to any one. Her husband attained to great eminence in his profession, made a handsome fortune, came home and purchased an estate in the neighbourhood where he was born.

There is no man among those who in that generation figured in public life, of whom a story like this could be so readily believed as of Windham. He was one whose endowments and accomplishments would have recommended him at the Court of Elizabeth, — and whose speeches, when he did not abase himself to the level of his hearers, might have commanded attention in the days of Charles I.

A FRAGMENT ON BEARDS.

Yet have I more to say which I have thought upon, for I am filled as the moon at the full! ECCLESIASTICUS.

THE reader must not expect that we have done with our beards yet; shaving, as he no doubt knows but too well, is one of those things at which we may cut and come again, and in the present Chapter

To shave, or not to shave, that is the question ;

a matter which hath not hitherto been fully considered. The question as relates to the expenditure of time, has been, profitably I trust, disposed of; and that of its effect upon health has been, as Members of Parliament say, poo-pooh'd. But the propriety of the practice is yet to be investigated upon other grounds.

Van Helmont tells us that Adam was created without a beard, but that after he had fallen and sinned, because of the sinful propensities which he derived from the fruit of the forbidden Tree, a beard was made part of his punishment and disgrace, bringing him thus into nearer resemblance with the beasts towards whom he had made his nature approximate; *Ut multorum quadrupedum compar, socius et similis esset, eorundem signaturam præ se ferret, quorum more ut salax, ita et vultum pilis hirtum ostenderet.* The same stigma was not inflicted upon Eve, because even in the fall she retained much of her original modesty, and therefore deserved no such opprobrious mark.

Van Helmont observes also that no good Angel ever appears with a beard, and this, he says, is a capital sign by which Angels may be distinguished, — a matter of great importance to those who are in the habit of seeing them. *Si apparuerit barbatus Angelus, malus esto. Eudæmon enim nunquam barbatus apparuit, memor casûs ob quem viro barba succrevit.* He marvelled therefore that men should suppose the beard was given them for an ornament, when Angels abhor it, and when they see that they have it in common with he-goats. There must be something in his remark; for take the most beautiful Angel that ever Painter designed, or Engraver copied, put him on a beard, and the celestial character will be so entirely destroyed, that the simple appendage of a tail will cacodemonise the Eudæmon.

This being the belief of Van Helmont, who declares that he had profited more by reveries and visions than by study, though he had studied much and deeply, ought he, in conformity to his own belief, to have shaved, or not? Much might be alleged on either side: for to wear the beard might seem in a person so persuaded, a visible sign of submission to the Almighty will, in thus openly bearing the badge of punishment, the mark of human degradation which the Almighty has been pleased to appoint: but, on the other hand, a shaven face might seem with equal propriety, and in like manner denote, a determination in the man to put off, as far as in him lay, this outward and visible sign of sin and shame, and thereby assert that fallen nature was in him regenerate,

Belle est vraiment l'opinion première;
Belle est encores l'opinion dernière;
A qui des deux est-ce doncq' que je suis? *

Which of the two opinions I might incline to is of no consequence, because I do not agree with Van Helmont concerning the origin of the beard; though as to what he affirms concerning good Angels upon his own alleged knowledge, I cannot contradict him upon mine, and have moreover freely confessed that when we examine our notions of Angels they are found to support him. But he himself seems to have thought both opinions probable, and therefore, according to the casuists, safe; so, conforming to the fashion of his times, without offence to his own conscience, he neither did the one thing, nor the other; or perhaps it may be speaking more accurately to say that he did both; for he shaved his beard, and let his mustachios grow.

Upon this subject, P. Gentien Hervet, Regent of the College at Orleans, printed three discourses in the year 1536. In the first of these, *De radendâ barbâ*, he makes it appear that we are bound to shave the beard. In the second, *De alendâ barbâ*, he proves we ought to let the beard grow. And in the third, *De vel radendâ vel alendâ barbâ*, he considers that it is lawful either to shave or cultivate the beard at pleasure. *Si bien*, says the Doctor in Theology, M. Jean Baptiste Thiers, in his grave and erudite *Histoire des Perruques*, published *aux depens de l'Autheur*, at Paris in 1690, — *Si*

* Pasquier.

bien, que dans la pensée de ce sçavant Theologien, le question des barbes, courtes ou longues, est une question tout-a-fait problematique, et où par conséquent on peut prendre tel party que l'on veut, pour ou contre.

[The following Extracts were to have been worked up in this Chapter.]

D'Israeli quotes an author who, in his Elements of Education, 1640, says, "I have a favourable opinion of that young gentleman who is curious in fine mustachios. The time he employs in adjusting, dressing and curling them, is no lost time: for the more he contemplates his mustachios, the more his mind will cherish, and be animated by, masculine and courageous notions."

There are men whose beards deserve not so honourable a grave as to stuff a botcher's cushion, or to be entombed in an ass's packsaddle. SHAKSPEARE.

"Human felicity," says Dr. Franklin, "is produced not so much by great pieces of good fortune that seldom happen, as by little advantages that occur every day. Thus if you teach a poor young man to shave himself and keep his razor in order, you may contribute more to the happiness of his life than in giving him a thousand guineas. This sum may be soon spent, the regret only remaining of having foolishly consumed it: but in the other case he escapes the frequent vexation of waiting for barbers, and of their sometimes dirty fingers, offensive breaths and dull razors; he shaves when most convenient to him, and enjoys daily the pleasure of its being done with a good instrument."

By Jupiter,
Were I the wearer of Antonius' beard
I would not shave 't to day. SHAKSPEARE.

D'Israeli says that a clergyman who had the longest and largest beard of any Englishman in Elizabeth's reign, gave as a reason for wearing it the motive it afforded "that no act of his life might be unworthy the gravity of his appearance."

FRAGMENT ON MORTALITY.

WHEN Fuller in his Pisgah Sight of Palestine, comes to the city of Aigalon, where Elon, Judge of Israel, was buried, "of whom nothing else is recorded save his name, time of his rule (ten years), and place of his interment; slight him not," he says, "because so little is reported of him, it tending much to the praise of his policy in preventing foreign invasions, and domestic commotions, so that the land enjoyed peace, as far better than victory, as health is to be preferred before a recovery from sickness. Yea, times of much doing are times of much suffering, and many martial achievements are rather for the Prince's honour, than the people's ease."

"To what purpose," says Norris, "should a man trouble both the world's and his own rest, to make himself great? For besides the emptiness of the thing, the Play will quickly be done, and the Actors must all retire into a state of equality, and then it matters not who personated the Emperor, or who the Slave."

The Doctor's feelings were in unison with both these passages; — with the former concerning the quiet age in which it was his fortune to flourish, and with the latter in that it was his fortune to flourish in the shade. "It is with times," says Lord Bacon, "as it is with ways; some are more up hill and down hill, and some are more flat and plain; and the one is better for the liver, and the other for the writer."

He assented also to the Christian-Platonist of Bemerton when he asked, "to what purpose should a man be very earnest in the pursuit of Fame? He must shortly die, and so must those too who admire him." But nothing could be more opposed to his way of thinking than what follows in that philosopher, — "Nay, I could almost say, to what purpose should a man lay himself out upon study and drudge so laboriously in the mines of learning? He is no sooner a little wiser than his brethren, but Death thinks him ripe for his sickle; and for aught we know, after all his pains and industry, in the next world, an ideot, or a mechanic will be as forward as he." In the same spirit Horace Walpole said in his old age, "What is knowledge to me, who stand on the verge, and must leave my old stores as well as what I may add to them, — and how little could that be!"

When Johnson was told that Percy was uneasy at the thought of leaving his house, his study, his books — when he should die, — he replied — "a man need not be uneasy on these grounds, for as he will retain his consciousness, he may say with the Philosopher, *omnia mea mecum porto*."

"Let attention," says the thoughtful John Miller in his Bampton Lectures, which deserve to be side by side with those of the lamented Van Mildert, "let attention be requested to what seems here an accessory sign of the adaptation of all our heavenly Father's dealings to that which he 'knows to be in man' — I mean his merciful shortening of the term of this present natural life, subsequently to the period when all-seeing justice had been compelled to destroy the old world for its disobedience.

"I call it merciful, because, though we can conceive no length of day which could enable man with his present faculties to exhaust all that is made subject to his intellect, yet observing the scarcely credible rapidity of some minds and the no less wonderful retention of others, we may well conceive a far severer, nay too severe a test of resignation and patience to arise from length of years. To learn is pleasant; but to be 'ever learning, and never able to come to sure knowledge of the truth,' (if it were only in matters of lawful, and curious, and ardent speculation,) is a condition which we may well imagine to grow wearisome by too great length of time. 'Hope delayed' might well 'make the heart sick' in many such cases. We may find an infidel amusing himself on the brink of the grave with many imaginary wishes for a little longer respite, that he might witness the result of this or that speculation; but I am persuaded that the heart which really loves knowledge most truly and most wisely will be affected very differently. From every fresh addition to its store, (as far as concerns itself,) it will only derive increase to that desire wherewith it longs to become disentangled altogether from a state of imperfection, and to be present in the fulness of that light, wherein 'everything that is in part shall be done away.' Here, then, in one of the most interesting and most important of all points, (the shortening of human life,) we find a representation in Scripture which may be accounted favourable to its credibility and divine authority on the safest grounds of reason and experience. For certainly, as to the bare matter of fact, such representation corresponds in the strictest manner, (as far as we have known and have seen,) with the state of life as at present existing; and accepting it as true, we can perceive at once a satisfactory explanation of it by referring it, as a provision for man's well being, to the wisdom and mercy of an Omnipotent Spirit who knew, and knows 'what is in man.'"

FRAGMENT OF SIXTH VOLUME.

Reader, we are about to enter upon the sixth volume of this our Opus; and as it is written in the forms of Herkeru, Verily the eye of Hope is upon the high road of Expectation.

Well begun, says the Proverb, is half done. Horace has been made to say the same thing by the insertion of an apt word which pentametrises the verse,

Dimidium facti qui bene cæpit habet.

D. Juan de Villagutierre Soto-Mayor in setting forth the merits of Columbus for having discovered the New World, and thereby opened the way for its conquest by the Spaniards, observes that *el principio en todas las operaciones humanas es el mas dificultoso estado; y assi una vez vencido, se reputa y debe reputarse por la mitad della obra, ò por la principal de ella; y el proseguir despues en lo comenzado no contiene tanta dificultad.*

When Gabriel Chappuis dedicated the eighteenth book of Amadis, by him translated from the Spanish, to the Noble and Virtuous Lord Jan Anthoine Gros, Sieur de S. Jouere, &c., he says, after a preamble of eulogies upon the Dedicates and the Book, *Vous recevrez donc, s'il vous plaist ce petit livre d'aussy bon œil que ont fait ceux ausquels j'ay dedié les trois livres précédens, m'asseurant que s'il vous plaist en avoir la lecture, vous y trouverez grande delectation, comme à la verité l'histoire qui y est descrite, et mesmes en tous les précédens et en ceux qui viendront apres, a esté inventée pour delecter; mais avec tant de beaux traits, et une infinité de divers accidens et occurrences qu'il est impossible qu'avec le plaisir et le delectation, l'on n'en tire un grand proffet, comme vous experementerez, moyennant la grace de Dieu.*

J'ay fait le précédent Chapitre un peu court; peut-être que celui-ci sera plus long; je n'en suis pourtant pas bien assuré, nous l'allons voir. SCARRON.

DEBORAH'S strong affection for her father was not weakened by marriage; nor his for her by the consequent separation. Caroline Bowles says truly, and feelingly, and beautifully,

It is not love that steals the heart from love;
'Tis the hard world and its perplexing cares,
Its petrifying selfishness, its pride,
Its low ambition, and its paltry aims.

There was none of that "petrifying selfishness" in the little circle which lost so much when Deborah was removed from her father's parsonage. In order that that loss might be less painfully felt, it was proposed by Mr. Allison that Sunday should always be kept at the Grange when the season or the weather permitted. The Doctor came if he could; but for Mrs. Dove it was always to be a holiday.

"The pleasures of a volatile head," says Mrs. Carter, "are much less liable to disappointment, than those of a sensible heart." For such as can be contented with rattles and raree-shows, there are rattles and raree-shows in abundance to content them; and when one is broken it is mighty easily replaced by another. But the pleasures arising from the endearments of social relations, and the delicate sensibilities of friendly affection, are more limited, and their objects incontrovertible; they are accompanied with perpetual tender solicitude, and subject to accidents not to be repaired beneath the Sun. It is no wonder, however, that the joys of folly should have their completion in a world with which they are to end, while those of higher order must necessarily be incompleat in a world where they are only to begin.*

---

* From the writing of the latter paragraph I should judge this to be one of the latest sentences Southey ever wrote. — In the MS. it was to have followed c. cxxxiv. vol. iv. p. 361. — P. 337. of this Edition.

FRAGMENT WHICH WAS TO HAVE ANSWERED THE QUESTION PROPOSED IN THE TWO HUNDRED AND FORTY-SECOND CHAPTER.

Io udii già dire ad un valente uomo nostro vicino, gli uomini abbiano molte volte bisogno sì di lagrimare, come di ridere; e per tal cagione egli affermava essere state da principio trovate le dolorose favole, che si chiamarono Tragedie, accioche raccontate ne' teatri, come in qual tempo si costumava di fare, tirassero le lagrime agli occhi di coloro, che avevano di ciò mestiere; e cosi eglino piangendo della loro infirmita guarissero. Ma come ciò sia a noi non istà bene di contristare gli animi delle persone con cui favelliamo; massimamente colà dove si dimori per aver festa e sollazzo, e non per piagnere; che se pure alcuno è, che infermi per vaghezza di lagrimare, assai leggier cosa fia di medicarlo con la mostarda forte, o porlo in alcun luogo al fumo.

GALATEO, DEL M. GIOVANNI DELLA CASA.

THE Reader may remember, when he is thus reminded of it, that I delayed giving an account of Pompey, in answer to the question who he was, till the Dog-days should come. Here we are, (if *here* may be applied to time,) in the midst of them, July 24, 1830.

Horace Walpole speaks in a letter of two or three Mastiff-days, so much fiercer were they that season than our common Dog-days. This year they might with equal propriety be called Iceland-Dog-days. Here we are with the thermometer every night and morning below the temperate point, and scarcely rising two degrees above it at middle day. And then for weather, — as Voiture says, *Il pleut pla-ple-pli-plo-plus.*

If, then, as Robert Wilmot hath written, "it be true that the motions of our minds follow the temperature of the air wherein we live, then I think the perusing of some mournful matter, tending to the view of a notable example, will refresh your wits in a gloomy day, and ease your weariness of the louring night:" and the tragical part of my story might as fitly be told now in that respect, as if "weary winter were come upon us, which bringeth with him drooping days and weary nights." But who does not like to put away tragical thoughts? Who would not rather go to see a broad farce than a deep tragedy? Sad thoughts, even when they are medicinal for the mind, are as little to the mind's liking, as physic is grateful to the palate when it is needed most.

FRAGMENT ON HUTCHINSON'S WORKS.*

These superstitions are unquestionably of earlier date than any existing records, and commenced with the oldest system of idolatry, the worship of the heavenly bodies. Hutchinson's view is that when Moses brought the Jews out of their captivity, all men believed that "Fire, Light, or the Operation of the Air, did everything in this material system:" those who believed rightly in God, knew that these secondary causes acted as his instruments, but "those who had fallen and lost communication with the Prophets and the truth of tradition, and were left to reason, (though they reasoned as far as reason could reach,) thought the Heavens of a divine nature, and that they not only moved themselves and the heavenly bodies but operated all things on earth; and influenced the bodies, and governed the minds and fortunes of men: and so they fell upon worshipping them, and consulting them for times and seasons." "The Devil," he says, "chose right; this was the only object of false worship which gave any temptation; and it had very specious inducements." And it was because he thus prevailed over "the Children of disobedience," that the Apostle stiles him "the Prince of the Powers of the Air." "This made the Priests and Physicians of the antient heathen cultivate the knowledge of these Powers, and afterwards made them star-gazers and observe the motions of those bodies for their conjunctions and oppositions, and all the stuff of their lucky and unlucky days and times, and especially to make advantage of their eclipses, for which they were stiled Magi, and looked upon as acquaintance of their Gods; and so much of the latter as is of any use, and a great deal more, we are obliged to them for." "But these," he says, "who thought that the Heavens ordered the events of things by their motions and influences, and that they were to be observed and foreseen by men, robbed God of his chief attributes, and were ordered then, and ought still, to be punished with death."

Hutchinson is one of the most repulsive writers that ever produced any effect upon his contemporaries. His language is such as almost justified Dr. Parr in calling it the Hutchinsonian jargon; and his system is so confusedly brought forward that one who wishes to obtain even a general knowledge of it, must collect it as he can from passages scattered through the whole of his treatises. Add to these disrecommendations that it is propounded in the coarsest terms of insolent assumption, and that he treats the offence of those who reject the authority of scripture,—that is of his interpretation of Hebrew, and his exposition of the Mosaic philosophy,—as "an infectious scurvy or leprosy of the soul which can scarcely be cured by anything but eternal brimstone."

The Paradise Lost, he calls, "that cursed farce of Milton, where he makes the Devil his hero:" and of the ancient poets and historians he says that "the mischief which these vermin did by praising their heroes in their farces or princes for conquering countries, and thereby inciting other princes to imitate them, were the causes of the greatest miseries that have befallen mankind." But Sir Isaac Newton was the great object of his hatred. "Nothing but villainy," he said, "was to be expected from men who had made a human scheme, and would construe every text concerning it, so as to serve their purpose; he could only treat them as the most treacherous men alive. I hope," he says, "I have power to forgive any crimes which are committed only against myself; I am not required, nor have I any power to forgive treason against the king, much less to forgive any crimes whereby any attempt to dispossess Jehovah Aleim. Nay, if I know of them and do not reveal them, and do not my endeavour to disappoint them in either, I am accessary. I shall put these things where I can upon the most compassionate side; the most favourable wish I can make for them is, that they may prove their ignorance so fully, that it may abate their crimes; but if their followers will shew that

* A Chapter was to have been devoted to the Hutchinsonian philosophy, and I am inclined to believe that this was a part of it.

he or his accomplices knew anything, I must be forced to make Devils of them. There are many other accidents besides design or malice, which make men atheists, — studying or arguing to maintain a system, forged by a man who does not understand it, and in which there must be some things false, makes a man a villain whether he will or no.

"He (Newton) first framed a philosophy, which is two thirds of the business of the real scriptures, and struck off the rest. And when he found his philosophy was built upon, and to be supported by emptiness, he was forced to patch up a God to constitute space. His equipage appears to have been the translation of the apostate Jews, and some blind histories of the modern heathen *Deus*, and an empty head to make his *Deus;* Kepler's banter of his powers, and some tacit acknowledgements, as he only supposed, of the ignorantest heathens; an air-pump to make, and a pendulum or swing to prove a vacuum; a loadstone, and a bit of amber, or jet, to prove his philosophy; a telescope, a quadrant, and a pair of compasses to make infinite worlds, circles, crooked lines, &c.; a glass bubble, prisms and lenses, and a board with a hole in it, to let light into a dark room to form his history of light and colours; and he seems to have spent his time, not only when young, as some boys do, but when he should have set things right, in blowing his phlegm through a straw, raising bubbles, and admiring how the light would glare on the sides of them."

No mention of Hutchinson is made in Dr. Brewster's Life of Newton: his system was probably thought too visionary to deserve notice, and the author unworthy of it because he had been the most violent and foul-mouthed of all Sir Isaac's opponents. The Mathematical Principles of Natural Philosophy, he called a cobweb of circles and lines to catch flies. "Mathematics," he said, "are applicable to any *data*, real or imaginary, true or false, more pestilent and destructive positions had been fathered upon that science than upon all others put together, and mathematicians had been put to death, both by Heathens and Christians, for attributing much less to the heavenly bodies than Newton had done." He compared his own course of observations with Newton's. His had been in the dark bowels of the earth, with the inspired light of scripture in his hand,—there he had learned his Hebrew, and there he had studied the causes and traced the effects of the Deluge. "The opportunities," he said, "were infinitely beyond what any man can have by living in a box, peeping out at a window, or letting the light in at a hole: or in separating and extracting the spirit from light, which can scarce happen in nature, or from refracting the light, which only happens upon the rainbow, bubbles, &c., or by making experiments with the loadstone, talc or amber, which differ in texture from most other bodies, and are only found in masses of small size; or by arranging a pendulum, which perhaps has not a parallel case in nature: or by the effects produced by spirit or light upon mixing small parcels of extracted fluids or substances, scarce one of which ever happened, or will happen in nature: or by taking cases which others have put, or putting cases which never had, nor ever will have any place in nature: or by forming figures or lines of crooked directions of motions or things, which most of them have no place, so the lines no use in nature, other than to serve hypotheses of imaginary Powers, or courses, which always have been useless, when any other Powers, though false, have been assigned and received; and must all finally be useless, when the true Powers are shewn."

Such passages show that Hutchinson was either grossly incapable of appreciating Newton's discoveries, or that he wilfully and maliciously depreciated them. His own attainments might render the first of these conclusions improbable, and the second would seem still more so upon considering the upright tenour of his life. But the truth seems to be, that having constructed a system with great labour, and no little ability, upon the assumption that the principles of natural philosophy as well as of our faith are contained in the scriptures, and that the true interpretation of scripture depended upon the right understanding of the Hebrew primitives, which knowledge the apostate Jews had lost, and he had recovered, his belief in this system had all the intolerance of fanaticism or supposed infallibility; and those who strongly contravened it, deserved in his opinion the punishments appointed in the Mosaic law for idolatry and blasphemy. Newton and Clarke were in this predicament. Both, in his judgement, attributed so much to secondary causes, — those Powers which had been the first objects of idolatry, that he considered their Deity to be nothing more than the Jupiter of the philosophising heathens; and he suspects that their esoteric doctrine resolved itself into Pantheism. Toland indeed had told him that there was a scheme in progress for leading men through Pantheism and Atheism, and made him acquainted with all their designs, divine or diabolical, and political or anarchical! and all the villanies and forgeries they had committed to accomplish them. First they sought to make men believe in a God who could not punish, and then — that there was no God, and Toland was engaged, for pay, in this scheme of propagandism, "because he had some learning, and more loose humour than any of them." The Pantheisticon was written with this view. Toland was only in part the author, other hands assisted, and Hutchinson says, he knew "there was a physician, and a patient of his a divine, who was very serviceable in their respective stations in prescribing proper doses, even to the very last." But they "carried the matter too far," "they discovered a secret which the world had not taken notice of, and which it was highly necessary the world should know." For "though it be true to a proverb, that a man should not be hanged for being a fool, they shewed the principles of these men so plainly, which were to have no superior, to conform to any religion, laws, oaths, &c., but be bound by none, and the consequences of propagating them, that they thereby shewed the wisdom of the heathen people, who, because they could not live safely, stoned such men; and the justice of the heathen Emperors and Kings, who put such to death, because they could have no security from them, and if their doubts, or notions had prevailed, all must have gone to anarchy or a commonwealth, as it always did, when and where they neglected to cut them off."

That atheism had its propagandists then as it has now is certain, and no one who has watched the course of opinion among his contemporaries can doubt that Socinianism, or semi-belief, gravitates towards infidelity. But to believe that Newton and Clarke were engaged in the scheme which is here imputed to them, we must allow more weight to Toland's character than to their's, and to Hutchinson's judgement.

What has here been said of Hutchinson exhibits him in his worst light, — and it must not hastily be concluded that because he breathed the fiercest spirit of intolerance, he is altogether to be disliked as a man, or despised as an author. Unless his theory, untenable as it is, had been constructed with considerable talent, and supported with no common learning, — he could never have had such men as Bishop Horne and Jones of Nayland among his disciples. Without assenting to his system, a biblical student may derive instruction from many parts of his works.

There is one remarkable circumstance in his history. When he was a mere boy a stranger came to board with his father, who resided at Spennythorn in the North-Riding of Yorkshire, upon an estate of forty pounds a-year. The father's intention was to educate this son for the office of steward to some great landed proprietor, and this stranger agreed to instruct him in every branch of knowledge requisite for such an employment, upon condition of being boarded free of expence, engaging at the same time to remain till he had compleated the boy's education. What he had thus undertaken he performed well; "he was, perhaps," says Hutchinson, "as great a mathematician as either of those whose books he studied, and taught me as much as

I could see any use for, either upon the earth or in the heavens, without poisoning me with any false notions fathered upon the mathematics." The curious part of this story is that it was never known who this scientific stranger was, for he carefully and effectually concealed everything that could lead to a discovery. Hutchinson was born in 1674, and his education under this tutor was compleated at the age of nineteen.

FRAGMENT RELATIVE TO THE GRAMMAR SCHOOL AT DONCASTER AND THE LIVING OF ROSSINGTON.*

THE Grammar School was next door to Peter Hopkins's, being kept in one of the lower apartments of the Town Hall. It was a free school for the sons of freemen, the Corporation allowing a salary of £50 *per annum* to the schoolmaster, who according to the endowment must be a clergyman. That office was held by Mr. Crochley, who had been bred at Westminster, and was elected from thence to Christ Church, Oxford, in 1742. He came to Doncaster with a promise from the Corporation that the living of Rossington, which is in their gift and is a valuable benefice, should be given him provided he had fifty scholars when it became vacant. He never could raise their numbers higher than forty-five; the Corporation adhered to the letter of their agreement; the disappointment preyed on him, and he died a distressed and broken-hearted man.

Yet it was not Crochley's fault that the school had not been more flourishing. He was as competent to the office as a man of good natural parts could be rendered by the most compleat course of classical education. But in those days few tradesmen ever thought of bestowing upon their sons any farther education than was sufficient to qualify them for trade; and the boys who were desirous to be placed there, must have been endued with no ordinary love of learning, for a grammar school is still anything rather than a *Ludus Literarius*.

Two or three years before the Doctor's marriage a widow lady came to settle at Doncaster, chiefly for the sake of placing her sons at the Grammar School there, which, though not in high repute, was at least respectably conducted. It was within five minutes' walk of her own door, and thus the boys had the greatest advantage that schoolboys can possibly enjoy, that of living at home, whereby they were saved from all the misery and from most of the evil with which boarding-schools, almost without an exception, abounded in those days, and from which it may be doubted whether there are any yet that are altogether free. Her name was Horseman, she was left with six children, and just with such means as enabled her by excellent management to make what is called

---

* The Parish of Rossington in the union and soke of Doncaster was for many generations the seat of the Fossard and Mauley families. In the reign of Henry VII., it was granted by that monarch to the corporation of Doncaster.

The following extract is from Mr. John Wainwright's History and Antiquities of Doncaster and Conisbro'.

"Connected with the history of this village, is a singular and curious specimen of Egyptian manners, as practised by the itinerant gypsies of the British Empire. In a letter, which we had the pleasure of receiving from the Rev. James Stoven, D.D., the worthy and learned rector of this place, it is remarked, that about one hundred and twenty years ago, the gypsies commenced here a curious custom, which they practised once in almost every year, occasioned by the interment, in the churchyard of this place, (of) one of their principal leaders, Mr. Charles Bosville, on the 30th of June, 1708 or 9. Having, from a boy, been much acquainted with this village, I have often heard of their (the gypsies) abode here, and with them Mr. James Bosville, their king, under whose authority they conducted themselves with great propriety and decorum, never committing the least theft or offence. They generally slept in their farmers' barns, who, at those periods, considered their property to be more safely protected than in their absence. Mr. Charles Bosville (but how related to the king does not appear,) was much beloved in this neighbourhood, having a knowledge of medicine, was very attentive to the sick, well bred in manners, and comely in person. After his death, the gypsies, for many years, came to visit his tomb, and poured upon it hot ale; but by degrees they deserted the place. — (These circumstances must yet hang on their remembrance; as, only a year ago, 1821, an ill-drest set of them encamped in our lanes, calling themselves Boswell's.) — These words in the parentheses came within my own knowledge."

It is added in a note — "*Boswell's Gang*, is an appellation, very generally applied to a collection of beggars, or other idle itinerants, which we often see encamped in groups in the lanes and ditches of this part of England."

In quoting this, I by no means assent to the statement that Gypsies are Egyptians. — They are of Hindostanee origin.

a respectable appearance, the boys being well educated at the cheapest rate, and she herself educating two daughters, who were fortunately the eldest children. Happy girls! they were taught what no Governess could teach them, to be useful as soon as they were capable of being so; to make their brothers' shirts and mend their stockings; to make and mend for themselves; to cipher so as to keep accounts; to assist in household occupations, to pickle and preserve, to make pastry, to work chair-bottoms, to write a fair hand, and to read Italian. This may seem incongruous with so practical a system of domestic education. But Mrs. Horseman was born in Italy, and had passed great part of her youth there.

The father, Mr. Duckinton, was a man of some fortune, whose delight was in travelling, and who preferred Italy to all other countries. Being a whimsical person he had a fancy for naming each of his children after the place where it happened to be born. One daughter therefore was baptized by the fair name of Florence, Mrs. Horseman was christened Venetia, like the wife of Sir Kenelm Digby, whose husband was more careful of her complexion than of her character. Fortunate it was that he had no daughter born at Genoa or at Nantes, for if he had, the one must have concealed her true baptismal name under the alias of Jenny; and the other have subscribed herself Nancy, that she might not be reproached with the brandy cask. The youngest of his children was a son, and if he had been born in the French capital would hardly have escaped the ignominious name of Paris, but as Mr. Duckinton had long wished for a son, and the mother knowing her husband's wishes had prayed for one, the boy escaped with no worse name than Deodatus.

FRAGMENT OF INTERCHAPTER.

Kissing has proverbially been said to go by favour. So it is but too certain, that Preferment does in Army and Navy, Church and State; and so does Criticism.

That Kissing should do so is but fair and just; and it is moreover in the nature of things.

That Promotion should do so is also in the nature of things — as they are. And this also is fair where no injustice is committed. When other pretensions are equal, favour is the feather which ought to be put into the scale. In cases of equal fitness, no wrong is done to the one party, if the other is preferred for considerations of personal friendship, old obligations, or family connection; the injustice and the wrong would be if these were overlooked.

To what extent may favour be reasonably allowed in criticism?

If it were extended no farther than can be really useful to the person whom there is an intention of serving, its limits would be short indeed. For in that case it would never proceed farther than truth and discretion went with it. Far more injury is done to a book and to an author by injudicious or extravagant praise, than by intemperate or malevolent censure.

Some persons have merrily surmised that Job was a reviewer because he exclaimed, "Oh that mine enemy had written a book!" Others on the contrary have inferred that reviewing was not known in his days, because he wished that his own words had been printed and published.

[The timbers were laid for a Chapter on wigs, and many notes and references were collected. — This Fragment is all that remains.]

Bernardin St. Pierre, who, with all his fancies and oddities, has been not undeservedly a popular writer in other countries as well as in his own, advances in the most extravagant of his books, (the *Harmonies de la Nature*,) the magnificent hypothesis that men invented great wigs because great wigs are *semblables aux criniers des lions*, like lion's manes. But as wigs are rather designed to make men look grave than terrible, he might with more probability have surmised that they were intended to imitate the appearance of the Bird of Wisdom.

The Doctor wore a wig: and looked neither like a Lion, nor like an Owl in it. Yet when he first put it on, and went to the looking-glass, he could not help thinking that he did not look like a Dove.

But then he looked like a Doctor, which was as it became him to look. He wore it professionally.

It was not such a wig as Dr. Parr's, which was of all contemporary wigs *facile princeps*. Nor was it after the fashion of that which may be seen in "immortal buckle," upon Sir Cloudesley Shovel's monument in Westminster Abbey —— &c.

MEMOIRS OF CAT'S EDEN.

[The following Fragments were intended to be worked up into an Interchapter on the History of Cats. The first fairly written out was to have been, it would appear, the commencement. The next is an Extract from Eulia Effendi. "That anecdote about the King of the Cats, Caroline, you must write out for me, as it must be inserted," said the lamented Author of "The Doctor, &c." to Mrs. Southey. The writer of the lines is not known, they were forwarded to the Author when at Killerton. The "Memoirs of Cats of Greta Hall" was to have furnished the particulars, which the first fragment states had got abroad.

What was to have been the form of the Interchapter the Editor does not know, neither does Mrs. Southey. The playful letter is given exactly as it was written. A beautiful instance, as will be acknowledged by all, of that confidence which should exist between a loving father and a dutiful daughter. Sir Walter Scott wrote feelingly when he said,

Some feelings are to mortals given
With less of earth in them than heaven:
And if there be a human tear
From passion's dross refined and clear,
A tear so limpid and so meek,
It would not stain an angel's cheek,
'Tis that which pious fathers shed
Upon a duteous daughter's head !]

FRAGMENT OF INTERCHAPTER.

More than prince of cats, I can tell you.
Romeo and Juliet.

An extract from the Register of Cat's Eden has got abroad, whereby it appears that the Laureate, Dr. Southey, who is known to be a philofelist, and confers honours upon his Cats according to their services, has raised one to the highest rank in peerage, promoting him through all its degrees by the following titles, His Serene Highness the Archduke Rumpelstilzchen, Marquis Macbum, Earl Tomlemagne, Baron Raticide, Waowlher and Skaratchi.

The first of these names is taken from the German Collection of *Kinder und Haus-Märchen.* A Dwarf or Imp so called was to carry off the infant child of the Queen as the price of a great service which he had rendered her, but he had consented to forego his right if in the course of three days she could find out what was his name. This she never could have done, if the King had not on the first day gone hunting, and got into the thickest part of the wood, where he saw a ridiculous Dwarf hopping about before a house which seemed by its dimensions to be his home, and singing for joy; these were the words of his song,

Heute back ich, morgen brau ich,
Uebermorgen hohl ich der Frau Königinn: ihr Kind,
Ach wie gut ist, das niemand weiss,
Dass ich Rumpelstilzchen heiss!

I bake to-day, and I brew to-morrow,
Mrs. Queen will see me the next day to her sorrow,
When according to promise her child I shall claim,
For none can disclose, because nobody knows
That Rumpelstilzchen is my name.

Now if Rumpelstilzchen had had as many names as a Spanish Infante, the man must have a good memory who could have carried them away upon hearing them once.

"The Cats of Diorigi are celebrated all over Greece, for nowhere are to be found cats so pretty, so vigilant, so caressing and well-bred as at Diorigi. The Cats of the Oasis in Egypt, and of Sinope, are justly renowned for their good qualities, but those of Diorigi are particularly fat, brilliant, and playing different colours. They are carried from here to Persia, to Ardebeil where they are shut up in cages, proclaimed by the public criers and sold for one or two *tomans*. The Georgians also buy them at a great price, to save their whiskers which are commonly eaten up by mice. The criers of Ardebeil, who cry these cats, have a particular melody to which they sing their cry in these words,

O you who like a Cat
That catches mouse and rat,
Well-bred, caressing, gay
Companion to sport and play,
Amusing and genteel,
Shall never scratch and steal.

Singing these words they carry the cats on their head and sell them for great prices, because the inhabitants of Ardebeil are scarce able to save their woollen cloth from the destruction of mice and rats. Cats are called Hurre, Katta, Senorre, Merabe, Matshi, Weistaun, Wemistaun, but those of Diorigi are particularly highly esteemed. Notwithstanding that high reputation and price of the Cats of Diorigi, they meet with dangerous enemies in their native place, where sometimes forty or fifty of them are killed secretly, tanned, and converted into fur for the winter time. It is a fur scarce to be distinguished from Russian ermelin, and that of the red cats is not to be distinguished from the fox that comes from Ozalov."*

A labouring man returning to his cottage after night-fall, passed by a lone house in ruins, long uninhabited. Surprised at the appearance of light within, and strange sounds issuing from the desolate interior, he stopped and looked in through one of the broken windows, and there in a large old gloomy room, quite bare of furniture except that the cobwebs hung about its walls like tapestry, he beheld a marvellous spectacle. A small coffin covered with a pall stood in the midst of the floor, and round and round and round about it, with dismal lamentations in the feline tongue, marched a circle of Cats, one of them being covered from head to foot with a black veil, and walking as chief mourner. The man was so frightened with what he saw that he waited to see no more, but went straight home, and at supper told his wife what had befallen him.

Their own old Cat, who had been sitting, as was her wont, on the elbow of her Master's chair, kept her station very quietly, till he came to the description of the chief Mourner, when, to the great surprise and consternation of the old couple, she bounced up, and flew up the chimney exclaiming — "Then I am King of the Cats."

Keswick, January 9th.

Dear Master,
Let our boldness not offend,
If a few lines of duteous love we send;
Nor wonder that we deal in rhyme, for long
We've been familiar with the founts of song;
Nine thorougher tabbies you would rarely find,
Than those who laurels round your temples bind:
For how, with less than nine lives to their share,
Could they have lived so long on poet's fare?
Athens surnamed them from their mousing powers,
And Rome from that harmonious MU of ours,
In which the letter U, (as we will trouble you
To say to Todd) should supersede ew —
This by the way — we now proceed to tell,
That all within the bounds of home are well;
All but your faithful cats, who inly pine;
The cause your Conscience may too well divine.
Ah! little do you know how swiftly fly
The venomed darts of feline jealousy;
How delicate a task to deal it is
With a Grimalkin's sensibilities,
When Titten's tortoise fur you smoothed with bland
And coaxing courtesies of lip and hand,
We felt as if, (poor Puss's constant dread,)
Some school-boy stroked us both from tail to head;
Nor less we suffer'd while with sportive touch
And purring voice, you played with grey-backed Gutch;
And when with eager step, you left your seat,
To get a peep at Richard's snow-white feet,
Himself all black; we long'd to stop his breath
With something like his royal namesake's death;
If more such scenes our frenzied fancies see,
Resolved we hang from yonder apple tree —
And were not that a sad catastrophe!
O! then return to your deserted lake,
Dry eyes that weep, and comfort hearts that ache;
Our mutual jealousies we both disown,
Content to share, rather than lose a throne.
The Parlour, Rumple's undisputed reign,
Hurley's the rest of all your wide domain.
Return, return, dear Bard κατ' ἐξοχήν,
Restore the happy days that once have been,
Resign yourself to Home, the Muse and us.

(*Scratch'd*) Rumplestitchkin,
Hurlyburlybuss.

MEMOIR OF THE CATS OF GRETA HALL.

For as much, most excellent Edith May, as you must always feel a natural and becoming concern in whatever relates to the house wherein you were born, and in which the first part of your life has thus far so happily

* Evlia Effendi.

been spent, I have, for your instruction and delight, composed these Memoirs of the Cats of Greta Hall: to the end that the memory of such worthy animals may not perish, but be held in deserved honour by my children, and those who shall come after them. And let me not be supposed unmindful of Beelzebub of Bath, and Senhor Thomaz de Lisboa, that I have not gone back to an earlier period, and included them in my design. Far be it from me to intend any injury or disrespect to their shades! Opportunity of doing justice to their virtues will not be wanting at some future time, but for the present I must confine myself within the limits of these precincts.

In the autumn of the year 1803, when I entered upon this place of abode, I found the hearth in possession of two cats, whom my nephew Hartley Coleridge, (then in the 7th year of his age,) had named Lord Nelson and Bona Marietta. The former, as the name implies, was of the worthier gender: it is as decidedly so in Cats, as in grammar and in law. He was an ugly specimen of the streaked-carrotty, or Judas-coloured kind; which is one of the ugliest varieties. But *nimium ne crede colori*. In spite of his complection, there was nothing treacherous about him. He was altogether a good Cat, affectionate, vigilant, and brave; and for services performed against the Rats was deservedly raised in succession to the rank of Baron, Viscount, and Earl. He lived to a good old age; and then being quite helpless and miserable, was in mercy thrown into the river. I had more than once interfered to save him from this fate; but it became at length plainly an act of compassion to consent to it. And here let me observe that in a world wherein death is necessary, the law of nature by which one creature preys upon another is a law of mercy, not only because death is thus made instrumental to life, and more life exists in consequence, but also because it is better for the creatures themselves to be cut off suddenly, than to perish by disease or hunger, — for these are the only alternatives.

There are still some of Lord Nelson's descendants in the town of Keswick. Two of the family were handsomer than I should have supposed any Cats of this complection could have been; but their fur was fine, the colour a rich carrot, and the striping like that of the finest tyger or tabby kind. I named one of them William Rufus; the other Danayn le Roux, after a personage in the Romance of Gyron le Courtoys.

Bona Marietta was the mother of Bona Fidelia, so named by my nephew aforesaid. Bona Fidelia was a tortoiseshell cat. She was filiated upon Lord Nelson, others of the same litter having borne the unequivocal stamp of his likeness. It was in her good qualities that she resembled him, for in truth her name rightly bespoke her nature. She approached as nearly as possible in disposition, to the ideal of a perfect cat: — he who supposes that animals have not their difference of disposition as well as men, knows very little of animal nature. Having survived her daughter Madame Catalani, she died of extreme old age, universally esteemed and regretted by all who had the pleasure of her acquaintance.

Bona Fidelia left a daughter and a granddaughter; the former I called Madame Bianchi — the latter Pulcheria. It was impossible ever to familiarise Madame Bianchi, though she had been bred up in all respects like her gentle mother, in the same place, and with the same persons. The nonsense of that arch-philosophist Helvetius would be sufficiently confuted by this single example, if such rank folly, contradicted as it is by the experience of every family, needed confutation. She was a beautiful and singular creature, white, with a fine tabby tail, and two or three spots of tabby, always delicately clean; and her wild eyes were bright and green as the Duchess de Cadaval's emerald necklace. Pulcheria did not correspond as she grew up to the promise of her kittenhood and her name; but she was as fond as her mother was shy and intractable. Their fate was extraordinary as well as mournful. When good old Mrs. Wilson died, who used to feed and indulge them, they immediately forsook the house, nor could they be allured to enter it again, though they continued to wander and moan around it, and came for food. After some weeks Madame Bianchi disappeared, and Pulcheria soon afterwards died of a disease endemic at that time among cats.

For a considerable time afterwards, an evil fortune attended all our attempts at re-establishing a Cattery. Ovid disappeared and Virgil died of some miserable distemper. You and your cousin are answerable for these names: the reasons which I could find for them were, in the former case, the satisfactory one that the said Ovid might be presumed to be a master in the Art of Love; and in the latter, the probable one that something like Ma-ro might be detected in the said Virgil's notes of courtship. There was poor Othello: most properly named, for black he was, and jealous undoubtedly he would have been, but he in his kittenship followed Miss Wilbraham into the street, and there in all likelihood came to an untimely end. There was the Zombi —(I leave the Commentators to explain that title, and refer them to my History of Brazil to do it,) — his marvellous story was recorded in a letter to Bedford, — and after that adventure he vanished. There was Prester John, who turned out not to be of John's gender, and therefore had the name altered to Pope Joan. The Pope I am afraid came to a death of which other Popes have died. I suspect that some poison which the rats had turned out of their holes proved fatal to their enemy. For some time I feared we were at the end of our Cat-a-logue: but at last Fortune, as if to make amends for her late severity, sent us two at once, — the-never-to-be-enough-praised Rumpelstilzchen, and the equally-to-be-admired Hurlyburlybuss.

And "first for the first of these" as my huge favourite, and almost namesake Robert South, says in his Sermons.

When the Midgeleys went away from the next house, they left this creature to our hospitality, cats being the least moveable of all animals because of their strong local predilections; — they are indeed in a domesticated state the serfs of the animal creation, and properly attached to the soil. The change was gradually and therefore easily brought about, for he was already acquainted with the children and with me; and having the same precincts to prowl in was hardly sensible of any other difference in his condition than that of obtaining a name; for when he was consigned to us he was an anonymous cat; and I having just related at breakfast, with universal applause, the story of Rumpelstilzchen from a German tale in Grimm's Collection, gave him that strange and magnisonant appellation; to which, upon its being ascertained that he came when a kitten from a bailiff's house, I added the patronymic of Macbum. Such is his history; his character may with most propriety be introduced after the manner of Plutarch's parallels, when I shall have given some previous account of his great compeer and rival Hurlyburlybuss, — that name also is of Germanic and Grimmish extraction.

Whence Hurlyburlybuss came was a mystery when you departed from the Land of Lakes, and a mystery it long remained. He appeared here, as Mango Capac did in Peru, and Quetzalcohuatl among the Aztecas, no one knew from whence. He made himself acquainted with all the philofelists of the family — attaching himself more particularly to Mrs. Lovell, but he never attempted to enter the house, frequently disappeared for days, and once, since my return, for so long a time that he was actually believed to be dead, and veritably lamented as such. The wonder was whither did he retire at such times — and to whom did he belong; for neither I in my daily walks, nor the children, nor any of the servants, ever by any chance saw him anywhere except in our own domain. There was something so mysterious in this, that in old times it might have excited strong suspicion, and he would have been in danger of passing for a Witch in disguise, or a familiar. The mystery, however, was solved about four weeks ago, when, as we were returning from a walk up the Greta, Isabel saw him on his transit across the road and the wall from Shulicrow, in a direction toward the Hill. But to this day we are ignorant who has the honour to be his owner in the eye of the law; and the owner is equally ignorant of the high favour in which Hurlyburlybuss is held, of the heroic name which he has obtained, and that his fame has extended far and wide — even unto Norwich in the East, and Escott and Crediton and Kellerton in the West, yea — that with Rumpelstilzchen he has been celebrated in song, by some hitherto undiscovered poet, and that his glory will go down to future generations.

The strong enmity which unhappily subsists between these otherwise gentle and most amiable cats is not unknown to you. Let it be imputed, as in justice it ought, not to their individual characters, (for Cats have characters, — and for the benefit of philosophy, as well as *felisophy*, this truth ought generally to be known,) but to the constitution of Cat nature, — an original sin, or an original necessity, which may be only another mode of expressing the same thing:

> Two stars keep not their motion in one sphere,
> Nor can one purlieu brook a double reign
> Of Hurlyburlybuss and Rumpelstilzchen.

When you left us, the result of many a fierce conflict was, that Hurly remained master of the green and garden, and the whole of the out of door premises; Rumpel always upon the appearance of his victorious enemy retiring into the house as a citadel or sanctuary. The conqueror was, perhaps, in part indebted for this superiority to his hardier habits of life, living always in the open air, and providing for himself; while Rumpel, (who though born under a bum-bailiff's roof was nevertheless kittened with a silver spoon in his mouth,) passed his hours in luxurious repose beside the fire, and looked for his meals as punctually as any two-legged member of the family. Yet I believe that the advantage on Hurly's side is in a great degree constitutional also, and that his superior courage arises from a confidence in his superior strength, which, as you well know, is visible in his make. What Bento and Maria Rosa used to say of my poor Thomaz, that he was *muito fidalgo*, is true of Rumpelstilzchen, his countenance, deportment, and behaviour being such that he is truly a gentleman-like Tom-cat. Far be it from me to praise him beyond his deserts, — he is not beautiful, the mixture, tabby and white, is not good, (except under very favourable combinations,) and the tabby is not good of its kind. Nevertheless he is a fine cat, handsome enough for his sex, large, well-made, with good features, and an intelligent countenance, and carrying a splendid tail, which in Cats and Dogs is undoubtedly the seat of honour. His eyes, which are soft and expressive, are of a hue between chrysolite and emerald. Hurlyburlybuss's are between chrysolite and topaz. Which may be the more esteemed shade for the *olho de gato* I am not lapidary enough to decide. You should ask my Uncle. But both are of the finest water. In all his other features Hurly must yield the palm, and in form also; he has no pretensions to elegance, his size is ordinary and his figure bad: but the character of his face and neck is so masculine, that the Chinese, who use the word bull as synonymous with male, and call a boy a bull-child, might with great propriety denominate him a bull-cat. His make evinces such decided marks of strength and courage, that if cat-fighting were as fashionable as cock-fighting, no Cat would stand a fairer chance for winning a Welsh main. He would become as famous as the Dog Billy himself, whom I look upon as the most distinguished character that has appeared since Buonaparte.

Some weeks ago Hurlyburlybuss was manifestly emaciated and enfeebled by ill health, and Rumpelstilzchen with great magnanimity made overtures of peace. The whole progress of the treaty was seen from the parlour window. The caution with which Rumpel made his advances, the sullen dignity with which they were received, their mutual uneasiness when Rumpel, after a slow and wary approach, seated himself whisker-to-whisker with his rival, the mutual fear which restrained not only teeth and claws, but even all tones of defiance, the mutual agitation of their tails which, though they did not expand with anger, could not be kept still for suspense, and lastly the manner in which Hurly retreated, like Ajax still keeping his face toward his old antagonist, were worthy to have been represented by that painter who was called the Rafaelle of Cats. The overture I fear was not accepted as generously as it was made; for no sooner had Hurlyburlybuss recovered strength than hostilities were recommenced with greater violence than ever; Rumpel, who had not abused his superiority while he possessed it, had acquired mean time a confidence which made him keep the field. Dreadful were the combats which ensued, as their ears, faces and legs bore witness. Rumpel had a wound which went through one of his feet. The result has been so far in his favour that he no longer seeks to avoid his enemy, and we are often compelled to interfere and separate them. Oh it is aweful to hear the "dreadful note of preparation" with which they prelude their encounters!—the long low growl slowly rises and swells till it becomes a high sharp yowl,—and then it is snapped short by a sound which seems as if they were spitting fire and venom at each other. I could half persuade myself that the word felonious is derived from the feline temper as displayed at such times. All means of reconciling them and making them understand how goodly a thing it is for cats to dwell together in peace, and what fools they are to quarrel and tear each other, are in vain. The proceedings of the Society for the Abolition of War are not more utterly ineffectual and hopeless.

All we can do is to act more impartially than the Gods did between Achilles and Hector, and continue to treat both with equal regard.

And thus having brought down these Memoirs of the Cats of Greta Hall to the present day, I commit the precious memorial to your keeping, and remain

Most dissipated and light-heeled daughter,
Your most diligent and light-hearted father,
Robert Southey.

Keswick, 18 *June*, 1824.

FRAGMENT OF INTERCHAPTER.

[The following playful effusion was likewise, as the "Memoirs of Cat's Eden," intended for "The Doctor, &c.," but how it was to have been moulded, so as to obscure the incognito, I do not know. It will tend, if I mistake not, to show the easy versatility, —the true *εὐτραπελία*,—of a great and a good man's mind. "Fortune," says Fluellen, "is turning and inconstant, and variations, and mutabilities,"—but one who, in the midst of constant and laborious occupations, could revel in such a recreation as this "Chapter on the Statutes" was Fortune's master, and above her wheel.

ARS UTINAM MORES ANIMUMQUE EFFINGERE POSSET:
PULCHRIOR IN TERRIS NULLA TABELLA FORET.*

It may be added that there was another very curious collection of Letters intended for "The Doctor, &c.," but they have not come to my hand. They were written in a peculiar dialect, and would have required much mother wit and many vocabularies to have decyphered them. She who suggested them,—a woman "of infinite jest,—of most excellent fancy,"—a good woman, and a kind,—is now gathered to her rest!]

ΕΙΣ ΤΟΥΣ ΑΝΔΡΙΑΝΤΑΣ.

Ὁ μὲν διάβολος ἐνέπνευσέ τισι παρανόμοις ἀνθρώποις, καὶ εἰς τοὺς τῶν βασιλέων ὕβρισαν ἀνδριάντας.

Chrysost. Hom. ad Popul. Antiochen.

My dear daughter,

Having lately been led to compose an inscription for one of our Garden statues, an authentic account of two such extraordinary works of art has appeared to me so desirable that I even wonder at myself for having so long delayed to write one. It is the more incumbent on me to do this, because neither of the artists have thought proper to inscribe their names upon these master-pieces,—either from that modesty which often accompanies the highest genius,

* Mart. Epigr.

or from a dignified consciousness that it was unnecessary to set any mark upon them, the works themselves sufficiently declaring from what hands they came.

I undertake this becoming task with the more pleasure because our friend Mrs. Keenan has kindly offered to illustrate the intended account by drawings of both Statues, — having, as you may well suppose, been struck with admiration by them. The promise of this co-operation induces me not to confine myself to a mere description, but to relate on what occasion they were made, and faithfully to record the very remarkable circumstances which have occurred in consequence; circumstances I will venture to say, as well attested and as well worthy of preservation as any of those related in the History of the Portuguese Images of Nossa Senhora, in ten volumes quarto, — a book of real value, and which you know I regard as one of the most curious in my collection. If in the progress of this design I should sometimes appear to wander in digression, you will not impute it to any habitual love of circumlocution; and the speculative notions which I may have occasion to propose, you will receive as mere speculations and judge of them accordingly.

Many many years ago I remember to have seen these popular and rustic rhymes in print,

God made a great man to plough and to sow,
God made a little man to drive away the crow;

they were composed perhaps to make some little man contented with that office, and certain it is that in all ages and all countries it has been an object of as much consequence to preserve the seed from birds when sown, as to sow it. No doubt Adam himself when he was driven to cultivate the ground felt this, and we who are his lineal descendants, (though I am sorry to say we have not inherited a rood of his estates,) have felt it also, in our small but not unimportant concern, the Garden. Mrs. L., the Lady of that Garden, used to complain grievously of the depredations committed there, especially upon her pease. Fowls and Ducks were condemned either to imprisonment for life, or to the immediate larder for their offences of this kind; but the magpies (my protegées) and the sparrows, and the blackbirds and the thrushes, bade defiance to the coop and the cook. She tried to fright them away by feathers fastened upon a string, but birds were no more to be frightened by feathers than to be caught by chaff. She dressed up two mopsticks; not to be forgotten, because when two youths sent their straw hats upon leaving Keswick to K. and B., the girls consigned the hats to these mopsticks, and named the figures thus attired in due honour of the youths, L. N., and C. K. These mopsticks, however, were well dressed enough to invite thieves from the town, — and too well to frighten the birds. Something more effectual was wanted, and Mrs. L. bespoke a man of Joseph Glover.

Such is the imperfection of language that, write as carefully and warily as we can, it is impossible to use words which will not frequently admit of a double construction; upon this indeed it is that the Lawyers have founded the science of the Law, which said science they display in extracting any meaning from any words, and generally that meaning that shall be most opposite to the intention for which they were used. When I say that your Aunt L. bespoke a man of Joseph Glover, I do not mean that she commissioned him to engage a labourer: nor that she required him actually to make a man, like Frankenstein, — though it must be admitted that such a man as Frankenstein made, would be the best of all scarecrows, provided he were broken in so as to be perfectly manageable. To have made a man indeed would have been more than even Paracelsus would have undertaken to perform; for according to the receipt which that illustrious Bombast ab Hohenheim has delivered to posterity, an homunculus cannot be produced in a hotbed in less than forty weeks and forty days; and this would not have been in time to save the pease; not to mention that one of his homunculi had it been ready could not have served the purpose, for by his account, when it was produced, it was smaller even than Mark Thumb. Such an order would have been more unreasonable than any of those which Juno imposed upon Hercules; whereas the task imposed by Mrs. L. was nothing more than Glover thought himself capable of executing, for he understood the direction plainly and simply in its proper sense, as a carpenter ought to understand it.

An ordinary Carpenter might have hesitated at undertaking it, or bungled in the execution. But Glover is not an ordinary Carpenter. He says of himself that he should have been a capital singer, only the pity is, that he has no voice. Whether he had ever a similar persuasion of his own essential but unproducible talents for sculpture or painting I know not:—but if ever genius and originality were triumphantly displayed in the first effort of an untaught artist, it was on this occasion. Perhaps I am wrong in calling him untaught; — for there is a supernatural or divine teaching; — and it will appear presently that if there be any truth in heathen philosophy, or in that of the Roman Catholics, (which is very much the same in many respects,) some such assistance may be suspected in this case.

With or without such assistance, but certainly *con amore*, and with the aid of his own genius, if of no other, Glover went to work: ere long shouts of admiration were heard one evening in the kitchen, so loud and of such long continuance that inquiry was made from the parlour into the cause, and the reply was that Mrs. L.'s man was brought home. Out we went, father, mother and daughters, (yourself among them,—for you cannot have forgotten that memorable hour,) My Lady and the Venerabilis,—and Mrs. L. herself, as the person more immediately concerned. Seldom as it happens that any artist can embody with perfect success the conceptions of another, in this instance the difficult and delicate task had been perfectly accomplished. But I must describe the Man,—calling him by that name at present, the power, *æon* or intelligence which had incorporated itself with that ligneous resemblance of humanity not having at that time been suspected.

Yet methinks more properly might he have been called youth than man, the form and stature being juvenile. The limbs and body were slender, though not so as to convey any appearance of feebleness, it was rather that degree of slenderness which in elegant and refined society is deemed essential to grace. The countenance at once denoted strength and health and hilarity, and the incomparable carpenter had given it an expression of threatful and alert determination, suited to the station for which he was designed and the weapon which he bore. The shape of the face was rather round than oval, resembling methinks the broad harvest moon; the eyes were of the deepest black, the eyebrows black also; and there was a blackness about the nose and lips, such as might be imagined in the face of Hercules, while he was in the act of lifting and strangling the yet unsubdued and struggling Antæus. On his head was a little hat, low in the crown and narrow in the brim. His dress was a sleeved jacket without skirts,—our ancestors would have called it a gipion; *jubon* it would be rendered if ever this description were translated into Spanish, *gibao* in Portuguese; *jupon* or *gippon* in old French. It was fastened from the neck downward with eight white buttons, two and two, and between them was a broad white stripe, the colour of the gipion being brown: whether the stripe was to represent silver lace, or a white facing like that of the naval uniform, is doubtful and of little consequence. The lower part of his dress represented innominables and hose in one, of the same colour as the gipion. And he carried a fowling-piece in his hand.

Great was the satisfaction which we all expressed at beholding so admirable a man; great were the applauses which we bestowed upon the workman with one consent; and great was the complacency with which Glover himself regarded the work of his own hands. He thought, he said, this would please us. Please us indeed it did, and so well did it answer that after short trial Mrs. L. thinking that a second image would render the whole garden secure, and moreover that it was not good for her Man to be alone,

J. Glover Fecit.

THE STATUES

(Page 689).

London, Longman & Co 1849

directed Glover to make a woman also. The woman accordingly was made. Flesh of his flesh and bone of his bone, she could not be, the Man himself not being made of such materials; but she was wood of his wood and plank of his plank,—which was coming as nearly as possible to it, made of the same tree and fashioned by the same hand.

The woman was in all respects a goodly mate for the man, except that she seemed to be a few years older; she was rather below the mean stature, in that respect resembling the Venus de Medicis; slender waisted yet not looking as if she were tight-laced, nor so thin as to denote ill health. Her dress was a gown of homely brown, up to the neck. The artist had employed his brightest colours upon her face; even the eyes and nose partook of that brilliant tint which is sometimes called the roseate hue of health or exercise, sometimes the purple light of love. The whites of her eyes were large. She also was represented in a hat, but higher in the crown and broader in the rim than the man's, and where his brim was turned up, her's had a downward inclination giving a feminine character to that part of her dress.

She was placed in the garden: greatly as we admired both pieces of workmanship, we considered them merely as what they seemed to be; they went by the names of Mrs. L.'s Man and Woman; and even when you departed for the south they were still known only by that vague and most unworthy designation. Some startling circumstances after awhile excited a more particular attention to them. Several of the family declared they had been frightened by them; and K. one evening came in saying that Aunt L.'s woman had *given her* a jump. Even this did not awaken any suspicion of their supernatural powers as it ought to have done, till on a winter's night, one of the maids hearing a knock at the back door opened it; and started back when she saw that it was the woman with a letter in her hand! This is as certain as that Nosso Senhor dos Passos knocked at the door of S. Roque's convent in Lisbon and was not taken in,—to the infinite regret of the monks when they learned that he had gone afterwards to the Graça Convent and been admitted there. It is as certain that I have seen men, women and children of all ranks kissing the foot of the said Image in the Church, and half Lisbon following his procession in the streets. It is as certain as all the miracles in the Fasti, the Metamorphoses, and the Acta Sanctorum.

Many remarkable things were now called to mind both of the man and woman;—how on one occasion they had made Miss Christian's maid miscarry of—half a message; and how at another time when Isaac was bringing a basket from Mr. Calvert's, he was frightened into his wits by them. But on Sunday evening last the most extraordinary display of wonderful power occurred, for in the evening the woman, instead of being in her place among the pease, appeared standing erect on the top of Mr. Fisher's haymow in the forge field, and there on the following morning she was seen by all Keswick, who are witnesses of the fact.

You may well suppose that I now began to examine into the mystery, and manifold were the mysteries which I discovered, and many the analogies in their formation of which the maker could never by possibility have heard; and many the points of divine philosophy and theurgic science which they illustrated. In the first place two Swedenborgian correspondencies flashed upon me in the material whereof they were constructed. They were intended to guard the Garden; there is a proverb which says, set a thief to catch a thief, and therefore it is that they were *fir* statues. Take it in English and the correspondence is equally striking; they were made of *deal*, because they were to do a *deal* of good. The dark aspect of the male figure also was explained; for being stationed there contra *fures*, it was proper that he should have a furious countenance. Secondly there is something wonderful in their formation:—they are bifronted, not merely bifaced like Janus, but bifronted from top to toe. Let the thief be as cunning as he may he cannot get behind them.—They have no backs, and were they disposed to be indolent and sit at their posts it would be impossible. They can appear at the kitchen door, or on the haymow, they can give the children and even the grown persons of the family a jump, but to sit is beyond their power, however miraculous it may be; for impossibilities cannot be effected even by miracle, and as it is impossible to see without eyes, or to walk without legs, — or for a ship to float without a bottom, so is it for a person in the same predicament as such a ship — to sit.

Yet farther mysteries; both hands of these marvellous statues are right hands and both are left hands, they are at once ambidexter and ambisinister. It was said by Dryden of old Jacob Tonson that he had two left legs: but these marvellous statues have two left legs and two right legs each, and yet but four legs between them, that is to say but two a-piece. In the whole course of my reading I have found no account of any statues so wonderful as these. For though the Roman Janus was bifronted, and my old acquaintance Yamen had in like manner a double face, and many of the Hindoo and other Oriental Deities have their necks set round with heads, and their elbows with arms, yet it is certain that all these Gods have backs, and sides to them also. In this point no similitude can be found for our Images. They may be likened to the sea as being bottomless, — but as being without a back, and in the mystery of having both hands and legs at once right and left, they are unequalled; none but themselves can be their parallel.

Now, my daughter, I appeal to you and to all other reasonable persons, — I put the question to your own plain sense, — is it anyways likely that statues so wonderful, so inexpressibly mysterious in their properties should be the mere work of a Keswick carpenter, though aided as he was by Mrs. L.'s directions? Is it not certain that neither he, nor Mrs. L., had the slightest glimpse, the remotest thought of any such properties, — she when she designed, he when he executed the marvellous productions? Is it possible that they should? Would it not be preposterous to suppose it?

This supposition therefore being proved to be absurd, which in mathematics is equal to a demonstration that the contrary must be true, it remains to inquire into the real origin of their stupendous qualities. Both the ancient Heathens and the Romanists teach that certain Images of the Gods or of the Saints have been made without the aid of human hands, and that they have appeared no one knew whence or how. The Greeks called such images Diopeteis, as having fallen from the sky, and I could enumerate, were it needful, sundry Catholic Images which are at this day venerated as being either of angelic workmanship or celestial origin. We cannot, however, have recourse to this solution in the present case; for Glover is so veracious a man that if he had found these figures in his workshop without knowing how they came there, — or if he had seen them grow into shape while he was looking on, — he would certainly not have concealed a fact so extraordinary. All Keswick would have known it. It must have become as notorious as Prince Hohenlohe's miracles.

There remains then another hypothesis, which is also common to the ancient Pagans and the Romanists; — that some superior powers finding a congruity in the Images have been pleased to communicate to them a portion of their influence, and even of their presence, and so, if I may be allowed the word, have actually become *inligneate* in them. Were my old acquaintance, Thomas Taylor, here, who entirely believes this, he would at once determine which of his Heathen Deities have thus manifested their existence. Who indeed that looks at the Youth but must be reminded of Apollo? Said I that his face resembled in its rotundity the Moon? the Sun would have been the fitter similitude, — the sun shorn of its beams: — Phœbus, — such as he appeared when in the service of Admetus. And for his female companion, her beauty and the admiration which it excites in all beholders, identify her with no less certainty for Venus. We have named them therefore the Apollo de Lovell, and the Venus de

Glover; in justice to both artists; and in farther honour of them and of the Images themselves have composed the following inscription:

No works of Phidias we; but Mrs. L.
  Designed, and we were made by Joseph Glover.
Apollo, I, and yonder Venus stands,
  Behold her, and you cannot chuse but love her.
If antient sculptors could behold us here,
  How would they pine with envy and abhorrence!
For even as I surpass their Belvedere,
  So much doth she excel the pride of Florence.

EPILUDE OF MOTTOES.

Careless! bring your apprehension along with you.
CONGREVE.

If I have written a sentence, or a word, that can bear a captious or unreasonable construction, I earnestly intreat a more lenient interpretation. When a man feels acutely, he may perhaps speak at times more pointedly than he ought; yet, in the present instance, I am conscious of no sentiment which I could wish to alter. BISHOP JEBB.

νὴ τὸν Ποσειδῶ, καὶ λέγει γ', ἅπερ λέγει,
δίκαια πάντα, κοὐδὲν αὐτῶν ψεύδεται. ARISTOPHANES.

Will you be true?

TRO. Who, I? alas, it is my vice, my fault.
While others fish with craft for great opinion,
I with great truth catch mere simplicity.
Whilst some with cunning gild their copper crowns,
With truth and plainness I do wear mine bare.
Fear not my truth; the moral of my wit
Is — "plain and true;" there's all the reach of it.
SHAKESPEARE.

— come augel che pria s' avventa e teme
Stassi fra i rami paventoso e solo
Mirando questo ed or quell' altro colle;
Così mi levo e mi ritengo insieme,
L' ale aguzzando al mio dubbioso volo.
GIUSTO DE' CONTI.

Whosoever be reader hereof maie take it by reason for a riche and a newe labour; and speciallie princes and governours of the common wealth, and ministers of justice, with other. Also the common people eche of theim maie fynd the labour conveniente to their estate. And herein is conteigned certaine right highe and profounde sentences, and holsome counsaylles, and mervaillous devyses agaynste the encumbraunce of fortune; and ryght swete consolacions for theim that are overthrowen by fortune. Finally it is good to them that digeste it, and thanke God that hath given such grace to the Auctour in gevyng us example of vertuous livyng, with hye and salutary doctrynes, and marvailous instructions of perfectness. — A ryght precious meale is the sentences of this boke; but fynally the sauce of the saied swete style moveth the appetyte. Many bookes there be of substanciall meates, but they bee so rude and so unsavery, and the style of so small grace, that the first morcell is lothsome and noyfull; and of suche bookes foloweth to lye hole and sounde in lybraries; but I trust this will not. Of trouth great prayse is due to the auctour of his travayle.
LORD BERNERS.

The current that with gentle murmur glides,
Thou know'st, being stopp'd, impatiently doth rage;
But when his fair course is not hindered,
He makes sweet music with the enamel'd stones,
Giving a gentle kiss to every sedge
He overtaketh in his pilgrimage;
And so by many winding nooks he strays,
With willing sport, to the wild ocean.
Then let me go, and hinder not my course;
I'll be as patient as a gentle stream,
And make a pastime of each weary step,
Till the last step have brought me to my rest.
SHAKESPEARE.

Sith you have long time drawn the weeds of my wit and fed yourselves with the cockle of my conceits, I have at last made you gleaners of my harvest, and partakers of my experience. — Here shall you find the style varying according to the matter, suitable to the style, and all of these aimed to profit. If the title make you suspect, compare it with the matter, it will answer you; if the matter, apply it with the censures of the learned, they will countenance the same; of the handling I repent me not, for I had rather you should condemn me for default in rhetorick, than commend my style and lament my judgement. Thus resolved both of the matter, and satisfied in my method, I leave the whole to your judgements; which, if they be not depraved with envy, will be bettered in knowledge, and if not carried away with opinion, will receive much profit. THOMAS LODGE.

This good Wine I present, needs no Ivy-bush. They that taste thereof shall feel the fruit to their best content, and better understanding. The learned shall meet with matter to refresh their memories; the younger students, a directory to fashion their discourse; the weakest capacity, matter of wit, worth and admiration.

T. L. D. M. P's. Epistle Prefatory to the Learned Summarie upon the famous Poem of William of Salust, Lord of BARTAS.

This fellow pecks up wit, as pigeon's pease,
And utters it again when Jove doth please;
He is wit's pedlar, and retails his wares.
LOVE'S LABOUR LOST.

Imagination, thro' the trick
Of Doctors, often makes us sick;
And why, let any sophist tell,
May it not likewise make us well!
CHURCHILL.

His mind fastens
On twenty several objects, which confound
Deep sense with folly. WEBSTER.

It is a crown unto a gentle breast,
  To impart the pleasure of his flowing mind,
(Whose sprightly motion never taketh rest)
  To one whose bosom he doth open find.
THOMAS SCOTT.

— Be prepared to hear:
And since you know you cannot see yourself
So well as by reflection, I, your glass,
Will modestly discover to yourself
That of yourself which you yet know not of.
SHAKESPEARE.

And whereas in my expression I am very plain and downright, and in my teaching part seem to tautologize, it should be considered, (and whoever has been a teacher will remember,) that the learners must be plainly dealt with, and must have several times renewed unto them the same thing. — Therefore I have chosen so to do in several places, because I had rather (in such cases) speak three words too many, than one syllable too few.

THOMAS MACE.

Lire et repasser souvent
Sur Athenes et sur Rome,
C'est dequoy faire un Sçavant,
Mais non pas un habile homme.

Méditez incessamment,
Dévorez livre apres livre,
C'est en vivant seulement
Que vous apprendrez à vivre.

Avant qu'en sçavoir les loix,
La clarté nous est ravie :
Il faudroit vivre deux fois
Pour bien conduire sa vie.

DE CHARLEVAL.

If we could hit on't, gallants, there are due
Certain respects from writers, and from you.

PROLOGUE TO THE ADVENTURES OF FIVE HOURS.

— Here you have a piece so subtly writ
Men must have wit themselves to find the wit.

EPILOGUE TO THE ADVENTURES OF FIVE HOURS.

All puddings have two ends, and most short sayings
Two handles to their meaning.

LORD DIGBY.

Reader, Now I send thee like a Bee to gather honey out of flowers and weeds; every garden is furnished with either, and so is ours. Read and meditate; thy profit shall be little in any book, unless thou read alone, and unless thou read all and record after.

HENRY SMITH.

The most famous of the Pyramids was that of Hermes. — Through each door of this Pyramid was an entrance into seven apartments, called by the names of the Planets. In each of them was a golden Statue. The biggest was in the apartment of Osiris, or the Sun. It had a book upon its forehead, and its hand upon its mouth. Upon the outside of the Book was written this inscription. *I must be read in a profound silence.*

TRAVELS OF CYRUS.

— Facio ego ut solent, qui quanto plus aliquem mirantur et explicare volunt quod sentiunt, eo minus id assequuntur quod volunt, ut quamquam magnum aliquid animo concipiunt, verba tamen desint, et moliri potius quàm dicere potuisse videantur.

HERMOLAUS BARBARUS JO. PICO MIRANDULÆ.

Nihil mihi potest esse beatius quam scire; discendum verò ut sciamus. Ego quidem sapientiæ ambitum, tanquam animi nostri ærarium quoddam semper judicavi, id quod communia commentationum nostrarum vectigalia inferenda censeo, sed proba; unde sibi suum quisque in usum sumat sine invidia atque simultate.

J. C. SCALIGER.

Feliz yerba es la yedra, si se enrama
A un muro altivo, á quien no alcanza el corte
De la envidia; puer queda con su altura,
El mas vistoso, y ella mas segura.

BALBUENA, EL BERNARDO.

— en poco tiempo te he dicho
lo que passò en mucho tiempo.

CALDERON, EL MAESTRO DE DANZAR.

I'll range the plenteous intellectual field,
And gather every thought of sovereign power
To chase the moral maladies of man;
Thoughts which may bear transplanting to the skies,
Nor wholly wither there where Seraphs sing,
Refined, exalted, — not annull'd — in heaven.

YOUNG.

Let every man enjoy his whim;
What's he to me, or I to him.

CHURCHILL.

And whereas I may seem too smart or satyrical in some particular places, I do not at all repent me, as thinking what is said to such ill-deserving persons much too little.

THOMAS MACE.

— Play the fool with wits,
'Gainst fools be guarded, 'tis a certain rule,
Wits are safe things; there's danger in a fool.

CHURCHILL.

And in this thought they find a kind of ease,
Bearing their own misfortune on the back
Of such as have before endured the like.

RICHARD II.

Our life indeed has bitterness enough
To change a loving nature into gall:
Experience sews coarse patches on the stuff
Whose texture was originally all
Smooth as the rose-leaf's, and whose hues were bright
As are the colours of the weeping cloud
When the sun smiles upon its tears.

MRS. LENOX CONYNGHAM.

Thus much we know, eternal bliss and pure,
By God's unfailing promise, is secure
To them who their appointed lot endure
Meekly, striving to fulfil,
In humble hopefulness, God's will.

MRS. LENOX CONYNGHAM.

I thowt how hard it is to denye
A ladye's preyer, wych after the entent
Of the poete is a myghty comaundement;
Wherfore me thoht as in this caas
That my wyt war lakkyd bettyr it was
That my wyl, and therfore to do
My ladyes preyer I assentyd to.

OSBERN BOKENAM.

Al peco de los años
lo eminente se rinde;
que á lo facil del tiempo
no ay conquista dificil.

CALDERON.

We only meet on earth
That we may know how sad it is to part:
And sad indeed it were, if in the heart
There were no store reserved against a dearth,
No calm Elysium for departed Mirth,
Haunted by gentle shadows of past pleasure,
Where the sweet folly, the light-footed measure,
And graver trifles of the shining hearth
Live in their own dear image.

HARTLEY COLERIDGE.

Sweet are the thoughts that smother from conceit:
For when I come and sit me down to rest,
My chair presents a throne of majesty;
And when I set my bonnet on my head,
Methinks I fit my forehead for a crown;
And when I take a truncheon in my fist,
A sceptre then comes tumbling in my thoughts.

ROBERT GREENE.

Quanquam verò hoc mihi non polliceri possum, me ubique veritatem quam sectatus sum, assecutum esse; sed potius eo fine ea proposui, ut et alios ad veritatis investigationem invitarem: tamen ut rectè Galenus habet, τολμητέον τε καὶ ζητητέον τὸ ἀληθὲς, εἰ γὰρ καὶ μὴ τύχομεν αὐτοῦ πάντως, δήπου πλησιέστερον ἢ νυν ἐσμὲν ἀφιξόμεθα. *Audendum est, et veritas investiganda, quam etiamsi non assequamur, omnino tamen propius quam nunc sumus, ed eam perveniemus. Quo verò ego animo ad scribendum accessi, eo ut alii ad legendum accedant, opto.*
SENNERTUS.

I do confess the imperfect performance. Yet I must take the boldness to say, I have not miscarried in the whole; for the mechanical part of it is regular. That I may say with as little vanity, as a builder may say he has built a house according to the model laid down before him, or a gardener that he has set his flowers in a knot of such or such a figure. CONGREVE.

As wheresoever these leaves fall, the root is in my heart, so shall they have ever true impressions thereof. Thus much information is in very leaves, that they can tell what the Tree is; and these can tell you I am a friend and an honest man. DONNE.

On ne recognoistroit les monts, sans les valées;
Et les tailles encor artistement meslées
En œuvre mosaÿque, ont, pour plus grand beauté,
Divers prix, divers teint, diverse quantité.
Dieu vueille qu'en mes chants la plus insigne tache
Semble le moucheron qu'une pucelle attache
A sa face neigeuse, et que bien peu d'erreurs
Donnent lustre aux beaux traicts de mes hautes fureurs.
DU BARTAS, LA MAGNIFICENCE.

Hills were not seen but for the vales betwixt;
The deep indentings artificial mixt
Amid mosaicks, for mere ornament,
Have prizes, sizes and dyes different.
And, Oh, God grant, the greatest spot you spy
In all my frame, may be but as the fly,
Which on her ruff, (whiter than whitest snows,)
To whiten white, the fairest virgin sows,
(Or like the velvet on her brow, or like
The dunker mole on Venus' dainty cheek.)
And that a few faults may but lustre bring
To my high furies where I sweetest sing.
SYLVESTER.

Be as capricious and sick-brained as ignorance and malice can make thee, here thou art rectified; or be as healthful as the inward calm of an honest heart, learning, and temper can state thy disposition, yet this book may be thy fortunate concernment and companion.
SHIRLEY.

Humble and meek befitteth men of years,
Behold my cell, built in a silent shade,
Holding content for poverty and peace,
And in my lodge is fealty and faith,
Labour and love united in one league.
I want not, for my mind affordeth wealth,
I know not envy, for I climb not high;
Thus do I live, and thus I mean to die.
ROBERT GREENE.

The events of to-day make us look forward to what will happen to-morrow; those of yesterday carry our views into another world. DANBY.

Mine earnest intent is as much to profit as to please, *non tam ut populo placerem, quam ut populum juvarem:* and these my writings shall take, I hope, like gilded pills, which are so composed as well to tempt the appetite and deceive the palate, as to help and medicinally work upon the whole body. My lines shall not only recreate, but rectify the mind. BURTON.

— Sit thou a patient looker on;
Judge not the play, before the play is done,
Her plot has many changes; every day
Speaks a new scene, the last act crowns the play.
QUARLES.

Lord, if thy gracious bounty please to fill
The floor of my desires, and teach me skill
To dress and chuse the corn, take those the chaff that will.
QUARLES.

Je n'ay pas plus faict mon livre, que mon livre m'a faict,— livre consubstantiel à son autheur. MONTAIGNE.

—se le parole che usa lo scrittore portan seco un poco, non dirà di difficultà, ma d'acutezza recondita, et non così nota, come quelle che si dicono parlando ordinariamente, danno una certa maggior auttorità alla scrittura, et fanno che il lettore va più ritenuto, et sopra di se, et meglio considera, et si diletta dell' ingegno et dottrina di chi scrive; et col buon giudicio affaticandosi un poco gusta quel piacere, che s' ha nel conseguir le cose difficili. Et se l' ignorantia di chi legge è tanta, che non posse superar quella difficultà, non è la colpa dello scrittore.
CASTIGLIONE, IL CORTIGIANO.

Certo estava eu que o Doutor sabia de tudo o que disse naõ só os termos e fundamentos, mas acuda o mas difficultoza, e substancial; — mas o praticar dellas de modo, que en as entendesse, he graça de seu saber, e naõ sufficiencia do meu ingenho. FRANCISCO RODRIGUES LOBO.

Sir, Our greatest business is more in our power than the least, and we may be surer to meet in Heaven than in any place upon earth; and whilst we are distant here, we may meet as often as we list in God's presence, by soliciting in our prayers for one another. DONNE.

Or ti riman, Lettor, sovra 'l tuo banco,
Dietro pensando a ciò che si preliba,
S' esser vuoi lieto assai prima che stanco.
Messo t' ho innanzi; omai per te ti ciba;
Che a se ritorce tutta la mia cura
Quella materia ond' io son fatto scriba. DANTE.

I have been often told that nobody now would read any thing that was plain and true; — that was accounted dull work, except one mixed something of the sublime, prodigious, monstrous, or incredible; and then they would read the one for the sake of the other. — So rather than not be read, I have put in a proportionable little of the monstrous. If any thing be found fault with, it is possible I may explain and add. HUTCHINSON.

Who seeketh in thee for profit and gain
Of excellent matter soon shall attain. T. H.

Pay me like for like; give me good thoughts for great studies; and at leastwise shew me this courtly courtesy to afford me good words, which cost you nothing, for serious thoughts hatched up with much consideration. Thus commending my deserts to the learned, and committing my labour to the instruction of the ignorant, I bid you all heartily farewell. LAZARUS PIOT.

Even at this time, when I humbly thank God, I ask and have his comfort of sadder meditations, I do not condemn in myself that I have given my wit such evaporations as these. DONNE.

L'ENVOY.

Gentle Reader — for if thou art fond of such works as these, thou art like to be the Gentleman and the Scholar — I take upon me to advertise thee that the Printer of The Doctor, &c. is William Nicol of the Shakspeare Press — the long-tried Friend of the lamented Southey and of their mutual Friend, the late Grosvenor Bedford of Her Majesty's Exchequer —

Felices animæ, et quales neque candidiores
Terra tulit!

The Sonnet following, Gentle Reader, I do thee to wit, is the composition of the above kind-hearted and benevolent William Nicol — and I wish it to be printed, because on Grosvenor Bedford's short visit to Southey in 1836, he expressed himself much pleased with it. May be, if thou art fond of the gentle craft, it may please thee too, and so I wish thee heartily farewell!

Who wrote The Doctor? Who's the scribe unknown?—
Time may discover, when the grave has closed
Its earthy jaws o'er us, who now are posed
To father that which greatest pen might own;
Learning diffuse, quaint humour, lively wit,
Satire severe and bold, or covert, sly,
Turning within itself the mental eye
To fancies strange that round its orbit flit,
Unknown to others and by self scarce seen;
Teaching, in sweetest English, England's plan, —
When England was herself, her laurels green —
Honour to God and charity to man:
Who wrote the Doctor? her best Son, I ween,
Whether his works, or his fair life you scan.

THE END.

London:
Spottiswoodes and Shaw,
New-street-Square.

E. Nash. del.

J. T. Willmore.

Portrait of the Author.